JOHN R. CARROLL

SELECTED PHYSICAL PROPERTIES

Density of air (STP)	1.29 kg/meter^3
Density of water (20°C)	$1.00 \times 10^3 \text{ kg/meter}^3$
Density of mercury (20°C)	$13.5 \times 10^3 \text{ kg/meter}^3$
Heat of fusion of water (0°C)	79.7 cal/gm
Heat of vaporization of water (100°C)	540 cal/gm
Standard atmosphere	$1.01 \times 10^5 \text{ nt/meter}^2 = 14.7 \text{ lb/in}^2$
Speed of sound in dry air (STP)	$331 \text{ meters/sec} = 1090 \text{ ft/sec}$
Acceleration of gravity (standard)	$9.81 \text{ meters/sec}^2 = 32.2 \text{ ft/sec}^2$
Mean radius of earth	$6.37 \times 10^6 \text{ meters} = 3960 \text{ miles}$
Mean earth-sun distance	$1.49 \times 10^8 \text{ km} = 92.9 \times 10^6 \text{ miles}$
Mean earth-moon distance	$3.80 \times 10^5 \text{ km} = 2.39 \times 10^5 \text{ miles}$

11 HAL

Physics

For Students of Science and Engineering

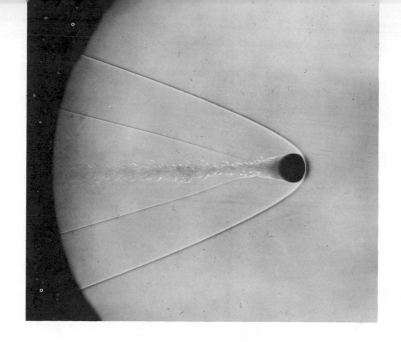

DAVID HALLIDAY

Professor of Physics

University of Pittsburgh

ROBERT RESNICK

Professor of Physics

Rensselaer Polytechnic Institute

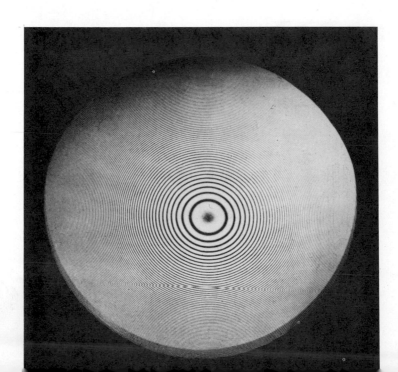

Physics

For Students of Science and Engineering

COMBINED EDITION

PART I FIRST EDITION
PART II SECOND EDITION

New York · *London* · *John Wiley & Sons, Inc.*

BOOKS BY HALLIDAY (D.)

Introductory Nuclear Physics. Second Edition

BOOKS BY HALLIDAY (D.) AND RESNICK (R.)

Physics for Students of Science and Engineering
   Part II, Second Edition
Physics for Students of Science and Engineering
   Parts I First Edition and II Second Edition Combined

BOOKS BY RESNICK (R.) AND HALLIDAY (D.)

Physics for Students of Science and Engineering
   Part I

FOURTH PRINTING, MAY, 1964

Copyright © 1960, 1962 by John Wiley & Sons, Inc.

All rights reserved. This book or any part
thereof must not be reproduced in any form
without the written permission of the publisher.

Library of Congress Catalog Card Number: 62-15336
Printed in the United States of America

Preface to First Edition

The time lag between developments in basic science and their application to engineering practice has shrunk enormously in the past few decades. The base of engineering, once largely empirical, is now largely scientific. Today the need is to stress principles rather than specific procedures, to select areas of contemporary interest rather than of past interest, and to condition the student to the atmosphere of change he will encounter during his career. These developments require a revision of the traditional course in general physics for engineers and scientists.

The most frequent criticisms made in varying degrees of textbooks used in such a course are these: (a) the content is encyclopedic in that topics are not treated with sufficient depth, the discussions are largely descriptive rather than explanatory and analytical, and too many topics are surveyed; (b) the content is not sufficiently "modern," and applications are drawn mostly from past engineering practice rather than from contemporary physics; (c) the organization of the material is too compartmentalized to reveal the essential unity of physics and its principles; (d) the approach is highly deductive and does not stress sufficiently the connection between theory and experiment. Of course, it is unlikely that a textbook will ever be written that is not criticized on one ground or another.

In writing this textbook we have been cognizant of these criticisms and have given much thought to ways of meeting them. We have considered the possibility of reorganizing the subject matter. The adoption of an atomic approach from the beginning or a structure built around energy in

v

its various aspects suggest themselves. We have concluded that our goals can best be achieved by modifying the selection and treatment of topics within the traditional organization. To shuffle freely the cards of subject matter content or to abandon entirely a sequence which represents the growth of physical thought invites both a failure to appreciate the Newtonian and Maxwellian syntheses of classical physics and a superficial understanding of modern physics. A solid underpinning of classical physics is essential to build the superstructure of contemporary physics in our opinion.

To illustrate how we hope to achieve our goals within this framework, we present here the principal features of our book.

1. Many topics are treated in greater depth than has been customary heretofore, and much contemporary material has been woven into the body of the text. For example, gravitation, kinetic theory, electromagnetic waves, and physical optics, among others, are treated in greater depth. Contemporary topics, such as atomic standards, collision cross section, intermolecular forces, mass-energy conversion, isotope separation, the Hall effect, the free-electron model of conductivity, nuclear stability, nuclear resonance, and neutron diffraction, are discussed where they are pertinent.

To permit this greater depth and inclusion of contemporary material, we have omitted entirely or treated only indirectly much traditional material, such as simple machines, surface tension, viscosity, calorimetry, change of state, humidity, pumps, practical engines, musical scales, architectural acoustics, electrochemistry, thermoelectricity, motors, alternating-current circuits, electronics, lens aberrations, color, photometry, and others.

2. We have tried to reveal the unity of physics in many ways. Throughout the book we stress the general nature of key ideas common to all areas of physics. For example, the conservation laws of energy, linear momentum, angular momentum, and charge are used repeatedly. Wave concepts and properties of vibrating systems, such as resonance, are used in mechanics, sound, electromagnetism, optics, atomic physics, and nuclear physics. The field concept is applied to gravitation, fluid flow, electromagnetism, and nuclear physics.

The interrelation of the various disciplines of physics is emphasized by the use of physical and mathematical analogies and by similarity of method. For example, the correspondences between the mass-spring system and the LC circuit or between the acoustic tube and the electromagnetic cavity are emphasized, and the interweaving of microscopic and macroscopic approaches is noted in heat phenomena and electrical and magnetic phenomena. We have tried to make a smooth transition between particle mechanics and kinetic theory, stressing that, in their classical aspects, both belong to the Newtonian synthesis. We have also sought a smooth transition between electromagnetism and wave optics, pointing frequently to the Maxwellian synthesis.

We discuss the limitations of classical ideas and the domain of their validity, and we emphasize the generalizing nature of contemporary ideas applicable in a broader domain. Throughout we aim to show the relation of theory to experiment and to develop an awareness of the nature and uses of theory.

3. Our approach to quantum physics is not the traditional descriptive one. Rather we seek to develop the contemporary concepts fairly rigorously, at a length and depth appropriate to an introductory course. In the early chapters we pave the way by pointing to the limitations of classical theory, by stressing the aspects of classical physics that bear on contemporary physics, and by choosing illustrative examples that have a modern flavor. Thus we stress fields rather than circuits, particles rather than extended bodies, and wave optics rather than geometrical optics. Among the illustrative examples are molecular potential energy curves, binding energy of a deuteron, nuclear collisions, the nuclear model of the atom, the Thomson atom model, molecular dipoles, drift speed of electrons, stability of betatron orbits, nuclear magnetic resonance, the red shift, and others too numerous to mention.

The point of view is that of developing the fundamental ideas of quantum physics. The customary descriptive chapter on nuclear physics is, for example, not present. Instead, the wave-particle duality, the uncertainty principle, the complementarity principle, and the correspondence principle are stressed.

4. The mathematical level of our book assumes a concurrent course in calculus. The derivative is introduced in Chapter 3 and the integral in Chapter 7. The related physical concepts of slope and area under a curve are developed steadily. Calculus is used freely in the latter half of the book. Simple differential equations are not avoided, although no formal procedures are needed or given for solving them. Vector notation and vector algebra, including scalar and vector products, are used throughout. Displacement is taken as the prototype vector, and the idea of invariance of vector relations is developed.

5. The number of problems is unusually large, but few are "plug-in" problems. Many involve extensions of the text material, contemporary applications, or derivations. The questions at the end of each chapter are intended to be thought-provoking; they may serve as the basis for class discussion, for essay papers, or for self-study. Only rarely can the questions be answered by direct quotation from the text.

6. The book contains an unusually large number of worked-out examples, with the "plug-in" variety used only to emphasize a numerical magnitude. Algebraic, rather than numerical, solutions are stressed. Examples sometimes extend the text treatment or discuss the fine points, but usually they are applications of the principles, often of contemporary physics.

7. The textbook has been designed to fit physics courses of various lengths. In small print there is a great deal of supplementary material of an advanced, historical, or philosophical character, to be omitted or included to varying degrees depending on interest and course length. In addition, many chapters may be regarded as optional. Each teacher will make his own choice. At our institutions Chapter 14 (statics of rigid bodies) and Chapters 41 and 42 (geometrical optics) are omitted. Other possibilities suggested, depending on emphasis or depth desired, or the nature of succeeding courses, are Chapter 12 (rotational dynamics), Chapters 17 and 18 (fluids), Chapter 24 (kinetic theory—II), Chapter 32 (emf and circuits), Chapter 46 (polarization), and Chapters 47 and 48 (quantum physics).

8. We have adopted the mks system of units throughout, although the British engineering system is also used in mechanics. Having observed the gradual exclusion, year by year, of the cgs system from advanced textbooks, we have seen fit to limit ourselves to the bare definition of the basic cgs quantities. An extensive list of conversion factors appears in Appendix H.

We wish to thank the engineering and science students at both Rensselaer Polytechnic Institute and the University of Pittsburgh who have borne with us through two successive preliminary editions. Constructive criticisms from our colleagues at each institution and from some eight reviewers have resulted in many changes. Benjamin Chi of R.P.I. has been of major service in all aspects of the preparation of the manuscript. Finally, we express our deep appreciation to our wives, not only for aid in typing and proofreading but for the patience and encouragement without which this book might never have been written.

DAVID HALLIDAY
ROBERT RESNICK

January 1960
Pittsburgh, Pennsylvania
Troy, New York

Preface to Part II, Second Edition

This revision of Part II of *Physics for Students of Science and Engineering*, which we hope will make our book more useful to students and instructors, is based on classroom experience at many institutions during the last two years. The basic outline of the book and its underlying philosophy remain unchanged. We have, however, modified the treatment of many topics, among them Ampère's, Faraday's, Gauss's and Lenz's laws and Huygens' principle, to make them clearer and more explicit than before. The experimental basis of the laws of physics has received increased stress, and new experimental material, such as the radiation pressure measurements of Nichols and Hull, optical masers, relativistic particle accelerators, and fiber optics illustrate the basic concepts. More than half the figures have been redrawn for greater clarity, and new figures and photographs have been inserted in key places. The questions and problems have been re-evaluated, and more than 200 are new.

In a few places we have supplied new sections either to extend or to improve the understanding of the basic material. For example, there are sections in reduced type on the electric vectors (E, D, and P) and on the magnetic vectors (B, H, and M). RC circuits are discussed, the Compton effect has been included in the treatment of the wave-particle duality, and a discussion of electromagnetic fields as seen by observers in relative motion has been added.

Other significant changes are (1) references to the literature available to students have been supplemented and brought up to date; (2) the sign conventions for geometrical optics have been put on a more physical basis; (3) attention has been called to examples or problems that contain important new material by using italicized titles; and (4) we have further systemized and simplified the notation in several places, particularly in wave optics.

We continue to be indebted to Dr. Benjamin Chi for assistance in preparing the illustrations and for his detailed criticism of the optics chapters. One of us (DH) wishes to thank Professor G. Wataghin for courtesies extended at the University of Turin while this revision was in progress. Finally, we extend special thanks to those students and instructors who have been kind enough to write to us about their experiences with the first edition.

DAVID HALLIDAY
ROBERT RESNICK

January 1, 1962
Pittsburgh, Pennsylvania
Troy, New York

Contents

Physics

For Students of Science and Engineering

Physical Measurement

CHAPTER 1

1-1 Measurement

When plans were being made to lay the first Atlantic telegraph cable, the company in charge of the construction hired a young engineer, William Thomson (1824–1907), as a consultant. In order to solve some of the problems raised by this undertaking, Thomson made many accurate electrical measurements. Often he used precision instruments which he himself had invented. His advice, based on his own experiments, was ignored, chiefly because the basic principles involved were not clearly understood or accepted by those in authority. The subsequent failures and costly mistakes of the project later led to a more careful consideration of Thomson's views. Their adoption led to the successful completion of the cable in 1858.* This early experience may have helped Thomson form his often quoted view: "I often say that when you can measure what you are speaking about, and express it in numbers, you know something about it; but when you cannot express it in numbers, your knowledge is of a meagre and unsatisfactory kind; it may be the beginning of knowledge, but you have scarcely, in your thoughts, advanced to the stage of Science, whatever the matter may be."

Although other scientists would deny that they should deal only with ideas that are strictly measurable, none would deny the great importance of exact measurement to science. There have been many instances in the history of science in which small but significant discrepancies between theory and accurate measurements have led to the development of new and more general

---

* In 1892, Thomson was raised to the peerage as Lord Kelvin. He had become one of Britain's foremost scientists. Among his other achievements, he was one of the founders of the science of thermodynamics.

theories. Such slight discrepancies could not have been detected if scientists had been satisfied with only a qualitative explanation of the phenomena.

1–2 Physical Quantities, Standards, and Units

The building blocks of physics are the physical quantities in terms of which the laws of physics are expressed. Among these quantities are force, time, velocity, density, temperature, charge, magnetic susceptibility, and a host of others. Many of these terms, such as force and temperature, are part of our everyday vocabulary. When these terms are so used, their meanings may be vague or different from their scientific meanings.

For the purposes of physics the basic quantities must be defined clearly and precisely. One view held at present is that the definition of a physical quantity has been given when the procedures for measuring that quantity have been given. This view is called the *operational* point of view because the definition is, at root, a set of laboratory operations leading ultimately to a number with a unit. The operations may include arithmetical or algebraic calculations.

Sometimes physical quantities are divided into *fundamental* quantities and *derived* quantities. Such a division of quantities is arbitrary in that a given quantity can be regarded as a fundamental one in a particular set of operations and a derived one in another.

Derived quantities are those whose defining operations are based on the use of other physical quantities. Examples of quantities usually viewed as derived are velocity, acceleration, and volume.

Fundamental quantities are not defined in terms of other physical quantities. The number of quantities regarded as fundamental is the minimum number needed to give a consistent and unambiguous description of all the quantities of physics. Examples of quantities usually viewed as fundamental are length and time. Their operational definitions involve two steps: first, the choice of a *standard*; and second, the establishment of procedures for obtaining multiples or submultiples of the standard, that is, for obtaining *units* of the quantity. Once our standard is chosen and units have been determined, a direct comparison of a quantity to be measured with the standard can often be made, so that a number and a unit are determined as the measure of that quantity.

An ideal standard has two prime characteristics: It is accessible, and it is invariable. Often the two requirements are incompatible and a compromise has to be made between them. Historically, greater emphasis was placed first on accessibility, but as techniques of measurement improved the need for greater invariability in the standards grew. The familiar yard, foot, and inch, for example, are descended directly from the human arm, foot, and upper thumb. Today, such rough measures of length are not satisfactory, and a much less variable standard must be used, even at the expense of accessibility.

Suppose that we have chosen our standard of length and determined units of length. If by direct comparison of a bar with the unit of length called the centimeter we conclude that the bar is twelve times as long as the centimeter, we say that the length of the bar is twelve centimeters.

It is important to realize, however, that there are many instances in which quantities cannot be measured in this direct way. For such cases an indirect approach, using more involved operational procedures, is necessary. Certain assumptions are made in order to relate the results of an indirect measurement to the direct operation. For example, suppose that the distance from a rocket launching station to the surface of the moon must be known at a certain time. One indirect approach to determine this distance would be to send out a radar signal from the station which will be reflected from the surface of the moon back to a receiver at the sending station. If the time between sending and receiving the signal is measured and the speed of the radar signal is known, the distance can be obtained as the product of the speed and one-half the time interval. We assume here that the speed of the signal is constant and that the signal has traveled in a straight line. The speed must be measured in a subsidiary experiment, and it is here that the standard of length appears in the operational procedure.

Astronomical distances, such as distances between stars and the earth, cannot be measured in a direct way. A few stars are close enough so that triangulation measurements can be made; here the position of the star with respect to the background of much more distant stars is observed at six-month intervals, when the earth has moved from one point of its orbit to a diametrically opposite point. From these observed data the desired distance can be obtained from trigonometry.

Just as we use indirect methods for measuring large distances, such as astronomical ones, so we must also use an indirect approach to measure very small distances, such as those within atoms and molecules. We shall encounter many examples of indirect methods in later chapters.

1–3 Frames of Reference

The idea of "motion" contains two primitive concepts, those of position and time. If we are to specify uniquely the position of a point, we may do so by noting its distance from three arbitrarily selected mutually perpendicular planes, which then constitute our reference system. A point must always be located *relative* to some frame of reference. We cannot attach meaning to the "absolute" location of a point. To do so would require that all observers be able to distinguish from all possible reference frames a particular "absolute" frame which seemed to offer some fundamental and unique advantage. At one time the earth was thought to be such a frame, but this was shown to be false. In the world about us we have not been able to find such an "absolute" frame of reference. Similar considerations hold for the determination of the time interval between two events, such as the time of passage of a particle from one point to another point. Once a particular reference system has been chosen, however, position and time can be specified relative to it.

We shall assume that observations are made relative to a specified frame of reference. Often our frame will be the earth itself. But whatever it is, we shall always specify it. How physical laws, or physical measurements such as time or length intervals, are affected by the reference frame in which they are described is the basic program of relativity theory.

In the sections immediately following, we shall discuss standards and units of length and of time. These ideas will then be combined (Chapter 3) into a detailed study of motion.

1–4 Length

The international standard of length is a bar of platinum-iridium alloy called the *standard meter*, which is kept at the International Bureau of Weights and Measures near Paris, France. The distance between two lines engraved on gold plugs near the end of the bar, when the bar is at a temperature of 0°C, is called *one meter*. One-hundredth of this distance is called *one centimeter*.* This bar is the primary standard of length. Because of its inaccessibility, copies of this primary standard are made, called secondary standards. They are distributed to the standardizing agencies of various nations, such as the National Bureau of Standards in Washington. A copy of this standard, known as Meter No. 27, was delivered to President Benjamin Harrison on January 2, 1890 (Fig. 1–1). The accuracy of the wooden meter stick is fixed by manufacturing specifications derived from the secondary standard, and it is accurate enough for most common determinations of length.

Historically, the meter was arrived at by seeking some convenient fraction of the distance from pole to equator along the meridian line through Paris. The meter was defined as one-ten-millionth of this distance. However, accurate measurements taken after the standard was originally determined show that it differs slightly (about 0.023%) from its intended value.

More recently, the distance between the two lines on the standard bar was very precisely compared with the wavelength of the orange light emitted by atoms of a single pure isotope of krypton (krypton-86) in an electrical discharge. The reasons for the choice of this atom and the specific color and the technique used will be discussed in a later chapter. Krypton-86 atoms are universally available and the orange light from them can be reproduced in any laboratory. The wavelength of this light is therefore a truly accessible standard. Furthermore, since all krypton atoms (of a given isotope) are exactly alike, the wavelength of the light used is invariable. The wavelength is uniquely characteristic of krypton-86 and is unaltered with time. This wavelength may soon be adopted as the new standard of length. The meter is to be defined as 1,650,763.73 times this wavelength. All precise measurements of length are now made with light waves.

The orange krypton-86 light wave is the most sharply defined wavelength currently available for length measurements. For ordinary laboratory measurements, spectroscopic lamps containing a single pure isotope of

---

* The subdivision of the meter into 100 equal divisions can be made with a dividing engine, which is essentially an accurately made screw which advances through equal distances for each rotation of the screw.

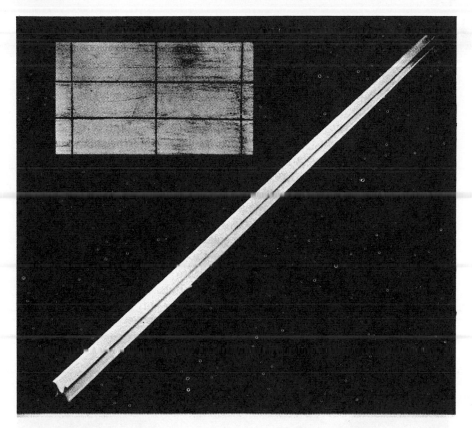

Fig. 1–1 Meter No. 27 at the National Bureau of Standards. The detail in the upper left-hand corner shows three marks scratched near the end of the bar, the center one marking the end of the meter.

mercury (mercury-198) have been made generally available by the U. S. National Bureau of Standards. The mercury 198 is obtained by transmutation of gold in a nuclear reactor at the Oak Ridge National Laboratory. Length measurements made with the green light emitted from this lamp are accurate to 1 part in a billion, or 100 times better than the accuracy possible with the standard meter.

The *yard*, originally embodied by a physical standard like the meter, is now defined legally in all English-speaking nations as

$$1 \text{ yard} = 0.9144 \text{ meter, exactly.}$$

Hence, the same physical standard serves for the yard, the meter, and the centimeter.

1–5 Time

The measurement of time is essentially a process of counting. Any phenomenon whatever that repeats itself can be used as a measure of time; the measurement consists of counting the repetitions. Of the many such phenomena that occur in nature, we have adopted the spinning of the earth about its axis. This motion, as reflected in the apparent motions of the stars and the sun, is a readily available standard.

Our standard of time for all purposes until recent years was the *mean solar second*, still the legal standard. The mean solar second is defined as the 1/86,400 part of the mean solar day. The solar day is the interval between two consecutive passages of the sun across the plane of the meridian at the place in question. Owing to the variable speed of the earth in its rotation about the sun, the solar day varies somewhat throughout the year. The mean solar day is the average taken over the year. In practice, measurements are made of the time between two successive passages of the same fixed star across the meridian plane at the place of observation; this is called the sidereal day (Latin: *sidus, sideris*, of a star). Since an exact relation between the sidereal day and the mean solar day can be calculated (Fig. 1–2), the length of the mean solar second is thereby precisely determined by transit observations of the stars.

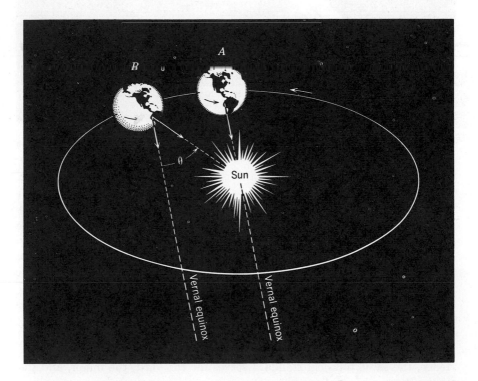

Fig. 1–2 Solar and sidereal time. An observer on the earth on March 21 sees that both the sun and a fixed direction in the heavens called the vernal equinox are directly above at the same time. This represents solar and sidereal noon. Many days later, when the earth has moved to *B*, the vernal equinox is directly above *before* the sun is by $\theta°/360°$ of a day. Thus sidereal noon occurs before solar noon by this time interval.

The rotation of the earth can be observed only when clouds do not obscure the celestial bodies. Hence, a good mechanical clock is needed to keep time during the interval between astronomical observations, at which time the small corrections needed can be applied to it. Actually, quartz crystal clocks, based on electrically induced mechanical vibrations, are used to keep time for the few weeks it is necessary to rely on them. The best of these clocks has kept mean solar time for a year with a maximum error of about 0.02 second. Time signals, based on such a clock, are broadcast from the U. S. Naval Observatory on a special-frequency radio station, WWV.*

When the times of occurrence of previous solar eclipses are calculated from a mean solar clock, they are found to differ from the times at which the eclipses were actually observed to occur. The discrepancy is a gradually changing one, being greater for early eclipses than for recent ones. Such eclipse calculations involve a comparison of the earth's rotation with its orbital motion. This discrepancy suggests that a clock based on the earth's orbital motion would get further and further out of step with the mean solar clock based on the earth's rotation as time went on. The inconsistency is explained in terms of a variation of the earth's speed of rotation. In relation to the orbital motion this variation amounts to as much as 1 part in 10^8, or 1 second every few years.

Among the motions of the solar system that can be observed accurately enough to be used as clocks are the rotation of the earth about its axis, the revolution of the earth about the sun, the revolution of the moon around the earth, that of Mercury and Venus around the sun, and those of the four large moons of Jupiter around that planet. Of these nine clocks, it is found that eight agree with one another, the one outstanding disagreement being the rotation of the earth about its axis. Hence, many observations have led to the conclusion that the earth's speed of rotation varies. The chief variation is a gradual slowing down of the rotation, at such a rate that the length of the day is increased by 0.001 second in a century. The cumulative effect on the measure of time over twenty centuries amounts to several hours. This would account for the discrepancies just noted in the occurrence of eclipses. The cause of this slowing down is known to be tidal friction between the water and the land. In addition there are irregularities in the rotation of the earth. A regular seasonal variation has been explained in terms of the seasonal motion of the winds. Causes of other variations are obscure but may be associated with melting of polar icecaps or shifts in other earth masses. All this suggests that the earth's rotation is not an ideal clock.†

---

* These signals are broadcast each second, the time interval being accurate to 2 parts in 10^8. The carrier frequencies used are 2.5, 5, 10, 15, 20, and 25 megacycles, accurate to 1 part in 10^5. At 5-minute intervals WWV alternately broadcasts a 440-cycle-per-second tone (A) and a 600-cycle-per-second tone.

† At this point we can see more clearly what is meant by a standard being invariable. The term invariability is not used here in any absolute sense but rather in a purely pragmatic or operational sense. In the case of time, for example, we start with the observations

In certain special studies astronomers have already used a new fundamental time standard, the period of the earth's revolution around the sun. This motion is believed to be understood exactly. In fact, in September 1955 the General Assembly of the International Astronomical Union meeting in Dublin accepted a new standard of time based on this motion. How the mean solar second, still used as the standard by physicists and engineers, can be related to this new standard is explained in the resolution adopted by that body.

This new standard may soon be directly available, however, owing to the recent development of atomic clocks. The atomic physicist has demonstrated the possibility of using atomic vibrations as the basis of a secondary time standard.* It is possible, for example, to count the vibrations of the molecules of ammonia gas under electrical excitation. The ammonia molecule is constructed like a pyramid with three hydrogen atoms at its base and a nitrogen atom at the apex (Fig. 1–3a). The molecule inverts itself like an umbrella turning inside out so that the pyramid points in the opposite direction. The inversion takes place spontaneously and periodically (at regular intervals) about 24 billion times per second. The inversion frequency of an isolated ammonia molecule (number of vibrations per second) depends only on the nature of the nitrogen and hydrogen atoms. The frequency cannot be changed since no small changes within the molecule can occur. If the molecule is varied the smallest possible amount, by removing one electron, for example, it is almost completely disrupted and changed. This is certainly different from the situation in regard to the earth, where innumerable small changes can occur. The ammonia molecule has the same physical characteristics no matter when or where the ammonia is produced and ammonia is obviously very accessible. Hence, the ammonia molecule is ideal for a time standard.

The problem is to attach some sort of dial to this molecule so that we can actually tell time by it. Recently, high-frequency electronic techniques have made it possible to synchronize electronic circuit oscillations with the molecular motions (Fig. 1–3b) and to have these motions control the oscillations. These electronic circuits can in turn control a standard clock of the usual type (Fig. 1–3c). Current models of this ammonia "atomic clock" are already better than quartz crystal clocks. This frequency can be accurately controlled to 2 parts in a billion.

Another type of atomic clock now being developed at the Bureau of Standards and elsewhere is controlled by the magnetic behavior of cesium atoms. Here the vibration is controlled by applied magnetic forces acting on the atom. The cesium atoms are in an atomic beam and are not free to collide with each other as do the molecules in the ammonia clock. Consequently the frequency can be measured to better than 1 part in 10 billion (1 second in 300 years) or 400 times better than a clock based on the earth's rotation.

---

of the celestial bodies and the theories of their motion. We find that when the rotation of the earth is taken as our measure of time, there are discrepancies between theory and observation. Now it is a fundamental principle of experimental science that carefully made observations are not to be doubted. Clearly then either the theory or the measure of time must be at fault. As scientists we prefer to choose the one that leaves us with the simplest model of the universe. This points to our time standard as the culprit. The alternative would be to find a new and more complicated theory of motion not otherwise needed. Hence, an invariable measure of time is simply the measure of time defined by the accepted laws of motion.

* See an article "Atomic Clocks" by Harold Lyons, in *Scientific American*, February 1957.

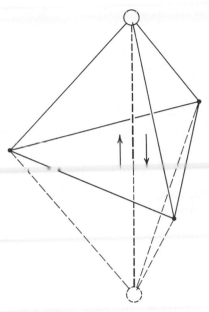

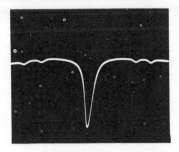

(b) The absorption curve of ammonia as recorded on an oscilloscope. The trace shows the power received from a beam of radio waves transmitted through the gas. Frequency varies along the horizontal axis. The dip in the curve shows that at the resonant frequency most of the wave energy is absorbed. The range of frequencies indicated by the width of the dip limits the accuracy of ammonia clocks.

Fig. 1–3 The ammonia clock. (a) The ammonia molecule has the shape of a pyramid with hydrogen atoms ● forming a triangular base and a nitrogen atom ○ at the apex. The nitrogen atom oscillates up and down through the base as indicated by the arrows.

(c) The first model of the ammonia clock was completed at the National Bureau of Standards in 1949. The wave guide containing the ammonia gas is seen wound around the face of the electric clock. The cabinets below house the crystal oscillator and other electronic circuits. (From Scientific American, February, 1957.)

Once the frequency of an atomic frequency standard has been determined to sufficient accuracy with respect to the new standard second, this atomic standard may be used as a new time standard. The trend toward atomic standards of both length and time is apparent.

With atomic clocks it will become possible to study a number of problems of great scientific and practical importance, ranging from changes in the earth's rotation and checks on the theory of relativity to improvements in navigation.

1–6 Systems of Units

As already pointed out, there is a certain amount of arbitrariness in the choice of the fundamental quantities.* For example, length, time, and mass can be chosen as fundamental quantities; then all other mechanical quantities, such as force, torque, density, etc., can be expressed in terms of (or derived from) these fundamental quantities. However, we might equally well choose force instead of mass as a fundamental quantity. But having picked the fundamental quantities and determined units for them we thereby automatically determine the units of the derived quantities.

Three different systems of units are most commonly used in science and engineering. They are the *meter-kilogram-second* or mks system, the *centimeter-gram-second* or cgs system, and the British engineering system (or *foot-pound-second* system). The gram and the kilogram are mass units, and the pound is a force unit; these will be defined and discussed in Chapter 5. The units used in the mks system turn out to be the standards themselves.

We shall use the mks system principally throughout the text, except in the mechanics sections where the fps system will also be used. The units used in the fps system are derived from the original legal standards of the

Table 1–1

SOME MULTIPLES AND SUBMULTIPLES OF METRIC QUANTITIES

$\dfrac{1}{1,000,000}$	$\dfrac{1}{1000}$	$\dfrac{1}{100}$	$\dfrac{1}{10}$	Quantity (examples)	10	100	1000	1,000,000
micro-	milli-	centi-	deci-	meter gram second	deka-	hekto-	kilo-	mega-
10^{-6}	10^{-3}	10^{-2}	10^{-1}	1	10^1	10^2	10^3	10^6

English-speaking countries. The metric systems are used universally in scientific work. A list of some multiples and submultiples of the metric units, which are simply related by powers of ten, is given in Table 1–1.

* See an article "Dimensions, Units, and Standards" by A. G. McNish, in *Physics Today*, April 1957.

QUESTIONS

1. Do you think that a definition of a physical quantity for which no method of measurement is known or given has meaning?

2. According to operational philosophy, if we cannot prescribe a feasible operation for the determination of a physical quantity, the quantity is undetectable by physical means and should be given up as having no physical reality. Not all scientists accept this view. What are the merits and drawbacks of this point of view in your opinion?

3. What characteristics, other than accessibility and invariability, would you consider desirable for a physical standard?

4. If someone told you that every dimension of every object had shrunk to half its former value overnight, how could you refute his statement?

5. How would you refute the following statement: "Once you have picked a physical standard, by the very meaning of standard it is invariable"?

6. Why is it necessary to specify the temperature at which comparisons with the standard meter bar are to be made? Can length be called a fundamental quantity if another physical quantity, such as temperature, must be specified in choosing a standard?

7. Can length be measured along a curved line? If so, how?

8. Can you suggest a way to measure (a) the radius of the earth, (b) the distance between the sun and the earth; (c) the size of the sun?

9. Explain how a time standard is derived from a frequency standard.

10. What criteria should a good clock satisfy?

11. Why isn't the year an integral number of whole days?

12. Name several repetitive phenomena occurring in nature which could serve as reasonable time standards.

13. Looking ahead to the days of space travel, when man ceases to be earth-bound and colonizes other planets, what drawbacks would our present standards of length and time have? What drawbacks would atomic standards have?

14. Can you think of a way to define a length standard in terms of a time standard or vice versa? (Think about a pendulum clock.) If so, can length and time both be considered as fundamental quantities?

PROBLEMS

1. Express your height in the metric system of units.

2. In track meets both 100 yards and 100 meters are used as distances for dashes. Which is longer? By how many meters is it longer? By how many feet?

3. A rocket attained a height of 300 kilometers. What was its highest altitude in miles?

4. Machine-tool men would like to have master gauges good to 0.0000001 inch. Show that the platinum-iridium meter is not measurable to this accuracy but that the krypton orange wavelength is. Use data given in the chapter.

5. Assuming that the length of the day uniformly increases by 0.001 second in a century, show how to calculate the cumulative effect on the measure of time over twenty centuries.

6. Calculate the exact relation between a solar day and a sidereal day (see Fig. 1–2). (Hint: There is exactly one less mean solar day in a year than there are sidereal days in a year.)

7. A naval destroyer is testing five clocks. Exactly at noon, as determined by WWV time signal, on the successive days of a week the clocks read as follows:

	Sun.	Mon.	Tues.	Wed.	Thurs.	Fri.	Sat.
A	12:36:40	12:36:56	12:37:12	12:37:27	12:37:44	12:37:59	12:38:14
B	11:59:59	12:00:02	11:59:57	12:00:07	12:00:02	11:59:56	12:00:03
C	15:50:45	15:51:43	15:52:41	15:53:39	15:54:37	15:55:35	15:56:33
D	12:03:59	12:02:52	12:01:45	12:00:38	11:59:31	11:58:24	11:57:17
E	12:03:59	12:02:49	12:01:54	12:01:52	12:01:32	12:01:22	12:01:12

How would you arrange these five clocks in the order of their relative value as good time-keepers? Justify your choice.

8. (*a*) The radius of the nucleus of an atom is about 10^{-15} meter; the radius of the observable universe is about 10^{28} centimeters. Find the ratio of these extreme distances. (*b*) The mean life of a neutral pi-meson (an elementary nuclear particle) is about 10^{-15} second. The age of the universe is about 4×10^9 years. Find the ratio of these extreme intervals.

Vectors

CHAPTER 2

2-1 Vectors and Scalars

A change of position of a particle is called its *displacement*. If a particle moves from position A to position B (Fig. 2–1a), we can represent its displacement by drawing a line from A to B; the direction of displacement can be shown by putting an arrowhead at B indicating that the displacement was *from A to B*. The path of the particle need not necessarily be a straight line from A to B; the straight line represents only the net effect of the motion, not the actual motion.

In Fig. 2–1b, for example, we plot the path followed by a particle from A to B to C. The path from A to B is not the same as the displacement AB. If we were to take snapshots of the particle at the times when it was at the positions A and B, we could obtain the net effect of the motion during this time, even though we would not know the actual path taken between these points. The same considerations apply to the path from A to C or from B to C.

Furthermore, a displacement such as $A'B'$ (Fig. 2–1a), which is parallel to AB, similarly directed, and of equal length to AB, will represent the same *change* in position as AB. We make no distinction between these two displacements. A displacement is therefore characterized by a *length* and a *direction*.

We can represent a subsequent displacement, from B to C, in a similar way (Fig. 2–1c). The net effect of the two displacements will be the same as a displacement from A to C. We speak then of AC (dashed line) as the *sum* or *resultant* of the displacements AB and BC. Notice that this sum is not an algebraic sum and that a number alone cannot uniquely specify it.

13

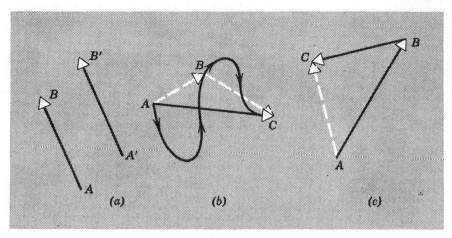

Fig. 2-1 Displacement vectors. (a) Vectors AB and $A'B'$ are equivalent since they have the same length and point in the same direction. (b) A particle travels the curved path from A to B and then from B to C. The displacement, however, is a straight line directed from A to C. (c) The sum of two displacements, from A to B and from B to C, is represented by the (dashed) vector AC.

Quantities that behave like displacements are called *vectors*. Vectors, then, are quantities that have both magnitude and direction and that combine according to certain rules of addition. These rules will be stated below. The displacement vector can be considered as the prototype. Some other physical quantities which are vectors are force, velocity, acceleration, electric field intensity, and magnetic induction.

Quantities that can be completely specified by a number and unit and that therefore have magnitude only are called *scalars*. Some physical quantities which are scalars are mass, length, time, density, energy, and temperature. Scalars can be manipulated by the rules of ordinary algebra.

2-2 Addition of Vectors, Geometrical Method

To represent a vector on a diagram we draw an arrow. We choose the length of the arrow to be proportional to the magnitude of the vector (that is, we choose a scale), and we choose the direction of the arrow to be the direction of the vector, with the arrowhead giving the sense of the direction. For example, a displacement of 40 ft north of east on a scale of 1 unit per 10 ft would be represented by an arrow 4 units long, drawn at an angle of 45° to the horizontal direction with the arrowhead at the top right extreme. A vector such as this can be represented by a symbol such as **d**, with the bold-face signifying both properties of a vector, magnitude and direction.* Often

---

* Boldface type is used in most texts to represent a vector quantity. This scheme is convenient in printing but is not well suited to typing or handwriting. A convenient notation for handwriting is one that employs a little arrow above the symbol to denote a vector quantity, such as $\vec{a}$.

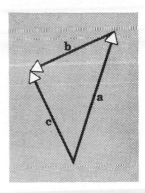

Fig. 2-2 The vector sum $\mathbf{a} + \mathbf{b} = \mathbf{c}$. (Compare with Fig. 2-1c.)

we shall be interested only in the magnitude of the vector (its "absolute value"); then we use the italic letter symbol rather than the boldface symbol.

Consider now Fig. 2-2 in which we have redrawn the vectors of Fig. 2-1c with appropriate symbols. The relation among these displacements (vectors) can now be written symbolically as

$$\mathbf{a} + \mathbf{b} = \mathbf{c}. \tag{2-1}$$

The rules to be followed in performing the addition geometrically are these: On a diagram drawn to scale lay out the displacement $\mathbf{a}$; then draw $\mathbf{b}$ with its tail at the head of $\mathbf{a}$, and draw a line from the tail of $\mathbf{a}$ to the head of $\mathbf{b}$ to construct the vector sum $\mathbf{c}$. This is a displacement equivalent in length and direction to the successive displacements $\mathbf{a}$ and $\mathbf{b}$. This procedure can be generalized to obtain the sum of any number of successive displacements.

Since vectors are new quantities, we must expect new rules for their manipulation. The symbol "+" here simply has a different meaning than it does in arithmetic or ordinary algebra. It tells us to carry out a different set of operations.

Some important properties of vector addition can now be verified (Fig. 2-3). First of all,

$$\mathbf{a} + \mathbf{b} = \mathbf{b} + \mathbf{a}, \tag{2-2}$$

$$(\mathbf{d} + \mathbf{e}) + \mathbf{f} = \mathbf{d} + (\mathbf{e} + \mathbf{f}). \tag{2-3}$$

That is, it makes no difference in what order or in what grouping we add

Fig. 2-3 On the left is illustrated the commutative law for vector sums which states that $\mathbf{a} + \mathbf{b} = \mathbf{b} + \mathbf{a}$. On the right is illustrated the associative law which states that $\mathbf{d} + (\mathbf{e} + \mathbf{f}) = (\mathbf{d} + \mathbf{e}) + \mathbf{f}$.

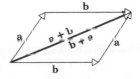

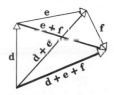

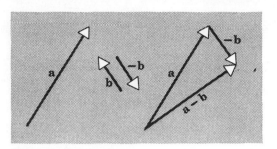

Fig. 2–4 The vector difference $\mathbf{a} + (-\mathbf{b}) = \mathbf{a} - \mathbf{b}$.

vectors; the sum is the same.* In this respect, vector addition and scalar addition follow the same rules.

The operation of subtraction can be included in our vector algebra by deciding that the negative of a vector means a vector of equal magnitude but opposite direction. Then

$$\mathbf{a} - \mathbf{b} = \mathbf{a} + (-\mathbf{b}), \tag{2–4}$$

as shown in Fig. 2–4.

Remember, that, although we have used displacements to illustrate these operations, the rules will apply to *all* vector quantities.

2–3 Resolution and Addition of Vectors, Analytical Method

The geometrical method of combining vectors is not very useful when we deal with vectors in three dimensions; often this method is inconvenient even for the two-dimensional case. Another general way of handling this problem is to use an analytical method involving the resolution of a vector into components along the coordinate axes.

Consider, for example, a vector $\mathbf{a}$ in the x–y plane (Fig. 2–5a). The components of the vector $\mathbf{a}$ are the projections of the vector on the coordinate axes. If θ is the angle that the vector makes with the positive x-axis, measured counterclockwise from this axis, and if a is the magnitude of the vector, the x component a_x and the y component a_y are given by

$$a_x = a \cos \theta, \qquad a_y = a \sin \theta. \tag{2–5}$$

Depending on the angle θ, a_x or a_y can be positive or negative, indicating that the component is either along the positive x- or y-axes or the negative x- or y-axes, respectively. For example, in Fig. 2–5b, b_y is negative and b_x is positive.

In the figure the vectors are drawn out from the origin of the coordinate system for convenience; notice, however, that the magnitudes of the projections are independent of the location of the vectors with respect to the origin. They depend only on the directions of the coordinate axes relative to the vector. Hence, the components of a vector are not unique but depend on the orientation of the coordinate system we use to describe the vector.

---

* These properties are called the commutative and associative laws of addition, respectively.

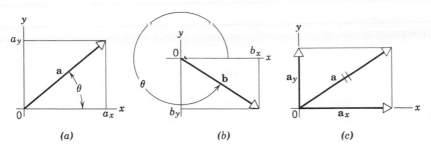

Fig. 2-5 Resolution of a vector into its components.

From the geometrical picture we can see at once that two vectors, one of magnitude a_x along the x-axis, called $\mathbf{a}_x$, and one of magnitude a_y along the y-axis, called $\mathbf{a}_y$, add to give us the original vector $\mathbf{a}$. Hence, $\mathbf{a}$ can be replaced by its equivalent $\mathbf{a}_x$ and $\mathbf{a}_y$, which are now drawn as vectors along the coordinate axes (Fig. 2–5c).

Once a vector is resolved into its components, the components themselves can be used to specify the vector. Instead of the two numbers a (magnitude of the vector) and θ (direction of the vector relative to x-axis), we now have the two numbers a_x and a_y. We can pass back and forth between the description of a vector in terms of its components a_x, a_y and a description in terms of magnitude and direction a and θ. To obtain a and θ from a_x and a_y, we note that

$$a = \sqrt{a_x{}^2 + a_y{}^2} \tag{2–6}$$

from the Pythagorean theorem, and

$$\tan \theta = a_y/a_x. \tag{2–7}$$

The quadrant in which θ lies is determined from the sign of a_x and a_y.

In order to add several vectors by the analytical method, we now use the rule for vector addition stated in terms of the vector components, namely: *The component, along any given direction, of the sum of several vectors is the algebraic sum of the components of the several vectors, taken along the same direction.* For example, for two vectors in the x–y plane, if

$$\mathbf{c} = \mathbf{a} + \mathbf{b}, \tag{2–8}$$

then

$$c_x = a_x + b_x, $$
$$c_y = a_y + b_y. \tag{2–9}$$

These two algebraic equations, Eqs. 2–9 taken together, are equivalent to the single vector equation, Eq. 2–8. From c_x and c_y the magnitude c, of the vector $\mathbf{c}$, can be computed from the Pythagorean theorem

$$c = \sqrt{c_x{}^2 + c_y{}^2}; \tag{2–10}$$

and the angle θ which **c** makes with the x-axis can be obtained, for example, from

$$\tan \theta = c_y/c_x. \tag{2–11}$$

The quadrant in which θ lies is determined from considering the sign of c_y and c_x.

The advantage of the method of breaking up vectors into components, rather than adding directly with the use of suitable trigonometric relations, is that we always deal with right triangles and thereby simplify the calculations.

These considerations can be generalized to many vectors and to three dimensions.   (See Problems 5 and 10.)

In adding vectors by the analytical method, the choice of coordinate axes determines how simple the process will be.   Sometimes the components of the vectors with respect to a particular set of axes are known to begin with, so that the choice of axes is obvious.   Other times a judicious choice of axes can greatly simplify the job of resolution of the vectors into components. For example, the axes can be oriented so that at least one of the vectors lies parallel to an axis.

▶ **Example 1.**   An airplane travels 130 miles on a straight course making an angle of 22.5° east of due north.   How far north and how far east did the plane travel from its starting point?

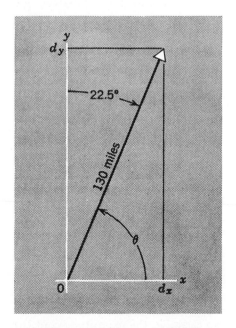

Fig. 2–6 Example 1.

We choose the x-axis along the east direction and the y-axis along the north direction.   Next (Fig. 2–6), we draw in a displacement vector from the origin (starting point), making an angle of 22.5° with the y-axis (north) inclined along the positive

x direction (east). The length of the vector is chosen to represent a magnitude of 130 miles. If we call this vector $\mathbf{d}$, then d_x gives the distance traveled east of tho starting point and d_y gives the distance traveled north of the starting point. We have

$$\theta = 90.0° - 22.5° = 67.5°,$$

so that

$$d_x = d \cos \theta = (130 \text{ miles}) \cos 67.5° = 130 \text{ miles } (0.383) = 50 \text{ miles},$$

$$d_y = d \sin \theta = (130 \text{ miles}) \sin 67.5° = 130 \text{ miles } (0.924) = 120 \text{ miles}.$$

Example 2. An automobile travels due east on a level road for 30 miles. It then turns due north at an intersection and travels 40 miles before stopping. Find the resultant displacement of the car.

Take the x-axis along the east direction and the y-axis along the north direction. The two successive displacements, $\mathbf{a}$ and $\mathbf{b}$, are then drawn as shown in Fig. 2–7.

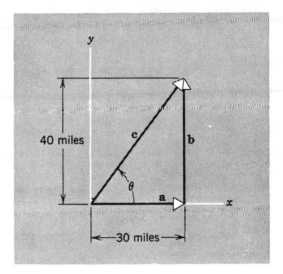

Fig. 2–7   Example 2.

The resultant displacement $\mathbf{c}$ is obtained from $\mathbf{c} = \mathbf{a} + \mathbf{b}$. Since $\mathbf{b}$ has no x component and $\mathbf{a}$ has no y component, we obtain

$$c_x = a_x + b_x = 30 \text{ miles} + 0 = 30 \text{ miles},$$

$$c_y = a_y + b_y = 0 + 40 \text{ miles} = 40 \text{ miles},$$

$$c = \sqrt{c_x{}^2 + c_y{}^2} = \sqrt{(30 \text{ miles})^2 + (40 \text{ miles})^2} = 50 \text{ miles},$$

$$\tan \theta = c_y/c_x = \frac{40 \text{ miles}}{30 \text{ miles}} = 1.33 \qquad \theta = \tan^{-1}(1.33) = 53°.$$

The resultant vector displacement $\mathbf{c}$ has a magnitude of 50 miles and makes an angle of 53° north of east. ◀

2–4 Multiplication of Vectors *

It has been implicitly assumed in the previous discussion that the vectors being added together are of like kind; that is, displacement vectors are added to displacement vectors, or velocity vectors are added to velocity vectors. Just as it would be meaningless to add together scalar quantities of different kinds, such as mass and temperature, so it would be meaningless to add together vector quantities of different kinds, such as displacement and electric field strength.

However, like scalars, vectors of different kinds can be multiplied by one another to generate quantities of new physical dimensions. Because of the fact that vectors have direction as well as magnitude, vector products cannot follow exactly the same rules as the algebraic rules of scalar multiplication.

We must establish new rules of multiplication for vectors. Among the many possibilities, we would pick the rules that will give physically meaningful results. We find it useful to define three kinds of multiplication operations involving vectors. They are (1) multiplication of a vector by a scalar, (2) multiplication of two vectors in such a way as to yield a scalar, and (3) multiplication of two vectors in such a way as to yield another vector. There are still other useful possibilities, but we need not consider them here.

The multiplication of a vector by a scalar has a simple meaning: The product of a scalar k and a vector $\mathbf{a}$, written $k\mathbf{a}$, is a new vector, each of whose components is the product of k and the corresponding component of $\mathbf{a}$. The magnitude of the new vector is k times the magnitude of $\mathbf{a}$. The new vector has the same direction as $\mathbf{a}$ if k is positive and the opposite direction if k is negative.

To divide a vector quantity by a scalar quantity we simply multiply the vector by the reciprocal of the scalar.

When we multiply a vector quantity by another vector quantity, we must distinguish between the *scalar* (or *dot*) *product* and the *vector* (or *cross*) *product*. The scalar product of two vectors is the product of the magnitude of one vector by the magnitude of the component of the second vector in the direction of the first. Let our vectors be $\mathbf{A}$ and $\mathbf{B}$, where the angle † between $\mathbf{A}$ and $\mathbf{B}$ is ϕ (Fig. 2–8). Then the *scalar product* of $\mathbf{A}$ and $\mathbf{B}$, written as $\mathbf{A} \cdot \mathbf{B}$, is defined by

$$\mathbf{A} \cdot \mathbf{B} = AB \cos \phi. \tag{2–12}$$

Here A is the magnitude of the vector $\mathbf{A}$ and B is the magnitude of the vector $\mathbf{B}$, both quantities being scalars, that is, having only magnitude; $\cos \phi$, the cosine of the angle between A and B, is merely a number. Therefore the *scalar product of two vectors is itself a scalar quantity*. Scalar quan-

---

* The material of this section will be used later in the text. The scalar product is first used in Chapter 7, the vector product in Chapter 11. The instructor can postpone this section accordingly. Its presentation here gives a complete and unified treatment of vector algebra and serves as a convenient reference for later work.

† We can, of course, obtain two different angles between a pair of vectors, depending on the sense of rotation. We always choose the *smaller* of the two in vector multiplication.

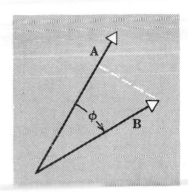

Fig. 2-8 The magnitude of **A** is A. The magnitude of the projection of **B** along **A** is $B \cos \phi$. The product $AB \cos \phi$ is the scalar product of **A** and **B**.

tities derived in this way have the same numerical value irrespective of the coordinate system used to represent the vectors. This becomes clear when we recall that the magnitude of a vector does not depend on the choice of reference frame, nor does the angle *between the two vectors* change when we change the reference frame in which we represent them.

We could have defined **A·B** to be any operation we want. We could have defined it, for example, to be $A^{\frac{1}{3}}B^3 \tan (\theta/2)$, but this would never be of any use to us in physics. With our definition of the scalar product, a number of important physical quantities can be described as the scalar product of two vectors.

Some physical quantities that are the scalar product of two vectors are mechanical work, gravitational potential energy, electrical potential, electric power, and electromagnetic energy density. When such quantities are discussed later, their connection with the scalar product of vectors will be pointed out.

The *vector product* of two vectors, **A** and **B**, is written as **A × B** and is another vector, **C**, where **C = A × B**. The *magnitude* of **C** is given by

$$C = AB \sin \phi \qquad (2\text{-}13)$$

where ϕ is the angle between **A** and **B**.

The *direction* of **C** is perpendicular to the plane formed by **A** and **B**. To specify the sense of the vector **C** we must refer to Fig. 2-9. Imagine rotating a right-hand screw whose axis is perpendicular to the plane formed by **A** and **B** so as to turn it *from* **A** *to* **B** through the angle ϕ between them. Then the direction of advance of the screw gives the direction of the vector product **A × B** (Fig. 2-9a). Another convenient way to obtain the direction of a vector product is the following. Imagine an axis perpendicular to the plane of **A** and **B** through their origin. Now wrap the fingers of the *right hand* around this axis and push the vector **A** into the vector **B** through the smaller angle between them with the fingertips, keeping the thumb erect; the direction of the erect thumb then gives the direction of the vector product **A × B** (Fig. 2-9b).

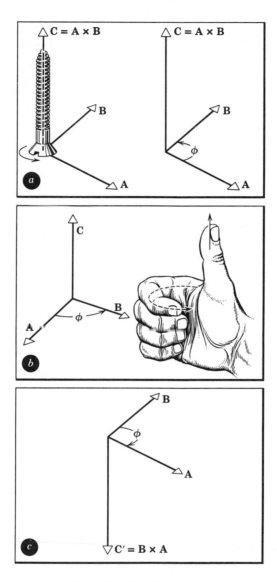

Fig. 2–9 The cross product. (*a*) In **C** = **A** × **B**, the direction of **C** is that in which a screw advances when turned from **A** to **B** through the smaller angle. (*b*) The direction of **C** can also be obtained by the so-called "right-hand rule": If the hand is held so that the curled fingers follow the rotation of **A** into **B**, the thumb will point in the direction of **C**. (*c*) The cross product changes sign when the order of the factors is reversed: **A** × **B** = −(**B** × **A**).

Notice that **B** × **A** is not the same vector as **A** × **B**, so that the order of factors in a vector product is important. This is not true for scalars because the order of factors in algebra or arithmetic does not affect the resulting product. Actually, **A** × **B** = −**B** × **A** (Fig. 2-9c). This can be deduced from the fact that the magnitude $AB \sin \phi$ equals the magnitude $BA \sin \phi$, but the direction of **A** × **B** is opposite to that of **B** × **A**; this is so because the right-hand screw advances in one direction when rotated from **A** to **B** through ϕ but advances in the opposite direction when rotated from **B** to **A** through ϕ. The student can obtain the same result by applying the right-hand rule.

In the particular case where ϕ is 90°, **A**, **B**, and **C** (= **A** × **B**) are all at right angles to one another and give the directions of a three-dimensional right-handed coordinate system.

The reason for defining the vector product in this way is that it proves to be useful in physics. We often encounter physical quantities which are vectors whose product, as just defined, is a vector quantity having important physical meaning. Some examples of physical quantities that are vector products are torque, angular momentum, the force on a moving charge in a magnetic field, and the flow of electromagnetic energy. When such quantities are discussed later in the book, their connection with the vector product of vectors will be pointed out.

The scalar product is the simplest product of two vectors. The order of multiplication does not affect the product. The vector product is the next simplest case. Here the order of multiplication does affect the product, but only by a factor of minus one, which implies a direction reversal. Other products of vectors are useful but more involved. For example, a tensor can be generated by multiplying each of the three components of one vector by the three components of another vector. Hence, a tensor has nine numbers associated with it, a vector three, and a scalar only one. Some physical quantities that can be represented by tensors are mechanical and electrical stress, moments and products of inertia, and strain. Still more complex physical quantities are possible. In this book, however, we are concerned only with scalars and vectors.

2-5 Physical Significance of Vector Quantities

It is appropriate at this point to stress the fundamental physical significance of vector quantities. Suppose we have three vectors **A**, **B**, and **C** where **A** has the components A_x, A_y, A_z with respect to our xyz frame of reference, **B** has the components B_x, B_y, B_z, and **C** has the components C_x, C_y, C_z. Let us further suppose that there exists a relation connecting **A**, **B**, and **C**, for example

$$\mathbf{A} + \mathbf{B} = \mathbf{C}.$$

That is, $A_x + B_x = C_x$, $A_y + B_y = C_y$, and $A_z + B_z = C_z$ (Fig. 2-10).

Now suppose we were to transform our axes, that is, suppose we choose to describe our vectors with respect to another frame of reference, say $x'y'z'$. Corresponding to the fact that a given vector will generally have different components in different frames of reference, **A** will now have components A_x', A_y', A_z', **B** will now have components B_x', B_y', B_z', and **C** will now have components C_x', C_y', C_z'. The vectors are now described by different components. However, the new components are found to be related in that

$$A_x' + B_x' = C_x', \qquad A_y' + B_y' = C_y', \qquad \text{and} \qquad A_z' + B_z' = C_z'.$$

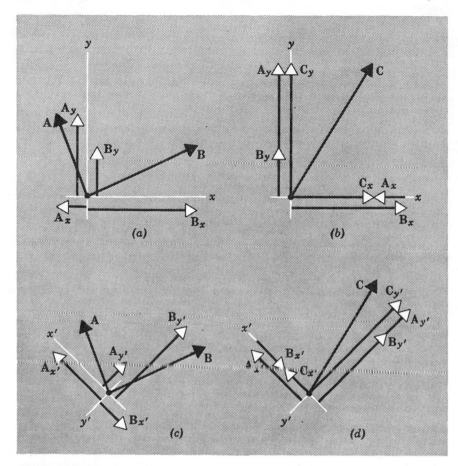

Fig. 2-10 (a) Vectors **A** and **B** are shown resolved into their components in coordinate system (x, y). (b) The x- and y-components are combined and then added to give **C**. (c, d) The same procedure is carried out in a different coordinate system (x', y'), but the resultant **C** is the same as before. We see that vector-algebraic operations (in this case, vector addition) give the same result regardless of the coordinate system chosen.

That is, in the new coordinate system we find once again that **A** + **B** = **C**. This will be true whether our new reference frame was obtained by rotation or by translation of our original reference frame.

In words, we find that *the relation connecting the vectors remains unchanged by the transformation of coordinates*. This is an important result. It says that if the equations of physics are vector equations, they will have the same form regardless of the orientation of the axis of the coordinate system involved. By use of vector quantities and vector equations, we make sure that physical statements are independent of rotation and translation of the coordinate system. This is a highly desirable result, even if not unexpected.

QUESTIONS

1. Can two vectors of different magnitude be combined to give a zero resultant? Can three vectors? Explain.
2. Can a vector be zero if one of its components is not zero?
3. Does it make any sense to call a quantity a vector when its magnitude is zero?
4. Name several scalar quantities. Is the value of a scalar quantity dependent on the coordinate system chosen?
5. We can order events in time. For example, event B may precede event C but follow event A, giving us a time order of events A, B, C. Hence, there is a sense of time, distinguishing past, present, and future. Is time a vector, therefore? If not, why not?

PROBLEMS

1. A man flies from Washington to Manila. Describe the displacement vector. What is its magnitude if the latitude and longitude of the two cities are 39°N, 77°W and 15°N, 121°E?
2. Two vectors **A** and **B** are added. Show that the magnitude of the resultant cannot be greater than $A + B$ or smaller than $|A - B|$, where the vertical bars signify absolute value.
3. A car is driven eastward for a distance of 50 miles, then northward for 30 miles, and then in a direction 30° east of north for 25 miles. Draw the vector diagram and determine the total displacement of the car from its starting point.
4. Consider two displacements, one of magnitude 3 meters and another of magnitude 4 meters. Show how the displacement vectors may be combined to get a resultant displacement of magnitude (a) 7 meters, (b) 1 meter, and (c) 5 meters.
5. Generalize the analytical method of vector resolution and addition to the case of *three or more vectors*.
6. A golfer takes three strokes to get his ball into the hole once he is on the green. The first stroke displaces the ball 12 ft north, the second stroke 6.0 ft southeast, and the third stroke 3.0 ft southwest. What displacement was needed to get the ball into the hole on the first stroke?
7. A particle undergoes three successive displacements in a plane, as follows: 4 meters southwest, 5 meters east, 6 meters in a direction 60° north of east. Choose the y-axis pointing north and the x-axis pointing east and find (a) the components of each displacement, (b) the components of the resultant displacement, (c) the magnitude and direction of the resultant displacement, and (d) the displacement that would be required to bring the particle back to the starting point.
8. Use a scale of 2 meters to the inch and add the displacements of Problem 7 graphically. Determine *from your graph* the magnitude and direction of the resultant.
9. Find the sum of the vector displacements **a**, **b**, and **c**, which are all in a plane and are specified by their components as follows:

$$a_x = 12 \text{ meters} \qquad b_x = -10 \text{ meters} \qquad c_x = 6 \text{ meters}$$

$$a_y = 4 \text{ meters} \qquad b_y = 0 \text{ meter} \qquad c_y = 2 \text{ meters}$$

10. Generalize the analytical method of resolving and adding two vectors to *three dimensions*.
11. Find the sum of the vector displacements **c** and **d** whose components in miles along three perpendicular directions are

$$c_x = 5, \quad c_y = 0, \quad c_z = -2; \qquad d_x = -3, \quad d_y = 4, \quad d_z = 6.$$

12. Find the sum of the vector displacements **a**, **b**, and **c**, whose components in miles along three perpendicular directions are

$$a_x = -7 \qquad a_y = 4 \qquad a_z = 0$$
$$b_x = 9 \qquad b_y = -3 \qquad b_z = 1$$
$$c_x = 6 \qquad c_y = 3 \qquad c_z = 7$$

13. A room has the dimensions 10 ft × 12 ft × 14 ft. A fly starting at one corner ends up at a diametrically opposite corner. (a) What is the magnitude of its displacement? (b) Could the length of its path be less than this distance? Greater than this distance? Equal to this distance? (c) Choose a suitable reference frame and find the components of the displacement vector in this frame.

14. In the previous problem, if the fly does not fly but crawls, what is the length of the shortest path it can take?

15. Carry out the problem in Example 2, using some *other* coordinate system, and show that the same result occurs.

16. A vector **d** has a magnitude 2.5 meters and points due north. What are the magnitudes and directions of the vectors (a) −**d**, (b) **d**/2.0, (c) −2.5**d**, and (d) 4.0**d**?

17. Two vectors of lengths A and B make an angle θ with each other when placed tail to tail. Prove, by taking components along two perpendicular axes, that the length of the resultant vector is

$$R = \sqrt{A^2 + B^2 + 2AB \cos \theta}.$$

18. Use the standard (right-hand) xyz coordinate system. Given vector **A** in the $+x$ direction, vector **B** in the $+y$ direction, and the scalar quantity d: (a) What is the direction of **A** × **B**? (b) What is the direction of **B** × **A**? (c) What is the direction of **B**/d? (d) What is the magnitude of **A**·**B**?

19. A vector **A** of magnitude ten units and another vector **D** of magnitude six units point in directions differing by 60°. Find (a) the scalar product of the two vectors and (b) the vector product of the two vectors. Do the products have the same dimensions as the original vectors?

20. Show for any vector **A** (with magnitude A) that **A**·**A** = A^2 and that **A** × **A** = 0.

21. Show that the magnitude of a vector product gives numerically the area of the parallelogram formed with the two component vectors as sides. Does this suggest how an element of area oriented in space could be represented by a vector?

22. Show that **A**·(**B** × **C**) is numerically equal to the volume of the parallelepiped formed on the three vectors **A**, **B**, and **C**.

23. Prove that **A**·**B** = **B**·**A**.

24. Show that if vector **A** has components A_x, A_y and vector **B** components B_x, B_y, then **A**·**B** = $A_x B_x + A_y B_y$. [Hint: **A** = **A**$_x$ + **A**$_y$, **B** = **B**$_x$ + **B**$_y$ so that **A**·**B** = (**A**$_x$ + **A**$_y$)· (**B**$_x$ + **B**$_y$).]

25. Show that the area of the triangle contained between the vectors **A** and **B** is $\frac{1}{2}|$**A** × **B**$|$ where the vertical bars signify absolute value.

Motion in One Dimension

CHAPTER 3

3–1 Mechanics

Mechanics is the oldest of the physical sciences. Historically, its fundamental concepts were used and generalized to construct other areas of physics. An understanding of the principles of mechanics therefore provides a foundation for an understanding of all physics.

Basically, mechanics is the study of the motion of material objects. The part that describes the motion is called *kinematics;* the part that relates the motion to the forces causing the motion and to the properties of the moving system is called *dynamics.* In this chapter and the next we discuss kinematics. The more general case of dynamics will be taken up in Chapter 5. First we consider motion in one dimension and in the next chapter two- and three-dimensional motion.

3–2 Particle Kinematics

A real object can rotate as it moves. For example, a baseball may be spinning while it is moving as a whole in some trajectory. Also, a body may vibrate as it moves, as for example a falling water droplet. These complications can be avoided by considering the motion of a very small body called a *particle.* Mathematically, a particle is treated as a point, an object without extent, so that rotational and vibrational considerations are not involved.

Actually, there is no such thing in nature as an object without extent. The concept of "particle" is nevertheless very useful because real bodies often behave, at least in approximation, as though they were particles. A body need not be "small" in the usual sense of the word in order to be treated as a particle. For example, if we consider the distance from the

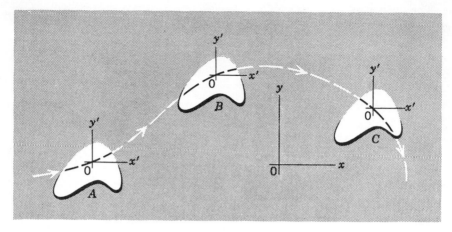

Fig. 3–1 Translational motion of an object.

earth to the sun, with respect to this distance the earth and the sun can usually be considered to be particles. We can deduce considerable information about the motion of the sun and planets, without appreciable error, by treating these bodies as particles. Baseballs, molecules, and electrons can often be treated as particles. Even if a body is too large to be considered a particle for a particular problem, the body can always be thought of as composed of a large number of particles and the results of particle motion may be useful in the analysis of the problem. As a simplification, therefore, we confine our present treatment to the motion of a particle.

Real bodies that have only motion of translation can be assumed to behave like particles. Motion is called *translational* if the axes of a coordinate system which is imagined rigidly attached to the object, say x' and y', always remain parallel to the axes of some fixed coordinate system, say x and y. In Fig. 3–1, for example, we show the translational motion of a plane object moving from positions A to B to C. Notice that the path taken is not necessarily a straight line. Notice too that throughout the motion every point of the body undergoes the same displacements as every other point. We can assume the body to be a particle because in describing the motion of one point on the body we have described the motion of the body as a whole.

3–3   Average Velocity

The velocity of a particle is the rate at which its position changes with time. Let a particle be displaced from one point A to another point B in a time interval t. If $\mathbf{d}$ represents the displacement vector joining A and B, the *average velocity* of the particle during the interval is defined by

$$\bar{\mathbf{v}} = \frac{\mathbf{d}}{t} = \frac{\text{displacement (a vector)}}{\text{elapsed time (a scalar)}}. \tag{3–1}$$

A bar above a symbol indicates an average value for the quantity in question.

The quantity $\bar{v}$ is a vector, for it is obtained by dividing the vector **d** by the scalar t. Velocity, therefore, involves both direction and magnitude. The magnitude is expressed in distance units divided by time units, as for example, meters per second or miles per hour.

The velocity given is called an *average* velocity because the measurement of the net displacement and the elapsed time do not tell us anything at all about the motion *between* A and B. The path may have been curved or straight; the motion may have been steady or erratic. The average velocity involves simply the total displacement and the total elapsed time. For example, suppose a man leaves his house and goes on an automobile trip, returning to his house a time t after he left it. Note that his average velocity for the trip is zero because his displacement *for the particular time interval* t is zero.

Equation 3-1 can also be written as

$$\mathbf{d} = \bar{v}t, \tag{3-2}$$

from which the displacement can be obtained if the average velocity and the time interval are known.

If we were to measure the time of arrival at each of many points along the actual route between A and B, we could describe the motion in more detail. If the average velocity turned out to be the same (in magnitude and direction) between any two points along the path, we would conclude that the particle moved with *constant velocity*, that is, along a straight line (constant direction) at a uniform rate (constant magnitude).

3-4   Instantaneous Velocity

Suppose that a particle is moving in such a way that its average velocity, measured for a number of different time intervals, does *not* turn out to be constant. This particle is said to move with variable velocity. Then we must seek to determine a velocity of the particle at any given instant of time, called the *instantaneous velocity*.

Velocity can vary by a change in magnitude, by a change in direction, or both. In the next chapter, we consider motion along a curved path in which the velocity can change continuously in direction as well as in magnitude. Here we consider only motion in one dimension in which the velocity can change continuously in magnitude but can be directed only in one of two directions along a straight line. For simplicity, we consider first motion in a fixed direction along a straight line.

We choose the x-axis to be along the straight line (Fig. 3-2). Let x_1 be the displacement of the particle from the origin at the time t_1 and x_2 the displacement at the time t_2, a little later. The elapsed time $t_2 - t_1$ is denoted by Δt. The displacement during this interval is $x_2 - x_1$, or Δx. The average velocity between the two points is therefore $\Delta x / \Delta t$. If we had chosen a different displacement, say $x_3 - x_1$, we might have obtained a different result, for the velocity may not be constant in magnitude. However, if we

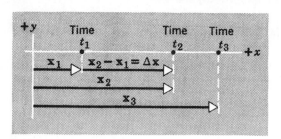

Fig. 3-2   A motion in one dimension.

choose the point x_2 successively closer and closer to the point x_1, the corresponding ratios $\Delta x/\Delta t$ will approach a definite limiting value. Although the displacement then becomes extremely small, the time interval by which it is divided becomes small also and the ratio is not necessarily a small quantity. This *limiting value of* $\Delta x/\Delta t$ is called the instantaneous velocity at the point x_1, or the velocity of the particle at the instant t_1.

If Δx *is the displacement in a small interval of time* Δt, *following the time t,* *the velocity at the time t is the limiting value approached by* $\Delta x/\Delta t$ *as both* Δx *and* Δt *approach zero.* Then if **v** represents the instantaneous velocity,

$$\mathbf{v} = \lim_{\Delta t \to 0} \frac{\Delta \mathbf{x}}{\Delta t}.$$

The direction of **v** is the limiting direction of the vector change in displacement $\Delta \mathbf{x}$. When the particle moves in the positive direction along x, the instantaneous velocity vector is directed toward $+x$; when it moves in the negative direction along x, the instantaneous velocity vector is directed toward $-x$.

In the notation of the calculus, the limiting value of $\Delta x/\Delta t$, as Δt approaches zero, is written $d\mathbf{x}/dt$ and is called the *derivative* of **x** with respect to t. Then we have

$$\mathbf{v} = \lim_{\Delta t \to 0} \frac{\Delta \mathbf{x}}{\Delta t} = \frac{d\mathbf{x}}{dt}. \tag{3-3}$$

The magnitude v of the instantaneous velocity is called *speed* and is simply the absolute value of **v**. That is,

$$v = |\mathbf{v}| = \left| \frac{d\mathbf{x}}{dt} \right|.$$

Speed, being the magnitude of a vector, is intrinsically positive.

Notice that when the velocity is constant the velocity at any instant equals the average velocity over any time interval.

▶ **Example 1.** As an example of the limiting process consider the following table of data taken for a motion along the x-axis (the first four columns are experimental data). The symbols refer to Fig. 3-2. The particle was at the point x_1 (100 cm from

0) when the watch read t_1 (1.00 sec). It was at x_2 at the time t_2. As we pick different positions for x_2, we find

x_1, cm	t_1, sec	x_2, cm	t_2, sec	$x_2 - x_1$ $= \Delta x$, cm	$t_2 - t_1$ $= \Delta t$, sec	$\Delta x / \Delta t$, cm/sec
100.0	1.00	200.0	11.00	100.0	10.00	10.0
100.0	1.00	180.0	9.60	80.0	8.60	9.3
100.0	1.00	160.0	7.90	60.0	6.90	8.7
100.0	1.00	140.0	5.90	40.0	4.90	8.2
100.0	1.00	120.0	3.56	20.0	2.56	7.8
100.0	1.00	110.0	2.33	10.0	1.33	7.5
100.0	1.00	105.0	1.69	5.0	0.69	7.3
100.0	1.00	103.0	1.42	3.0	0.42	7.1(4)
100.0	1.00	101.0	1.14	1.0	0.14	7.1(3)

Hence, as Δt approaches zero, x_2 approaches x_1 and $\Delta x / \Delta t$ approaches the limiting value of 7.1 cm/sec. Therefore, $v = \lim_{\Delta t \to 0} (\Delta x / \Delta t) = 7.1$ cm/sec at the time t_1. The instantaneous velocity of the particle at x_1 is represented by a vector v_1 pointing toward $+x$ and having a length corresponding to 7.1 cm/sec.

Example 2. In order to further clarify the ideas introduced so far, let us now consider another example. Figure 3–3a represents a graph of displacement versus time for a particular motion along the x-axis with variable speed. We see from the graph that at the time $t = 0$ the particle is at P, 1 ft from the origin. As time goes on the particle moves to Q, 5 ft from the origin, and then back to R, 2 ft from the origin. The *average velocity* for this entire 4-sec interval is then the total displacement, 1 ft in the $+x$ direction, divided by the elapsed time, 4 sec, or $\frac{1}{4}$ ft/sec toward $+x$. This can be obtained directly from the slope of the dashed line PR, where by slope we mean the ratio of the net displacement TR to the net time TP.*

The *instantaneous velocity* at any point, however, is obtained from the slope of the curve at that instant. Equation 3–3 is, in fact, the relation by which the slope of the curve is defined in the calculus. In our example, the slope at S is $+1.7$ ft/sec, and the slope at Q is zero, as shown in the figure. When we determine the slope, dx/dt, at each instant t, we can plot on a graph the instantaneous velocity v, versus the time t, as in Fig. 3–3b. The instantaneous velocity at P is a little less than $+4$ ft/sec; it then decreases steadily, becoming zero at Q, and thereafter it is negative, being about -6 ft/sec at R.

The student should visualize the motion represented by Fig. 3–3, bearing in mind that it occurs along a straight line. The velocity vectors at various points along the straight line from P to Q during the first 2 sec are shown in Fig. 3–3c. The student should construct a similar diagram for the motion from Q to R during the last 2 sec. ◀

Just as a particle is a physical concept making use of the mathematical concept of a point, so here velocity is a physical concept using the mathematical concept of differentiation. In fact, the calculus was invented originally by the English physicist, Isaac Newton (1642–1727), in order to have a proper mathematical tool for treating fundamental mechanical problems. On the other hand, some abstract mathematical concepts do not find application to physical reality until after they have been rather developed.

---

* Notice that the slope is *not* the tangent of the angle RPT measured on the graph. This angle depends on the scales we choose for the ordinate and the abscissa and is arbitrary.

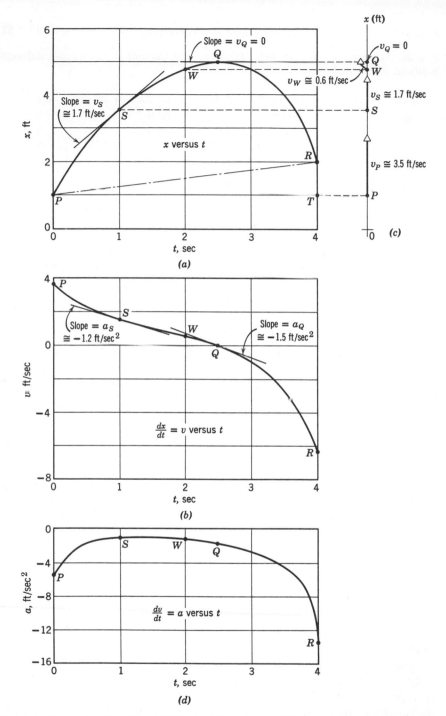

Fig. 3-3 Examples 2 and 3. (a) The position of a particle is plotted against time. The particle progresses in the $+x$ direction until 2.5 sec have elapsed; then it begins moving in the opposite direction. The slope of the curve gives the velocity of the particle, which is plotted in (b). The velocity vectors are also drawn in (c), which illustrates the position of the particle on the x-axis at instants $P, S, W,$ and Q. From the slope of the velocity curve (b), the acceleration, plotted in (d), is found.

3–5   Average Acceleration

Often the velocity of a moving body changes as the motion proceeds. The body is then said to have an acceleration. *The acceleration of a particle is the rate of change of its velocity with time.* If at the instant t_1 a particle is moving with the instantaneous velocity $\mathbf{v}_1$, and at a later instant t_2 it moves with the instantaneous velocity $\mathbf{v}_2$, the *average acceleration* $\bar{\mathbf{a}}$ is the change of velocity divided by the time interval. That is

$$\bar{\mathbf{a}} = \frac{\mathbf{v}_2 - \mathbf{v}_1}{t_2 - t_1} = \frac{\Delta \mathbf{v}}{\Delta t}. \tag{3–4}$$

The quantity $\bar{\mathbf{a}}$ is a vector, for it is obtained by dividing a vector, $\Delta \mathbf{v}$, by a scalar, Δt. Acceleration is therefore characterized by magnitude and direction. The magnitude of the acceleration is expressed in velocity units divided by time units, as for example meter/sec per sec (written meters/sec² and read "meters per second squared"), cm/sec², and ft/sec².

We call $\bar{\mathbf{a}}$ of Eq. 3–4 the *average* acceleration because nothing has been said about the time variation of velocity *during* the interval Δt. We know only the net change in velocity and the total elapsed time.

If the change in velocity (a vector) divided by the time interval were to remain constant, regardless of the time intervals over which we measured the acceleration, we would have *constant* acceleration. Constant acceleration, therefore, implies that the velocity always changes in the same direction and that the speed changes with time at a constant rate. If the velocity were to remain constant both in magnitude *and* direction, the acceleration would be zero.

3–6   Instantaneous Acceleration

If a particle is moving in such a way that its average acceleration, measured for a number of different time intervals, does *not* turn out to be constant, the particle is said to have a variable acceleration. The acceleration can vary in magnitude, or in direction, or both. In such cases we seek to determine the acceleration of the particle at any given time, called the instantaneous acceleration. The *instantaneous acceleration* is defined by

$$\mathbf{a} = \lim_{\Delta t \to 0} \frac{\Delta \mathbf{v}}{\Delta t} = \frac{d\mathbf{v}}{dt}. \tag{3–5}$$

That is, the acceleration of a particle at time t is *the limiting value of $\Delta \bar{\mathbf{v}}/\Delta t$ at time t* as both $\Delta \mathbf{v}$ and Δt approach zero. The magnitude of the instantaneous acceleration a is the magnitude of $\mathbf{a}$. The direction of the instantaneous acceleration is the limiting direction of the vector change in velocity $\Delta \mathbf{v}$.

Notice that when the acceleration is constant the instantaneous acceleration equals the average acceleration.

Two special cases of accelerated motion are of great interest in physics. One is that of constant acceleration. Here (Section 3–7) the motion is along a straight line (no change in direction), but the speed changes uniformly with time. The second case (Section 4–4) is that of motion in a circle at constant speed. Here the velocity vector changes continuously in direction but its magnitude remains constant. Both cases represent accelerated motion.

▶ **Example 3.** The motion of Fig. 3–3 is one of variable acceleration and occurs along the x-axis. To find the acceleration at each instant we must determine dv/dt at each instant. This is simply the slope of the curve v versus t at that instant. The slope at S is -1.2 ft/sec^2 and the slope at Q is -1.5 ft/sec^2 as shown in the figure. The result of calculating the slope for all points is shown in Fig. 3–3d. Notice that the acceleration is negative at all instants. The acceleration vector, therefore, points along the negative x direction. This means that the velocity is decreasing in magnitude with time, as is clearly seen from Fig. 3–3b. The length of the acceleration vector changes with time, so that the motion is in fact one of variable acceleration. ◀

3–7   Rectilinear Motion with Constant Acceleration

For motion in a straight line, called *rectilinear* motion, the displacement, velocity, and acceleration vectors all lie along the same line. Therefore, we need find only the relations between x, v, and a treated as scalars. A negative value for x, v, or a will simply mean that the corresponding vector quantity points in the negative x direction. We have already implicitly used this meaning in drawing and interpreting Fig. 3–3. The sign does not depend on where the vector is but on the direction in which it is pointing (Fig. 3–4).

Let us now consider rectilinear motion with constant acceleration. In the case of constant acceleration, the average acceleration $\bar{a}$, equals the instantaneous acceleration, a, so that

$$a = \frac{v_2 - v_1}{t_2 - t_1}, \qquad \text{a constant.} \tag{3–6}$$

Let $t_1 = 0$ and let t_2 be any arbitrary time t. Let v_0 represent the speed when $t = 0$, and let v be the speed at time t. We call v_0 the initial speed. With these conventions, our previous equation becomes

$$a = \frac{v - v_0}{t - 0},$$

or
$$v = v_0 + at. \tag{3–7}$$

This equation states that the speed v at the time t is the sum of the speed

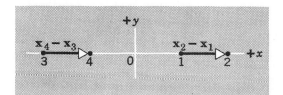

Fig. 3–4 Displacements $x_4 - x_3$ and $x_2 - x_1$ are positive since they both point toward $+x$.

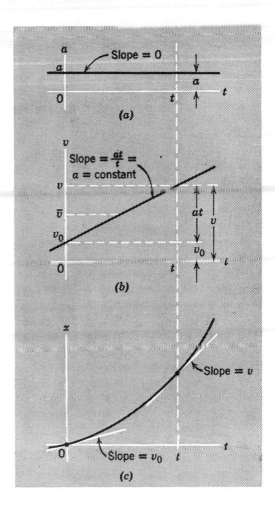

Fig. 3-5 One-dimensional motion with constant acceleration. (a) The acceleration has a constant value, and thus its slope is zero. (b) The velocity increases uniformly according to $v = v_0 + at$. Its slope has the constant value a, the acceleration. (c) The displacement increases quadratically according to $x = v_0 t + at^2/2$. Its slope increases uniformly and at each instant has the value v, the velocity.

v_0 at the time zero plus the increase in speed during the time t, which is at.

Figure 3-5 shows a graph of v versus t (Fig. 3-5b) for constant acceleration (Fig. 3-5a). Notice that the slope of the velocity curve is a constant, in accordance with the fact that a, which is dv/dt, is constant.

When the speed changes uniformly with time, the average speed in any time interval equals one-half the sum of the speeds at the beginning and at the end of the interval. Therefore, the average speed $\bar{v}$ between $t = 0$ and $t = t$ is

$$\bar{v} = \frac{v_0 + v}{2}. \tag{3-8}$$

This relation would not be true if the acceleration were not constant, for then the curve v versus t would not be a straight line.

From Eq. 3–2 we can now obtain the displacement x at any time t for a particle which is at the origin at $t = 0$, namely,

$$x = \bar{v}t,$$

or
$$x = \frac{v_0 + v}{2} \cdot t. \tag{3–9}$$

These two equations, Eqs. 3–7 and 3–9, are sufficient for obtaining all information about motion with constant acceleration.

Notice that aside from initial conditions of the motion, that is, the values of x and v at $t = 0$ (taken here as $x = 0$ and $v = v_0$), there are four parameters of the motion. These are x, the displacement; v, the speed; a, the acceleration; and t, the elapsed time. If we know only that the acceleration is constant, but not necessarily its value, from any two of these parameters we can obtain the other two. For example, if a and t are known, Eq. 3–7 gives v, and having obtained v, we find x from Eq. 3–9.

In most problems in uniformly accelerated motion, two parameters are known and a third is sought. It is convenient, therefore, to obtain relations between any three of the four parameters. Equation 3–7 contains v, a, and t but *not* x; Eq. 3–9 contains x, v, and t but *not* a. Clearly, to complete our system of equations we need two more relations, one containing x, a, and t but *not* v and another containing x, v, and a but *not* t. These are easily obtained by combining Eqs. 3–7 and 3–9.

Thus, if we substitute into Eq. 3–9 the value of v from Eq. 3–7, we thereby eliminate v and obtain
$$x = v_0 t + \tfrac{1}{2}at^2. \tag{3–10}$$

When Eq. 3–7 is solved for t and this value for t is substituted into Eq. 3–9, we obtain
$$v^2 = v_0{}^2 + 2ax. \tag{3–11}$$

Equations 3–7, 3–9, 3–10, and 3–11 represent the complete set of equations for motion with constant acceleration, for the special case of the particle at the origin when $t = 0$. If the particle were at $x = x_0$ when $t = 0$, these equations could still be used if $x - x_0$ were substituted for x.

▶ **Example 4.** The curve of Fig. 3-5c is a displacement-time graph for motion with constant acceleration; that is, it is a graph of Eq. 3–10. The slope of the tangent to the curve at time t equals the speed v at that time. Notice that the slope increases continuously with time from v_0 at $t = 0$. The *rate of increase* of this slope should give the acceleration a, which is *constant* in this case. The curve is a *parabola*, Eq. 3–10 being the equation for a parabola having slope v_0 at $t = 0$. We obtain, upon successive differentiation of Eq. 3–10,

$$x = v_0 t + \tfrac{1}{2}at^2,$$

$$dx/dt = v_0 + at \quad \text{or} \quad v = v_0 + at,$$

which is the speed v at time t, and

$$dv/dt = a,$$

the constant acceleration.

The displacement-time graph for uniformly accelerated motion will, therefore, always be parabolic. The student should now be able to draw the curves of v versus t and a versus t corresponding to the motion of Fig. 3–5c exactly, as was done before for the motion of Fig. 3–3a. ◄

A special case of motion with constant acceleration is that in which the acceleration is zero. Then $a = 0$ and $v = v_0$, a constant, so that $x = v_0t$.

3–8 Dimensional Consistency

The student should not feel compelled to memorize relations such as those just discussed. The important thing is to be able to follow the line of reasoning used to obtain the results. These relations will be recalled automatically after the student has used them repeatedly to solve numerous problems, in part as a result of the familiarity acquired with them but chiefly as a result of the better understanding obtained of them through application.

Of course, we are at liberty to use any convenient *units* of time and distance in these equations. If we choose to express time in seconds and distance in feet, for self-consistency we should express velocity in ft/sec and acceleration in ft/sec². If we are given data in which the units of one quantity, as velocity, are not consistent with the units of another quantity, as acceleration, then before using the data in our equations we should transform both quantities to units that are consistent with one another. Having chosen the units of our fundamental quantities, we automatically determine the units of our derived quantities consistent with them. This procedure enables us to substitute numbers into an equation without specifying the units until the final result is obtained. In carrying out any calculation, always remember to attach the proper units to the final result, for the result is meaningless without this label.

▶ **Example 5.** For example, suppose we wish to find the speed of a particle which is uniformly accelerated 5.00 cm/sec² at $\frac{1}{2}$ hr after the initial time t_0, if the particle has a speed of 10 ft/sec at t_0. We decide to choose the foot as our length unit and the second as our time unit. Then

$$a = 5.00 \text{ cm/sec}^2 = 5.00 \text{ cm/sec}^2 \cdot \left(\frac{1 \text{ in.}}{2.54 \text{ cm}}\right) \cdot \left(\frac{1 \text{ ft}}{12 \text{ in.}}\right) = \frac{5.00}{30.5} \text{ ft/sec}^2$$

$$= 0.164 \text{ ft/sec}^2.$$

The time interval,

$$t - t_0 = \tfrac{1}{2} \text{ hr} = \tfrac{1}{2} \text{ hr} \cdot \left(\frac{60 \text{ min}}{1 \text{ hr}}\right) \cdot \left(\frac{60 \text{ sec}}{1 \text{ min}}\right) = 1800 \text{ sec}.$$

From our equation we then have

$$v = v_0 + at = 10 \text{ ft/sec} + 0.164 \text{ (ft/sec}^2\text{)}(1800 \text{ sec}) = 305 \text{ ft/sec}. \quad ◄$$

A useful way of checking the possible validity of an equation is to check the *dimensions* of all its terms. The dimensions of any physical quantity can always be expressed as some combination of the fundamental quantities, such as mass, length, and time, from which they are derived. The dimensions of velocity are length (L) divided by time (T); the dimensions of acceleration are length divided by time squared, etc. *In any legitimate physical equation the dimensions of all the terms must be the same.* This means, for example, that we cannot equate a term whose total dimension is a velocity to one whose total dimension is an acceleration. The dimensional labels attached to various quantities may be treated just like algebraic quantities and may be combined, canceled, etc., just as if they were factors in the equation. For example, to check Eq. 3–10, $x = v_0 t + \frac{1}{2}at^2$, dimensionally, we note that x has the dimension of a length. Therefore, each term must have the dimension of a length. Thus the dimension of the term $v_0 t$ is

$$\frac{\text{length}}{\text{time}} \times \text{time} = \text{length},$$

or

$$\frac{(L)}{(T)} \times (T) = (L),$$

and of $\frac{1}{2}at^2$ is

$$\frac{\text{length}}{\text{time}^2} \times \text{time}^2 = \text{length},$$

or

$$\frac{(L)}{(T^2)} \times (T^2) = (L).$$

The equation is, therefore, *dimensionally correct.*

The student should check the dimensions of all the equations he uses. Often we can obtain deeper insight into the meaning of a physical quantity when we know the fundamental dimensions of which it is compounded. In any case, an equation is certainly incorrect if its various terms have different dimensions.

▶ **Example 6.** The speed of an automobile traveling due west is uniformly reduced from 45.0 miles/hr to 30.0 miles/hr in a distance of 264 ft.

(a) What is the magnitude and direction of the constant acceleration?

We are given x and v and we seek a. The time is not involved. Equation 3–11 is, therefore, appropriate. We have $v = 30.0$ miles/hr, $v_0 = 45.0$ miles/hr, $x = 264$ ft $= 0.0500$ mile. From Eq. 3–11, $v^2 = v_0^2 + 2ax$, we obtain

$$a = \frac{v^2 - v_0^2}{2x},$$

or

$$a = \frac{(30.0 \text{ miles/hr})^2 - (45.0 \text{ miles/hr})^2}{2(0.0500 \text{ mile})} = -1.125 \times 10^4 \text{ miles/hr}^2 = 4.58 \text{ ft/sec}^2.$$

The direction of the acceleration is due east. The car is slowing down as it moves westward, so that $\mathbf{v} - \mathbf{v}_0$, which gives the direction of $\mathbf{a}$, points due east.

(b) How much time has elapsed during this deceleration?

By using only the original data, Eq. 3–9 is appropriate. From Eq. 3–9, $x = (v_0 + v)t/2$, we obtain

$$t = \frac{2x}{v + v_0},$$

or

$$t = \frac{(2)(0.0500 \text{ mile})}{(45.0 + 30.0) \text{ miles/hr}} = \frac{1}{750} \text{ hr} = 4.80 \text{ sec}.$$

By using the derived data of part a, Eq. 3–7 is appropriate. We have as a check Eq. 3–7, $v = v_0 + at$,

$$t = \frac{v - v_0}{a},$$

or $t = \dfrac{(30.0 - 45.0) \text{ miles/hr}}{-1.125 \times 10^4 \text{ miles/hr}^2} = 1.33 \times 10^{-3} \text{ hr} = 4.80 \text{ sec}.$

(c) Assuming that the car continues to decelerate at the same rate, how much time would elapse in bringing it to rest from 45.0 miles/hr?

Equation 3–7 is useful here. We have $v_0 = 45.0$ miles/hr, $a = -1.125 \times 10^4$ miles/hr², and the final speed $v = 0$. Then from Eq. 3–7, $v = v_0 + at$, we obtain

$$t = \frac{v - v_0}{a},$$

or $t = \dfrac{(0 - 45.0) \text{ miles/hr}}{-1.125 \times 10^4 \text{ miles/hr}^2} = 4.00 \times 10^{-3} \text{ hr} = 14.4 \text{ sec}.$

(d) What total distance is required to bring the car to rest from 45.0 miles/hr?

Equation 3–10 is appropriate here. We have $v_0 = 45.0$ miles/hr, $a = -1.125 \times 10^4$ miles/hr², $t = 4.00 \times 10^{-3}$ hr. From Eq. 3–10, $x = v_0 t + \frac{1}{2}at^2$,

$$x = (45.0 \text{ miles/hr})(400 \times 10^{-3} \text{ hr}) - \tfrac{1}{2}(1.125 \times 10^4 \text{ miles/hr}^2)(4.00 \times 10^{-3} \text{ hr})^2$$

$$= 0.0900 \text{ mile} = 475 \text{ ft}.$$

Example 7. The nucleus of a helium atom (alpha-particle) travels along the inside of a straight hollow tube 2.0 meters long which forms part of a particle accelerator. (a) Assuming uniform acceleration, how long is the particle in the tube if it enters at a speed of 1000 meters/sec and leaves at 9000 meters/sec? (b) What is its acceleration during this interval?

(a) We are given x and v and we seek t. The acceleration a is not involved. Hence, we use Eq. 3–9, $x = (v_0 + v)t/2$, or

$$t = \frac{2x}{v_0 + v},$$

$$t = \frac{(2)(2.0 \text{ meters})}{(1000 + 9000) \text{ meters/sec}} = 4.0 \times 10^{-4} \text{ sec},$$

or about 400 microseconds.

(b) The acceleration follows at once from

$$v = v_0 + at,$$

or $a = \dfrac{v - v_0}{t} = \dfrac{(9000 - 1000) \text{ meters/sec}}{4.0 \times 10^{-4} \text{ sec}} = 2.0 \times 10^7 \text{ meters/sec}^2,$

or 20 million meters per second per second!

Although this acceleration is enormous by standards of the previous example, it occurs over an extremely short time.

How would you describe the direction of the acceleration?   ◀

3–9   Freely Falling Bodies

The most common example of motion with (nearly) constant acceleration is that of a body falling toward the earth. In the absence of air resistance it is found that all bodies, regardless of their size, weight, or composition, fall with the same acceleration at the same point of the earth's surface, and if the distance covered is not too great, the acceleration remains constant throughout the fall. This ideal motion, in which air resistance and the small change in acceleration with altitude are neglected, is called "free fall."

The acceleration of a freely falling body is called the acceleration due to gravity and is denoted by the symbol **g**. Near the earth's surface its magnitude is approximately 32.0 ft/sec^2, 9.80 meters/sec^2, or 980 cm/sec^2, and it is directed down toward the center of the earth. The variation of the exact value with latitude and altitude will be discussed later (Chapter 16).

The nature of the motion of a falling object was long ago a subject of interest in natural philosophy. Aristotle had asserted that "the downward movement . . . of any body endowed with weight is quicker in proportion to its size." It was not until many centuries later when Galileo Galilei (1564–1642), an Italian scientist of the Renaissance, appealed to experiment to discover the truth, and then publicly proclaimed it, that Aristotle's authority on the matter was seriously challenged. In the later years of his life, Galileo wrote the treatise entitled *Dialogues Concerning Two New Sciences* in which he detailed his studies of motion.* This treatise may be considered as marking the beginning of the science of dynamics.

Aristotle's belief that a heavier object will fall faster is a commonly held view. It appears to receive support from a well-known lecture demonstration in which a ball and a sheet of paper are dropped at the same instant, the ball reaching the floor much sooner than the paper. However, when the lecturer first crumples the paper tightly and then repeats the demonstration both ball and paper strike the floor at essentially the same time. In the former case it is the effect of greater resistance of the air which makes the paper fall more slowly than the ball. In the latter case the effect of air resistance on the paper is reduced and is about the same for both bodies, so that they fall at about the same rate. Of course, a direct test can be made by dropping bodies in vacuum. Even in easily obtainable partial vacuums we can show that a feather and a ball of lead thousands of times heavier drop at rates that are practically indistinguishable.

In Galileo's time, however, there was no effective way to obtain a partial vacuum, nor did equipment exist to time freely falling bodies with sufficient precision to obtain reliable numerical data. Nevertheless, Galileo proved his result by showing first that the character of the motion of a ball rolling down an incline was the same as that of a ball in free fall. The incline merely served to reduce the effective acceleration of gravity and to slow the motion thereby. Time intervals measured by the volume of water discharged from a tank could then be used to test the speed and acceleration of this motion. Galileo showed that if the acceleration along the incline is constant, the acceleration due to gravity must also be constant; for the acceleration along the incline is simply a component of the vertical acceleration of

---

* Galileo made noteworthy contributions to astronomy by the application of his telescope. His strong evidence in favor of the Copernican hypothesis of the solar system served to refute the Ptolemaic system and on this account raised strong feelings against him in the minds of the leaders of the Church. Twice he was brought before the Inquisition. He was ordered not to publish anything in support of the Copernican system and was compelled to publicly disclaim his belief in it. It was during a period of fear and uncertainty that he wrote his dialogue on motion, not published until after his death.

† It is said that Galileo publicly demonstrated his results by simultaneously dropping two objects, one very much heavier than the other, from the top of the Leaning Tower of Pisa, showing that both struck the ground at the same time. This story is not definitely confirmed by historical research, but the truth of his hypothesis could certainly have been demonstrated in this way.

gravity, and along an incline of constant slope the ratio of the two accelerations remains fixed.

He found from his experiments that the distance covered in consecutive time intervals were proportional to the odd numbers 1, 3, 5, 7, $\cdots$, etc. Total distances for consecutive intervals thus were proportional to $1 + 3, 1 + 3 + 5, 1 + 3 + 5 + 7$, etc., that is, to the squares of the integers 1, 2, 3, 4, etc. But if the distance covered is proportional to the square of the elapsed time, velocity acquired is proportional to the elapsed time, a result which is true only if motion is uniformly accelerated. He found that the same results held regardless of the mass of the ball used.

3–10   Equations of Motion in Free Fall

We shall take as our reference frame a frame rigidly attached to the earth. The y-axis will be taken as positive vertically upward. Then the acceleration due to gravity g will be a vector pointing vertically down (toward the center of the earth) in the negative y direction. (This choice is rather arbitrary. In other problems it may be convenient to choose down as positive.) Our equations for constant acceleration are applicable here. We simply replace x by y in Eqs. 3–7, 3–9, 3–10, and 3–11, obtaining

$$v = v_0 + at,$$

$$y = \frac{v_0 + v}{2} \cdot t,$$

$$y = v_0 t + \tfrac{1}{2}at^2,$$

$$v^2 = v_0{}^2 + 2ay,$$

$$(3–12)$$

and put $a = -g$ for problems in free fall. Here $y = 0$ at $t = 0$, and g is the magnitude * of the acceleration due to gravity, 32.0 ft/sec².

▶ **Example 8.** A body is dropped from rest and falls freely. Determine the position and speed of the body after 1.00, 2.00, 3.00, and 4.00 sec have elapsed.

We choose the starting point as the origin. We know the initial speed and the acceleration and we are given the time. To find the position we use

$$y = v_0 t - \tfrac{1}{2}gt^2.$$

Then, $v_0 = 0$ and $g = 32.0$ ft/sec², and with $t = 1.00$ sec we obtain

$$y = 0 - (\tfrac{1}{2}) \cdot (32.0 \text{ ft/sec}^2)(1.00 \text{ sec})^2 = -16.0 \text{ ft.}$$

To find the speed with $t = 1.00$ sec, we use

$$v = v_0 - gt$$

and obtain $v = 0 - (32.0 \text{ ft/sec}^2)(1.00 \text{ sec}) = -32.0 \text{ ft/sec.}$

After 1 sec of falling from rest, the body is 16.0 ft below its starting point and has a velocity directed downward whose magnitude is 32.0 ft/sec.

---

* For convenience in numerical problems we have taken 32.0 ft/sec² as the magnitude of the acceleration due to gravity. Actually g varies over the surface of the earth (Chapter 16), and a better average value to three significant figures is 32.2 ft/sec². In the metric system, for computational convenience, we take $g = 9.80$ meters/sec².

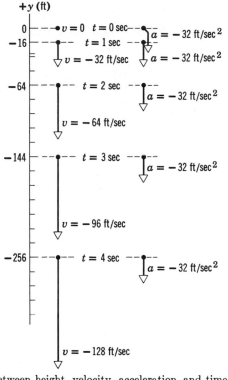

Fig. 3–6 Relations between height, velocity, acceleration, and time for an object experiencing free fall.

The student should now show that at

$t = 1.00$ sec,	$y = -16.0$ ft	$v = -32.0$ ft/sec	$a = -32$ ft/sec^2;
$t = 2.00$ sec,	$y = -64.0$ ft	$v = -64.0$ ft/sec	$a = -32$ ft/sec^2;
$t = 3.00$ sec,	$y = -144$ ft	$v = -96.0$ ft/sec	$a = -32$ ft/sec^2;
$t = 4.00$ sec,	$y = -256$ ft	$v = -128$ ft/sec	$a = -32$ ft/sec^2.

The results are illustrated in Fig. 3–6.

Example 9. A ball is thrown vertically upward from the ground with a speed of 80.0 ft/sec.

(a) How long does it take to reach its highest point?

At its highest point, $v = 0$, and we have $v_0 = 80$ ft/sec. To obtain the time t we use

$$v = v_0 - gt,$$

or

$$t = (v_0 - v)/g,$$

$$t = \frac{(80 - 0) \text{ ft/sec}}{32 \text{ ft/sec}^2} = 2.5 \text{ sec.}$$

(b) How high does the ball rise?

Using only the original data, we choose the relation

$$v^2 = v_0^2 - 2gy,$$

or

$$y = (v_0^2 - v^2)/2g,$$

$$= \frac{(80 \text{ ft/sec})^2 - 0}{2 \times 32 \text{ ft/sec}^2} = 100 \text{ ft.}$$

(c) At what times will the ball be 96 ft above the ground?
Using

$$y = v_0 t - \tfrac{1}{2} g t^2,$$

we have

$$\tfrac{1}{2} g t^2 - v_0 t \overset{\cdot}{+} y = 0,$$

or

$$(\tfrac{1}{2})(32 \text{ ft/sec}^2) \cdot t^2 - (80 \text{ ft/sec}) t + 96 \text{ ft} = 0,$$

$$t^2 - 5t + 6 = 0,$$

$$(t - 3) \cdot (t - 2) = 0,$$

$$t = 2 \text{ sec},$$

and

$$t = 3 \text{ sec}.$$

At $t = 2$ sec, the ball is moving *upward* with a speed

$$v = v_0 - gt = 80 \text{ ft/sec} - (32 \text{ ft/sec}^2)(2 \text{ sec}) = 16 \text{ ft/sec}.$$

At $t = 3$ sec, the ball is moving *downward* with the same speed,

$$v = v_0 - gt = 80 \text{ ft/sec} - (32 \text{ ft/sec}^2)(3 \text{ sec}) = -16 \text{ ft/sec}.$$

Notice that in this 1 sec the velocity changed by -32 ft/sec, corresponding to an acceleration of -32 ft/sec^2.   ◀

QUESTIONS

1. Can you think of physical phenomena involving the earth in which the earth cannot be treated as a particle?

2. Each second a rabbit moves half the remaining distance from his nose to a head of lettuce. Does he ever get to the lettuce? What is the limiting value of his average speed? Draw graphs showing his velocity and position as time increases.

3. Average speed can mean the magnitude of the average velocity vector. Another meaning given to it is that average speed is the total length of path traveled divided by the elapsed time. Are these meanings different? If so, give an example.

4. Is the average speed of a particle $\tfrac{1}{2}(v_0 + v)$ when the acceleration is not uniform? Prove your answer with the use of graphs.

5. (a) Can a body have zero velocity and still be accelerating? (b) Can a body have a constant speed and still have a varying velocity? (c) Can a body have a constant velocity and still have a varying speed?

6. Can an object have an eastward velocity while experiencing a westward acceleration?

7. Can the direction of the velocity of a body change when its acceleration is constant?

8. When the acceleration is not uniform, the motion is jerky. In fact, the time rate of change of acceleration is called "jerk" in technical language. Can you cite some examples of nonuniformly accelerated motion?

9. Devise a scheme for keeping time with a "water clock" such as Galileo used. Can you avoid repetitive operations and still keep accurate time?

10. Consider a ball thrown vertically up. Taking air resistance into account, would you expect the time during which the ball rises to be longer or shorter than the time during which it falls?

11. A man standing at some height above the ground throws one ball out so that it has an upward component of velocity u and then throws another ball out so that it has a downward component of velocity u. Which ball, if either, has the larger vertical component of velocity when it hits the ground? Neglect air resistance.

12. From what you know about angular measure, what *dimensions* would you assign to an angle? Can a quantity have units without having dimensions?

13. If m is a light stone and M is a heavy one, according to Aristotle M should fall faster than m. Galileo attempted to show that Aristotle's belief was logically inconsistent by the following argument. Tie m and M together to form a double stone. Then, in falling, m should retard M, since it tends to fall more slowly, and the combination would fall faster than m but more slowly than M; but according to Aristotle the double body $(M + m)$ is heavier than M and hence should fall faster than M.

If you accept Galileo's reasoning as correct, can you conclude that M and m must fall at the same rate? What need is there for experiment in that case?

If you believe Galileo's reasoning is incorrect, explain why.

PROBLEMS

1. Compare your average speed in the following two cases. (a) You walk 240 ft at a speed of 4 ft/sec and then run 240 ft at a speed of 10 ft/sec along a straight track. (b) You walk for 1 min at a speed of 4 ft/sec and then run for 1 min at 10 ft/sec along a straight track.

2. A train moving at an essentially constant speed of 60 miles/hr moves eastward for 40 min, then in a direction 45° east of north for 20 min, and finally westward for 50 min. What is the average velocity of the train during this run?

3. Two trains, each having a speed of 30 miles/hr, are headed at each other on the same straight track. A bird that can fly 60 miles/hr flies off one train when they are 60 miles apart and heads directly for the other train. On reaching the other train it flies directly back to the first train, and so forth. How many trips can the bird make from one train to the other before they crash?

4. A particle moving along a horizontal line has the following positions at various instants of time:

x (meters) =	0.08	0.05	0.04	0.05	0.08	0.13	0.68
t (sec) =	0	1	2	3	4	5	10

(a) Plot displacement (not position) versus time. (b) Find the average velocity of the particle in the intervals 0 to 1 sec, 0 to 2 sec, 0 to 3 sec, 0 to 4 sec. (c) Find the slope of the curve drawn in part a at the points $t = 1, 2, 3, 4$, and 5 sec. (d) Plot the slope (units?) versus time. (e) From the curve of part d determine the acceleration of the particle at times $t = 2, 3$, and 4 sec.

5. A tennis ball is dropped onto the floor from a height of 4.0 ft. It rebounds to a height of 3.0 ft. If the ball was in contact with the floor for 0.010 sec, what was its average acceleration during contact?

6. The graph of x versus t (see Fig. 3–7a) is for a particle in rectilinear motion. State for each interval whether the velocity is $+$, $-$, or 0, and whether the acceleration is $+$,

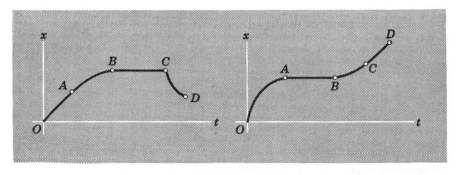

Fig. 3–7a　　　　　　　　　　　Fig. 3–7b

—, or 0. The intervals are OA, AB, BC, and CD. From the curve is there any *interval* over which the acceleration is obviously *not constant?* (Ignore the behavior at the end points of the intervals.)

7. Answer the previous questions for the motion described by the graph of Fig. 3–7b.

8. An arrow while being shot from a bow was accelerated over a distance of 2.0 ft. If its speed at the moment it left the bow was 200 ft/sec. what was the average acceleration imparted by the bow? Justify any assumptions you need to make.

9. An electron with initial speed $v_0 = 10^4$ meters/sec enters a region where it is electrically accelerated (Fig. 3–8). It emerges with a speed 4×10^6 meters/sec. What was its acceleration, assumed constant? (Such a process occurs in the electron gun in a cathode-ray tube, used in television receivers and oscilloscopes.)

10. Suppose that you were called upon to give some advice to a lawyer concerning the fundamental physics involved in one of his cases. The question is whether or not a driver was exceeding a 30 miles/hr (44 ft/sec) speed limit before he made an emergency stop, brakes locked and wheels sliding. The length of skid marks on the road was 19.2 ft. The policeman made the reasonable assumption that the maximum deceleration of the car would not exceed the acceleration of a freely falling body and arrested the driver for speeding. Was he speeding? Explain.

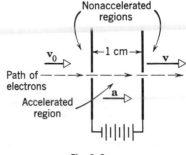

Fig. 3–8

11. A meson is shot with constant speed 5.00 $\times$ 10^6 meters/sec into a region where an electric field produces an acceleration on the meson, of magnitude 1.25×10^{14} meters/sec^2 directed opposite to the initial velocity. How far does the meson travel before coming to rest? How long does the meson remain at rest?

12. A train started from rest and moved with constant acceleration. At one time it was traveling 30 ft/sec, and 160 ft farther on it was traveling 50 ft/sec. Calculate (a) the acceleration, (b) the time required to travel the 160 ft mentioned, (c) the time required to attain the speed of 30 ft/sec, (d) the distance moved from rest to the time the train had a speed of 30 ft/sec.

13. At the instant the traffic light turns green, an automobile starts with a constant acceleration of 6 ft/sec^2. At the same instant a truck, traveling with a constant speed of 30 ft/sec, overtakes and passes the automobile. (a) How far beyond the starting point will the automobile overtake the truck? (b) How fast will the car be traveling at that instant? (It is instructive to plot a qualitative graph of x versus t for each vehicle.)

14. A car moving with constant acceleration covers the distance between two points 180 ft apart in 6 sec. Its speed as it passes the second point is 45 ft/sec. (a) What is its speed at the first point? (b) What is its acceleration? (c) At what prior distance from the first point was the car at rest?

15. The engineer of a train moving at a speed v_1 sights a freight train a distance d ahead of him on the same track moving in the same direction with a slower speed v_2. He puts on the brakes and gives his train a constant deceleration a. Show that

$$\text{if} \quad d > \frac{(v_1 - v_2)^2}{2a}, \quad \text{there will be no collision;}$$

$$\text{if} \quad d < \frac{(v_1 - v_2)^2}{2a}, \quad \text{there will be a collision.}$$

(It is instructive to plot a qualitative graph of x versus t for each train.)

16. A rocket-driven sled running on a straight level track is used to investigate the physiological effects of large accelerations on humans. One such sled can attain a speed

of 1000 miles/hr in 1.8 sec starting from rest. (a) Assume the acceleration is constant and compare it to g. (b) What is the distance traveled in this time?

17. An artillery shell is fired directly up from a gun; a rocket, propelled by burning fuel, takes off vertically from a launching area. Plot qualitatively (numbers not required) *possible* graphs of a versus t, of v versus t, and of y versus t for each. Take $t = 0$ at the instant the shell leaves the gun barrel or the rocket leaves the ground. Continue the plots until the rocket and the shell fall back to earth; neglect air resistance; assume that up is positive and down is negative.

18. A rocket is fired vertically and ascends with constant vertical acceleration of 64 ft/sec² for 1 min. Its fuel is then all used and it continues as a free particle. (a) What is the maximum altitude reached? (b) What is the total time elapsed from take-off until the rocket strikes the earth?

19. A stone is dropped into the water from a bridge 144 ft above the water. Another stone is thrown vertically down 1 sec after the first is dropped. Both stones strike the water at the same time. (a) What was the initial speed of the second stone? (b) Plot speed versus time on a graph for each stone, taking zero time as the instant the first stone was released.

20. A ball is thrown vertically upward with a speed of 80 ft/sec. (a) How high will it rise? (b) How long will it take to reach this height? (c) With what speed must a ball be thrown vertically upward in order to rise to a height of 50 ft? (d) How long will it be in the air?

21. A dog sees a flower pot sail up and then back down past a window 5 ft high. If the total time the pot is in sight is 1 sec, find the height above the window that the pot rises.

22. A balloon is ascending at the rate of 12 meters/sec at a height 80 meters above the ground when a package is dropped. How long does it take the package to reach the ground?

23. A parachutist after taking off falls 50 meters without friction. When the parachute opens, he decelerates downward 2 meters/sec². He reaches the ground with a speed of 3 meters/sec. (a) How long is the parachutist in the air? (b) At what height did he take off?

24. An elevator ascends with an upward acceleration of 4.0 ft/sec². At the instant its upward speed is 8.0 ft/sec, a loose bolt drops from the ceiling of the elevator 9.0 ft from the floor. Calculate (a) the time of flight of the bolt from ceiling to floor, and (b) the distance it has fallen relative to the elevator shaft.

25. The position of a particle moving along the x-axis depends on the time according to the equation

$$x = at^2 - bt^3,$$

where x is in feet and t in seconds. (a) What dimensions and units must a and b have? For the following, let their numerical values be 3 and 1 respectively. (b) What distance does the particle cover in the first 4 sec? (c) What is its displacement during the first 4 sec? (d) What is the particle's speed at the end of each of the first 4 sec? (e) What is the particle's acceleration at the end of each of the first 4 sec?

Motion in a Plane

CHAPTER 4

4–1 Displacement and Velocity in Curved Motion

Consider a particle moving along a curved path from P to Q in the x–y plane (Fig. 4–1). At P the displacement of the particle from the origin is $\mathbf{s}$.

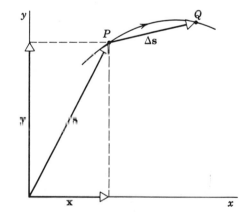

Fig. 4–1 A particle moves along a curved path from P to Q.

If $\mathbf{x}$ and $\mathbf{y}$ are the vector components of $\mathbf{s}$ along the coordinate axes, then

$$\mathbf{s} = \mathbf{x} + \mathbf{y}.$$

At Q the displacement of the particle from the origin can be written as $\mathbf{s} + \Delta\mathbf{s}$, where $\Delta\mathbf{s}$ is the displacement of the particle in going from P to Q.

Let the particle move along the curved path from P to Q in a time interval Δt. Then the *average velocity* during Δt is $\Delta\mathbf{s}/\Delta t$; its direction is that of $\Delta\mathbf{s}$, along the chord PQ. Now let the point Q be chosen successively nearer and nearer to P. As the time interval Δt and the length of chord approach zero,

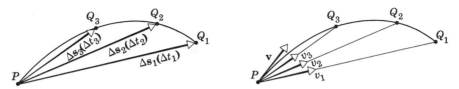

Fig. 4–2 Successively shorter displacements, with corresponding shorter time intervals, are shown. In the limit as Δt approaches zero, $\Delta s/\Delta t$ approaches **v**.

the direction of the chord approaches that of the line tangent to the curve at P (Fig. 4–2). The *instantaneous velocity* of the particle at point P is

$$\mathbf{v} = \lim_{\Delta t \to 0} \frac{\Delta \mathbf{s}}{\Delta t} = \frac{d\mathbf{s}}{dt},$$

a vector whose direction is along the line tangent to the curve at the position of the particle and whose magnitude is the speed of the particle, ds/dt.

As the particle moves along its path, its projections onto the x- and y-axes move along these axes in rectilinear motion. The velocities of the projections (Fig. 4–3) are the rectangular components of the velocity **v** of the particle:

$$\mathbf{v}_x = \frac{d\mathbf{x}}{dt} \quad \text{and} \quad \mathbf{v}_y = \frac{d\mathbf{y}}{dt},$$

$$\mathbf{v} = \frac{d\mathbf{s}}{dt} = \mathbf{v}_x + \mathbf{v}_y.$$

If $\mathbf{v}_x$ and $\mathbf{v}_y$ are determined independently, we simply add them vectorially to obtain the resultant velocity **v**.

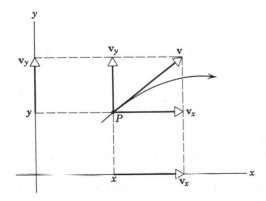

Fig. 4–3 A particle moving along a curve is shown at the instant it passes through point P. Here its velocity is **v**, tangent to the path. The rectangular components of the velocity are $\mathbf{v}_x$ and $\mathbf{v}_y$, which are also shown projected onto the coordinate axes.

4–2 Motion in a Plane with Constant Acceleration

When a particle moves in a straight line, its velocity vector can have any magnitude but must be directed along that line. When a particle instead moves along a curved path in a plane, its velocity vector may have any direction in the plane as well as any magnitude. The velocity vector is tangent to the curve at each point of the motion. These two results are related by the fact that the velocity along the curve is the vector sum of the component velocities along the x- and y-axes.

Likewise, when a particle moves in a straight line, its acceleration vector can have any magnitude but must be directed along that line. When a particle moves along a curved path in a plane instead, its acceleration vector may have any direction in the plane as well as any magnitude. Let us determine the acceleration in curved motion by adding vectorially the component accelerations along the x- and y-axes.

Consider again the particle moving along the curve PQ. At some instant its velocity $\mathbf{v}$ has a definite value and the velocity of the projected motion along the x-axis, $\mathbf{v}_x$, has a definite value. As time goes on the particle moves along the curve and both $\mathbf{v}$ and $\mathbf{v}_x$ will, in general, change. The x component of the motion can be treated as accelerated motion along a straight line. The instantaneous acceleration in the x direction is given simply by $\mathbf{a}_x = d\mathbf{v}_x/dt$. Likewise, the y component of the motion can be treated as accelerated motion along a straight line and the instantaneous acceleration in the y direction is given by $\mathbf{a}_y = d\mathbf{v}_y/dt$.

Hence, the acceleration $\mathbf{a}$ of the particle moving in curved motion in a plane is obtained at once as the sum of the component accelerations; that is,

$$\mathbf{a} = \mathbf{a}_x + \mathbf{a}_y$$

or
$$\mathbf{a} = \frac{d\mathbf{v}_x}{dt} + \frac{d\mathbf{v}_y}{dt} = \frac{d}{dt}(\mathbf{v}_x + \mathbf{v}_y) = \frac{d\mathbf{v}}{dt}.$$

In Fig. 4–4 we show the acceleration $\mathbf{a}$ and its rectangular components $\mathbf{a}_x$ and $\mathbf{a}_y$ for an assumed motion along the curve. Note that the acceleration

Fig. 4–4 The acceleration **a** and its rectangular components $\mathbf{a}_x$ and $\mathbf{a}_y$ for the motion of Fig. 4–3 are shown.

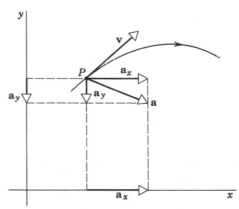

vector does *not* have the same direction as the velocity vector, in general. In Section 4–5 we shall see how we can obtain the acceleration directly from the motion along the curve.

In order to clarify these concepts, let us first consider the specific case of motion in a plane with *constant* acceleration. If **a** is constant, its components $\mathbf{a}_x$ and $\mathbf{a}_y$ must also be constant. We then have a situation in which there is rectilinear motion with constant acceleration simultaneously along each of two perpendicular directions. Let v_{0x} and v_{0y} represent the x and y components, respectively, of the velocity $\mathbf{v}_0$ at the time $t = 0$, and let v_x and v_y be the corresponding components of **v** at the time t. Then, using the results of Section 3–7, we obtain for the x motion

$$v_x = v_{0x} + a_x t \tag{4-1a}$$

and for the y motion $\qquad v_y = v_{0y} + a_y t. \tag{4-1b}$

These two scalar equations are equivalent to the single vector equation

$$\mathbf{v} = \mathbf{v}_0 + \mathbf{a}t. \tag{4-1}$$

Likewise, $\qquad\qquad x = v_{0x}t + \tfrac{1}{2}a_x t^2 \tag{4-2a}$

and $\qquad\qquad\qquad y = v_{0y}t + \tfrac{1}{2}a_y t^2. \tag{4-2b}$

These two scalar equations are equivalent to the single vector equation

$$\mathbf{s} = \mathbf{v}_0 t + \tfrac{1}{2}\mathbf{a}t^2. \tag{4-2}$$

An example of curved motion with constant acceleration is projectile motion. This is the two-dimensional motion of a particle thrown obliquely into the air. The ideal motion of a baseball, a golf ball, or a bullet is an example of projectile motion. We assume that the motion takes place in empty space so that the effect the air itself would have on their motion can be neglected. Let us now consider projectile motion in detail.*

4–3 Projectile Motion

The motion of a projectile is subject to a constant acceleration **g**, directed downward. There is no horizontal component of acceleration.

Let us choose the origin of our coordinates to be the point at which the projectile begins its flight, Fig. 4–5. Hence, the origin will be the point at which the ball leaves the thrower's hand or the fuel in a rocket burns out, for example. We start counting time when the projectile begins its flight; that is, we set t equal to zero at the origin. The velocity at that initial time is $\mathbf{v}_0$ and makes an angle θ_0 with the $+x$-axis. The component of the initial velocity vector along the x-axis, v_{0x}, equals $v_0 \cos \theta_0$ and that along the y-axis, v_{0y}, equals $v_0 \sin \theta_0$.

---

*See Galileo Galilei, *Dialogues Concerning Two New Sciences*, the "Fourth Day," for a fascinating discussion of Galileo's research on projectiles.

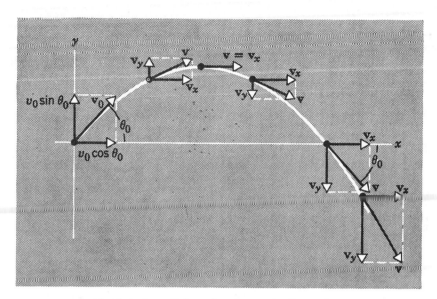

Fig. 4-5 A particle undergoing projectile motion.

Since there is no horizontal acceleration, the x component of the velocity will be constant. In Eq. 4-1a we put $a_x = 0$ and $v_{0x} = v_0 \cos \theta_0$, so that

$$v_x = v_0 \cos \theta_0. \tag{4-3}$$

The y component of the velocity will change with time in accordance with vertical motion with constant acceleration. In Eq. 4-1b we put $a_y = -g$ and $v_{0y} = v_0 \sin \theta_0$, so that

$$v_y = v_0 \sin \theta_0 - gt. \tag{4-4}$$

The *magnitude* of the resultant velocity vector at any instant is

$$v = \sqrt{v_x^2 + v_y^2}.$$

The angle θ that the velocity vector makes with the horizontal at that instant is given by

$$\tan \theta = v_y/v_x.$$

The velocity vector is tangent to the path of the particle at every point (Fig. 4-5). The acceleration vector is directed down at every point.

The x coordinate of the particle at any time (from Eq. 4-2a, with $a_x = 0$ and $v_{0x} = v_0 \cos \theta_0$) is

$$x = (v_0 \cos \theta_0)t. \tag{4-5}$$

The y coordinate (from Eq. 4-2b with $a_y = -g$ and $v_{0y} = v_0 \sin \theta_0$) is

$$y = (v_0 \sin \theta_0)t - \tfrac{1}{2}gt^2. \tag{4-6}$$

Time is taken as zero at the origins of both the x and y motions, so that t is the same for both. By eliminating t from these two equations, we obtain

$$y = (\tan \theta_0)x - \frac{g}{2(v_0 \cos \theta_0)^2} x^2.$$

Since v_0, θ_0, and g are constants, this equation has the form

$$y = bx - cx^2,$$

the equation of a parabola. Hence, the trajectory of a projectile is parabolic.

▶ **Example 1.** A bomber is flying at a constant horizontal velocity of 240 miles/hr at an elevation of 10,000 ft toward a point directly above its target. At what angle of sight ϕ should a bomb be released to strike the target (Fig. 4–6)?

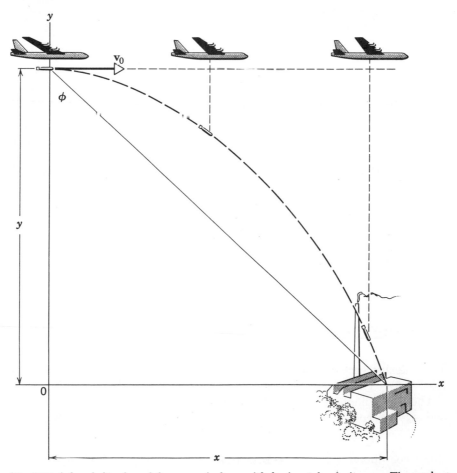

Fig. 4–6 A bomb is released from an airplane with horizontal velocity v_0. The angle ϕ is that at which the bombsight must be oriented for the bomb to find its target.

The motion of the bomb at the instant of release is the same as that of the bomber. Hence, the initial projectile velocity v_0 is horizontal and its magnitude is 240 miles/hr. We have

$$v_{0x} = 240 \text{ miles/hr} = 352 \text{ ft/sec},$$

and
$$v_{0y} = 0.$$

Here the angle of projection θ_0 is zero.

The time of fall is obtained from Eq. 4–6, $y = v_{0y}t - \frac{1}{2}gt^2$, with $v_{0y} = 0$ and $y = -10,000$ ft. This gives

$$t = \sqrt{-\frac{2y}{g}} = \sqrt{-\frac{2(-10,000) \text{ ft}}{32.0 \text{ ft/sec}^2}} = 25.0 \text{ sec}.$$

The horizontal distance traveled by the bomb in this time is given by Eq. 4–5,

$$x = v_{0x}t,$$

$$x = (352 \text{ ft/sec})(25.0 \text{ sec}) = 8800 \text{ ft},$$

so that the angle of sight (Fig. 4–6) should be

$$\phi = \tan^{-1}\left(\frac{x}{y}\right) = \tan^{-1}\left(\frac{8800}{10,000}\right) = 41.6°.$$

Does the motion of the bomb appear to be parabolic when viewed from the bomber?

Example 2. A soccer player kicks a ball at an angle of 37° from the horizontal with an initial speed of 50 ft/sec. (A right triangle, one of whose angles is 37°, has sides in the ratio 0.4.3, or 0.8:10.) Assuming that the ball moves in a vertical plane:

(a) Find the time t_1 at which the ball reaches the highest point of its trajectory.

At the highest point, the vertical component of velocity v_y is zero. By using Eq. 4–4,

$$v_y = v_0 \sin \theta_0 - gt,$$

we obtain
$$t = \frac{v_0 \sin \theta_0 - v_y}{g}.$$

With $v_y = 0,$ $v_0 = 50 \text{ ft/sec},$ $\theta_0 = 37°,$ $g = 32 \text{ ft/sec}^2,$

we have
$$t_1 = \frac{[50(\tfrac{6}{10}) - 0] \text{ ft/sec}}{32 \text{ ft/sec}^2} = \tfrac{15}{16} \text{ sec}.$$

(b) How high does the ball go?

The maximum height is reached at $t = \tfrac{15}{16}$ sec. By using Eq. 4–6,

$$y = (v_0 \sin \theta_0)t - \frac{1}{2}gt^2,$$

we have
$$y_{max} = (50 \text{ ft/sec})(\tfrac{6}{10})(\tfrac{15}{16} \text{ sec}) - \tfrac{1}{2}(32 \text{ ft/sec}^2)(\tfrac{15}{16})^2 \text{ sec}^2 = 14 \text{ ft}.$$

(c) What is the horizontal range of the ball and how long is it in the air?

The horizontal distance from the starting point at which the ball returns to its original elevation (ground level) is the range R. We set $y = 0$ in Eq. 4–6 and find the time t_2 required to traverse this range. We obtain

$$t_2 = \frac{2v_0 \sin \theta_0}{g} = \frac{(100 \text{ ft/sec})(\tfrac{6}{10})}{32 \text{ ft/sec}^2} = \tfrac{15}{8} \text{ sec}.$$

Notice that $t_2 = 2t_1$. This corresponds to the fact that the same time is required for the ball to go up (reach its maximum height from ground) as is required for the ball to come down (reach the ground from its maximum height).

The range R can then be obtained by inserting this value t_2 for t in Eq. 4–5. We obtain

$$x = (v_0 \cos \theta_0)t,$$

$$R = (v_0 \cos \theta_0)t_2 = (50 \text{ ft/sec})(\tfrac{8}{10})(\tfrac{15}{8}\text{sec}) = 75 \text{ ft}.$$

(*d*) What is the velocity of the ball as it strikes the ground?

From Eq. 4–3 we obtain

$$v_x = v_0 \cos \theta = (50 \text{ ft/sec})(\tfrac{8}{10}) = 40 \text{ ft/sec}.$$

From Eq. 4–4 we obtain for $t = t_2 = \tfrac{15}{8}$ sec,

$$v_y = v_0 \sin \theta - gt = (50 \text{ ft/sec})(\tfrac{6}{10}) - (32 \text{ ft/sec}^2)(\tfrac{15}{8} \text{ sec}) = -30 \text{ ft/sec}.$$

Hence,

$$v = \sqrt{v_x{}^2 + v_y{}^2} = \sqrt{(40 \text{ ft/sec})^2 + (-30 \text{ ft/sec})^2} = 50 \text{ ft/sec},$$

$$\tan \theta = v_y/v_x = -\tfrac{30}{40},$$

so that $\theta = 37°$ in the fourth quadrant. Notice that $\theta = \theta_0$, as we expect from symmetry (Fig. 4–5).

Example 3. In a favorite lecture demonstration a gun is sighted at an elevated target which is released in free fall by a trip mechanism as the bullet leaves the muzzle. No matter what the initial speed of the bullet, it always hits the falling target.

The simplest way to understand this is the following. If there were no acceleration due to gravity, the target would not fall and the bullet would move along the line of

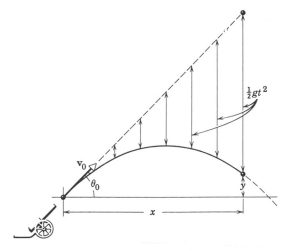

Fig. 4–7 Example 3. In the motion of a projectile, its position at any time t can be thought of as the sum of two vectors: $v_0 t$, directed along v_0, and $gt^2/2$, directed downward.

sight directly into the target (Fig. 4–7). The effect of gravity is to cause each body to accelerate down at the same rate from the position it would otherwise have. Therefore, in the time t, the bullet will fall a distance $\tfrac{1}{2}gt^2$ from the position it would have had along the line of sight and the target will fall the same distance from its starting point. When the bullet reaches the line of fall of the target, it will be the same distance below the target's initial position as the target is, and hence the collision (Fig. 4–7). If the bullet moves faster than shown in the figure (v_0 larger), it will have a greater range and will cross the line of fall at a higher point; but since it gets there sooner, the target will fall a correspondingly smaller distance in the same time and collide with it. A similar argument holds for slower speeds.

This reasoning is equivalent to thinking of the projectile's velocity as the sum of v_0, the initial velocity, and gt, the velocity acquired in time t by a body in free fall. This corresponds to writing

$$v = v_0 + gt$$

which is the same as Eq. 4–1, with $a = g$. The displacement of the projectile at any time t is then thought of as the sum of two displacements $v_0 t$, directed along v_0, and $gt^2/2$, directed downward. This corresponds to writing

$$s = v_0 t + \tfrac{1}{2} gt^2$$

which is the same as Eq. 4–2 with $a = g$.   ◄

4–4 Uniform Circular Motion

In Section 3–5 we saw that acceleration arises from a change in velocity. In the simple case of free fall the velocity changed in magnitude only, but not in direction. In the case of a particle moving in a circle with constant speed, called uniform circular motion, the velocity vector changes continuously in direction but not in magnitude. We seek now to obtain the acceleration in uniform circular motion.

The situation is shown in Fig. 4–8a. Let P be the position of the particle at the time t and P' its position at the time $t + \Delta t$. The velocity at P is $\mathbf{v}$, a vector tangent to the curve at P. The velocity at P' is $\mathbf{v}'$, a vector tangent

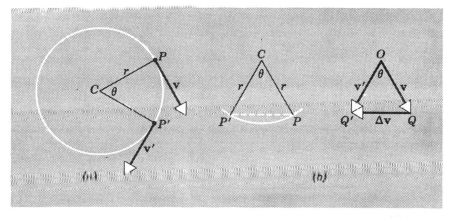

Fig. 4–8 Uniform circular motion. The particle travels around a circle at constant speed. Its velocity at two points P and P' is shown. Its change in velocity in going from P to P' is Δv.

to the curve at P'. Vectors $\mathbf{v}$ and $\mathbf{v}'$ are equal in magnitude, the speed being constant, but their directions are different. The length of path traversed during Δt is the arc length PP', which is equal to $v\,\Delta t$, v being the constant speed.

Now redraw the vectors $\mathbf{v}$ and $\mathbf{v}'$, as in Fig. 4–8b, so that they originate at a common point. We are free to do this as long as the magnitude and direction of each vector is the same as in Fig. 4–8a. This diagram (Fig. 4–8b) enables us to see clearly the *change in velocity* as the particle moved from P to P'. This change, $\mathbf{v}' - \mathbf{v} = \Delta\mathbf{v}$, is the vector which must be added to $\mathbf{v}$ to get $\mathbf{v}'$. Notice that it points inward, approximately toward the center of the circle.

Now the triangle OQQ' formed by $\mathbf{v}$, $\mathbf{v}'$, and $\Delta\mathbf{v}$ is similar to the triangle CPP' formed by the chord PP' and the radii CP and CP'. This is so because both are isosceles triangles having the same vertex angle; the angle θ between $\mathbf{v}$ and $\mathbf{v}'$ is the same as the angle POP' because $\mathbf{v}$ is perpendicular to CP and $\mathbf{v}'$ is perpendicular to CP'. We can, therefore, write

$$\frac{\Delta v}{v} = \frac{v\,\Delta t}{r}, \qquad \text{approximately,}$$

the chord PP' being taken equal to the arc length PP'. This relation becomes more nearly exact as Δt is diminished, since the chord and the arc then approach each other. Notice also that $\Delta\mathbf{v}$ approaches closer and closer to a direction perpendicular to $\mathbf{v}$ and $\mathbf{v}'$ as Δt is diminished and, therefore, approaches closer and closer to a direction pointing to the exact center of the circle. It follows from this relation that

$$\frac{\Delta v}{\Delta t} = \frac{v^2}{r}, \qquad \text{approximately,}$$

and in the limit when $\Delta t \to 0$ this expression becomes exact. We, therefore, obtain

$$a = \lim_{\Delta t \to 0} \frac{\Delta v}{\Delta t} = \frac{v^2}{r} \qquad (4\text{-}7)$$

as the magnitude of the acceleration. The direction of $\mathbf{a}$ is instantaneously along a radius inward toward the center of the circle.

Figure 4–9 shows the instantaneous relation between $\mathbf{v}$ and $\mathbf{a}$ at various points of the motion. The magnitude of $\mathbf{v}$ is constant, but its direction

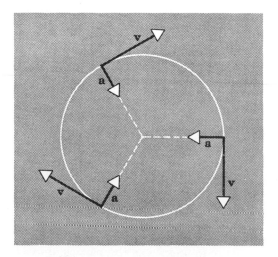

Fig. 4–9 In uniform circular motion the acceleration $\mathbf{a}$ is always directed toward the center of the circle and hence is perpendicular to $\mathbf{v}$.

changes continuously. This gives rise to an acceleration **a** which is also constant in magnitude (but not zero) but continuously changing in direction. The velocity **v** is always tangent to the circle in the direction of motion; the acceleration **a** is always directed radially inward. Because of this, **a** is called a *radial*, or *centripetal*, acceleration. "Centripetal" means "seeking a center."

Both in free fall and in projectile motion **a** is constant in direction and magnitude and we can use the equations developed for constant acceleration. This is not true for uniform circular motion, for then **a** varies in direction and is not constant.

The units of centripetal acceleration are the same as those of an acceleration resulting from a change in the magnitude of a velocity. Dimensionally, we have

$$\frac{v^2}{r} = \left(\frac{\text{length}}{\text{time}}\right)^2 \bigg/ \text{length} = \frac{\text{length}}{\text{time}^2} \text{ or } \frac{(L)}{(T^2)},$$

which are the dimensions of acceleration. The units, therefore, may be ft/sec², meters/sec², among others.

The acceleration resulting from a change in direction of a velocity is just as real and just as much an acceleration in every sense as that arising from a change in magnitude of a velocity. By definition, acceleration is the time rate of change of velocity and velocity, being a vector, can change in direction as well as magnitude. If a physical quantity is a vector, its directional aspects cannot be ignored, for their effects will prove to be every bit as important and real as those produced by changes in magnitude. It is, therefore, a matter of real consequence whether a quantity is a scalar or a vector.

It is worth emphasizing at this point that there need not be any motion in the direction of an acceleration and that there is no fixed relation in general between the directions of **a** and **v**. In Fig. 4–10 we illustrate instances

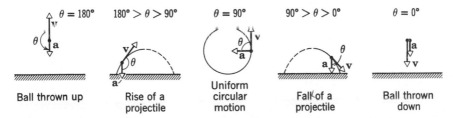

Fig. 4–10 Showing the relation between **v** and **a** for various motions.

in which the angle between **v** and **a** varies from 0 to 180°. Only in one case, $\theta = 0°$, is the motion in the direction of **a**.

▶ **Example 4.** The moon revolves about the earth, making a complete revolution in 27.3 days. Assume that the orbit is circular and has a radius of 239,000 miles. What is the magnitude of the acceleration of the moon toward the earth?

We have $r = 239{,}000$ miles $= 385 \times 10^6$ meters.

The time for one complete revolution, called the period, is $T = 27.3$ days $= 23.6 \times 10^5$ sec. The speed of the moon (assumed constant) is therefore

$$v = \frac{2\pi r}{T} = 1020 \text{ meters/sec.}$$

The centripetal acceleration is

$$a = \frac{v^2}{r} = \frac{(1020 \text{ meters/sec})^2}{385 \times 10^6 \text{ meters}} = 0.00273 \text{ meter/sec}^2, \text{ or only } 2.8 \times 10^{-4}g.$$

Example 5. Calculate the speed of an artificial earth satellite, assuming for simplicity that it is traveling just above the surface of the earth. The radius of the earth R_e is about 4000 miles.

Like any free object near the earth's surface the satellite has an acceleration g toward the earth's center. It is this acceleration that causes it to follow the circular path. Hence, the centripetal acceleration is g, and from

$$a = \frac{v^2}{r},$$

we have

$$g = \frac{v^2}{R_e},$$

or $v = \sqrt{R_e g} = \sqrt{(4000 \text{ miles})(5280 \text{ ft/mile})(32.0 \text{ ft/sec}^2)} = 2.60 \times 10^4 \text{ ft/sec}$

$= 17{,}700 \text{ miles/hr.}$ ◀

4–5 Tangential Acceleration in Circular Motion

We now consider the more general case of circular motion in which the speed is not constant. This motion is illustrated in Fig. 4–11a. In moving from P to P', the particle undergoes a change in velocity from $\mathbf{v}$ to $\mathbf{v}'$, where $\mathbf{v}'$ has a greater magnitude than $\mathbf{v}$ as well as a different direction. In Fig. 4–11b we have redrawn the vectors. We see that $\Delta\mathbf{v}$, which is the vector

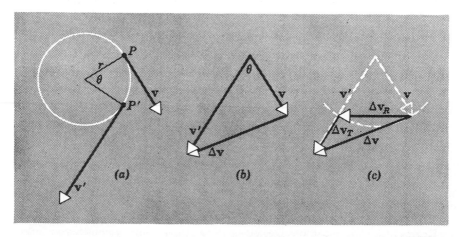

Fig. 4–11 In nonuniform circular motion the speed is variable. The change in velocity $\Delta\mathbf{v}$ in going from P to P' is made up of two parts: $\Delta\mathbf{v}_R$ caused by the change in direction of $\mathbf{v}$, and $\Delta\mathbf{v}_T$ caused by the change in magnitude of $\mathbf{v}$.

change in velocity, does not necessarily point toward the center of the circle.

The *average acceleration* in the interval $\Delta t = t' - t$ as the particle moves from P to P' is $\Delta \mathbf{v}/\Delta t$.

The vector $\Delta \mathbf{v}$ can be resolved into a radial component $\Delta \mathbf{v}_R$ and a tangential component $\Delta \mathbf{v}_T$. The radial component arises from a change in the *direction* of the velocity, whereas the tangential component arises from a change in the *magnitude* of the velocity (Fig. 4–11c). The ratio $\Delta \mathbf{v}_R/\Delta t$ is the radial component $\mathbf{a}_R$ of the average acceleration, and the ratio $\Delta \mathbf{v}_T/\Delta t$ is the tangential component $\mathbf{a}_T$ of the average acceleration.

The radial and tangential components of the *instantaneous acceleration* are then

$$\mathbf{a}_R = \lim_{\Delta t \to 0} \frac{\Delta \mathbf{v}_R}{\Delta t},$$

and

$$\mathbf{a}_T = \lim_{\Delta t \to 0} \frac{\Delta \mathbf{v}_T}{\Delta t}.$$

The limiting value of $\Delta \mathbf{v}_R/\Delta t$ is the same as for motion in a circle with constant speed. Therefore, $\mathbf{a}_R$ has the magnitude v^2/r and points inward along the radius, as before; $\mathbf{a}_T$ has the magnitude dv/dt, the rate of change of the *magnitude* of the velocity, and points along the tangent in the direction of increasing velocity.

The magnitude of the *resultant* instantaneous acceleration is

$$a = \sqrt{a_T{}^2 + a_R{}^2}, \tag{4–8}$$

with

$$a_T = \frac{dv}{dt} \quad \text{and} \quad a_R = \frac{v^2}{r}. \tag{4–9}$$

Because the speed v is not constant, a_R will vary from point to point. If the speed v does not change at a constant rate, a_T will vary from point to point also.

If the motion is not circular, these formulas can still be applied if for r we substitute the radius of curvature of the path at the instantaneous position of the particle. Then a_T gives the component of acceleration tangent to the curve at that position, and a_R gives the component of acceleration normal to the curve at that position.

4–6 Relative Velocity and Acceleration

In earlier sections we considered the addition of velocities in a particular reference frame. Let us now consider the relation between the velocity of an object as determined by one observer (= one reference frame) and the velocity of the same object as determined by another observer (= another reference frame) who is moving with respect to the first.

Consider one observer fixed to the earth, so that his reference frame is the earth. The other observer is moving on the earth—for example, a passenger

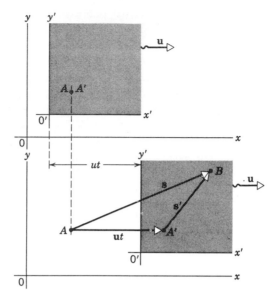

Fig. 4–12 Two coordinate frames, x, y and x', y', are shown; x', y' moves to the right, relative to x, y, with speed u.

sitting on a moving train—so that his reference frame is the train. These observers each follow the motion of the same object, say an automobile on the road or a man walking through the train. Each observer will record a displacement, a velocity, and an acceleration for this object measured *relative to his reference frame.* How will these measurements compare? In this section we consider only the case in which the second frame is in motion with respect to the first with a *constant* velocity **u**.

In Fig. 4–12 the coordinate system represented by the x- and y-axes can be thought of as fixed to the earth. The shaded region indicates another reference frame represented by x'- and y'-axes which moves along the x-axis with a constant velocity **u**, as measured in the x–y system; it can be thought of as drawn on the floor of a railroad flatcar.

Initially a particle (say a ball on the flatcar) is at a position called A in the x–y frame and called A' in the x'–y' frame. At a time t later the flatcar and its x'–y' reference frame have moved a distance ut to the right and the particle has moved to B. The *displacement* of the particle from its initial position *in the x–y system* is the vector **s** from A to B. The *displacement* of the particle from its initial position *in the x'–y' frame* is the vector **s**' from A' to B. These are different vectors because the reference point A' of the moving frame has been displaced a distance ut along the x-axis during the motion. From the figure we see that **s** is the vector sum of **s**' and **u**t:

$$\mathbf{s} = \mathbf{s}' + \mathbf{u}t.$$

If the time interval is taken as an infinitesimal one, dt, the displacements become infinitesimal, the vector from A to A' becomes $\mathbf{u}\,dt$, and the other vectors become $d\mathbf{s}$ and $d\mathbf{s}'$, so that

$$d\mathbf{s} = d\mathbf{s}' + \mathbf{u}\,dt.$$

Dividing throughout by dt, we have

$$\frac{d\mathbf{s}}{dt} = \frac{d\mathbf{s}'}{dt} + \mathbf{u}.$$

But $d\mathbf{s}/dt = \mathbf{v}$, the instantaneous velocity of the particle measured in the x–y frame, and $d\mathbf{s}'/dt = \mathbf{v}'$, the instantaneous velocity of the same particle measured in the x'–y' frame, so that

$$\mathbf{v} = \mathbf{v}' + \mathbf{u}. \tag{4–10}$$

Hence, the velocity of the particle relative to the x–y frame, $\mathbf{v}$, is the vector sum of the velocity of the particle relative to the x'–y' frame, $\mathbf{v}'$, and the velocity of the primed frame relative to the unprimed one, $\mathbf{u}$.

▶ **Example 6.** (a) The compass of an airplane indicates that it is heading due east. Ground information indicates a wind blowing due north. Show on a diagram the velocity of the plane with respect to the ground.

The object is the airplane. The earth is one reference frame (unprimed) and the air is the other reference frame (primed) moving with respect to the first. Then,

$\mathbf{u}$ is a vector giving the velocity of the air with respect to the ground,
$\mathbf{v}'$ is a vector giving the velocity of the plane with respect to the air, and
$\mathbf{v}$ is the velocity of the plane with respect to the ground.

In this case $\mathbf{u}$ points north and $\mathbf{v}'$ points east. Then the relation $\mathbf{v} = \mathbf{v}' + \mathbf{u}$ determines the velocity of the plane with respect to the ground, as shown in Fig. 4–13a.

The angle α is the angle N of E of the plane's course with respect to the ground and is given by

$$\tan \alpha = u/v'.$$

The airplane's speed with respect to the ground is given by

$$v = \sqrt{(v')^2 + u^2}.$$

For example, if the air-speed indicator shows that the plane is moving relative to the air at a speed of 200 miles/hr, and if the speed of the wind with respect to the ground is 40.0 miles/hr, then

$$v = \sqrt{(200)^2 + (40.0)^2} \text{ miles/hr} = 204 \text{ miles/hr}$$

is the ground speed of the plane and

$$\alpha = \tan^{-1} \frac{40.0}{200} = 11° \, 20'$$

gives the course of the plane N of E.

(b) Now draw the vector diagram showing the direction the pilot must steer the plane through the air for the plane to travel due east with respect to the ground.

He would naturally head partly into the wind. His speed relative to the earth will, therefore, be less than before. The vector diagram is shown in Fig. 4–13b. The student should calculate θ and v, using the previous data for $\mathbf{u}$ and $\mathbf{v}'$.   ◀

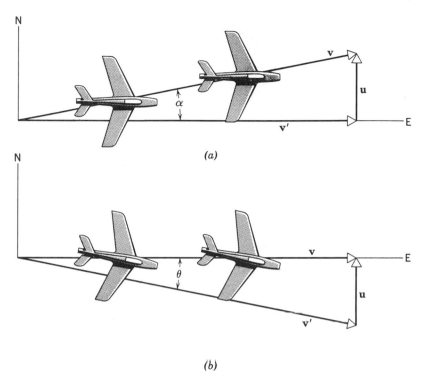

Fig. 4–13 Example 6.

We have seen that different velocities are assigned to a particle by different observers when the observers are in relative motion. These velocities *always differ by* the relative velocity of the two observers, which here is *a constant velocity*. It follows that when the particle velocity changes the *change will be the same* for both observers. Hence, they each measure the *same acceleration* for the particle. The acceleration of a particle is the same in *all* references frames moving relative to one another with constant velocity; that is, $\mathbf{a} = \mathbf{a'}$.

QUESTIONS

1. A bus with a vertical windshield moves along in a rainstorm at speed v_b. The raindrops fall vertically with a terminal speed v_r. At what angle do the raindrops strike the windshield?

2. In projectile motion when air resistance is negligible, is it ever necessary to consider three-dimensional motion rather than two-dimensional?

3. In broad jumping does it matter how high you jump? What factors determine the span of the jump?

4. How could you determine the height of a hill by standing at the top with only a stone and a watch?

5. Describe qualitatively the acceleration acting on a bead which moves inward along a spiral with constant speed.

6. A boy sitting in a railroad car moving at constant velocity throws a ball straight up into the air. Will the ball fall behind him? In front of him? Into his hand? What happens if the car accelerates forward? Goes around a curve?

7. A certain aviator, pulling out of a dive, follows the arc of a circle. He was said to have "experienced 3 g's" in pulling out of the dive. Explain clearly what this statement means.

8. A man on the observation platform of a train moving with constant velocity drops his pocket watch while leaning over the rail. Describe the path of the watch as seen by (a) the man on the train and (b) a person standing on the ground near the track.

PROBLEMS

1. A ball rolls off the edge of a horizontal table top 4.0 ft high. If it strikes the floor at a point 5.0 ft horizontally away from the edge of the table, what was its speed at the instant it left the table?

2. A ball rolls off the top of a stairway with a horizontal velocity of magnitude 5.0 ft/sec. The steps are exactly 8 in. high and 8 in. wide. Which step will the ball hit first? Draw a diagram illustrating the problem.

3. A shell is fired horizontally from a powerful gun located 144 ft above a horizontal plane, with a muzzle speed of 800 ft/sec. (a) How long does the shell remain in the air? (b) What is its range? (c) What is the magnitude of the vertical component of its velocity as it strikes the target?

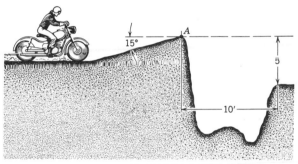

4. An object is projected *down* at an angle α with the horizontal from the top of a cliff of height h with an initial speed v. Find (a) the time t elapsing before it hits the ground, and (b) the distance d from the foot of the cliff to the point of landing. (c) Solve numerically for $v = 300$ ft/sec, $\alpha = 30.0°$, and $h = 600$ ft.

Fig. 4–14

5. Solve the preceding problem, assuming that the object is projected *upward* at an angle α with the horizontal.

6. Calculate the minimum speed with which a motorcycle rider must leave the 15° ramp at A in order to just clear the ditch (Fig. 4–14).

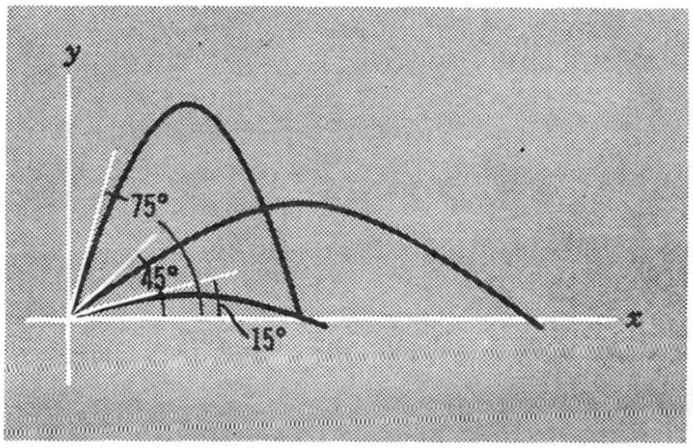

7. Show that the maximum height reached by a projectile is $y_{max} = (v_0 \sin \theta_0)^2/2 \, g$.

8. Show that the horizontal range of a projectile having an initial speed v_0 and angle of projection θ_0 is $R = (v_0^2/g) \sin 2\theta_0$. Then show that a projection angle of 45° gives the maximum horizontal range (Fig. 4–15).

9. In Galileo's *Two New Sciences* the author states that "for elevations (angles of projection) which

Fig. 4–15

exceed or fall short of 45° by equal amounts, the ranges are equal. . . ." Prove this statement, starting with the range formula of the previous problem (Fig. 4–15).

10. A batter hits a pitched ball at a height 4 ft above ground so that its angle of projection is 45° and its horizontal range is 350 ft. The ball is fair down the left field line where a 24-ft-high fence is located 320 ft from home plate. Will the ball clear the fence?

11. A football is kicked off with an initial speed of 64 ft/sec at a projection angle of 45°. A receiver on the goal line 60 yd away in the direction of the kick starts running to meet the ball at that instant. What must his speed be if he is to catch the ball before it hits the ground?

12. In a cathode-ray tube a beam of electrons is projected horizontally with a speed of 10^9 cm/sec into the region between a pair of horizontal plates 2.0 cm long. An electric field between the plates exerts a constant downward acceleration on the electrons of magnitude 10^{17} cm/sec^2. Find (a) the vertical displacement of the beam in passing through the plates, and (b) the velocity of the beam (direction and magnitude) as it emerges from the plates.

13. (a) Show that if the acceleration of gravity changes by an amount dg, the range of a projectile (cf. Problem 8) of given initial speed v_0 and angle of projection θ_0 changes by dR where $dR/R = -dg/g$. (b) If the acceleration of gravity changes by a small amount Δg (say by going from one place to another), the range for a given projectile system will change as well. Let the change in range be ΔR. If Δg, ΔR are small enough, we may write $\Delta R/R = -\Delta g/g$. In 1936 Jesse Owens (United States) established the world's running broad-jump record of 8.09 meters at the Olympic games at Berlin ($g = 9.8128$ meters/sec^2). By how much would his record have differed if he had competed instead in 1956 at Melbourne ($g = 9.7999$ meters/sec^2)? (In this connection see an interesting article "Bad Physics in Athletic Measurements" by P. Kirkpatrick, *American Journal of Physics*, February 1944).

14. Prove that in motion in a plane with constant acceleration

$$\mathbf{s} = (\mathbf{v}_0 + \mathbf{v})t/2$$

and

$$\mathbf{v} \cdot \mathbf{v} = \mathbf{v}_0 \cdot \mathbf{v}_0 + 2\mathbf{a} \cdot \mathbf{s}.$$

These are the generalizations of Eqs. 3–9 and 3–11 to more than one dimension.

15. An earth satellite moves in a circular orbit 400 miles above the earth's surface. The time for 1 revolution (the period) is found to be 98 min. Find the acceleration of gravity at the orbit from these data.

16. The earth revolves about the sun in a (nearly) circular orbit with a (nearly) constant speed of 30 km/sec. What is the acceleration of the earth toward the sun?

17. Consider a projectile at the top of its trajectory. (a) What is its speed in terms of v_0 and θ_0? (b) What is its acceleration? (c) How is the direction of its acceleration related to that of its velocity? (d) Over a short distance a circular arc is a good approximation to a parabola. What then is the radius of the circular arc approximating the projectile's motion near the top of its path?

18. A magnetic field will deflect a charged particle perpendicular to its direction of motion. An electron experiences a radial acceleration of 3.0×10^{14} meters/sec^2 in one such field. What is its speed if the radius of its curved path is 0.15 meter?

19. In Bohr's model of the hydrogen atom an electron revolves around a proton in a circular orbit of radius 5.28×10^{-11} meter with a speed of 2.18×10^6 meters/sec. What is the acceleration of the electron in the hydrogen atom?

20. Find the magnitude of the centripetal acceleration of a particle on the tip of a fan blade, 0.30 meter in diameter, rotating at 1200 rev/min.

21. By what factor would the speed of the earth's rotation have to increase for a body on the equator to require a centripetal acceleration of g to keep it on the earth? Such a body now requires a centripetal acceleration of only about 3.0 cm/sec^2.

22. A particle travels with constant speed on a circle of radius 3.0 meters and completes 1 revolution in 20 sec (Fig. 4–16). Starting from the origin O, find (a) the magnitude and

direction of the displacement vectors 5.0 sec, 7.5 sec, and 10 sec later; (b) the magnitude and direction of the displacement in the 5.0-sec interval from the fifth to the tenth second; (c) the average velocity vector in this interval; (d) the instantaneous velocity vector at the

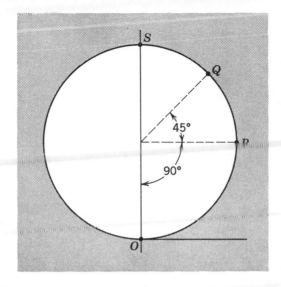

Fig. 4–16

beginning and at the end of this interval; (e) the average acceleration vector in this interval; and (f) the instantaneous acceleration vector at the beginning and at the end of this interval.

23. A man can row a boat 4.0 miles/hr in still water. (a) If he is crossing a river where the current is 2.0 miles/hr, in what direction will his boat be headed if he wants to reach a point directly opposite from his starting point? (b) If the river is 4.0 miles wide, how long will it take him to cross the river? (c) How long will it take him to row 2.0 miles *down* the river and then back to his starting point? (d) How long will it take him to row 2.0 miles *up* the river and then back to his starting point? (e) In what direction should he head the boat if he wants to cross in the smallest possible time?

24. A pilot is supposed to fly due east from A to B and then back again to A due west. The velocity of the plane in air is v' and the velocity of the air with respect to the ground is **u**. The distance between A and B is l and the plane's air speed v' is constant. (a) If $u = 0$ (still air), show that the time for the round trip is $t_0 = 2l/v'$. (b) Suppose that the air velocity is due east (or west), show that the time for a round trip is then

$$t_E = \frac{t_0}{1 - \dfrac{u^2}{(v')^2}}.$$

(c) Suppose that the air velocity is due north (or south). Show that the time for a round trip is then

$$t_N = \frac{t_0}{\sqrt{1 - \dfrac{u^2}{(v')^2}}}.$$

25. Prove by a velocity diagram similar to Fig. 4–12 that observers moving at a constant velocity relative to one another measure the same acceleration for a moving particle.

Particle Dynamics—I

CHAPTER 5

5–1 Particle Dynamics

In the previous two chapters we described the motion of particles, particularly straight-line and planar motion. We did not ask what caused the motion. Our discussion, therefore, was essentially geometrical. In this and later chapters we shall study the causes of motion and the way in which bodies influence one another's motion. This part of mechanics is called *dynamics.*

As before, we confine our attention at first to translational motion. Bodies will be treated as though they were single particles. The treatment of extended bodies and groups of particles will be given later in the text.

5–2 Newton's First Law of Motion

Man quite naturally appeals to his everyday experiences in seeking to understand nature. As far as motion is concerned, he sees, among many other things, falling stones, sliding blocks, bullets shot from rifles, and the apparent motions of the heavenly bodies. By studying these motions he hopes to find fundamental laws that apply to all or at least to many of his experiences involving motion.

For centuries the problem of motion and its causes was studied in this way. It became a central theme of natural philosophy. It was not until the time of Galileo and Newton, however, that dramatic progress was made in solving the problem. Isaac Newton (1642–1727), born in England the year of Galileo's death, is the principal architect of classical mechanics.*

---

* Newton also invented the (fluxional) calculus, conceived the idea of universal gravitation and discovered its law, and discovered the composition of white light. His formulation of mechanics and his ideas of absolute space and time were not seriously challenged until Albert Einstein developed the theory of relativity in 1905, over 200 years later.

He carried to full fruition the ideas of Galileo and others who preceded him. His system of mechanics is summarized in three laws of motion, presented first (in 1686) in the *Principia Mathematica Philosophiae Naturalis.*

Before Galileo's time most philosophers thought that some external influence or "force" was needed to keep a body moving. They thought that a body was in its "natural state" when it was at rest. In order for a body to move in a straight line at constant speed, for example, they believed that some external agent had to continually propel it; otherwise it would "naturally" stop moving.

If we wanted to test these ideas experimentally, we would first have to find a way in which to free a body from all external influences, or forces. We would soon find that we really cannot do this, because even bodies very far from our test body can influence it and change its motion. However, in certain cases we can make the external forces very small. If we study the motion as we make these forces smaller and smaller, we shall have some idea of what the motion would be like if the external forces were truly zero.

We cannot remove the earth but we can minimize its influence on motion by placing our test body, say a block, on a rigid horizontal plane. If we let the block slide along this plane, we notice that it gradually slows down and stops. This observation was used, in fact, to support the idea that motion stopped when the external force, in this case the hand initially pushing the block, was removed. Galileo argued against this idea, however. His reasoning is as follows.

Let us repeat our experiment, now using a smoother block and a smoother surface. We notice that the velocity decreases more slowly than before. Let us continue to use still smoother blocks and surfaces. We find that the block decreases in velocity at a slower and slower rate and travels farther each time before coming to rest. We can now extrapolate our ideas and say that if all friction could be eliminated, the body would continue indefinitely in a straight line with constant speed. This was Galileo's conclusion. Galileo asserted that some external force was necessary to *change* the velocity of a body but that no external force was necessary to *maintain* the velocity of a body. Our hand, for example, exerts a force on the block when it sets it in motion. The rough plane exerts a force on it when it slows it down. Both of these forces produce a change in the velocity, that is, they produce an acceleration.

This principle of Galileo was adopted by Newton as the first of his three laws of motion. Newton stated his first law of motion in these words: *"Every body persists in its state of rest or of uniform motion in a straight line unless it is compelled to change that state by forces impressed on it."*

It is important to realize that this principle has not actually been proved but that it represents a generalization from experience. We often use this procedure in science. Whether or not the procedure is a good one depends on whether or not the deductions from the generalization agree with experiment.

In order to prove Newton's first law we need to define the word *force* which appears in the statement of the law. So far we have not done so.

Rather we have loosely identified force with what we call *external influence*. In so doing we have leaned heavily on the intuitive feeling that all of us have about the nature of force. In science, however, our concepts must rest on a firmer foundation than intuitive feelings. They must be defined in a quantitative, operational way. Logically, we could take the first law as a definition of force. Force would thereby be defined as the cause of acceleration. This definition would not be a quantitative one, however, although it would be in accord with our intuitive ideas about force.

The fact that a body once started in motion retains a uniform linear motion in the absence of applied forces is often described by assigning a property to matter called *mass*.* Mass is regarded then as the property of matter that determines its resistance to a change in its motion. In Section 5–4 we discuss how the mass of a body is defined and measured.

5–3 Force

The primitive concept of a force is a push or a pull exerted by our muscles. We know that by pushing or pulling on an object, such as the block in our previous example, we can change its velocity. In fact, the harder we push or pull, the more we change its velocity (that is, the greater its acceleration). These statements merely confirm our intuitive acceptance of the first law of motion in which force is regarded as the cause of acceleration. For purposes of science, however, we must make our definition of force exact by setting up a procedure for measuring it.

Let us arbitrarily pick out an object as a standard object and let it be free to move on a horizontal table having negligible friction. If we apply a force to this object, the object will be accelerated. We can measure this acceleration and use the value found as a measure of the force. For example, we can attach a spring to the standard object. We pull on the other end of the spring in such a way that the spring is stretched a fixed length beyond its normal unstretched length, for a short time at least. Meanwhile, by suitable distance and time measurements we measure the resulting acceleration of the standard object.

Suppose that with our spring stretched 0.03 meter we measure the acceleration to be 1 meter/sec^2. We take this force, which accelerates the standard object at the rate of 1 meter/sec^2, as our *unit force*. We can now stretch the same spring different lengths, or we can use other springs of different stiffness. For each stretching the force exerted is determined as a definite number of units of force, depending on the acceleration produced on the standard object. Thus, a force of 13 units is one that will accelerate the standard object 13 meters/sec^2, a force of 6 units is one that will accelerate the standard object 6 meters/sec^2, and so forth. We now have a definite procedure for measuring the force exerted by a spring, and we are able to exert different forces of known magnitudes on objects.

The question arises whether our definition of force is a good one. It

---

* Often this property is called inertia. Mass is then regarded as the quantitative measure of inertia.

appears to be simple and uncomplicated. However, will it prove to be a useful concept in mechanics? The answer lies in experiment.

Let us now attach two springs to our standard object and let both pull simultaneously *in the same direction*, one exerting a force of F_1 units and the other a force of F_2 units. We find by experiment that the acceleration produced is $F_1 + F_2$ meters/sec^2, the same acceleration that a single spring of $F_1 + F_2$ force units would produce acting alone. That is, forces of magnitude F_1 and F_2 applied in the same direction at the same time cause the same acceleration as a single force of $F_1 + F_2$ acting alone. This result does not follow abstractly from our definition of force. Instead, it is proved by direct experiment.

Let us proceed further by experiment. We find an important consequence of our definition of force, which is that force so defined is a vector quantity. It is clear that a force involves direction as well as magnitude. However, it does not follow from this that force is a vector. We must also show that forces obey the laws of addition of vectors. We discussed these in Section 2–2 for the prototype vector quantity, displacement. Hence, whether or not force is a vector quantity can only be proved by experiment.

Let us apply a force of six units in magnitude to our standard object, pulling along the positive x-axis of some reference frame. At the same time, let us apply a force of eight units in magnitude pulling along the positive y-axis of our frame. Notice that the forces now act *in different directions*. The resulting acceleration is found to have a magnitude of 10 meters/sec^2 and to lie along a straight line making an angle with the x-axis whose tangent is four-thirds. That is, the resultant acceleration is the same in both magnitude and direction as would be obtained from a single force which is the *vector sum* of the two separate forces. Forces, therefore, add like displacements and are vectors.

This result is often stated as follows: *When several forces act on a body, each produces its own acceleration independently. The resulting acceleration is the vector sum of the several independent accelerations.*

Our experiments were conducted on a standard object which was taken to be at rest before we applied the forces. We obtain the same results when the object is initially in motion; that is, the same acceleration is produced by a given force acting on a given body no matter what the initial velocity of the body. If this were not so, our procedure for measuring force would have to be restricted to measuring the acceleration produced on the standard object when it is instantaneously at rest. However, experiment shows that we do not need to restrict the definition of force in this way in classical physics.

5–4 Concept of Mass: Newton's Second Law of Motion

The student will have noticed that our previous study of forces has been confined to the effect produced by various forces on a single body, namely the standard object which was chosen arbitrarily. The obvious question arises: What effect would these forces have on other objects? Since our object was chosen arbitrarily in the first place, we know that the previous results hold for any given object, that is, the force is directly proportional to the acceleration.

The significant question is "What effect will the *same force* have on *different objects?*" Everyday experience gives us a qualitative answer. The same force will produce different accelerations on different bodies. A baseball will be accelerated more by a given force than will an automobile. In order to obtain a quantitative answer to this question we must make measurements. To do this, we need a method to measure mass, the property of a body which determines the effect of a force applied to it.

The procedure for measuring mass is suggested by experience. For a given force, the greater the mass the less the acceleration produced by that force. We now generalize this experience and define mass in terms of the acceleration produced by a given force. To be exact, if m_1 is the mass of body 1 and m_2 is the mass of body 2, we *define* the ratio of the masses to be

$$\frac{m_1}{m_2} = \frac{a_2}{a_1} \qquad \text{(given force } \mathbf{F}\text{)} \qquad\qquad (5\text{--}1)$$

where a_2 is the magnitude of the acceleration of body 2 and a_1 is the magnitude of the acceleration of body 1 produced by the same applied force $\mathbf{F}$. If body 2 has only half the acceleration of body 1 when both are acted on by the same force, then by definition m_2 is twice as great as m_1. If m_1 is the standard mass, then m_2 would be two standard masses.

If we were to change the force from $\mathbf{F}$ to $\mathbf{F}'$ and once again measure the ratio of accelerations a_2'/a_1' produced on the same two bodies 1 and 2 as used before, we would find

$$\frac{a_2'}{a_1'} = \frac{a_2}{a_1},$$

so that

$$\frac{m_1}{m_2} = \frac{a_2}{a_1} = \frac{a_2'}{a_1'}.$$

The ratio of the masses is found to be the same, regardless of the particular force we use in the experiments. Since the masses are accelerated different amounts by different forces, we conclude that the mass of a body, as we have defined it, is independent of the velocity of the body.

Furthermore, experiment shows that we can consistently assign mass numbers to any body by this procedure. For example, if we compare a third body with body 1 and find m_3 from the relation

$$\frac{m_1}{m_3} = \frac{a_3}{a_1} \qquad \text{(given force } \mathbf{F}\text{)},$$

experiment shows that when body 2 and body 3 are compared

$$\frac{a_3}{a_2} = \frac{m_2}{m_3} \qquad \text{(given force } \mathbf{F}\text{)},$$

where m_2 and m_3 are the values already determined by comparing bodies 2 and 3 independently with body 1.

In order to find a number to assign for the mass of a body, we simply agree to assign to the standard object (which was accelerated 1 meter/sec^2 by a unit force) a mass of one unit. Then the masses of all other objects are defined by Eq. 5–1 in terms of this unit mass. We, therefore, have an operational procedure for measuring mass quantitatively, a procedure which is simple, self-consistent, and intuitively satisfactory.

We can now summarize all the experiments and definitions in one equation, the fundamental equation of classical mechanics,

$$\mathbf{F} = m\mathbf{a}. \tag{5–2}$$

In this equation $\mathbf{F}$ represents the (vector) *sum* of *all* the forces acting *on* the body, m is the mass of the body, and $\mathbf{a}$ is its (vector) acceleration. That all our results are contained in this one equation is obvious from the form

$$\mathbf{a} = \frac{\mathbf{F}}{m},$$

which states that *the acceleration caused by one or many forces acting on a body is proportional in magnitude to the resultant of the forces, and parallel to it in direction, and is inversely proportional to the mass of the body.* This can be taken as a statement of *Newton's second law of motion.*

Notice that the first law of motion is contained in the second law as a special case, for if $\mathbf{F} = 0$, then $\mathbf{a} = 0$. In other words, if the resultant force on a body is zero, the acceleration of the body is zero. Therefore, in the absence of applied forces a body will move with constant velocity or be at rest (zero velocity). This is the exact content of the first law of motion. Therefore, of Newton's three laws of motion only two are independent, namely the second and the third (Section 5–5). The division of translational particle dynamics that includes only systems for which the resultant force $\mathbf{F}$ is zero is called *statics.*

Notice that Eq. 5–2 is a vector equation. We can write this single vector equation as three scalar equations,

$$F_x = ma_x,$$

$$F_y = ma_y, \tag{5–3}$$

$$F_z = ma_z,$$

relating the x, y, and z components of the resultant force (F_x, F_y, and F_z) to the x, y, and z components of acceleration (a_x, a_y, a_z) for the mass m. It should be emphasized that F_x is the *sum* of the x components of *all* the forces, F_y is the *sum* of the y components of *all* the forces, and F_z is the *sum* of the z components of *all* the forces acting on m.

Mass is a scalar quantity. It follows from experiment that if objects of mass m_1 and m_2 are fastened together, they behave mechanically as a single object of mass ($m_1 + m_2$).

Newton expressed the second law of motion in a way more general than Eq. 5–2. To quote him, "The change of motion is proportional to the motive power impressed; and is made in the direction of the right [that is, straight] line in which that force is impressed." Newton's term *motion* is called *momentum* today and is the quantity $m\mathbf{v}$. Hence, Newton states that the force acting on a body is equal to the rate of change of momentum of the body, or in our terminology, $\mathbf{F} = d\,(m\mathbf{v})/dt$. If we assume that the mass of a body is constant in time, this equation reduces to Eq. 5–2, for then

$$\mathbf{F} = \frac{d}{dt}\,(m\mathbf{v}) = m\,\frac{d\mathbf{v}}{dt} = m\mathbf{a} \qquad \text{(constant mass)}.$$

5–5   Newton's Third Law of Motion

Forces acting on a body originate in other bodies. Any single force is only one aspect of a mutual interaction between *two* bodies. We find that whenever one body exerts a force on a second body, the second body always exerts a force on the first. Furthermore, these forces are equal in magnitude but opposite in direction. A single isolated force is, therefore, an impossibility.

If one of the two forces involved in the interaction between two bodies is called an "action" force, the other force is called the "reaction" force. *Either* force may be considered the "action" and the other the "reaction." Cause and effect is *not* implied here, but a mutual simultaneous interaction *is* implied.

This property of forces was first stated by Newton in his third law of motion: *"To every action there is always opposed an equal reaction; or, the mutual actions of two bodies upon each other are always equal, and directed to contrary parts."*

In other words, if body A exerts a force on body B, body B exerts an equal but oppositely directed force on body A; and furthermore the forces lie along the line joining the bodies. It is important to notice that the action and reaction forces, which always occur in pairs, act on *different* bodies. If they were to act on the same body, we could never have accelerated motion because the resultant force on every body would always be zero.

Imagine a boy kicking open a door. The force exerted by the boy (B) on the door (D) accelerates the door (it flies open); at the same time, the door (D) exerts an equal but opposite force on the boy (B), which decelerates the boy (his foot loses forward velocity). The boy will be painfully aware of the "reaction" force to his "action," particularly if his foot is bare.

The following examples illustrate the application of the third law and clarify its meaning.

▶ **Example 1.** Consider a man pulling horizontally on a rope attached to a block on a horizontal table as in Fig. 5–1. The man pulls on the rope with a force $\mathbf{F}_{MR}$. The rope exerts a reaction force $\mathbf{F}_{RM}$ on the man. Therefore, $\mathbf{F}_{MR} = -\mathbf{F}_{RM}$. Also, the rope exerts a force $\mathbf{F}_{RB}$ on the block, and the block exerts a reaction force $\mathbf{F}_{BR}$ on the rope. Therefore, $\mathbf{F}_{RB} = -\mathbf{F}_{BR}$.

Suppose that the rope has a mass m_R. Then, in order to start the block and rope moving from rest, we must have an acceleration, say $\mathbf{a}$. The only forces acting *on the rope* are $\mathbf{F}_{MR}$ and $\mathbf{F}_{BR}$, so that the resultant force on it is $\mathbf{F}_{MR} + \mathbf{F}_{BR}$, and this

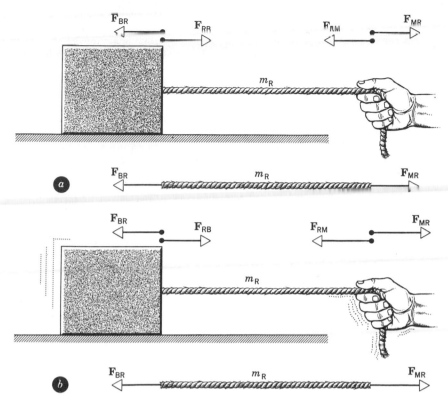

Fig. 5–1 Example 1. A man pulls on a rope attached to a block. (*a*) The forces exerted on the rope by the block and by the man are equal and opposite. Thus the resultant horizontal force on the rope is zero, as is shown in the free-body diagram. The rope does not accelerate. (*b*) The force exerted on the rope by the man exceeds that exerted by the block. The net horizontal force has magnitude $F_{MR} - F_{BR}$ and points to the right. Thus the rope is accelerated to the right.

The block is also acted upon by a frictional force not shown here.

must be different from zero if the rope is to accelerate. In fact, from the second law we have

$$\mathbf{F}_{MR} + \mathbf{F}_{BR} = m_R\mathbf{a}.$$

Since all forces act along the same line, we can drop the vector notation and write the relation between the magnitude of the vectors, namely

$$F_{MR} - F_{BR} = m_R a.$$

We see, therefore, that in general $\mathbf{F}_{MR}$ does not have the same magnitude as $\mathbf{F}_{BR}$ (Fig. 5–1*b*). These two forces act on the *same* body and are *not* action and reaction pairs.

Notice that the magnitude of $\mathbf{F}_{MR}$ always equals the magnitude of $\mathbf{F}_{RM}$, and the magnitude of $\mathbf{F}_{RB}$ always equals the magnitude of $\mathbf{F}_{BR}$. However, only in the special case when the acceleration of the system is zero, $a = 0$, will we have the pair of forces $\mathbf{F}_{MR}$ and $\mathbf{F}_{RM}$ equal in magnitude to the pair of forces $\mathbf{F}_{RB}$ and $\mathbf{F}_{BR}$ (Fig. 5–1*a*). In this special case only we could imagine that the rope merely transmits the force exerted by the man to the block, without change. This same result holds in principle if $m_R = 0$. In practice, we never find a massless rope. However, we can often neglect the mass of a rope in problems, and then the rope is assumed to transmit a force unchanged. In such cases we need not actually consider the rope in a force diagram. The force exerted at any point in the rope is called the *tension* at that point. The tension is the same at all points in the rope only if it is unaccelerated or assumed to be massless.

Example 2. Consider a spring attached to the ceiling and at the other end holding a block at rest (Fig. 5–2a). Since no body is accelerating, all the forces on any body will cancel. For example, the forces on the suspended block are **T**, the tension in the stretched spring, pulling vertically up on the mass, and **W**, the pull of the earth acting vertically down on the body, called its weight. These are drawn in Fig. 5–2b, where we show only the block for clarity. There are no other forces on the block.

The resultant of all the forces acting on the block is **T** + **W**. In Newton's second law, **F** represents the *sum* of *all* the forces acting *on* a body, so that for the block

$$\mathbf{F} = \mathbf{T} + \mathbf{W}.$$

The block is at rest so that its acceleration is zero, or

$$\mathbf{a} = 0.$$

Hence, from the relation $\qquad\qquad \mathbf{F} = m\mathbf{a},$

we obtain $\qquad\qquad\qquad \mathbf{T} + \mathbf{W} = 0,$

or $\qquad\qquad\qquad\qquad \mathbf{T} = -\mathbf{W}.$

The forces act along the same line, so that their magnitudes are equal, or

$$T = W.$$

Therefore, the tension in the spring is an exact measure of the weight of the block. We shall make use of this particular result later in presenting a static procedure for measuring forces.

It is instructive to examine the forces exerted on the spring also; they are shown in Fig. 5–2c. **T′** is the pull of the block on the spring and is the reaction force of the action force **T**. **T′**, therefore, has the same magnitude as **T**, which is W. **P** is the upward pull of the ceiling on the spring, and **w** is the weight of the spring, that is, the pull of the earth on it. Since the spring is at rest and all forces act along the same line, we have

$$\mathbf{P} + \mathbf{T'} + \mathbf{w} = 0,$$

or $\qquad\qquad\qquad\qquad P = W + w.$

The ceiling, therefore, pulls up on the spring with a force whose magnitude is the sum of the weights of the block and spring.

From the third law of motion, the force exerted by the spring on the ceiling, **P′**, must be equal in magnitude to **P**, which is the reaction force to the action force **P′**. **P′**, therefore, has a magnitude $W + w$.

In general, the spring exerts different forces on the bodies attached at its different ends, for $P' \neq T$. In the special case in which the weight of the spring is negligible, $w = 0$, and $P' = W = T$. Therefore, a *weightless* spring (or cord) may be considered to transmit a force from one end to the other without change.

It is instructive to classify all the forces in this problem according to action and reaction pairs. The reaction to **W**, a force exerted by the earth on the block, must be a force exerted by the block on the earth. Similarly, the reaction to **w** is a force exerted by the spring on the earth. Because the earth is so massive, we do not expect

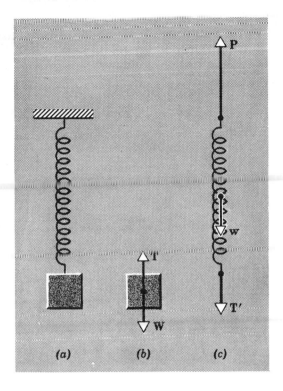

Fig. 5–2 Example 2. (*a*) A block is suspended by a spring. (*b*) A free-body diagram showing all the vertical forces exerted on the block. (*c*) A similar diagram for the vertical forces on the spring.

these forces to impart a noticeable acceleration to the earth. Since the earth is not shown in our diagrams, these forces have not been shown. The forces **T** and **T'** are action-reaction pairs, as are **P** and **P'**. Notice that although **T** = −**W** in our problem, these forces are *not* an action-reaction pair because they act on the *same* body. ◀

5–6 Mass Standards, Systems of Mechanical Units

Unit force was defined as a force that causes an acceleration of one unit when applied to the standard object, which in turn was assigned unit mass. As a consequence of these definitions, no numerical factor appeared in Eq. 5–2. This procedure determines the mks (meter, kilogram, second) and the cgs (centimeter, gram, second) system of units.

The standard of mass, called the *kilogram*, is a particular platinum cylinder kept at the International Bureau of Weights and Measures in Paris. One-thousandth of the mass of this standard is defined as the *gram*, a derived unit of mass. The kilogram is taken as the unit of mass in the mks system (Fig. 5–3). The gram is taken as the unit of mass in the cgs system.

Recalling that our length and time standards may soon be atomic standards, some have speculated that the standard kilogram may someday be replaced by an atomic standard of mass. This new standard might consist of a specification of a number of atoms of a certain type whose collective mass is 1 kilogram. At the present time, however, the accuracy with which masses

Fig. 5–3 National standard kilograms No. 4 and No. 20; No. 20, uncovered, is the primary mass standard for the United States.

can be compared, as on a balance, exceeds the accuracy with which we can determine the exact number of atoms that make up a given mass.

In the mks system unit force is the force that will accelerate a 1-kilogram mass at the rate of 1 meter/sec^2; this unit is called the *newton*. In the cgs system unit force is the force that will accelerate a 1-gram mass at the rate of 1 cm/sec^2; this unit is called the *dyne*.

Thus, in the mks system

$$\mathbf{F} \text{ [nt]} = m \text{ [kg]} \times \mathbf{a} \text{ [meters/sec}^2\text{]},$$

and in the cgs system

$$\mathbf{F} \text{ [dynes]} = m \text{ [gm]} \times \mathbf{a} \text{ [cm/sec}^2\text{]}.$$

Since 1 kg = 10^3 gm and 1 meter/sec^2 = 10^2 cm/sec^2, it follows that 1 nt = 10^5 dynes. The cgs system is gradually falling out of use in physics. We seldom use it in this book.

In each of our systems of units we have chosen mass, length, and time as our fundamental quantities. Standards were adopted for these fundamental quantities and units defined in terms of these standards. Force appears as a derived quantity, determined from the relation $\mathbf{F} = m\mathbf{a}$.

In the British engineering system of units, however, *force*, length, and time are chosen as the fundamental quantities and mass is a derived quantity. In this system, mass is determined from the relation $m = F/a$. The standard and unit of force in this system is the *pound*. Actually, the pound of force was originally defined to be the pull of the earth on a certain standard body at a certain place on the earth. We can get this force in an operational way by hanging the standard body from a spring at the particular point where the earth's pull on it is defined to be 1 lb of force. If the body is at rest, the earth's pull on the body, its weight W, is balanced by the tension in the spring. Therefore, $T = W = 1$ lb, in this instance. We can now use this spring (or any other one thus calibrated) to exert a force of 1 lb on any other body; to do this we simply attach the spring to another body and stretch it the same amount as the pound force had stretched it. The standard body can be compared to the kilogram and it is found to have the mass 0.45359237 kg. The acceleration due to gravity at the certain place on the earth is found to be 32.1740 ft/sec². The pound of force can, therefore, be defined from $F = ma$ as the force that accelerates a mass of 0.45359237 kg at the rate of 32.1740 ft/sec².

This procedure enables us to compare the pound-force with the newton. Using the fact that 32.1740 ft/sec² equals 9.8066 meters/sec², we find that

$$1 \text{ lb} = (0.45359237 \text{ kg})(32.1740 \text{ ft/sec}^2)$$
$$= (0.45359237 \text{ kg})(9.8066 \text{ meters/sec}^2)$$
$$\cong 4.45 \text{ nt}.$$

The unit of mass in the British engineering system can now be derived. It is defined as the mass of a body whose acceleration is 1 ft/sec² when the force on it is 1 lb; this mass is called the *slug*. Thus, in this system

$$F \text{ [lb]} = m \text{ [slugs]} \times a \text{ [ft/sec}^2].$$

Legally, the pound is a unit of mass. But in engineering practice the pound is treated as a unit of force or weight. This has given rise to the terms pound-mass and pound-force. The pound-mass is a body of mass 0.45359237 kg; no standard block of metal is preserved as the pound-mass, but like the yard it is defined in terms of the mks standard. The pound-force is the force that gives a standard pound an acceleration equal to the standard acceleration of gravity, 32.1740 ft/sec². As we shall see later, the acceleration of gravity varies with distance from the center of the earth, and this "standard acceleration" is, therefore, the value at a particular distance from the center of the earth. (Any point at sea level and 45°N latitude is a good approximation.)

In this book only forces will be measured in pounds. Thus the corresponding unit of mass is the slug.

The units of force, mass, and acceleration in the three systems are summarized in Table 5–1.

Table 5–1

UNITS IN $F = ma$

Systems of Units	Force	Mass	Acceleration
Mks	newton (nt)	kilogram (kg)	meter/sec²
Cgs	dyne	gram (gm)	cm/sec²
Engineering	pound (lb)	slug	ft/sec²

The *dimensions* of force are the same as those of mass times acceleration. In a system in which mass, length, and time are the fundamental quantities, the dimensions of force are, therefore, mass $\times$ length/time^2, or in abbreviated form (MLT^{-2}), where (M) represents the dimension of mass, (L) the dimension of length, and (T) the dimension of time. We shall arbitrarily adopt mass, length, and time as our fundamental mechanical quantities.

5–7   Weight and Mass

The *weight* of a body is the gravitational force exerted on it by the earth. Weight, being a force, is a vector quantity. The direction of this vector is the direction of the gravitational force, that is, toward the center of the earth. The magnitude of the weight is expressed in force units, such as pounds or newtons.

When a body of mass m is allowed to fall freely, its acceleration is the acceleration of gravity $\mathbf{g}$ and the force acting on it is its weight $\mathbf{W}$. Newton's second law, $\mathbf{F} = m\mathbf{a}$, when applied to a freely falling body, gives us $\mathbf{W} = m\mathbf{g}$. Both $\mathbf{W}$ and $\mathbf{g}$ are vectors directed toward the center of the earth. We can, therefore, write

$$W = mg, \tag{5–4}$$

where W and g are the magnitudes of the weight and acceleration vectors. To keep an object from falling we have to exert on it an upward force equal in magnitude to W, so as to make the total force zero. In Fig. 5–2a the tension in the spring supplies this force.

We stated previously that g is found experimentally to have the same value for all objects *at the same place*. From this it follows that the ratio of the weights of two objects must be equal to the ratio of their masses. Therefore, a chemical balance, which actually is an instrument for comparing two downward forces, can be used in practice to compare masses. If a sample of salt in one pan of a balance is pulling down on that pan with the same force as is a standard 1 gram-mass on the other pan, we know * that the mass of salt is equal to 1 gram. We are likely to say that the salt "weighs" 1 gram, although a gram is a unit of mass, not weight. In dynamics, however, it is important to distinguish very carefully between weight and mass.

We have already seen that the weight of a body, the downward pull of the earth on that body, is a vector quantity. The mass of a body is a scalar quantity. The quantitative relation between weight and mass is given by $\mathbf{W} = m\mathbf{g}$. Because $\mathbf{g}$ varies from point to point on the earth, $\mathbf{W}$, the weight of a body of mass m, is actually different in different localities. Thus, the weight of a 1 kg-mass in a locality where g is 9.80 meters/sec^2 is 9.80 nt; in a locality where g is 9.78 meters/sec^2, the same 1 kg-mass weighs 9.78 nt. If these weights were determined by measuring the amount of stretch required in a spring to balance them, the difference in weight of the same 1 kg-mass at the two different localities would be evident in the slightly

---

* Corrections for buoyancy, owing to the different volumes of air displaced by the salt and the standard, must be made. These are discussed in Chapter 17.

different stretch of the spring at these two localities. Hence, unlike the mass of a body, which is an intrinsic property of the body, the weight of a body depends on its location relative to the center of the earth. Spring scales read differently, balances the same, at different parts of the earth.

We shall generalize the concept of weight in Chapter 16 in which universal gravitation is discussed. There we shall see that the weight of a body is zero in regions of space where the gravitational effects are nil, although the inertial effects, and hence the mass of the body, remain unchanged from those on earth.

It would take the same effort to accelerate a body in gravity-free space as it does to accelerate it along a horizontal frictionless surface on earth, for its mass is the same in each place. But it takes much more effort to hold the body up against the pull of the earth on the earth's surface than it does high up in space, for its weight is different in each place.

Often instead of being given the mass we are given the weight of a body on which forces are exerted. The acceleration **a** produced by the force **F** acting on a body whose weight has a magnitude W can be obtained by combining Eq. 5–2 and Eq. 5–4. Thus from $\mathbf{F} = m\mathbf{a}$ and $W = mg$ we obtain

$$m = \frac{W}{g},\qquad(5\text{–}5)$$

so that

$$\mathbf{F} = \frac{W}{g}\,\mathbf{a}.\qquad(5\text{–}6)$$

The quantity W/g plays the role of m in the equation $F = ma$ and is in fact the mass of a body whose weight has the magnitude W. For example, a man whose weight is 160 lb at a point where $g = 32.0$ ft/sec^2 has a mass $m = W/g = (160 \text{ lb})/(32.0 \text{ ft/sec}^2) = 5.00$ slugs. Notice that his weight at another point where $g = 32.2$ ft/sec^2 is $W = mg = (5.00 \text{ slugs})(32.2 \text{ ft/sec}^2) = 161$ lb.

5–9 A Static Procedure for Measuring Forces

In Section 5–3 we presented a procedure for measuring forces based on determining how the state of motion of a body was changed when a force was applied to it. That method may be called a dynamic method for measuring force. Another procedure for measuring forces is based on measuring the change in the shape or size of a body on which the force is applied when the body is unaccelerated. This method may be called a static method for measuring force. The dynamic method is used to define force quantitatively and leads to the second law of motion. The static method makes use of both the first law of motion, which is a special case of the second law, and the third law.

The idea of the static method is to use the fact that when a body, under the action of several forces, has zero acceleration, the vector sum of all the forces acting on the body must be zero. This is, of course, merely the content of the first law of motion. A single force acting on a body would produce an acceleration; this acceleration can be made zero if we apply another force to the body equal in magnitude but oppositely directed. In practice we seek to keep the body at rest. If now we choose some force as our unit force, we are in a position to measure forces. The pull of the earth on a standard body at a particular point can be taken as the unit force, for example.

The instrument most commonly used to measure forces in this way is the spring balance. It consists of a coiled spring having a pointer at one end that moves over a scale. A force exerted on the balance changes the length of the spring. If a body weighing 1 lb is hung from the spring, the spring stretches until the pull of the spring on the body is equal in magnitude but opposite in direction to its weight. A mark can be made on the scale next to the pointer and labeled "1-lb force." Similarly, 2-lb, 3-lb, etc., weights may be hung from the spring and corresponding marks can be made on the scale next to the pointer in each case. In this way the spring is calibrated. We assume that the force exerted on the spring is always the same when the pointer stands at the same position. The calibrated balance can now be used to measure any unknown force, not merely the pull of the earth on some body.

The third law is tacitly used in our static procedure because we assume that the force exerted by the spring on the body is the same in magnitude as the force exerted by the body on the spring. This latter force is the force we wish to measure. The first law is used because we assume $\mathbf{F}$ is zero when $\mathbf{a}$ is zero. It is worth noting again here that if the acceleration were not zero, the body of weight W would not stretch the spring to the same length as it did with $\mathbf{a} = 0$. In fact, if the spring and attached body of weight W were to fall freely under gravity so that $\mathbf{a} = \mathbf{g}$, the spring would not stretch at all and its tension would be zero.

5–9 Some Application of Newton's Laws of Motion

Newton's second law states that the vector sum of all the forces acting on a body is equal to the mass of the body times its acceleration. Hence, the first step in problem solving is to pick the body to be considered. As obvious as this seems, lack of clarity as to what exactly has been or should be picked for the body leads to more mistakes than any other point in setting up problems. Once the body has been picked, we next determine *all* the forces acting *on* the body. It is helpful to make a separate diagram showing only the body picked and *all* the forces acting *on* it. This is called a free-body diagram. Next, we pick a convenient reference system and apply Newton's second law to each component of force and acceleration.

The following examples illustrate the applications of Newton's laws of motion. Each body is treated as if it were a particle of definite mass, and the forces acting on it are assumed to act at a point. The acceleration of gravity is taken to be 32.0 ft/sec² or 9.80 meters/sec² unless otherwise specified. Strings and pulleys are considered to have negligible mass.

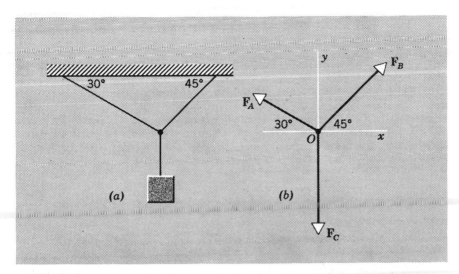

Fig. 5–4 Example 3. (*a*) A mass is suspended by strings. (*b*) A free-body diagram showing all the forces acting on the knot. The strings are assumed to be weightless.

▶ **Example 3.** Figure 5-4*a* shows a weight hung by strings. Consider the knot at the junction of the three strings to be the body. The body remains at rest under the action of the three forces shown in Fig. 5–4*b*. Suppose we are given the magnitude of one of these forces. How can we determine the magnitude of the other forces?

$\mathbf{F}_A$, $\mathbf{F}_B$, and $\mathbf{F}_C$ are *all* the forces acting *on* the body. Since the body is unaccelerated (actually at rest), $\mathbf{F}_A + \mathbf{F}_B + \mathbf{F}_C = 0$. Choosing the *x*- and *y*-axes as shown, we can write this vector equation equivalently as three scalar equations:

$$F_{Ax} + F_{Bx} = 0,$$

$$F_{Ay} + F_{By} + F_{Cy} = 0,$$

using Eq. 5–3. The third scalar equation for the *z*-axis is simply

$$F_{Az} = F_{Bz} = F_{Cz} = 0.$$

That is, the vectors all lie in the *x y* plane and have no *z* components.
From the figure we see that

$$F_{Ax} = -F_A \cos 30° = -0.866 F_A,$$

$$F_{Ay} = F_A \sin 30° = 0.500 F_A,$$

and

$$F_{Bx} = F_B \cos 45° = 0.707 F_B,$$

$$F_{By} = F_B \sin 45° = 0.707 F_B.$$

Also,

$$F_{Cy} = -F_C = -W,$$

because the string *C* merely serves to transmit the force on one end to the junction at its other end. Substituting these results into our original equations, we obtain

$$-0.866 F_A + 0.707 F_B = 0,$$

$$0.500 F_A + 0.707 F_B - W = 0.$$

If we are given the magnitude of any one of these three forces, we can solve these equations for the other two. For example, if $W = 100$ lb, we obtain $F_A = 73.3$ lb and $F_B = 89.6$ lb.

Example 4. We wish to analyze the motion of a block on a smooth incline.

(a) *Static case:* Figure 5–5a shows a block of mass m kept at rest on a smooth plane, inclined at an angle θ with the horizontal, by means of a string attached to the vertical wall. The forces acting *on* the block are shown in Fig. 5–5b. $\mathbf{F}_1$ is the force exerted *on* the block by the string; $m\mathbf{g}$ is the pull of the earth *on* the block, that is, its weight; and $\mathbf{F}_2$ is the force exerted *on* the block by the inclined surface. $\mathbf{F}_2$, called the normal force, is normal to the surface of contact because there is no frictional force between

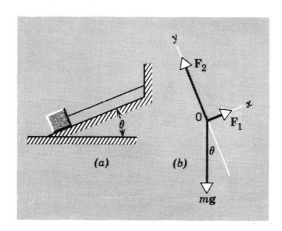

Fig. 5–5 Example 4. (a) A block is held on a smooth inclined plane by a string. (b) A free-body diagram showing all the forces acting on the block.

the surfaces. If there were a frictional force, $\mathbf{F}_2$ would have a component parallel to the incline. Because we wish to analyze the motion of *the block*, we choose *ALL the forces acting ON the block*. The student will note that the block will exert forces on other bodies (the string, the earth, the surface of the incline) in accordance with the action-reaction principle; these forces, however, are not needed to determine the motion of the block.

Suppose θ and m are given. How do we determine the values of F_1 and F_2? Since the block is unaccelerated, we obtain

$$\mathbf{F}_1 + \mathbf{F}_2 + m\mathbf{g} = 0.$$

It is convenient to choose the x-axis of our reference frame to be along the incline and the y-axis to be normal to the incline (Fig. 5–5b). With this choice of coordinates, only one force, $m\mathbf{g}$, must be resolved into components in solving the problem. The two scalar equations obtained by resolving $m\mathbf{g}$ along the x- and y-axes are

$$F_1 - mg \sin \theta = 0,$$

$$F_2 - mg \cos \theta = 0,$$

from which F_1 and F_2 can be obtained if θ and m are given.

(b) *Dynamic case:* Now suppose that the string is to be cut. Then the force $\mathbf{F}_1$, the pull of the string on the block, will be removed. The resultant force on the block will no longer be zero, and the block will, therefore, accelerate. What is its acceleration?

From Eq. 5–3 we have $F_x = ma_x$ and $F_y = ma_y$. Using these relations we obtain

$$F_0 - mg \cos \theta - ma_y = 0,$$

$$- mg \sin \theta = ma_x,$$

which yields $\qquad a_y = 0, \qquad a_x = -g \sin \theta.$

The acceleration is directed down the incline with a magnitude of $g \sin \theta$.

Example 5. Consider a block of mass m pulled along a smooth horizontal surface by a horizontal force **P**, as shown in the force diagram Fig. 5–6. **N** is the normal force

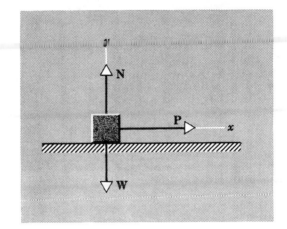

Fig. 5–6 Example 5. A block is being pulled along a smooth table. The forces acting on the block are shown.

exerted on the block by the frictionless surface and **W** is the weight of the block.

(a) If the block has a mass of 2 kg, what is the normal force?

From the second law of motion with $a_y = 0$ we obtain

$$F_y = ma_y,$$

or $\qquad N - W = 0.$

Hence, $N = W = mg = (2 \text{ kg})(9.8 \text{ meters/sec}^2) = 20 \text{ nt}.$

(b) What force P is required to give the block a horizontal velocity of 4 meters/sec in 2 sec starting from rest?

The acceleration a_x follows from

$$a_x = \frac{v - v_0}{t} = \frac{4 \text{ meters/sec} - 0}{2 \text{ sec}} = 2 \text{ meters/sec}^2.$$

From the second law, $F_x = ma_x$, or $P = ma_x$. The force P is then

$$P = ma_x = (2 \text{ kg})(2 \text{ meters/sec}^2) = 4 \text{ nt}.$$

Example 6. Figure 5–7a shows a block of mass m_1 on a smooth horizontal surface pulled by a string which is attached to a block of mass m_2 hanging over a pulley. We assume that the pulley has no mass and is frictionless and that it merely serves to change the direction of the tension in the string at that point. Find the acceleration of the system and the tension in the string.

Suppose we choose the block of mass m_1 as the body whose motion we investigate. The forces on this block, taken to be a particle, are shown in Fig. 5–7b. **T**, the tension in the string, pulls on the block to the right; $m_1\mathbf{g}$ is the downward pull of the earth

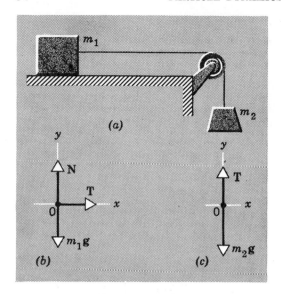

Fig. 5–7 Example 6. (a) Two masses are connected by a string: m_1 lies on a smooth table, m_2 hangs freely. (b) A free-body diagram showing all the forces acting on m_1. (c) A similar diagram for m_2.

on the block and **N** is the vertical force exerted on the block by the smooth table. The block will accelerate in the x direction only, so that $a_{1y} = 0$. We, therefore, can write

$$N - m_1g = 0 = m_1a_{1y},$$
$$T = m_1a_{1x}. \tag{5-7}$$

From these equations we conclude only that $N = m_1g$. We do not know T, so we cannot solve for a_{1x}.

To determine T we must consider the motion of the suspended block of mass m_2. The forces acting on the suspended block are shown in Fig. 5–7c. Because the string and block are accelerating, we cannot conclude that T equals m_2g. In fact, if T were to equal m_2g, the resultant force on the suspended block would be zero, a condition holding only if the system is not accelerated.

The equation of motion for the suspended block is

$$m_2g - T = m_2a_{2y}. \tag{5-8}$$

It is clear that, because the string has a fixed length and because the direction of the tension in the string at the pulley changes,

$$a_{2y} = a_{1x},$$

and we can therefore represent the acceleration of the system as simply a. We then obtain from Eqs. 5–7 and 5–8

$$m_2g - T = m_2a, \tag{5-9}$$
$$T = m_1a.$$

These yield
$$m_2g = (m_1 + m_2)a, \tag{5-10}$$

$$a = \frac{m_2}{m_1 + m_2} g,$$

$$T = \frac{m_1m_2}{m_1 + m_2} g, \tag{5-11}$$

which gives us the acceleration of the system a and the tension in the string T.

Notice that the tension in the string is always less than $m_2 g$. This is clear from Eq. 5–11, which can be written

$$T = m_2 g \frac{m_1}{m_1 + m_2}.$$

Notice also that a is always less than g, the acceleration due to gravity. Only when m_1 equals zero, which means that there is no block at all on the table, do we obtain $a = g$ (from Eq. 5–10). In this case $T = 0$ (from Eq. 5–9).

We can interpret Eq. 5–10 in a simple way. The net unbalanced force on the system of mass $m_1 + m_2$ is represented by $m_2 g$. Hence, from $F = ma$, we obtain Eq. 5–10 directly.

To make the example specific, suppose $m_1 = 2.0$ kg and $m_2 = 1.0$ kg. Then

$$a = \frac{m_2}{m_1 + m_2} g = \tfrac{1}{3}g = 3.3 \text{ meters/sec}^2,$$

$$T = \frac{m_1 m_2}{m_1 + m_2} g = (\tfrac{2}{3})(9.8) \text{ kg-m/sec}^2 = 6.5 \text{ nt}.$$

Example 7. Consider two unequal masses connected by a string which passes over a frictionless and massless pulley, as shown in Fig. 5–8a. Let m_2 be greater than m_1. Find the tension in the string and the acceleration of the masses.

We consider an *upward* acceleration *positive*. If the acceleration of m_1 is a, the acceleration of m_2 must be $-a$. The forces acting on m_1 and on m_2 are shown in Fig. 5–8b in which T represents the tension in the string.

The equation of motion for m_1 is

$$T - m_1 g = m_1 a$$

and for m_2 is

$$T - m_2 g = -m_2 a.$$

Combining these equations, we obtain

$$a = \frac{m_2 - m_1}{m_2 + m_1} g, \tag{5–12}$$

$$T = \frac{2 m_1 m_2}{m_1 + m_2} g.$$

For example, if $m_2 = 2.0$ slugs and $m_1 = 1.0$ slug,

$$a = (32/3.0) \text{ ft/sec}^2 = g/3,$$

$$T = (\tfrac{4}{3})(32) \text{ slug-ft/sec}^2 = 43 \text{ lb}.$$

Notice that the magnitude of T is always intermediate between the weight of the mass m_1 (32 lb in our example) and the weight of the mass m_2 (64 lb in our example). This is to be expected, since T must exceed $m_1 g$ to give m_1 an upward acceleration, and $m_2 g$ must exceed T to give m_2 a downward acceleration. In the special case when $m_1 = m_2$, we obtain $a = 0$ and $T = m_1 g = m_2 g$, which is the static result to be expected.

Figure 5–8c depicts the forces acting on the massless pulley. If we treat the pulley as a particle, all the forces can be taken to act through its center. P is the upward pull of the support on the pulley and T is the downward pull of each segment of the string on the pulley. Since the pulley has no translational motion,

$$P = T + T = 2T.$$

If we were to drop our assumption of a massless pulley and assign a mass m to it, we would then be required to include a downward force mg on the support. Also,

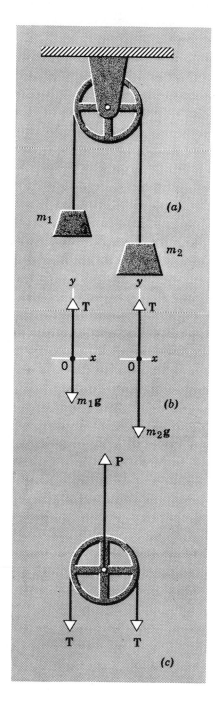

Fig. 5–8 Example 7. (a) Two unequal masses are suspended by a string from a pulley (Atwood's machine). (b) Free-body diagrams for m_1 and m_2. (c) Free-body diagram for the pulley, assumed weightless.

as we shall see later, the rotational motion of the pulley results in a different tension in each segment of the string. Friction in the bearings also affects the rotational motion of the pulley and the tension in the strings.

Example 8. Consider an elevator moving vertically with an acceleration a. We wish to determine the force exerted by a passenger on the floor of the elevator.

Acceleration will be taken *positive upward* and *negative downward*. Thus positive acceleration in this case means that the elevator either is moving upward with in-

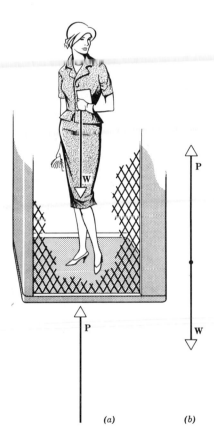

Fig. 5–9 Example 8. (a) A passenger stands on the floor of an elevator. (b) A free-body diagram for the passenger.

(a)   (b)

creasing speed or is moving downward with decreasing speed. Negative acceleration means that the elevator is moving upward with decreasing speed or downward with increasing speed.

From Newton's third law of motion the force exerted by the passenger on the floor will always be equal in magnitude but opposite in direction to the force exerted by the floor on the passenger. We can, therefore, calculate either the action force or the reaction force. When the forces acting on the passenger are used, we solve for the latter force. When the forces acting on the floor are used, we solve for the former force.

The situation is shown in Fig. 5–9: The passenger's weight is **W** and the force exerted on her by the floor is called **P**. The resultant force acting on her is **P** + **W**.

Forces will be taken as positive when directed upward. From the second law of motion we have

$$F = ma,$$

$$P - W = ma, \tag{5-13}$$

where m is the mass of the passenger and a is her (and the elevator's) acceleration.

Suppose, for example, that the passenger weighs 128 lb, and the acceleration is 2.00 ft/sec² upward. We have

$$m = \frac{W}{g} = \frac{128 \text{ lb}}{32.0 \text{ ft/sec}^2} = 4.00 \text{ slugs,}$$

and from Eq. 5–13,

$$P - 128 \text{ lb} = (4.00 \text{ slugs})(2.00 \text{ ft/sec}^2)$$

or

$$P = 136 \text{ lb.}$$

If we were to measure this force directly by having the passenger stand on a spring scale fixed to the elevator floor (or suspended from the ceiling), we would find the scale reading to be 136 lb for a woman whose weight is 128 lb. The passenger feels herself pressing down on the floor with greater force (the floor is pressing upward on her with greater force) than when she and the elevator are at rest. Everyone experiences this feeling when an elevator starts upward from rest.

If the acceleration were taken as 2.00 ft/sec² downward, then $a = -2.00$ ft/sec² and $P = 120$ lb for the passenger. The passenger who weighs 128 lb feels herself pressing down on the floor with less force than when she and the elevator are at rest. Everyone experiences this feeling when an elevator starts downward from rest.

If the elevator cable were to break and the elevator were to fall freely with an acceleration $a = -g$, then P would equal $W + (W/g)(-g) = 0$. Then the passenger and floor would exert no forces on each other. The passenger's apparent weight, as indicated by the spring scale on the floor, would be zero pounds.   ◀

5–10 Critique of Newton's Laws of Motion

In the Introduction to his *Principles of Mechanics* published in 1894, Heinrich Hertz writes, "It is exceedingly difficult to expound to thoughtful hearers the very introduction to mechanics without being occasionally embarrassed, without feeling tempted now and again to apologize, without wishing to get as quickly as possible over the rudiments and on to examples which speak for themselves. I fancy that Newton himself must have felt this embarrassment." In a similar vein F. A. Kaempffer in a recent article* writes, "Newton's second law is certainly one of the most obscure of all the understandable relations underlying our description of the physical world in which we find ourselves. Anyone who has ever tried to explain this law to a person who insisted on asking questions will know the difficulty of giving good reasons for the . . . facts embodied in it. . . ."

What are some of the questions that cause such difficulty? One such question is: To what extent do the laws of motion depend on the definition of an appropriate reference system and how can we determine such a reference system experimentally? The acceleration **a** of a body depends in general on the reference system relative to which it is measured. If the force **F** on a body is computed from the second law, $\mathbf{F} = m\mathbf{a}$, we may obtain different values for **F** when different reference systems are used. The question then is whether there is one particular reference system which gives the "true" value of the force. If there is such a system, we know that any other system moving relative to it with *constant velocity* will also do, for (Section 4–6)

* "On Possible Realizations of Mach's Program," *Canadian Journal of Physics*, February 1958.

the acceleration of a body is the same in all systems moving relative to one another with constant velocity. Notice that the meaning of the first law is involved in this question also, for if forces are defined in terms of accelerations, the only way we know that the force is zero is that the acceleration is zero; but whether or not a is zero depends on the choice of reference system.

Newton was aware of these difficulties, as were others, but could find no satisfactory answer to them. One answer often given is to choose a reference system at rest with respect to the fixed stars or any system moving relative to this with constant velocity. When we measure the acceleration of a body relative to such a system and compute the force from $\mathbf{F} = m\mathbf{a}$, we are always able to identify this computed force with some "real" force, such as the pull of a spring or the gravitational pull of the earth. But what do we do in a frame that is *accelerated* with respect to the fixed stars? The earth, after all, is such a frame, for it rotates on its axis and revolves about the sun. The best we can do here is to show that the effects of this acceleration are small and neglect them, or else introduce "fictitious" forces attributable to this acceleration, using our intuition to guide us.

There are still other serious questions of logic that can be raised in regard to Newton's laws. Do these laws *define* the concept of force so that they are not laws at all but just definitions? And if so, what makes this definition "useful"? Or is force defined in another way so that $\mathbf{F} = m\mathbf{a}$ is really a law connecting quantities previously defined? And if so, what general significance do we give to the concept of "force"? There is no way to make Newton's laws (in the conventional form) rigorous and logical by any simple twisting of words or special interpretation. They can be made so only by a broad generalization and reformulation beyond the scope of this book.*

In a definitive article† L. Eisenbud writes "The logical difficulties in the Newtonian formulation of the laws of motion do not, of course, alter the fact that the laws have provided an extremely well-tested basis for the analysis of motions. We must conclude, therefore, that the Newtonian statements *implicitly* contain the necessary basis for an adequate theory of motion. . . . It is not unfair to say that Newton's laws operate by a method similar to that of a stage magician. The magician directs the attention of his audience on matters of no significance to the effects produced while his essential manipulations are obscured. Newton's laws tend to concentrate our attention on the empty concept of force; the operative content of the laws, however, is not explicitly stated." Eisenbud then goes on to reformulate the classical laws of motion in a logical manner and in such a way as to bring out the essential significance of the force and mass concepts.

Newton's laws of motion represent the first great synthesis in physics. At the very least we must regard him as an intuitive genius. Most of engineering and much of physics today rest on his work. However, there comes a time when the concepts in any theory must come under careful scrutiny, usually when we seek even greater precision or try to apply the theory to areas beyond its original scope. At such times the probing and questioning will lead to basic revisions of the theory, often in the form of a generalization of it which describes even better and still more of the world we live in. This in fact is exactly how the theory of relativity grew out of the logical difficulties of classical physics. Probably no concept in any theory is perfectly precise, but if we are to progress at all the theory must be developed as if every concept were precise. Only after we understand the scope of one theory can we appreciate and fully understand generalizations of it represented by newer theories. Newton's laws of motion represent a giant step along the way to our current understanding of nature. They are valid and precise over a wide area of scientific practice.

---

* See *Introduction to Theoretical Physics*, second edition, by Leigh Page, for such a reformulation.

† "On the Classical Laws of Motion" by Leonard Eisenbud, *American Journal of Physics*, March 1958.

QUESTIONS

1. List carefully the essential steps taken to arrive at the relation $\mathbf{F} = m\mathbf{a}$.

2. What is your mass in slugs? Your weight in newtons?

3. Why do you fall forward when a moving train decelerates to a stop and fall backward when a train accelerates from rest? What would happen if the train rounded a curve at constant speed?

4. A horse is urged to pull a wagon. The horse refuses to try, citing Newton's third law for this situation as his defense: " 'The pull of the horse on the wagon is equal but opposite to the pull of the wagon on the horse.' If I can never exert a greater force on the wagon than it exerts on me, how can I ever start the wagon moving?" asks the horse. How would you reply?

5. A block of mass m is supported by a cord C from the ceiling, and another cord D is attached to the bottom of the block (Fig. 5-10). Explain the following observations: If you give a sudden jerk to D it will break, but if you pull on D steadily C will break

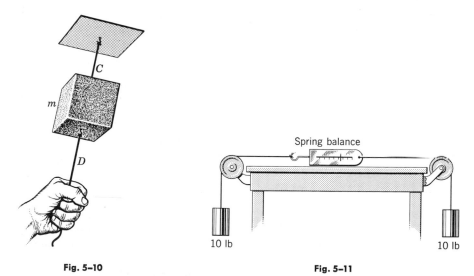

Fig. 5–10   Fig. 5–11

6. Two 10-lb weights are attached to a spring scale as shown in Fig. 5–11. Does the scale read 0 lb, 10 lb, 20 lb, or give some other reading?

7. Criticize the statement, often made, that the mass of a body is a measure of the "quantity of matter" in it.

8. Using force, length, and time as fundamental quantities, what are the dimensions of mass?

9. Do you see any particular advantage or disadvantage to any of the three systems of units presented in this chapter? Are they equally logical and equally practical?

10. Is the current standard of mass accessible, invariable, reproducible, indestructible? Does it have simplicity for comparison purposes? Would an atomic standard be better in any respect?

11. In a tug of war, three men pull on a rope to the left at A and three men pull to the right at B with forces of equal magnitude. Now a weight of 5 lb is hung vertically from the center of the rope. (a) Can the men get the rope AB to be horizontal? (b) If not, explain. If so, determine the magnitude of the forces required at A and B to do this.

12. Under what circumstances would your weight be zero? Does your answer depend on the choice of a reference system?

13. Two objects of equal mass rest on opposite pans of a trip scale. Does the scale remain balanced when it is accelerated up or down in an elevator?

14. A massless rope is strung over a frictionless pulley. A monkey holds onto one end of the rope and a mirror, having the same weight as the monkey, is attached to the other end of the rope at the monkey's level. Can the monkey get away from his image seen in the mirror (a) by climbing up the rope, (b) by climbing down the rope, (c) by releasing the rope?

15. Comment on the following statements: "The first law is *not* merely a superfluous statement of a special case which is covered by the second law, namely the case of $F = 0$. The first law implies that only an unbalanced force, *and no other agent*, can be the cause of acceleration of a body. This is not implied by the second law."

PROBLEMS

1. Two blocks, mass m_1 and m_2, are connected by a light spring on a horizontal frictionless table. Find the ratio of their accelerations, a_1 and a_2, after they are pulled apart and then released.

2. Illustrate any method for adding vectors by obtaining the resultant of the following combination of forces acting on a particle (Fig. 5–12).

$$F_1 = 5.00 \text{ nt,}$$

$$F_2 = 4.00 \text{ nt,}$$

$$F_3 = 8.66 \text{ nt,}$$

$$F_4 = 14.0 \text{ nt.}$$

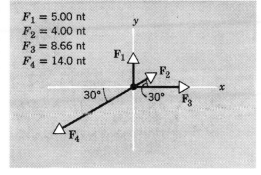

$F_1 = 5.00$ nt
$F_2 = 4.00$ nt
$F_3 = 8.66$ nt
$F_4 = 14.0$ nt

Fig. 5–12

3. A body of mass m is acted on by two forces $\mathbf{F}_1$ and $\mathbf{F}_2$, as shown in Fig. 5–13. If $m = 5$ kg, $F_1 = 3$ nt, and $F_2 = 4$ nt, find the vector acceleration of the body.

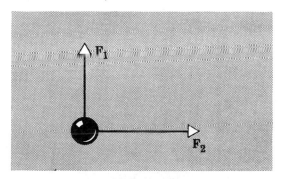

Fig. 5–13

4. A car moving initially at a speed of 50 miles/hr and weighing 3000 lb is brought to a stop in a distance of 200 ft. Find the braking force and the time required to stop. Assuming the same braking force, find the distance and time required to stop if the car was going 25 miles/hr initially.

5. (a) An electron travels in a straight line from the cathode of a vacuum tube to its anode, which is exactly 1 cm away. It starts with zero speed and reaches the anode with a speed of 6.0×10^6 meters/sec. Assume constant acceleration and compute the force on the electron. Take the electron's mass to be 9.1×10^{-31} kg.

(b) This force is electrical in origin. Compare it with the gravitational force on the electron, which we neglected when we assumed straight-line motion. Is this assumption valid?

6. A body of mass 2 slugs is acted on by the downward force of gravity and a horizontal force of 128 lb. Find its acceleration and its velocity as a function of time, assuming it starts from rest.

7. An electron is projected horizontally from an electron gun at a speed of 1.2×10^7 meters/sec into an electric field which exerts a constant vertical force of 4.5×10^{-15} nt on it. The mass of the electron can be taken to be 9.1×10^{-31} kg. Determine the vertical distance the electron is deflected during the time it has moved forward 3 cm horizontally.

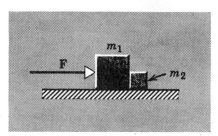

Fig. 5–14

8. A space traveler whose mass is 75 kg. leaves the earth. Compute his weight (a) on the earth, (b) 400 miles above the earth (where $g = 8.1$ meters/sec^2), and (c) in interplanetary space. What is his mass at each of these locations?

9. Two blocks are in contact as shown on a frictionless table. A horizontal force is applied to one block, as shown in Fig. 5–14. If $m_1 = 2$ kg, $m_2 = 1$ kg, and $F = 3$ nt, find the force of contact between the two blocks.

10. Three blocks are connected, as shown in Fig. 5–15, on a horizontal frictionless table and pulled to the right with a force $T_3 = 60$ nt. If $m_1 = 10$ kg, $m_2 = 20$ kg, and $m_3 = 30$ kg, find the tensions T_1 and T_2.

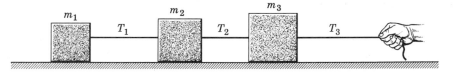

Fig. 5–15

11. A charged sphere of mass 3.0×10^{-4} kg is suspended from a string. An electric force acts horizontally on the sphere so that the string makes an angle of $37°$ with the vertical when at rest (Fig. 5–16). Find (a) the magnitude of the electric force and (b) the tension in the string.

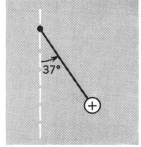

Fig. 5–16

12. Compute the initial upward acceleration of a V2 rocket of mass 1.3×10^4 kg if the initial upward thrust of its engine is 2.6×10^5 nt. Can you neglect the weight of the rocket (the downward pull of the earth on it)?

13. A block of mass $m_1 = 3$ slugs on a smooth inclined plane of angle 30° is connected by a cord over a small frictionless pulley to a second block of mass $m_2 = 2$ slugs hanging vertically (Fig. 5–17). (a) What is the acceleration of each body? (b) What is the tension in the cord?

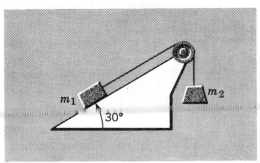

Fig. 5–17

14. How could a 100-lb object be lowered from a roof using a cord with a breaking strength of 87 lb without breaking the rope?

15. A block is projected up a frictionless inclined plane with a speed v_0. The angle of incline is θ. (a) How far up the plane does it go? (b) How long does it take to get there? (c) What is its speed when it gets back to the bottom? Find numerical answers for $\theta = 30°$ and $v_0 = 8$ ft/sec.

16. A block slides down a frictionless incline making an angle θ with an elevator floor. Find its acceleration relative to the incline in the following cases: (a) Elevator descends at constant speed v. (b) Elevator ascends at constant speed v. (c) Elevator descends with acceleration a. (d) Elevator descends with deceleration a. (e) Elevator cable breaks.

17. An elevator weighing 6000 lb is pulled upward by a cable with an acceleration of 4 ft/sec². What is the tension in the cable? What is the tension when the elevator is accelerating downward at 4 ft/sec²?

18. A lamp hangs vertically from a cord in a descending elevator. The elevator has a deceleration of 8 ft/sec² before coming to a stop. (a) If the tension in the cord is 20 lb, what is the mass of the lamp? (b) What is the tension in the cord when the elevator ascends with an acceleration of 8 ft/sec²?

19. A plumb bob hanging from the ceiling of a railroad car acts as an accelerometer. (a) Derive the general expression relating the horizontal acceleration a of the car to the angle θ, made by the bob with the vertical. Plot θ versus a. (b) Find a when $\theta = 20°$. Find θ when $a = 5$ ft/sec².

20. Refer to Fig. 5–5. Let the mass of the block be 2 slugs and the angle θ equal 30°. (a) Find the tension in the string and the normal force acting on the block. (b) If the string is cut, find the acceleration of the block. Neglect friction.

21. Refer to Fig. 5–7a. Let $m_1 = 4$ slugs and $m_2 = 2$ slugs. Find the tension in the string and the acceleration of the two blocks.

22. Refer to Fig. 5–8a. Let $m_1 = 1.0$ kg and $m_2 = 0.5$ kg. Find the acceleration of the two blocks and the tension in the string.

23. A uniform flexible chain l feet long, weighing λ lb/ft, passes over a small frictionless, massless pulley. It is released from a rest position with x ft of chain hanging from one side and $l - x$ ft from the other side. (a) Under what circumstances will it accelerate? (b) Assuming these circumstances are met, find the acceleration a as a function of x.

24. A triangular block of mass M with angles 30°, 60°, and 90° rests with its 30–90° side on a horizontal table. A cubical block of mass m rests on the 60–30° side (Fig. 5–18).

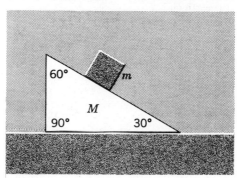

Fig. 5–18

(*a*) What horizontal acceleration a must M have relative to the table to keep m stationary relative to the triangular block, assuming frictionless contacts? (*b*) What horizontal force F must be applied to the system to achieve this result, assuming a frictionless table top? (*c*) Suppose no force is supplied to M and both surfaces are frictionless. Describe the resulting motion.

Particle Dynamics—II

CHAPTER 6

6-1 Introduction

In this chapter we continue our discussion of particle dynamics. Newton's laws were illustrated in Chapter 5, primarily with elastic and gravitational forces, and most examples involved constant accelerations. Here we extend the application to include frictional forces and consider accelerations that change in direction with time.

6-2 Frictional Forces

The fact that a body projected along an ordinary horizontal table eventually comes to rest means that the body experiences resistance to its motion. This resistance changes the velocity of the body and is, therefore, measured by a force. This force is called the *force of friction.*

Up to this point we have ignored the effects of friction. All our surfaces were considered to be "smooth," by which we meant that no frictional forces existed between the surfaces. Actually, whenever the surface of one body slides over that of another, each body exerts a frictional force on the other parallel to the surfaces. The frictional force on each body is in a direction opposite to its motion relative to the other body. Frictional forces automatically oppose the motion and can never aid it. Even when there is no relative motion, frictional forces may exist between surfaces.

Consider a block at rest on a horizontal table. Attach a spring to it to measure the force required to set the block in motion. We find that the block will not move even with the application of a small force. We say that our applied force is balanced by an opposite frictional force exerted on the block by the table, acting along the surface of contact. As we increase

95

the applied force we find some definite force at which the block just begins to move. Once motion has started, this same force produces accelerated motion. By reducing the force once motion has started, we find that it is possible to keep the block in uniform motion without acceleration; this force may be small, but it is never zero.

The frictional forces acting between surfaces at rest with respect to each other are called forces of *static friction*. The maximum force of static friction will be the same as the smallest force necessary to start motion. Once motion is started, the frictional forces acting between the surfaces usually decrease so that a smaller force is necessary to maintain uniform motion. The forces acting between surfaces in relative motion are called forces of *kinetic friction*.

For any two given types of surface that are dry and not lubricated, it is found experimentally that the maximum force of static friction between them is approximately independent of the area of contact over wide limits but is proportional to the normal force which holds the two surfaces together. The normal force is the pinching force that your finger would feel if it were placed between the opposing surfaces. The ratio of the magnitude of the maximum force of static friction to the magnitude of this normal force is called the *coefficient of static friction* for those surfaces. If f_s represents the magnitude of the force of static friction, we can write

$$f_s \leqq \mu_s N, \tag{6-1}$$

where μ_s is the coefficient of static friction and N is the magnitude of the normal force. The equality sign holds only when f_s has its maximum value.

For any two given types of surface, which are dry and not lubricated, it is found that the force of kinetic friction is approximately independent of the area of contact or of the speed with which the surfaces move, over wide limits, but is proportional to the normal force which holds the two surfaces in contact. The ratio of the magnitude of the force of kinetic friction to the magnitude of this normal force is called the *coefficient of kinetic friction*. If f_k represents the magnitude of the force of kinetic friction, we can write

$$f_k = \mu_k N, \tag{6-2}$$

where μ_k is the coefficient of kinetic friction.

Both μ_s and μ_k are dimensionless constants, each being the ratio of two forces. Usually for a given pair of surfaces $\mu_s > \mu_k$. The actual values of μ_s and μ_k depend on the nature of both the surfaces in contact, being larger if the surfaces are rough and smaller, in general, if they are smooth. Both μ_s and μ_k can exceed unity, although commonly they are less than one.

Notice that Eqs. 6–1 and 6–2 are relations between the *magnitudes only* of the normal and frictional forces. These forces are always directed perpendicularly to one another.

In Fig. 6–1 we show the typical behavior of a block being set in uniform motion from rest on a rough surface.

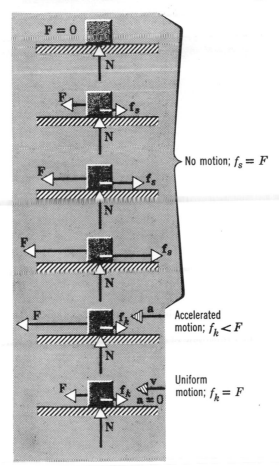

Fig. 6–1 A block being put into motion as an applied force **F** overcomes frictional forces. In the first four drawings the applied force is gradually increased from zero to magnitude $\mu_s N$. No motion occurs until this point because the frictional force always just balances the applied force. The instant F becomes greater than $\mu_s N$, the block goes into motion, as is shown in the fifth drawing. In general, $\mu_k N < \mu_s N$; this leaves an unbalanced force to the left and the block accelerates. In the last drawing F has been reduced to equal $\mu_k N$. The net force is zero, and the block continues with constant velocity.

The three laws describing friction say that when one solid body slides over another the frictional force is (a) proportional to the normal force, (b) independent of the area of contact, and (c) independent of the sliding speed. The first two laws were originally stated by Leonardo da Vinci and the third one by the French physicist Charles A. de Coulomb in 1785.

Because of its increasing importance in precision machinery, friction is being intensively investigated today.* Most investigators agree that friction arises from the cohesion of molecules in the surfaces of contact with one another. The bonding between molecules may be so strong at some points that small fragments are torn off one and stick to the other (Fig. 6–2). This has been demonstrated by experiments with radioactive tracer materials.†

Two surfaces actually touch each other only at a relatively small number of raised spots. The actual microscopic contact area is very different from the apparent macroscopic area of contact. Hence, the frictional resistance is proportional to the actual area of contact. Under ordinary circumstances, however, this actual area of contact is proportional to the load, increasing as the normal force increases. Since

---

* See "Stick and Slip" by Ernest Rabinowicz, in *Scientific American*, May 1956.

† See "Friction" by Frederick Palmer, in *Scientific American*, February 1951.

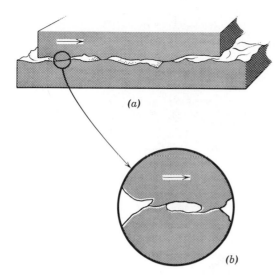

Fig. 6–2 Sliding friction. (*a*) The upper body is sliding to the right over the lower body in this enlarged diagram, grinding off small particles as it moves up and down crevices. (*b*) A further enlarged portion of (*a*); at the points of closest contact, the bodies actually become momentarily welded together; force is required to break these welds apart and maintain the motion.

the normal force is readily measured and the actual area of contact is not, it is simpler to express the coefficient of friction as the ratio of f to N. Hence, the first two laws of friction are considered to be generally true today.

The third law of friction is known not to be true. For example, Table 6–1 shows the coefficients of kinetic friction for steel on steel, unlubricated, at various relative

Table 6–1[a]

Coefficient of Kinetic Friction, Steel on Steel, Unlubricated

Speed, in./sec	0.0001	0.001	0.01	0.1	1	10	100
Coefficient of kinetic friction, μ_k	0.53	0.48	0.39	0.31	0.23	0.19	0.18

[a] Taken from *American Institute of Physics Handbook*, McGraw-Hill Book Company.

speeds. Notice that μ_k falls with increasing speed. In many practical problems, however, the speeds do not vary by as large a factor in the range of interest as they do in the very wide range of this table, and results are usually expressed by giving a coefficient of friction typical of the range. This amounts to using Eq. 6–2 with μ_k representing an average value, one that is not greatly different from the value at any particular speed in the range.

The coefficient of friction between surfaces depends on many variables, such as the nature of the materials themselves, surface finish, humidity, surface films, temperature, and extent of contamination. It is not surprising, therefore, that there is no exact theory of dry friction. The laws of friction are *empirical* laws, being based not on a theory giving insight into the causes of friction but only on observation of the effects. Considering the complex nature of friction, they hold surprisingly well, and it is useful to tabulate values of μ in handbooks.

The motion of one body rolling on another is opposed by a force which arises from the deformation of the surfaces where the bodies are in contact. This resisting force is called *rolling friction*.

Friction between *lubricated* surfaces, although complicated, *is* susceptible to exact theoretical analysis. The behavior of a film of lubricating fluid is well understood.

Examples of the application of these empirical laws follow.

▶ **Example 1.** A block is at rest on an inclined plane making an angle θ with the horizontal, as in Fig. 6–3a. As the angle of incline is raised, it is found that slipping just begins at an angle of inclination θ_s. What is the coefficient of static friction between block and incline?

The forces acting on the block, considered to be a particle, are shown in Fig. 6–3b. **W** is the weight of the block, **N** the normal force exerted on the block by the inclined surface, and $\mathbf{f}_s$ the tangential force of friction exerted by the inclined surface on the block. Notice that the resultant force exerted by the inclined surface on the block, $\mathbf{N} + \mathbf{f}_s$, is no longer perpendicular to the surface of contact, as was true for smooth surfaces ($\mathbf{f}_s = 0$). The block is at rest, so that

$$\mathbf{N} + \mathbf{f}_s + \mathbf{W} = 0.$$

Resolving our forces into x and y components, along the plane and the normal to the plane, respectively, we obtain

$$N - W \cos \theta = 0,$$
$$f_s - W \sin \theta = 0. \tag{6-3}$$

However, $f_s \leq \mu_s N$. If we increase the angle of incline slowly until slipping just begins, for that angle, $\theta = \theta_s$, we can use $f_s = \mu_s N$. Substituting these into Eqs. 6–3, we obtain

$$N = W \cos \theta_s$$

and

$$\mu_s N = W \sin \theta_s,$$

so that

$$\mu_s = \tan \theta_s.$$

Hence, measurement of the angle of inclination at which slipping just starts provides a simple experimental method for determining the coefficient of static friction between two surfaces.

The student can make use of similar arguments to show that the angle of inclination θ_k required to maintain a *constant speed* for the block as it slides down the plane once it has been started by tapping is given by

$$\mu_k = \tan \theta_k,$$

where $\theta_k < \theta_s$.

With the aid of a ruler the student can now determine μ_s and μ_k for a coin sliding down his textbook.

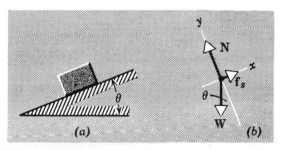

Fig. 6–3 Example 1. (*a*) A block at rest on a rough inclined plane. (*b*) A free-body force diagram for the block.

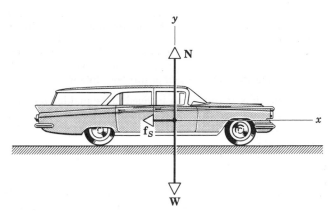

Fig. 6–4 Example 2. The forces on a decelerating automobile.

Example 2. Consider an automobile moving along a straight horizontal road with a speed v_0. If the coefficient of static friction between the tires and the road is μ_s, what is the shortest distance in which the automobile can be stopped?

The forces acting on the automobile, considered to be a particle, are shown in Fig. 6–4. The car is assumed to be moving in the positive x direction. If we assume that f_s is a constant force, we have uniformly decelerated motion.

From the relation (Eq. 3–11)

$$v^2 = v_0{}^2 + 2ax,$$

with the final speed $v = 0$, we obtain

$$x = -v_0{}^2/2a,$$

where the minus sign means that **a** points in the negative x direction.

To determine a, apply the second law of motion to the x component of the motion:

$$-f_s = ma = (W/g)a \qquad \text{or} \qquad a = -g(f_s/W).$$

From the y components we obtain

$$N - W = 0 \qquad \text{or} \qquad N = W,$$

so that

$$\mu_s = f_s/N = f_s/W$$

and

$$a = -\mu_s g.$$

Then the distance of stopping is

$$x = -v_0{}^2/2a = v_0{}^2/2g\mu_s. \tag{6–4}$$

The greater the initial speed, the longer the distance required to come to a stop; in fact, this distance varies as the square of the initial velocity. Also, the greater the coefficient of static friction between the surfaces, the less the distance required to come to a stop.

We have used the coefficient of static friction in this problem, rather than the coefficient of sliding friction, because we assume there is no sliding between the tires and the road. We have neglected rolling friction. Furthermore, we have assumed that the maximum force of static friction ($f_s = \mu_s N$) operates because the problem seeks the shortest distance for stopping. With a smaller static frictional force the distance for stopping would obviously be greater. The correct braking technique required here is to keep the car just on the verge of skidding. If the surface is smooth and the brakes are applied fully, sliding may occur. In this case μ_k replaces μ_s, and the distance required to stop is seen to increase from Eq. 6–4.

As a specific example, if $v_0 = 60$ miles/hr $-$ 88 ft/sec, and $\mu_s = 0.60$ (a typical value), we obtain

$$x = \frac{v_0^2}{2\mu_s g} = \frac{(88 \text{ ft/sec})^2}{2(0.60)(32 \text{ ft/sec}^2)} = 200 \text{ ft.}$$

Notice that the mass of the car does not appear in Eq. 6–4. How can you explain the practice of "weighing down" a car in order to increase safety in driving on icy roads?

The student should now investigate how, in principle, forces of friction would modify the results of the examples of Section 5–9.   ◀

6–3   Centripetal and Centrifugal Forces

The acceleration of a particle which moves in a circular path at constant speed v is a vector of magnitude v^2/r, directed at any instant toward the center of the circle (Section 4–4). There must be a force acting on this particle to cause it to accelerate. According to Newton's second law, the magnitude of this force must be mv^2/r, where m is the mass of the particle. This force acts inward "toward the center" of the curved path and is responsible for the circular motion. It is called a *centripetal* force.

The term "centripetal" refers to the fact that such a force applied to a body changes the *direction* of the velocity of that body in such a way that the acceleration points in "toward the center" of curvature. Centripetal forces are no different in principle from any other forces. In practice, however, we often distinguish forces by their specific effects on motion; hence the specific names for them. Newton's second law is meant to apply to every kind of force.

According to the third law of motion, the agent supplying the centripetal force acting *on* the particle must experience a reaction force exerted *by* the particle on that agent. This reaction force must be directed opposite to the centripetal force, so that it points out along the radius of curvature "away from the center" of curvature. It is called the *centrifugal* force. Notice that the centripetal force and the centrifugal force act on *different* bodies.

Consider a stone on the end of a string whirled in a circle with constant speed on a horizontal frictionless surface, as in Fig. 6–5. The string is at-

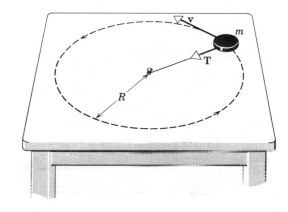

Fig. 6–5 A body m moves with constant speed in a horizontal circular path. The only horizontal force acting on m is the centripetal force **T**.

tached to a pin set in the surface. The centripetal force is the force **T** with which the string pulls *on the stone*. This force is the net force acting on the stone. It accelerates the stone by constantly changing the direction of its velocity so that the stone moves in a circle. The magnitude of this centripetal force **T** is mv^2/R, and it is always directed toward the pin at the center. If the string were to be cut where it joins the stone, there would be no force exerted on the stone. The stone would then move with constant speed in a straight line along the direction of the tangent to the circle at the point at which the string was cut. Hence, to keep the stone moving in a circle, a force must be applied to it pulling it *inward* toward the center.

The centrifugal force is the force exerted by the stone *on the string*. This force is equal in magnitude to **T** but is oppositely directed, pulling outward on the string. If the string is massless, it simply transmits this force to the pin at the center, which then pulls in on the string with the same force. Hence, the string need not enter into the analysis of the motion unless it has significant mass.

Let us consider some examples of centripetal force.

▶ **Example 3.** Figure 6–6a represents a small body of mass m revolving in a horizontal circle with constant speed v at the end of a string of length L. As the body swings around, the string sweeps over the surface of a cone. This device is called a *conical pendulum*. Find the time required for one complete revolution of the body.

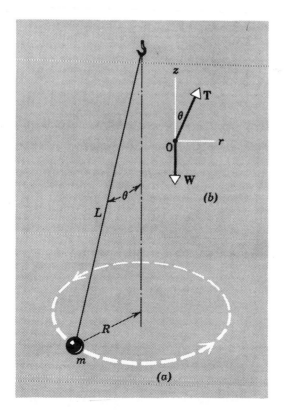

Fig. 6–6 Example 3. (*a*) A mass m suspended from a string of length L swings so as to describe a circle. The string describes a right circular cone of semiangle θ. (*b*) A free-body force diagram for m.

If the string makes an angle θ with the vertical, the radius of the circular path is $R = L \sin \theta$. The forces acting on the body of mass m are **W**, its weight, and **T**, the pull of the string, as shown in Fig. 6–6b. It is clear that $\mathbf{T} + \mathbf{W} \neq 0$. Hence, the resultant force acting on the body is nonzero and the acceleration of the body moving in a circle is also nonzero. We can resolve **T** at any instant into a radial and a vertical component,

$$T_r = T \sin \theta \qquad \text{and} \qquad T_z = T \cos \theta.$$

Since the body has no vertical acceleration,

$$T_z - W = 0$$

or

$$T \cos \theta - W = 0$$

or

$$T \cos \theta = mg.$$

The radial acceleration is v^2/R. This acceleration is supplied by T_r, the radial component of **T**, which is the centripetal force acting on m. Hence,

$$T_r = T \sin \theta = mv^2/R.$$

Dividing this equation by the one above, we obtain

$$\tan \theta = v^2/Rg,$$

or

$$v^2 = Rg \tan \theta,$$

which gives the constant speed of the bob. If we let τ represent the time for one complete revolution of the body, then

$$v = \frac{2\pi R}{\tau} = \sqrt{Rg \tan \theta}$$

or

$$\tau = \frac{2\pi R}{v} = \frac{2\pi R}{\sqrt{Rg \tan \theta}} = 2\pi \sqrt{R/(g \tan \theta)}.$$

But $R = L \sin \theta$, so that

$$\tau = 2\pi \sqrt{(L \cos \theta)/g}.$$

This equation gives the relation between τ, L, and θ. Notice that τ, called the *period* of motion, does not depend on m.

If $L = 3.0$ ft and $\theta = 30°$, what is the period of the motion? We have

$$\tau = 2\pi \sqrt{\frac{(3.0 \text{ ft})(0.866)}{32 \text{ ft/sec}^2}} = 1.8 \text{ sec.}$$

Example 4. In many amusement parks we find a device called the *rotor*. The rotor is a hollow cylindrical room which can be set rotating about the central vertical axis of the cylinder. A person enters the rotor, closes the door, and stands up against the wall. The rotor gradually increases its rotational speed from rest until, at a predetermined speed, the floor below the person is opened downward, revealing a deep pit. The passenger does not fall but remains "pinned up" against the wall of the rotor. Find the coefficient of friction necessary to prevent falling.

The forces acting on the passenger are shown in Fig. 6–7. **W** is the passenger's weight, $\mathbf{f}_s$ is the force of static friction between passenger and rotor wall, and **P** is the centripetal force exerted by the wall on the passenger necessary to keep him moving in a circle. Let the radius of the rotor be R and the final speed of the passenger be v. Since the passenger does not move vertically, but experiences a radial acceleration v^2/R at any instant, we have

$$f_s - W = 0$$

and

$$P(=ma) = (W/g)(v^2/R).$$

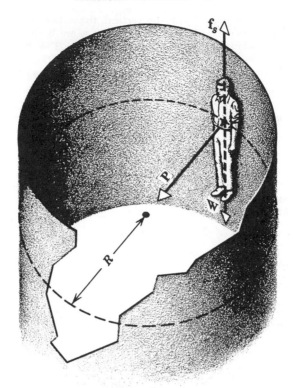

Fig. 6–7 The forces on a person in a "rotor" of radius R.

If μ_s is the coefficient of static friction between passenger and wall necessary to prevent slipping, then $f_s = \mu_s P$ and

$$f_s = W = \mu_s P$$

or

$$\mu_s = \frac{W}{P} = \frac{gR}{v^2}.$$

This equation gives the minimum coefficient of friction necessary to prevent slipping for a rotor of radius R when a particle on its wall has a speed v. Notice that the result does not depend on the passenger's weight.

As a practical matter the coefficient of friction between the textile material of clothing and a typical rotor wall (canvas) is about 0.40. For a typical rotor the radius is 7.0 ft so that v must be about 24 ft/sec or 16 miles/hr or more. ◀

There are a large number of practical mechanical devices which utilize centripetal forces: engine governors, cream separators, ultracentrifuges used in chemical and biological research, clothes driers, and so forth. We shall see later (Chapter 16) that planetary and satellite motions are also examples of motion with a centripetal force.

The centripetal forces discussed in our previous problems are examples of forces that vary with the time. All the other forces considered so far in dynamics were constant forces giving rise to constant accelerations. Forces can vary with time in direction or in magnitude, or in both ways. The centripetal forces discussed previously vary with time in direction only. The analysis of this type of motion is relatively simple because the magnitudes of the centripetal forces and accelerations remain constant and because the directions of these vector quantities vary in such a simple way (so as **always** to be directed along a radius).

An example of a force that varies with time in magnitude only is an impulsive force exerted by one body on another body during a collision. A force that varies with time in both direction *and* magnitude is the force exerted by a spring on an oscillating mass suspended from it. Both of these forces are important in practice. The dynamics of systems acted on by such forces will be considered in detail in later chapters.

6–4   The Limitations of Newtonian Mechanics

In Section 5–10 we discussed some of the questions raised by Newton's formulation of the laws of mechanics. The questions had to do with the logic and consistency of the operational procedures needed to deduce these laws. No question was raised about the correctness of the laws themselves. It is a fact, however, that the laws themselves fail to predict the correct results of observation in some areas of physics. Let us now investigate the limitations of Newtonian mechanics.

In Newtonian mechanics it is assumed that all observers, regardless of their relative motion, will measure the same length for a given stick and the same time interval between two particular successive pistol shots, say. That is, space and time are absolute concepts in classical physics. One consequence of these classical ideas is that the behavior of measuring instruments is not affected by their motion, as long as they are not rapidly accelerated. In seeking to clarify the problem of the relation of physical laws to the coordinate system used to represent them, Albert Einstein was forced to revise the classical notion of absolute time and space. The behavior of measuring instruments was found to be rather generally affected by their motion.

Einstein's results were embodied in his *theory of relativity*. He concluded that the laws of physics were invariant with respect to all frames of reference, that is, they had the same form in all frames. In order for this result to hold, Newton's equations of motion had to be modified. These modifications were found to be correct when the deductions from them were compared with experiment. Here, indeed, was a triumph for clarity and precision of thought!

Some specific examples of the changes in mechanics predicted by relativity and verified by experiment are these: For one, the observed mass of a body depends on its speed in relation to the observer. As a consequence the acceleration produced by a given force is *not* independent of the motion of the body. We shall discuss this in connection with momentum and energy in later chapters. Secondly, length and time intervals are not absolute but depend on the relative motion of observer and the event he measures. One specific consequence is that the classical velocity addition theorem (Eq. 4–10) must be modified. The most general consequence is that the readings of measuring instruments depend on their state of motion.

However, the student need not be alarmed at this state of affairs. For one thing classical physics forms the starting point for modern theories. An understanding of the concepts of classical physics makes it much easier to understand contemporary physics. For another thing, Newton's mechanics is accurate to a very high degree for a very wide range of phenomena. Newtonian mechanics has been successful in accounting for almost all the dynamic phenomena of our ordinary experience, from planetary motion to the motion of some atomic systems. It is only for particles moving at extremely high speeds, near the speed of light, that we must use relativistic mechanics. Ordinary objects cannot reach such speeds. For example, the fractional change in mass of an object moving 2000 miles/hr, a very high speed by ordinary standards, is only about 1 part in 10^{11} (100 billion). In fact, to obtain a mass change of only 0.5% requires a speed about one-tenth the speed of light, or approximately 20,000 *miles/sec*. This is 36,000 times greater than the previous speed! Only when we deal in the realm of atomic and nuclear particles do we attain such speeds. In atomic and nuclear physics, therefore, we will find it necessary to use relativistic mechanics. It follows from all this that Einstein's mechanics must *include* Newton's mechanics as a limiting case for speeds small compared to the speed of light. There is an analogous situation in trigonometry, for example, where the laws of spherical trigonometry approach those of plane trigonometry as a limiting case when the distances involved become small compared to the radius of the sphere.

Another assumption made throughout classical physics is that it is possible, at least in principle, to devise instruments to measure any quantity with as small an error as we please. This assumption fails in the extreme case of very small magnitudes. It is of consequence in the atomic and nuclear domain. In this realm we must use *quantum* (or wave) *mechanics* instead of classical mechanics. Once again, we find that quantum mechanics includes Newtonian mechanics as a limiting case for dimensions large compared to atomic dimensions. The development of quantum mechanics was due initially to W. Heisenberg in 1925 and E. Schroedinger in 1926 and was generalized by P. A. M. Dirac in 1927. Relativistic quantum mechanics represents the highest development of mechanics to date. It gives us pause for thought to learn that even these theories seem in need of revision in the light of current problems in nuclear research.

We have pointed out the difficulties of classical concepts and laws so that the student will be prepared to accept later modifications in the theory. Many engineers, as well as scientists, work today in areas in which modifications cannot be ignored. Certainly Newton could not have foreseen all these limitations. His theory is a triumph of human intellect, considering the circumstances and the time. Even today, 270 years after the publication of the *Principia*, engineers and scientists find his mechanics completely adequate for many of the phenomena they deal with. In any case, Newtonian mechanics forms the foundation upon which all subsequent physics is built.

QUESTIONS

1. It is now known that there is a limit beyond which further polishing of a surface *increases* rather than decreases frictional resistance. Can you give a plausible explanation of this fact?

2. Increasing the apparent macroscopic area of contact between surfaces should increase the actual microscopic area of contact proportionally. Why then does not the coefficient of friction depend on the apparent area of contact?

3. Is friction ever useful? If so, give examples.

4. When walking on ice, is it better to take short steps or long steps? Explain.

5. How could a person who is at rest on a sheet of completely frictionless ice covering a pond reach shore? Could he do this by walking, rolling, swinging his arms, or kicking his feet? How could a person be placed in such a position in the first place?

6. Your car skids across the center line on an icy highway. Should you turn the front wheels in the direction of skid or in the opposite direction (*a*) when you want to avoid a collision with an oncoming car, (*b*) when no other car is near but you want to regain control of the steering?

7. If you want to stop the car in the shortest distance on an icy road, should you (*a*) push hard on the brakes to lock the wheels, (*b*) push just hard enough to prevent slipping, or (*c*) "pump" the brakes?

8. A coin is put on a phonograph turntable. The motor is started, but before the final speed of rotation is reached, the coin flies off. Explain.

9. Why are train roadbeds and highways banked on curves?

10. How does the earth's revolution affect the apparent weight of a body at the equator?

11. Today it is believed that all forces fall into one of four categories: nuclear (very strong); electromagnetic (strong); Fermi or weak interaction, as in β-decay (weak); and gravitational (very weak). Into what category would you put frictional forces? Elastic forces?

PROBLEMS

1. A fireman weighing 160 lb slides down a vertical pole with an average acceleration of 10 ft/sec.^{2} What is the average vertical force he exerts on the pole?

2. A railroad flatcar is loaded with crates having a coefficient of static friction 0.25 with the floor. If the train is moving at 30 miles/hr, in how short a distance can the train be stopped without letting the crates slide?

3. Frictional heat generated by the moving ski is the chief factor promoting sliding in skiing. The ski sticks at the start but once in motion will melt the snow beneath it. Waxing the ski makes it water repellent and reduces friction with the film of water. A magazine reports that a new type of plastic ski is even more water repellent and that on a gentle 700-ft slope in the Alps, a skier reduced his time from 61 to 42 sec with the new skis (a) Determine the average accelerations for each pair of skis. (b) Assuming a 3° slope compute the coefficient of kinetic friction for each case.

4. A student wants to determine the coefficients of static friction and kinetic friction between a box and a plank. He places the box on the plank and gradually raises the plank. When the angle of inclination with the horizontal reaches 30°, the box starts to slip and slides 4.0 meters down the plank in exactly 4.0 sec. Show how he can determine the coefficients from these observations.

5. A hockey puck weighing 0.25 lb slides on the ice for 50 ft before it stops. (a) If its initial speed was 20 ft/sec, what is the force of friction between puck and ice? (b) What is the coefficient of kinetic friction?

6. A 10-lb block of steel is at rest on a horizontal table. The coefficient of static friction between block and table is 0.50. (a) What is the magnitude of the horizontal force that will just start the block moving? (b) What is the magnitude of a force acting upward 60° from the horizontal that will just start the block? (c) If the force acts down at 60° from the horizontal, how large can it be without causing the block to move?

7. A piece of ice slides down a 45° incline in twice the time it takes to slide down a frictionless 45° incline. What is the coefficient of kinetic friction between the ice and incline?

8. A horizontal force F of 12 lb pushes a block weighing 5 lb against a vertical wall (Fig. 6–8). The coefficient of static friction between the wall and the block is 0.6 and the

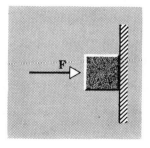

Fig. 6–8

coefficient of kinetic friction is 0.4. Assume the block is not moving initially. (a) Will the block start moving? (b) What is the force exerted on the block by the wall?

9. Block B weighs 160 lb. The coefficient of static friction between block and table is 0.25. Find the maximum weight of block A for which the system will be in equilibrium as shown in Fig. 6–9.

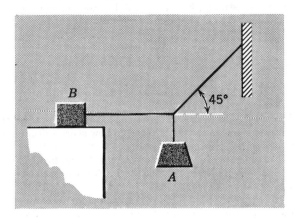

Fig. 6–9

10. A 4-kg block is put on top of a 5-kg block. In order to cause the top block to slip on the bottom one, a horizontal force of 12 nt must be applied to the top block (Fig. 6–10). Assume a frictionless table and find (*a*) the maximum horizontal force F which can be applied to the lower block so that the blocks will move together, and (*b*) the resulting acceleration of the blocks.

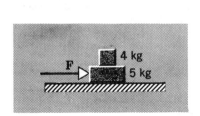

Fig. 6–10

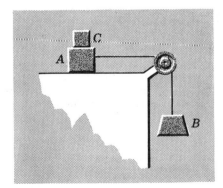

Fig. 6–11

11. In Fig. 6–11 A is a 10-lb block and B is a 5-lb block. (*a*) Determine the minimum weight (block C) which must be placed on A to keep it from sliding, if μ_s between A and the table is 0.20. (*b*) The block C is suddenly lifted off A. What is the acceleration of block A, if μ_k between A and the table is 0.20?

12. The handle of a floor mop of mass m makes an angle θ with the vertical direction. Let μ_k be the coefficient of kinetic friction between mop and floor, and μ_s be the coefficient of static friction between mop and floor. Neglect the mass of the handle. (*a*) Find the magnitude of the force F directed along the handle required to slide the mop with uniform velocity across the floor. (*b*) Show that if θ is smaller than a certain angle θ_0, the mop cannot be made to slide across the floor no matter how great a force is directed along the handle. (*c*) What is the angle θ_0?

13. A block slides down an inclined plane of slope angle ϕ with constant velocity. It is then projected up the same plane with an initial speed v_0. How far up the incline will it move before coming to rest? Will it slide down again?

14. Body B weighs 100 lb and body A weighs 32 lb (Fig. 6–12). Given $\mu_s = 0.56$ and $\mu_k = 0.25$, (a) find the acceleration of the system if B is initially at rest, and (b) find the acceleration if B is moving initially.

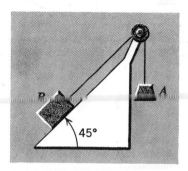

Fig. 6–12

15. A block of mass m at the end of a string is whirled around in a vertical circle of radius R. Find the critical speed below which the string would become slack at the highest point.

16. A 5000-lb airplane loops the loop at a speed of 200 miles/hr. Find (a) the radius of the largest circular loop possible, and (b) the force on the plane at the bottom of this loop.

17. In the Bohr model of the hydrogen atom, the electron revolves in a circular orbit around the nucleus. If the radius of the orbit is 5.3×10^{-11} meters and the electron makes 6.6×10^{15} rev/sec, find (a) the acceleration (magnitude and direction) of the electron, and (b) the centripetal force acting on the electron. (This force is due to the attraction between the positively charged nucleus and the negatively charged electron.) The mass of the electron is 9.1×10^{-31} kg.

18. Assume that the standard kilogram would weigh exactly 9.80 nt at sea level on the earth's equator if the earth did not rotate about its axis. Then take into account the fact that the earth does rotate so that this mass moves in a circle of radius 6.40×10^6 meters (earth's radius) at a constant speed of 465 meters/sec. (a) Determine the centripetal force needed to keep the standard moving in its circular path. (b) Determine the force exerted by the standard kilogram on a spring balance from which it is suspended at the equator (its weight).

19. A circular curve of highway is designed for traffic moving at 40 miles/hr. (a) If the radius of the curve is 400 ft, what is the correct angle of banking of the road? (b) If the curve is not banked, what is the minimum coefficient of friction between tires and road that would keep traffic from skidding at this speed?

20. An old streetcar rounds a corner on unbanked tracks. If the radius of the tracks is 30 ft and the car's speed is 10 miles/hr, what angle with the vertical will be made by the loosely hanging hand straps? Is there a force acting on these straps? If so, is it a centripetal or a centrifugal force? Do your answers depend on what reference frame you choose?

21. A mass m on a frictionless table is attached to a hanging mass M by a cord through a hole in the table (Fig. 6–13). Find the conditions (v and r) with which m must spin for M to stay at rest.

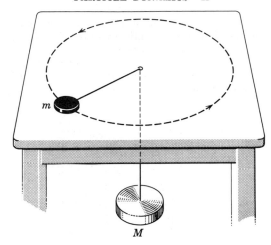

Fig. 6–13

22. The following extracts are taken from Christian Huygens' (1629–1695) *Horologium Oscillatorium*, in which he presents theorems on centrifugal force. His proofs were found among his papers after his death. Give your proofs.

(a) If a moving body travels in the circumference of a circle with a speed the same as that which it would acquire by falling from a height equal to a quarter of the diameter, it will exert a centrifugal force equal to its weight; that is, it will stretch the string which holds it to the center with the same force as it would if suspended from it.

(b) If two moving bodies, suspended by threads of unequal length, swing around so that they traverse circumferences parallel to the horizon, whereas the other end of the thread remains fixed so that the altitudes of the cones which the threads describe in this motion are equal, then the times in which their paths are described are equal.

Work and Energy

CHAPTER 7

7-1 Introduction

The fundamental problem of particle dynamics is to find how a particle will move when we know the forces that act on it. By "how a particle will move" we mean how its position varies with time. If the motion is one-dimensional, the problem is to find x as a function of time, $x(t)$. In the previous two chapters we solved this problem for the special case of a constant force. The method used is this. We find the resultant force $\mathbf{F}$ acting on the particle. We then substitute $\mathbf{F}$ and the particle mass m into Newton's second law of motion. This gives us the acceleration $\mathbf{a}$ of the particle; or

$$\mathbf{a} = \mathbf{F}/m.$$

If the force $\mathbf{F}$ and the mass m are constant, the acceleration $\mathbf{a}$ must be constant. Let us choose the x-axis to be along the direction of this constant acceleration. We can then find the speed of the particle from Eq. 3–7,

$$v = v_0 + at,$$

and the position of the particle from Eq. 3–10,

$$x = v_0 t + \tfrac{1}{2}at^2.$$

This equation gives us directly what we usually want to know, namely $x(t)$, the position of the particle as a function of time.

The problem is more difficult, however, when the force acting on a particle is *not constant*. In such a case we still obtain the acceleration of the particle, as before, from Newton's second law of motion. However, in order to get the speed or position of the particle, we can no longer use the formulas previously developed for constant acceleration because the acceleration now is *not* constant. In general, to solve such problems, we must use the mathematical process of integration, which is developed in this chapter.

We confine our attention to forces that vary with the position of the particle. This type of force is very common in physics. Some examples are the gravitational forces between bodies, such as the sun and earth or earth and moon, and the force exerted by a stretched spring on a body to which it is attached. The procedure used to determine the motion of a particle subject to such a force leads us to the concepts of work and kinetic energy. These in turn will lead us (in Chapter 8) to the broader concept of energy, a concept which has played a major role in the development of physics.

7–2 Work Done by a Constant Force

Consider a particle acted on by a force. In the simplest case the force **F** is constant and the motion takes place in a straight line in the direction of the force. In such a situation we define the *work done by the force on the particle* as the product of the magnitude of the force F and the distance d through which the particle moves. We write this as

$$W = Fd.$$

However, the constant force acting on a particle may not act in the direction in which the particle moves. In this case we define the *work done by the force on the particle* as the product of the component of the force along the line of motion by the distance d the body moves along that line. In Fig. 7–1 a constant force **F** makes an angle θ with the x-axis and acts on a particle whose displacement along the x-axis is **d**. If W represents the work done by **F** during this displacement, then according to our definition

$$W = (F \cos \theta)d. \tag{7-1}$$

Of course, other forces must act on a particle that moves in this way (its weight and the frictional force exerted by the plane, to name two). A particle acted on by only a single force may have a displacement in a direction other than that of this single force, as in projectile motion. But it cannot

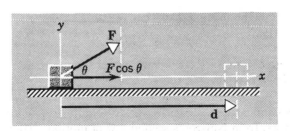

Fig. 7–1 A force **F** makes the block undergo a displacement **d**. The component of **F** that does the work has magnitude $F \cos \theta$; the work done is **F**·**d** $= Fd \cos \theta$.

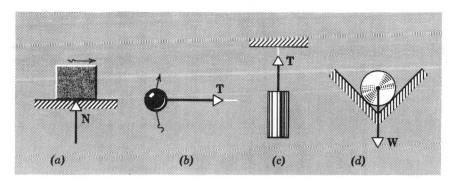

Fig. 7–2 Work is not always done when a force is applied to a body. In (a) the block moves to the right as a normal force N is exerted upon it. In (b) the ball moves in a circle under the influence of centripetal force **T**. In both (a) and (b) the applied force is perpendicular to the displacement; the work is zero since $W = \mathbf{F} \cdot \mathbf{d} = Fd \cos \theta = Fd \cos 90° = 0$. In (c) a cylinder hangs from the ceiling; the cord exerts a force **T** on the cylinder. In (d) a cylinder rests in a groove; the earth exerts the force **W** on the cylinder. In both (c) and (d) there is no displacement, so the work done is zero.

move in a straight line unless the line has the same direction as that of the single force applied to it. *Equation 7–1 refers only to the work done on the particle by the particular force* **F**. *The work done on the particle by the other forces must be calculated separately.* The total work done on the particle is the sum of the works done by the separate forces.

When θ is zero, the work done by **F** is simply Fd, in agreement with our previous equation. Thus, when a horizontal force draws a body horizontally, or when a vertical force lifts a body vertically, the work done by the force is the product of the magnitude of the force by the distance moved. When θ is 90°, the force has no component in the direction of motion. That force then does no work on the body. For instance, the vertical force holding a body a fixed distance off the ground does no work on the body, even if the body is moved horizontally over the ground. Also, the centripetal force acting on a body in motion does no work on that body because the force is always at right angles to the direction in which the body is moving. Of course, a force does no work on a body that does not move, for its displacement is then zero. In Fig. 7–2 we illustrate common examples in which a force applied to a body does no work on that body.

Notice that we can write Eq. 7–1 either as $(F \cos \theta)d$ or $F(d \cos \theta)$. This suggests that the work can be calculated in two different ways: Either we multiply the magnitude of the displacement by the component of the force in the direction of the displacement or we multiply the magnitude of the force by the component of the displacement in the direction of the force. These two methods always give the same result.

Work is a *scalar*, although the two quantities involved in its definition, force and displacement, are vectors. In Section 2–4 we defined the *scalar product* of two vectors as the scalar quantity that we find when we multiply the magnitude of one vector by the projection of a second vector along the direction of the first. We promised in that section that we would soon run across physical quantities that behave like scalar products. Equation 7–1 shows that work is such a quantity. In the terminology of vector algebra we can write this equation as

$$W = \mathbf{F} \cdot \mathbf{d}, \tag{7-2}$$

where the dot indicates a scalar (or dot) product. Equation 7–2 for $\mathbf{F}$ and $\mathbf{d}$ corresponds to Eq. 2–12 for $\mathbf{A}$ and $\mathbf{B}$.

Work can be either positive or negative. If the particle on which a force acts has a component of motion opposite to the direction of the force, the work done by that force is negative. This corresponds to an obtuse angle between the force and displacement vectors. For example, when a person lowers an object to the floor, the work done on the object by the upward force of his hand holding the object is negative. In this case θ is 180°, for $\mathbf{F}$ points up and $\mathbf{d}$ points down.

Work as we have defined it (Eq. 7–2) proves to be a very useful concept in physics. Our special definition of the word *work* does not correspond to the colloquial usage of the term. This may be confusing. A person holding a heavy weight at rest in the air may say that he is doing hard work—and he may work hard in the physiological sense—but from the point of view of physics we say that he is not doing any work. We say this because the applied force causes no displacement. The word *work* is used only in the strict sense of Eq. 7–2. In many scientific fields words are borrowed from our everyday language and are used to name a very specific concept (and conversely). The words *basic* and *cell*, for example, mean quite different things in chemistry and biology than in everyday language.

The *unit* of work is the work done by a unit force in moving a body a unit distance in the direction of the force. In the mks system the unit of work is 1 *newton-meter*, called 1 *joule*. In the British engineering system the unit of work is the *foot-pound*. Using the relations between the newton and the pound, and the meter and foot, we obtain 1 joule = 0.7376 ft-lb or 1 ft-lb = 1.356 joules.

▶ **Example 1.** A block of mass 10.0 kg is to be raised from the bottom to the top of an incline 5.00 meters long and 3.00 meters off the ground at the top. Assuming frictionless surfaces, how much work must be done by a force parallel to the incline pushing the block up at *constant speed?*

The situation is shown in Fig. 7–3a. The forces acting on the block are shown in Fig. 7–3b. We must first find P, the magnitude of the force pushing the block up the incline. Because the motion is not accelerated, the resultant force parallel to the plane must be zero. Thus

$$P - mg \sin \theta = 0,$$

or
$$P = mg \sin \theta = (10.0 \text{ kg})(9.80 \text{ meters/sec}^2)(\tfrac{3}{5}) = 58.8 \text{ nt}.$$

Then the work done by $\mathbf{P}$, from Eq. 7–1 with $\theta = 0°$, is

$$W = \mathbf{P} \cdot \mathbf{d} = Pd \cos 0° = Pd = (58.8 \text{ nt})(5.00 \text{ meters}) = 294 \text{ joules}.$$

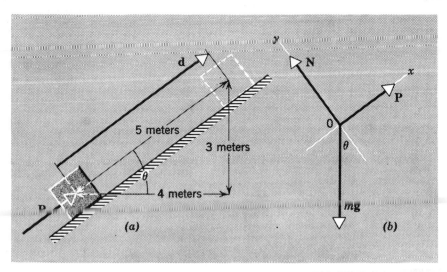

Fig. 7–3 Example 1. (a) A force **P** displaces a block a distance **d** up an inclined plane which makes an angle θ with the horizontal. (b) A free-body force diagram for the block.

If you were to raise the block vertically without using the incline, the work done would be the vertical force mg times the vertical distance or

$$(98.0 \text{ nt})(3.00 \text{ meters}) = 294 \text{ joules},$$

the same as before. The only difference is that with the incline we could apply a smaller force ($P = 58.8$ nt) to raise the block than is required without the incline ($mg = 98.0$ nt); on the other hand we had to push the block a greater distance (5.00 meters) up the incline than we had to raise the block directly (3.00 meters).

Example 2. A boy pulls a 10-lb sled 30 ft along a horizontal surface at a *constant speed*. What work does he do on the sled if the coefficient of kinetic friction is 0.20 and his pull makes an angle of 45° with the horizontal?

The situation is shown in Fig. 7–4a and the forces acting on the sled are shown in Fig. 7–4b. **P** is the boy's pull, **w** the sled's weight, **f** the frictional force, and **N** the normal force exerted by the surface on the sled. The work done by the boy on the sled is

$$W = \mathbf{P \cdot d} = Pd \cos \theta.$$

To evaluate this we first must determine P, whose value has not been given. To obtain P we refer to the force diagram.

The sled is unaccelerated, so that from the second law of motion we obtain

$$P \cos \theta - f = 0,$$

and

$$P \sin \theta + N - w = 0.$$

We know also that f and N are related by

$$f = \mu_k N.$$

In each of these equations there are two unknown quantities. To find P we eliminate f and N from these three equations and solve the remaining equation for P. The student should verify that

$$P = \mu_k w / (\cos \theta + \mu_k \sin \theta).$$

Fig. 7–4 Example 2. (a) A boy displaces a sled an amount **d** by pulling with a force **P** on a rope that makes an angle θ with the horizontal. (b) A free-body force diagram for the sled.

With $\mu_k = 0.20$, $w = 10$ lb, and $\theta = 45°$ we obtain

$$P = (0.20)(10 \text{ lb})/(0.707 + 0.141) = 2.4 \text{ lb.}$$

Then with $d = 30$ ft, the work done by the boy on the sled is

$$W = Pd \cos \theta = (2.4 \text{ lb})(30 \text{ ft})(0.707) = 51 \text{ ft-lb.}$$

The vertical component of the boy's pull **P** does no work on the sled. Notice, however, that it reduces the normal force between the sled and the surface ($N = w - P \sin \theta$) and thereby reduces the magnitude of the force of friction ($f = \mu_k N$).

Would the boy do more work, less work, or the same amount of work on the sled if he pulled horizontally instead of at 45° from the horizontal?

Do any of the other forces acting on the sled do work on it?   ◄

7–3 Work Done by a Variable Force

Let us now consider the work done by a force that is not constant. We consider first a force that varies in magnitude only. Let the force be given as a function of position $F(x)$ and assume that the force acts in the x direction. Suppose a body is moved along the x direction by this force. What is the work done by this variable force in moving the body from x_1 to x_2?

In Fig. 7–5 we plot F versus x. Let us divide the total displacement into a large number of small equal intervals Δx (Fig. 7–5a). Consider the small displacement Δx from x_1 to $x_1 + \Delta x$. During this small displacement the force F has a nearly constant value and the work it does, ΔW, is approximately

$$\Delta W = F \, \Delta x, \tag{7–3}$$

where F is the value of the force at x_1. Likewise, during the small displacement from $x_1 + \Delta x$ to $x_1 + 2\Delta x$, the force F has a nearly constant value and the work it does is approximately $\Delta W = F \, \Delta x$, where F is the value of the force at $x_1 + \Delta x$. The total work done by F in displacing the body from x_1 to x_2, W_{12}, is approximately the sum of a large number of terms like that of Eq. 7-3, in which F has a different value for each term. Hence,

$$W_{12} = \sum_{x_1}^{x_2} F \, \Delta x \qquad (7-4)$$

where the Greek letter sigma (Σ) stands for sum over all intervals from x_1 to x_2.

To make a better approximation we can divide the total displacement from x_1 to x_2 into a larger number of equal intervals, as in Fig. 7-5b, so that

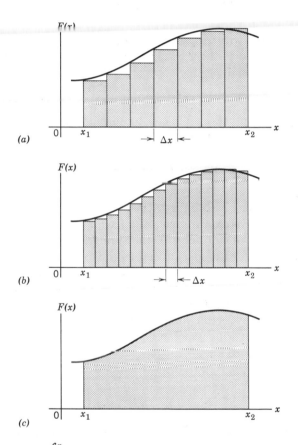

(a)

(b)

(c)

Fig. 7-5   Computing $\int_{x_1}^{x_2} F(x) \, dx$ amounts to finding the area under the curve $F(x)$ between the limits x_1 and x_2. This can be done approximately as in the top drawing (a) by dividing the area into a few strips, each of width Δx. The areas of the rectangles are then summed to give a rough value of the area. In the middle drawing (b) the strips are further subdivided and the value for the area becomes more exact as the errors at the tops of the rectangles become smaller. In the bottom drawing (c) the strips are only infinitesimal in width. The measurement of area is exact, since the errors at the tops of the rectangles go to zero as the strip width dx goes to zero.

Δx is smaller and the value of F at the beginning of each interval is more typical of its values within the interval. It is clear that we can obtain better and better approximations by taking Δx smaller and smaller so as to have a larger and larger number of intervals. We can obtain an exact result for the work done by F if we let Δx go to zero and the number of intervals go to infinity. Hence, the exact result is

$$W_{12} = \lim_{\Delta x \to 0} \sum_{x_1}^{x_2} F \, \Delta x. \tag{7–5}$$

The relation
$$\lim_{\Delta x \to 0} \sum_{x_1}^{x_2} F \, \Delta x = \int_{x_1}^{x_2} F \, dx,$$

defines the integral of F with respect to x from x_1 to x_2. Numerically, this quantity is exactly equal to the area between the force curve and the x-axis between the limits x_1 and x_2 (Fig. 7–5c). Hence, graphically an integral can be interpreted as an area. The symbol $\int$ is a distorted S and symbolizes the integration process. We can write the total work done by F in displacing a body from x_1 to x_2 as

$$W_{12} = \int_{x_1}^{x_2} F(x) \, dx. \tag{7–6}$$

As an example, consider a spring attached to a wall. Let us apply a force to the spring so as to stretch it horizontally from a length x_1 to a length x_2. We shall assume that the end point of the spring is not accelerated by the applied force but moves with constant speed. Strictly speaking, if there is to be no acceleration at the beginning and the end of the stretching, we must have zero speed. However, we can choose the speed to be very slow and neglect the small acceleration at the beginning and the small deceleration at the end (or else we can imagine that we are computing the work done over an interval in which the speed is constant and not concern ourselves with the other intervals).

The force exerted by a spring that has been stretched to a distance x from its unstretched length x_0 is

$$F = -k(x - x_0), \tag{7–7}$$

where k is a constant called the *force constant* of the spring. The direction of the force is always opposite to the displacement from x_0. When the spring is stretched, then $x > x_0$; when the spring is compressed, then $x < x_0$. Equation 7–7 shows that the force always changes in sign when the particle passes through the origin x_0; the force always points toward x_0. Real springs will obey this relation, known as *Hooke's law*, if we do not stretch them beyond a limited range. We can think of k as the magnitude of the force per unit elongation. Thus, very stiff springs have large values of k. If we choose our origin so that $x_0 = 0$, Eq. 7–7 becomes simply $F = -kx$.

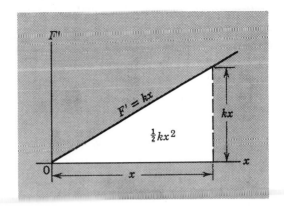

Fig. 7–6 The force exerted in stretching a spring is $F' = kx$. The area under the force curve is the work done in stretching the spring a distance x and can be found by integrating or using the formula for the area of a triangle.

To stretch the spring without accelerating it, we must exert a force F' on the spring equal but opposite to the force F exerted by the spring on us. The applied force * is, therefore, $F' = kx$.

The work done by this force in stretching the spring from x_1 to x_2 is

$$W_{12} = \int_{x_1}^{x_2} F'(x)\, dx = \int_{x_1}^{x_2} kx\, dx = \tfrac{1}{2}kx_2{}^2 - \tfrac{1}{2}kx_1{}^2.$$

If we let $x_1 = 0$ and $x_2 = x$, we obtain

$$W = \int_0^x kx\, dx = \tfrac{1}{2}kx^2. \tag{7–8}$$

This is the work done in stretching a spring from 0 to x.

We can also evaluate this integral by computing the area under the force-displacement curve and the x-axis from $x = 0$ to $x = x$. This is drawn as the white area in Fig. 7–6. The area is a triangle of base x and altitude kx. The white area is, therefore,

$$(\tfrac{1}{2})(x)(kx) = \tfrac{1}{2}kx^2,$$

in agreement with Eq. 7 8.

The force **F** may vary in direction as well as in magnitude, and the particle may move along a curved path. To compute the work in this general case we must know the angle θ between the force **F** and the displacement ds at each point of the path. In general, then, we have

$$dW = \mathbf{F} \cdot \mathbf{ds} = F \cos\theta\, ds. \tag{7–9}$$

* If the applied force were different from $F = kx$, we would have a net unbalanced force acting on the spring and its motion would be accelerated. To compute the work done we would have to specify exactly what the applied force is at each point. No matter what the force turned out to be, the work done would always be the same for the same displacement x_1 to x_2, providing the spring has the same speed initially and finally. However, it is much easier to use the simple force $F = kx$ in calculating the work done. Such an applied force leads to unaccelerated motion. It is in order to be able to use this simple force that we specified unaccelerated motion in the first place.

Here $d\mathbf{s}$ is the vector differential displacement of magnitude ds, and θ is the angle between $\mathbf{F}$ and $d\mathbf{s}$. Figure 7–7 shows this for two points on the curved path.

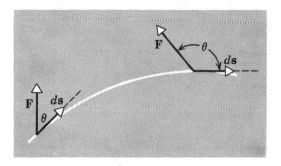

Fig. 7–7 How $\mathbf{F}$ and $d\mathbf{s}$ might change along a path. Note that $d\mathbf{s}$ always points in the direction of the velocity of the moving object, since $\mathbf{v} = d\mathbf{s}/dt$ and hence is tangent to the path at all points.

As an example, consider a particle of mass m suspended from a weightless cord of length l. This is called a simple pendulum. Let us displace the particle along a circular path of radius l from $\phi = 0$ to $\phi = \phi_0$ by applying a force that is always *horizontal*. We can apply such a force by pulling horizontally on the particle with an attached string, for example. The particle will then have been displaced a vertical distance h. Figure 7–8a shows the situation and Fig. 7–8b shows the forces acting on the particle in the arbitrary position ϕ. $\mathbf{F}$ is the applied force, $\mathbf{T}$ the tension in the cord, and $m\mathbf{g}$ the weight of the particle.

Fig. 7–8 (*a*) The simple pendulum. A mass point m is suspended on a string of length l. Its maximum displacement is ϕ_0. (*b*) A free-body force diagram for the mass.

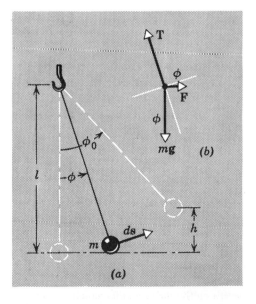

Again we assume that there is no acceleration (the reason is the same as before), so that in practice the motion must be very slow. The force $\mathbf{F}$ is always horizontal, but the displacement $d\mathbf{s}$ is along the arc. The direction of $d\mathbf{s}$ depends on the value of ψ and is tangent to the circle at each point. $\mathbf{F}$ will vary in magnitude in such a way as to balance the horizontal component of the tension.

From the first law we obtain

$$mg = T \cos \phi \qquad \text{and} \qquad F = T \sin \phi$$

On eliminating T from these equations, we obtain

$$F = mg \tan \phi.$$

The work done in a displacement $d\mathbf{s}$ by a force $\mathbf{F}$ is

$$dW = \mathbf{F} \cdot d\mathbf{s} = (mg \tan \phi)(\cos \phi)(ds) = mg \sin \phi \, ds.$$

Notice that the angle between $\mathbf{F}$ and $d\mathbf{s}$, called θ in Eq. 7–9, is equal to ϕ in this case. To determine the work done in a displacement from $\phi = 0$ to $\phi = \phi_0$, we integrate along the arc. We use the relation $ds = l \, d\phi$ and obtain

$$W = \int_{\phi=0}^{\phi=\phi_0} \mathbf{F} \cdot d\mathbf{s} = \int_{\phi=0}^{\phi=\phi_0} mg \sin \phi \, ds = \int_0^{\phi_0} mgl \sin \phi \, d\phi = mgl(1 - \cos \phi_0).$$

But $h = l(1 - \cos \phi_0)$, so that we obtain the simple result $W = mgh$.

The student should now try to compute the work done in displacing the particle along the arc with constant speed by applying a force that is always directed along the arc. The result will be the same as before, $W = mgh$. Notice that both of these results are the same as the work that would be done in raising a mass m vertically through a height h.

What work has been done on the particle by the tension $\mathbf{T}$ in the string?

7–4 Power

We have not considered the time involved in doing work. The same amount of work is done in raising a given body through a given height whether it takes one second or one year to do so. However, the *rate at which work is done* is often more interesting to us than the total work performed.

We define *power* as the time rate at which work is done. The average power delivered by an agent is the total work done by the agent divided by the total time interval, or

$$\bar{P} = W/t.$$

The instantaneous power delivered by an agent is

$$P = dW/dt. \tag{7–10}$$

If the power is constant in time, then $P = \bar{P}$ and

$$W = Pt.$$

In the mks system the unit of power is 1 joule/second, which is called 1 *watt*. This unit of power is named in honor of James Watt whose steam engine is the predecessor of today's more powerful engines. In the British engineering system, the unit of power is 1 ft-lb/sec. This unit is quite small for practical purposes, so a larger unit, called the *horsepower*, has been adopted. Actually Watt himself suggested as a unit of power the power delivered by a horse as an engine. One horsepower was chosen to equal 550 ft-lb/sec. One horsepower is equal to about 746 watts or about three-fourths of a kilowatt. A horse would not last very long at that rate.

Work can also be expressed in units of power × time. This is the origin of the term *kilowatt-hour*, for example. One kilowatt-hour is the work done in 1 hr by an agent working at a constant rate of 1 kw.

▶ **Example 3.** An automobile uses 100 hp and moves at a uniform speed of 60 miles/hr (= 88 ft/sec). What is the forward thrust on the car?

$$P = \frac{W}{t} = \frac{\mathbf{F} \cdot \mathbf{d}}{t} = \mathbf{F} \cdot \mathbf{v}.$$

The forward thrust **F** is in the direction of motion given by **v**, so that

$$P = Fv,$$

$$F = \frac{P}{v} = \left(\frac{100 \text{ hp}}{88 \text{ ft/sec}}\right)\left(\frac{550 \text{ ft-lb/sec}}{1 \text{ hp}}\right) = 630 \text{ lb.}$$

Why doesn't the car accelerate?   ◀

7–5 Kinetic Energy

In all our previous examples of work done by forces, we dealt with *unaccelerated* objects. Recall that we assumed motion with constant speed in each case. The *resultant force* acting on the object was always zero. Let us suppose now that the *resultant force* acting on an object is *not zero*, so that the object is *accelerated*. The conditions are the same in all respects to those that exist when a single unbalanced force acts on the object.

The simplest situation to consider is that of a *constant resultant force* **F**. Such a force, acting on a particle of mass m, will produce a constant acceleration **a**. Let us choose the x-axis to be in the common direction of **F** and **a**. What is the work done by this force on the particle in causing a displacement x? We have (for constant acceleration) the relations

$$a = \frac{v - v_0}{t}$$

and

$$x = \frac{v + v_0}{2} \cdot t,$$

Eqs. 3–7 and 3–9 respectively. Here v_0 is the particle's speed at $t = 0$ and v its speed at the time t. Then the work done is

$$W = Fx = max$$

$$= m\frac{v - v_0}{t}\frac{v + v_0}{2}t = \tfrac{1}{2}mv^2 - \tfrac{1}{2}mv_0^2. \tag{7–11}$$

We call one-half the product of the mass of a body and the square of its speed the kinetic energy of the body. If we represent kinetic energy by the symbol K, then

$$K = \tfrac{1}{2}mv^2. \tag{7–12}$$

We may then state Eq. 7–11 in this way: *The work done by the* resultant *force acting on a particle is equal to the change in the kinetic energy of the particle.*

Although we have proved this result for a constant force only, it holds whether the resultant force is constant or variable. Let the resultant force vary in magnitude (but not in direction), for example. Take the displacement to be in the direction of the force. Let this direction be the x-axis. The work done by the resultant force in displacing the particle from x_0 to x is

$$W = \int \mathbf{F} \cdot d\mathbf{s} = \int_{x_0}^{x} F \, dx.$$

But from Newton's second law we have $F = ma$, and the acceleration a can be written as

$$a = \frac{dv}{dt} = \frac{dv}{dx} \cdot \frac{dx}{dt} = \frac{dv}{dx} v = v \frac{dv}{dx}.$$

Hence,

$$W = \int_{x_0}^{x} F \, dx = \int_{x_0}^{x} mv \frac{dv}{dx} \, dx = \int_{v_0}^{v} mv \, dv = \tfrac{1}{2}mv^2 - \tfrac{1}{2}mv_0^2. \quad (7\text{-}13)$$

A more general case is that in which the force varies both in direction and magnitude and the motion is along a curved path, as in Fig. 7-7. (See Problem 6.) Once again we find that the work done on a particle by the resultant force is equal to the change in the kinetic energy of the particle.

The work done *on* a particle by the *resultant* force is *always* equal to the change in the kinetic energy of the particle:

$$W \text{ (of the } resultant \text{ force)} = K - K_0 = \Delta K. \quad (7\text{-}14)$$

Equation 7-14 is known as the *work-energy theorem* for a particle.

Notice that when the speed of the particle is constant, there is no change in kinetic energy and the work done by the resultant force is zero. With uniform circular motion, for example, the speed of the particle is constant and the centripetal force does no work on the particle. A force at right angles to the direction of motion merely changes the *direction* of the velocity and not its magnitude. Only when the resultant force has a component along the direction of motion does it change the speed of the particle or its kinetic energy. Hence, work is done on a particle only by that component of the resultant force along the line of motion. This coincides with our definition of work in terms of a scalar product, for in $\mathbf{F} \cdot d\mathbf{s}$ only the component of $\mathbf{F}$ along $d\mathbf{s}$ contributes to the product.

If the kinetic energy of a particle decreases, the work done on it by the resultant force is negative. The displacement and the component of the resultant force along the line of motion are oppositely directed. The work done *on* the particle by the force is the negative of the work done *by* the particle on whatever produced the force. This is a consequence of Newton's third law of motion. Hence, Eq. 7-14 can be interpreted to say that the kinetic energy of a particle decreases by an amount just equal to the amount of work which the particle *does*. A body has energy stored in it because of its motion; as it does work it slows down and loses some of this energy.

Therefore, *the kinetic energy of a body in motion is equal to the work it can do before it is brought to rest.* This result holds whether the applied forces are constant or variable.

The units of kinetic energy and of work are the same. Kinetic energy, like work, is a scalar quantity. The kinetic energy of a group of particles is simply the (scalar) sum of the kinetic energies of the individual particles in the group.

▶ **Example 4.** A neutron, one of the constituents of a nucleus, is found to pass two points 6.0 meters apart in a time interval of 1.8×10^{-4} sec. Assuming its speed was constant, find its kinetic energy. The mass of a neutron is about 1.7×10^{-27} kg.

The speed is obtained from

$$v = \frac{d}{t} = \frac{6.0 \text{ meters}}{1.8 \times 10^{-4} \text{ sec}} = 3.3 \times 10^4 \text{ meters/sec.}$$

The kinetic energy is

$$K = \tfrac{1}{2}mv^2 = (\tfrac{1}{2})(1.7 \times 10^{-27} \text{ kg})(3.3 \times 10^4 \text{ meters/sec})^2 = 9.3 \times 10^{-19} \text{ joules.}$$

For purposes of nuclear physics the joule is a very large energy unit. A unit more commonly used is the electron volt (ev), which is equivalent to 1.60×10^{-19} joules. The kinetic energy of the neutron in our example can then be expressed as

$$K = (9.3 \times 10^{-19} \text{ joules}) \left(\frac{1 \text{ ev}}{1.60 \times 10^{-19} \text{ joules}} \right) = 5.8 \text{ ev}$$

Example 5. Assume the force of gravity to be constant for small distances above the surface of the earth. A body is dropped from rest at a height h above the earth's surface. What will its kinetic energy be just before it strikes the ground?

The gain in kinetic energy is equal to the work done by the resultant force, which here is the force of gravity. This force is constant and directed along the line of motion, so that the work done by gravity is

$$W = \mathbf{F} \cdot \mathbf{d} = mgh.$$

Initially the body has a speed $v_0 = 0$ and finally a speed v. The gain in kinetic energy of the body is

$$\tfrac{1}{2}mv^2 - \tfrac{1}{2}mv_0^2 = \tfrac{1}{2}mv^2 - 0.$$

Equating these two equivalent terms we obtain

$$K = \tfrac{1}{2}mv^2 = mgh$$

as the kinetic energy of the body just before it strikes the ground.

The speed of the body is then

$$v = \sqrt{2gh}.$$

The student should show that in falling from a height h_1 to a height h_2 a body will increase its kinetic energy from $\tfrac{1}{2}mv_1^2$ to $\tfrac{1}{2}mv_2^2$, where

$$\tfrac{1}{2}mv_2^2 - \tfrac{1}{2}mv_1^2 = mg(h_1 - h_2).$$

In this example we are dealing with a constant force and a constant acceleration. The methods developed in previous chapters should be useful here too. Can you show how the results obtained by energy considerations could be obtained directly from the laws of motion for uniformly accelerated bodies?

Example 6. A block weighing 8.0 lb slides on a horizontal frictionless table with a speed of 4.0 ft/sec. It is brought to rest in compressing a spring in its path. By how much is the spring compressed if its force constant is 0.25 lb/ft?

The kinetic energy of the block is

$$K = \tfrac{1}{2}mv^2 = \tfrac{1}{2}(w/g)v^2.$$

This kinetic energy is equal to the work W that the block can do before it is brought to rest. The work done in compressing the spring a distance x feet beyond its unstretched length is

$$W = \tfrac{1}{2}kx^2,$$

so that

$$\tfrac{1}{2}kx^2 = \tfrac{1}{2}(w/g)v^2$$

or

$$x = \sqrt{\frac{w}{gk}} \, v = \sqrt{\frac{8.0}{(32)(0.25)}} \, 4.0 \text{ ft} = 4.0 \text{ ft}. \qquad \blacktriangleleft$$

7-6 Significance of the Work-Energy Theorem

The work-energy theorem is very useful for solving problems in which the work done by the resultant force is easily computed and in which we are interested in finding the particle's speed at certain positions. Note that this theorem follows directly from Newton's second law.

Of greater significance, perhaps, is the fact that the work-energy theorem is the starting point for a sweeping generalization in physics. It has been emphasized that the work-energy theorem is valid when W is interpreted as the work done by the *resultant* force acting on the particle. However, it is helpful in many problems to compute separately the work done by certain types of force and give special names to the work done by each type. This leads to the concepts of different types of energy and the principle of the conservation of energy, which is the subject of the next chapter.

QUESTIONS

1. Can you think of other words like "work" whose colloquial meanings are often very different from their scientific meanings?

2. In a tug of war one team is slowly giving way to the other. What work is being done and by whom?

3. A man rowing a boat upstream is at rest with respect to the shore. (*a*) Is he doing any work? (*b*) If he stops rowing and moves down with the stream, is any work being done on him?

4. The work done by the resultant force is always equal to the change in kinetic energy. Can it happen that the work done by one of the component forces alone will be greater than the change in kinetic energy? If so, give examples.

5. Does the work done in raising a box onto a platform depend on how fast it is raised?

6. When two children play catch on a train, does the kinetic energy of the ball depend on the speed of the train? Does the coordinate system chosen as a reference affect your answer? If so, would you call kinetic energy a scalar quantity?

PROBLEMS

1. A 100-lb block of ice slides down an incline 5.0 ft long and 3.0 ft high. A man pushes up on the ice parallel to the incline so that it slides down at constant speed. The coefficient of friction between the ice and the incline is 0.10. Find (*a*) the force exerted by the man, (*b*) the work done by the man on the block, (*c*) the work done by gravity on the block, (*d*) the work done by the surface of the incline on the block, (*e*) the work done by the resultant force on the block, and (*f*) the change in kinetic energy of the block.

2. A man pushes a 60-lb block 30 ft along a level floor at constant speed with a force directed 45° below the horizontal. If the coefficient of kinetic friction is 0.20, how much work does the man do on the block?

3. A crate weighing 500 lb is suspended from the end of a rope 40 ft long. The crate is then pushed aside 4 ft from the vertical and held there. (*a*) What is the force needed to keep the crate in this position? (*b*) Is work being done in holding it there? (*c*) Was work done in moving it aside? If so, how much? (*d*) Does the tension in the rope perform any work on the crate?

4. (*a*) Estimate the work done by the force shown on the graph (Fig. 7–9) in displacing a particle from $x = 1$ to $x = 3$ meters. Refine your method to see how close you can come

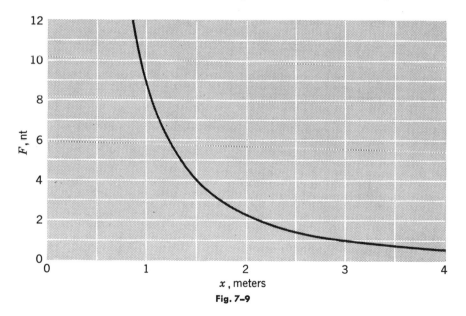

Fig. 7–9

to the exact answer of 6 joules. (*b*) The curve is given analytically by $F = a/x^2$ where $a = 9$ nt-m^2. Show how to get the work done by the rules of integration.

5. The scalar product of two vectors can also be computed directly from the components of those vectors. Let the vector **F** have components F_x and F_y in the plane defined by **F** and **d**, and let **d** have the components d_x and d_y. Prove that the scalar product of **F** and **d** is then equal to $F_x d_x + F_y d_y$.

6. When the force **F** varies both in direction and magnitude and the motion is along a curved path s, the work done by **F** is

$$dW = \mathbf{F}\cdot d\mathbf{s} = F \cos \theta \, ds,$$

where the integration is taken along the curved path. Notice that both F and θ, the angle between **F** and ds, may vary from point to point (see Fig. 7–7). Using the result of the previous problem, show that for two-dimensional motion

$$W = \tfrac{1}{2}mv^2 - \tfrac{1}{2}mv_0^2,$$

where v is the final speed and v_0 the initial speed.

7. Generalize the results of the previous two problems to three dimensions.

8. A net force of 5.0 nt acts on a 15-kg body initially at rest. Compute the work done in the first, second, and third second and the instantaneous power that exists at the end of the third second.

9. A horse pulls a wagon with a force of 40 lb at an angle of 30° with the horizontal and moves along at a speed of 6 miles/hr. (*a*) How much work does the horse do in 10 min? (*b*) What is the power output of the horse?

10. The force required to tow a boat at constant velocity is proportional to the velocity. If it takes 10 hp to tow a certain boat at a speed of 2.5 miles/hr, how much horsepower does it take to tow it at a speed of 7.5 miles/hr?

11. A running man has half the kinetic energy that a boy of half his mass has. The man speeds up by 1 meter/sec and then has the same kinetic energy as the boy. What were the original speeds of man and boy?

12. From what height would an automobile have to fall to gain the kinetic energy equivalent to what it would have when going 60 miles/hr?

13. A proton (nucleus of the hydrogen atom) is being accelerated in a linear accelerator. In each stage of such an accelerator the proton is accelerated along a straight line by 3.6×10^{15} meters/sec^2. If a proton enters such a stage moving initially with a speed of 2.4×10^7 meters/sec and the stage is 3.5 cm long, compute (*a*) its speed at the end of the stage and (*b*) the gain in kinetic energy resulting from the acceleration. Take the mass of the proton to be 1.67×10^{-27} kg and express the energy in electron volts.

14. A 30-gm bullet initially traveling 500 meters/sec penetrates 12 cm into a wooden block. What average force does it exert?

15. Show *from considerations of work and kinetic energy* that the minimum stopping distance for a car of mass m moving with speed v along a level road is $v^2/2\mu_s g$, where μ_s is the coefficient of static friction between tires and road. (See Example 2, Chapter 6.)

16. A truck can move up a road having a grade of 1-ft rise every 50 ft with a speed of 15 miles/hr. The resisting force is equal to one-twenty-fifth the weight of the truck. How fast will the same truck move down the hill with the same horsepower?

17. A proton starting from rest is accelerated in a cyclotron to a final speed of 3.0×10^7 meters/sec (about one-tenth the speed of light). How much work, in electron volts, is done on the proton by the electrical force of the cyclotron which accelerates it?

18. A satellite rocket weighing 100,000 lb acquires a speed of 4000 miles/hr in 1 min after launching. (*a*) What is its kinetic energy at the end of the first minute? (*b*) What is the average power expended during this time, neglecting frictional and gravitational forces?

The Conservation of Energy

CHAPTER 8

8–1 Introduction

We have seen that the work done on a body by the resultant force acting on it equals the change in kinetic energy of the body. It is very helpful in many problems to compute separately the work done by certain types of force and to give special names to the work done by each type. This leads to the concept of different types of energy, such as potential energy and heat energy. This process of categorizing different types of energy culminates in the formulation of one of the great principles of science, the conservation of energy.

8–2 Conservative and Nonconservative Forces

Let us first distinguish between two types of force, *conservative* and *nonconservative*. To make the distinction clear, let us consider an example of each type.

If a ball is thrown vertically into the air from the ground, its speed, and hence its kinetic energy, decreases steadily until it becomes zero at the highest point of its motion. Then the ball reverses its direction and its speed and kinetic energy increase steadily as the ball returns to ground. Neglecting air resistance, the ball returns to its initial position with the same speed and kinetic energy as it had originally; only the direction of motion has changed. In this case the ball loses kinetic energy during one part of its motion but regains it all during the other part of its motion as it returns to its starting point. We have interpreted the kinetic energy of a body as its ability to do work by virtue of its motion. It is clear that in a round trip the ability of the ball to do work remains the same—it has been conserved. Forces that produce such an effect are called *conservative*. Gravitational forces are conservative.

It, however, a body subject to a force returns to its initial position with less or more kinetic energy than it had there originally, in a round trip its ability to do work has changed. We say that such a force is *nonconservative*. The force of friction is a nonconservative force. When a ball is thrown into the air, taking into account the resistance to motion offered by the air, we find that the ball returns to its original position with *less* kinetic energy than it had before. The frictional force of the air opposes the motion of the ball whether the ball is rising or falling and, therefore, lowers the speed it would otherwise have at any position. In a round trip the ball loses kinetic energy. The induction force in a betatron (Section 35–7) is a nonconservative force. Instead of dissipating kinetic energy it generates it, so that a particle will return to its initial position with more kinetic energy than it had there originally. In a round trip the particle gains kinetic energy.

We can define conservative force from another point of view, that of the work done by the force. If there is no change in the kinetic energy of a body, the work done on it by the resultant force must be zero. This follows from the work-energy theorem, for

$$W = \Delta K = 0.$$

In the example of the tossed ball the resultant force acting on it (neglecting air resistance) is gravity. The negative work done by gravity on the ball as it rose was just equal, but opposite in sign, to the positive work done by gravity as the ball returned to its initial position. Therefore, the total work done by the force of gravity in a round trip is zero. Similarly, if there is a change in kinetic energy, the work done by the resultant force is not zero. The force of friction, for example, opposes the motion of the ball whether it is rising or falling and does negative total work on it in a round trip, thereby reducing its kinetic energy.

In general, *a force is conservative if the work done by the force in moving a body through any round trip is zero. A force is nonconservative if the work done by the force in moving the body through any round trip is not zero.*

These definitions can be expressed in another equivalent way.

Consider a motion in which a particle goes from a point A to a point B along path 1 and back from B to A along path 2, as shown in Fig. 8–1a. If the force is conservative, the work done in a round trip is zero, so that

$$W_{AB,1} + W_{BA,2} = 0$$

or $W_{AB,1} = -W_{BA,2}.$

(a)   (b)

Fig. 8–1

That is, the work in going from A to B along path 1 is the negative of the work in going from B to A along path 2. However, if we go from A to B along path 2, as shown in Fig. 8–1b, we merely reverse the direction of the previous motion along 2, so that

$$W_{AB,2} = -W_{BA,2}.$$

Hence,
$$W_{AB,1} = W_{AB,2}$$

or the work done on the particle by a conservative force in going from A to B is the same for either path.

Paths 1 and 2 can be any paths at all, as long as they go from A to B, and A and B can be chosen to be any two points at all. We obtain the same result in all cases, providing the force is conservative. Furthermore, by a similar argument, it is clear that if the same work is done in going from one given point to another given point, regardless of the path, then, in any round trip in which two paths are traversed in opposite directions, the total work done will be zero. Hence, we arrive at another equivalent definition of conservative and nonconservative forces.

A force is conservative if the work done by it in moving a body between two given points depends only on these points and not on the path followed. A force is nonconservative if the work done by that force in moving a body between two points depends on the path taken between those points.

Consider a specific example of each.

Imagine that we are to raise a block to a height h above the ground by going from A to B via several different paths, as shown in Fig. 8–2. We already know that in a round trip the total work done by a conservative force is zero. The work done *on* the block by gravity along the return path BCA is simply mgh. Hence, if gravity is a conservative force, the work done *by* gravity *on* the block along any of the paths from A to B must be $-mgh$, for only if this is true can the total work done by gravity in a round trip be zero. This means that gravity does negative work on the block as it moves from A to B, or, to put it another way, work must be done *against* gravity along the paths AB. The student can directly compute the result that the work done by gravity along any path AB equals $-mgh$. For any of these paths can be decomposed into infinitesimal displacements which

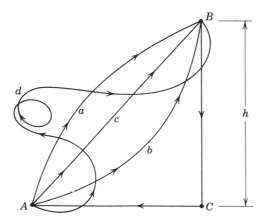

Fig. 8-2 A block is raised from A to B via various paths a, b, c, and d.

are alternately horizontal and vertical; no work is done by gravity in horizontal displacements, and the net vertical displacement is the same in all cases. Hence, the work done on the body moving from A to B depends only on the positions A and B and not at all on the path taken.

The work done in a round trip by a nonconservative force depends on the nature of the path followed and cannot generally be zero. For example, consider a block pushed along a table with friction. Work must be done against friction in moving the block from A to B. Friction does negative work on the block; it will bring a sliding block to rest and dissipate its kinetic energy. To return the block from B to A, work must be done against friction again because the force of friction is always directed opposite to the direction of motion. Again friction does negative work. For the complete round trip, the total work done can never be zero because the work done by friction is always negative. To complete the discussion, we need only point out that as we vary the path from A to B, and hence the total distance traversed, the work done by friction varies. It is *not* independent of the path taken between two fixed points.

The definitions of conservative force which we have given are equivalent to one another. Which definition we use depends only on convenience. The round-trip approach can be used to show clearly that energy is conserved when conservative forces act. For purposes of developing the idea of potential energy, however, the path independence statement is preferable.

8–3 Potential Energy

The work done by a conservative force depends only on the starting and the end point of the motion and not on the path followed between them. Such a force can depend only on the position of the particle. It does not depend on the velocity of the particle or on time, for example.

Consider the case of motion in a straight line. The work done by the resultant force F in displacing a body is equal to the gain in kinetic energy of that body, or

$$\int_{x_0}^{x} F \, dx = \tfrac{1}{2}mv^2 - \tfrac{1}{2}mv_0^2. \tag{8-1}$$

In one dimension all forces that depend only on position are conservative. If F depends only on x, the kinetic energy of the body depends *only* on its position. At different positions along the line of motion the kinetic energy may be different, but at a particular point on the line the kinetic energy will always be the same. The example of a ball thrown vertically in the air (without air resistance) illustrates this point.

The decrease of energy of motion (kinetic energy) is associated with an increase of energy of position (potential energy). Let the symbol U represent potential energy. Then the relation

$$\Delta K = -\Delta U$$

expresses the fact that any change in kinetic energy is associated with an opposite change in potential energy. But from the work-energy theorem (Eq. 8–1)

$$\Delta K = \int_{x_0}^{x} F(x)\, dx.$$

Comparing these equations we see that the change in potential energy is defined as

$$\Delta U = -\int_{x_0}^{x} F(x)\, dx, \tag{8–2}$$

and is a function of position only.

Because $-\int_{x_0}^{x} F(x)\, dx = \int_{x}^{x_0} F(x)\, dx$, we can write this as

$$U(x) - U(x_0) = \int_{x}^{x_0} F(x)\, dx. \tag{8–3}$$

The change in potential energy is the work done by the force when the particle moves from x to some standard reference point x_0.

If we now combine Eqs. 8–1 and 8–2, we obtain

$$U(x) - U(x_0) = -\int_{x_0}^{x} F(x)\, dx = \tfrac{1}{2}mv_0^2 - \tfrac{1}{2}mv^2$$

or

$$U(x) + \tfrac{1}{2}mv^2 = U(x_0) + \tfrac{1}{2}mv_0^2. \tag{8–4}$$

Notice that force and acceleration have been eliminated from this equation. Only position and speed remain. The quantity on the right depends only on the initial position x_0 and the initial speed v_0, which have definite values; it is, therefore, *constant during the motion*. This constant is called the *total mechanical energy E*. We have obtained the *law of conservation of kinetic plus potential energy*:

$$\tfrac{1}{2}mv^2 + U(x) = K + U = E. \tag{8–5}$$

This law can hold, as we have seen, only when the resultant force is conservative.

In many problems we find that although some of the individual forces are not conservative, they are negligibly small. In such instances we can use Eq. 8–5 as a good approximation. For example, air resistance may be present but may have so little effect on the motion that we ignore it. Notice that, instead of starting with Newton's laws, we can simplify problem solving when conservative forces alone are involved by starting with Eq. 8–5. This relation is derived from Newton's laws, of course, but it is one step closer to the solution. We often solve problems without analyzing the forces or writing down Newton's laws by looking instead for something in the motion that is constant; here the mechanical energy E is constant and we can write down Eq. 8–5 as the first step.

The relation between the force and the potential energy can also be written as

$$F(x) = -\frac{d}{dx}U(x). \tag{8-6}$$

Substitution of Eq. 8–6 into Eq. 8–2 gives an identity. Equation 8–6 expresses the physical meaning of potential energy. *The potential energy is a function of position whose negative derivative gives the force.*

The effect of changing the coordinate of the standard point x_0 is to add a constant to $U(x)$. Since it is the derivative of U which enters into dynamical equations as the force, and the derivative of a constant is zero, the choice of the standard point is immaterial. In simpler terms the choice of a reference point for potential energy is immaterial because we are always concerned only with *differences* in potential energy, rather than with any absolute value of potential energy at a given point. Thus in Eqs. 8–4 and 8–5 a change in reference position would merely add the same constant to both sides of the equation. The *change* in potential energy would be unaffected.

With a constant force there is no particular advantage in any one position over any other. Convenience usually determines that the potential energy be taken as zero at some particular point for some particular problem. Thus, for the (assumed) constant force of gravity for small distances above the earth, the potential energy would be taken as zero on the surface of the earth. When the force depends on position, however, it is usually most convenient to choose the potential energy as zero at the point where the force is zero. For an elastic spring the potential energy would be taken as zero when the spring is at its natural unstretched length.

There is a certain arbitrariness in specifying kinetic energy also. In order to determine speed and hence kinetic energy, we must specify a reference frame. The speed of a man sitting on a train is zero if the train is taken as a reference frame, but it is not zero to an observer on the ground who sees the man move by with uniform velocity. The value of the kinetic energy depends on the reference frame used by the observer. The important thing about mechanical energy, however, is not its actual value during a given motion (this depends on the observer) but the fact that this value does not change during the motion for any particular observer when the forces are conservative.

8–4 One-Dimensional Conservative Systems

Let us now consider two examples of conservative forces, the force of gravity and the elastic restoring force of a stretched spring.

For the force of gravity the one-dimensional motion is vertical. We take positive y upward. The force of gravity is then in the negative y direction, or downward. We have $F = -mg$, a constant. The potential energy is obtained from Eq. 8–3;

$$U(y) - U(0) = \int_y^0 F\,dy = \int_y^0 (-mg)\,dy = mgy.$$

The potential energy can be taken as zero where $y = 0$, so that $U(0) = 0$, and

$$U(y) = mgy. \tag{8-7}$$

The gravitational potential energy is then mgy. The relation $F = -dU/dy$ is satisfied, for $-d(mgy)/dy = -mg$. We choose $y = 0$ to be at the surface of the earth for convenience, so that the gravitational potential energy is zero at the earth's surface and increases linearly with altitude y.

The conservation of kinetic plus potential energy, Eq. 8–4, gives us the relation

$$mgy + \tfrac{1}{2}mv^2 = \tfrac{1}{2}mv_0^2.$$

This is equivalent mathematically to the well-known result

$$v^2 = v_0^2 - 2gy.$$

If our particle moves from a height h_1 to a height h_2, we can use Eq. 8–5 to obtain

$$\tfrac{1}{2}mv_1^2 + mgh_1 = \tfrac{1}{2}mv_2^2 + mgh_2.$$

This result is equivalent to that of Example 5, Chapter 7. The total mechanical energy E is constant and is conserved during the motion, even though the kinetic energy and the potential energy vary from point to point.

A second example of a conservative force is that exerted by an elastic spring on a mass attached to it moving on a horizontal frictionless surface. If we take $x_0 = 0$ as the position of the end of the spring when unextended, the force exerted *on* the mass when the spring is stretched a distance x from its unextended length is $F = -kx$. The potential energy is obtained from Eq. 8–3,

$$U(x) - U(0) = \int_x^0 F\,dx = \int_x^0 (-kx)\,dx.$$

If we choose $U(0) = 0$, the potential energy, as well as the force, is zero at the unextended position of the spring, and

$$U(x) = \int_x^0 (-kx)\,dx = \tfrac{1}{2}kx^2.$$

The result is the same whether we stretch or compress the spring, that is, whether x is plus or minus.

The relation $F = -dU/dx$ is satisfied, for $-d(\tfrac{1}{2}kx^2)/dx = -kx$. The elastic potential energy of the spring is then

$$U(x) = \tfrac{1}{2}kx^2. \tag{8-8}$$

The particle of mass m will undergo a motion in which the total energy E is conserved (Fig. 8–3). From Eq. 8–4 we have

$$\tfrac{1}{2}kx^2 + \tfrac{1}{2}mv^2 = \tfrac{1}{2}mv_0^2.$$

Here v_0 is the speed of the particle at $x = 0$. Physically we achieve such a result by stretching the spring with an applied force to some position, x_m,

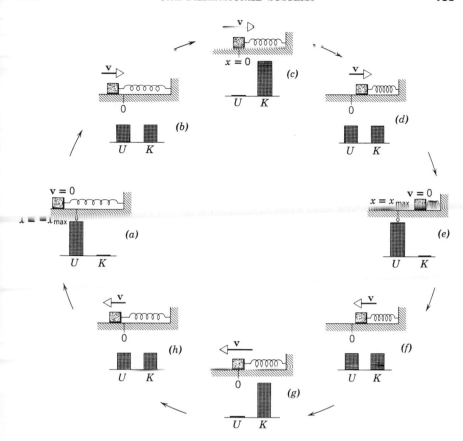

Fig. 8–3 A mass attached to a spring slides back and forth on a frictionless surface. The system is called a harmonic oscillator. The motion of the mass through one cycle is illustrated. Starting at the left (9 o'clock) the mass is in its extreme left position and momentarily at rest: $K = 0$. The spring is extended to its maximum length: $U = U_{\max}$. (K and U are illustrated in the bar graphs below each sketch.) An eighth-cycle later (next drawing) the mass has gained kinetic energy, but the spring is no longer so elongated; K and U have here the same value, $K = U = U_{\max}/2$. At the top the spring is neither elongated nor compressed and the speed is at a maximum: $U = 0$, $K = K_{\max} = U_{\max}$. The cycle continues, with the total energy $E = K + U$ always the same: $E = K_{\max} = U_{\max}$. The harmonic oscillator will be analyzed more closely in Chapter 15.

and then releasing the spring. Notice that at $x = 0$ the energy is all kinetic. At $x = x_m$ (the maximum value of x), v must be zero, so that here the energy is all potential. At $x = x_m$, we have

$$\tfrac{1}{2}kx_m{}^2 = \tfrac{1}{2}mv_0{}^2$$

or

$$x_m = \sqrt{m/k}\, v_0.$$

For motion between x_1 and x_2, Eq. 8–5 gives

$$\tfrac{1}{2}kx_1{}^2 + \tfrac{1}{2}mv_1{}^2 = \tfrac{1}{2}kx_2{}^2 + \tfrac{1}{2}mv_2{}^2.$$

We have seen that *the kinetic energy of a body is the work that a body can do by virtue of its motion.* We found the universal result $K = \frac{1}{2}mv^2$. We cannot give a similar universal formula by which potential energy can be expressed. *The potential energy of a body or a system of bodies is the work that a body or system of bodies can do by virtue of the relative position of its parts.* In each case we must determine how much work the body or system can do in passing from one relative position to another and then take this as the difference in potential energy of the body or system between these two positions.

The potential energy of the spring depends on the relative position of the parts of the spring. Work can be obtained by allowing the spring to return from its extended to its unextended length, during which time it exerts a force through a distance. If a mass is attached to the spring, as in our example, the mass will be accelerated by this force and the potential energy will be converted to kinetic energy. In the gravitational case an object occupies a position with respect to the earth. The potential energy is actually a property of the object and the earth, considered as a system of bodies. It is the relative position of the parts of this system that determines its potential energy. The potential energy is greater when the parts are far apart than when they are close together. The loss of potential energy is equal to the work done in this process. This work is converted into kinetic energy of the bodies. In our example we ignored the kinetic energy acquired by the earth itself as an object fell toward it. In principle, this object exerts a force on the earth and causes it to acquire an acceleration. The resulting speed, however, is extremely small, and in spite of the enormous mass of the earth, its kinetic energy is negligible compared to that acquired by the falling object. This will be proved in a later chapter. In other instances, such as in planetary motion where the masses of the objects in our system may be comparable, we cannot ignore any part of the system. In general, *potential energy* is not assigned to either body separately but *is considered a joint property of the system.*

▶ **Example 1.** What is the change in gravitational potential energy when a 1600-lb elevator moves from street level to the top of the Empire State Building, 1250 ft above street level?

Gravitational potential energy is $U = mgy$. Then

$$\Delta U = U_2 - U_1 = mg(y_2 - y_1).$$

But $\qquad mg = W = 1600 \text{ lb} \qquad \text{and} \qquad y_2 - y_1 = 1250 \text{ ft},$

so that $\qquad \Delta U = 1600 \times 1250$ ft-lb = an increase of 2 million ft-lb.

Example 2. As an example of the simplicity and usefulness of the energy method of solving dynamical problems, consider the problem illustrated in Fig. 8–4. A block of mass m slides down a curved frictionless surface. The force exerted by the surface on the block is always normal to the surface and to the direction of the motion of the block, so that this force does no work. Only the gravitational force does work on the

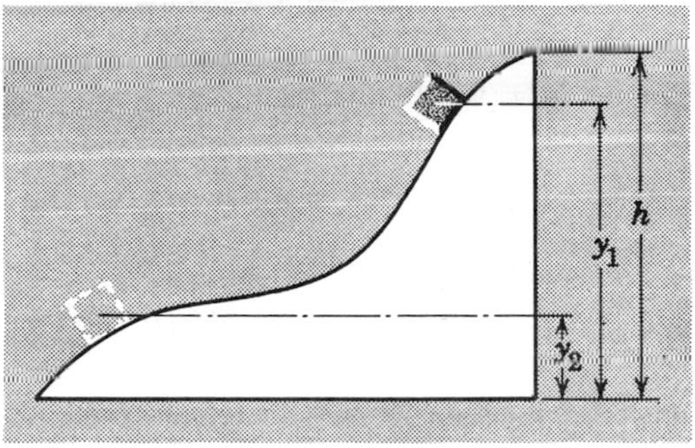

Fig. 8–4 A block sliding down a frictionless curved surface.

block and that force is conservative. The mechanical energy is, therefore, conserved and we can write at once

$$mgy_1 + \tfrac{1}{2}mv_1{}^2 = mgy_2 + \tfrac{1}{2}mv_2{}^2.$$

This gives $\qquad\qquad v_2{}^2 = v_1{}^2 + 2g(y_1 - y_2).$

The speed at the bottom of the curved surface depends only on the initial speed and the change in vertical height but does not depend at all on the shape of the surface. In fact, if the block is initially at rest at $y_1 = h$, and if we set $y_2 = 0$, we obtain

$$v_2 = \sqrt{2gh}.$$

At this point the student should recall the independence of path feature of work done by conservative forces and should be able to justify applying the ideas developed for one-dimensional motion to this two-dimensional example.

In this problem the value of the force depends on the slope of the surface at each point. Hence, the acceleration is not constant but is a function of position. To obtain the speed by starting with Newton's laws we would first have to determine the acceleration at each point and then integrate the acceleration over the path. We avoid all this unnecessary labor by starting at once from the fact that the mechanical energy is constant throughout the motion.

Example 3. The spring in a spring gun has a force constant of 4.0 lb/in. It is kept compressed 2.0 in. from its natural length, and a ball weighing 0.03 lb is put into the barrel against it. Assuming no friction and a horizontal gun barrel, with what speed will the ball leave the gun when released?

The force is conservative so that mechanical energy is conserved in the process. The initial mechanical energy is the elastic potential energy of the spring, $\tfrac{1}{2}kx^2$, and the final mechanical energy is the kinetic energy of the ball, $\tfrac{1}{2}mv^2$. Hence,

$$\tfrac{1}{2}kx^2 = \tfrac{1}{2}mv^2$$

or $\qquad v = \sqrt{\dfrac{k}{m}}\, x = \sqrt{\dfrac{48 \text{ lb/ft}}{(0.03 \text{ lb})/(32 \text{ ft/sec}^2)}}\, (\tfrac{1}{6} \text{ ft}) = 38 \text{ ft/sec.}$ ◀

8–5   The Complete Solution of the Problem for One-Dimensional Forces Depending on Position Only

Equation 8–4 gives the relation between coordinate and speed for one-dimensional motion when the force depends on position only. The force and the acceleration have been eliminated in arriving at this equation. To complete the solution of the dynamical problem we must eliminate the speed and determine position as a function of time.

We can do this in a formal way, as follows. From Eq. 8–5 we have

$$\tfrac{1}{2}mv^2 + U(x) = E.$$

Solving for v, we obtain

$$v = \frac{dx}{dt} = \sqrt{\frac{2}{m}[E - U(x)]}, \tag{8–9}$$

or

$$\frac{dx}{\sqrt{\dfrac{2}{m}[E - U(x)]}} = dt$$

Then the function $x(t)$ may be found by solving for x the equation

$$\int_{x_0}^{x} \frac{dx}{\sqrt{\dfrac{2}{m}[E - U(x)]}} = \int_{t_0}^{t} dt = t - t_0. \tag{8–10}$$

Here the particle is taken to be at x_0 at the time t_0 and E is the constant total energy. In actually applying this equation, the sign of the square root taken corresponds to whether v is positive or negative. When v is positive during some parts of the motion and negative during others, it may be necessary to carry out the integration separately for each part of the motion.

Even when this integral cannot be evaluated or when the resulting equation cannot be solved to give an explicit solution for $x(t)$, the equation of energy conservation gives us useful information about the solution. For example, for a given total energy E, Eq. 8–9 tells us that the particle is restricted to those regions on the x-axis where $E > U(x)$. We cannot have an imaginary speed or a negative kinetic energy physically, so that $E - U(x)$ must be zero or greater. Furthermore, we can obtain a good qualitative description of the types of motion possible by plotting $U(x)$ versus x. This description depends on the fact that the speed is proportional to the square root of the difference between E and U.

For example, consider the potential energy function shown in Fig. 8–5. This could be thought of as an actual profile of a frictionless roller coaster, but in general it can represent the potential energy of a nongravitational system. Since we must have $E > U(x)$ for real motion, the lowest total energy possible is E_0. At this value of the total energy, $E_0 = U$ and the kinetic energy must be zero. The particle must be at rest at the point x_0. At a slightly higher energy E_1 the particle can move between x_1 and x_2 only. As it moves from x_0 its speed decreases on approaching either x_1 or x_2. At x_1 or x_2 the particle stops and reverses its direction. These points x_1 and x_2 are, therefore, called *turning points* of the motion. At a total energy E_2 there are four turning points, and the particle can oscillate in either one of the two potential valleys. At the total energy E_3 there is only one turning point of the motion, at x_3. If the particle is initially moving in the negative x direction, it will stop at x_3 and then move in the positive x direction. It will speed up as U decreases and slow down as U increases. At energies above E_4 there are no turning points, and the particle will move in one direction only. Its speed will change according to the value of the potential at each point.

At a point where $U(x)$ has a minimum value, such as at $x = x_0$, the slope of the curve is zero so that the force is zero, that is, $F = -dU/dx = 0$. A particle at rest at this point will remain at rest. Furthermore, if the particle is displaced slightly in either direction, the force, $F = -dU/dx$, will tend to return it, and it will oscillate about the equilibrium point (where $F = 0$). This equilibrium point is, therefore, called a point of *stable equilibrium*.

At a point where $U(x)$ has a maximum value, such as at $x = x_4$, the slope of the curve is zero so that the force is zero, that is, $F = -dU/dx = 0$. A particle at rest at

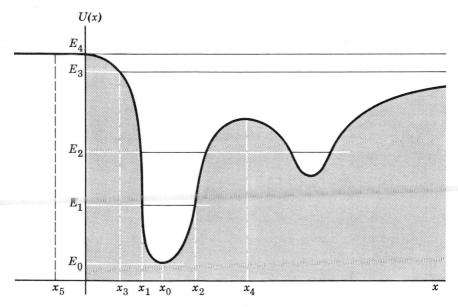

Fig. 8–5   A potential energy curve.

this point will remain at rest. However, if the particle is displaced even the slightest distance from this point, the force, $F = -dU/dx$, will tend to push it farther away from the equilibrium position ($F = 0$). Such an equilibrium point is, therefore, called a point of *unstable equilibrium*.

In an interval in which $U(x)$ is constant, such as near $x = x_5$, the slope of the curve is zero so that the force is zero, that is, $F = -dU/dx = 0$. Such an interval is called one of neutral equilibrium, since a particle can be displaced slightly without experiencing either a repelling or a restoring force.

From this it is clear that if we know the potential energy function for the region of x in which the body moves, we know a great deal about the motion of the body

▶ **Example 4.** The potential energy function for the force between two atoms in a diatomic molecule can be expressed approximately as follows:

$$U(x) = \frac{a}{x^{12}} - \frac{b}{x^6}$$

where a and b are positive constants and x is the distance between atoms.

(a) At what values of x is $U(x)$ equal to zero? At what value of x is $U(x)$ a minimum?

In Fig. 8–6a we show $U(x)$ versus x. The values of x at which $U(x)$ equals zero are found from

$$\frac{a}{x^{12}} - \frac{b}{x^6} = 0.$$

Hence, $x^6 = \frac{a}{b}$ $x = \sqrt[6]{\frac{a}{b}}.$

$U(x)$ also becomes zero as $x \to \infty$ [see figure or put $x = \infty$ into equation for $U(x)$], so that $x = \infty$ is also a solution.

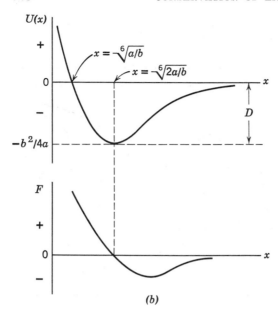

Fig. 8-6 Example 4. (a) The potential energy and (b) the force between two atoms in a diatomic molecule as a function of the distance x between atoms.

The value of x at which $U(x)$ is a minimum is found from

$$\frac{d}{dx} U(x) = 0.$$

That is,

$$\frac{-12a}{x^{13}} + \frac{6b}{x^7} = 0$$

or

$$x^6 = \frac{2a}{b} \qquad x = \sqrt[6]{\frac{2a}{b}}.$$

(b) Determine the force between the atoms.
From Eq. 8–6

$$F(x) = -\frac{d}{dx} U(x),$$

$$F = -\frac{d}{dx}\left(\frac{a}{x^{12}} - \frac{b}{x^6}\right) = \frac{12a}{x^{13}} - \frac{6b}{x^7}.$$

We plot the force as a function of the separation between the atoms in Fig. 8–6b When the force is positive (from $x = 0$ to $x = \sqrt[6]{2a/b}$), the atoms are repelled from one another (force directed toward increasing x). When the force is negative (from $x = \sqrt[6]{2a/b}$ to $x = \infty$), the atoms are attracted to one another (force directed toward decreasing x). At $x = \sqrt[6]{2a/b}$ the force is zero; this is the equilibrium point and is a point of stable equilibrium.

(c) Assume that one of the atoms remains at rest and that the other moves along x. Describe the possible motions.

From the analysis of this section it is clear that the atom oscillates about the equilibrium separation at $x = \sqrt[6]{2a/b}$, much as a particle sliding up and down the frictionless hills of the potential valley.

(d) The energy needed to break up the molecule into separate atoms is called the dissociation energy. What is the dissociation energy of the molecule?

If one atom has enough kinetic energy to get over the potential hill, it will no longer be bound to the other atom. Hence, the dissociation energy D equals the change in potential energy from the minimum value at $x = \sqrt[6]{2a/b}$ to the value at $x = \infty$. This is simply

$$U(x = \infty) - U\left(x = \sqrt[6]{\frac{2a}{b}}\right) = 0 - \left(\frac{a}{4a^2/b^2} - \frac{b}{2a/b}\right) = \frac{b^2}{4a}.$$

If the kinetic energy at the equilibrium position is equal to or greater than this value, the molecule will dissociate.   ◀

8–6   Two- and Three-Dimensional Conservative Systems

The previous discussion of potential energy and of energy conservation was limited to one-dimensional systems in which the force was directed along the line of motion. The discussion is easily generalized to three-dimensional motion.

If the work done by the force **F** depends only on the end points of the motion and is independent of the path taken between these points, the force is conservative. We define the potential energy U by analogy with the one-dimensional system and find that it is a function of three space coordinates, that is, $U = U(x,y,z)$. Again we find that mechanical energy is conserved; that is,

$$K + U = E, \quad \text{a constant,}$$

or

$$\tfrac{1}{2}mv_x^2 + \tfrac{1}{2}mv_y^2 + \tfrac{1}{2}mv_z^2 + U(x,y,z) = E. \tag{8–11}$$

Equation 8–11 enables us to determine the speed of the particle as a function of position.

▶ **Example 5.** Consider the simple pendulum, Section 7–3, Fig. 7–8a. The motion of the system is in the x y plane, that is, it is a two-dimensional motion. The tension in the cord is always at right angles to the motion of the suspended particle, so that this force does no work on the particle. If the pendulum is displaced through some angle and is then released, only the gravitational force of attraction exerted on the particle by the earth does work on it. Since this force is conservative, we can use the equation of energy conservation in two dimensions,

$$\tfrac{1}{2}mv_x^2 + \tfrac{1}{2}mv_y^2 + U(x,y) = E.$$

But $v_x^2 + v_y^2$ equals v^2, where v is the speed of the particle along the arc, and U equals mgy, where y is taken as zero at the lowest point of the arc ($\phi = 0°$). Then,

$$\tfrac{1}{2}mv^2 + mgy = E.$$

The particle is pulled through an angle ϕ_0 before being released. The potential energy there is mgh, corresponding to a height $y = h$ above the reference point. At the release point ($\phi = \phi_0$) the speed and the kinetic energy are zero so that the potential energy equals the total mechanical energy at that point.

Hence,

$$E = mgh$$

and

$$\tfrac{1}{2}mv^2 + mgy = mgh,$$

or

$$\tfrac{1}{2}mv^2 = mg(h - y).$$

The maximum speed occurs at $y = 0$, where $v = \sqrt{2gh}$.
The minimum speed occurs at $y = h$, where $v = 0$.
At $y = 0$ the energy is entirely kinetic, the potential energy being zero.
At $y = h$ the energy is entirely potential, the kinetic energy being zero.
At intermediate positions the energy is partly kinetic and partly potential.

Notice that $U \leq E$ at all points of the motion; the pendulum cannot rise higher than $y = h$, its initial release point. ◀

8–7 Nonconservative Forces

Up until now we have considered only conservative systems. Starting from the work-energy theorem

$$W \text{ (of resultant force)} = \Delta K,$$

we found that when the resultant force is conservative the work it does can be expressed as a decrease in potential energy, or

$$-\Delta U = \Delta K.$$

This led to the idea of the conservation of kinetic plus potential energy. That is, from

$$\Delta K + \Delta U = 0,$$

we find

$$\Delta(K + U) = 0,$$

or

$$K + U = \text{constant}.$$

We called this constant the total mechanical energy E of the system.

Suppose that among the forces acting on a system some are *not* conservative. The work done by the resultant force is the sum of the work of the nonconservative forces and the work of the conservative forces. Let us write this as

$$W_{\text{conserv}} + W_{\text{nonconserv}} = \Delta K.$$

But the work done by the conservative forces can be expressed as a decrease in potential energy, or

$$W_{\text{conserv}} = -\Delta U,$$

so that

$$W_{\text{nonconserv}} = \Delta K + \Delta U,$$

or

$$W_{\text{nonconserv}} = \Delta(K + U) = \Delta E.$$

That is, the total mechanical energy of the system E is *not* constant but changes by the amount of work done on the system by the nonconservative forces. *Only when there are no nonconservative forces, or when we can neglect the work they do, can we assume conservation of mechanical energy.*

Consider the case in which friction is the only nonconservative force. Friction is a dissipative force. It tends to diminish the total mechanical energy of the system. Dissipative forces do negative work on a body. The frictional force, for example, is always directed opposite to the displacement.

Then, if W_f represents the work done *by* friction *on* a body,

$$W_{\text{nonconserv}} = W_f = \Delta(K + U) = \Delta E$$

or $$W_f = (K + U) - (K_0 + U_0). \tag{8–12}$$

Since W_f is negative, the final mechanical energy $K + U$ is less than the initial mechanical energy $K_0 + U_0$.

What happened to the "lost" mechanical energy? In the case of friction it is transformed into heat. Heat is developed when surfaces are rubbed together, for example. The heat energy developed is exactly equal to the mechanical energy dissipated. We shall have much more to say about heat energy in later chapters.

Just as the work done by a conservative force on an object is the negative of the potential energy gain, so the work done by a frictional force *on* an object is the negative of the heat energy gained. In other words, the heat energy produced is equal to the work done *by* the object. Then we can replace W_f in Eq. 8–12 by a term on the right-hand side of the equation representing the heat energy produced, say Q, or

$$0 = \Delta E + Q.$$

This asserts that there is no change in the sum of the mechanical and heat energy of the system when only conservative and frictional forces act on the system. Writing this equation as

$$Q = -\Delta E,$$

we see that the loss of mechanical energy equals the gain in heat energy.

▶ **Example 6.** A 10-lb block is thrust up a 30° inclined plane with an initial speed of 16 ft/sec. It is found to travel 5.0 ft along the plane, stop, and slide back to the bottom. Compute the force of friction f acting on the block and find the speed v of the block when it returns to the bottom of the inclined plane.

Consider first the *upward* motion. At the top, where this motion ends,

$$K + U = 0 + (10 \text{ lb})(5.0 \text{ ft})(\sin 30°) = 25 \text{ ft-lb}.$$

At the bottom, where this motion begins,

$$K_0 + U_0 = \left(\frac{1}{2}\right)\left(\frac{10 \text{ lb}}{32 \text{ ft/sec}^2}\right)(16 \text{ ft/sec})^2 + 0 = 40 \text{ ft-lb},$$

$$W_f = -fs = -f(5.0 \text{ ft}).$$

But $$(K + U) - (K_0 + U_0) = W_f,$$

so that $$25 \text{ ft-lb} - 40 \text{ ft-lb} = -f(5.0 \text{ ft})$$

and $$f = 3.0 \text{ lb}.$$

Now consider the *downward* motion. The block returns to the bottom of the inclined plane with a speed v ft/sec. Then, at the bottom, where this motion ends,

$$K + U = \left(\frac{1}{2}\right)\left(\frac{10}{32}\right)v^2 + 0.$$

At the top, where this motion begins,

$$K_0 + U_0 = 0 + (10 \text{ lb})(5.0 \text{ ft})(\sin 30°) = 25 \text{ ft-lb},$$

$$W_f = -(3.0 \text{ lb})(5.0 \text{ ft}) = -15 \text{ ft-lb}.$$

But

$$(K + U) - (K_0 + U_0) = W_f,$$

so that

$$\left(\frac{1}{2}\right)\left(\frac{10}{32}\right) v^2 \text{ ft-lb} - 25 \text{ ft-lb} = -15 \text{ ft-lb},$$

$$v = 8.0 \text{ ft/sec.} \qquad \blacktriangleleft$$

8–8   The Conservation of Energy

We have seen that when nonconservative forces act the work-energy theorem can be written as

$$W_{\text{nonconserv}} = \Delta K + \Delta U.$$

The work done by the conservative forces appears here as a change in potential energy. Actually, many conservative forces have been found in physics, so there are many different kinds of potential energy, such as gravitational, elastic, electrical, and nuclear potential energies. Therefore we should write this equation as

$$W_{\text{nonconserv}} = \Delta K + \Sigma \Delta U$$

to allow for the change in each potential energy function associated with each of the conservative forces.

There are also many nonconservative forces in physics. We have seen that when friction is the *only* nonconservative force, $W_{\text{nonconserv}} = W_f$ and $W_f = -Q$ where Q is the heat produced in the interaction. Hence the work done by friction corresponds to a form of energy called heat energy, and here we find it possible to write the work-energy theorem as

$$0 = \Delta K + \Sigma \Delta U + Q.$$

In general, if there are other nonconservative forces besides friction and W' represents the work done by these forces, the work-energy theorem becomes

$$W' = \Delta K + \Sigma \Delta U + Q.$$

Now whatever W' is, it has always been possible to find a new form of energy which corresponds to this work. We can then represent W' by another change of energy term on the right-hand side of the equation, with the result that we can always write the work-energy theorem as

$$0 = \Delta K + \Sigma \Delta U + Q + \text{(change in other forms of energy)}.$$

In other words, the total energy—kinetic plus potential plus heat plus all other forms—does not change. *Energy may be transformed from one kind to another but it cannot be created or destroyed; the total energy is constant.*

This statement is a generalization from our experience, so far not contradicted by observation of nature. It is called the *principle of the conservation of energy*. Often in the history of physics this principle seemed to fail. But its apparent failure stimulated the search for the reasons. Experimentalists searched for physical phenomena besides motion that accompany the forces of interaction between bodies. Such phenomena have always been found. With work done against friction, heat is produced; in other interactions energy in the form of sound, light, electricity, etc., may be produced. Hence the concept of energy was generalized to include forms other than kinetic and potential energy of directly observable bodies. This procedure, which relates the mechanics of bodies observed to be in motion to phenomena which are not mechanical or in which motion is not directly detected, has linked mechanics to all other areas of physics. The energy concept now permeates all of physical science and has become one of the unifying ideas of physics.*

In subsequent chapters we shall study various transformations of energy— from mechanical to heat, mechanical to electrical, nuclear to heat, etc. It is during such transformations that we measure the energy changes in terms of work, for it is during these transformations that forces arise and do work.

Although the principle of the conservation of kinetic plus potential energy is often useful, we see that it is a restricted case of the more general principle of the conservation of energy. Kinetic and potential energy is conserved only when conservative forces act. Total energy is *always* conserved.

8–9 Mass and Energy

One of the great conservation laws of science has been the law of conservation of matter. From a philosophical point of view an early statement of this general principle was given by the Roman poet Lucretius, a contemporary of Julius Caesar, in his celebrated work *De Rerum Natura*. Lucretius wrote "Things cannot be born from nothing, cannot when begotten be brought back to nothing." It was a long time before this concept was established as a firm scientific principle. The principal experimental contribution was made by Antoine Laurent Lavoisier (1743–1794), regarded by many as the father of modern chemistry. He wrote in 1789 "We must lay it down as an incontestable axiom, that in all the operations of art and nature, nothing is created; an equal quantity of matter exists both before and after the experiment . . . and nothing takes place beyond changes and modifications in the combinations of these elements."

This principle, subsequently called the conservation of mass, proved extremely fruitful in chemistry and physics. Serious doubts as to the general validity of this principle were raised by Albert Einstein in his papers introducing the theory of relativity. Subsequent experiments on fast-moving electrons and on nuclear matter confirmed his conclusions.

Einstein's findings suggested that if physical laws were to be retained in the classical form the mass of a particle had to be redefined as

$$m = \frac{m_0}{\sqrt{1 - v^2/c^2}} \tag{8–13}$$

---

* See for example, "Concept of Energy in Mechanics," by R. B. Lindsay in *The Scientific Monthly*, October 1957.

Here m_0 is the mass of the particle when at rest with respect to the observer, called the *rest mass*; m is the mass of the particle measured as it moves at a speed v relative to the observer; and c is the speed of light having a constant value of approximately 3×10^8 meters/sec. Experimental checks of this equation can be made, for example, by deflecting high-speed electrons in magnetic fields and measuring the radii of curvature of their path. The paths are circular and the magnetic force a centripetal one ($F = mv^2/r$, F and v being known). At ordinary speeds the difference between m and m_0 is too small to be detectable. Electrons, however, can be emitted from radioactive nuclei with speeds greater than nine-tenths that of light. In such cases the results (Fig. 8–7) confirm Eq. 8–13.

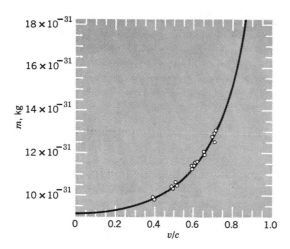

Fig. 8–7 The way an electron's mass increases as its speed relative to the observer increases. The solid line is a plot of $m = m_0(1 - v^2/c^2)^{-\frac{1}{2}}$, and the circles are adapted from experimental values obtained by Bucherer and Neumann in 1914 (*Annalen der Physik*, vol. 45, p. 529). The curve tends toward infinity as $v \to c$.

It is convenient to let the ratio v/c be represented by β. Then Eq. 8–13 becomes

$$m = m_0(1 - \beta^2)^{-\frac{1}{2}}.$$

To find the kinetic energy of a body, we compute the work done by the resultant force in setting the body in motion. In Section 7–5 we obtained

$$K = \int_0^v \mathbf{F} \cdot d\mathbf{s} = \frac{1}{2} m_0 v^2$$

for kinetic energy, when we assumed a constant mass m_0. Suppose now instead we take into account the variation of mass with speed and use $m = m_0(1 - \beta^2)^{-\frac{1}{2}}$ in our previous equation. We find (Problem 24, Chapter 9) that the kinetic energy is no longer given by $\frac{1}{2} m_0 v^2$ but instead is

$$K = mc^2 - m_0 c^2 = (m - m_0)c^2 = \Delta mc^2. \tag{8–14}$$

The kinetic energy of a particle is, therefore, the product of c^2 and the increase in mass Δm resulting from the motion.

Now, at small speeds we expect the relativistic result to agree with the classical result. By the binomial theorem we can expand $(1 - \beta^2)^{-\frac{1}{2}}$ as

$$(1 - \beta^2)^{-\frac{1}{2}} = 1 + \tfrac{1}{2}\beta^2 + \tfrac{3}{8}\beta^4 + \tfrac{5}{16}\beta^6 + \cdots.$$

At small speeds $\beta = v/c \ll 1$ so that all terms beyond β^2 are negligible. Then

$$K = (m - m_0)c^2 = m_0 c^2[(1 - \beta^2)^{-\frac{1}{2}} - 1]$$

$$= m_0 c^2(1 + \tfrac{1}{2}\beta^2 + \cdots - 1) \cong \tfrac{1}{2}m_0 c^2 \beta^2 = \tfrac{1}{2}m_0 v^2,$$

which is the classical result. Notice also that when K equals zero, $m = m_0$ as expected.

The basic idea that energy is equivalent to mass can be extended to include energies other than kinetic. For example, when we compress a spring and give it elastic potential energy U, its mass increases from m_0 to $m_0 + U/c^2$. When we add heat in amount Q to an object, its mass increases by an amount Δm, where Δm is Q/c^2. We arrive at a principle of *equivalence of mass and energy:* For every unit of energy E of *any* kind supplied to a material object, the mass of the object increases by an amount

$$\Delta m = E/c^2.$$

This is the famous Einstein formula

$$E = \Delta m c^2. \tag{8–15}$$

In fact, since mass itself is just one form of energy, we can now assert that a body at rest has an energy $m_0 c^2$ by virtue of its rest mass. This is called its rest energy. If we now consider a closed system, the principle of the conservation of energy, as generalized by Einstein, becomes

$$\Sigma\,(m_0 c^2 + \mathcal{E}) = \text{constant}$$

or

$$\Delta(\Sigma\, m_0 c^2 + \Sigma\, \mathcal{E}) = 0$$

where $\Sigma\, m_0 c^2$ is the total rest energy and $\Sigma\, \mathcal{E}$ is the total energy of *all other* kinds. As Einstein wrote, "Pre-relativity physics contains two conservation laws of fundamental importance, namely the law of conservation of energy and the law of conservation of mass; these two appear there as completely independent of each other. Through relativity theory they melt together into *one* principle."

Because the factor c^2 is so large, we would not expect to be able to detect changes in mass in ordinary mechanical experiments. A change in mass of 1 gm would require an energy of 9×10^{13} joules. But when the mass of a particle is quite small to begin with and high energies can be imparted to it, the relative change in mass may be noticeable. This is true in nuclear phenomena, and it is in this realm that classical mechanics breaks down and relativistic mechanics receives its most striking verification.

The most beautiful example of exchange of energy between mass and other forms is given by the phenomenon of pair annihilation or pair production. In this phenomenon an electron and a positron, elementary material particles differing only in the sign of their electric charge, can combine and literally disappear. In their place we find high-energy radiation, called γ-radiation, whose radiant energy is exactly equal to the rest mass energies of the disappearing particles. The process is reversible, so that a materialization of mass from radiant energy can occur when a high enough energy γ-ray, under proper conditions, disappears; in its place appears a positron-electron pair whose total energy (rest mass + kinetic) is equal to the radiant energy lost.

▶ **Example 7.** Consider a quantitative example. On the atomic mass scale the unit of mass is 1.66×10^{-27} kg approximately. On this scale the mass of the proton (the nucleus of a hydrogen atom) is 1.00757 and the mass of the neutron (a neutral particle, one of the constituents of all nuclei except hydrogen) is 1.00893. A deuteron (the nucleus of heavy hydrogen) is known to consist of a neutron and a proton; the mass of the deuteron is found to be 2.01416. The mass of the deuteron is *less than* the combined masses of neutron and proton by 0.00234 atomic mass units. The discrepancy is equivalent in energy to

$$E = \Delta mc^2 = (0.00234 \times 1.66 \times 10^{-27} \text{ kg})(3.00 \times 10^8 \text{ meters/sec})^2$$

$$= 3.50 \times 10^{-13} \text{ joules} = 2.19 \times 10^6 \text{ ev.}$$

When a neutron and a proton combine to form a deuteron, this exact amount of energy is given off in the form of γ-radiation. Similarly, it is found that the same amount of energy must be *added* to the deuteron to break it up into a proton and a neutron. This energy is therefore called the *binding energy* of the deuteron.   ◀

QUESTIONS

1. Mountain roads rarely go straight up the slope but wind up gradually. Explain why.

2. Is any work being done on a car moving with constant speed along a straight level road?

3. Explain how the range of your car's headlights limits the safe driving speed at night.

4. What happens to the potential energy an elevator loses in coming down from the top of a building to a stop at the ground floor?

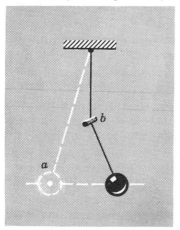

Fig. 8–8

5. When the bob of a simple pendulum is released at a, a nail catches the string at b (Fig. 8–8). It is observed that no matter what the position of the nail the bob always rises to the level of a. Explain.

6. Give physical examples of unstable equilibrium. Of neutral equilibrium. Of stable equilibrium.

7. Give specific examples of the conversion of mechanical energy to other forms of energy.

8. Explain, using work and energy ideas, how a child pumps a swing up to large amplitudes from a rest position.

9. An object is dropped and observed to bounce to one and one-half times its original height. What conclusion can you draw from this observation?

10. A spring is kept compressed by tying its ends together tightly. It is then placed in acid and dissolves. What happened to its stored potential energy?

PROBLEMS

1. The string in Fig. 8 9 is 4 ft long. When the ball is released, it will swing down the dotted arc. How fast will it be going when it reaches the lowest point in its swing?

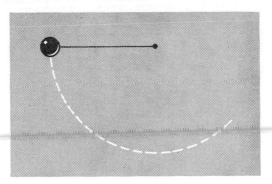

Fig. 8–9

2. Show that for the same initial speed v_0, the speed v of a projectile will be the same at all points at the same elevation, regardless of the angle of projection.

3. (a) A light rigid rod of length l has a mass m attached to its end, forming a simple pendulum. It is inverted and then released. What is its speed v at the lowest point and what is the tension T in the suspension at that instant? (b) The same pendulum is next put in a horizontal position and released from rest. At what angle from the vertical will the tension in the suspension equal the weight in magnitude?

4. Prove the following theorem taken from Huygens' *Horologium Oscillatorium:* "If a simple pendulum swings with its greatest lateral oscillation, that is, if it descends through the whole quadrant of a circle, when it comes to the lowest point of the circumference it stretches the string with three times as great a force as it would if it were simply suspended by it."

5. Two identical cylindrical vessels with their bases at the same level contain water to heights h_1 and h_2 respectively. The area of either base is A. Find the work done by gravity in equalizing the levels when the two vessels are connected.

6. An object is attached to a vertical spring and slowly lowered to its equilibrium position. This stretches the spring by an amount d. If the same object is attached to the same vertical spring but permitted to fall instead, through what distance does it stretch the spring?

7. A small block of mass m slides along the frictionless loop-the-loop track shown in Fig. 8–10. (a) If it starts from rest at P, what is the resultant force acting on it at Q?

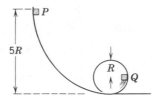

Fig. 8–10

(b) At what height above the bottom of the loop should the block be released so that the force it exerts against the track at the top of the loop is equal to its weight?

8. A body of mass m on a frictionless plane inclined at an angle θ with the horizontal is attached to one end of a spring of force constant k, the other end being fixed (Fig. 8–11).

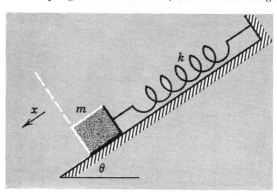

Fig. 8–11

(a) Find the mechanical energy when the body is pulled a distance x_1 from the unstretched position of the spring. (b) If the initial mechanical energy is E_1, show that the speed of the body at any position x from the unstretched position of the spring is obtained from

$$\tfrac{1}{2}mv^2 = E_1 + mgx\sin\theta - \tfrac{1}{2}kx^2.$$

9. A body moving along the x-axis is subject to a force repelling it from the origin, given by $F = kx$. (a) Find the potential energy function U for the motion and write down the conservation of energy condition. (b) Describe the motion of the system and show that this is the kind of motion we would expect near a point of unstable equilibrium.

10. If the attractive force between a particle of mass m_1 and one of mass m_2 is given by

$$F = k\,\frac{m_1 m_2}{x^2}$$

where k is a positive constant and x is the distance between the particles, find (a) the potential energy function and (b) the work required to increase the separation of the masses from $x = x_1$ to $x = x_1 + d$.

11. The force of attraction between the positively charged nucleus and the negatively charged electron in the hydrogen atom is given by

$$F = k\,\frac{e^2}{r^2}$$

where e is the charge of the electron, k is a constant, and r is the separation between electron and nucleus. Assume that the nucleus is fixed. The electron, initially moving in a circle of radius R_1 about the nucleus, jumps suddenly into a circular orbit of smaller radius R_2. (a) Calculate the change in kinetic energy of the electron, using Newton's second law. (b) Using the relation between force and potential energy, calculate the decrease in potential energy of the atom. (c) Show by how much the total energy of the atom has decreased in this process. (This energy is given off in the form of radiation.)

12. An α-particle (helium atom nucleus) in a large nucleus is bound by a potential like that shown in Fig. 8–12. (a) Construct a

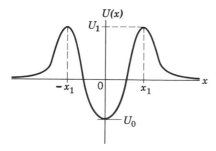

Fig. 8–12

function of x which has this general shape, with a minimum value U_0 at $x = 0$ and a maximum value U_1 at $x = x_1$ and $x = -x_1$. (b) Determine the force between the α particle and the nucleus as a function of x. (c) Describe the possible motions.

13. Show that when friction is present in an otherwise conservative mechanical system, the rate at which mechanical energy is dissipated equals the frictional force times the speed at that instant, or

$$\frac{d}{dt}(K + U) = -fv.$$

14. A body of mass m starts from rest down a plane of length l inclined at an angle θ with the horizontal. (a) Take the coefficient of friction to be μ and find the body's speed at the bottom. (b) How far, d, will it slide horizontally on a similar surface after reaching the bottom of the incline. Solve by using energy methods and solve again using Newton's laws directly.

15. A 1.0-kg block collides with a horizontal weightless spring of force constant 2.0 nt/meters (Fig. 8–13). The block compresses the spring 4.0 meters from the rest position.

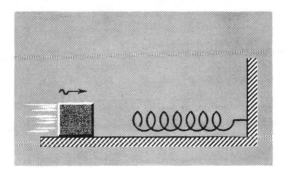

Fig. 8–13

Assuming that the coefficient of kinetic friction between block and horizontal surface is 0.25, what was the speed of the block at the instant of collision?

16. A 40-lb body is pushed up a frictionless 30° inclined plane 10 ft long by a horizontal force F. (a) If the speed at the bottom is 2 ft/sec and at the top is 10 ft/sec, how much work is done by F? (b) Suppose the plane is not frictionless and that $\mu_k = 0.15$. What work will this same force do? How far up the plane does the body go?

17. A chain is held on a frictionless table with one-fifth of its length hanging over the edge. If the chain has a length l and a mass m, how much work is required to pull the hanging part back on the table?

18. An escalator joins one floor with another one 25 ft above. The escalator is 40 ft long and moves along its length at 2.0 ft/sec. (a) What power must its motor deliver if it is required to carry a maximum of 100 persons per minute, of average mass 5 slugs? (b) A 160-lb man walks up the escalator in 10 sec. How much work does the motor do on him? (c) If this man turned around at the middle and walked down the escalator so as to stay at the same level in space, would the motor do work on him? If so, what power does it deliver for this purpose? (d) Is there any (other?) way the man could walk along the escalator without consuming power from the motor?

19. An electron (rest mass 9.1×10^{-31} kg) is moving with a speed $0.99c$. (a) What is its total energy? (b) Find the ratio of the Newtonian kinetic energy to the relativistic kinetic energy in this case.

20. What is the speed of an electron with a kinetic energy of (a) 100,000 ev, (b) 1,000,000 ev?

21. (a) The rest mass of a body is 0.01 kg. What is its mass when it moves at a speed of 3.0×10^7 meters/sec relative to the observer? At 2.7×10^8 meters/sec? (b) Compare

the classical and relativistic kinetic energies for these cases. (c) What if the observer, or measuring apparatus, is riding on the body?

22. The United States consumed 563×10^{12} watt-hr of electrical energy in 1956, according to the *Britannica Yearbook*. How many kilograms of matter would have to be completely destroyed to yield this energy?

23. It is believed that the sun obtains its energy by a fusion process in which four hydrogen atoms are transformed into a helium atom with the emission of energy in various forms of radiation. If a hydrogen atom has a rest mass of 1.0081 atomic mass units (see Example 7) and a helium atom has a rest mass of 4.0039 atomic mass units, calculate the energy released in each fusion process.

24. A vacuum diode consists of a cylindrical anode enclosing a cylindrical cathode. An electron with a potential energy relative to the anode of 4.8×10^{-16} joule leaves the surface of the cathode with zero initial speed. Assume that the electron does not collide with any air molecules and that the gravitational force is negligible. (a) What kinetic energy would the electron have when it strikes the anode? (b) Take 9.1×10^{-31} kg as the mass of the electron and find its final speed. (c) Were you justified in using classical relations for kinetic energy and mass rather than the relativistic ones?

Conservation
of Linear Momentum

9-1 Center of Mass

So far we have treated objects as though they were particles, having mass
but no size. In translational motion each point on a body experiences the
same displacement as any other point as time goes on, so that the motion of
one particle represents the motion of the whole body.   But even when a
body in translational motion rotates or vibrates, we can represent its translational motion by the motion of a point called the *center of mass* of the body.
Likewise, when we deal with a system containing many particles, we can
describe the translational motion of the entire system by the motion of the
center of mass of the system.   In this section we define the center of mass
and show how to calculate its position.   In the next section we discuss its
motion.

Consider first the simple case of a system of two particles m_1 and m_2 at
distances x_1 and x_2 respectively, from some origin O. We locate a point C,
called the center of mass of the system, a distance $\bar{x}$ from the origin O, where
$\bar{x}$ is defined by

$$\bar{x} = \frac{m_1 x_1 + m_2 x_2}{m_1 + m_2}. \tag{9-1}$$

This point (Fig. 9-1) has the property that the product of the total mass of
the system times the distance of this point from the origin is equal to the
sum of the products of the mass of each particle by its distance from the
origin; that is,

$$(m_1 + m_2)\bar{x} = m_1 x_1 + m_2 x_2. \tag{9-1a}$$

In Eq. 9-1 $\bar{x}$ can be regarded as the *mass-weighted mean* of x_1 and x_2.

153

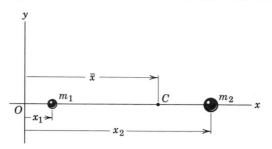

Fig. 9–1 The center of mass of the two masses m_1 and m_2 lies on the line joining m_1 and m_2 at C, a distance $\bar{x}$ from the origin.

An analogy might help to fix this idea. Suppose, for example, that we are given two boxes of nails. In one box we have n_1 nails all having the same length l_1; in the other box we have n_2 nails all having the same length l_2. We are asked to get the mean length of the nails. If $n_1 = n_2$, the mean length is simply $(l_1 + l_2)/2$. But if $n_1 \neq n_2$, we must allow for the fact that there are more nails of one length than another by a "weighting" factor for each length. For l_1 this factor is $n_1/(n_1 + n_2)$ and for l_2 this factor is $n_2/(n_1 + n_2)$, the fraction of the total number of nails in each box. Then the weighted-mean length is

$$\bar{l} = \left(\frac{n_1}{n_1 + n_2}\right) l_1 + \left(\frac{n_2}{n_1 + n_2}\right) l_2$$

or

$$\bar{l} = \frac{n_1 l_1 + n_2 l_2}{n_1 + n_2}.$$

The center of mass, defined in Eq. 9–1, is then a weighted-mean displacement where the "weighting" factor for each particle is the fraction of the total mass that each particle has.

If we have n particles, $m_1, m_2, \cdots, m_n$, *along a straight line*, by definition the center of mass of these particles relative to some origin is

$$\bar{x} = \frac{m_1 x_1 + m_2 x_2 + \cdots + m_n x_n}{m_1 + m_2 + \cdots + m_n} = \frac{\Sigma\, m_i x_i}{\Sigma\, m_i}, \tag{9–2}$$

where $x_1, x_2, \cdots, x_n$ are the distances of the masses from the origin from which $\bar{x}$ is measured. The symbol Σ represents a summation operation, in this case over all n particles. The sum

$$\Sigma\, m_i = M$$

is the total mass of the system. We can then rewrite Eq. 9–2 in the form

$$M\bar{x} = \Sigma\, m_i x_i. \tag{9–2a}$$

Suppose now that we have three particles *not in a straight line;* they will lie in a plane, as in Fig. 9–2. The center of mass C is defined and located by the coordinates $\bar{x}$ and $\bar{y}$ where

$$\bar{x} = \frac{m_1 x_1 + m_2 x_2 + m_3 x_3}{m_1 + m_2 + m_3},$$

$$\bar{y} = \frac{m_1 y_1 + m_2 y_2 + m_3 y_3}{m_1 + m_2 + m_3},$$

(9–3)

in which x_1, y_1 are the coordinates of the particle of mass m_1; x_2, y_2 are those of m_2; and x_3, y_3 are those of m_3. The coordinates $\bar{x}$, $\bar{y}$ of the center of mass are measured from the same arbitrary origin.

For a large number of particles lying in a plane, the center of mass is at $\bar{x}$, $\bar{y}$ where

$$\bar{x} = \frac{\Sigma\, m_i x_i}{\Sigma\, m_i} \qquad \bar{y} = \frac{\Sigma\, m_i y_i}{\Sigma\, m_i}.$$

(9–4)

For a large number of particles not necessarily confined to a plane but *distributed in space,* the center of mass is at $\bar{x}$, $\bar{y}$, $\bar{z}$, where

$$\bar{x} = \frac{\Sigma\, m_i x_i}{\Sigma\, m_i} \qquad \bar{y} = \frac{\Sigma\, m_i y_i}{\Sigma\, m_i} \qquad \bar{z} = \frac{\Sigma\, m_i z_i}{\Sigma\, m_i}.$$

(9–5)

Equation 9–5 is the most general case for a collection of particles. Equations 9–1 through 9–4 are special instances of this one. The location of the center of mass is independent of the coordinate system used to locate it (see Problem 1). *The center of mass of a system of particles depends only on the masses of the particles and the positions of the particles relative to one another.*

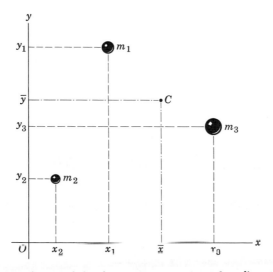

Fig. 9–2 The center of mass of the three masses m_1, m_2, and m_3 lies at point C, with coordinates $\bar{x}$, $\bar{y}$. C lies in the same plane as that of the triangle formed by the three masses.

A rigid body, such as a meter stick, can be thought of as a system of closely packed particles. Hence, it also has a center of mass. The number of particles (atoms, for example) in the body is so large and their spacing so small, however, that we can treat the body as though it has a continuous distribution of mass. To obtain the expression for the center of mass of a continuous body, let us begin by subdividing the body into n small elements of mass Δm_i located approximately at the points x_i, y_i, z_i. The coordinates of the center of mass are then given approximately, by

$$x = \frac{\Sigma \, \Delta m_i x_i}{\Sigma \, \Delta m_i} \qquad \bar{y} = \frac{\Sigma \, \Delta m_i y_i}{\Sigma \, \Delta m_i} \qquad \bar{z} = \frac{\Sigma \, \Delta m_i z_i}{\Sigma \, \Delta m_i}.$$

Now let the elements of mass be further subdivided so that the number of elements n tends to infinity. The points x_i, y_i, z_i will locate the mass elements more precisely as n is increased and will locate them exactly as n becomes infinite. The continuous body is then subdivided into an infinite number of infinitesimal mass elements. The coordinates of the center of mass can now be given precisely as

$$\bar{x} = \lim_{\Delta m_i \to 0} \frac{\Sigma \, \Delta m_i x_i}{\Sigma \, \Delta m_i} = \frac{\int x \, dm}{\int dm} = \frac{1}{M} \int x \, dm,$$

$$\bar{y} = \lim_{\Delta m_i \to 0} \frac{\Sigma \, \Delta m_i y_i}{\Sigma \, \Delta m_i} = \frac{\int y \, dm}{\int dm} = \frac{1}{M} \int y \, dm, \qquad (9\text{--}6)$$

$$\bar{z} = \lim_{\Delta m_i \to 0} \frac{\Sigma \, \Delta m_i z_i}{\Sigma \, \Delta m_i} = \cdot \frac{\int z \, dm}{\int dm} = \frac{1}{M} \int z \, dm.$$

In these expressions dm is the differential element of mass at the point x, y, z, and $\int dm$ equals M, where M is the total mass of the object. For a continuous body the summation of Eq. 9–5 is replaced by the integration of Eq. 9–6.

If the vector $\mathbf{r}$ is the distance from a suitable origin of an element of mass dm of a continuous body, the center of mass $\bar{\mathbf{r}}$ is at

$$\bar{\mathbf{r}} = \frac{\int \mathbf{r} \, dm}{\int dm}. \qquad (9\text{--}6a)$$

The components of $\bar{r}$ along the x-y-z-axes having the same origin are $\bar{x}$, $\bar{y}$, and $\bar{z}$ of Eq. 9–6. Hence, Eq. 9–6a is the single vector equation which is exactly equivalent to the three scalar equations of Eq. 9–6. Notice the economy of expression permitted by use of vectors.

Very often we deal with homogeneous objects having a point, a line, or a plane of symmetry. Then the center of mass will lie at the point, on the line, or in the plane of symmetry. For example, the center of mass of a homogeneous sphere (which has a point of symmetry) will be at the center of the sphere, the center of mass of a cone (which has a line of symmetry) will be on the axis of the cone, etc.

▶ **Example 1.** Locate the center of mass of three particles of mass $m_1 = 1.0$ kg, $m_2 = 2.0$ kg, and $m_3 = 3.0$ kg at the corners of an equilateral triangle 1.0 meter on a side.

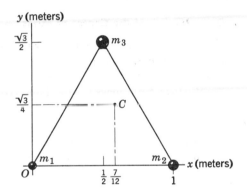

Fig. 9–3 Example 1. Finding the center of mass C of three unequal masses forming an equilateral triangle.

Choose the x-axis along one side of the triangle as shown in Fig. 9–3. Then,

$$\bar{x} = \frac{\Sigma\, m_i x_i}{\Sigma\, m_i} = \frac{(1.0\ \text{kg})(0) + (2.0\ \text{kg})(1.0\ \text{meter}) + (3.0\ \text{kg})(\tfrac{1}{2}\ \text{meter})}{(1.0 + 2.0 + 3.0)\ \text{kg}} = \tfrac{7}{12}\ \text{meter},$$

$$\bar{y} = \frac{\Sigma\, m_i y_i}{\Sigma\, m_i} = \frac{(1.0\ \text{kg})(0) + (2.0\ \text{kg})(0) + (3.0\ \text{kg})(\sqrt{3}/2\ \text{meter})}{(1.0 + 2.0 + 3.0)\ \text{kg}} = \tfrac{\sqrt{3}}{4}\ \text{meter}.$$

The center of mass C is shown in the figure. Why isn't it at the geometric center of the triangle?

Example 2. Find the center of mass of the triangular plate of Fig. 9–4.

If a body can be divided into parts such that the center of mass of each part is known, the center of mass of the body can usually be found simply. The triangular plate may be divided into narrow strips parallel to one side. The center of mass of each strip lies on the line which joins the middle of that side to the opposite vertex. But we can divide up the triangle in three different ways, using this process for each of three sides. Hence, the center of mass lies at the intersection of the three lines

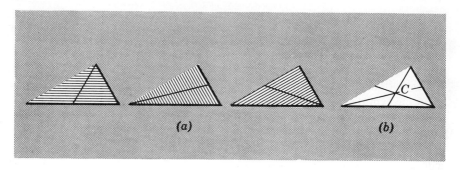

Fig. 9–4 Example 2. Finding the center of mass C of a triangular plate, using the method of intersections.

which join the middle of each side with the opposite vertices. This is the only point that is common to the three lines. ◀

9–2 Motion of the Center of Mass

We are now in a position to discuss one of the physical consequences of the center-of-mass concept.

Consider the motion of a group of particles whose masses are m_1, m_2, $\cdots$, m_n and whose total mass is M. Then from Eq. 9–2a,

$$M x = m_1 x_1 + m_2 x_2 + \cdots + m_n x_n,$$

where the $\bar{x}$ is the x coordinate of the center of mass. Differentiating this equation with respect to the time, we obtain

$$M \frac{d\bar{x}}{dt} = m_1 \frac{dx_1}{dt} + m_2 \frac{dx_2}{dt} + \cdots + m_n \frac{dx_n}{dt}$$
$$= m_1 v_{1x} + m_2 v_{2x} + \cdots + m_n v_{nx}, \tag{9–7}$$

where v_{1x} is the x component of the velocity of the first particle, etc., and $d\bar{x}/dt$ is the x component of the velocity of the center of mass. Similar equations can be obtained for the y and z components of the motion.

Differentiating Eq. 9–7 with respect to the time, we obtain

$$M \frac{d^2\bar{x}}{dt^2} = m_1 \frac{d^2x_1}{dt^2} + m_2 \frac{d^2x_2}{dt^2} + \cdots + m_n \frac{d^2x_n}{dt^2}$$
$$= m_1 a_{1x} + m_2 a_{2x} + \cdots + m_n a_{nx}, \tag{9–8}$$

where a_{1x} is the x component of the acceleration of the first particle, etc., and $d^2\bar{x}/dt^2$ is the x component of the acceleration of the center of mass. If the x component of the resultant force acting on the first particle is called F_{1x}, then, from Newton's second law $F_{1x} = m_1 a_{1x}$. Likewise, $F_{2x} = m_2 a_{2x}$, etc. Equation 9–8 can, therefore, be written as follows:

$$M a_x = F_{1x} + F_{2x} + \cdots + F_{nx}, \tag{9–9}$$

where a_x is the x component of the acceleration of the center of mass. Similar equations hold for the y and z components. The three scalar equations can be combined into one vector equation:

$$Ma = F_1 + F_2 + \cdots + F_n. \qquad (9\text{–}10)$$

Hence, *the total mass of the group of particles times the acceleration of its center of mass is equal to the vector sum of all the forces acting on the group of particles.*

Among all these forces will be *internal* forces exerted by the particles on each other. However, from Newton's third law these internal forces will occur in equal and opposite pairs, so that they contribute nothing to the sum. Hence, the internal forces can be removed from the problem. The right hand sum in Eq. 9–10 represents the sum of only the *external* forces acting on all the particles. We can then rewrite Eq. 9–10 as simply

$$Ma = F_{\text{ext}}. \qquad (9\text{–}11)$$

This states that *the center of mass of a system of particles moves as though all the mass of the system were concentrated at the center of mass and all the external forces were applied at that point.*

Notice that we obtain this simple result without specifying the nature of the system of particles. The system can be a rigid body, in which the particles are in fixed positions with respect to one another, or it can be a collection of particles in which there may be all kinds of internal motion. Whatever the system is, and however its individual parts may be moving, its center of mass moves according to Eq. 9–11.

Hence, instead of treating bodies as particles as we have done in previous chapters, we can treat them as collections of particles. Then we can obtain the translational motion of the body by assuming that all the mass of the body is concentrated at its center of mass and all the external forces are applied at that point.* The motion of the center of mass represents the translational motion of the whole body. This, in fact, is the procedure that we followed implicitly in all our force diagrams and problem solving.

Aside from justifying and making more concrete our previous procedure, we have now found how to describe the translational motion of a *system* of particles and how to describe the *translational* motion of a body which may be rotating as well. In this chapter and the next we apply this result to the linear motion of a system of particles. In later chapters we shall see how it simplifies the analysis of rotational motion.

▶ **Example 3.** Consider three particles of different masses acted on by external forces, as shown in Fig. 9–5. Find the acceleration of the center of mass of the system.

---

* When the external force is gravity, it acts through the center of gravity of the body. In every case we have considered, the center of gravity coincides with the center of mass, which is a more general concept. The conditions under which these points are different for a body will be discussed in Chapter 14.

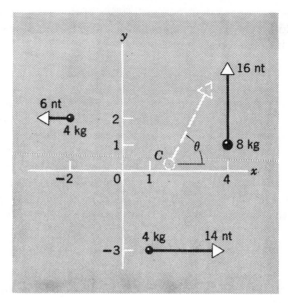

Fig. 9–5 Example 3. Finding the motion of the center of mass of three masses, each subjected to a different force.

First we find the coordinates of the center of mass. From Eq. 9–3,

$$\bar{x} = \frac{(8.0 \times 4) + (4.0 \times -2) + (4.0 \times 1)}{16} \text{ meters} = \tfrac{7}{4} \text{ meters},$$

$$\bar{y} = \frac{(8.0 \times 1) + (4.0 \times 2) + (4.0 \times -3)}{16} \text{ meters} = \tfrac{1}{4} \text{ meter}.$$

These are shown as C in Fig. 9–5.

To obtain the acceleration of the center of mass, we first determine the resultant external force acting on the system consisting of the three particles. The x component of this force is

$$F_x = 14 \text{ nt} - 6.0 \text{ nt} = 8.0 \text{ nt},$$

and the y component is

$$F_y = 16 \text{ nt}.$$

Hence, the resultant external force F is

$$F = \sqrt{(8.0)^2 + (16)^2} \text{ nt} = 18 \text{ nt},$$

and makes an angle θ with the x-axis given by

$$\tan \theta = \frac{16 \text{ nt}}{8.0 \text{ nt}} = 2.0 \quad \text{or} \quad \theta = 63°.$$

Then, from Eq. 9–11, the acceleration of the center of mass is

$$a = \frac{F}{M} = \frac{18 \text{ nt}}{16 \text{ kg}} = 1.1 \text{ meters/sec}^2,$$

making an angle of 63° with the x-axis.

Although the three particles will change their relative positions as time goes on, the center of mass will move, as shown, with this acceleration. ◄

9-3 Linear Momentum of a Particle

The momentum of a particle is a vector **p** defined as the product of its mass m and its velocity **v**. That is,

$$\mathbf{p} = m\mathbf{v}. \tag{9-12}$$

Momentum, being the product of a scalar by a vector, is a vector quantity.

Newton, in his famous *Principia*, expressed the second law of motion in terms of momentum (which he called "quantity of motion"). Expressed in modern terminology Newton's second law reads: *Rate of change of momentum is proportional to the resultant force and is in the direction of that force.*

In symbolic form the second law is

$$\mathbf{F} = \frac{d\mathbf{p}}{dt}. \tag{9 13}$$

When the mass of a body is constant, the second law can be put in the form $\mathbf{F} = m\mathbf{a}$, which we have used up to now. That is, if m is a constant, then

$$\mathbf{F} = \frac{d\mathbf{p}}{dt} = \frac{d}{dt}(m\mathbf{v}) = m\frac{d\mathbf{v}}{dt} = m\mathbf{a} \qquad (m \text{ constant}).$$

Suppose, however, that we are dealing with a body whose mass varies with time. Then $\mathbf{F} = m\mathbf{a}$ will no longer be a valid equation of motion. Allowing for a change in mass with time, the second law asserts

$$\mathbf{F} = \frac{d}{dt}(m\mathbf{v})$$

$$= \mathbf{v}\frac{dm}{dt} + m\frac{d\mathbf{v}}{dt} \tag{9-14}$$

$$= \mathbf{v}\frac{dm}{dt} + m\mathbf{a}.$$

Only when dm/dt is zero do we obtain the form $\mathbf{F} = m\mathbf{a}$.

As long as we apply Newton's second law to a fixed system, that is, a system with a fixed number of particles, then, because mass is conserved in classical physics, the two formulations of Newton's second law are equivalent. Often we deal with a system in which mass enters or leaves while the system is under observation. For example, our system might be a rocket and its fuel load; as time goes on the rocket burns its fuel and expels it in the form of hot gases. The simplest way to treat such systems is by using a momentum principle. Therefore, the importance of the formulation $\mathbf{F} = d(m\mathbf{v})/dt$ in classical physics is primarily that it gives prominence to momentum $m\mathbf{v}$. As we shall soon see, momentum is a very useful concept.

In relativity theory the second law in the form $\mathbf{F} = m\mathbf{a}$ is not valid. However, it turns out that Newton's second law in the form $\mathbf{F} = d\mathbf{p}/dt$ *is* still a valid law if the momentum $\mathbf{p}$ is defined not as $m_0\mathbf{v}$ but as

$$\mathbf{p} = \frac{m_0\mathbf{v}}{\sqrt{1 - v^2/c^2}}. \tag{9–15}$$

This result suggested a new definition of mass (compare Eq. 9–12 and Eq. 9–15)

$$m = \frac{m_0}{\sqrt{1 - v^2/c^2}},$$

so that momentum could still be written as $\mathbf{p} = m\mathbf{v}$. In this equation v is the speed of the particle, c is the speed of light, and m_0 is the "rest mass" of the body (its mass when $v = 0$). From this definition we must expect the mass of a particle to increase with its speed. In atomic and nuclear systems particles may acquire enormous speeds, comparable to the speed of light. This concept can be put to a direct test in such systems because the increase in mass over the rest mass for such particles is large enough to measure accurately. Results of all such experiments indicate that this effect is real and given exactly by the equation above. (See Fig. 8–7.)

Although there is no evidence that Newton regarded the mass of a given particle as a variable, he apparently understood the importance of the quantity $m\mathbf{v}$. His stature is enhanced by the fact that his formulation of the second law in terms of momentum can be preserved even in relativity theory.

9–4   Linear Momentum of a System of Particles

Suppose that instead of a single particle we have a system of n particles. Let the particles have masses $m_1, m_2, \cdots, m_n$ so that the total mass M of the system is

$$M = m_1 + m_2 + \cdots + m_n.$$

The particles may interact with each other and external forces may act on them as well (Fig. 9–6). Each particle will have a velocity and a momentum. Particle 1 of mass m_1 and velocity $\mathbf{v}_1$ will have a momentum $\mathbf{p}_1 = m_1\mathbf{v}_1$, for example. The system as a whole will have a *total momentum* $\mathbf{P}$ which is simply the vector sum of the momenta of the individual particles. That is,

$$\mathbf{P} = \mathbf{p}_1 + \mathbf{p}_2 + \cdots + \mathbf{p}_n.$$

Now let us differentiate this equation with respect to the time. We obtain

$$\frac{d\mathbf{P}}{dt} = \frac{d\mathbf{p}_1}{dt} + \frac{d\mathbf{p}_2}{dt} + \cdots + \frac{d\mathbf{p}_n}{dt}. \tag{9–16}$$

However, we have seen that $d\mathbf{p}_1/dt$ is the force $\mathbf{F}_1$ exerted on particle 1, $d\mathbf{p}_2/dt$ is the force $\mathbf{F}_2$ exerted on particle 2, and so forth. Therefore, we can write Eq. 9–16 as

$$\frac{d\mathbf{P}}{dt} = \mathbf{F}_1 + \mathbf{F}_2 + \cdots + \mathbf{F}_n. \tag{9–17}$$

Now the right side of this equation is simply the vector sum of all the forces acting on the particles. These forces include all external forces, which are exerted on the particles by agents outside the system. They also include all the internal forces, which are the forces exerted by the particles on each other. According to Newton's third law of motion, however, the internal forces contribute nothing to the sum because they occur in equal and opposite pairs. If $\mathbf{F}_1$ includes a force exerted on particle 1 by particle 2, for example, then $\mathbf{F}_2$ includes an equal but opposite force exerted by particle 1 on particle 2. Therefore, the right side of Eq. 9-17 can be replaced by the sum of the *external forces* alone without changing its value. We then obtain the equation

$$\frac{d\mathbf{P}}{dt} = \mathbf{F}_{\text{ext}}. \tag{9-18}$$

This equation is the generalization of the single-particle equation (Eq. 9-13) to the many-particle system (Fig. 9-6). Equation 9-18 reduces to Eq. 9-13 for the special case of one particle, there being only external forces on a one-particle system.

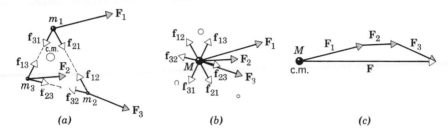

(a)   *(b)*   *(c)*

Fig. 9-6 Relationship between the various forces acting on a system of three masses m_1, m_2, and m_3. (*a*) *All* the forces acting on each mass are shown here, as well as the location "c.m.," the center of mass. On m_1 act forces $\mathbf{f}_{21}$ and $\mathbf{f}_{31}$ exerted by m_2 and m_3 respectively, as well as $\mathbf{F}_1$, a force from some external agent. Similar sets of forces act on m_2 and m_3. However, according to Newton's third law, internal forces $\mathbf{f}_{31}$ and $\mathbf{f}_{13}$ must be equal and opposite and must both lie along the line of centers of m_1 and m_3. Similar statements hold for the other two pairs of action-reaction forces. (*b*) If we are interested only in the motion of the system as a whole, we may consider all the forces to act on a mass $M = m_1 + m_2 + m_3$, located at the center of mass. Owing to the equality of the action-reaction pairs of internal forces as just stated, they cancel each other identically, leaving only the three external forces $\mathbf{F}_1$, $\mathbf{F}_2$, and $\mathbf{F}_3$. These are added graphically in (*c*) to yield a net force $\mathbf{F}$ acting on the center of mass of the system.

Consider now the motion of a system of particles. We have seen in Section 9-2 that whatever the internal motion of a body or system of particles may be, the motion of the center of mass can be obtained by imagining all the mass to be concentrated at that point and all the external forces to be applied there. That is, from Eq. 9-11 we have

$$\mathbf{F}_{\text{ext}} = \frac{d}{dt} (M \mathbf{v}_{\text{cm}}). \tag{9-19}$$

On combining Eqs. 9–18 and 9–19, we obtain

$$\frac{d\mathbf{P}}{dt} = \frac{d}{dt}(M\mathbf{v}_{cm}).$$ (9–20)

Therefore, $\mathbf{P} = M\mathbf{v}_{cm}.$ (9–21)

The total momentum of a system of particles is equal to the product of the total mass and the velocity of the center of mass.

9–5 Conservation of Linear Momentum

Suppose that the sum of the external forces acting on a system is zero. Then, from Eq. 9–18,

$$\frac{d\mathbf{P}}{dt} = 0 \quad \text{or} \quad \mathbf{P} = \text{constant.}$$

When the resultant external force acting on a system is zero, the total vector momentum of the system remains constant. This simple but quite general result is called *the principle of the conservation of linear momentum.* We shall see that it is applicable to many important physical situations.

The total momentum of a system can only be changed by external forces acting on the system. The internal forces, being equal and opposite, produce equal and opposite changes in momentum which annul one another. For a system of particles

$$\mathbf{p}_1 + \mathbf{p}_2 + \cdots + \mathbf{p}_n = \mathbf{P},$$

so that when the total momentum $\mathbf{P}$ is constant we have

$$\mathbf{p}_1 + \mathbf{p}_2 + \cdots + \mathbf{p}_n = \text{constant} = \mathbf{P}_0.$$ (9–22)

The momenta of the individual particles may change, but their sum remains constant if there is no net external force.

Momentum is a vector quantity. Equation 9–22 is, therefore, equivalent to three scalar equations, one for each coordinate direction. Hence, the conservation of linear momentum supplies us with three conditions on the motion of a system to which it applies. The conservation of energy on the other hand supplies us with only one condition on the motion of a system to which it applies, because energy is a scalar.

The law of the conservation of linear momentum holds true even in atomic and nuclear physics, although Newtonian mechanics does not. Hence, this conservation law must be more fundamental than Newtonian principles. In our derivation of this principle we must have made more rigid assumptions than we needed to. This is true even in the framework of classical mechanics. The student should bear in mind the key role played by Newton's third law in this deduction of momentum conservation. This law was used to justify the assumption that the sum of the internal forces acting on all the particles is zero. However, it is somewhat artificial to regard the internal forces in a piece of matter as resulting from pairs of equal and opposite forces between the various pairs of atoms. These internal forces are actually many-body forces, depending not only on the relative separation and orientation of two atoms but also on the positions and orientations of neighboring atoms. If it were possible to prove our assumption without using Newton's third law, the law of conservation of linear momentum would not depend on the validity of the third law of motion. Actually we can prove this assumption on the basis of a much less stringent requirement than that the third law should hold. The proof lies outside the scope of this text.*

9-6   Some Applications of the Momentum Principle

▶ **Example 4.** Consider first a problem in which an external force acts on a system of particles. Recall our previous discussion of projectile motion (Chapter 4). Now let us imagine that our projectile is a shell that explodes while in flight. The path of the shell is shown in Fig. 9-7. We assume that the air resistance is negligible. The system is the shell, the earth is our reference frame, and the external force is that of gravity. At the point x_1 the shell explodes and shell fragments are blown in all directions. What can we say about the motion of this system thereafter?

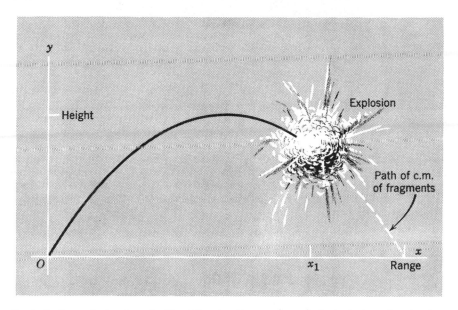

Fig. 9-7 Example 4. A projectile, following the usual parabolic trajectory, bursts at x_1. The center of mass of all the fragments continues along the same parabolic path.

The forces of the explosion are all *internal forces;* they are forces exerted by part of the system on other parts of the system. These forces may change the momenta of all the *individual fragments* from the values they had when they made up the shell, but they cannot change the *total* vector momentum of the system. Only an external force can change the total momentum. The external force, however, is simply that due to gravity. Since a system of particles as a whole moves as though all its mass were concentrated at the center of mass with the external force applied there, the center of mass of the fragments will continue to move in the parabolic trajectory that the unexploded shell would have followed. The change in the total momentum of the system attributable to gravity is the same whether the shell explodes or not.

* See an article "On Newton's Third Law and the Conservation of Momentum" by E. Gerjuoy, in *American Journal of Physics*, November 1949.

What can you say about the *mechanical energy* of the system before and after the explosion?

Example 5. Consider now two blocks A and B, of masses m_A and m_B, coupled by a spring and resting on a horizontal frictionless table. Let us pull the blocks apart and stretch the spring, as in Fig. 9–8, and then release the blocks. Describe the subsequent motion.

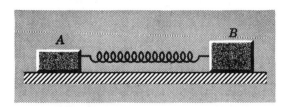

Fig. 9–8 Example 5. Two blocks A and B, resting on a frictionless surface, are connected by a spring. If held apart and then released, the sum of their momenta remains zero.

If the system consists of the two blocks and spring, then after we have released the blocks there is no net external force acting on the system. The only forces are internal ones arising from the spring. These cancel in pairs when we are thinking about the system as a whole. We can, therefore, apply the conservation of linear momentum to the motion. The momentum of the system before the blocks were released was zero, so the momentum must remain zero thereafter. The total momentum can be zero even though the blocks move because momentum is a *vector* quantity. One block will have positive momentum (A moves in the $+x$ direction) and the other block will have negative momentum (B moves in the $-x$ direction). From the conservation of momentum we have

$$\text{initial momentum} = \text{final momentum},$$

$$0 = m_B\mathbf{v}_B + m_A\mathbf{v}_A.$$

Therefore, $$m_B\mathbf{v}_B = -m_A\mathbf{v}_A$$

or $$\mathbf{v}_A = -\frac{m_B}{m_A}\,\mathbf{v}_B.$$

For example, if m_A is 2 slugs and m_B is 1 slug, then $\mathbf{v}_A$ is one-half $\mathbf{v}_B$ in magnitude and is oppositely directed.

The kinetic energy of block A is $\frac{1}{2}m_A v_A{}^2$ and can be written as $(m_A v_A)^2/2m_A$ and that of block B is $\frac{1}{2}m_B v_B{}^2$ and can be written as $(m_B v_B)^2/2m_B$. But

$$\frac{K_A}{K_B} = \frac{2m_B(m_A v_A)^2}{2m_A(m_B v_B)^2} = \frac{m_B}{m_A},$$

in which $m_A v_A$ equals $m_B v_B$ because of momentum conservation. The kinetic energies of the blocks are inversely proportional to their respective masses. Because mechanical energy is conserved also, the blocks will continue to oscillate back and forth, the energy being partly kinetic and partly potential. What is the motion of the center of mass of this system?

If mechanical energy is not conserved, as would be true if friction were present, the motion will die out as the energy is dissipated. Can we apply the conservation of linear momentum in this case? Explain.

Example 6. As an example of recoil, consider radioactive decay. An α-particle (the nucleus of a helium atom) is emitted from a uranium-238 nucleus, originally at rest, with a speed of 1.4×10^7 meters/sec and a kinetic energy of 4.1 Mev (million electron volts). Find the recoil speed of the residual nucleus (thorium-234).

We think of the system (thorium + α-particle) as initially bound and forming the uranium nucleus. The system then fragments into two separate parts. The momentum of the system before fragmentation is zero. In the absence of external forces, the momentum after fragmentation is also zero. Hence,

$$\text{initial momentum} = \text{final momentum},$$

$$0 = M_\alpha \mathbf{v}_\alpha + M_{\text{Th}} \mathbf{v}_{\text{Th}},$$

$$\mathbf{v}_{\text{Th}} = -\frac{M_\alpha}{M_{\text{Th}}} \mathbf{v}_\alpha.$$

The ratio of the α-particle mass to the thorium nucleus mass, M_α/M_{Th}, is 4/234 and $v_\alpha = 1.4 \times 10^7$ meters/sec. Hence,

$$v_{\text{Th}} = -(4/634)(1.40 \times 10^7 \text{ meters/sec}) = -2.4 \times 10^5 \text{ meters/sec}.$$

The minus sign indicates that the residual thorium nucleus recoils in a direction exactly opposite to the motion of the α-particle, so as to give a resultant vector momentum of zero.

How can we compute the kinetic energy of the recoiling nucleus (see previous example)? Where does the energy of the fragments come from?

Example 7. Consider now the apparently simple example of a ball thrown up from the earth by a person and then caught by him on its return. To simplify matters we can consider the person to be part of the earth since he does not lose contact with it. We also assume that air resistance is negligible.

The system being considered consists of the earth and the ball. The gravitational forces between the parts of the system are now internal forces. Let us choose a frame of reference in which the earth is at rest initially. When the ball is thrown up, the earth must recoil. The momentum of the system (earth + ball) is zero initially and no external forces act. Therefore, momentum is conserved and the total momentum remains zero throughout the motion. The upward momentum acquired by the ball is balanced by an equal and opposite downward momentum of the earth. We have

$$\text{initial momentum} = \text{final momentum},$$

$$0 = m_B \mathbf{v}_B + m_E \mathbf{v}_E,$$

$$m_B \mathbf{v}_B = -m_E \mathbf{v}_E.$$

Here m_B and m_E are the masses of ball and earth respectively and $\mathbf{v}_B$ and $\mathbf{v}_E$ are the velocities of the ball and the earth. Owing to the enormous mass of the earth in comparison with the ball, the recoil speed of the earth is negligibly small.

As the ball and earth separate, the internal force of gravitational attraction pulls them together until they cease separating and begin to approach one another. As the ball falls toward the earth, the earth falls toward the ball with an equal but oppositely directed momentum. As the ball is caught, its momentum is neutralized by (and it neutralizes) the momentum of the earth. Both objects lose their relative motion, the total momentum is still zero, and the original situation before throwing is restored.

You will recall that when we discussed the conservation of energy in the presence of gravitational potential, we neglected to consider the motion of the earth itself. We took the surface of the earth as our zero level of gravitational potential energy.

The reference position did not matter, since we were concerned only with *changes* in potential energy. However, in computing changes in kinetic energy, we assumed that the earth remained stationary, as in the case of the ball thrown up from the earth.

In principle, we cannot ignore the change in the kinetic energy of the earth itself. For example, when the ball falls toward the earth, the earth is slightly accelerated toward the ball. We neglected this fact before because we assumed that the change in kinetic energy of the earth is negligible. This result is not obvious, because although the earth's speed will certainly be small, its mass is enormous and the kinetic energy acquired may be significant. To settle the point we compute the ratio of the kinetic energy of the earth to that of the ball. Using $m_E v_E = -m_B v_B$ from momentum conservation, we have

$$\frac{K_E}{K_B} = \frac{\frac{1}{2}m_E v_E^2}{\frac{1}{2}m_B v_B^2} = \frac{\frac{1}{2}(m_E v_E)^2}{\frac{1}{2}(m_B v_B)^2} \cdot \frac{m_B}{m_E} = \frac{m_B}{m_E}.$$

Since the mass of the ball m_B is negligibly small compared to the mass of the earth m_E, the kinetic energy acquired by the earth, K_E, is negligibly small compared to that of the ball, K_B. For example, if $m_B = 6$ kg (a rather massive ball), then, since $m_E = 6 \times 10^{24}$ kg, $K_E/K_B = 10^{-24}$!

Notice that this problem is identical in principle to Example 5. The differences are only those of detail; in one the potential energy is elastic and in the other the potential energy is gravitational; in one the masses are pictured as of the same order of magnitude, and in the other they are of different orders of magnitude.

Example 8. The motion of a rocket is an interesting application of Newton's third law of motion and the momentum principle. The rocket forces a jet of hot gases from its tail; this is the action force. The jet of hot gases exerts a force on the rocket, propelling it forward; this is the reaction force. These forces are internal forces in the system (rocket + gas). From the momentum point of view, the hot gases acquire momentum in the backward direction and the rocket acquires an equal amount of momentum in the forward direction.

An instructive analogy is that shown in Fig. 9–9. A machine gun is mounted on a car on a horizontal frictionless surface. As each bullet is fired from the gun, that bullet acquires a backward momentum mu. The car, therefore, acquires a forward momentum mu for each bullet fired. If n is the number of bullets fired per unit time, the change in momentum of the car per unit time is nmu. However, the change in momentum with time is simply the force, so the reaction force exerted on the car is nmu.

In a similar way a reaction force is exerted on the rocket by the gas particles ejected from the tail of the rocket. This force gives the rocket a forward acceleration. In each case we have assumed that the external forces are zero, so that the total momentum of each system is constant. Our coordinate system is a frame attached to the center of mass. The center of mass, if at rest initially, remains at rest in the absence of external forces. The individual parts of the system (bullets and car or gases and rocket) may change their momentum, however, with respect to this frame.

Let us now solve the rocket problem exactly. We can get the equation of motion of a rocket from the momentum principle. This principle applies to a definite system of particles. If we consider the rocket as our system at any instant, we must remember that, at a time dt later, this system will comprise the rocket plus the material ejected from the rocket during that time. Both must be considered in computing the change in momentum.

Let the mass of the rocket at any given instant be M, a variable, and let its velocity be **v** relative to some fixed coordinate system. In a time interval dt an amount of mass dM is ejected from the rocket motor. If the gases ejected from the rocket motor have an exhaust velocity **u** relative to the rocket, the velocity of the exhaust relative

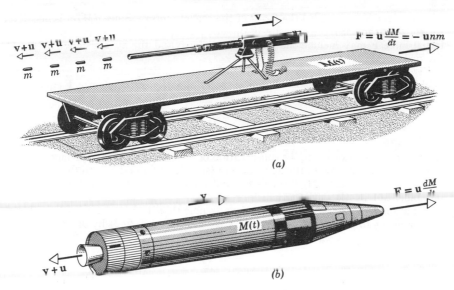

Fig. 9–9 Example 8. (*a*) A machine gun is fixed to a car that rolls without friction. The car moves with a velocity **v** relative to the ground. The bullets move with velocity **u** relative to the car, or with velocity **v** + **u** relative to the ground. The gun shoots *n* bullets, each of mass *m*, each second. The net force on the system, **F**, is $-\mathbf{u}nm$. (*b*) A rocket moves through space without friction, with velocity **v** relative to the ground. The exhaust is expelled with a velocity **u** relative to the rocket, or with velocity **v** + **u** relative to the ground. The rate at which the exhaust is expelled is dM/dt. The net force on the rocket, **F**, is $\mathbf{u}\,dM/dt$.

to the fixed coordinate system is **v** + **u**. Hence, the rate of change of momentum of the rocket is

$$\frac{d}{dt}(M\mathbf{v}) = M\frac{d\mathbf{v}}{dt} + \mathbf{v}\frac{dM}{dt},$$

and the rate of change of momentum in the rocket exhaust is

$$-(\mathbf{v} + \mathbf{u})\frac{dM}{dt}.$$

The minus sign appears here because the change in mass of the exhaust is the negative of the change in mass of the rocket. This second term simply gives the rate at which momentum appears in the exhaust, for $-dM/dt$ is the rate at which mass appears in the exhaust and **v** + **u** is the velocity of this ejected mass.

The total rate of change of momentum of the system is the sum of these two terms and is equal to the resultant external force **F** acting on the system, or

$$\mathbf{F} = M\frac{d\mathbf{v}}{dt} + \mathbf{v}\frac{dM}{dt} - \mathbf{v}\frac{dM}{dt} - \mathbf{u}\frac{dM}{dt}$$

$$= M\frac{d\mathbf{v}}{dt} - \mathbf{u}\frac{dM}{dt}.$$

This equation can be rewritten as

$$\mathbf{F} + \mathbf{u}\frac{dM}{dt} = M\frac{d\mathbf{v}}{dt}. \tag{9–23}$$

The term $\mathbf{u}\, dM/dt$ is called the *thrust* of the rocket motor. Since dM/dt is negative, we see that the thrust is opposite in direction to the exhaust velocity $\mathbf{u}$. The external force $\mathbf{F}$ may include the gravitational force and the air resistance acting on the rocket.

For a rocket $\mathbf{F}$ will be zero when the rocket is essentially out of any gravitational field in the vacuum of free space. *In this special case of no external force*, $\mathbf{F}$ equals zero and Eq. 9–23 becomes

$$\mathbf{u}\, \frac{dM}{dt} = M\, \frac{d\mathbf{v}}{dt}. \tag{9–24}$$

This corresponds exactly to the conservation of momentum and is the result deduced originally by analogy with the machine gun (see Fig. 9–9a and b). In the case of the machine gun on a car, dM/dt equals nm and $\mathbf{u}\, dM/dt$ gives the thrust on, or change in momentum of, the car at any instant.

Equation 9–24 can be easily solved if we assume that $\mathbf{u}$, the velocity of the exhaust gases relative to the rocket, is constant. We multiply Eq. 9–24 by dt/M, obtaining

$$d\mathbf{v} = \mathbf{u}\, \frac{dM}{M}.$$

Integrating,* we obtain

$$\int_{\mathbf{v}_0}^{\mathbf{v}} d\mathbf{v} = \mathbf{u} \int_{M_0}^{M} \frac{dM}{M}$$

or

$$\mathbf{v} - \mathbf{v}_0 = -\mathbf{u}\, \ln\left(\frac{M_0}{M}\right) = -\mathbf{u}\, \ln\left(1 + \frac{M_0 - M}{M}\right). \tag{9–25}$$

Here M_0 and $\mathbf{v}_0$ are the initial mass and velocity of the rocket, and M and $\mathbf{v}$ are the final mass and velocity of the rocket, respectively. Thus, the change in speed of the rocket in any interval of time depends only on the exhaust velocity (being opposite in direction from it) and on the fraction of mass exhausted during that time interval.

As a numerical example, consider a rocket weighing 30,000 lb when initially at rest and 10,000 lb after all its fuel is burned out, the exhaust velocity of the gases being 6000 ft/sec. The speed v at burnout time, *in the absence of external forces*, would be (from Eq. 9–25)

$$v = (6000 \text{ ft/sec}) \ln\left(\frac{30,000}{10,000}\right) = 6600 \text{ ft/sec} = 4500 \text{ miles/hr}.$$

The minus sign in Eq. 9–25 indicates that the direction of the rocket's velocity is opposite to that of the exhaust velocity. If the external forces of air resistance and gravity were accounted for, the final speed would be smaller.

Figure 9–10 shows the U. S. Air Force Atlas rocket and lists some of its properties.

Now let us take into account the force of gravity in a vertical rocket firing, using these same data. The upward force $\mathbf{u}\, dM/dt$ will be constant if the rate at which the gas is ejected is constant. Let us assume that this rate is constant at 10 slugs/sec. Then the constant upward force is

$$u\, \frac{dM}{dt} = (6000 \text{ ft/sec})(10 \text{ slugs/sec}) = 60,000 \text{ lb}.$$

This upward force is opposed by the downward pull of gravity, which is 30,000 lb initially and 10,000 lb finally. Hence, the net upward force initially is 30,000 lb and

---

* The integral $\int dx/x$ equals $\ln x$. See any text on calculus for proof.

(a)

Range	5500–6200 miles
Maximum speed	15,000 mph
Number of stages	2
Over-all length	75 ft
Diameter	10 ft
Gross weight	243,000 lb
Major constructional material	Steel
Guidance	Inertial
Power plants	
Propellents	Liquid oxygen and kerosene
Thrust	
First (booster) stage (2)	150,000 lb each
Second stage	100,000 lb

(b)

Fig. 9–10 (a) A photograph of the Atlas, the U. S. Air Force intercontinental ballistic missile. The rocket begins its flight with all engines in operation, producing about a 400,000-lb thrust, but in a few seconds booster engines fall away and the second stage continues with a thrust of about 100,000 lb. This photograph shows the two small "vernier" engines which serve to stabilize the rocket against rolling. These verniers operate throughout the entire powered flight. Other data are listed in (b)

finally 50,000 lb. · The ratio of the net upward force to the force of gravity (the weight of the rocket) is, therefore, initially

$$\frac{30,000}{30,000} = 1$$

and finally

$$\frac{50,000}{10,000} = 5.$$

The initial upward acceleration of the rocket is g and the final upward acceleration of the rocket is $5g$, where g is the magnitude of the acceleration of gravity.

What happens after the fuel burns out?

Example 9. As a final example consider the conveyer belt problem. This is a clear-cut example of a force associated with change of mass alone, the velocity being constant.

Imagine material to be dropped continuously from a hopper onto a moving belt, as in Fig. 9–11. Call the rate at which mass is dropped on the belt dm/dt. Let m be

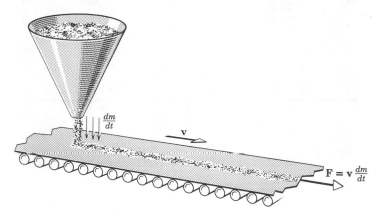

Fig. 9–11 Example 9. Sand drops from a hopper at a rate dm/dt onto a conveyer belt moving with velocity **v**. The force **F** required to keep the belt moving at constant velocity is **v** dm/dt.

the mass of material on the belt and let M be the mass of the belt. The problem is to find the force **F** required to keep the belt moving at *constant* velocity **v**.

The total momentum **P** of the system (belt + material on the belt and in the hopper) is

$$\mathbf{P} = (m + M)\mathbf{v},$$

where we have assumed the hopper to be at rest. The momentum principle requires that

$$\mathbf{F} = \frac{d\mathbf{P}}{dt}$$

$$= (m + M)\frac{d\mathbf{v}}{dt} + \mathbf{v}\frac{dm}{dt} + \mathbf{v}\frac{dM}{dt}.$$

But M is constant, so that $dM/dt = 0$, and **v** is constant, so that $(m + M)\,d\mathbf{v}/dt = 0$. Hence,

$$\mathbf{F} = \mathbf{v}\frac{dm}{dt}.$$

This solves the problem and gives the force on the belt. Notice that (in the absence of friction) the mass of the belt does not really enter the problem.

If we compute the power supplied by the force, we obtain

$$P = \mathbf{F} \cdot \mathbf{v} = \mathbf{v} \cdot \mathbf{F} = \mathbf{v} \cdot \mathbf{v} \frac{dm}{dt} = v^2 \frac{dm}{dt}.$$

But
$$v^2 \frac{dm}{dt} = \frac{d}{dt}(mv^2),$$

for constant velocity, so that

$$P = \frac{d}{dt}(mv^2) = \frac{d}{dt}(m + M)v^2,$$

where the added term $d(Mv^2)/dt$ is zero. This result can also be written as

$$P = 2 \frac{d}{dt}[\tfrac{1}{2}(m + M)v^2] = 2 \frac{dK}{dt}.$$

Hence, the power supplied by the force is twice the rate of increase of kinetic energy of the entire system. Therefore, mechanical energy is not conserved. Where is the other half of the power going in this case?

In which of the previous examples did we have conservation of momentum without conservation of mechanical energy? ◀

QUESTIONS

1. Must there necessarily be any mass at the center of mass of a system?

2. Does the center of mass of a solid body necessarily lie within the body? If not, give examples.

3. How is the center of mass concept related to the concept of geographic center of the country? To the population center of the country? What can you conclude from the fact that the geographic center differs from the population center?

4. Can a body have energy without having momentum? Explain. Can a body have momentum without having energy? Explain.

5. A light and a heavy body have equal kinetic energies of translation. Which one has the larger momentum?

6. A bird is in a wire cage hanging from a spring balance. Is the reading of the balance when the bird is flying about greater than, less than, or the same as that when the bird sits in the cage?

7. Can a sailboat be propelled by air blown at the sails from a fan attached to the boat? Explain.

8. Why is the following statement false: "A rocket cannot move under its own power in outer space because there is no air for its exhaust to push against"?

9. The final velocity of the final stage of a multistage rocket is much greater than the final velocity of a single-stage rocket of the same total weight and fuel supply. Explain this fact.

10. Using the principle of conservation of linear momentum, explain how a propeller-driven airplane and a propeller-driven boat move forward.

PROBLEMS

1. Show that the choice of origin is immaterial in locating the center of mass of a system of two particles (Fig. 9–1). Then extend the proof to show that the location of the center of mass of a system is independent of the coordinate system used to locate it.

2. Show that the center of mass of two particles is on the line joining them at a point whose distance from each particle is inversely proportional to the mass of that particle.

3. Experiments using the diffraction of electrons show that the distance between the centers of the carbon (C) and oxygen (O) atoms in the carbon monoxide gas molecule is 1.13×10^{-10} meter. Locate the center of mass of a CO molecule relative to the carbon atom.

4. The mass of the moon is about 0.013 times the mass of the earth, and the distance from the center of the moon to the center of the earth is about 60 times the radius of the earth. How far is the center of mass of the earth-moon system from the center of the earth? Take the earth's radius to be 4000 miles.

5. In the ammonia (NH_3) molecule, the three hydrogen (H) atoms form an equilateral triangle, the distance between centers of the atoms being 1.628×10^{-10} meter, so that the center of the triangle is 9.39×10^{-11} meter from each hydrogen atom. The nitrogen (N) atom is at the apex of a pyramid, the three hydrogens constituting the base. (See Fig. 1–3.) The hydrogen-nitrogen distance is 1.014×10^{-10} meter. Locate the center of mass relative to the nitrogen atom.

6. A cubistic sculptor decides to portray a bird (Fig. 9–12). Luckily the final model is actually able to stand upright. The model is formed of a single sheet of metal of uniform thickness. Of the points shown, which is most likely to be the center of mass?

7. Find the center of mass of a homogeneous semicircular plate. Let a be the radius of the circle.

8. Two particles P and Q are initially at rest 1.0 meter apart. P has a mass of 0.10 kg and Q a mass of 0.30 kg. P and Q attract each other with a constant force of 1.0×10^{-2} nt. No external forces act on the system. Describe the motion of the center of mass. At what distance from P's original position do the particles collide?

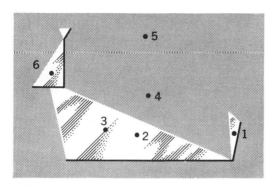

Fig. 9–12

9. Two bodies, each made up of weights from a set, are connected by a light cord which passes over a light, frictionless pulley with a diameter of 5.0 cm. The two bodies are at the same level. Each originally has a mass of 500 gm. (a) Locate their center of mass. (b) Twenty grams are transferred from one body to the other, but the bodies are prevented from moving. Locate the center of mass. (c) The two bodies are now released. Describe the motion of the center of mass and determine its acceleration.

10. What is the momentum of a 4000-lb car whose speed is 30 mph? At what speed would a 10-ton truck have the same momentum? The same kinetic energy?

11. A 200-lb man standing on a surface of negligible friction kicks forward a 0.1-lb stone lying at his feet so that it acquires a speed of 10 ft/sec. What velocity does the man acquire as a result?

12. An opossum (Fig. 9–13) weighing 6.0 lb is standing on a flatboat so that he is 20 ft from a pier on the shore. He walks 8 ft on the boat toward the pier and then halts. The boat weighs 60 lb, and there is no friction between it and the water. How far is he from

Fig. 9–13 Copyright 1959 Walt Kelly. Reproduced by permission.

the pier at the end of this time? (Hint: The center of mass of the boat + opossum does not move. Why?)

13. A railroad flat car of weight W can roll without friction along a straight horizontal track as shown. Initially a man of weight w is standing on the car which is moving to the right with speed v_0. What is the change in velocity of the car if the man runs to the left (Fig. 9–14) so that his speed relative to the car is u just before he jumps off at the left end?

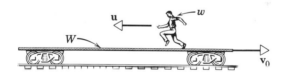

Fig. 9–14

14. Assume that the car in Problem 13 is initially at rest. It holds n men each of weight w. If each man in succession runs with a relative velocity u and jumps off the end, do they impart to the car a greater velocity than if they all run and jump at the same time? Prove your answer.

15. A vessel at rest explodes, breaking into three pieces. Two pieces, having equal mass, fly off perpendicular to one another with the same speed of 30 meters/sec. The third piece has three times the mass of each other piece. What is the direction and magnitude of its velocity immediately after the explosion?

16. A radioactive nucleus, initially at rest, decays by emitting an electron and a neutrino at right angles to one another. The momentum of the electron is 1.2×10^{-22} kg-m/sec and that of the neutrino is 6.4×10^{-23} kg-m/sec. (a) Find the direction and magnitude of the momentum of the recoiling nucleus. (b) The mass of the residual nucleus is 5.8×10^{-26} kg. What is its kinetic energy of recoil?

17. A projectile is fired from a gun at an angle of 45° with the horizontal and with a muzzle speed of 1500 ft/sec. At the highest point in its flight the projectile explodes into two fragments of equal mass. One fragment falls vertically. How far from the gun does the other fragment land, assuming a level terrain?

18. A machine gun fires 50-gm bullets at a speed of 1000 meters/sec. The gunner, holding the machine gun in his hands, can exert an average force of 180 nt against the gun. Determine the maximum number of bullets he can fire per minute.

19. A 6000-kg rocket is set for a vertical firing. If the exhaust speed is 1000 meters/sec, how much gas must be ejected per second to supply the thrust needed (a) to overcome the weight of the rocket, (b) to give the rocket an initial upward acceleration of 19.6 meters/ sec^2?

20. Show that the rocket speed is equal to the exhaust speed when the ratio M_0/M is e (about 2.8). Specify the coordinate system within which this result holds. Show also that the rocket speed is twice the exhaust speed when M_0/M is e^2 (about 7.9).

21. A jet airplane is traveling 600 ft/sec. The engine takes in 2400 ft^3 of air having a mass of 4.8 slugs each second. The air is used to burn 0.20 slug of fuel each second. The energy is used to compress the products of combustion and to eject them at the rear of the plane at 1600 ft/sec relative to the plane. Find the thrust of the jet engine and the delivered horsepower.

22. A freight car, open at the top, weighing 10 tons, is coasting along a level track with negligible friction at 2.0 ft/sec when it begins to rain hard. The raindrops fall vertically with respect to the ground. What is the speed of the car when it has collected 0.5 ton of rain? What assumptions, if any, must you make to get your answer?

23. A freight car filled with sand has a hole so that sand leaks out through the bottom at a constant rate, $-dm/dt = \lambda$. A force F acts on the car in the direction of its motion. Call the instantaneous speed v and write the equation of motion of the freight car.

24. Consider a particle acted on by a force having the same direction as its velocity. (a) Using the relation $F = d(mv)/dt$, show that

$$F \, ds = mv \, dv + v^2 \, dm.$$

(b) Using the relation $v^2 = (1 - m_0{}^2/m^2)c^2$, show that

$$mv \, dv = \frac{m_0{}^2 c^2}{m^2} \, dm.$$

(c) Substitute the relations for $mv \, dv$ and v^2 into result (a) and show that

$$W = \int F \, ds = (m - m_0)c^2.$$

Collisions

10–1 Introduction

Much of our information about atomic and nuclear particles is obtained experimentally by observing the effects of collisions between them. On a larger scale such things as the properties of gases can be understood better in terms of particle collisions. In this chapter we consider the mechanics of particle collisions, and find that from the conservation of momentum principle and the conservation of energy principle we can deduce much information about collision phenomena.

10–2 Impulse and Momentum

In a collision a large force acts on each colliding particle for a short time: A bat striking a baseball or one nuclear particle colliding with another are specific examples. During the very short time interval in which, for example, the bat is in contact with the ball, a very large force is exerted on the ball (Fig. 10–1). This force varies with time in a complex way that in general cannot be determined. Both the ball and the bat are deformed during the collision. Forces of this type are called *impulsive* forces.

Let us assume that the curve of Fig. 10–2 shows the magnitude of the actual force exerted on a body during a collision. We assume that the force has a constant direction. The collision begins at time t_1 and ends at time t_2, the force being zero before and after collision.

From Eq. 9–13 we can write the change in momentum $d\mathbf{p}$ of a body in the time dt during which a force $\mathbf{F}$ acts on it as

$$d\mathbf{p} = \mathbf{F}\,dt. \tag{10–1}$$

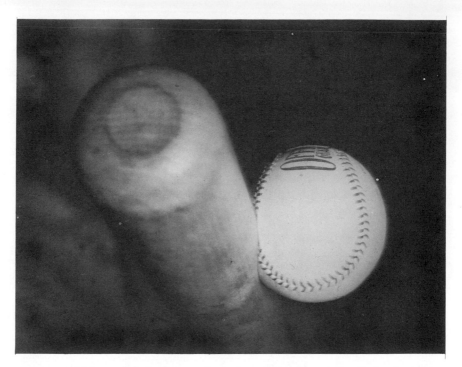

Fig. 10–1 A high-speed flash photograph of a bat striking a baseball. Notice the deformation of the ball, indicating the enormous magnitude of the impulsive force at this instant.

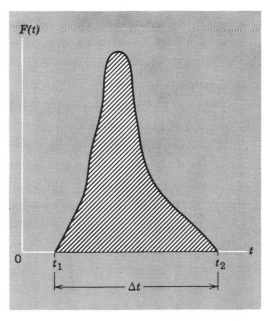

Fig. 10–2 How an impulsive force $F(t)$ might vary with time during a collision starting at time t_1 and ending at t_2.

We can obtain the change in momentum of the body during a collision by integration over the time of collision. That is,

$$\mathbf{p}_2 - \mathbf{p}_1 = \int_1^2 d\mathbf{p} = \int_1^2 \mathbf{F}\, dt. \tag{10–2}$$

The integral of a force over the time interval during which the force acts is called the *impulse* of the force. Hence, the change in momentum of a body acted on by an impulsive force is equal to the impulse. Both impulse and momentum are vectors and both have the same units and dimensions.

The impulsive force represented in Fig. 10–2 is assumed to have a constant direction. The impulse of this force $\int_{t_1}^{t_2} \mathbf{F}\, dt$ is represented in magnitude by the area under the force-time curve.

10–3 Collision Phenomena

Consider now a collision between two particles, such as the particles of masses m_1 and m_2, shown in Fig. 10–3. During the brief collision these

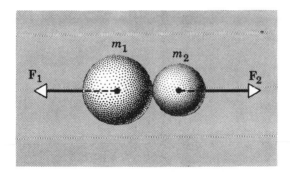

Fig. 10–3 Two "particles" m_1 and m_2, in collision, experience equal and opposite forces along their line of centers, according to Newton's third law.

particles exert large forces on one another. At any instant $\mathbf{F}_1$ is the force exerted on particle 1 by particle 2 and $\mathbf{F}_2$ is the force exerted on particle 2 by particle 1. By Newton's third law these forces at any instant are equal in magnitude but oppositely directed. Furthermore, each force acts during the same time interval, namely the time of the collision, $\Delta t = t_2 - t_1$.

The change in momentum of particle 1 resulting from the collision is

$$\Delta \mathbf{p}_1 = \int_{t_1}^{t_2} \mathbf{F}_1\, dt = \overline{\mathbf{F}}_1\, \Delta t.$$

Here $\overline{\mathbf{F}}_1$ is the average value of the force $\mathbf{F}_1$ during the time interval $\Delta t = t_2 - t_1$.

The change in momentum of particle 2 attributable to the collision is

$$\Delta \mathbf{p}_2 = \int_{t_1}^{t_2} \mathbf{F}_2 \, dt = \overline{\mathbf{F}}_2 \, \Delta t.$$

Here $\overline{\mathbf{F}}_2$ is the average value of the force $\mathbf{F}_2$ during the time interval $\Delta t = t_2 - t_1$.

If no other forces act on the particles, then $\Delta \mathbf{p}_1$ and $\Delta \mathbf{p}_2$ give the total change in momentum for each particle. But we have seen that at each instant $\mathbf{F}_2$ equals $-\mathbf{F}_1$, so that $\overline{\mathbf{F}}_1$ equals $-\overline{\mathbf{F}}_2$, and therefore,

$$\Delta \mathbf{p}_1 = -\Delta \mathbf{p}_2.$$

If we consider the two particles as constituting a system, the total momentum of the system is

$$\mathbf{P} = \mathbf{p}_1 + \mathbf{p}_2,$$

and the total *change* in momentum of the system as a result of the collision is zero, that is,

$$\Delta \mathbf{P} = \Delta \mathbf{p}_1 + \Delta \mathbf{p}_2 = 0.$$

Hence, in the absence of external forces the total momentum of the system is constant. The impulsive forces acting during the collision are internal forces which have no effect on the total momentum of the system.

If we consider next a system of three, four, or, in fact, any number of particles undergoing collisions with one another, by a simple extension of the method used for two particles we can show that the momentum of the system is conserved. The only requirement is that no external forces act on the system.

Now the student may wonder why collision phenomena have been discussed in terms of impulse. Actually, the principle of conservation of momentum has been deduced before. All we must recognize for systems within which collisions are occurring is that the collisional forces are *internal* forces, and the conservation principle follows at once for such systems.

One reason for looking into the impulse nature of a collision is to illustrate for an important class of problems how momentum conservation comes about. A more important reason, however, is to enable us to explain why we almost always assume momentum conservation during a collision, *even when external forces act on the system*.

When a bat strikes a baseball, a golf club strikes a golf ball, or one billiard ball strikes another, it is certainly true that external forces act on the system. Gravity or friction exerts forces on these bodies, for example; these external forces may not be the same on each colliding body, nor are they necessarily annulled by other external forces. It is nevertheless quite safe to neglect these external forces during collision and to assume momentum conservation, provided, as is almost always true, the external forces are negligible compared to the impulsive forces of collision. As a result the change in momentum of a particle undergoing a collision arising from an external force is

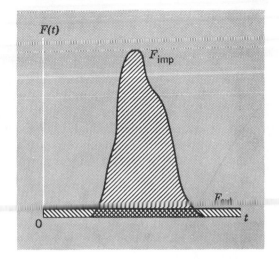

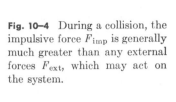

Fig. 10-4 During a collision, the impulsive force F_{imp} is generally much greater than any external forces F_{ext}, which may act on the system.

negligible compared to the change in momentum of that particle arising from the impulsive collisional force (Fig. 10–4).

For example, when a bat strikes a baseball, the collision lasts only a fraction of a second. Since the change in momentum is large and the time of collision is very small, it follows from

$$\Delta \mathbf{p} = \overline{\mathbf{F}} \, \Delta t$$

that the average impulsive force $\overline{\mathbf{F}}$ is extremely large. Compared to this force, the external force of gravity is negligible. *During the collision* we can safely ignore this external force in determining the change in motion of the ball.

If we refer again to Fig. 10–2, we can now emphasize that $t_2 - t_1$ is an extremely short time interval and that the magnitude of $\mathbf{F}$ may be quite large compared to other external forces. Consider for a moment how we can obtain the same impulse as that of Fig. 10–2 with shorter and shorter times of collision. Call the impulse J. Then

$$J = \int F \, dt = \overline{F} \, \Delta t,$$

so that we are trying to keep J constant as Δt gets smaller. This can be done by assuming a larger and larger force F, or $\overline{F}$. In the limit when $\Delta t \to 0$, $F \to \infty$ in order that J be constant at a finite value. If collisions take place in zero time, clearly external forces are negligible compared to the infinite collisional force.

In practice, therefore, *all that is required to justify using momentum conservation during collisions is that the time of collision be small.* This is almost always the case. We can then say that the momentum of a system of particles just before the particles collide is equal to the momentum of the system just after the particles collide.

10–4 Collisions in One Dimension

The problem of determining the motion of bodies after collision from the motion before collision can be solved only if we know the forces of collision exactly and can solve the equations of motion. Often these forces are not known. However, the principle of conservation of momentum must hold during the collision as well as that of the conservation of total energy. Although we may not know the details of the interaction, these principles can be used to predict the results of the collision.

Collisions are not limited to cases in which two bodies come into contact in the usual sense. Bodies that do not come into contact but exert forces on one another and disturb each other's motion can also be said to collide. Atoms may interact through the electric or magnetic forces they exert on one another, nuclei through nuclear forces, or astronomical bodies through gravitational forces. By treating the interacting bodies as a system, we can use the conservation principles to study the motion of these bodies.

Collisions are usually classified according to whether or not *kinetic energy* is conserved in the collision. When kinetic energy is conserved in a collision, the collision is said to be *elastic*. Otherwise, the collision is *inelastic*. Collisions between atomic and subatomic particles are sometimes elastic. These are in fact the only truly elastic collisions known. We can often treat collisions as approximately elastic, however, such as those between ivory or glass balls. Most collisions are inelastic. When two bodies stick together after collision, the collision is said to be completely inelastic. For example, the collision between a bullet and its target is completely inelastic when the bullet remains embedded in the target. The term completely inelastic does *not* mean that all the initial kinetic energy is lost; as we shall see, it means rather that the loss is as great as is consistent with momentum conservation.

Even if the forces of collision are not known, the motion of the particles after collision can be determined from the motion before collision, providing the collision is completely inelastic, or, if the collision is elastic, providing the collision is a one-dimensional one. For a one-dimensional collision the relative motion after collision is along the same line as the relative motion before collision. We restrict ourselves to one-dimensional motion for the present.

Consider first an elastic one-dimensional collision. We can imagine two smooth nonrotating spheres moving initially along the line joining their centers, then colliding head-on and moving along the same straight line without rotation after collision. The situation is illustrated in Fig. 10–5. Because of their spherical shape, these bodies exert forces on each other during the collision that are along the initial line of motion, so that the final motion is along the same line.

The masses of the spheres are m_1 and m_2, the velocity components being u_1 and u_2 before collision and v_1 and v_2 after collision. We take the positive

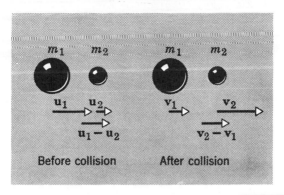

Fig. 10–3 Two elastic spheres before and after a collision. The velocity $u_1 - u_2$ of m_1 relative to m_2 before collision is equal to the velocity $v_2 - v_1$ of m_2 relative to m_1 after collision.

direction of the momentum and velocity to be to the right. Then from conservation of momentum we obtain

$$m_1 u_1 + m_2 u_2 = m_1 v_1 + m_2 v_2,$$

and from conservation of kinetic energy we obtain

$$\tfrac{1}{2} m_1 u_1^2 + \tfrac{1}{2} m_2 u_2^2 = \tfrac{1}{2} m_1 v_1^2 + \tfrac{1}{2} m_2 v_2^2.$$

The momentum equation can be written as

$$m_1(u_1 - v_1) = m_2(v_2 - u_2), \qquad (10\text{–}3)$$

and the energy equation can be written as

$$m_1(u_1^2 \quad v_1^2) - m_2(v_2^2 - u_2^2). \qquad (10\text{–}4)$$

Dividing Eq. 10–4 by Eq. 10–3, we obtain

$$u_1 + v_1 = v_2 + u_2. \qquad (10\text{–}5)$$

Notice that in an elastic one-dimensional collision, the relative velocity of approach before collision is equal to the relative velocity of separation after collision, for Eq. 10–5 can also be written as

$$u_1 - u_2 = v_2 - v_1.$$

To determine the velocity components v_1 and v_2 after collision from the velocity components u_1 and u_2 before collision, we can use any two of the three previous numbered equations. Thus, from Eq. 10–5

$$v_2 = u_1 + v_1 - u_2.$$

Inserting this into Eq. 10–3 and solving for v_1, we find that

$$v_1 = \left(\frac{m_1 - m_2}{m_1 + m_2}\right) u_1 + \left(\frac{2 m_2}{m_1 + m_2}\right) u_2.$$

Likewise, inserting $v_1 = v_2 + u_2 - u_1$ (from Eq. 10–5) into Eq. 10–3 and solving for v_2, we obtain

$$v_2 = \left(\frac{2m_1}{m_1 + m_2}\right) u_1 + \left(\frac{m_2 - m_1}{m_1 + m_2}\right) u_2.$$

There are several cases of special interest. For example, when the colliding particles have the same mass, m_1 equals m_2 and the two previous equations become

$$v_1 = u_2 \qquad v_2 = u_1.$$

That is, in a one-dimensional elastic collision of two particles of equal mass, the particles simply exchange velocities during collision.

Another case of interest is that in which one particle m_2 is initially at rest. Then u_2 equals zero and

$$v_1 = \left(\frac{m_1 - m_2}{m_1 + m_2}\right) u_1 \qquad v_2 = \left(\frac{2m_1}{m_1 + m_2}\right) u_1.$$

Of course, if $m_1 = m_2$ also, then $v_1 = 0$ and $v_2 = u_1$ as we expect. The first particle is "stopped cold" and the second one "takes off" with the velocity the first one originally had. If, however, m_2 is very much greater than m_1, we obtain

$$v_1 \cong -u_1 \qquad \text{and} \qquad v_2 \cong 0.$$

That is, when a light particle collides with a very much more massive particle at rest, the velocity of the light particle is approximately reversed and the massive particle remains approximately at rest. For example, suppose that a ball is dropped vertically onto a horizontal surface attached to the earth. This is in effect a collision between the ball and the earth. If the collision is elastic, the ball will rebound with a reversed velocity and will reach the same height from which it fell.

If, finally, m_2 is very much smaller than m_1, we obtain

$$v_1 \cong u_1 \qquad v_2 \cong 2u_1.$$

This means that the velocity of the massive incident particle is virtually unchanged by the collision with the light stationary particle, but that the light particle rebounds with approximately twice the velocity of the incident particle. The motion of a bowling ball is hardly affected by collision with an inflated beach ball of the same size, but the beach ball bounces away quickly.

Neutrons produced in a reactor from the fission of uranium atoms move very fast and must be slowed down if they are to produce more fissions. Assuming that they make elastic collisions with the nuclei at rest, what material should be picked to moderate the neutrons in the reactor? We know from the considerations noted that if the stationary targets were massive nuclei, like lead, the neutrons would simply bounce back with practically the same speed they had initially. If the stationary targets were very much lighter than the neutrons, like electrons, the neutrons would move on with practically the same velocity they had initially. However, if the stationary targets are particles of nearly the same mass, the neutrons will be brought almost to rest in a collision with them. Hence, hydrogen, whose nucleus (proton) has nearly the same mass as a neutron, should be most effective. Other considerations affect the choice of a moderator for neutrons, but momentum considerations alone limit the choice to the lighter elements.

If a collision is inelastic, we can no longer use the conservation of kinetic energy. The final kinetic energy may be less than the initial value, the difference being ultimately converted to heat or to potential energy of deformation in the collision, for example; or the final kinetic energy may exceed the initial value, as when potential energy is released in the collision. In any case, the conservation of momentum still holds. We must use the conservation of total energy, however, rather than the conservation of kinetic energy.

Let us consider finally a completely inelastic collision. The two particles will remain in contact after collision, so that there will be a final common velocity $\mathbf{v}$. It is not necessary to restrict the discussion to one-dimensional motion. Using only the conservation of momentum principle, we find

$$m_1\mathbf{u}_1 + m_2\mathbf{u}_2 = (m_1 + m_2)\mathbf{v}. \tag{10–6}$$

This determines $\mathbf{v}$ when $\mathbf{u}_1$ and $\mathbf{u}_2$ are known.

▶ **Example 1.** A baseball weighing 0.35 lb is struck by a bat while it is in horizontal flight with a speed of 90 ft/sec. After leaving the bat the ball travels with a speed of 110 ft/sec in a direction opposite to its original motion. Determine the impulse of the collision.

We cannot determine the impulse from the definition $J = \int F\, dt$ because we do not know the force exerted on the ball as a function of time. However, we have seen (Eq. 10–2) that the change in momentum of a particle acted on by an impulsive force is equal to the impulse. Hence,

$$\text{impulse} = \text{change in momentum} = \mathbf{p}_2 - \mathbf{p}_1$$

$$= m\mathbf{v}_2 - m\mathbf{v}_1 = \frac{W}{g}(\mathbf{v}_2 - \mathbf{v}_1).$$

The magnitude of the impulse is then

$$\left(\frac{0.35}{32}\text{ slugs}\right)(-110 \text{ ft/sec} - 90 \text{ ft/sec}) = -2.2 \text{ lb-sec}.$$

The minus sign indicates that the direction of the impulse is opposite that of the original velocity which we arbitrarily choose as positive.

The force of the collision cannot be determined from the data we are given. Actually, any force whose impulse is −2.2 lb-sec will produce the same change in momentum. For example, if the bat and ball were in contact for 0.001 sec, the average force during this time would be

$$\bar{F} = \frac{\Delta p}{\Delta t} = \frac{-2.2 \text{ lb-sec}}{0.001 \text{ sec}} = -2200 \text{ lb}.$$

For shorter contact times the average forces would be greater. The actual force would have a maximum value greater than this average value.

How far would gravity cause the baseball to fall during its collision time?

Example 2. (a) By what fraction is the kinetic energy of a neutron (mass m_1) decreased in a head-on elastic collision with an atomic nucleus (mass m_2) initially at rest?

The initial kinetic energy K_i is $\frac{1}{2}m_1u_1^2$. The final kinetic energy K_f is $\frac{1}{2}m_1v_1^2$. Hence, the fractional decrease in kinetic energy is

$$\frac{K_i - K_f}{K_i} = \frac{u_1^2 - v_1^2}{u_1^2} = 1 - \frac{v_1^2}{u_1^2}.$$

But, for such a collision

$$v_1 = \left(\frac{m_1 - m_2}{m_1 + m_2}\right)u_1,$$

so that

$$\frac{K_i - K_f}{K_i} = 1 - \left(\frac{m_1 - m_2}{m_1 + m_2}\right)^2 = \frac{4m_1m_2}{(m_1 + m_2)^2}.$$

(b) Find the fractional decrease in the kinetic energy of a neutron when it collides in this way with a lead nucleus, a carbon nucleus, and a hydrogen nucleus. The ratio of nuclear mass to neutron mass is 206 for lead, 12 for carbon, and 1 for hydrogen.

For lead, $m_2 = 206m_1$,

$$\frac{K_i - K_f}{K_i} = \frac{4 \times 206}{(207)^2} = 0.02 \quad \text{or} \quad 2\%.$$

For carbon, $m_2 = 12m_1$,

$$\frac{K_i - K_f}{K_i} = \frac{4 \times 12}{(13)^2} = 0.28 \quad \text{or} \quad 28\%.$$

For hydrogen, $m_2 = m_1$,

$$\frac{K_i - K_f}{K_i} = \frac{4 \times 1}{(2)^2} = 1 \quad \text{or} \quad 100\%.$$

These results explain why neutrons are slowed down just a little by a 50-cm-thick lead plate but are completely absorbed in a layer of paraffin (hydrogeneous) 20 cm thick.

Example 3. The ballistic pendulum is used to measure bullet speeds. The pendulum, consisting of a large wooden block of mass M, hangs vertically by two cords. A bullet of mass m, traveling with a horizontal speed u, strikes the pendulum and remains embedded in it (Fig. 10–6). If the collision time (the time required for the bullet to come to rest with respect to the block) is very small compared to the time of swing of the pendulum, the supporting cords remain approximately vertical during the collision. Therefore, no external horizontal force acts on the system during collision, and the horizontal component of momentum is conserved. The speed of the system after collision v is much less than that of the bullet before collision. This final speed can be easily determined, so that the original speed of the bullet can be calculated from momentum conservation.

The initial momentum of the system is that of the bullet mu, and the momentum of the system just after collision is $(m + M)v$, so that

$$mu = (m + M)v.$$

After the collision is over, the pendulum and bullet swing up to a maximum height y, where the kinetic energy left after impact is converted into gravitational potential

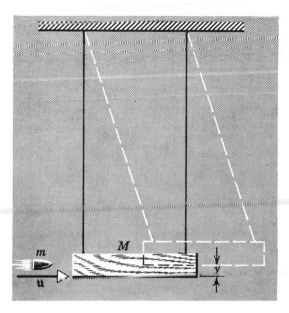

Fig. 10–6 Example 3. A ballistic pendulum consisting of a large wooden block of mass M is suspended by cords. When a bullet of mass m and velocity $\mathbf{u}$ is fired into it, the block swings, rising a maximum distance y.

energy. Then, using the conservation of mechanical energy for this part of the motion, we obtain

$$\tfrac{1}{2}(m + M)v^2 = (m + M)gy.$$

Solving these two equations for u, we obtain

$$u = \frac{m + M}{m}\,\sqrt{2gy}.$$

Hence, the initial speed of the bullet can be determined by measuring m, M, and y.

The kinetic energy of the bullet initially is $\tfrac{1}{2}mu^2$ and the kinetic energy of the system bullet-in-pendulum just after collision is $\tfrac{1}{2}(m + M)v^2$. The ratio is

$$\frac{\tfrac{1}{2}(m + M)v^2}{\tfrac{1}{2}mu^2} = \frac{m}{m + M}.$$

For example, if the bullet has a mass $m = 5$ gm and the block has a mass $M = 2000$ gm, only about one-fourth of 1% of the original kinetic energy remains; over 99% is converted to other forms of energy, such as heat. ◀

The motion of the center of mass of two particles is unaffected by their collision, for the collision does not change the total momentum of the system of two particles, only the distribution of momentum between the two particles. The momentum of the system can be written (Eq. 9–21) as $\mathbf{P} = (m_1 + m_2)\mathbf{v}_{cm}$. If no external forces act on the system, then $\mathbf{P}$ is constant before and after the collision, and the center of mass moves with uniform velocity throughout.

If we choose a frame of reference attached to the center of mass, then in this center-of-mass coordinate system $\mathbf{v}_{cm} = 0$ and $\mathbf{P} = 0$. There is a great simplicity and

symmetry in describing collisions with respect to the center of mass, and it is customary to do so in nuclear physics. For whether collisions are elastic or inelastic, momentum is conserved, and in the center of mass coordinates the total momentum is zero.
These results hold in two and three dimensions as well as in one because momentum
is a vector quantity.

As an example, consider a head-on elastic collision between two particles m_1 and m_2.
Let m_2 equal $3m_1$ and let m_2 be at rest, so that u_2 equals zero in the laboratory coordinate system. The total momentum of the two particles is just that of the incident
particle m_1u_1, so that

$$m_1u_1 = (m_1 + m_2)v_{cm}$$

or
$$v_{cm} = \left(\frac{m_1}{m_1 + m_2}\right)u_1 = \tfrac{1}{4}u_1.$$

After the collision, m_1 has a velocity $v_1 = -\tfrac{1}{2}u_1$ and m_2 has a velocity $v_2 = \tfrac{1}{2}u_1$.
The total momentum of the two particles $(m_1v_1 + m_2v_2)$ is the same as before the
collision, and the motion of the center of mass is unchanged (check this). In Fig.
10–7a we draw a series of "snapshots" of the collision taken at equal time intervals as
seen in the laboratory coordinate system. In Fig. 10–7b we draw the same situation
as seen in the center-of-mass coordinate system where v_{cm} is zero. Notice the symmetry of the particles' motions when described in this way. The particle incident
from the left has a speed $\tfrac{3}{4}u_1$ with respect to the center of mass (where u_1 is the speed
of m_1 in the laboratory system) and recedes with this same speed. The particle
incident from the right has a speed $\tfrac{1}{4}u_1$ with respect to the center of mass and recedes
with this same speed.

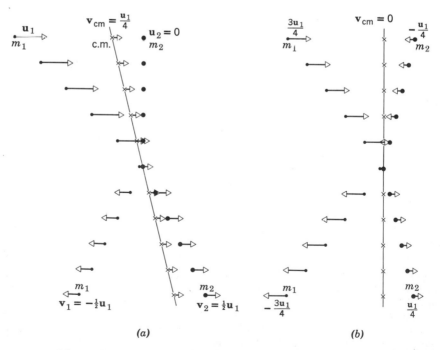

(a) (b)

Fig. 10–7 (a) An elastic collision in the laboratory coordinate system. (b) The same
elastic collision in the center-of-mass coordinate system.

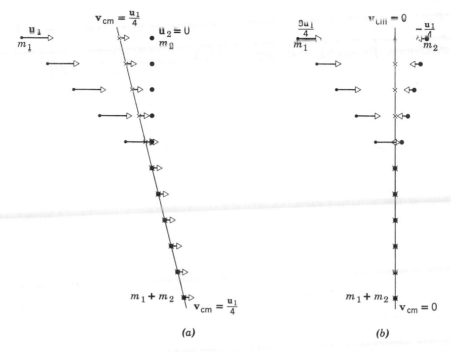

Fig. 10–8 (a) A completely inelastic collision in the laboratory coordinate system. (b) The same completely inelastic collision in the center-of-mass coordinate system.

If the collision is completely inelastic, the motion after collision is simply that of two particles moving along together at the center of mass. In Figs. 10–8a and 10–8b we show how this inelastic collision would be described in the laboratory and the center-of-mass coordinate systems, respectively. These figures differ from the previous ones only after the collision when the motion of the center of mass describes that of the entire system.

10–5 The "True" Measure of a Force

The distinction between kinetic energy and momentum and the relationship of these concepts to force were not clearly understood until late in the eighteenth century. Scientists argued whether kinetic energy or momentum was the true measure of the effect of a force on a body. Descartes argued that when bodies interact, all that can happen is the transfer of momentum from one body to another, for the total momentum of the universe remains constant; hence, the only true measure of a force is the change in momentum it produces in a given time. Liebnitz attacked this view and argued that the true measure of a force is the change it produces in kinetic energy (called by him *vis viva* or living force, taken to be twice what we now call kinetic energy).

In his treatise on mechanics (1743), D'Alembert dismissed the argument as being pointless and arising from a confusion of terminology. The cumulative effect of a force can be measured by its integrated effect over *time*,

$\int F\,dt$, which produces a change in momentum, *or* by its integrated effect over *space*, $\int F\,dx$, which produces a change in kinetic energy. Both concepts are useful and valid, although different. Which one we use depends on what we are interested in or what is more convenient. As our present study of collisions illustrates, we frequently use both concepts in the same problem.

10–6 Collisions in Two and Three Dimensions

Except for a completely inelastic collision, the use of the conservation laws alone cannot determine the motion of particles after a collision from a knowledge of the motion before the collision when the motion is two- or three-dimensional. For example, for a two-dimensional elastic collision, which is the simplest case, we have four unknowns, namely the two components of velocity for each of two particles after collision; but we have only three known relations between them, one for the conservation of kinetic energy and a conservation of momentum relation for each of the two dimensions. Hence, we need more information than just the initial conditions. When we do not know the actual forces of interaction, as is often the case, the additional information must be obtained from experiment. It is simplest to specify the angle of recoil of one of the colliding particles.

Let us consider what happens when one particle is projected at a target particle which is at rest. This case is not as restrictive as it may seem, for we can always pick our coordinate system to be one in which the target particle is at rest before collision. Furthermore, much experimental work in nuclear physics involves projecting nuclear particles at a target which is stationary in the laboratory coordinate system. Then the motion is in a plane determined by the lines of recoil of the colliding particles. The initial motion need not be along the line joining the centers of the two particles. The force of interaction may not be a contact force but may instead be a force acting at a distance, such as magnetic, electrical, gravitational, or nuclear forces.

A typical situation is shown in Fig. 10–9. The distance b between the initial line of motion and a line parallel to it through the center of the target particle is called the *impact parameter*. This is a measure of the directness of the collision, $b = 0$ corresponding to a head-on collision. The direction of motion of the incident particle m_1 after collision makes an angle θ_1 with the initial direction, and the target particle m_2, initially at rest, moves in a direction after collision making an angle θ_2 with the initial direction of the incident projectile. Applying the conservation of momentum, which is a vector relation, we obtain two scalar equations; for the x component of motion we have

$$m_1 u_1 = m_1 v_1 \cos\theta_1 + m_2 v_2 \cos\theta_2,$$

and for the y component

$$0 = m_1 v_1 \sin\theta_1 - m_2 v_2 \sin\theta_2.$$

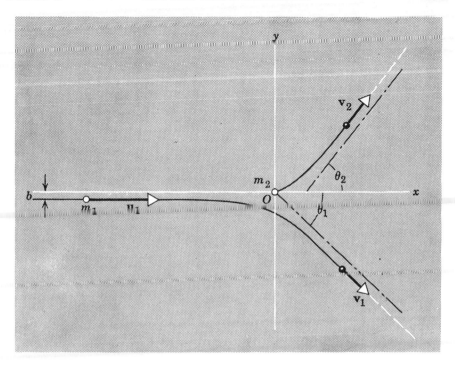

Fig. 10–9 Two particles, m_1 and m_2, undergoing a collision. The open circles indicate their positions before collision, the shaded ones those after collision. Initially m_2 is at rest. The impact parameter b is the distance by which the collision misses being head-on.

Let us now assume that the collision is *elastic*. Here the conservation of kinetic energy applies and we obtain a third equation,

$$\tfrac{1}{2}m_1u_1{}^2 = \tfrac{1}{2}m_1v_1{}^2 + \tfrac{1}{2}m_2v_2{}^2.$$

If we know the initial conditions (m_1, m_2, and u_1), we are left with four unknowns (v_1, v_2, θ_1, and θ_2) but only three equations relating them. We can determine the motion after collision only if we specify a value for one of these quantities, such as θ_1.

▶ **Example 4.** A gas molecule having a speed of 300 meters/sec collides elastically with another molecule of the same mass which is initially at rest. After the collision the first molecule moves at an angle of 30° to its initial direction. Find the speed of each molecule after collision and the angle made with the incident direction by the recoiling target molecule.

This example corresponds exactly to the situation just discussed, with $m_1 = m_2$, $u_1 = 300$ meters/sec, and $\theta_1 = 30°$. Setting m_1 equal to m_2, we have the relations

$$u_1 = v_1 \cos\theta_1 + v_2 \cos\theta_2,$$

$$v_1 \sin\theta_1 = v_2 \sin\theta_2,$$

$$u_1{}^2 = v_1{}^2 + v_2{}^2.$$

We must solve for v_1, v_2, and θ_2. To do this we square the first equation (rewriting it as $u_1 - v_1 \cos \theta_1 = v_2 \cos \theta_2$), and add this to the square of the second equation (noting that $\sin^2 \theta + \cos^2 \theta = 1$); we obtain

$$u_1{}^2 + v_1{}^2 - 2u_1v_1 \cos \theta_1 = v_2{}^2.$$

Combining this with the third equation,

$$u_1{}^2 = v_1{}^2 + v_2{}^2,$$

we obtain

$$2v_1{}^2 = 2u_1v_1 \cos \theta_1$$

or

$$v_1 = u_1 \cos \theta_1 = (300 \text{ meters/sec})(\cos 30°) = 260 \text{ meters/sec}.$$

From the third equation

$$v_2{}^2 = u_1{}^2 - v_1{}^2 = (300 \text{ meters/sec})^2 - (260 \text{ meters/sec})^2,$$

$$v_2 = 150 \text{ meters/sec}.$$

Finally, from the second equation

$$\sin \theta_2 = \frac{v_1}{v_2} \sin \theta_1$$

$$= (\tfrac{260}{150})(\sin 30°) = 0.866$$

or

$$\theta_2 = 60°.$$

The two molecules move apart at right angles ($\theta_1 + \theta_2 = 90°$ in Fig. 10–9).

The student should be able to show that in an elastic collision between particles of equal mass, one of which is initially at rest, the recoiling particles always move off at right angles to one another. ◀

In Fig. 10–10, we show photographs of four elastic nuclear collisions. In each the incident particle is an α-particle (nucleus of helium atom) and the target nucleus is at rest before collision. Notice that as the target mass increases, the angle between the recoiling particles increases. (See Problem 18.) In case (b), where the target is also an α-particle, the recoiling particles move off at right angles.

Most collisions are *inelastic*, even on a microscopic scale. Atoms, molecules, and even nuclei have internal energy associated with the positions and motions of their constituent parts. These particles, therefore, may absorb or give up kinetic energy in collisions. It may even happen that the recoiling particles are not the same as the colliding particles. In all these cases, however, the law of conservation of momentum holds, and if we take into account the internal energy of the particles, we can also use the law of conservation of *total* energy. The methods of this section can be extended, therefore, to cover the whole range of atomic, molecular, and nuclear collisions. This extension, however, is beyond the scope of the text.

10–7 Collision Cross Section

When the force of interaction between the colliding particles is known, we can find the resulting motion directly from the initial conditions. The force law itself is a fourth equation applying to the motion. The impact parameter is then an initial condition which must be specified. Examples frequently

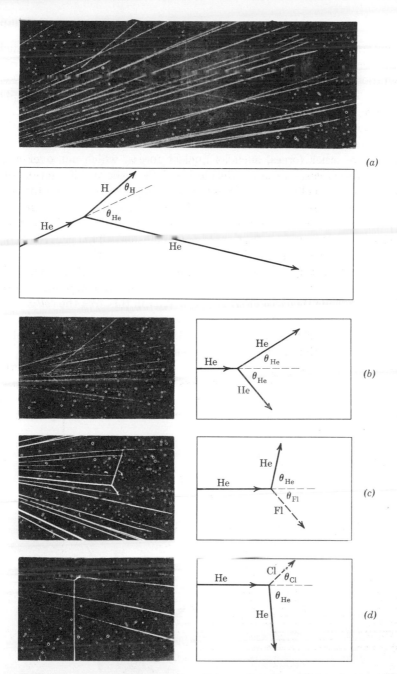

Fig. 10-10 Photographs of trajectories of particles undergoing collisions inside a Wilson cloud chamber, a device that makes these paths visible. The chamber contains saturated water vapor. If the vapor is slightly compressed and then allowed to expand quickly, the water vapor will condense in droplets along the trajectory. The incident particle in all four tracks (a, b, c, d) is a helium (He) nucleus of mass 4 atomic mass units (amu). In (a) the target is a hydrogen (H) atom (1 amu); after collision the He and H particles exit in directions θ_{He} and θ_{H}. The other tracks are similar, except that in (b) the target is another He atom, whereas in (c) and (d) the targets are fluorine and chlorine atoms, respectively.

encountered in physics are collisions between astronomical bodies, such as the motion of a comet near a planet, in which the force is the known force of gravitation, or collisions between electrically charged particles, in which the force is the known Coulomb force between charged particles. These forces are long-range ones, so that the changes in the motion of colliding bodies subject to such forces of interaction are gradual rather than abrupt as they are for contact collisions.

There are other forces, such as nuclear forces, which act over a short range. In such cases we must decide just how weak an interaction should be to be called a collision. This involves stating just how large the impact parameter can be so that, for purposes of the problem at hand, a large enough deflection occurs to call the interaction a collision. If the impact parameter exceeds this value, we say that there is no collision. This procedure determines the effective range of the force of interaction. Hence, we can define an area about the target particle such that a collision occurs if the initial line of motion of the incident particle passes through this area and does not occur if it passes outside this area (Fig. 10–11). We call this area the *collision cross section σ*. Because a fast-moving particle interacts for a shorter time with the target than a slow-moving particle, the collision cross section will generally depend on the incident speed (or energy).

Often, as in nuclear physics, the exact nature of the force of interaction is not known. Then we determine the cross section experimentally and use the results to deduce something about the nature of the force. In nuclear physics the collision cross section is determined experimentally by firing a

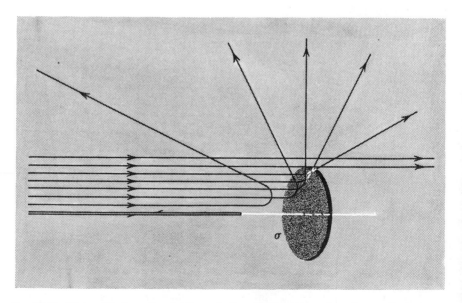

Fig. 10–11 The scattering cross section σ is the effective area a target presents to a projectile to be scattered. If the initial line of motion of the projectile passes through σ, we say that the projectile has been scattered; otherwise, not.

beam of particles at a thin foil of material containing a great many target nuclei. We cannot control the impact parameter because the distance from a target nucleus to the line of flight of a projectile may be different for each pair of "colliding" particles. The impact parameters are randomly distributed, and we must analyze the interactions statistically.

The area of the foil exposed to the beam is A and the thickness of the foil is Δs. If there are n target particles per unit volume of foil, the total number of available target particles is $nA\,\Delta s$. If each target particle offers a cross-sectional area σ for collision, the total area available for collisions is $(nA\,\Delta s)\sigma$. Hence, the chance that a collision will occur when one particle passes through the foil is the ratio of this area to the total area of the foil exposed to the beam, or $n\,\Delta s\,\sigma$. To determine σ experimentally, we measure the *fraction of the incident particles which make a collision* and set this fraction equal to $n\,\Delta s\,\sigma$. That is, N/N_0 equals $n\,\Delta s\,\sigma$. From knowledge of the thickness of the foil and the density of target particles we then solve for σ.

Instead of the cross section for the occurrence of any collision, called the *total* cross section, we are often interested in the cross section for some special kind of collision. For example, in molecular collisions the incident molecule may ionize the target molecule; it may merely transfer energy to the target molecule; it may dissociate the target molecule, and so forth. To obtain the cross section for one particular kind of collision, we simply measure the fraction of the incident particles which makes this kind of collision with the target particles. The total collision cross section is the sum of all such partial cross sections.

▶ **Example 5.** (a) About 1910 Geiger and Marsden, working under Lord Rutherford at Manchester University, performed a series of classic experiments that established the fact that atoms consisted of a small nucleus surrounded by a cloud of electrons rather than a ball of distributed positive and negative charges, as Thomson had suggested earlier.

This experiment was in essence that shown in Fig. 10–12. Here α-particles from a polonium source are allowed to impinge on a gold foil 4.0×10^{-7} meter thick. It is found that although most of the α-particles pass through the foil (forward scattering),

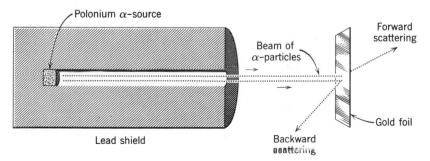

Fig. 10–12 Example 5. α-Particles stream from a polonium source and a beam is formed by the lead shield. Some of the α-particles are scattered backward by the gold foil target; the rest pass through the foil.

about 1 in 6.17×10^6 are scattered backward, that is, are deflected through an angle greater than $90°$. The number of gold atoms per unit volume in the foil is $5.9 \times 10^{28}/$ meter^3. What is the scattering cross section in barns for backward scattering (1 barn $= 10^{-28}$ meter^2)?

From

$$n \, \Delta s \, \sigma = \text{fraction scattered backward}$$

we have $\quad (5.9 \times 10^{28}/\text{meter}^3)(4.0 \times 10^{-7} \text{ meter})\sigma = 1/(6.17 \times 10^6)$

or $\quad \sigma = 6.9 \times 10^{-28} \text{ meter}^2 = 6.9 \text{ barns.}$

This is the cross section for backward scattering.

(b) Rutherford reasoned that the backward scattering could not be caused by electrons in the atom; the α-particles were so much more massive than the atoms that they would hardly be deflected at all by electrons, let alone be scattered backward. He then suggested the nuclear model of the atom, attributing the scattering to collisions between α-particles and the massive positive core of the atom, the nucleus.

Assuming that the cross section for backward scattering is approximately equal to the area offered by a gold nucleus for direct collisions, estimate the size of a gold nucleus.

If the radius of the gold nucleus is taken to be r, we have

$$\sigma \cong \pi r^2,$$

$$r^2 \cong \sigma/\pi = 6.9 \times 10^{-28} \text{ meter}^2/\pi,$$

or $\quad r \cong 1.5 \times 10^{-14} \text{ meter.}$

This is the approximate radius of a gold *nucleus*.

This compares with the value of about 1.5×10^{-10} meter for the gold *atom*.

Hence, the massive nucleus is concentrated in a very small region of the atom (about 1 part in 10^{12} by volume). ◄

QUESTIONS

1. Explain how conservation of momentum applies to a handball bouncing off a wall.

2. How can you reconcile the sailing of a sailboat into the wind with the conservation of momentum principle?

3. A sand glass is being weighed on a sensitive balance, first when sand is dropping in a steady stream from the upper to the lower part and then again after the upper part is empty. Are the two weights the same or not? Explain your answer.

4. It is obvious from inspection of Eqs. 10–3 and 10–4 that a valid solution to the problem of finding the final velocities of two particles in a one-dimensional elastic collision is $v_1 = u_1$ and $v_2 = u_2$. What does this mean physically? Explain.

5. When the forces of interaction between two particles have an infinite range, such as the mutual gravitational attraction between two bodies, can the cross section for collision be finite?

6. Why does the computation of the radius of the gold nucleus in Example 5 give only an approximate answer?

7. Could we determine in principle the cross section for a collision by using only one bombarding particle and one target particle? In practice?

PROBLEMS

1. A cue strikes a billiard ball, exerting an average force of 50 nt over a time of 10 milliseconds. If the ball has mass 0.20 kg, what speed does it have after impact?

2. A 1-kg ball drops vertically onto the floor with a speed of 25 meters/sec. It rebounds with an initial speed of 10 meters/second. (a) What impulse acts on the ball during contact? (b) If the ball is in contact for 0.02 sec, what is the average force exerted on the floor?

3. A croquet ball (mass 0.50 kg) is struck by a mallet, receiving the impulse shown in the graph (Fig. 10–13). What is the ball's velocity just after the force has become zero?

4. A ball of mass m and speed v strikes a wall perpendicularly and rebounds with undiminished speed. If the time of collision is t, what is the average force exerted by the ball on the wall?

5. A bullet weighing 1.0×10^{-2} lb is fired horizontally into a 4.0-lb wooden block at rest on a horizontal surface. The coefficient of kinetic friction between block and surface is 0.20. The bullet comes to rest in the block which moves 6.0 ft. Find the speed of the bullet.

6. A 6.0-kg box sled is traveling across the ice at a speed of 9.0 meters/sec when a 12-kg package is dropped into it vertically. Describe the subsequent motion of the sled.

7. A bullet of mass 10 gm strikes a ballistic pendulum of mass 2.0 kg. The center of mass of the pendulum rises a vertical distance of 12 cm. Assuming the bullet remains embedded in the pendulum, calculate its initial speed.

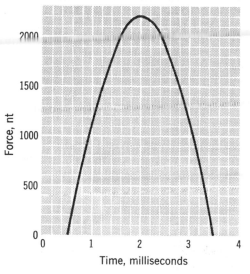

Fig. 10–13

8. A steel ball weighing 1.0 lb is fastened to a cord 27 in. long and is released when the cord is horizontal. At the bottom of its path the ball strikes a 5.0-lb steel block initially at rest on a level surface (Fig. 10–14). The collision is elastic. Find the speed of the ball and the speed of the block just after the collision.

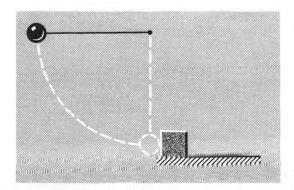

Fig. 10–14

9. A railroad freight car weighing 32 tons and traveling 5.0 ft/sec overtakes one weighing 24 tons traveling 3.0 ft/sec in the same direction. (a) Find the speed of the cars after collision and the loss of kinetic energy during collision if the cars couple together. (b) If the collision is elastic, the freight cars do not couple but separate after collision. What are their speeds?

10. An elevator is moving *up* at 6.0 ft/sec in a shaft. At the instant the elevator is 60 ft from the top, a ball is dropped from the top of the shaft. The ball rebounds elastically from the elevator roof. To what height can it rise relative to the top of the shaft? Do the same problem assuming the elevator is moving *down* at 6.0 ft/sec.

11. A box is put on a scale which is adjusted to read 0 lb when the box is empty. A stream of pebbles is then poured into the box from a height h ft above its bottom at a rate of μ pebbles per second. Each pebble has a mass m slugs. If the collisions between the pebbles and box are completely inelastic, find the scale reading t sec after the pebbles begin to fill the box. Determine a numerical answer when $\mu = 100$ sec^{-1}, $h = 25$ ft, $mg = 0.01$ lb, and $t = 10$ sec.

12. An electron collides elastically with a hydrogen atom initially at rest. The initial and final motions are along the same straight line. What fraction of the electron's initial kinetic energy is transferred to the hydrogen atom? The mass of the hydrogen atom is 1840 times the mass of the electron.

13. An electron, mass m, collides head on with an atom, mass M, initially at rest. As a result of the collision a characteristic amount of energy E is stored internally in the atom. What is the minimum initial velocity v_0 that the electron must have? (Hint: Conservation principles lead to a quadratic equation for the final electron velocity v and a quadratic equation for the final atom velocity V. The minimum value v_0 follows from the requirement that the radical in the solutions for v and V be real.)

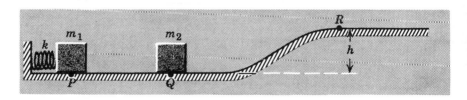

Fig. 10–15

14. Path PQR is a frictionless surface along which m_1 and m_2 can slide. Mass m_1 is initially held against (although not attached to) a spring with spring constant k at point P, compressing the spring a distance x_0. The mass is then released and collides elastically with m_2 which is at rest at Q (Fig. 10–15). (a) Assume $m_1 < m_2$. How much, x, will the spring be compressed when m_1 bounces back against it after the collision? (b) What is the value of x if $m_1 = m_2$? (c) Again assume $m_1 < m_2$. How much must the original compression x_0 be if m_2 is to just reach point R before stopping? [Can you make use of part of your work for (a)?]

15. A bullet of mass m is fired with a velocity $\mathbf{v}$ into a pendulum (initially at rest), consisting of a putty ball of mass M suspended by a wire of length l (Fig. 10–16). The bullet remains lodged in the putty ball after collision. Find (a) the vertical height to which the putty ball rises, and (b) the kinetic energy of the bullet and putty ball immediately after impact.

16. In a common lecture demonstration on momentum, six billiard balls are placed in contact with each other along a straight line. The balls can slide along a wire support but cannot roll.

(a) Assume the billiard balls are identical, each having a mass M. Show that if the collisions are elastic, when one ball is slammed into the other five in contact (Fig. 10–17), its incident speed v is transferred to the last ball; when two balls are slammed into the other four in contact, their common incident speed v is transferred to the last two balls, etc.

(b) Let the last mass on the right, m, be smaller than the remaining masses M. Suppose that a ball of mass M collides from the left with speed v_0 into the other five in contact. Show that if the collision is elastic it is impossible for m to be the only mass set in motion. If we assume that only two balls are set in motion, what must their speeds be?

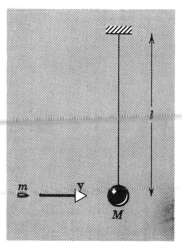

Fig. 10–16

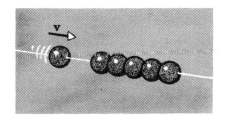

Fig. 10–17

(c) Let the last mass on the right be M', where M' is greater than the mass M of each of the remaining balls. Mass M now collides elastically from the left with incident speed v_0. (Notice that the next-to-last mass on the right transfers its momentum toward the left.) What is the velocity of M' and of the first mass M at the left end of the row? What happens if M' is very large compared to M?

17. (a) Show that in a one-dimensional elastic collision the speed of the center of mass of two particles, m_1 moving with initial speed u_1 and m_2 moving with initial speed u_2, is

$$v_{\rm cm} = \left(\frac{m_1}{m_1 + m_2}\right) u_1 + \left(\frac{m_2}{m_1 + m_2}\right) u_2.$$

(b) Use the expressions obtained for v_1 and v_2, the particles' speeds after collision, to derive the same result for $v_{\rm cm}$ *after* the collision.

18. Show that, in the case of an elastic collision between a particle of mass m_1 with a particle of mass m_2 initially *at rest*, (a) the maximum angle through which m_1 can be deflected by the collision is given by $\cos^2 \theta_m = 1 - m_2^2/m_1^2$, so that $0 \leq \theta_m \leq \pi/2$, when $m_1 > m_2$; (b) $\theta_1 + \theta_2 = \pi/2$, when $m_1 = m_2$; (c) θ_1 can take on all values between 0 and π, when $m_1 < m_2$.

19. A billiard ball moving at a speed of 2.2 meters/sec strikes an identical stationary ball a glancing blow. After the collision one ball is found to be moving at a speed of 1.1 meters/sec in a direction making a $60°$ angle with the original line of motion. Find the velocity of the other ball.

20. An α-particle collides with an oxygen nucleus, initially at rest. The α-particle is scattered at an angle of $72°$ from its initial direction of motion and the oxygen nucleus recoils at an angle of $41°$ on the other side of this initial direction. What is the ratio of the speeds of these particles? The mass of oxygen nucleus is four times that of the α-particle.

21. Two balls A and B, having different but unknown masses, collide. A is initially at rest when B has a speed v. After collision B has a speed $v/2$ and moves at right angles to

its original motion. Find the direction in which ball A moves after collision. Can you determine the speed of A from the information given? Explain.

22. Two vehicles A and B are traveling west and south, respectively, toward the same intersection (Fig. 10–18) where they collide and lock together. Before the collision A (total weight, 900 lb) is moving with a speed of 40 mph, and B (total weight, 1200 lb) has a speed of 60 mph. Find the magnitude and direction of the velocity of the (interlocked) vehicles immediately after collision.

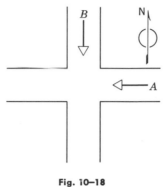

Fig. 10–18

23. In 1932 Chadwick in England demonstrated the existence and properties of the neutron (one of the fundamental particles making up the atom) with the device shown in Fig. 10–19. In an evacuated chamber, a sample of radioactive polonium decays to yield α-rays (helium nuclei). These nuclei impinge on a block of beryllium inducing a process whereby neutrons are emitted. (The reaction is: He and Be combine to form radioactive carbon, which decays to stable carbon + neutrons.) The neutrons strike a film of paraffin

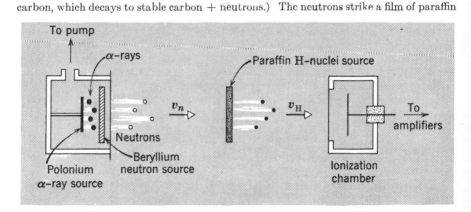

Fig. 10–19

(CH_4), releasing hydrogen nuclei which are detected in an ionization chamber. In other words, an elastic collision takes place in which the momentum of the neutron is partially transferred to the hydrogen nucleus.

(a) Find an expression for the maximum speed v_H that the hydrogen nucleus (mass m_H) can achieve. Let the incoming neutrons have mass m_n and speed v_n. (Hint: Will more energy be transferred in a head-on collision or in a glancing collision?)

(b) One of Chadwick's goals was to find the mass of his new particle. Inspection of expression (a) which contains this parameter, however, shows that *two* unknowns are present, v_n and m_n (v_H is known; it can be measured with the ionization chamber). To eliminate the unknown v_n, he substituted a paracyanogen (CN) block for the paraffin.

The neutrons then underwent elastic collisions with nitrogen nuclei instead of hydrogen nuclei. Of course, expression (a) still holds if v_N is written for v_H and m_N for m_H.

Therefore if v_H and v_N are measured in separate experiments, v_n can be eliminated between the two expressions for hydrogen and nitrogen to yield a value for m_n. Chadwick's values were

$$v_H = 3.3 \times 10^9 \text{ cm/sec},$$

$$v_N = 0.47 \times 10^9 \text{ cm/sec}.$$

What was his value for m_n? How does this compare with the established value $m_n = 1.008987$ amu? (Take $m_H = 1.0$ amu, $m_N = 14$ amu.)

24. A sphere of radius r_1 impinges on a sphere of radius r_2. What is the cross section for a contact collision?

25. A beam of fast neutrons impinges on a 5-mg sample of Cu^{65}, a stable isotope of copper (Fig. 10–20). A possibility exists that the copper nucleus may capture a neutron to form Cu^{66}, which is radioactive and decays to Zn^{66}, which is again stable. If a study of the electron emission of the copper sample implies that 4.6×10^{11} neutron captures occur each second, what is the neutron capture cross section in barns for this process? The intensity of the neutron beam is 1.1×10^{18} neutrons/(meter²)(sec).

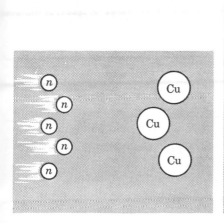

Fig. 10–20

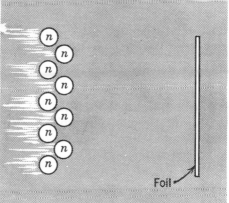

Fig. 10–21

26. As in Problem 25, slow neutrons strike an aluminum foil 10^{-5} meter thick (Fig. 10–21). Some neutrons are captured by the aluminum which becomes radioactive and decays by emitting an electron (β^-) and forming silicon:

$$n + Al^{27} \rightarrow Al^{28} \rightarrow Si^{28} + \beta^-.$$

Suppose that the neutron flux is 3×10^{16}/(meter²)(sec), and the neutron capture cross section is 0.23 barn. How many transmutations will occur each second?

27. In a thick foil there are a great many layers of target particles so that the number of projectile particles reaching a layer will depend on how many have been scattered out by previous layers. Let the number of particles reaching a layer at a depth s be N and the number lost by scattering from that layer be $-dN$; then show that

$$-\frac{dN}{N} = n\sigma \, ds$$

and

$$N = N_0 e^{-n\sigma s}$$

where N_0 is the number of particles incident on the face of the foil ($s = 0$).

Rotational Kinematics

11-1   Rotational Motion

Up to this point we have restricted our study of motion to translational motion. In translational motion each point on a body experiences the same displacement as any other point, as time goes on, so that the motion of one particle represents the motion of the whole body. Let us now investigate rotational motion.

We shall consider a *rigid body* only, that is, a body whose parts all have a fixed location with respect to each other when the body is subjected to external forces. This eliminates the possibility of vibrational motion. Of course, no real substance is perfectly rigid or incompressible, but a great many bodies, such as a steel beam or a wooden wheel, are rigid enough that their vibrational motion can be ignored in many problems.

A particle, or a real body in translational motion, can be located completely by specifying the three coordinates x, y, and z of the point representing it with respect to some Cartesian reference frame. Three coordinates are usually *not* sufficient for locating a rigid body, however, because such a body can rotate as well as move translationally. In general, six coordinates are required; three, such as x, y, and z, can locate some point on the body, and three other coordinates, such as angles, can specify the orientation of the body with respect to the frame of reference.

Figure 11-1 illustrates a rigid-body motion which combines translational and rotational motion. This figure is a simple extension of Fig. 3-1 in which the same body used there is now allowed to rotate as it moves translationally. Not only must we specify the location of a point O in the body relative to the reference frame (x- and y-axes), but we must also specify how the coordinate

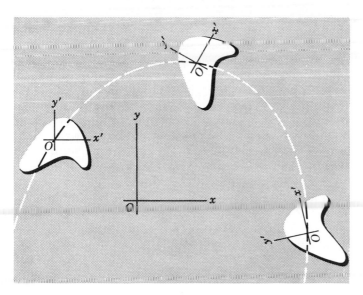

Fig. 11–1 A rigid body undergoing both rotational and translational motion. Notice that the coordinate axes fixed on the body (x', y') are not oriented the same way throughout the motion. Compare with Fig. 3–1.

axes through O, which are fixed in the body (x'- and y'-axes), are oriented relative to the reference frame.

Although the general motion of a rigid body combines translational and rotational motion, it is possible to separate these motions into a purely translational part and a purely rotational part. We saw in Chapter 9 that for any system of particles, whether rigid or not, the center of mass of the system moves as though all the mass of the system were concentrated there and all the external forces were applied at that point. Hence, the motion of the center of mass of a rigid body can be determined directly from Eq. 9–11,

$$\mathbf{F}_{ext} = M\mathbf{a},$$

where M is the mass of the rigid body, $\mathbf{a}$ is the acceleration of its center of mass, and $\mathbf{F}_{ext}$ is the sum of all the external forces acting on the body. This motion is a pure translation, the center of mass being merely a point. It is, therefore, a great simplification to represent the translational motion of a rigid body by the motion of its center of mass. This reduces the translational motion of a rigid body to the known motion of a single particle.

It now remains to determine the rotational motion of the body. First, it is necessary to *describe* rotational motion. This description, called rotational kinematics, involves defining the variables of angular motion and relating them to one another, just as in particle kinematics we defined the variables of linear motion and found their relation to one another. Next, we seek to relate the rotational motion of a body to its properties and the causes of motion. This is the aim of rotational dynamics. In this chapter we study the kinematics of rotation. The dynamics of rotation is developed in the next chapter.

11-2   Rotational Kinematics

A rigid body moves with pure translational motion if each particle of the body undergoes the same displacement as every other particle in any given time interval. A rigid body moves with pure rotational motion, on the other hand, *if every particle of the body moves in a circle, the centers of which are on a single straight line, called the axis of rotation.* If we draw a line from each particle perpendicular to the axis of rotation, each of these lines will turn through equal angles in the same time.

We assume for the present that the axis of rotation is fixed with respect to the reference frame in which we describe the motion. Later we shall consider rotation about an axis which is moving with respect to our reference frame. Some examples of rotational motion are motion of a phonograph turntable about its axis and the motion of a flywheel or grindstone about its axis.

Figure 11-2 represents a rigid body that rotates about a fixed axis through O perpendicular to the plane of the diagram. Line OP is a line in the body from P to O perpendicular to the axis. This line is fixed with respect to the rigid body and rotates with it. We can specify the position of the entire body by an angle θ which the line OP makes with some reference line fixed in space, such as Ox. The angle θ is called the angular position of the body with respect to the reference position. We arbitrarily choose the positive sense of rotation to be counterclockwise, so that θ increases for counterclockwise motion and θ decreases for clockwise motion.

It is convenient to measure the angle θ in radians, rather than in degrees. A radian is an angle at the center of the circle subtended by an arc whose length is equal to its radius; an angle θ in radians is, therefore, given by

$$\theta = \frac{s}{R},$$

as shown in Fig. 11-3.

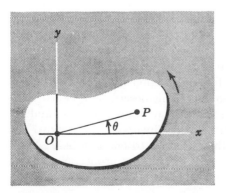

Fig. 11-2 A rigid body rotating about a fixed axis perpendicular to the page and passing through O. Point P is fixed to the body and lies in the x-y plane.

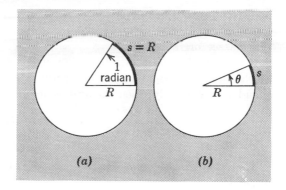

Fig. 11–3 (a) A radian is the angle subtended by an arc s equal to the radius R. (b) $s/R = \theta$ radians.

The radian is a pure number having no physical dimension, since it is a ratio of two lengths. Since the circumference of a circle of radius R is $2\pi R$, there are 2π radians in a complete circle, that is,

$$\theta = \frac{2\pi R}{R} = 2\pi.$$

Therefore, 2π radians $= 360°$, π radians $= 180°$, and 1 radian $\cong 57.3°$. The degree is likewise a pure number.

Let our body be rotating counterclockwise. At the time t_1 the reference line OP will make an angle θ_1 with Ox and at time t_2 an angle θ_2 (Fig. 11–4). The *angular displacement* will be $\theta_2 - \theta_1 = \Delta\theta$ during the time interval $t_2 - t_1 = \Delta t$. Then the *average angular speed* of the body $\bar{\omega}$ in this time interval is defined as

$$\bar{\omega} = \frac{\theta_2 - \theta_1}{t_2 - t_1} = \frac{\Delta\theta}{\Delta t}.$$

The *instantaneous angular speed* ω is defined as the limit approached by this ratio as Δt approaches zero:

$$\omega = \lim_{\Delta t \to 0} \frac{\Delta\theta}{\Delta t} = \frac{d\theta}{dt}. \tag{11–1}$$

For a rigid body all lines fixed in it rotate through the same angle in the same time, so that the angular speed ω is the same for each particle in the

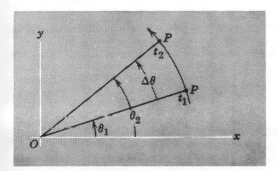

Fig. 11–4 The reference line OP, fixed in the body of Fig. 11–2, is displaced through $\Delta\theta = \theta_2 - \theta_1$ in the time interval $\Delta t = t_2 - t_1$.

body. Thus, ω is characteristic of the body as a whole. Angular speed has the dimensions of an inverse time (T^{-1}); its units are commonly taken to be radians/sec or rev/min.

If the angular speed of a body is not constant, the body has an angular acceleration. Let ω_1 and ω_2 be the instantaneous angular speeds at the times t_1 and t_2 respectively; then the *average angular acceleration* $\bar{\alpha}$ is defined as

$$\bar{\alpha} = \frac{\omega_2 - \omega_1}{t_2 - t_1} = \frac{\Delta\omega}{\Delta t}.$$

The *instantaneous angular acceleration* is the limit of this ratio as Δt approaches zero, or

$$\alpha = \lim_{\Delta t \to 0} \frac{\Delta\omega}{\Delta t} = \frac{d\omega}{dt}. \tag{11-2}$$

Angular acceleration has the dimensions of an inverse time squared (T^{-2}); its units are commonly taken to be radians/sec^2 or rev/min^2.

We have defined our angular quantities in a way similar to the definitions of the corresponding linear quantities of Chapter 3. For linear motion x corresponds to θ, v corresponds to ω, and a corresponds to α. The linear quantities differ dimensionally from the corresponding angular ones by a length factor. This difference arises from the relation $\theta = s/R$, or $s = R\theta$, in which the displacement along the arc s is a linear quantity; the angular displacement is θ, and the radius R has the dimensions of length.

11-3　Rotational Quantities as Vectors

The linear displacement, velocity, and acceleration are vectors. The corresponding angular quantities seem to be vectors also, for in addition to a magnitude we must specify a direction for them, namely the direction of the axis of rotation in space. Because we considered rotation only about an axis whose direction is fixed, we were able to treat θ, ω, and α as though they were scalar quantities. If the direction of the axis changes, we can no longer avoid the question "Are rotational quantities really vectors?" We can find out only by seeing whether or not they obey the laws of vector algebra, among which are the laws of vector addition.

Consider first the angular displacement θ. The magnitude of the angular displacement is the angle through which the body turns, and the direction of the angular displacement is the direction of the axis about which it turns. Angular displacements, however, do *not* add as vectors and are *not* vectors in the strict sense. As an example, consider giving two successive rotations θ_1 and θ_2 to a book which initially lies flat on a table. Let rotation θ_1 be a 90° clockwise turn about a vertical axis through the center of the book as viewed from above. Let θ_2 be a 90° clockwise turn about a north-south axis through the center of the book as viewed looking north. In one case, apply operation θ_1 first and then θ_2. In the other case, apply operation θ_2 first and then θ_1. Now, if angular displacements are vector quantities, they must add like vectors. In particular, they must obey the law of vector addition $\boldsymbol{\theta}_1 + \boldsymbol{\theta}_2 = \boldsymbol{\theta}_2 + \boldsymbol{\theta}_1$, which asserts that the order in which vectors are added does not affect their sum. This law is obviously violated for finite angular displacements (Fig. 11-5a). The student should try this for himself. Hence, finite angular displacements are *not* vector quantities.

Suppose that instead of 90° rotations we had made 3° rotations. The result of $\boldsymbol{\theta}_1 + \boldsymbol{\theta}_2$ would still differ from the result of $\boldsymbol{\theta}_2 + \boldsymbol{\theta}_1$, but the difference would be much

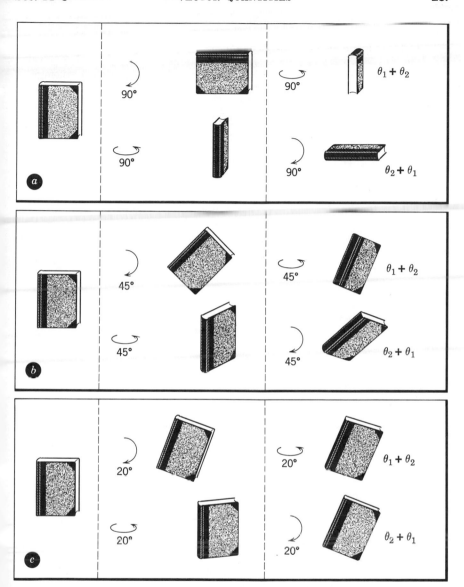

Fig. 11–5   (a) A book rotated θ_1 (90° clockwise as seen from the front) and then θ_2 (90° counterclockwise as seen from above) has a different final orientation than if rotated first through θ_2 and then θ_1.   This property is called the noncommutivity of finite angles under addition: $\theta_1 + \theta_2 \neq \theta_2 + \theta_1$.   (b) The middle group is the same except that the angular displacements are smaller, being 45°.   Although the final orientations still differ, they are evidently much nearer each other.   (c) The lower group repeats the experiment for 20° displacements.   We see here that $\theta_1 + \theta_2 \cong \theta_2 + \theta_1$.

It is clear that as θ_1, $\theta_2 \to 0$, the final positions approach each other.   Finite angles under addition tend toward commutivity as the angles become very small.   Infinitesimal angles do commute under addition, making it possible to treat them as vectors.

smaller.   In fact, as the two angular displacements are made smaller, the difference between the two sums disappears very rapidly (Fig. 11–5b, c).   If the angular displacements are made infinitesimal, the order of addition no longer affects the result. Hence, *we can regard infinitesimal angular displacements as vectors in the strict sense.*

Quantities defined in terms of infinitesimal angular displacements may themselves be vectors.   For example, the angular velocity is defined as $\boldsymbol{\omega} = d\boldsymbol{\theta}/dt$.

Since $d\boldsymbol{\theta}$ is a vector and dt a scalar, the quotient is a vector.   Therefore, the angular velocity is a vector.   In Fig. 11–6 we represent the angular velocity $\boldsymbol{\omega}$ of a uniformly

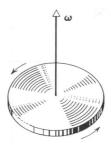

Fig. 11–6   The angular velocity vector $\boldsymbol{\omega}$ of a uniformly rotating disk.

rotating object by an arrow drawn along the axis of rotation.   The length of the arrow is made proportional to the magnitude of the angular velocity.   The sense of the rotation determines the direction in which the arrow points along the axis.   If the fingers of the *right hand* curl around the axis in the direction of rotation of the body, the extended thumb points along the direction of the angular velocity vector.   This rule corresponds to the vector pointing *into* the face of a clock for a *clockwise* rotation and *out* from the face of the clock for a *counterclockwise* rotation.   For the rigid body of Fig. 11–2, therefore, the angular velocity vector will be perpendicular to the page through O pointing up out of the page for a counterclockwise rotation and pointing down into the page for a clockwise rotation.   The angular velocity of the turntable of a phonograph is a vector pointing down.   Notice that nothing moves in the direction of the angular velocity vector.   The vector represents the angular velocity of the rotational motion taking place in the plane perpendicular to it.

We often represent a vector perpendicular to the plane of the page by the symbol ⊙ when the arrowhead points up out of the page (the dot represents the point of the arrow) and by the symbol ⊗ when the arrowhead points down into the page (the cross represents the tail of the arrow).

Angular acceleration is also a vector quantity.   This follows from the definition $\boldsymbol{\alpha} = d\boldsymbol{\omega}/dt$ in which $d\boldsymbol{\omega}$ is a vector and dt a scalar.   Later we shall encounter other rotational quantities that are vectors, such as torque and angular momentum.

The advantage of representing rotational quantities by vectors stems from the fact that we can then add such quantities by the usual rules for vector addition.

11–4   Rotation with Constant Angular Acceleration

The simplest type of accelerated rotational motion is rotation about a fixed axis with constant acceleration.   We can derive expressions for the angular speed and the angular displacement of this motion either by direct integration or by algebra from the average angular speed.   The procedure is the same as that used for uniformly accelerated linear motion.   The linear equations are repeated below on the left, and on the right we list the corresponding equations which replace them in rotational motion.

(3–7) $v = v_0 + at,$ $\qquad\qquad \omega = \omega_0 + \alpha t,$ $\qquad\qquad$ (11–3)

(3–9) $x = \dfrac{v_0 + v}{2} t,$ $\qquad\qquad \theta = \dfrac{\omega_0 + \omega}{2} t,$ $\qquad\qquad$ (11–4)

(3–10) $x = v_0 t + \frac{1}{2} a t^2,$ $\qquad\qquad \theta = \omega_0 t + \frac{1}{2} \alpha t^2,$ $\qquad\qquad$ (11–5)

(3–11) $v^2 = v_0{}^2 + 2ax,$ $\qquad\qquad \omega^2 = \omega_0{}^2 + 2\alpha\theta.$ $\qquad\qquad$ (11–6)

Here ω_0 is the angular speed at the time $t = 0$ and θ, ω, and α are considered positive when having a counterclockwise sense and negative otherwise. The student should check these equations dimensionally before verifying them.

Just as Eqs. 3–7 to 3–11 correspond to cases in which all the vectors involved lie parallel or antiparallel to a given direction (the straight line of motion), so Eqs. 11–3 to 11–6 correspond to cases in which all the vectors involved lie parallel or antiparallel to a given direction (the fixed axis of rotation).

▶ **Example 1.** A grindstone has a constant angular acceleration of 3.0 radians/sec². Starting from rest a line, such as OP, is horizontal (Fig. 11–7). Find (a) the angular

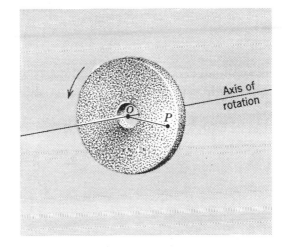

Fig. 11–7 Example 1. The line OP is attached to a grindstone rotating about an axis through O.

displacement of the line OP (and hence of the grindstone) and (b) the angular speed of the grindstone 2.0 sec later.

(a) α and t are given; we wish to find θ. Hence, we use Eq. 11–5,

$$\theta = \omega_0 t + \tfrac{1}{2}\alpha t^2.$$

At $t = 0$, we have $\omega = \omega_0 = 0$ and $\alpha = 3.0$ radians/sec². Therefore, after 2 sec,

$$\theta = (0)(2.0 \text{ sec}) + \tfrac{1}{2}(3.0 \text{ radians/sec}^2)(2.0 \text{ sec})^2 = 6.0 \text{ radians} = 0.96 \text{ rev.}$$

(b) α and t are given; we wish to find ω. Hence, we use Eq. 11–3

$$\omega = \omega_0 + \alpha t,$$

and $\qquad\qquad \omega = 0 + (3.0 \text{ radians/sec}^2)(2.0 \text{ sec}) = 6.0 \text{ radians/sec.}$

Using Eq. 11–6 as a check, we have

$$\omega^2 = \omega_0{}^2 + 2\alpha\theta,$$

$$\omega^2 = 0 + (2)(3.0 \text{ radians/sec}^2)(6.0 \text{ radians}) = 36 \text{ radians}^2/\text{sec}^2,$$

$$\omega = 6.0 \text{ radians/sec}.$$

Example 2. Derive the equation $\omega = \omega_0 + \alpha t$ for constant angular acceleration. (a) Starting from the definition of angular acceleration,

$$\alpha = \frac{d\omega}{dt},$$

we have

$$\alpha \, dt = d\omega$$

or

$$\int \alpha \, dt = \int d\omega.$$

But α is a constant, so that

$$\alpha \int dt = \int d\omega.$$

If at $t = 0$ we call the angular speed ω_0, then

$$\alpha \int_0^t dt = \int_{\omega_0}^{\omega} d\omega$$

or

$$\alpha t = \omega - \omega_0$$

and

$$\omega = \omega_0 + \alpha t.$$

(b) We can also derive the result by making use of the fact that the average acceleration equals the instantaneous acceleration when the acceleration is constant. The average acceleration is

$$\bar{\alpha} = \frac{\omega - \omega_0}{t - t_0}.$$

For constant acceleration we have $\bar{\alpha} = \alpha$. Letting $t_0 = 0$, we obtain

$$\alpha = \frac{\omega - \omega_0}{t}$$

or

$$\omega = \omega_0 + \alpha t.$$

The student should compare this derivation with that of the corresponding linear relation $v = v_0 + at$ in Section 3–7. ◀

11–5 Relation between Linear and Angular Kinematics of a Particle in Circular Motion

In Sections 4–4 and 4–5 we discussed the linear velocity and acceleration of a particle moving in a circle. When a rigid body rotates about a fixed axis, every particle in the body moves in a circle. Hence, we can describe the motion of such a particle either in linear variables or in angular variables. The relation between the linear and angular variables enables us to pass back and forth from one description to another and is very useful.

Consider a particle at P in the rigid body, a distance r from the axis through O. This particle (or point) moves in a circle of radius r as the body rotates,

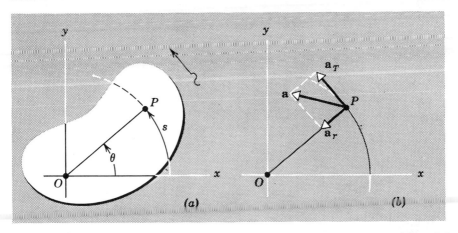

Fig. 11-8 (a) A rigid body rotates about an axis O perpendicular to the page. The point P sweeps out an arc s which subtends an angle θ. (b) The acceleration $\mathbf{a}$ of point P has components $\mathbf{a}_T$ (tangential) where $a_T = \alpha r$ ($r = \overline{OP}$) and $\mathbf{a}_r$ (radial) where $a_r = v^2/r = \omega^2 r$ (ω = angular speed).

as in Fig. 11–8a. The reference position is Ox. The particle moves through a distance s along the arc when the body rotates through an angle θ, such that

$$s = \theta r \tag{11–7}$$

where θ is in radians.

Differentiating both sides of this equation with respect to the time, and noting that r is constant, we obtain

$$\frac{ds}{dt} = \frac{d\theta}{dt} r.$$

But ds/dt is the linear speed of the particle at P and $d\theta/dt$ is the angular speed ω of the rotating body so that

$$v = \omega r. \tag{11–8}$$

This is a relation between the *magnitudes* of the linear velocity and the angular velocity; the linear speed of a particle in circular motion is the product of the angular speed and the distance r of the particle from the axis of rotation.

Differentiating Eq. 11–8 with respect to the time, we have

$$\frac{dv}{dt} = \frac{d\omega}{dt} r.$$

But dv/dt is the magnitude of the *tangential* component of acceleration of the particle (see Section 4–5) and $d\omega/dt$ is the magnitude of the angular acceleration of the rotating body, so that

$$a_T = \alpha r. \tag{11–9}$$

Hence, the magnitude of the tangential component of the linear acceleration of a particle in circular motion is the product of the magnitude of the angular acceleration and the distance r of the particle from the axis of rotation.

We have seen that the *radial* component of acceleration is v^2/r for a particle moving in a circle. This can be expressed in terms of angular speed by use of Eq. 11–8. We have

$$a_r = \frac{v^2}{r} = \omega^2 r. \tag{11–10}$$

The resultant acceleration of point P is shown in Fig. 11–8b.

Equations 11–7 through 11–10 enable us to describe the motion of one point on a rotating rigid body *either* in angular variables *or* in linear variables. We might ask why we need the angular variables when we are already familiar with the equivalent linear variables. The answer is that the angular description offers a distinct advantage over the linear description when various points on the same rotating body must be considered. Different points on the same rotating body do not have the same linear displacement, speed, or acceleration, but *all* points on a rotating rigid body do have the same *angular* displacement, speed, or acceleration at any instant. By the use of angular variables we can describe the motion of the body as a whole in a simple way.

▶ **Example 3.** If the radius of the grindstone of Example 1 is 0.50 meter, calculate (*a*) the linear or tangential speed of a particle on the rim, (*b*) the tangential acceleration of a particle on the rim, and (*c*) the centripetal acceleration of a particle on the rim, at the end of 2 sec.

We have $\alpha = 3.0$ radians/sec^2, $\omega = 6.0$ radians/sec after 2 sec, and $r = 0.50$ meter. Then,

(*a*)
$$v = \omega r$$
$$= (6.0 \text{ radians/sec})(0.50 \text{ meter})$$
$$= 3.0 \text{ meter/sec} \quad \text{(linear speed)};$$

(*b*)
$$a_T = \alpha r$$
$$= (3.0 \text{ radians/sec}^2)(0.50 \text{ meter})$$
$$= 1.5 \text{ meters/sec}^2 \quad \text{(tangential acceleration)};$$

(*c*)
$$a_r = v^2/r = \omega^2 r$$
$$= (6.0 \text{ radians/sec})^2(0.50 \text{ meter})$$
$$= 18 \text{ meters/sec}^2 \quad \text{(centripetal acceleration)}.$$

(*d*) Are the results the same for a particle halfway in from the rim, that is, at $r = 0.25$ meter?

The *angular* variables are the same for this point as for a point on the rim. That is, once again

$$\alpha = 3.0 \text{ radians/sec}^2, \qquad \omega = 6.0 \text{ radians/sec}.$$

But now $r = 0.25$ meter, so that for this particle

$$v = 1.5 \text{ meters/sec}, \qquad a_T = 0.75 \text{ meter/sec}^2, \qquad a_r = 9.0 \text{ meters/sec}^2. \quad ◀$$

The student should notice that the relations just deduced are relations between *scalar* quantities, namely the *magnitudes* of the linear and angular variables. Such

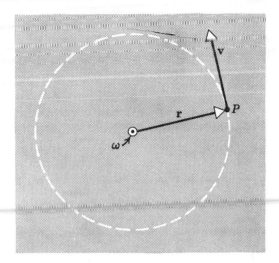

Fig. 11–9 For a point P rotating a distance r from an axis, its linear and angular velocities are related by $\mathbf{v} = \boldsymbol{\omega} \times \mathbf{r}$.

relations are adequate when the axis of rotation is fixed. If the axis of rotation is not fixed, we must use the corresponding vector relations. These can be deduced with the help of the vector product of two vectors, a multiplication operation for vectors discussed in Chapter 2. In fact, at any instant, the vector relations are

$$d\mathbf{s} = d\boldsymbol{\theta} \times \mathbf{r}, \tag{11–11}$$

$$\mathbf{v} = \boldsymbol{\omega} \times \mathbf{r}, \tag{11–12}$$

$$\mathbf{a}_T = \boldsymbol{\alpha} \times \mathbf{r}. \tag{11–13}$$

Each angular vector quantity is directed along the axis of rotation, perpendicular to $\mathbf{r}$ and to the other linear vectors, all of which lie in the plane of rotation. The vector or cross product of two vectors gives a third vector which is at right angles to the plane formed by the two vectors being multiplied, in accordance with the requirements stated.

The order of the factors in the product determines the sense of the product vector. Consider the expression

$$\mathbf{v} = \boldsymbol{\omega} \times \mathbf{r}.$$

In Fig. 11–9 $\boldsymbol{\omega}$ is up out of the page $\odot$ for a counterclockwise rotation and $\mathbf{r}$ is directed from the axis to the rotating point P. From the relation $\mathbf{v} = \boldsymbol{\omega} \times \mathbf{r}$ we find that $\mathbf{v}$ is along the tangent in the direction shown. This corresponds to a counterclockwise motion, as required. If $\boldsymbol{\omega}$ were into the page, then $\mathbf{v}$ would change direction, both in accordance with a clockwise rotation. That these equations give the correct relation between the magnitudes of our vectors is apparent from their form, which corresponds to Eqs. 11–7, 11–8, and 11–9, and from the fact that the three vectors in any equation are always at right angles to one another.

Notice that the tangential linear acceleration $\mathbf{a}_T$ is zero if the rotational acceleration $\boldsymbol{\alpha}$ is zero, but that a radial acceleration still exists here, corresponding to the fact that there is a centripetal acceleration for uniform circular motion. The vector relation between $\mathbf{a}_r$, $\mathbf{v}$, $\boldsymbol{\omega}$, and $\mathbf{r}$ is

$$\mathbf{a}_r = \boldsymbol{\omega} \times \mathbf{v} = \boldsymbol{\omega} \times (\boldsymbol{\omega} \times \mathbf{r}).$$

This gives the correct magnitude and direction for $\mathbf{a}_r$.

QUESTIONS

1. Could the angular quantities θ, ω, and α be expressed in terms of degrees instead of radians in the kinematical equations?

2. Explain why the radian measure of angle is equally satisfactory for all systems of units. Is the same true for degrees?

3. What is the angular speed of the second hand of a watch? Of the minute hand? Could you conveniently express the motion of these hands in terms of linear variables?

4. A wheel is rotating about an axis through its center perpendicular to the plane of the wheel. Consider a point on the rim. When the wheel rotates with *constant angular velocity*, does the point have a radial acceleration? A tangential acceleration? When the wheel rotates with *constant angular acceleration*, does the point have a radial acceleration? A tangential acceleration? Do the magnitudes of these accelerations change?

5. Suppose you were asked to determine the equivalent distance traveled by a phonograph needle in playing, say, a 12-in., $33\frac{1}{3}$ rpm, microgroove record. What information do you need? What assumptions would you make to arrive at an answer from theory alone?

6. (a) Describe the vector that would represent the angular velocity of the earth rotating about its axis. (b) Describe the vector that would represent the angular velocity of the earth rotating about the sun.

7. It is convenient to picture rotational vectors as lying along the axis of rotation. Is there any reason why they could not be pictured as merely parallel to the axis, but located anywhere? Recall that we are free to slide a displacement vector along its own direction or translate it sideways without changing its value.

PROBLEMS

1. The angular speed of an automobile engine is increased from 1200 rpm to 3000 rpm in 12 sec. (a) What is its angular acceleration, assuming it to be uniform? (b) How many revolutions does the engine make during this time?

2. A phonograph turntable rotating at 78 rev/min slows down and stops in 30 sec after the motor is turned off. (a) Find its (uniform) angular acceleration. (b) How many revolutions did it make in this time?

3. A wheel has a constant angular acceleration of 3 radians/sec². In a 4-sec interval it turns through an angle of 120 radians. Assuming the wheel started from rest, how long had it been in motion at the start of this 4-sec interval?

4. A heavy flywheel rotating on its axis is slowing down because of friction in its bearings. At the end of the first minute its angular velocity is 0.9 of its angular velocity ω_0 at the start. Assuming constant frictional forces, find its angular velocity at the end of the second minute.

5. The angle turned through by the flywheel of a generator during a time interval t is given by

$$\theta = at + bt^3 - ct^4,$$

where a, b, and c are constants. What is the expression for its angular acceleration?

6. A body moves in the x–y plane such that $x = R \cos \omega t$ and $y = R \sin \omega t$. Here x and y are the coordinates of the body, t is the time, and R and ω are constants. (a) Eliminate t between these equations to find the equation of the curve in which the body moves. What is this curve? What is the meaning of the constant ω? (b) Differentiate the equations for x and y with respect to the time to find the x and y components of the velocity of the body, v_x and v_y. Combine v_x and v_y to find the magnitude and direction of $\mathbf{v}$. Describe the motion of the body. (c) Differentiate v_x and v_y with respect to the time to obtain the magnitude and direction of the resultant acceleration.

7. The earth's orbit about the sun, although elliptical, is almost a circle. (a) Calculate the angular velocity of the earth about the sun and its average linear speed in its orbit. (b) Show how to find the centripetal acceleration of the earth with respect to the sun.

8. (a) What is the angular speed about the polar axis of a point on the earth's surface at a latitude of 45°N? What is the linear speed? (b) How do these compare with the similar values for a point at the equator?

9. An automobile traveling 60 miles/hr has wheels of 30-in. diameter. (a) What is the angular speed of the wheels about the axle? (b) If the wheels are brought to a stop uniformly in 30 turns, what is the angular acceleration? (c) How far does the car advance during this braking period?

10. (a) If an airplane propeller of radius 5 ft rotates at 2000 rpm and the airplane is propelled at a ground speed of 100 mph, what is the speed of a point on the tip of the propeller? (b) What kind of path does this point traverse?

11. What is the angular speed of a car rounding a circular turn of radius 360 ft at 30 miles/hr?

12. What is the centripetal acceleration of a point on the rim of a 12-in. record rotating at $33\frac{1}{3}$ rev/min?

13. A rigid body, starting at rest, rotates about a fixed axis with constant angular acceleration. (a) Express the radial acceleration and the tangential acceleration of a particle in the body in terms of the angular acceleration of the body. Let the particle be a distance r from the axis. (b) If the resultant acceleration of the particle at some instant makes an angle of 60° with the tangential acceleration, what total angle has the body turned through to that instant?

14. One method of measuring the speed of light makes use of a rotating toothed wheel. A beam of light passes through a slot at the outside edge of the wheel, travels to a distant mirror, and returns to the wheel just in time to pass through the next slot in the wheel. One such toothed wheel has a radius of 5.0 cm and 500 teeth at its edge. Measurements taken when the mirror was 500 meters from the wheel indicated a speed of light of 3.0×10^5 km/sec. (a) What was the (constant) angular speed of the wheel? (b) What was the linear speed of a point on its edge?

Rotational Dynamics

CHAPTER 12

12–1 Rotational Variables

The basic relation of all dynamics is $\mathbf{F} = m\mathbf{a}$. This form is particularly well suited to particle dynamics. For rotation, however, it would be more convenient to express the second law in terms of rotational quantities.

We have already found the rotational analog of linear acceleration $\mathbf{a}$, namely the rotational or angular acceleration $\boldsymbol{\alpha}$. In order to suggest what rotational variables are analogous to $\mathbf{F}$ and to m, we consider first a simple example.

Let us try to impart rotational acceleration to a meter stick which is free to rotate about a fixed frictionless axis passing perpendicularly through it near one end, as shown in Fig. 12–1. In order to eliminate friction and gravity for the present, imagine that the meter stick is on a horizontal frictionless surface. If we exert a force $\mathbf{F}_1$ at the point a, the stick will rotate, that is, it will accelerate rotationally from rest about the axis through O. If we exert the identical force $\mathbf{F}_1$ at the point b, the stick will again accelerate rotationally; however, the acceleration will be greater than before. Everyday experience, such as pushing revolving doors, confirms the fact that to obtain a greater rotational effect with a given force we apply the force at a point farther from the axis of rotation. Evidently, then, it is not the applied force alone which determines rotational acceleration. It is certainly true that increasing the *magnitude of the force* $\mathbf{F}_1$ will increase the rotational acceleration, but even with the same force we can increase the rotational acceleration merely by changing the *point of application* of the force.

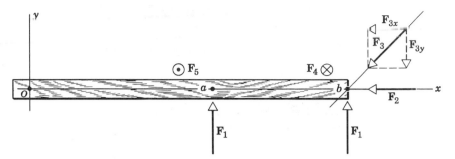

Fig. 12–1 A meter stick pivoted at O and free to rotate in the plane of the paper. Forces F_1 and F_3 tend to produce rotation about O; forces F_2, F_4 and F_5 do not.

Consider now applying a second force F_2, as shown in Fig. 12–1. Let this force have the same magnitude as F_1 and the same point of application b. Such a force whose line of action passes through the axis of rotation will cause no rotational motion at all. Evidently the *direction of the force* plays a role in determining the rotational acceleration it gives to a body.

Consider a force such as F_3 applied at b. We can resolve this force into components: one component, lying along the line Ob joining the axis and the point b, contributes nothing to the rotational motion; and the other component, at right angles to this line, causes a rotational acceleration in a sense opposite to that caused by F_1 (clockwise instead of counterclockwise). Clearly if the same force F_3 were applied at a point on the opposite side of the axis, it would give rise to a rotational acceleration having the same sense as that due to the force F_1 applied at b. Hence, the direction of the force at its point of application affects the *sense of the rotation* as well as the magnitude of the rotational acceleration.

Finally, consider forces such as F_4 and F_5 whose directions are perpendicular to the plane of the meter stick, as is the axis of rotation. We can imagine the meter stick to be rigidly mounted on its axis of rotation, so that it need not lie on a surface. Clearly these forces cannot cause a rotation about the fixed axis through O.

We must, therefore, find a quantity which can be considered as the cause of rotational acceleration and which is related in such a way to the applied force that it has all the properties discussed earlier. Such a quantity is called a *torque*, or a *moment of force*, and will be defined exactly in the next section. Torque will turn out to be the rotational analog of force.

In order to suggest the rotational analog to mass, we consider next a slight modification of our previous example. Let us have a meter stick, half of which is wood and half of which is steel, as in Fig. 12–2.

In Fig. 12–2 the axis is through the wooden part of the stick at O. Let us apply a force F of definite direction and magnitude at a definite point a. We obtain a definite rotational acceleration. Next, reverse the stick and let the axis be through the steel part of the stick at O', corresponding geomet-

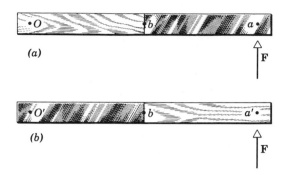

Fig. 12-2 A meter stick, half of which is wood, the other half steel. (*a*) The stick is pivoted at the wooden end at *O* and a force applied on the steel end at *a*. (*b*) The stick is pivoted at the steel end at *O′* and a force applied at the wooden end at *a′*.

rically to *O*. Apply the identical force **F** to the identical geometric point *a* as before. We now have a much greater rotational acceleration than before. The total mass of the meter stick was not changed by our choice of the axis of rotation and the applied force had the same magnitude, direction, and point of application with respect to the axis in each case. Yet the accelerations produced were different. All that has been changed is the *distribution of the mass with respect to the axis of rotation*. In one case most of the mass (the steel part) is close to the axis and in the second most of the mass is far from the axis.

That the distribution of mass with respect to the axis is decisive is simply confirmed by choosing an axis at *b*, through the center of the meter stick. Now the distribution of mass with respect to its distance from this axis is the same in both cases, and we find that the same rotational acceleration is produced in each case by a given force and point of application.

The same ideas can be shown to hold for the original meter stick of Fig. 12-1 or for any body in rotation. This will be done in Section 12-3. At this point we merely suggest that the analog in rotational motion to the particle mass of translational motion will not be the mass of the rigid body but a quantity that may be called *rotational inertia*, or moment of inertia, depending in some way on the distribution of the mass with respect to the axis of rotation.

We proceed now to develop these qualitative ideas in an exact and quantitative way.

12-2   Torque, or Moment of a Force

If a force **F** acts on a single particle at the point *P*, whose position with respect to the origin of coordinates *O* is given by the displacement vector **r** (Fig. 12-3), the *torque* **τ**, or the moment of the force, *about the origin O* is defined as

$$\boldsymbol{\tau} = \mathbf{r} \times \mathbf{F}. \tag{12-1}$$

The torque is a vector quantity; its magnitude is given by

$$\tau = rF \sin \theta, \qquad (12\text{--}2)$$

where θ is the angle between **r** and **F**; its direction is normal to the plane formed by **r** and **F**, with the sense given by the rule for the vector product of two vectors.

Notice that the torque produced by a force depends not only on the magnitude and on the direction of the force but also on the point of application of the force relative to the origin. In particular, when **F** acts through the origin, **r** is zero, so that the torque τ about the origin is zero.

Also, $F \sin \theta$ is the magnitude of the component of **F** perpendicular to **r**. Evidently, from Eq. 12–2, only this component of **F** contributes to the torque. In particular, when θ equals 0° or 180°, there is no perpendicular component; then the line of action of the force passes through the origin and the torque about the origin is zero. In this case Eq. 12–2 gives

$$\tau = rF \sin 0° \quad \text{or} \quad rF \sin 180° = 0.$$

If we reverse the direction of **F**, then θ changes by 180° and the direction of τ is reversed. Similarly, if we reverse **r**, then θ changes by 180°, thereby changing the point of application of **F** and again the direction of τ is re-

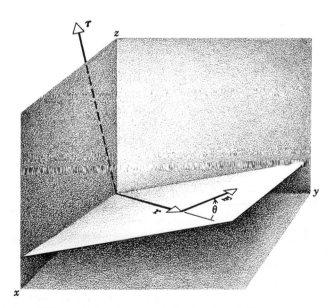

Fig. 12–3 A force **F** is applied at P, a point displaced **r** relative to the origin. The force makes an angle θ with the radius vector **r**. The torque τ about O is shown. Its direction is perpendicular to the plane formed by **r** and **F** with the sense given by the right-hand rule.

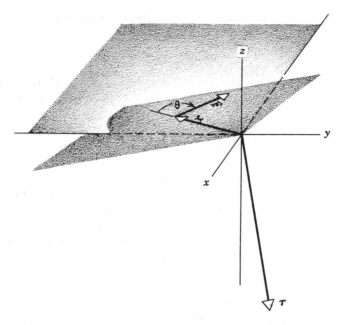

Fig. 12–4 Reversing **r** (the point of application of the force) reverses **τ**. Compare with Fig. 12–3.

versed, as shown in Fig. 12–4. These results follow from the fact that sin $(\theta + 180°) = -\sin\theta$ so that in Eq. 12–2 τ changes to $-\tau$.

This discussion gives the definition and the properties of torque and applies rather generally. We are interested expecially in rigid-body rotations, however, and particularly those in which the axis of rotation is fixed. Our body is then a collection of particles which always maintain the same positions with respect to one another. The vector **r** locates the point of application of the force relative to the fixed axis through O. In such a case the body can rotate only about the fixed axis. If a torque is applied to such a body, only the component of the torque parallel to the axis is effective in causing the body to rotate. The component of the torque normal to the axis is annulled by a torque applied to the body by the fixed axis itself. If the body is mounted with two points fixed in bearings, for example, the bearings supply this torque. This is the rotational analog to a block sliding on a horizontal table. Any force applied to the block normal to the table is automatically annulled by an opposite force exerted on the block by the table.

With rotation about a fixed axis, therefore, we need consider only force components which are in the plane perpendicular to the axis of rotation, for only forces in this plane can cause a rotation about the fixed axis. If our fixed axis of rotation is along the z-axis through the origin O, the only component of **τ** causing rotation is τ_z, the component parallel to the axis of rotation. Only those components of displacement and applied force which lie in a plane perpendicular to the z-axis (that is, in the x–y plane) contribute to τ_z. Hence, to simplify matters we shall, in this chapter, consider only the cases in which **r** and **F** actually lie in such a plane.

Consider now the case discussed earlier in a qualitative way, that of the meter stick free to rotate about an axis normal to it through a point O. In Fig. 12–5 we have redrawn the situation. The *torque about a fixed axis* perpendicular to the body through O attributable to the force **F** applied at b is

$$\boldsymbol{\tau} = \mathbf{r} \times \mathbf{F}, \tag{12-3}$$

where **r** is the vector displacement from O to b. The torque $\boldsymbol{\tau}$ is directed along the fixed axis of rotation and its magnitude is

$$\tau = rF \sin \theta. \tag{12-4}$$

The rotation will be counterclockwise if $0° < \theta < 180°$ and clockwise if $180° < \theta < 360°$; the student should check this statement using the right-hand rule for vector products.

The torque given by Eq. 12–4 can be computed directly by measuring r, F, and θ. Often in rigid-body rotations we think of the torque as the product of two terms, as follows. Since $F \sin \theta$ is the component $(F_\perp)$ of the force normal to **r**, we can write

$$\tau = rF \sin \theta = rF_\perp.$$

Hence, the torque about an axis can be thought of as the product of the distance from the axis to the point of application of the force and the component of the applied force perpendicular to the line joining these points.

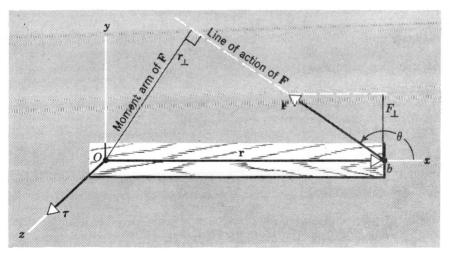

Fig 12–5 The torque is in magnitude $rF \sin \theta$, which is equal to $rF_\perp$ or to $Fr_\perp$. The *line of action of* **F** is simply a line drawn along the vector **F**. The *moment arm* of **F** or $r_\perp$ is a line segment drawn from the pivot O to the line of action of **F**, making a right angle with the line of action.

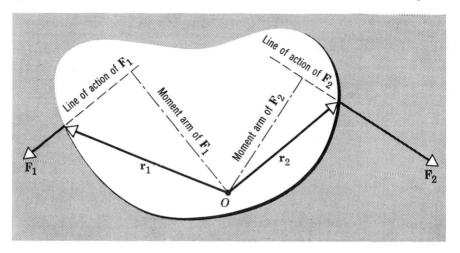

Fig. 12–6 Two forces acting on a body of arbitrary shape pivoted at O. The $\mathbf{F}$ and $\mathbf{r}$ vectors are in the plane of the paper and the resultant torque τ points down through O perpendicular to the page.

Another equivalent description is often more useful. The extended line along which a force vector lies is called the *line of action* of that force. Notice that $r \sin \theta$ is the perpendicular distance ($r_\perp$) from the axis to the line of action of the force $\mathbf{F}$. This quantity, $r_\perp$, is called the *moment arm* of the force about the axis. We can, therefore, write Eq. 12–4 as

$$\tau = F(r \sin \theta) = F r_\perp.$$

Hence, the torque about an axis can be thought of as simply the product of the magnitude of the force and its moment arm about that axis.

The student can now convince himself that our defintion of torque, or moment of force, has all the properties we required of it in our earlier qualitative discussion.

For a body of arbitrary shape free to rotate about an axis through O perpendicular to the plane of the paper, as in Fig. 12–6, the same considerations apply. In Fig. 12–6 two forces act on the body and tend to produce opposite rotations. The resultant torque has a magnitude

$$F_2 r_2 \sin \theta_2 - F_1 r_1 \sin \theta_1,$$

and is directed into the page along the axis of rotation through O.

Torque has the same dimensions as force times distance, or in terms of our assumed fundamental dimensions, (M), (L), (T), it has the dimensions (ML^2T^{-2}). These are the same as the dimensions of work. Nevertheless, torque and work are very different physical quantities. Torque is a vector quantity and work is a scalar quantity, for example. The unit of torque may be the nt-m or lb-ft, among other possibilities.

▶ **Example 1.** A wagon wheel is free to rotate about a horizontal axis through O. A force of 10 lb is applied to a spoke at the point P, 1.0 ft from the center, QP makes an angle of 30° with the horizontal (x-axis) and the force is in the plane of the wheel making an angle of 45° with the horizontal (x-axis). What is the torque on the wheel?

The angle between the displacement vector $\mathbf{r}$ from O to P and the applied force $\mathbf{F}$ (Fig. 12–7) is θ. But

$$\theta = 45° - 30° = 15°.$$

Then the magnitude of the torque is

$$\tau = rF \sin \theta,$$

$$= (1.0 \text{ ft})(10 \text{ lb})(\sin 15°) = 2.6 \text{ lb-ft}.$$

It is clear that we can obtain this same result from $\tau = rF_\perp$ or $\tau = r_\perp F$ as well. The torque ($\boldsymbol{\tau} = \mathbf{r} \times \mathbf{F}$) is a vector pointing out $\odot$ along the axis through O having a magnitude 2.6 lb-ft.   ◀

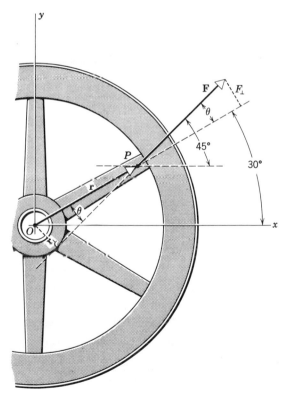

Fig. 12–7   Example 1.

12-3   Kinetic Energy of Rotation and Rotational Inertia

Each particle in a rotating body has a certain amount of kinetic energy. A particle of mass m at a distance r from the axis of rotation has a speed $v = \omega r$, where ω is the angular speed of the particle about the axis of rotation; its kinetic energy, therefore, is $\frac{1}{2}mv^2 = \frac{1}{2}mr^2\omega^2$. The total kinetic energy of the body is the sum of the kinetic energies of all its particles. If the body is rigid, as we assume in this chapter, ω is the same for all particles. The radius r may be different for different particles. Hence, the total kinetic energy K of the rotating body can be written as

$$K = \tfrac{1}{2}(m_1 r_1{}^2 + m_2 r_2{}^2 + \cdots)\omega^2 = \tfrac{1}{2}(\Sigma\, m_i r_i{}^2)\omega^2.$$

The term $\Sigma\, m_i r_i{}^2$ is the sum of the products of the masses of the particles by the squares of their respective distances from the axis of rotation. If we denote this quantity by I, then

$$I = \Sigma\, m_i r_i{}^2 \tag{12-5}$$

is called the *rotational inertia*, or moment of inertia, of the body about the particular axis of rotation. Note that *the rotational inertia of a body depends on the particular axis about which it is rotating* as well as on the shape of the body and the manner in which its mass is distributed.

Rotational inertia has the dimensions (ML^2) and is usually expressed in slug-ft^2 or kg-m^2.

In terms of rotational inertia we can now write the kinetic energy of the rotating body as

$$K = \tfrac{1}{2}I\omega^2. \tag{12-6}$$

This is analogous to the expression for the kinetic energy of translation of a body, $K = \frac{1}{2}mv^2$. We have already seen that the angular speed ω is analogous to the linear speed v. Now we see that the rotational inertia I is analogous to the mass, or the translational inertia m. Although the mass of a body does not depend on its location, the rotational inertia of a body does depend on the axis about which it is rotating.

We should understand that the rotational kinetic energy given by Eq. 12-6 is simply the sum of the ordinary translational kinetic energy of all the parts of the body and not a new kind of energy. Rotational kinetic energy is simply a convenient way of expressing the kinetic energy for a rotating rigid body.

▶ **Example 2.**   Consider a body consisting of two spherical masses of 5.0 kg each connected by a light rigid rod 1.0 meter long (Fig. 12-8). Treat the spheres as point particles and neglect the mass of the rod. Then determine the rotational inertia, or moment of inertia, of the body (a) about an axis normal to it through its center at O, and (b) about an axis normal to it through one sphere.

(a) If the axis is normal to the page through O, we have

$$I_o = \Sigma\, m_i r_i{}^2 = m_a r_a{}^2 + m_b r_b{}^2$$

$$= (5.0 \text{ kg})(0.5 \text{ meter})^2 + (5.0 \text{ kg})(0.5 \text{ meter})^2 = 2.5 \text{ kg-m}^2.$$

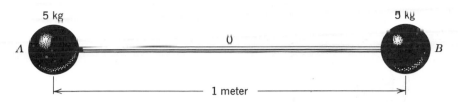

Fig. 12–8   Example 2.   Calculating the rotational inertia of a dumbbell.

(b) If the axis is normal to the page through A or B, we have

$$I_A = m_a r_a^2 + m_b r_b^2 = (5.0 \text{ kg})(0 \text{ meter})^2 + (5.0 \text{ kg})(1.0 \text{ meter})^2 = 5.0 \text{ kg-m}^2,$$

$$I_B = m_a r_a^2 + m_b r_b^2 = (5.0 \text{ kg})(1.0 \text{ meter})^2 + (5.0 \text{ kg})(0 \text{ meter})^2 = 5.0 \text{ kg-m}^2.$$

Hence, the rotational inertia of this rigid dumbbell model is twice as great about an axis through an end as it is about an axis through the center.   ◄

For a body that is not composed of discrete point masses but is instead a continuous distribution of matter, the summation process in $I = \Sigma\, m_i r_i^2$ becomes an integration process. We imagine the body to be subdivided into infinitesimal elements, each of mass dm. We let r be the distance from such an element to the axis of rotation. Then the rotational inertia is obtained from

$$I = \int r^2 \, dm, \qquad (12\text{–}7)$$

where the integral is taken over the whole body. The procedure by which the summation Σ of a discrete distribution is replaced by the integral $\int$ for a continuous distribution is the same as that discussed for the center of mass in Section 9–1.

For bodies of irregular shape the integral may be difficult to evaluate. For bodies of simple geometrical shape the integrals are relatively easy when an axis of symmetry is chosen as the axis of rotation.

Let us illustrate the procedure for an annular cylinder (or ring) about the cylinder axis (Fig. 12–9). The most convenient mass element is an infinitesimally thin cylindrical shell of radius r, thickness dr, and length L. If the density of the material, that is, the mass per unit volume, is called ρ, then

$$dm = \rho \, dV,$$

where dV is the volume of the cylindrical shell of mass dm. We have

$$dV = (2\pi r \, dr)L,$$

so that $$dm = 2\pi L \rho r \, dr.$$

Then the rotational inertia about the cylinder axis is

$$I = \int r^2 \, dm = 2\pi L \int_{R_1}^{R_2} \rho r^3 \, dr.$$

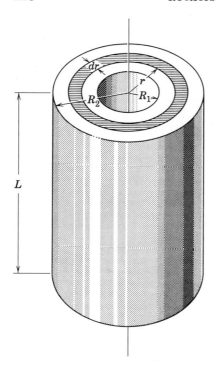

Fig. 12-9 Calculating the rotational inertia of a hollow cylinder.

Here R_1 is the radius of the inner cylindrical wall and R_2 is the radius of the outer cylindrical wall.

If this body did not have a uniform constant density, we would have to know how ρ depends on r or other coordinates before we could carry out the integration. Let us assume for simplicity that the density is uniform. Then

$$I = 2\pi L\rho \int_{R_1}^{R_2} r^3 \, dr = 2\pi L\rho \frac{R_2{}^4 - R_1{}^4}{4} = \rho\pi(R_2{}^2 - R_1{}^2)L \frac{R_2{}^2 + R_1{}^2}{2}.$$

The mass M of the entire annular cylinder is the product of its density ρ by its volume $\pi(R_2{}^2 - R_1{}^2)L$, or

$$M = \rho\pi(R_2{}^2 - R_1{}^2)L.$$

The rotational inertia of the *annular cylinder* (or ring) of mass M, inner radius R_1 and outer radius R_2, is therefore

$$I = \tfrac{1}{2}M(R_1{}^2 + R_2{}^2)$$

about the cylinder axis.

If the inner radius is zero, R_1 equals zero, and we have a solid cylinder (or disk). Then

$$I = \tfrac{1}{2}MR^2$$

about the cylinder axis, where R is the radius of the solid cylinder of mass M.

Table 12–1

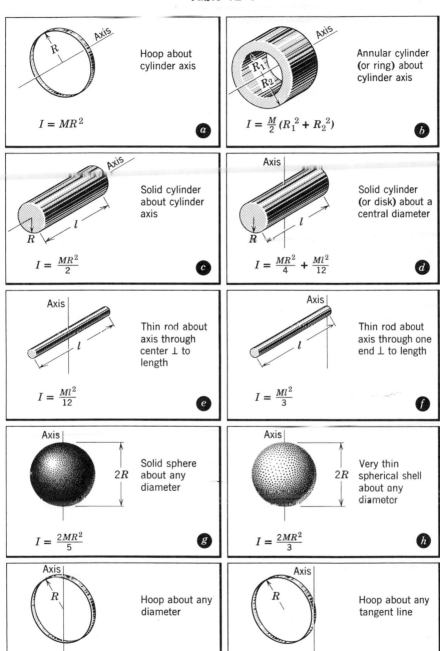

Hoop about cylinder axis

$$I = MR^2$$

(a)

Annular cylinder (or ring) about cylinder axis

$$I = \frac{M}{2}(R_1^2 + R_2^2)$$

(b)

Solid cylinder about cylinder axis

$$I = \frac{MR^2}{2}$$

(c)

Solid cylinder (or disk) about a central diameter

$$I = \frac{MR^2}{4} + \frac{Ml^2}{12}$$

(d)

Thin rod about axis through center ⊥ to length

$$I = \frac{Ml^2}{12}$$

(e)

Thin rod about axis through one end ⊥ to length

$$I = \frac{Ml^2}{3}$$

(f)

Solid sphere about any diameter

$$I = \frac{2MR^2}{5}$$

(g)

Very thin spherical shell about any diameter

$$I = \frac{2MR^2}{3}$$

(h)

Hoop about any diameter

$$I = \frac{MR^2}{2}$$

(i)

Hoop about any tangent line

$$I = \frac{3MR^2}{2}$$

(j)

A *hoop* can be thought of as a very thin-walled hollow cylinder. In that case

$$R_1 = R_2 = R,$$

and

$$I = MR^2$$

is the moment of a hoop of mass M and radius R about the cylinder axis.

This result for the hoop is obvious since every mass point in the hoop is the same distance R from the central axis. For the solid cylinder (or disk) having the same *mass* as the hoop, the rotational inertia (or moment of inertia) would naturally be less than that of the hoop, because most of the cylinder (or disk) is less than a distance R from the axis.

The rotational inertia of some common solids about certain axes are listed in Table 12–1. Each of these results can be derived by integration in a manner similar to that of our illustration. The total mass of the body is denoted by M in each equation.

There is a simple and very useful relation between the rotational inertia I of a body about any axis and its rotational inertia I_0 with respect to a parallel axis *through the center of mass*. If M is the total mass of the body and h the distance between the two axes, the relation is

$$I = I_o + Mh^2. \qquad\qquad (12\text{–}8)$$

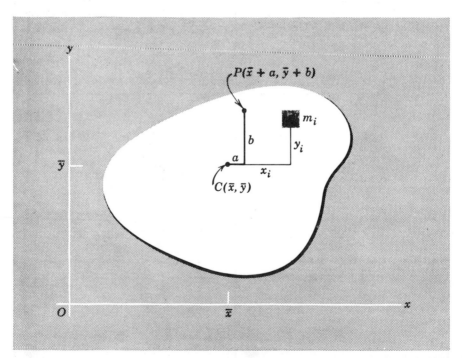

Fig. 12–10 Derivation of the parallel-axis theorem. Knowing the rotational inertia about C, we can find its value about P.

The proof of this relation (parallel-axis theorem) follows. Let C be the center of mass of the arbitrarily shaped body whose cross section is shown in Fig. 12–10. The center of mass has coordinates $\bar{x}$ and $\bar{y}$. We choose the x–y plane to include C, so that $\bar{z}$ equals zero. Consider an axis through C at right angles to the plane of the paper and another axis parallel to it through P at $(\bar{x} + a)$ and $(\bar{y} + b)$. The distance between the axes is $h = \sqrt{a^2 + b^2}$. Then the square of the distance of a particle from the axis through C is $x_i{}^2 + y_i{}^2$ where x_i and y_i measure the coordinates of a mass element m_i relative to the axis through C. The square of its distance from an axis through P is $(x_i - a)^2 + (y_i - b)^2$. Hence, the rotational inertia about an axis through P is

$$I = \Sigma\, m_i[(x_i - a)^2 + (y_i - b)^2]$$
$$= \Sigma\, m_i(x_i{}^2 + y_i{}^2) - 2a\, \Sigma\, m_i x_i - 2b\, \Sigma\, m_i y_i + (a^2 + b^2)\, \Sigma\, m_i.$$

From the definition of center of mass

$$\Sigma\, m_i x_i = \Sigma\, m_i y_i = 0,$$

so that the two middle terms are zero. The first term is simply the rotational inertia about an axis through the center of mass I_o and the last term is Mh^2. Hence, it follows that $I = I_o + Mh^2$.

With the aid of this formula several of the results of Table 12–1 can be deduced from previous results. For example, (f) follows from (e), and (j) follows from (i) with the aid of Eq. 12–8. The formula will prove to be especially useful in problems that combine rotational and translational motion.

12–4   Rotational Dynamics of a Rigid Body

The fundamental equation of dynamics is Newton's second law of motion. When expressed in the form $\mathbf{F} = m\mathbf{a}$, this equation is convenient for translational motion. For rotational motions it would be more convenient to express the second law in terms of rotational quantities, such as angular acceleration and rotational inertia. We now proceed to do this for the special case of a rotating rigid body.

Consider a rigid body (Fig. 12–11) pivoted about a fixed axis through O perpendicular to the plane of the diagram. We need to consider only forces in this plane, for those parallel to the axis cannot cause rotation about the fixed axis. Let an external force F, in the plane, be exerted on the body at some point P. If we watch the body for an infinitesimal time dt, the point P will move an infinitesimal distance ds along a circular path of radius r and the body will rotate through an infinitesimal angle $d\theta$, where

$$ds = r\, d\theta.$$

The diagram illustrates a finite rotation. For an infinitesimal rotation, ds is along the arc in the direction of the tangent to the circle at P. An infinitesimal rotation is a vector also, so that the vector relation between ds and $d\theta$ is $d\mathbf{s} = d\boldsymbol{\theta} \times \mathbf{r}$. Because $\mathbf{r}$ and $d\boldsymbol{\theta}$ are at right angles, the magnitude of $d\mathbf{s}$ is $ds = r\, d\theta$.

The work dW done by this force during this small rotation is

$$dW = \mathbf{F} \cdot d\mathbf{s} = F \cos \phi\, ds = (F \cos \phi)(r\, d\theta),$$

where $F \cos \phi$ is the component of $\mathbf{F}$ in the direction of $d\mathbf{s}$.

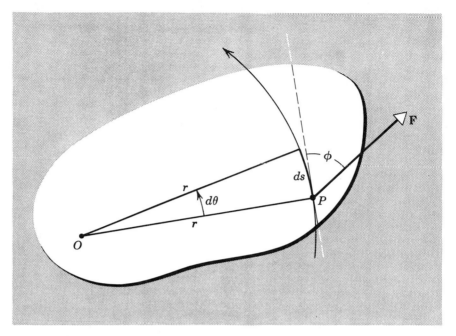

Fig. 12–11   A rigid body is pivoted at O.   A force $\mathbf{F}$ is shown producing an angular displacement $d\theta$ and moving P a distance ds. $\mathbf{F}$ makes an angle ϕ with the tangent of ds at P.

The term $(F \cos \phi)r$, however, is the magnitude of instantaneous torque exerted by $\mathbf{F}$ on the rigid body about an axis through O, so that

$$dW = \tau \, d\theta. \tag{12–9}$$

This differential expression for the work done in rotation (about a fixed axis) is equivalent to the expression $dW = F \, ds$ for the work done in translation (along a straight line).

To obtain the rate at which work is done in rotational motion (about a fixed axis), we divide both sides of Eq. 12–9 by the infinitesimal time interval dt during which the body is displaced through $d\theta$, obtaining

$$\frac{dW}{dt} = \tau \frac{d\theta}{dt}$$

or

$$P = \tau\omega.$$

This last expression is the rotational analog of $P = Fv$ for translational motion (along a straight line).

If now a number of forces $\mathbf{F}_1$, $\mathbf{F}_2$, etc., are applied to the body in the plane normal to its axis of rotation, the work done by these forces on the body in a small rotation $d\theta$ will be

$$dW = F_1 \cos \phi_1 r_1 \, d\theta + F_2 \cos \phi_2 r_2 \, d\theta + \cdots,$$
$$= (\tau_1 + \tau_2 + \cdots) \, d\theta = \tau \, d\theta,$$

where $r_1 \, d\theta$ equals ds_1, the displacement of the point at which $\mathbf{F}_1$ is applied, and ϕ_1 is the angle between $\mathbf{F}_1$ and $d\mathbf{s}_1$, etc., and where τ is now the *resultant* torque about the axis through O. In computing this sum each torque is considered positive or negative according to the sense in which it alone would tend to rotate the body about its axis. We can arbitrarily call the torque associated with a force positive if the effect of the force is to produce a counterclockwise rotation; then the torque is negative if the effect is to produce a clockwise rotation.

There is no internal motion of particles within a truly rigid body. The particles always maintain a fixed position relative to one another and move only with the body as a whole. Hence, there can be no dissipation of energy within a truly rigid body. We can, therefore, equate the rate at which work is being done on the body to the rate at which its kinetic energy is increasing. The rate at which work is being done on the rigid body is

$$\frac{dW}{dt} = \tau \frac{d\theta}{dt} = \tau\omega. \tag{12–10}$$

The rate at which the kinetic energy of the rigid body is increasing is

$$\frac{d}{dt}\left(\tfrac{1}{2}I\omega^2\right).$$

But I is constant because the body is rigid and the axis is fixed. Hence,

$$\frac{d}{dt}\left(\tfrac{1}{2}I\omega^2\right) = \tfrac{1}{2}I\frac{d}{dt}\left(\omega^2\right) = I\omega\frac{d\omega}{dt} = I\omega\alpha. \tag{12–11}$$

Equating Eq. 12–10 to Eq. 12–11, we obtain

$$\tau\omega = I\alpha\omega$$

or

$$\tau = I\alpha. \tag{12–12}$$

Equation 12–12 is the equivalent of Newton's second law of motion, $F = ma$, for the rotational motion of a rigid body. We have simply transformed the second law from translational terms, $\mathbf{F} = m\mathbf{a}$, to rotational terms, $\boldsymbol{\tau} = I\boldsymbol{\alpha}$. Here the sum of the torques $\boldsymbol{\tau}$ is analogous to the sum of the forces $\mathbf{F}$, the rotational inertia I is analogous to the mass m, and the angular acceleration $\boldsymbol{\alpha}$ is analogous to the linear acceleration $\mathbf{a}$.

Just as the value of the rotational inertia I of a body depends on the location of the axis about which the body is taken to rotate, so the value of the torque applied to a body by a force depends on the location of the axis of rotation relative to the point of application of the force.

The torques were all assumed to be directed along the fixed axis of rotation in our derivation so that for the analogous linear case the forces must be assumed to be along the same line. Forces and the torques are vectors, but when they are directed along a fixed line, they can have only two possible directions. By taking one direction as $+$ and the other as $-$, we can treat these vectors algebraically and deal with their magnitudes only.

In Table 12–2 we compare the motion of a particle along a straight line with the motion of a rigid body about a fixed axis.

Table 12–2

Rectilinear Motion		Rotation about a Fixed Axis	
Displacement	x	Angular displacement	θ
Velocity	$v = \dfrac{dx}{dt}$	Angular velocity	$\omega = \dfrac{d\theta}{dt}$
Acceleration	$a = \dfrac{dv}{dt}$	Angular acceleration	$\alpha = \dfrac{d\omega}{dt}$
Mass	m	Rotational inertia	I
Force	$F = ma$	Torque	$\tau = I\alpha$
Work	$W = \int F\,dx$	Work	$W = \int \tau\,d\theta$
Kinetic energy	$\frac{1}{2}mv^2$	Kinetic energy	$\frac{1}{2}I\omega^2$
Power	$P = Fv$	Power	$P = \tau\omega$
Linear momentum	mv	Angular momentum	$I\omega$

▼ **Example 3.** A uniform disk of radius R and mass M is mounted on an axle supported in fixed frictionless bearings, as in Fig. 12–12. A light cord is wrapped around the rim of the wheel and a steady downward pull T is exerted on the cord. Find the angular acceleration of the wheel and the tangential acceleration of a point on the rim.

The torque about the central axis is $\tau = TR$, and the rotational inertia of the disk about its central axis is $I = \frac{1}{2}MR^2$. From

$$\tau = I\alpha,$$

we have

$$TR = (\tfrac{1}{2}MR^2)\alpha$$

or

$$\alpha = \frac{2T}{MR}.$$

If the mass of the disk is taken to be $M = 0.20$ slug, its radius $R = 0.50$ ft, and the force $T = 1.0$ lb, then

$$\alpha = \frac{(2)(1.0\text{ lb})}{(0.20\text{ slug})(0.50\text{ ft})} = 20\text{ radians/sec}^2.$$

The tangential acceleration of a point on the rim is given by

$$a = R\alpha = (20\text{ radians/sec}^2)(0.50\text{ ft}) = 10\text{ ft/sec}^2.$$

Example 4. Suppose that we hang a body of mass m from the cord in the previous problem. Find the angular acceleration of the disk and the tangential acceleration of a point on the rim in this case.

Now, let T be the tension in the cord. Since the suspended body will accelerate downward, the downward pull of gravity on it, $m\mathbf{g}$, must exceed the upward pull of

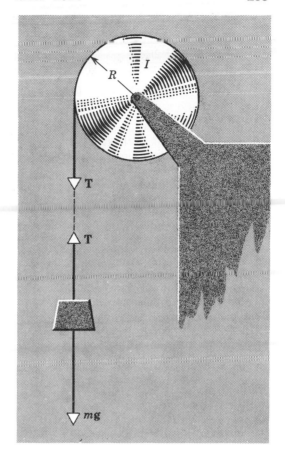

Fig. 12–12 Example 3. A steady downward force **T** produces rotation of the disk. Example 4. Here **T** is supplied by the falling mass m.

the cord on it, **T**. The acceleration a of the suspended body is the same as the tangential acceleration of a point on the rim of the disk. Therefore, from Newton's second law

$$mg - T = ma.$$

The resultant torque on the disk is TR and its rotational inertia is $\frac{1}{2}MR^2$, so that from

$$\tau = I\alpha$$

we obtain $$TR = \frac{1}{2}MR^2\alpha.$$

Using the relation $a = R\alpha$, we can write this last equation as

$$2T = Ma.$$

Solving the first and last equations simultaneously leads to

$$a = \left(\frac{2m}{M + 2m}\right)g,$$

and $$T = \left(\frac{Mm}{M + 2m}\right)g.$$

If now we let the disk have a mass $M = 0.20$ slug and a radius $R = 0.50$ ft as before, and we let the suspended body weigh 1.0 lb, we obtain

$$a = \frac{2mg}{M + 2m} = \frac{(2)(1.0 \text{ lb})}{(0.20 \text{ slug}) + (2)(\frac{1}{32} \text{ slug})} = 7.6 \text{ ft/sec}^2,$$

$$\alpha = \frac{a}{R} = \frac{(7.6 \text{ ft/sec}^2)}{0.50 \text{ ft}} = 15 \text{ radians/sec}^2.$$

Notice that the accelerations are less for a suspended 1.0-lb body than they were for a steady 1.0-lb pull on the string (Example 3). This corresponds to the fact that the tension in the string supplying the torque is now less than 1 lb, namely

$$T = \frac{Mmg}{M + 2m} = \frac{(0.20 \text{ slug})(1.0 \text{ lb})}{(0.20 + 2.0/32) \text{ slug}} = 0.76 \text{ lb}.$$

The tension in the string must be less than the weight of the suspended body if the body is to accelerate downward.

Example 5. Assuming that the disk of Example 4 starts from rest, compute the work done by the applied torque on the disk in 2.1 sec. Compute also the increase in rotational kinetic energy of the disk.

Since the applied torque is constant, the resulting angular acceleration is constant. The total angular displacement in constant angular acceleration is obtained from Eq. 11–5,

$$\theta = \omega_0 t + \tfrac{1}{2}\alpha t^2,$$

in which $\omega_0 = 0,$ $\alpha = 15 \text{ radians/sec}^2,$ $t = 2.1 \text{ sec},$

so that $\theta = 0 \mid (\tfrac{1}{2})(15 \text{ radians/sec}^2)(2.1 \text{ sec})^2 = 34 \text{ radians}.$

For constant torque the work done in a finite angular displacement is

$$W = \tau(\theta_2 - \theta_1),$$

in which $\tau = TR = (0.76 \text{ lb})(0.50 \text{ ft}) = 0.38 \text{ lb-ft},$

and $\theta_2 - \theta_1 = \theta = 34 \text{ radians}.$

Therefore $W = (0.38 \text{ lb-ft})(34 \text{ radians}) = 13 \text{ ft-lb}.$

This work must result in an increase in rotational kinetic energy of the disk. Starting from rest the disk acquires an angular speed ω.

The rotational energy is $\tfrac{1}{2}I\omega^2 = \tfrac{1}{2}(\tfrac{1}{2}MR^2)\omega^2$.

To obtain ω we use Eq. 11–3,

$$\omega = \omega_0 + \alpha t,$$

in which $\omega_0 = 0,$ $t = 2.1 \text{ sec},$ $\alpha = 15 \text{ radians/sec}^2,$

so that $\omega = 0 + (15 \text{ radians/sec}^2)(2.1 \text{ sec}) = 32 \text{ radians/sec}.$

Then $\tfrac{1}{2}I\omega^2 = (\tfrac{1}{4})(0.20 \text{ slug})(0.50 \text{ ft})^2(32 \text{ radians/sec})^2 = 13 \text{ ft-lb},$

as before. Hence, the increase in kinetic energy of the disk is equal to the work done by the resultant force on the disk, as it must be.

Example 6. Show that the conservation of mechanical energy holds for the system of Example 4.

The resultant force acting on the system is the force of gravity on the suspended body. This is a conservative force. Viewing the system as a whole, we see that the suspended body loses potential energy U as it descends,

$$U = mgy,$$

where y is the vertical distance through which the block descends. At the same time the suspended body gains kinetic energy of translation and the disk gains kinetic energy of rotation. The total gain in kinetic energy is

$$\tfrac{1}{2}mv^2 + \tfrac{1}{2}I\omega^2,$$

where v is the linear speed of the suspended mass. We must prove then that

$$mgy = \tfrac{1}{2}mv^2 + \tfrac{1}{2}I\omega^2.$$

For the linear motion starting from rest we have $v^2 = 2ay$. From Example 4, we obtained $a = 2\, mg/(M + 2m)$. Hence

$$mgy = \frac{mgv^2}{2a} = \frac{1}{2}\, mv^2 \left(\frac{g}{a}\right) = \frac{1}{2}\, mv^2 \left(\frac{M + 2m}{2m}\right) = \frac{1}{4}(M + 2m)v^2.$$

We also know that $\omega = v/r$ and $I = \tfrac{1}{2}Mr^2$. Substituting these relations into the right-hand side of the conservation equation, we obtain

$$\tfrac{1}{2}mv^2 + \tfrac{1}{2}I\omega^2 = \tfrac{1}{2}mv^2 + \tfrac{1}{2}(\tfrac{1}{2}Mr^2)(v^2/r^2) = \tfrac{1}{4}(M + 2m)v^2.$$

The mechanical energy is therefore conserved. ◀

12–5   The Combined Translational and Rotational Motion of a Rigid Body

Up until now we have considered only bodies rotating about some fixed axis. If a body is rolling, however, it is rotating about an axis and also moving translationally. Therefore it would seem that the motion of rolling bodies must be treated as a combination of translational and rotational motion. It is also possible, however, to treat a rolling body as though its motion is one of pure rotation. We wish to illustrate the equivalence of the two approaches.

Consider, for example, a cylinder rolling along a level surface, as in Fig. 12–13. At any instant the bottom of the cylinder is at rest on the surface, since it does not slide. The axis normal to the diagram through the point of

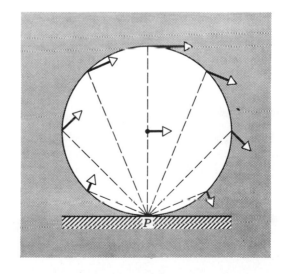

Fig. 12–13 A rolling body may at any instant be thought of as rotating about its point of contact P.

contact P is called the *instantaneous axis of rotation*. At that instant the linear velocity of every particle of the cylinder is directed at right angles to the line joining the particle and P and its magnitude is proportional to this distance. This is the same as saying that the cylinder is rotating about a fixed axis through P with a certain angular speed ω, *at that instant*. Hence, at a given instant the motion of the body is equivalent to a pure rotation. The total kinetic energy can, therefore, be written as

$$K = \tfrac{1}{2}I_p\omega^2, \tag{12–13}$$

where I_p is the rotational inertia about the axis through P.

Let us now use the parallel axis theorem, which tells us that

$$I_p = I_o + MR^2,$$

where I_o is the rotational inertia of the cylinder of mass M and radius R about a parallel axis through the center of mass. Equation 12–13 now becomes

$$K = \tfrac{1}{2}I_o\omega^2 + \tfrac{1}{2}MR^2\omega^2. \tag{12–14}$$

The quantity $R\omega$ is the speed with which the center of mass of the cylinder is moving with respect to the fixed point P. Let $R\omega = v_o$. Equation 12–14 then becomes

$$K = \tfrac{1}{2}I_o\omega^2 + \tfrac{1}{2}Mv_o^2. \tag{12–15}$$

Now notice that the speed of the center of mass with respect to P is the same as the speed of P with respect to the center of mass. Hence, the angular speed ω of the center of mass about P as seen by someone at P is the same as the angular speed of a particle at P about O as seen by someone at O (moving along with the cylinder). This is equivalent to saying that any reference line in the cylinder turns through the same angle in a given time whether it is observed from a fixed frame of reference or a moving frame of reference. We can, therefore, interpret Eq. 12–15, which was derived on the basis of a pure rotational motion, in another way; that is, the first term, $\tfrac{1}{2}I_o\omega^2$, is the kinetic energy the cylinder would have if it were merely rotating about an axis through its center of mass, without translational motion; and the second term, $\tfrac{1}{2}Mv_o^2$, is the kinetic energy the cylinder would have if it were moving translationally with the speed of its center of mass, without rotating. Notice that there is now no reference at all to the instantaneous axis of rotation. In fact, Eq. 12–15 applies to any body that is moving and rotating about an axis perpendicular to its motion whether or not it is rolling on a surface.

The combined effects of translation of the center of mass and rotation about an axis through the center of mass are equivalent to a pure rotation with the same angular speed about an axis through the point of contact of a rolling body.

To illustrate this result simply, let us consider the instantaneous speed of various points on the rolling cylinder. If the speed of the center of mass is v_o, the instantaneous angular speed about an axis through P is $\omega = v_o/R$. A point Q at the top of the cylinder will therefore have a speed $\omega 2R = 2v_o$ at

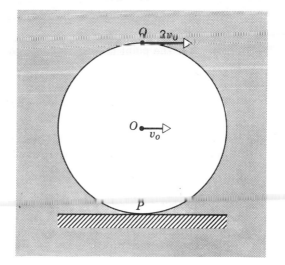

Fig. 12–14 Since Q and O have the same angular velocity about P, Q moves with twice the linear velocity of that of O, being twice as far from P.

that instant. The point of contact P is instantaneously at rest. Hence, from the point of view of pure rotation about P, the situation is as shown in Fig. 12–14.

Now let us regard the rolling as a combination of translation of the center of mass and rotation about the cylinder axis through O. If we consider translation only, all points on the cylinder have the same speed v_o as the center of mass. This is shown in Fig. 12–15a. If we consider the rotation only, the center is at rest, whereas the point Q at the top has a speed $+\omega R$ in the x direction and the point P at the bottom of the cylinder has a speed $-\omega R$ in the x direction. This is shown in Fig. 12–15b. Now let us combine

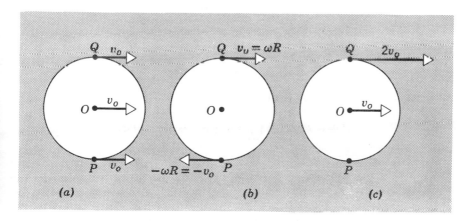

Fig. 12–15 (a) For pure translation, all points move with the same velocity. (b) For pure rotation about O, opposite points move with opposite velocities. (c) Combined rotation and translation is obtained by adding together corresponding vectors in (a) and (b).

these two results. Recalling that $\omega = v_0/R$, we obtain

for the point Q $\qquad v = v_0 + \omega R = v_0 + \dfrac{v_0}{R}R = 2v_0,$

for the point O $\qquad v = v_0 + \dot{0} = v_0,$

for the point P $\qquad v = v_0 - \omega R = v_0 - \dfrac{v_0}{R}R = 0.$

This result, shown in Fig. 12–15c is exactly the same as that obtained from the purely rotational point of view, Fig. 12–14.

▶ **Example 7.** Consider a solid cylinder of mass M and radius R rolling down an inclined plane without slipping. Find the speed of its center of mass when the cylinder reaches the bottom.

The situation is illustrated in Fig. 12–16. We can use the conservation of energy to solve this problem. The cylinder is initially at rest. In rolling down the incline

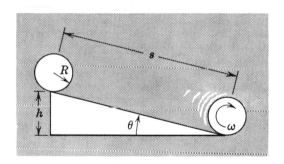

Fig. 12–16 Example 7. The motion of a cylinder rolling down an incline.

the cylinder loses potential energy of an amount Mgh, where h is the height of the incline. It gains kinetic energy equal to

$$\tfrac{1}{2}I_0\omega^2 + \tfrac{1}{2}Mv^2,$$

where v is the linear speed of the center of mass and ω is the angular speed about the center of mass at the bottom.

We have then the relation

$$Mgh = \tfrac{1}{2}I_0\omega^2 + \tfrac{1}{2}Mv^2,$$

in which $\qquad\qquad I_0 = \tfrac{1}{2}Mr^2 \qquad$ and $\qquad \omega = \dfrac{v}{r}.$

Hence $\qquad Mgh = \tfrac{1}{2}(\tfrac{1}{2}MR^2)\left(\dfrac{v}{R}\right)^2 + \tfrac{1}{2}Mv^2 = (\tfrac{1}{4} + \tfrac{1}{2})Mv^2,$

$$v^2 = \tfrac{4}{3}gh \qquad \text{or} \qquad v = \sqrt{\tfrac{4}{3}gh}.$$

The speed of the center of mass would have been $v = \sqrt{2gh}$ if the cylinder had *slid* down a *frictionless* incline. The speed of the rolling cylinder is, therefore, less than the speed of the sliding cylinder, because for the rolling cylinder part of the lost potential energy has been transformed into rotational kinetic energy, leaving less available for the translational part of the kinetic energy. Although the rolling cylinder arrives later at the bottom of the incline than an identical sliding cylinder started at the same time down a frictionless, but otherwise identical, incline, both arrive at the bottom with the same amount of energy; the rolling cylinder happens to be rotating as it moves, whereas the sliding one does not rotate as it moves.

Notice that static friction is needed to cause the cylinder to rotate. Remembering that friction is a dissipative force, how can you justify using the conservation of mechanical energy in this problem?

Example 8. The previous result was derived by use of energy methods. Solve the same problem using only dynamical methods.

The force diagram is shown in Fig. 12–17. $M\mathbf{g}$ is the weight of the cylinder acting vertically down through the center of mass,* $\mathbf{N}$ is the normal force exerted by the

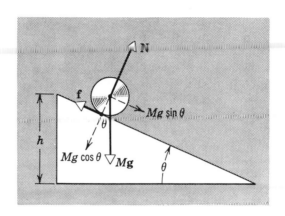

Fig. 12–17 Example 8. Dynamic solution of the motion of a cylinder rolling down an incline.

incline on the cylinder, and $\mathbf{f}$ is the force of static friction acting along the incline at the point of contact.

The *translational* motion of a body is obtained by assuming that all the external forces act at its center of mass. Using Newton's second law, we obtain

$$N - Mg\cos\theta = 0 \qquad \text{for motion normal to the incline,}$$

and
$$Mg\sin\theta - f = Ma \qquad \text{for motion along the incline.}$$

The *rotational* motion about the center of mass follows from

$$\tau = I_o\alpha.$$

Neither $\mathbf{N}$ nor $M\mathbf{g}$ can cause rotation about C because their lines of action pass through C, and they have zero moment arms. The force of friction has a moment arm R about C, so that

$$fR = I_o\alpha.$$

But
$$I_o = \tfrac{1}{2}MR^2 \qquad \text{and} \qquad \alpha = \frac{a}{R}$$

so that
$$f = \frac{I_o\alpha}{R} = \frac{Ma}{2}.$$

---

* In drawing the vector diagram for this problem we tacitly assume that the total weight of the body can be thought of as acting at the center of mass. We saw in Section 9–2 that this is justified for analyzing the translational motion. However, later in the problem we use this result in analyzing the rotational motion as well. We shall justify this procedure in Chapter 14, where it is shown that the *weight* of a body can be considered to act at its center of mass for both translational *and* rotational motion.

Substituting this into the second translational equation, we find

$$a = \tfrac{2}{3}g \sin \theta.$$

That is, the acceleration of the center of mass for the rolling cylinder ($\tfrac{2}{3}g \sin \theta$) is less than the acceleration of the center of mass for the cylinder sliding down the incline ($g \sin \theta$).

This result holds at any instant, regardless of the position of the cylinder along the incline. The center of mass moves with constant linear acceleration. To get the speed of the center of mass, starting from rest, we use the relation

$$v^2 = 2as,$$

so that

$$v^2 = 2(\tfrac{2}{3}g \sin \theta)s = \tfrac{4}{3}g \frac{h}{s} s = \tfrac{4}{3}gh$$

or

$$v = \sqrt{\tfrac{4}{3}gh}.$$

This result is the same as that obtained before by the energy method. The energy method is certainly simpler and more direct. However, if we are interested in knowing what the forces are, such as **N** and **f**, we must use a dynamical method.

This method determines the minimum force of static friction needed for rolling:

$$f = \frac{Ma}{2} = \frac{M}{2}(\tfrac{2}{3}g \sin \theta) = \tfrac{1}{3}Mg \sin \theta.$$

What would happen if the force of static friction between the surfaces were less than this value?

Example 9. A sphere and a cylinder, having the same mass and radius, start from rest and roll down the same incline. Which body gets to the bottom first?

For a sphere I_o equals $\tfrac{2}{5}MR^2$. Using the dynamical method we obtain

$$Mg \sin \theta - f = Ma, \qquad \text{translation of c.m.,}$$
$$fR = I_o\alpha = (\tfrac{2}{5}MR^2)\left(\frac{a}{R}\right), \qquad \text{rotation about c.m.,}$$

or

$$f = \tfrac{2}{5}Ma \quad \text{and} \quad a = \tfrac{5}{7}g \sin \theta, \qquad \text{sphere.}$$

For the cylinder (Example 8)

$$a = \tfrac{2}{3}g \sin \theta, \qquad \text{cylinder.}$$

Hence, the acceleration of the center of mass of the sphere is at all times greater than the acceleration of the center of mass of the cylinder. Since both bodies start from rest at the same instant, the sphere will reach the bottom first.

Which body has the greater rotational energy at the bottom? Which body has the greater translational energy at the bottom?

The student should note carefully that neither the mass nor the radius of the rolling object enters the previous results. How then would we expect the behavior of cylinders of different mass and radii to compare? How would we expect the behavior of spheres of different mass and radii to compare? How would the behavior of a cylinder and sphere having different masses and radii compare? ◀

QUESTIONS

1. State Newton's three laws of motion in words suitable for rotating bodies.
2. Can the mass of a body be considered as concentrated at its center of mass for purposes of computing its rotational inertia?

3. A person can distinguish between a raw egg and a hard-boiled one by spinning each one on the table. Explain how.

4. If two circular disks of the same weight and thickness are made from metals having different densities, which disk, if either, will have the larger rotational inertia?

5. The rotational inertia of a body of rather complicated shape is to be determined. The shape makes a mathematical calculation from $\int r^2\,dm$ exceedingly difficult. Suggest ways in which the rotational inertia could be measured *experimentally*.

6. Five solids are shown in cross section (Fig. 12–18). The cross sections have equal heights and equal maximum widths. The axes of rotation are perpendicular to the sections

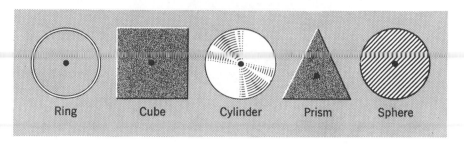

Ring   Cube   Cylinder   Prism   Sphere

Fig. 12–18

through the points shown. The solids have equal masses. Which one has the largest rotational inertia? Which the smallest?

7. A solid wooden sphere rolls down two different inclined planes of the same height but different inclines. Will it reach the bottom with the same speed in each case? Will it take longer to roll down one incline than the other? If so, which one and why?

8. Two heavy disks are connected by a short rod of much smaller radius. The system is placed on a narrow inclined plank so that the disks hang over the sides and the system rolls down on the rod without slipping (Fig. 12–19). Near the bottom of the incline the

Fig. 12–19

disks touch the horizontal table top and the system takes off with greatly increased translational speed. Explain carefully.

9. When a logger cuts down a tree he makes a cut on the side facing the direction in which he wants it to fall. Explain why. Would it be safe to stand directly behind the tree on the opposite side of the fall, even knowing to a certainty that it will fall the opposite way?

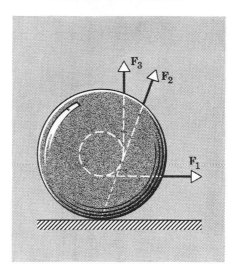

Fig. 12–20

Fig. 12–20

10. A Yo-yo is resting on a horizontal table and is free to roll (Fig. 12–20). If the string is pulled by a horizontal force such as F_1, which way will the Yo-yo roll? What happens when the force F_2 is applied (its line of action passes through the point of contact of Yo-yo and table)? If the string is pulled vertically with the force F_3, what happens?

PROBLEMS

1. (a) Show that, by resolving $\mathbf{F}$ into components F_x and F_y and $\mathbf{r}$ into components x and y, the torque about the z-axis can be written as $\tau_z = xF_y - yF_x$. (b) Use this method to compute the torque in Example 1.

2. (a) Show that the sum of the rotational inertia of a plane laminar body about any two perpendicular axes in the plane of the body is equal to the rotational inertia of the body about an axis through their point of intersection perpendicular to the plane. (b) Apply this to a circular disk to find its rotational inertia about a diameter as axis.

3. (a) Prove that the rotational inertia of a thin rod of length l about an axis through its center perpendicular to its length is $I = \frac{1}{12}Ml^2$. (See Table 12–1.) (b) Use the parallel-axis theorem to show that $I = \frac{1}{3}Ml^2$ when the axis of rotation is through one end perpendicular to the length of the rod.

4. Show that the rotational inertia of a rectangular plate of sides a and b about an axis perpendicular to the plate through its center is $\frac{1}{12}M(a^2 + b^2)$.

5. (a) Show that a solid cylinder of mass M and radius R is equivalent to a thin hoop of mass M and radius $R/\sqrt{2}$, for rotation about a central axis. (b) The radial distance from a given axis at which the mass of a body could be concentrated without altering the rotational inertia of the body about that axis is called the *radius of gyration*. Let k represent radius of gyration and show that

$$k = \sqrt{I/M}.$$

This gives the radius of the "equivalent hoop" in the general case.

6. The oxygen molecule has a total mass of 5.30×10^{-26} kg and a rotational inertia of 1.94×10^{-46} kg-m² about an axis through the center perpendicular to the line joining atoms. Suppose that such a molecule in a gas has a mean speed of 500 meters/sec and

that its rotational kinetic energy is two-thirds of its translational kinetic energy. Find its average angular velocity.

7. A hoop of radius 10 ft weighs 320 lb. It rolls along a horizontal floor so that its center of mass has a speed of 0.50 ft/sec. How much work has to be done to stop it?

8. An automobile engine develops 100 hp when rotating at a speed of 1800 rev/min. What torque does it deliver?

9. A thin rod of length l and mass m is suspended freely at its end. It is pulled aside and swung about a horizontal axis, passing through its lowest position with an angular speed ω. How high does its center of mass rise above its lowest position? Neglect friction and air resistance.

10. Assume the earth to be a sphere of uniform density. (a) What is its rotational kinetic energy? Take the radius of the earth to be 6.4×10^3 km and the mass of the earth to be 6.0×10^{24} kg. (b) Suppose this energy could be harnessed for man's use. For how long could the earth supply 1 kw of power to each of the 3.0×10^9 persons on earth?

11. A Yo-yo of mass M has a shaft of radius r about which a string is wound. A child lets the Yo-yo unwind as he holds the loose end of the string in a fixed position. The Yo-yo accelerates down, reaches the bottom, and climbs back up, the string winding around the shaft in the opposite sense. Find the tension in the string during the descent and the ascent, assuming r to be small enough to consider the string being vertical at all times. Let I represent the rotational inertia of the Yo-yo about its central axis.

12. A wheel of mass M and radius of gyration k (see Problem 5) spins on a fixed horizontal axle passing snugly through its hub. The hub rubs the axle, whose radius is a, the coefficient of friction being μ. The wheel is given an initial angular velocity ω_0. Find the time of rotation and the number of revolutions before the wheel comes to a stop.

13. In an Atwood's machine (Fig. 5–8) one block has a mass of 500 gm and the other a mass of 460 gm. The pulley, which is mounted in horizontal frictionless bearings, has a radius of 5.0 cm. When released from rest the heavier block is observed to fall 75 cm in 5 sec. Show how to determine the rotational inertia of the pulley from these data.

14. A 6.0-lb block is put on a plane inclined 30° to the horizontal and is attached by a cord parallel to the plane over a pulley at the top to a hanging block weighing 18 lb. The pulley weighs 2.0 lb and has a radius of 0.33 ft. The coefficient of kinetic friction between block and plane is 0.10. Find the acceleration of the hanging block and the tension in the cord on each side of the pulley. Assume the pulley to be a uniform disk.

15. A box 6 ft high by 4 ft wide by 3 ft deep containing a refrigerator sits in the back of a truck vertically. The weight of the refrigerator plus that of the box is 300 lb, and this is presumed to be uniformly distributed throughout the volume of the box. The box is tipped over by an acceleration of the truck. What was the minimum value that this acceleration must have had?

16. Take the center of mass of a car to be 2.5 ft above the road and its width between wheels to be 4.5 ft. (a) If the car races around an unbanked curve having a radius of 100 ft without skidding, what is the largest speed possible without its overturning? (b) What minimum value would the coefficient of friction need to be at this speed?

17. You are riding on a train and are standing with your feet 2 ft apart facing forward. If the train "rounds a curve" of radius 500 yards in a counterclockwise sense viewed from above, with a linear speed of 45 mph, what per cent of your weight rests on your left leg? Assume that your center of mass is 4 ft above the floor.

18. Show that a cylinder will slip on an inclined plane of inclination angle θ if the coefficient of static friction between plane and cylinder is less than $\frac{1}{3} \tan \theta$.

19. A sphere rolls up an inclined plane of inclination angle 30°. At the bottom of the incline the center of mass of the sphere has a translational speed of 16 ft/sec. (a) How far does the sphere travel up the plane? (b) How long does it take to return to the bottom?

20. A small sphere rolls without slipping on the inside of a large vertical hemisphere. It starts at the top from rest. (a) What is its kinetic energy at the bottom? What fraction is rotational? What translational? (b) What normal force does the small sphere exert on

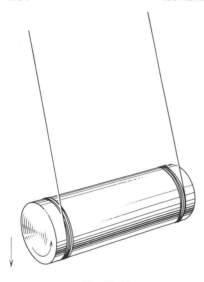

Fig. 12–21

the hemisphere at the bottom? Take the radius of the small sphere to be r, that of the hemisphere to be R, and let m be the mass of the sphere.

21. A cylinder of length 1.0 ft and radius 1.0 in. weighs 6 lb. Two cords are wrapped around the cylinder, one near each end, and the cord ends are attached to hooks on the ceiling. The cylinder is held horizontally with the two cords exactly vertical and is then released (Fig. 12–21). Find the tension in the cords as they unwind, and determine the linear acceleration of the cylinder as it falls.

22. A string is wrapped around a cylinder of mass M, radius R. The string is pulled vertically upward to prevent the center of mass from falling as the cylinder unwinds the string. (a) What is the tension in the string? (b) How much work has been done on the cylinder once it has reached an angular speed ω? (c) What is the length of string unwound in this time?

23. A solid cylinder of weight 50 lb and radius 3 in. has a light thin tape wound around it. The tape passes over a light smooth fixed pulley to a 10-lb body (Fig. 12–22). Find the tension in the tape and the linear acceleration of the cylinder up the incline, assuming no slipping.

24. A bowling ball is thrown down the alley in such a way that it slides with a speed v_0 initially without rolling. Prove that it will roll without any sliding when its speed falls to $\frac{5}{7}v_0$. The transition from pure sliding to pure rolling is gradual, so that both sliding *and* rolling take place during this interval. (Hint: Sliding ceases when the forward speed of the lowest point of the sphere is zero.)

25. A 10-ft-long ladder rests against a wall and makes an angle of 60° with the horizontal floor. If it starts to slip, where is the instantaneous axis of rotation?

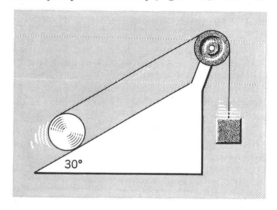

Fig. 12–22

26. (a) A tall chimney cracks near its base and falls over. Express the linear acceleration of the top of the chimney as a function of the angle θ made by the chimney with the vertical. Can this acceleration exceed g? (b) The chimney cracks up during the fall. Explain how this can happen.

27. A meter stick is held vertically with one end on the floor and is then allowed to fall. Find the speed of the other end when it hits the floor, assuming that the end on the floor does not slip.

The Conservation
of Angular Momentum

CHAPTER 13

13-1 Introduction

In rotational dynamics the concept of angular momentum plays a role similar to that played by linear momentum in linear dynamics. With the use of this concept we can generalize the equation of rotational dynamics and derive an important conservation principle. We shall develop this concept, applying it first to a single particle and then to a many-particle system. The rotational motion of rigid bodies will then be seen to be a special case of this more general approach. Angular momentum and its conservation principle play a very important part in the description of modern atomic and nuclear physics as well as in astronomy and macroscopic physics.

13-2 Angular Momentum of a Particle

Consider a particle of mass m and linear momentum $\mathbf{p}$ at a position $\mathbf{r}$ relative to the origin O of a coordinate system (Fig. 13-1). The *angular momentum* of the particle *about the point* 0 is a vector represented by the symbol $\mathbf{L}$ and defined as

$$\mathbf{L} = \mathbf{r} \times \mathbf{p}. \tag{13-1}$$

The magnitude of $\mathbf{L}$ is $\qquad L = rp \sin \theta, \tag{13-2}$

where θ is the angle from $\mathbf{r}$ to $\mathbf{p}$. The direction of $\mathbf{L}$ is perpendicular to the plane formed by $\mathbf{r}$ and $\dot{\mathbf{p}}$. The sense of $\mathbf{L}$ is given by the rule for vector products. One swings $\mathbf{r}$ into $\mathbf{p}$ through the smaller angle between them with the curled fingers of the right hand; the direction of the extended thumb then gives the direction of $\mathbf{L}$.

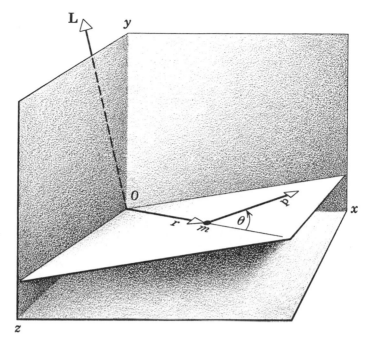

Fig. 13–1 A mass point m having momentum $\mathbf{p}$ is located at $\mathbf{r}$ relative to the origin O. The plane formed by $\mathbf{p}$ and $\mathbf{r}$ is shown, as well as the angle θ that $\mathbf{p}$ makes with $\mathbf{r}$. Since $\mathbf{L} = \mathbf{r} \times \mathbf{p}$, $\mathbf{L}$ is perpendicular to this plane. The value of $\mathbf{L}$ depends on the location of m relative to O, but not on how the coordinate axes x, y, and z are oriented about O.

Just as torque can be thought of as the moment of a force, so angular momentum can be thought of as the moment of (linear) momentum. The moment arm is the perpendicular distance from O to the line of action of $\mathbf{p}$. When the angle θ is $0°$ or $180°$, the line of action of $\mathbf{p}$ passes through O; with these two angles (Eq. 13–2) the angular momentum about O is zero. Angular momentum, like torque, refers to a particular origin about which moments are taken. The angular momentum vector is drawn through this origin, as in Fig. 13–1.

We can now show an important relation between torque and angular momentum. We have seen that $\mathbf{F} = d(m\mathbf{v})/dt$. First we take the vector product of $\mathbf{r}$ with both sides of this equation and obtain

$$\mathbf{r} \times \mathbf{F} = \mathbf{r} \times \frac{d}{dt} m\mathbf{v}.$$

But $\mathbf{r} \times \mathbf{F}$ is the moment of a force, or the torque, about O. We can then write

$$\boldsymbol{\tau} = \mathbf{r} \times \frac{d}{dt} m\mathbf{v}. \tag{13–3}$$

Next we differentiate Eq. 13-1 and obtain

$$\frac{d\mathbf{L}}{dt} = \frac{d}{dt}(\mathbf{r} \times \mathbf{p}).$$

Now the derivative of a vector product is taken in the same way as the derivative of an ordinary product, except that the order of the terms must not be changed. We have

$$\frac{d\mathbf{L}}{dt} = \left(\frac{d\mathbf{r}}{dt} \times \mathbf{p}\right) + \left(\mathbf{r} \times \frac{d\mathbf{p}}{dt}\right).$$

But $d\mathbf{r}$ is simply the vector displacement of the particle in the time dt so that $d\mathbf{r}/dt$ is the instantaneous velocity $\mathbf{v}$ of the particle. Also, $\mathbf{p}$ equals $m\mathbf{v}$, so that the equation can be rewritten as

$$\frac{d\mathbf{L}}{dt} = (\mathbf{v} \times m\mathbf{v}) + \left(\mathbf{r} \times \frac{d}{dt}m\mathbf{v}\right).$$

Now $\mathbf{v} \times m\mathbf{v}$ equals zero because the vector product of two parallel vectors is zero. Therefore,

$$\frac{d\mathbf{L}}{dt} = \mathbf{r} \times \frac{d}{dt}m\mathbf{v}. \tag{13-4}$$

Inspection of Eqs. 13-3 and 13-4 shows that

$$\boldsymbol{\tau} = \frac{d\mathbf{L}}{dt}, \tag{13-5}$$

which states that *the time rate of change of the vector angular momentum of a particle is equal to the (vector) torque acting on it.* This result is the rotational analog of Eq. 9-13, which stated that the time rate of change of the vector linear momentum of a particle is equal to the vector force acting on it.

The vector Eq. 13-5, like all vector equations, is equivalent to three scalar equations, namely

$$\tau_x = \frac{d}{dt}L_x, \qquad \tau_y = \frac{d}{dt}L_y, \qquad \tau_z = \frac{d}{dt}L_z. \tag{13-6}$$

Hence, the x component of the applied torque is given by the change with time of the x component of the angular momentum. Similar results hold for the y and z directions.

13-3   Angular Momentum of a System of Particles

The previous section was concerned with a single particle. Let us now consider a system consisting of many particles. To calculate the total angular momentum of a system of particles about some point, we must add vectorially the angular momenta of all the individual particles of the system about this point. As time goes on, the total angular momentum of the system about a fixed reference point may change. This change, $d\mathbf{L}/dt$, can arise from two sources: (*a*) torques exerted on the particles of the system by internal forces between the particles; (*b*) torques exerted on the particles of the system by external forces.

If Newton's third law holds exactly, that is, if the forces between any two particles not only are equal and opposite but are also directed along the line joining the two particles, the total internal torque is zero because the torque resulting from each internal action-reaction force pair is zero. Hence, the first source contributes nothing. For a fixed reference point, therefore, only the second source remains, and we can write

$$\tau_{ext} = \frac{d\mathbf{L}}{dt}, \tag{13-7}$$

where τ_{ext} stands for the *sum* of *all* the *external* torques acting on the system. In words, *the time rate of change of the total angular momentum of a system of particles about a fixed reference point is equal to the sum of the* external *torques acting on the system.**

Equation 13-7 is the generalization of Eq. 13-5 to many particles. When we have only one particle, there are no internal forces or torques, of course.

A rigid body is simply a special case of a system of particles, namely a system of particles whose relative positions are fixed. Hence, Eq. 13-7 is applicable to a rigid body. A rigid body is a relatively simple system because every particle in it has the same angular velocity $\boldsymbol{\omega}$ and angular acceleration $\boldsymbol{\alpha}$. We saw in Chapter 12 that the expression

$$\tau = I\boldsymbol{\alpha} \tag{13-8}$$

holds at any instant for a rigid body which is free to rotate about any axis, where I is the rotational inertia of the rigid body calculated with respect to that axis and τ is the sum of the applied (external) torques about that axis. Comparing this with Eq. 13-7, we obtain the result

$$\frac{d\mathbf{L}}{dt} = I\boldsymbol{\alpha}.$$

But $\boldsymbol{\alpha} = d\boldsymbol{\omega}/dt$, and if I is constant, $I\,d\boldsymbol{\omega}/dt = d(I\boldsymbol{\omega})/dt$ so that

$$\frac{d\mathbf{L}}{dt} = \frac{d}{dt}I\boldsymbol{\omega}$$

or
$$\mathbf{L} = I\boldsymbol{\omega}. \tag{13-9}$$

Hence, the angular momentum of a rigid body is the product of the rotational inertia and the angular velocity of the rigid body.

---

* It is worth noting that if our reference point is chosen to be the center of mass of the system, Eq. 13-7 is still valid even if the reference point is not fixed in space. That is, the rate of change of angular momentum of the system about the center of mass is independent of the motion of the center of mass.

Notice the analogy to the linear momentum equation

$$\mathbf{p} = m\mathbf{v},$$

Here mass m is analogous to the rotational inertia I, linear velocity $\mathbf{v}$ is analogous to angular velocity $\boldsymbol{\omega}$, and linear momentum $\mathbf{p}$ is analogous to angular momentum $\mathbf{L}$.

If we combine Eqs. 13–7 and 13–9 we obtain

$$\boldsymbol{\tau} = \frac{d}{dt} I \boldsymbol{\omega}. \tag{13-10}$$

When I is constant, we obtain $\boldsymbol{\tau} = I\boldsymbol{\alpha}$. It turns out, however, that Eq. 13–10 is valid even for a system of particles in which I is *not constant*. Just as we found that the expression

$$\mathbf{F} = m\mathbf{a}$$

had to be generalized to

$$\mathbf{F} = \frac{d}{dt} m\mathbf{v} = \frac{d}{dt} \mathbf{p}$$

to be generally valid, so we find that the expression

$$\boldsymbol{\tau} = I\boldsymbol{\alpha}$$

must be generalized to

$$\boldsymbol{\tau} = \frac{d}{dt} I \boldsymbol{\omega} = \frac{d}{dt} \mathbf{L}$$

to be generally valid. Angular momentum, therefore, plays the same fundamental role in rotational dynamics as does linear momentum in translational dynamics.

▶ **Example 1.** Consider a horizontal plate rotating about a vertical axis through O, as shown in Fig. 13–2. Derive the relation $\mathbf{L} = I\boldsymbol{\omega}$ directly from the definition of angular momentum.

The angular momentum of a particle of mass m_i, displaced from the axis through O by the vector $\mathbf{r}_i$, is

$$\mathbf{r}_i \times \mathbf{p}_i = \mathbf{r}_i \times m_i \mathbf{v}_i,$$

where $\mathbf{v}_i$ is the linear velocity of the ith particle. To find the total angular momentum of the plate we must sum over the contributions from all the particles of the plate. Hence,

$$\mathbf{L} = \Sigma \, \mathbf{r}_i \times m_i \mathbf{v}_i = \Sigma \, m_i (\mathbf{r}_i \times \mathbf{v}_i).$$

Now it is clear that $\mathbf{L}$ lies parallel to the axis through O, since $\mathbf{r}_i$ and $\mathbf{v}_i$ for each particle are in the plane of the plate. Thus $\mathbf{L}$ is in the same direction as the angular velocity vector $\boldsymbol{\omega}$ of the rigid body. Therefore, we need to calculate only the magnitude of $\mathbf{L}$.

From the meaning of a vector product, we obtain

$$L = \Sigma \, m_i (r_i v_i \sin \theta_i),$$

where θ_i is the angle between the vectors $\mathbf{r}_i$ and $\mathbf{v}_i$. However, this angle is 90° for any

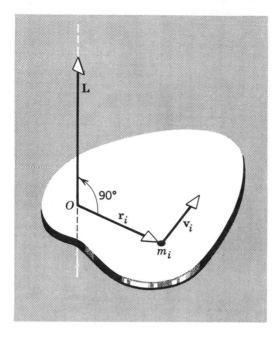

Fig. 13–2 Example 1. A horizontal plate rotating about a vertical axis through O. A mass point m_i located at r_i has velocity v_i. The sum of the angular momenta $\mathbf{L}_i = \mathbf{r}_i \times m_i \mathbf{v}_i$ add up to give the angular momentum of the plate, $\mathbf{L}$.

particle since $\mathbf{v}_i$ must be at right angles to $\mathbf{r}_i$ in a rigid body. Therefore, using $\theta_i = 90°$ and $v_i = \omega r_i$, we obtain

$$L = \Sigma\, m_i r_i \omega r_i = \Sigma\, (m_i r_i^2)\omega = I\omega.$$

Since $\boldsymbol{\omega}$ and $\mathbf{L}$ have the same directions, we have obtained the result

$$\mathbf{L} = I\boldsymbol{\omega}$$

for a flat rigid body directly from the definition of angular momentum.   ◄

13–4   Conservation of Angular Momentum

Suppose that the sum of the external torques acting on a system of particles is zero. Then in Eq. 13–7

$$\boldsymbol{\tau}_{\text{ext}} = 0,$$

$$d\mathbf{L}/dt = 0,$$

so that $$\mathbf{L} = \text{constant}.$$

When the resultant external torque acting on a system is zero, the total vector angular momentum of the system remains constant. This is *the principle of the conservation of angular momentum.*

For a system of n particles, the total angular momentum about some point is

$$\mathbf{L} = \mathbf{L}_1 + \mathbf{L}_2 + \cdots + \mathbf{L}_n.$$

Hence, when the total angular momentum $\mathbf{L}$ is constant, we have

$$\mathbf{L}_1 + \mathbf{L}_2 + \cdots + \mathbf{L}_n = \text{constant} = \mathbf{L}_0, \qquad (13\text{–}11)$$

where $\mathbf{L}_0$ is the constant total angular momentum vector. The angular momenta of the individual particles may change, but their sum remains constant in the absence of a net external torque.

Angular momentum is a vector quantity so that Eq. 13–11 is equivalent to three scalar equations, one for each coordinate direction through the reference point. The conservation of angular momentum, therefore, supplies us with three conditions on the motion of a system to which it applies.

If our system of particles is a rigid body, its angular momentum is $\mathbf{L} = I\boldsymbol{\omega}$, and Eq. 13–11 for the conservation of angular momentum then becomes

$$I\boldsymbol{\omega} = \text{constant} = I_0\boldsymbol{\omega}_0. \tag{13–12}$$

That is, the angular momentum of a rigid body rotating about an axis remains constant when the external torques about that axis are zero. Notice that $I\boldsymbol{\omega}$ must remain constant in *magnitude and* direction, for Eqs. 13–11 and 13–12 are *vector* equations. Since it is possible to change the distribution of mass about an axis as a body rotates, the rotational inertia I can vary. Whenever this happens, $\boldsymbol{\omega}$ must change in such a way that the product $I\boldsymbol{\omega}$ remains the same as the initial value $I_0\boldsymbol{\omega}_0$.

Acrobats, divers, ballet dancers, ice skaters, and others often make use of this principle. Because I depends on the square of the distance of the parts of the body from the axis of rotation, a large variation is possible by extending or pulling in the limbs. Consider the diver in Fig. 13–3. Let us assume that as he leaves the diving board he has a certain angular speed ω_0 about a horizontal axis through the center of mass, such that he would rotate through half a turn before he strikes water. If he wishes to make a one and one-half turn somersault instead, in the same time, he must triple his angular speed. Now there are no external forces acting on him except gravity, and gravity exerts no torque about his center of mass. His angular momentum, therefore, remains constant, and $I_0\omega_0 = I\omega$. Since $\omega = 3\omega_0$, the diver must change his rotational inertia about the horizontal axis through the center of mass from the initial value I_0 to a value I, such that I equals $\frac{1}{3}I_0$. This he does by pulling in his arms and legs toward the center of his body. The greater his initial angular speed and the more he can reduce his rotational inertia, the greater the number of revolutions he can make in a given time.

We should notice that the rotational kinetic energy of the diver is not constant. In fact, in our example, since

$$I_0\omega_0 = I\omega$$

and

$$I < I_0,$$

it follows that

$$\tfrac{1}{2}I\omega^2 > \tfrac{1}{2}I_0\omega_0{}^2,$$

and the diver's rotational kinetic energy *increases*. This increase in energy is supplied by the diver, who does work when he pulls the parts of his body together.

In a similar way the ice skater and ballet dancer can increase or decrease the angular speed of a spin about a vertical axis. A cat manages to land on its feet after a fall by using the same principles, the tail serving as a useful, but unessential, extra appendage.

Fig. 13-3 A diver leaves the diving board with arms and legs outstretched and with some initial angular velocity.   Since no torques are exerted on him about his center of mass, $\mathbf{L} = I\,\boldsymbol{\omega}$ is constant while he is in the air.   When he pulls his arms and legs in, since I decreases, ω increases.   When he again extends his limbs, his angular velocity drops back to its initial value.   Notice the parabolic motion of his center of mass, common to all two-dimensional motion under the influence of gravity.

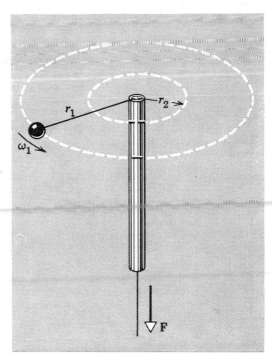

Fig. 13–4 Example 2. A mass at the end of a cord moves in a circle of radius r_1 with angular speed ω_1. The cord passes down through a tube. **F** supplies the centripetal force.

▶ **Example 2.** A small object of mass m is attached to a light string which passes through a hollow tube. The tube is held by one hand and the string by the other. The object is set into rotation in a circle of radius r_1 with a speed v_1. The string is then pulled down, shortening the radius of the path to r_2 (Fig. 13–4). Find the new linear speed v_2 and the new angular speed ω_2 of the object in terms of the initial values v_1 and ω_1 and the two radii.

The downward pull on the string is transmitted as a radial force on the object. Such a force exerts a zero torque on the object about the center of rotation. Since no torque acts on the object about its axis of rotation, its angular momentum in that direction is constant. Hence,

$$\text{initial angular momentum} = \text{final angular momentum,}$$

$$mv_1r_1 = mv_2r_2,$$

and

$$v_2 = v_1\left(\frac{r_1}{r_2}\right).$$

Since $r_1 > r_2$, the object speeds up on being pulled in.

In terms of angular speed, since v_1 equals $\omega_1 r_1$ and v_2 equals $\omega_2 r_2$,

$$mr_1{}^2\omega_1 = mr_2{}^2\omega_2$$

and

$$\omega_2 = \left(\frac{r_1}{r_2}\right)^2\omega_1,$$

so that there is an even greater increase in angular speed over the initial value. (See Problem 10.) What effect does the force of gravity (the object's weight) have on this analysis?

Example 3. A student sits on a stool that is free to rotate about a vertical axis. He holds his arms extended horizontally with an 8.0-lb weight in each hand. The instructor sets him rotating with an angular speed of 0.50 rev/sec. Assume that friction is negligible and exerts no torque about the vertical axis of rotation. Assume that the rotational inertia of the student remains constant at 4.0 slug-ft² as he pulls his hands to his sides and that the change in rotational inertia is due only to pulling the weights in. Take the original distance of the weights from the axis of rotation to be 3.0 ft and their final distance 0.50 ft. Find the final angular speed of the student.

The only external force is gravity acting through the center of mass, and that exerts no torque about the axis of rotation. Hence, the angular momentum is conserved about this axis and

$$\text{initial angular momentum} = \text{final angular momentum},$$

$$I_0\omega_0 = I\omega.$$

We have
$$I = I_{\text{student}} + I_{\text{weights}},$$

$$I_0 = 4.0 + 2\left(\frac{8.0}{32}\right)(3.0)^2 = 8.5 \text{ slug-ft}^2,$$

$$I = 4.0 + 2\left(\frac{8.0}{32}\right)\left(\frac{1}{2}\right)^2 = 4.1 \text{ slug-ft}^2,$$

$$\omega_0 = 0.50 \text{ rev/sec} = \pi \text{ radians/sec}.$$

Therefore,
$$\omega = \frac{I_0}{I}\omega_0 = \frac{8.5}{4.1}\pi \text{ radians/sec} = 2.1\pi \text{ radians/sec} \cong 1.0 \text{ rev/sec}.$$

The final angular speed is approximately doubled.

If we had allowed for the decrease in I caused by the arms being pulled in, the final angular speed would have been much greater.

What change would friction make? Is kinetic energy conserved as the student pulls in his arms and then puts them out again, assuming there is no friction? Explain.

Example 4. A classroom demonstration that illustrates the vector nature of the law of conservation of angular momentum is worth considering.

A student stands on a platform that can rotate only about a vertical axis. In his hand he holds the axle of a bicycle wheel with its axis vertical. The wheel is spinning about this vertical axis with an angular speed ω_0, but the student and platform are at rest. The student tries to change the direction of rotation of the wheel. What happens?

The initial total angular momentum is $I_0\boldsymbol{\omega}_0$, arising from the spinning wheel, I_0 being the rotational inertia of the wheel about its axis and $\boldsymbol{\omega}_0$ pointing vertically upward. Figure 13–5a shows the initial condition.

The student next turns the axis of the wheel through an angle θ from the vertical; to do this he supplies a torque about a horizontal axis. Since there is no component of torque about the *vertical* axis, the vertical component of angular momentum must be conserved. The wheel, however, is now spinning about an axis making an angle θ with the vertical so that it contributes a vertical component of angular momentum of only $I_0\omega_0\cos\theta$ to the system. Hence, the student and platform must supply the additional angular momentum about the vertical axes, and they begin to rotate about a vertical axis. This extra vertical angular momentum $I_p\omega_p$ when added to $I_0\omega_0\cos\theta$ must equal the initial vertical angular momentum of the system, $I_0\omega_0$. That is,

$$I_p\omega_p = I_0\omega_0(1 - \cos\theta).$$

This is shown in Fig. 13–5b. I_p is the rotational inertia of student and platform with respect to the vertical axis, and ω_p is their angular speed about this axis.

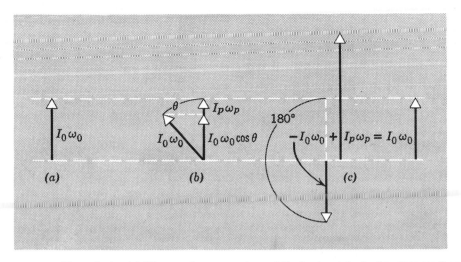

Fig. 13–5 Example 4. (a) The angular momentum of the horizontal wheel is shown. In (b), the wheel has been tilted an angle θ. Since no torque in the vertical direction has been exerted on the system, the angular momentum in that direction must be conserved. The deficit, $(1 - \cos \theta) I_0\omega_0$; is made up by rotation of the student. In (c), the wheel has been tilted 180°. The deficit is now $2I_0\omega_0$, which is now, as before, made up by the student.

If the student turns the wheel through an angle $\theta = 180°$, the student and platform acquire a vertical angular momentum of $2I_0\omega_0$. The total vertical angular momentum of the system is still being conserved at the initial value $I_0\omega_0$, as shown in Fig. 13–5c.

Consider the other components of angular momentum of the wheel alone. One component is in the plane of the drawing and is horizontal; it has a magnitude $I_0\omega_0 \sin \theta$. Another component is at right angles to the plane of the drawing and is horizontal. These components of angular momentum of the wheel, originally zero, arise from internal torques exerted on the wheel by the student to get and to keep its axis at the angle θ to the vertical. An internal reaction torque on the student accounts for the vertical angular momentum acquired by him and the platform. As time goes on the axis of the wheel traces out a cone of angle θ about the vertical. The time average angular momentum of the entire system has only a vertical component.

The precise analysis of the motion of this system depends only on the application of the equation $\tau = d\mathbf{L}/dt$ and the vector nature of the quantities involved. It will be left as an exercise for the interested student to work out.

Example 5. A symmetrical object rotating about an axis which is fixed at one point is called a *top*. The axis of rotation of a top can itself rotate about the fixed point. Assume that the angular velocity of the axis of rotation, called the precessional angular velocity, is very small compared to the angular velocity of the top about this axis, and show that the angular velocity of precession is inversely proportional to the magnitude of the angular momentum of the top.

In Fig. 13–6a we show a top spinning about its central axis with an angular momentum **L**. The fixed point, or pivot, is O and the axis of rotation makes an angle θ with the vertical. The upward force on the pivot at O exerts no torque about that point. The resultant torque about O is due to the weight $m\mathbf{g}$ acting through the center of mass and is given by

$$\boldsymbol{\tau} = \mathbf{r} \times m\mathbf{g}$$

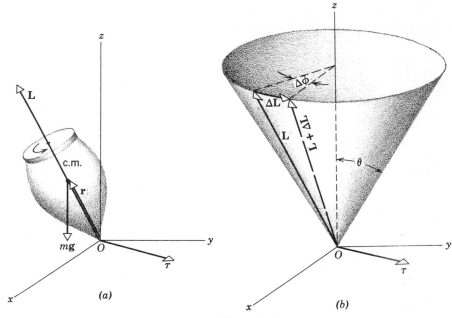

Fig. 13–6 Example 5.

where **r** locates the center of mass with respect to the pivot. In a short time Δt this torque produces a change in angular momentum (Eq. 13–5) given by

$$\Delta \mathbf{L} = \boldsymbol{\tau} \, \Delta t.$$

The direction of the torque, and also the change in angular momentum, is perpendicular to the axis of rotation, as shown in the figures.

The angular momentum of the top, after a time Δt, is the vector sum of **L** and $\Delta \mathbf{L}$. Since $\Delta \mathbf{L}$ is perpendicular to **L** and is assumed to be very small in magnitude compared to it, the new angular momentum vector has the same *magnitude* as the old one but a different *direction*. Hence, the head of the angular momentum vector swings around in the arc of a horizontal circle, as time goes on (Fig. 13–6*b*). Since the angular momentum vector lies along the axis of the top, this means that the axis turns about a vertical line through the pivot at O. This motion of the axis of rotation is called *precession*.

The angular velocity of the precession ω_p follows at once from Fig. 13–6*b*, for

$$\omega_p = \Delta\phi / \Delta t.$$

But, since $\Delta L \ll L$, $\qquad \Delta\phi \cong \Delta L / L \sin\theta = \tau \, \Delta t / L \sin\theta,$

and $\qquad\qquad\qquad\qquad \tau = mgr \sin\theta,$

so that $\qquad\qquad\qquad \omega_p = \dfrac{mgr \sin\theta \, \Delta t}{L \sin\theta \, \Delta t} = \dfrac{mgr}{L}.$

Notice that the precessional angular velocity is independent of θ and varies inversely as the magnitude of the angular momentum. If this is large, the precessional angular velocity will be small.

The precession of a spinning top illustrates directly the general relation (Eq. 13-5) $\tau = dL/dt$ and forms the prototype for the behavior of many atomic and nuclear systems, some of which will be discussed later.

13-5   Some Other Aspects of the Conservation of Angular Momentum

The conservation of angular momentum principle holds in atomic and nuclear physics as well as in celestial and macroscopic regions. Since Newtonian mechanics does not hold in the atomic and nuclear domain, this conservation law must be more fundamental than Newtonian principles. In our derivation of this principle we must have made more rigid assumptions than we needed to. This is true even in the framework of classical mechanics. The student should note the key role played by Newton's third law in our deduction of this conservation principle. This law was used to justify the assumption that the sum of the internal torques was zero. Actually we can prove this assumption on the basis of a much less stringent requirement than that the third law should hold.*

The law of conservation of angular momentum, as we have formulated it, holds for a system of bodies whenever the bodies can be treated as particles, that is, whenever effects due to the rotation of the individual bodies can be neglected. When the individual bodies have rotation, the conservation of angular momentum principle is still valid, providing we include the angular momentum associated with this rotation. However, the bodies then are no longer simple particles whose motion can be described by particle dynamics.

In atomic and nuclear physics we find that the "elementary particles" such as electrons, protons, and neutrons have angular momentum associated with an intrinsic spinning motion, as well as with motion about some external point. When we use the law of conservation of total angular momentum we must include this *spin* angular momentum in the total. A fundamental aspect of atomic, molecular, and nuclear systems is that their angular momenta can take on only definite discrete values, rather than a continuum of values. Angular momentum is said to be *quantized*. Hence, angular momentum plays a central role in the description of the behavior of such systems. (See Problems 19 and 20.) These ideas will be developed in later chapters.

If we were to regard the sun, planets, and satellites as particles having no intrinsic rotation, the angular momentum of the solar system would not be constant. But these bodies do have intrinsic rotations; in fact, tidal forces convert some of the intrinsic rotational angular momentum into orbital angular momentum of the planets and satellites. When we use the law of conservation of the angular momentum, we must include this rotational angular momentum in the total. The conservation of angular momentum plays a key role in the evaluation of theories of the origin of the solar system, the contraction of giant stars, and other problems in astronomy.† Some astronomical applications will be considered in Chapter 16.

The conservation laws of total energy, linear momentum, and angular momentum are fundamental to physics, being valid in all modern physical theories. We shall have occasion to use them many times in later chapters.

QUESTIONS

1. In Chapter 1 the melting of the polar icecaps was cited as a possible cause of the variation in the earth's time of rotation. Explain.

2. Many great rivers flow toward the equator. What effect does the sediment they carry to the sea have on the rotation of the earth?

---

* See E. Gerjuoy, *American Journal of Physics*, Vol. 17, No. 8, 477–487 (1949).

† See, for example, *Frontiers of Astronomy*, by Fred Hoyle, Harper & Brothers, 1955.

3. A stone is dropped along the center of a deep vertical mine shaft. Will the stone continue along the center of the shaft? If not, which side will it head toward, north, east, south, or west? Assume no air resistance and consider the earth's rotation.

4. A man turns on a rotating table with an angular speed ω. He is holding two equal masses at arm's length. Without moving his arms, he drops the two masses. What change, if any, is there in his angular speed? Is the angular momentum conserved? Explain.

5. You are walking along a narrow railroad track and you start to lose your balance. If you start falling to the right, which way do you turn your body to regain balance? Explain.

6. The destructive effect of a tornado (twister) is greater near the center of the disturbance than near the edge. Explain.

7. When a stopper is pulled from a filled basin, the water drains out while circulating like a small whirlpool. The rate of circulation is largest near the orifice. Explain.

8. The precessional motion of a top is often regarded as the angular equivalent of uniform circular motion, for the direction of the spin angular velocity ω, and not its magnitude, is changed. Elaborate on this analogy.

9. If the top of Fig. 13–6a were not spinning, it would tip over. If its spin angular momentum is large compared to the change caused by the applied torque, the top precesses. What happens in between when the top spins slowly?

10. A single-engine airplane must be "trimmed" to fly level. (Trimming consists of raising one aileron and lowering the opposite one.) Why is this necessary? Is this necessary on a bi-engine plane under normal circumstances?

PROBLEMS

1. Starting from Newton's third law, prove that the resultant internal torque on a system of particles is zero.

2. Show that the angular momentum about any point of a single particle moving with constant velocity remains constant throughout the motion.

3. If we are given r, p, and θ, we can calculate the angular momentum of a particle from Eq. 13–1. Sometimes, however, we are given the components of $\mathbf{r}$ (x, y, z) and $\mathbf{p}$ (p_x, p_y, p_z) instead. (a) Show that the components of $\mathbf{L}$ along the x-, y-, and z-axes are then given by

$$L_x = (\mathbf{r} \times \mathbf{p})_x = yp_z - zp_y,$$

$$L_y = (\mathbf{r} \times \mathbf{p})_y = zp_x - xp_z,$$

$$L_z = (\mathbf{r} \times \mathbf{p})_z = xp_y - yp_x.$$

(b) Show that if the particle moves only in the x–y plane, the resultant angular momentum vector has only a z component.

4. A wheel is rotating with an angular speed of 500 rev/min on a shaft whose rotational inertia is negligible. A second identical wheel, initially at rest, is suddenly coupled to the same shaft. What is the angular speed of the resultant combination of the shaft and the two wheels?

5. The moon revolves about the earth so that we always see the same face. By how much would its total angular momentum have to change if we were to be able to see all its surface during the course of a month?

6. By what amount would the diameter of the earth need to shrink in order to speed its rotation by one second per day?

7. In a playground there is a small merry-go-round of radius 4.0 ft and mass 12.0 slugs. The radius of gyration (see Problem 5, Chapter 12) is 3.0 ft. A child of mass 3.0 slugs runs at a speed of 10 ft/sec tangent to the rim of the merry-go-round when it is at rest and then jumps on. Neglect friction and find the angular velocity of the merry-go-round and child.

8. A cockroach, mass m, runs counterclockwise around the rim of a lazy-susan (a circular dish mounted on a vertical axle) of radius R and rotational inertia I with friction-

less bearings. The cockroach's speed (relative to the earth) is v, whereas the lazy-susan turns clockwise with angular speed ω_0. The cockroach finds a breadcrumb on the rim and of course, stops. What is the angular speed of the lazy-susan after the cockroach stops? Is energy conserved?

9. A man stands on a frictionless rotating platform which is rotating with a speed of 1 rev/sec; his arms are outstretched and he holds a weight in each hand. With his hands in this position the total rotational inertia of the man and platform is 6 kg-m². If by drawing in the weights the man decreases the rotational inertia to 2 kg-m², (a) what is the resulting angular speed of the platform? (b) By how much is the kinetic energy increased?

10. In Example 2 compare the kinetic energies of the object in two different orbits. Use the work-energy theorem to explain the difference quantitatively.

11. A hemispherical bowl of radius a is rotated about its vertical axis with angular speed ω. If a marble of mass m is placed in the rotating bowl, it ultimately settles at a point a distance d from the axis. Find d as a function of ω.

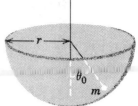

Fig. 13–7

12. A particle is projected horizontally along the interior of a smooth hemispherical bowl of radius r which is kept at rest (Fig. 13–7). We wish to find the initial speed v_0 required for the particle to just reach the top of the bowl. Find v_0 as a function of θ_0, the initial angular position of the particle. (Hint: Use conservation principles.)

13. A uniform flat disk of mass M and radius R rotates about a horizontal axis through its center with angular speed ω_0. (a) What is its kinetic energy? Its angular momentum? (b) A chip of mass m breaks off the edge of the disk at an instant such that the chip rises *vertically* above the point at which it broke off (Fig. 13–8). How high above the point does it rise before starting to fall? (c) What is the final angular speed of the broken disk? The final angular momentum and energy?

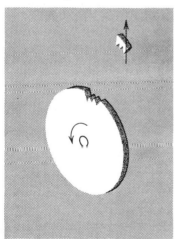

Fig. 13–8

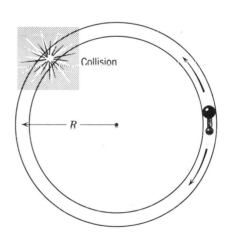

Collision

Fig. 13–9

14. On a large horizontal frictionless circular track, radius R, lie two small masses m and M, free to slide on the track. Between the two masses is squeezed a spring which, however, is *not fastened* to m and M. The two masses are held together by a string. (a) If the string breaks, the compressed spring (assumed massless) shoots off the two masses in opposite directions; the spring itself is left behind. The balls collide when they again meet on the track (Fig. 13–9). Where does this collision take place? (You might find it convenient to

express the answer in terms of the angle m or M travels through.) (b) If the potential energy initially stored in the spring was U_0, what is the time it takes after the string breaks for the collision to take place? (c) Assuming the collision to be perfectly elastic and head-on, where will the balls again collide after the first collision?

15. The time integral of a torque is called the *angular impulse*. Starting from $\tau = d\mathbf{L}/dt$, show that the resultant angular impulse equals the change in angular momentum. This is the angular analog of the linear impulse-momentum theorem.

16. A stick has a mass 0.30 slug and a length 4.0 ft. It is initially at rest on a smooth horizontal plane and is struck by an impulsive force of impulse 3 lb-sec at a distance $l = 1.5$ ft from the center (Fig. 13–10). Determine the subsequent motion.

17. A top is spinning 30 rev/sec about an axis making an angle of $30°$ with the vertical. Its mass is 0.5 kg and its rotational inertia is 5×10^{-4} kg-m². The center of mass is 4 cm from the pivot point. If the spin is clockwise as seen from above, what is the magnitude and direction of the angular velocity of precession?

18. Using data in the appendix, find (a) the angular momentum of the earth's spin about its own axis, (b) the angular momentum of the earth's orbital motion about the sun.

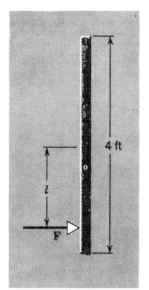

Fig. 13–10

19. (a) Assume that the electron moves in a circular orbit about the proton in a hydrogen atom. If the centripetal force on the electron is supplied by an electrical force $e^2/4\pi\epsilon_0 r^2$, where e is the magnitude of the charge of an electron and of a proton, r is the orbit radius, and ϵ_0 is a constant, show that the radius of the orbit is

$$r = \frac{e^2}{4\pi\epsilon_0 m v^2},$$

where m is the mass of the electron and v is its speed.

(b) Assume now that the angular momentum of the electron about the nucleus can only have values that are integral multiples n of $h/2\pi$, where h is a constant called Planck's constant. Show that the only electronic orbits possible are those with a radius

$$r = \frac{nh}{2\pi m v}.$$

(c) Combine these results to eliminate v and show that the only orbits consistent with both requirements have radii

$$r = \frac{n^2 \epsilon_0 h^2}{\pi m e^2}.$$

Hence, the allowed radii are proportional to the square of the integers $n = 1, 2, 3$, etc. When $n = 1$, r is smallest and has the value 0.528×10^{-10} meter.

20. In 1913, Niels Bohr (then a graduate student) postulated that any mechanical rotating system with rotational inertia I can have an angular momentum whose values can take on only integral multiples of a particular number $\hbar = 1.054 \times 10^{-34}$ joule-sec. (This number is $1/2\pi$ times Planck's constant h.) In other words,

$$L = I\omega = n\hbar,$$

where n is any positive integer or zero. We say that L is quantized, since it is no longer allowed to have any value whatsoever. (a) Show that this postulate restricts the kinetic energy the rotating system can have to a set of discrete values, that is, that the energy is quantized. (*b*) Consider the so-called *rigid rotator*, consisting of a mass m constrained to

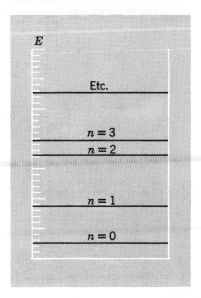

Fig. 13–11

rotate in a circle of radius R. With what angular speeds could the mass rotate if the postulate were correct? What values of kinetic energy may it assume?

(*c*) Draw an energy-level diagram of some sort indicating how the spacing between the energy levels varies as n increases. It might look something like Fig. 13–11. Certain low-energy diatomic molecules behave like a rigid rotator.

Statics of Rigid Bodies

CHAPTER 14

14–1 Mechanical Equilibrium

Particle motion is motion of translation. When a particle remains at rest or moves with uniform velocity, its acceleration is zero. The resultant of all the forces acting on such a particle is zero and the particle is said to be in mechanical equilibrium. The equilibrium is said to be static if the particle is at rest. The branch of mechanics concerned with the static equilibrium of a particle is called particle statics. We have seen (Chapter 5) that particle statics is a special case of particle dynamics.

Rigid-body motion is motion of rotation and translation. When a rigid body remains at rest or moves as a whole such that its linear velocity and its angular velocity are uniform, both the linear acceleration of the body and its angular acceleration are zero. The resultant of all the forces and the resultant of all the torques acting on such a body are zero, and the rigid body is said to be in mechanical equilibrium. The equilibrium is said to be static if the rigid body is at rest. The branch of mechanics concerned with the static equilibrium of a rigid body is called rigid-body statics. We shall see that rigid-body statics is simply a special case of rigid-body dynamics.

Statics is a subject of great practical importance in engineering. Its principles are used in the construction of bridges, experimental apparatus, and other structures. Many aspects of this subject will be treated in later courses in mechanics and engineering. Here we consider the general conditions for mechanical equilibrium and briefly illustrate their application to the special case of truly rigid bodies at rest.

14-2 The Conditions for Mechanical Equilibrium of a Rigid Body

For a rigid body to be in *translational* equilibrium, the linear acceleration **a** of its center of mass must equal zero. We have seen (Section 11-1) that the linear acceleration of the center of mass is given by

$$\mathbf{a} = \mathbf{F}_{ext}/M,$$

where M is the mass of the rigid body and $\mathbf{F}_{ext}$ is the sum of the external forces acting on the body. Hence, the first condition of equilibrium is: *The vector sum of all the external forces acting on a body in equilibrium is zero.*

Condition 1 can be written as

$$\mathbf{F} = \mathbf{F}_1 + \mathbf{F}_2 + \cdots = 0 \tag{14-1}$$

This vector equation leads to three scalar equations

$$
\begin{aligned}
F_x &= F_{1x} + F_{2x} + \cdots = 0, \\
F_y &= F_{1y} + F_{2y} + \cdots = 0, \\
F_z &= F_{1z} + F_{2z} + \cdots = 0,
\end{aligned}
\tag{14-2}
$$

which state that the sum of the components of the forces along each of three mutually perpendicular directions is zero.

For a rigid body to be in *rotational* equilibrium, its angular acceleration $\boldsymbol{\alpha}$ must equal zero. We have seen (Chapter 12) that for the rotational motion of a rigid body $\boldsymbol{\tau}_{ext}$ equals $I\boldsymbol{\alpha}$, so that the second condition for equilibrium is: *The vector sum of all the external torques acting on a body in equilibrium is zero.*

Condition 2 can be written as

$$\boldsymbol{\tau} = \boldsymbol{\tau}_1 + \boldsymbol{\tau}_2 + \cdots = 0. \tag{14-3}$$

This vector equation leads to three scalar equations

$$
\begin{aligned}
\tau_x &= \tau_{1x} + \tau_{2x} + \cdots = 0, \\
\tau_y &= \tau_{1y} + \tau_{2y} + \cdots = 0, \\
\tau_z &= \tau_{1z} + \tau_{2z} + \cdots = 0,
\end{aligned}
\tag{14-4}
$$

which state that the sum of all the torques acting on a body about each of three mutually perpendicular axes is zero.

If a body is to be in equilibrium, it must not have an angular acceleration about *any* axis. Of the infinite number of axes that can be chosen, it is necessary to consider only three mutually perpendicular ones. We can show this with the help of the following simple theorem: *If the sum of the applied torques about an axis O is τ_o, the sum of the applied torques about an axis P, which is parallel to O, is equal to τ_o plus the torque about P exerted by the resultant force applied to O.*

The proof of this theorem follows. Consider the rotation of a rigid body about an axis through O perpendicular to the page, as shown in Fig. 14-1. Only forces or

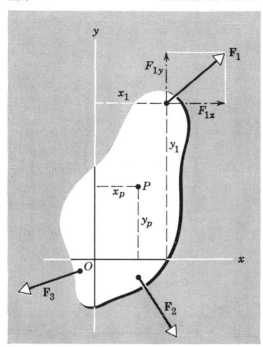

Fig. 14-1 The relation between the torque about O, produced by forces $\mathbf{F}_1$, $\mathbf{F}_2$, $\mathbf{F}_3$, and the torque about P.

components of forces in the plane of the page can cause rotation about an axis through O perpendicular to the page. The resultant torque about O is

$$\tau_o = \tau_{1o} + \tau_{2o} + \tau_{3o} + \cdots$$

$$= (F_{1x}y_1 - F_{1y}x_1) + (F_{2x}y_2 - F_{2y}x_2) + \cdots$$

Here we have taken clockwise torques as positive and counterclockwise torques as negative. The resultant torque about a parallel axis through P, where P has coordinates x_p, y_p with respect to O, is

$$\tau_p = [F_{1x}(y_1 - y_p) - F_{1y}(x_1 - x_p)] + [F_{2x}(y_2 - y_p) - F_{2y}(x_2 - x_p)] + \cdots$$

Combining these expressions we obtain

$$\tau_p = \tau_o + x_p(F_{1y} + F_{2y} + \cdots) - y_p(F_{1x} + F_{2x} + \cdots)$$

$$= \tau_o + x_p(F_y) - y_p(F_x).$$

In this expression F_x and F_y are the x and y components of the resultant force

$$\mathbf{F} = \mathbf{F}_1 + \mathbf{F}_2 + \cdots$$

If this resultant force were to act at the point O, its torque about the axis through P would be $F_y x_p - F_x y_p$. Hence, we have proved the theorem.

Now, with the use of this theorem, we can show that for a body in equilibrium the torque about *any* axis will be zero if the torque about each of three particular mutually perpendicular axes is zero. If a body is in equilibrium, the resultant force $\mathbf{F}$ acting on it is zero. If the torque about a particular axis O is zero, it follows that the torque about any parallel axis P is also zero. That is,

$$\tau_p - \tau_o + x_p(0) - y_p(0) = \tau_o = 0$$

because, for the equilibrium,

$$\tau_o = 0 \quad \text{and} \quad F_x = F_y = 0.$$

Likewise for each of the other two mutually perpendicular axes, if the torque is zero about them, the torque is zero about any axis parallel to them. We must note finally that if τ equals zero for each of three perpendicular axes, then τ equals zero with respect to any axis inclined to these. Therefore, we have shown that a body will be in rotational equilibrium about any axis whatsoever if it is in rotational equilibrium about three mutually perpendicular axes.

The net result is that we have *six independent conditions* on our forces for a body to be in equilibrium. These conditions are the six algebraic relations of Eqs. 14-2 and 14-4. These six conditions are a condition on each of the six degrees of freedom of a rigid body, three translational and three rotational.

Often we deal with problems in which all the forces lie in a plane. Then we have only three conditions on our forces: The sum of their components must be zero for each of two directions in the plane, and the sum of their torques about one axis perpendicular to the plane must be zero. These conditions correspond to the three degrees of freedom for motion in a plane, two of translation and one of rotation.

We shall limit ourselves henceforth mostly to planar problems in order to simplify the calculations. This does not impose any fundamental restriction on the general principles. Also, we shall consider only the case of static equilibrium, in which bodies are actually at rest.

14-3   Center of Gravity

One of the forces encountered in rigid-body motions is the force of gravity. Actually this is not just one force but the resultant of a great many forces. Each particle in the body is acted on by a gravitational force. If the body of mass M is imagined to be divided into a large number of particles, say n, the gravitational force exerted by the earth on the ith particle of mass m_i is $m_i\mathbf{g}$. This force is directed down toward the earth. If the acceleration due to gravity $\mathbf{g}$ is the same everywhere in a region, we say that a uniform gravitational field exists there; that is, $\mathbf{g}$ has the same magnitude and direction everywhere in that region. For a rigid body in a uniform gravitational field, $\mathbf{g}$ must be the same for each particle in the body and the weight forces on the particles must be parallel to one another. If we assume that the earth's gravitational field is uniform, we can show that all the individual weight forces acting on a body can be replaced by a single force $M\mathbf{g}$ acting down at the center of mass of the body.

Consider an axis through the center of mass of a body and choose the origin of coordinates to be at the center of mass C. Then the torque about

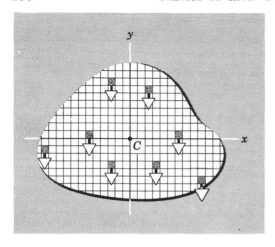

Fig. 14–2 Forces due to a uniform gravitational field on elemental masses making up a body.

the z-axis, through C and normal to the page, resulting from the vertical weight forces acting on each mass particle in the body (Fig. 14–2), is

$$\tau_z = m_1 g x_1 + m_2 g x_2 + \cdots + m_n g x_n$$

$$= \Sigma\, m_i g x_i = g(\Sigma m_i x_i).$$

Here x_i gives the x coordinate of the ith particle of mass m_i. However, $\Sigma\, m_i x_i$ equals zero, from the definition of center of mass (see Section 9–1), so that τ_z equals zero. Likewise, we can show that τ_x and τ_y, the torques about the x- and y-axes through the center of mass, are zero.

We obtain the same result if the body is continuous and is divided into an infinite number of particles ($n = \infty$). The student should be able to do this with the use of integral calculus (see Section 9–1).

Now if we recall our previous theorem, we can conclude that the torque about any axis parallel to z is the same as though the total downward force, $\Sigma\, m_i g = Mg$, were applied at the center of mass, and likewise for any axis parallel to x or to y. The result is that we can replace the gravitational forces acting on all the mass particles in the body by a single force $M\mathbf{g}$ equal to the

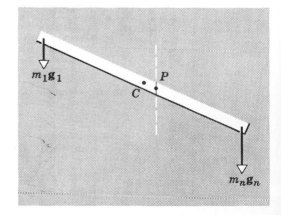

Fig. 14–3 The center of mass C and center of gravity P in reality do not coincide, since the earth's gravitational field is not uniform.

total weight of the body, acting at the center of mass. The point of application of the equivalent resultant gravitational force is often called the *center of gravity*.

The coincidence of the center of gravity and the center of mass came about because of the assumption that the earth's gravitational field was uniform. Actually this assumption is not strictly true, for the magnitude of **g** changes with distance from the center of the earth and furthermore the direction of **g** is radially in toward the center of the earth from any point (Chapter 16). To see the effect this has, let us consider a uniform stick many miles long inclined to the vertical in the earth's gravitational field, as in Fig. 14–3. The center of gravity of a body is the point at which the equivalent resultant gravitational force on it acts. This point must be the same as the point at which a single oppositely directed force is applied for the body to be kept in equilibrium. If the field were uniform, a single upward force Mg at the center of mass would keep the stick in translational and rotational equilibrium. But the field is not uniform, and the value of g at m_1 is less than the value of g at m_n. The point at which a single force must be applied to keep the body in equilibrium is, therefore, at a point P some distance below the center of mass. Furthermore, if the orientation of the body is changed, the position of the point P, required for application of an equilibrium force, changes. Hence, center of gravity really has little significance in such a case. Not only does it not coincide with the center of mass, but its position changes with respect to the body as the body is moved.

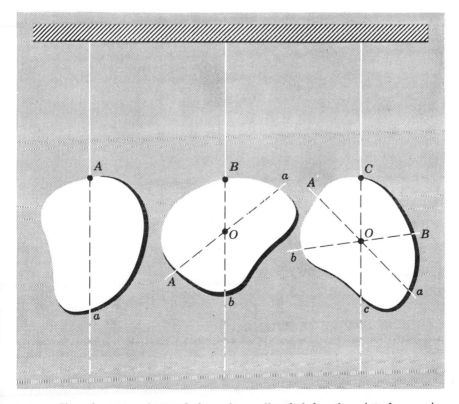

Fig. 14–4 Since the center of mass O always hangs directly below the point of suspension, hanging a plate from two different points determines O.

It is because almost all problems in mechanics involve objects having dimensions small compared to the distances over which **g** changes appreciably that we can assume that **g** is uniform over the body. The center of mass and the center of gravity can then be taken as the same point. In fact, we can make use of this coincidence to determine experimentally the center of mass in irregularly shaped objects. For example, let us locate the center of mass of a thin plate of irregular shape, as shown in Fig. 14–4. We suspend the body by a cord from some point A on its edge. When the body is at rest, the center of gravity must lie directly under the point of support somewhere on the line Aa, for only then can the torque resulting from the cord and the weight add to zero. We next suspend the body from another point B on its edge. Again, the center of gravity must lie somewhere on Bb. The only point common to the lines Aa and Bb is O, the point of intersection, so that this point must be the center of gravity. If now we suspend the body from any other point on its edge, as C, the vertical line Cc will pass through O. Since we have assumed a uniform field, the center of gravity coincides with the center of mass which is, therefore, located at O.

14–4 Examples of Static Equilibrium

In applying the conditions for static equilibrium (zero resultant force and zero resultant torque about any axis), we can clarify and simplify the procedure in many ways.

First, we should draw an imaginary boundary around the system under consideration. This assures that we see clearly just what body or system of bodies it is to which we are applying the laws of static equilibrium. This process is called isolating the system.

Second, we should draw vectors representing the magnitude, direction, and point of application of all *external* forces. An external force is one that acts from outside the boundary which was drawn earlier. Examples of external forces often encountered in statics are gravitational forces and forces transmitted by strings, wires, rods, and beams which cross the boundary. A question sometimes arises about the direction of a force. In this case make an imaginary cut through the member transmitting the force at the point where it crosses the boundary. If the ends of this cut tend to pull apart, the force acts outward. If you are in doubt, choose the direction arbitrarily. A negative value for a force in the solution means that the force acts in the direction opposite to that assumed. Note that only external forces acting on the system need be considered; all internal forces cancel one another in pairs.

Third, we should choose convenient coordinate axes along which to resolve the external forces before applying the first condition of equilibrium. The object here is to simplify the calculations. The preferable coordinates are usually obvious.

Fourth, we should choose a convenient axis about which to take torques. The object again is to simplify the calculations. An axis taken where two or more unknown forces concur will automatically reduce their torques to zero. The torque resulting from all external forces must be zero about any axis for equilibrium. Internal torques will cancel in pairs.

▶ **Example 1.** (*a*) A uniform steel meter bar rests on two scales at its ends (Fig. 14–5). The bar weighs 4.0 lb. Find the readings on the scales.

Our system is the bar. The forces acting on the bar are $\mathbf{W}$, the gravitational force acting down at the center of gravity, and $\mathbf{F}_1$ and $\mathbf{F}_2$, the forces exerted upward on the bar at its ends by the scales. These are shown in Fig. 14–5*a*. By Newton's third law, the force exerted by a scale on the bar is equal and opposite to that exerted by the bar on the scale. Therefore, to obtain the readings on the scales, we must determine the magnitudes of $\mathbf{F}_1$ and $\mathbf{F}_2$.

For translational equilibrium (Eq. 14–1) the condition is

$$\mathbf{F}_1 + \mathbf{F}_2 + \mathbf{W} = 0.$$

All forces act vertically so that if we choose the *y* axis to be vertical, no other axes need be considered. Then we get the scalar equation

$$F_1 + F_2 - 4.0 \text{ lb} = 0.$$

For rotational equilibrium, the resultant torque on the bar must be zero about any axis. We can have rotation about any axis perpendicular to the plane of the drawing. Let us choose an axis through the center of gravity. Then, taking clockwise rotation as positive and counterclockwise rotation as negative, the condition for rotational equilibrium (Eq. 14–3) is

$$F_1\left(\frac{l}{2}\right) - F_2\left(\frac{l}{2}\right) + W(0) = 0$$

or
$$F_1 - F_2 = 0.$$

Combining the two equations, we obtain

$$F_1 + F_2 = 2F_1 = 2F_2 = 4.0 \text{ lb},$$

$$F_1 = F_2 = 2.0 \text{ lb}.$$

Each scale reads 2.0 lb, as we might have expected.

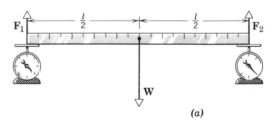

W

(*a*)

Fig. 14–5 (*a*) Example 1*a*. A uniform steel bar rests on two spring scales. (*b*) Example 1*b*. A weight *w* is suspended a quarter of the way from one end.

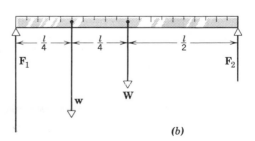

(*b*)

If we had chosen an axis through one end of the bar, we would have obtained the same result. For example, taking torques about an axis through the right end, we obtain

$$F_1(l) - W\left(\frac{l}{2}\right) + F_2(0) = 0$$

or
$$F_1 = \frac{W}{2} = \frac{4.0 \text{ lb}}{2} = 2.0 \text{ lb.}$$

Combining this with $F_1 + F_2 = 4.0$ lb, we obtain $F_2 = 2.0$ lb, as before.

(b) Suppose that a 6.0-lb block is placed at the 25-cm mark on the meter bar. What do the scales read now?

The external forces acting on the bar are shown in Fig. 14–5b, where **w** is the force exerted on the bar by the block. The first condition for equilibrium is

$$F_1 + F_2 - W - w = 0.$$

With $W = 4.0$ lb and $w = 6.0$ lb, we obtain

$$F_1 + F_2 = 10 \text{ lb.}$$

If we take an axis through the left end of the bar, the second condition for equilibrium is

$$w\left(\frac{l}{4}\right) + W\left(\frac{l}{2}\right) - F_2(l) = 0.$$

With $W = 4.0$ lb and $w = 6.0$ lb, we obtain

$$F_2 = 3.5 \text{ lb.}$$

Putting this result into the first equation, we obtain

$$F_1 + 3.5 \text{ lb} = 10 \text{ lb,}$$

$$F_1 = 6.5 \text{ lb.}$$

The left-hand scale reads 6.5 lb and the right-hand scale reads 3.5 lb at equilibrium.

Why do we obtain only two conditions on the forces in this problem rather than the three conditions expected for problems in which all forces lie in the same plane?

Example 2.   (a) A 60-ft ladder weighing 100 lb rests against a wall at a point 48 ft above the ground. The center of gravity of the ladder is one-third the way up. A 160-lb man climbs halfway up the ladder. Assuming that the wall is frictionless, find the forces exerted by the system on the ground and the wall.

The forces acting on the ladder are shown in Fig. 14–6. **W** is the weight of the man standing on the ladder, and **w** is the weight of the ladder itself. A force $\mathbf{F}_1$ is exerted by the ground on the ladder. F_{1v} is the vertical component and F_{1h} is the horizontal component of this force (due to friction). The wall, being frictionless, can exert only a force normal to its surface, called $\mathbf{F}_2$. We are given the following data:

$$W = 160 \text{ lb,} \qquad w = 100 \text{ lb,} \qquad a = 48 \text{ ft,} \qquad c = 60 \text{ ft.}$$

From the geometry we conclude that $b = 36$ ft. The line of action of **W** intersects the ground at a distance $b/2$ from the wall and the line of action of **w** intersects the ground at a distance $2b/3$ from the wall.

We choose the x-axis to be along the ground and the y-axis along the wall. Then, the conditions on the forces for translational equilibrium (Eq. 14–2) are

$$F_2 - F_{1h} = 0,$$

$$F_{1v} - W - w = 0.$$

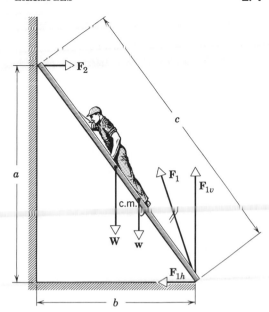

Fig. 14–6 Example 2.

For rotational equilibrium (Eq. 14–4) choose an axis through the point of contact with the ground and obtain

$$F_2(a) - W\left(\frac{b}{2}\right) - w\left(\frac{b}{3}\right) = 0.$$

Using the data given we obtain

$$F_2(48 \text{ ft}) - (160 \text{ lb})(18 \text{ ft}) - (100 \text{ lb})(12 \text{ ft}) = 0,$$

$$F_2 = 85 \text{ lb},$$

$$F_{1h} = F_2 = 85 \text{ lb},$$

$$F_{1v} = 160 \text{ lb} + 100 \text{ lb} = 260 \text{ lb}.$$

By Newton's third law the forces exerted by the ground and the wall on the ladder are equal but opposite to the forces exerted by the ladder on the ground and the wall, respectively. Therefore, the normal force on the wall is 85 lb, and the force on the ground has components of 260 lb down and 85 lb to the right.

(b) If the coefficient of static friction between the ground and the ladder is $\mu_s = 0.40$, how high up the ladder can the man go before it starts to slip?

Let x be the fraction of the total length of the ladder the man can climb before slipping begins. Then our equilibrium conditions are

$$F_2 - F_{1h} = 0,$$

$$F_{1v} - W - w = 0,$$

and

$$F_2 a - Wbx - w\left(\frac{b}{3}\right) = 0.$$

Now we obtain

$$F_2(48 \text{ ft}) - (160 \text{ lb})(36 \text{ ft})x + (100 \text{ lb})(12 \text{ ft}),$$

$$F_2 = (120x + 25) \text{ lb}.$$

Hence, $F_{1h} = (120x + 25)$ lb

and $F_{1v} = 260$ lb.

The maximum force of static friction is given by

$$F_{1h} = \mu_s F_{1v} = (0.40)(260 \text{ lb}) = 104 \text{ lb}.$$

Therefore, $F_{1h} = (120x + 25)$ lb $= 104$ lb

and $x = \frac{79}{120}$,

so that the man can climb up the ladder

$$60x \text{ ft} = 39.5 \text{ ft}$$

before slipping begins.

In this example the ladder is treated as a one-dimensional object, with only one point of contact at the wall and ground. The student should reflect on how this limits consideration of the less artificial case of two contact points at each end.

The reason for assuming that the wall is frictionless is discussed later. Can you guess what it is?

Example 3. (a) A uniform beam is hinged at the wall. A wire connected to the wall a distance d above the hinge is attached to the other end of the beam. This wire is horizontal when a weight w is hung from a string fastened to the end of the beam. If the beam has a weight W and a length l, find the tension in the wire and the forces exerted by the hinge on the beam.

The situation is pictured in Fig. 14–7, in which all the forces acting on the beam are shown. **F**, the force exerted by the hinge on the beam, has horizontal and vertical components F_h and F_v, respectively. **T** is the tension in the horizontal wire pulling on the beam and **w** is the tension in the string transmitting the weight of the suspended body to the beam. **W** is the weight of the beam, acting at the center of gravity.

Taking horizontal and vertical axes, we obtain for translational equilibrium,

$$T - F_h = 0,$$

$$F_v - W - w = 0.$$

Choosing an axis through the hinge (Why?) we obtain for rotational equilibrium,

$$\left(\frac{W}{2}\right) \sqrt{l^2 - d^2} + w \sqrt{l^2 - d^2} - Td = 0.$$

Our unknowns are T, F_v, and F_h. Let us assign the following numbers to the other quantities:

$$W = 300 \text{ lb}, \qquad w = 50 \text{ lb}, \qquad l = 10 \text{ ft}, \qquad d = 6.0 \text{ ft}.$$

Then, $\sqrt{l^2 - d^2} = 8.0$ ft

and, substituting numbers in the above equation,

$$(300/2)(4.0) + (50)(8.0) - T(6.0) = 0$$

or $T \cong 267$ lb,

$$F_h = T \cong 267 \text{ lb},$$

$$F_v = W + w = 350 \text{ lb}.$$

(b) Suppose that the suspended body is replaced by one weighing 200 lb and that then the beam makes an angle of 30° with the horizontal (Fig. 14–7b). Find the tension in the wire and the forces exerted by the hinge on the beam.

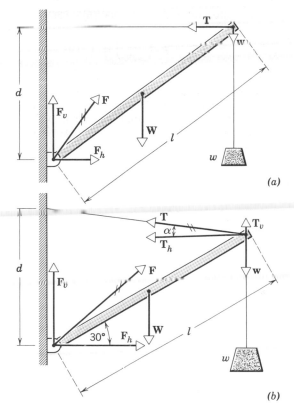

Fig. 14–7 (a) Example 3a. A hinged beam is held up by a horizontal cable making a 3-4-5 triangle. (b) Example 3b. The weight is increased, and the cable is lengthened so that the beam makes a 30° angle with the horizontal.

In this case the wire will no longer be horizontal. **T** will have horizontal and vertical components T_h and T_v, respectively.

Our translational equilibrium conditions are

$$F_v + T_v - W - w = 0,$$

$$F_h - T_h = 0.$$

Choosing an axis through the point of intersection of **T** and **w** (Why?), we obtain for rotational equilibrium

$$F_v(l \cos 30°) - F_h(l \sin 30°) - W(l \cos 30°)/2 = 0.$$

We are given the data

$$W = 300 \text{ lb}, \quad w = 200 \text{ lb}, \quad l = 10 \text{ ft}, \quad d = 6.0 \text{ ft}.$$

Therefore,

(1) $$F_v + T_v = 500 \text{ lb},$$

(2) $$F_h = T_h$$

and
$$F_v(10)(0.866) = F_h(5) + (300)(5)(0.866)$$
or

(3)
$$F_v = F_h\left(\frac{5.0}{8.66}\right) +, 150 \text{ lb}.$$

Notice that we have four unknowns now, namely F_v, F_h, T_v, and T_h. We need another relation between these quantities if we are to solve the problem. This relation follows from the fact that $\mathbf{T}_v$ and $\mathbf{T}_h$ must add to give a resultant vector $\mathbf{T}$ directed along the wire. The wire cannot supply or support a force transverse to its orientation. (Notice that this is not true for the beam, however.) Hence, our fourth relation is

$$T_v = T_h \tan \alpha,$$

where $\tan \alpha = (d - l\sin 30°)/l\cos 30° = 1.0/8.66$, so that

(4)
$$T_v = \frac{T_h}{8.66}.$$

Combining (1) and (4) we obtain

$$F_v = 500 \text{ lb} - T_h/8.66.$$

Combining (2) and (3) we obtain

$$F_v = T_h(5.0/8.66) + 150 \text{ lb}.$$

Solving these equations simultaneously we obtain

$$T_h = 505 \text{ lb}$$

and
$$F_v = 442 \text{ lb}.$$

From (2) we obtain
$$F_h = 505 \text{ lb}.$$

From (1) we obtain
$$T_v = 58 \text{ lb}.$$

The tension in the wire will then be

$$T = \sqrt{T_h{}^2 + T_v{}^2} = 509 \text{ lb},$$

and the hinge will exert a horizontal force of 505 lb and a vertical force of 442 lb on the beam.   ◀

In the preceding examples we have been careful to limit the number of unknown forces to the number of independent equations relating the forces. When all the forces act in a plane, we can have only three independent equations of equilibrium, one for rotational equilibrium about any axis normal to the plane and two others for translational equilibrium in the plane. However, we often have more than three unknown forces. For example, in the ladder problem of Example 2a, if we drop the artificial assumption of a frictionless wall, we have four unknown scalar quantities, namely, the horizontal and vertical components of the force acting on the ladder at the wall and the horizontal and vertical components of the force acting on the ladder at the ground. Since we have only three scalar equations, these forces cannot be determined. For any value assigned to one unknown force, the other three forces can be determined. But if we have no basis for assigning any particular value to an unknown force, there are an infinite number of solutions possible mathematically. We must, therefore, find another independent relation between the unknown forces if we hope to solve the problem uniquely.

Another simple example of such underdetermined structures is the automobile. In this case we wish to determine the forces exerted by the ground on each of the four tires when the car is at rest on a horizontal surface. If we assume that these forces are normal to the ground, we have four unknown scalar quantities. All other forces, such as the weight of the car and passengers, act normal to the ground. Therefore, we have only three independent equations giving the equilibrium conditions, one for translational equilibrium in the single direction of all the forces and two for rotational equilibrium about the two axes perpendicular to each other in a horizontal plane. Again the solution of the problem is indeterminate, mathematically. A four-legged table with all its legs in contact with the floor is a similar example.

Of course, since there is actually a unique solution to any real physical problem, we must find a physical basis for the additional independent relations between the forces that enable us to solve the problem. The difficulty is removed when we realize that structures are never perfectly rigid, as we have tacitly assumed throughout. Actually our structures will be somewhat deformed. For example, the automobile tires and the ground will be deformed, as will the ladder and wall. The laws of elasticity and the elastic properties of the structure determine the nature of the deformation and will provide the necessary additional relation between the four forces. A complete analysis, therefore, requires not only the laws of rigid body mechanics but also the laws of elasticity. In courses in civil and mechanical engineering, many such problems are encountered and analyzed in this way. We shall not consider the matter further here.

14–5 Stable, Unstable, and Neutral Equilibrium of Rigid Bodies in a Gravitational Field

In Chapter 8 we saw that the gravitational force is a conservative force. For conservative forces we can define a potential energy function $U(x, y, z)$ where U is related * to F by

$$F_x = -\frac{dU}{dx}, \qquad F_y = -\frac{dU}{dy}, \qquad F_z = -\frac{dU}{dz}.$$

At points where dU/dx is zero, a particle subject to this conservative force will be in translational equilibrium in the x direction, for then F_x equals zero. Likewise, at points where dU/dy or dU/dz are zero, a particle will be in translational equilibrium in the y and z directions, respectively. The derivative of U at a point will be zero when U has an extreme value (maximum or minimum) at that point or when U is constant with respect to the variable coordinate.

When U is a minimum, the particle is in *stable* equilibrium; any displacement from this position will result in a restoring force tending to return the particle to the equilibrium position. Another way of stating this is to say that if a body is in stable equilibrium, work must be done on it by an external agent to change its position. This results in an increase in its potential energy.

---

* Strictly speaking, these relations involve partial derivatives.

When U is a maximum, the particle is in *unstable* equilibrium; any displacement from this position will result in a force tending to push the particle farther from the equilibrium position. In this case no work must be done on the particle by an external agent to change its position; the work done in displacing the body is supplied internally by the conservative force, resulting in a decrease in potential energy.

When U is constant, the particle is in *neutral* equilibrium. In this case a particle can be displaced slightly without experiencing either a repelling or restoring force.

Notice that a particle can be in equilibrium with respect to one coordinate without necessarily being in equilibrium with respect to another coordinate, as for example a freely falling ball. Furthermore, a particle may be in stable equilibrium with respect to one coordinate and in unstable equilibrium with respect to another coordinate, as for example a particle at a saddle point (Fig. 14–8).

All these remarks apply to particles, that is, to translational motion. Suppose now we treat a rigid body. We must consider rotational equilibrium as well as translational equilibrium. The problem of a rigid body in a gravitational field is particularly simple, however, because *all the gravitational forces on the particles of the rigid body can be considered to act at one point, both for translational and rotational purposes.* We can replace this entire rigid body, for purposes of equilibrium under gravitational forces, by a single particle having the equivalent mass at the center of gravity.

For example, consider a cube at rest on one side on a horizontal table. The center of gravity is shown at the center of the central cross section of the cube in Fig. 14–9a. Let us supply a force to the cube so as to rotate it without its slipping about an axis

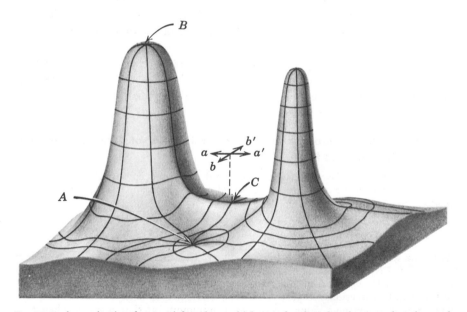

Fig. 14–8 A gravitational potential surface, which may be thought of as a real surface. A particle placed at A, B or C remains at rest; a plane tangent to any of these points is horizontal. We say that a particle here is *in equilibrium*. At A, a particle, if slightly displaced, tends to return to A. A represents a point of *stable equilibrium*. At B, a particle, if slightly displaced, tends to increase its displacement. Thus B represents a point of *unstable equilibrium*. At C, the particle, if slightly displaced in direction aa', will tend to return to C, but if it is displaced in direction bb', it will tend to increase its displacement. C is called a *saddle point* since a saddle has somewhat this shape. Neutral equilibrium, experienced by a particle anywhere on a plane horizontal surface, is not illustrated.

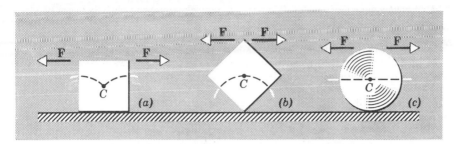

Fig. 14–9 Equilibrium of an extended body. (*a*) A block resting on one side is in *stable equilibrium* since its center of gravity *C* is raised if the block is tipped by a force **F**. (*b*) A block resting on one edge is in *unstable equilibrium* since *C* falls if the block is tipped by **F**. (*c*) A sphere or cylinder is in *neutral equilibrium* since *C* neither rises nor falls when **F** is applied. Compare these criteria for equilibrium with those given in Fig. 14–8. How are the criteria in the two figures related?

along an edge. Notice that the center of gravity is raised and that work is done on the cube, which increases its potential energy. If the force is removed, the cube tends to return to its original position, its increased potential energy being converted into kinetic energy as it falls back. This initial position is, therefore, one of *stable* equilibrium. In terms of a particle of equivalent mass at the center of gravity, this process is described by the dotted line which indicates the path taken by the center of gravity during this motion. The particle is seen to have a minimum potential energy in the position of stable equilibrium, as required. We can conclude that the rigid body will be in stable equilibrium if the application of any force can raise the center of gravity of the body but not lower it.

If the cube is rotated until it balances on an edge, as in Fig. 14–9*b*, then once again the cube is in equilibrium. This equilibrium position is seen to be unstable. The application of even the slightest horizontal force will cause the cube to fall away from this position with a decrease of potential energy. The particle of equivalent mass at the center of gravity follows the dotted path shown. At the position of unstable equilibrium this particle has a maximum potential energy, as required. We can conclude that the rigid body will be in unstable equilibrium if the application of any horizontal force tends to lower the center of gravity of the body.

The neutral equilibrium of a rigid body is illustrated by a sphere on a horizontal table (Fig. 14–9*c*). If the sphere is subjected to any horizontal force, the center of gravity is neither raised nor lowered but moves along the horizontal dotted line. The potential energy of the sphere is constant during the displacement, as is that of the particle of equivalent mass at the center of gravity. The system has no tendency to move in any direction when the applied force is removed. A rigid body will be in neutral equilibrium if the application of any horizontal force neither raises nor lowers the center of gravity of the body.

Under what circumstances would a *suspended* rigid body be in stable equilibrium? When would a *suspended* rigid body be in unstable equilibrium, and when would it be in neutral equilibrium?

QUESTIONS

1. Give several examples of moving bodies which are in equilibrium. Is there a coordinate system in which such a body is at rest? Is the body in equilibrium in such a system?

2. Give several examples of a body which is not in equilibrium, even though the resultant of all the forces acting on it is zero.

3. Which is more likely to break in use, a hammock stretched tightly between two trees or one that sags quite a bit? Prove your answer.

4. A ladder is at rest with its upper end against a wall and the lower end on the ground. Is it more likely to slip when a man stands on it at the bottom or at the top? Explain.

5. In Example 2, if the wall were rough, would the empirical laws of friction supply us with the extra condition needed to determine the extra (vertical) force exerted by the wall on the ladder?

6. In Example 3, what effect would friction at the hinge save?

7. A picture hangs from a wall by two wires. What orientation should the wires have to be under minimum tension? Explain how equilibrium is possible with any number of orientations and tensions, even though the picture has a definite mass.

8. Show how to use a spring balance to weigh objects well beyond the maximum reading of the balance.

9. Do the center of mass and the center of gravity coincide for a building? For a lake? Under what conditions does the difference between the center of mass and the center of gravity of a body become significant?

10. If a rigid body is thrown into the air without spinning, it does not spin during its flight, provided air resistance can be neglected. What does this simple result imply about the location of the center of gravity?

PROBLEMS

1. What force F applied horizontally at the axle of the wheel is necessary to raise the wheel over an obstacle of height h? Take r as the radius of the wheel and W as its weight (Fig. 14–10).

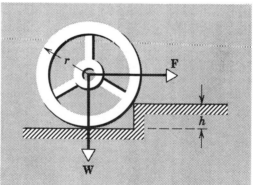

Fig. 14–10

2. A beam is carried by three men, one man at one end and the other two supporting the beam between them on a crosspiece so placed that the load is equally divided between the three men. Find where the crosspiece is placed.

3. A meter stick balances on a knife edge at the 50.0-cm mark. When two nickels are stacked over the 12.0-cm mark, the loaded stick is found to balance at the 45.5-cm mark. A nickel has a mass of 5.0 gm. What is the mass of the meter stick? Try this technique sometime and check your answer experimentally.

4. Prove that when only three forces act on a body in equilibrium, they must be coplanar, and their lines of action must meet at a point or at infinity.

5. In Fig. 14–11 a man is trying to get his car out of the mud on the shoulder of a road. He ties one end of a rope tightly around the front bumper and the other end tightly around

a telephone pole 60 ft away. He then pushes sideways on the rope at its midpoint with a force of 125 lb, displacing the center of the rope 1 ft from its previous position and the car almost moves. What force does the rope exert on the car? (The rope stretches somewhat under the tension.)

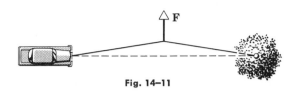

Fig. 14–11

6. A homogeneous sphere of radius r and weight W *slides* along the floor under the action of a constant horizontal force P applied to a string as shown in Fig. 14–12. If the coefficient of friction between sphere and floor is μ, show that the height h is given by

$$h = r\left(1 - \mu\frac{W}{P}\right).$$

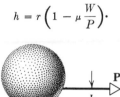

Fig. 14–12

7. A thin horizontal bar AB of negligible weight and length l is pinned to a vertical wall at A and supported at B by a thin wire BC that makes an angle θ with the horizontal. A weight P can be moved anywhere along the bar as defined by the distance x from the wall (Fig. 14–13). (a) Find the tensile force T in the thin wire as a function of x. (b) Find the horizontal and vertical components of the force exerted on the bar by the pin.

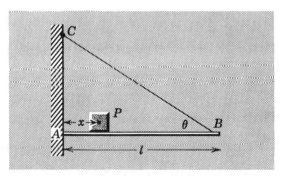

Fig. 14–13

8. A door 7.0 ft high and 3.0 ft wide weighs 60 lb. A hinge 1.0 ft from the top and another 1.0 ft from the bottom each support half the door's weight. Assume that the center of gravity is at the geometrical center of the door and determine the force exerted by each hinge on the door.

9. An automobile weighing 3000 lb has a wheel base of 120 in. Its center of gravity is located 70 in. behind the front axle. Determine the force exerted on each of the front

wheels (assumed the same) and the force exerted on each of the back wheels (assumed the same) by the level ground.

10. A balance is made up of a rigid rod free to rotate about a point not at the center of the rod. It is balanced by unequal weight pans placed at each end of the rod. When an unknown mass m is placed in the left-hand pan, it is balanced by a mass m_1 placed in the right-hand pan, and similarly when the mass m is placed in the right-hand pan, it is balanced by a mass m_2 in the left-hand pan. Show that

$$m = \sqrt{m_1 m_2},$$

and state any assumptions you make in doing this.

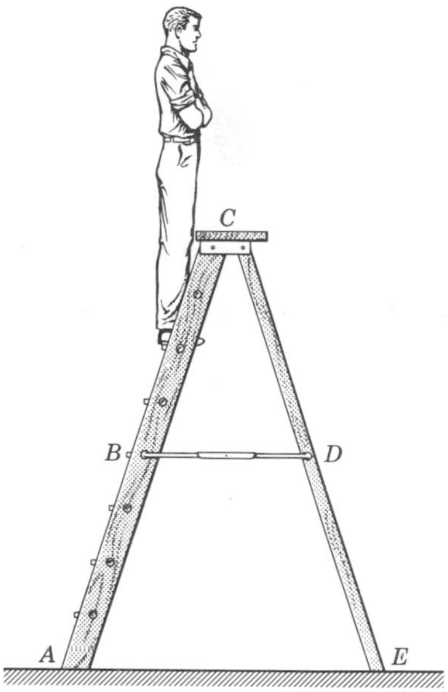

11. In the stepladder shown, AC and CE are 8.0 ft long and hinged at C. BD is a tie rod 2.5 ft long, halfway up. A man weighing 192 lb climbs 6.0 ft along the ladder (Fig. 14–14). Assuming that the floor is very smooth and neglecting the weight of the ladder, find the tension in the tie rod and the forces exerted on the ladder by the floor.

12. A bowl is shaped like a section of a hollow sphere of radius r. A bug can just barely crawl out. If the coefficient of static friction between the bowl and the bug's feet is one-third, how deep is the bowl?

13. A body is suspended at the geometrical center of a cube by three strings, two going to adjacent corners of the top face and the third to the middle of the opposite edge of the top face. The force exerted by a string on one of the corners is 10 nt in magnitude. What is the mass of the body? What would be its initial acceleration if the string to the middle of an edge were cut?

14. Spring 1 has a natural length of 0.5 meter and a force constant $k_1 = 25$ nt/meter. Spring 2 has a natural length of 1.0 meter and a force constant $k_2 = 10$ nt/meter. They are connected together and stretched so that the ends are fastened to walls 2.0 meters apart (Fig. 14–15). What are the stretched lengths of the springs at equilibrium? Notice that $L = l_1 + l_2 = 2.0$ meters.

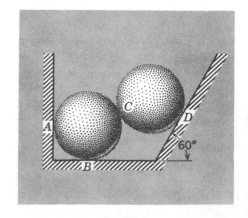

Fig. 14–14

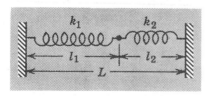

Fig. 14–15

Fig. 14–16

15. Two identical smooth spheres, each of weight $W = 100$ lb, are supported as shown in Fig. 14–16. Assuming smooth wall surfaces, find the reactions induced at the points of support A, B, C, and D. The line joining the centers of the spheres makes an angle of 30° with the horizontal.

16. A flexible chain weighing W lb hangs between two fixed points, A and B, at the same level, as shown in Fig. 14–17. Find (a) the vector force exerted by the chain on each end point and (b) the tension in the chain at the lowest point.

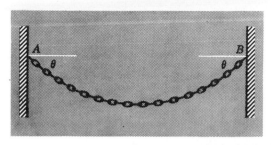

Fig. 14–17

17. A bowl having a radius of curvature r rests on a horizontal table. Show that the bowl will be in stable equilibrium about the center point at its bottom only if the center of mass of the material piled up in the bowl is not as high as r.

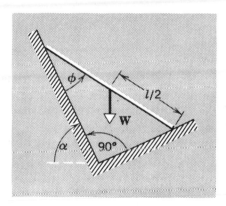

Fig. 14–18

18. Prove that the position of equilibrium for the uniform bar shown in Fig. 14–18 is an unstable one. The bar is of weight W and length l and is supported at its ends by two smooth inclined planes as shown.

Oscillations

CHAPTER 15

15–1 Harmonic Motion

A motion that is repeated at regular intervals of time is called *periodic*. Some examples of periodic motion are the swinging motion of a clock's pendulum, the vibration of a violin string, the rotation of the earth about its axis, and the motion of a mass at the end of a spring. In practice, many of these motions are only approximately periodic owing to the effect of frictional forces which dissipate the energy of motion. Thus, the pendulum gradually stops oscillating and the violin string soon ceases to vibrate. When these dissipative forces are taken into account, the motion is said to be *damped* periodic motion.

The solutions of the equations of periodic motion can always be expressed in terms of sines and cosines. The term *harmonic* is applied to expressions containing these functions. Hence, periodic motion is often called *harmonic motion*.

In harmonic motion neither the velocity nor the acceleration of the particle is constant. One example of single-particle motion discussed earlier in which this was true was uniform circular motion. In that case both the velocity and the acceleration of the particle were constant in magnitude, but they varied in direction. For harmonic motion the velocity and the acceleration are constant neither in direction nor in magnitude.

Any sort of motion that repeats itself in equal intervals of time is periodic. If the motion is back and forth over the same path, it is called *oscillatory* or *vibratory*. A *vibration* or *oscillation* is one round trip of the motion. The *period* of the motion, T, is the time required for one vibration, that is, for each successive repetition of the round-trip motion. The *frequency* of the motion, f, is the number of vibrations per unit of time. The frequency is, therefore, simply the reciprocal of the period, or

$$T = \frac{1}{f}. \tag{15-1}$$

The position at which no net force acts on the particle is called its *equilibrium* position. The *displacement* (linear or angular) is the distance (linear or angular) of the oscillating particle from its equilibrium position at any instant. The *amplitude* of the motion, A, is the maximum displacement.

15–2   The Simple Harmonic Oscillator

If a particle vibrates about an equilibrium position under the influence of a force that is proportional to the distance of the particle from the equilibrium position, the particle is said to have *simple harmonic motion*. The force is always such as to direct the particle back to its equilibrium position and is called a *restoring* force. This force gives the simplest kind of harmonic motion, as the name implies.

An example of a simple harmonic oscillator is a particle of mass m fastened to a spring whose force constant is k (discussed before in Section 8–4). Let us assume that the mass and spring are on a horizontal frictionless surface. We take the origin to be the equilibrium position and let the motion of the particle be along the x-axis. When the particle is displaced to the point x, the spring exerts a restoring force F on it, where

$$F = -kx. \tag{15-2}$$

The minus sign indicates that the force is directed to the left when x is positive and to the right when x is negative. The force on the particle is, therefore, always directed toward the equilibrium position at $x = 0$, as shown in Fig. 15–1.

Let us apply Newton's second law, $F = ma$, to the motion of Fig. 15–1. For F we substitute $-kx$ (from Eq. 15–2) and for a we put in d^2x/dt^2 $(= dv/dt)$. This gives us

$$-kx = m\frac{d^2x}{dt^2}$$

or
$$m\frac{d^2x}{dt^2} + kx = 0. \tag{15-3}$$

This equation involves derivatives and is, therefore, called a differential equation. To solve this equation means to find how the displacement x of the particle must depend on the time t in order for this equation for x to hold true. When we know how x depends on time, we know the motion of the particle; thus, Eq. 15–3 is called the *equation of motion* of a simple harmonic oscillator. We shall solve this equation and describe the motion in detail in the next section.

The simple harmonic oscillator problem is important for two reasons. First, any problem involving mechanical vibrations reduces to that of the

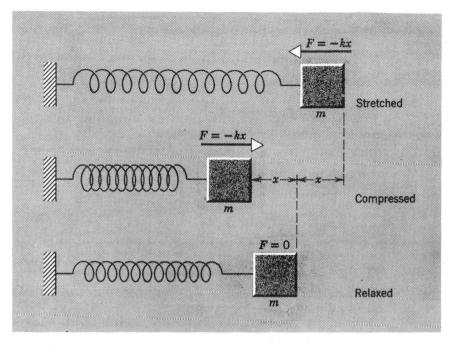

Fig. 15-1 The simple harmonic oscillator. The force exerted by the spring on the mass is shown in each case. The block slides on a frictionless horizontal table.

simple harmonic oscillator at small amplitudes of vibration or to a combination of such vibrations. Second, equations like Eq. 15–3 turn up in a great variety of physical problems—in acoustics, in optics, in mechanics, in electrical circuits, and even in atomic physics. The simple harmonic oscillator exhibits features common to all sorts of physical systems.

It was Robert Hooke (1635–1703) who first demonstrated the simple behavior of elastic substances. *Hooke's Law* can be stated as follows: When a solid is deformed, it resists the deformation with a force proportional to the amount of deformation, provided the deformation is not too great. For a one-dimensional deformation, Hooke's law can be written as $F = -kx$ (Eq. 15–2). Here x is the deformation, that is, the amount of compression or stretching from the undeformed position; F is the resisting force of the solid and k is the proportionality constant. The minus sign shows that the force opposes, or resists, the deformation. When the solid is deformed, it has potential energy U. We can write the potential energy as $U = \frac{1}{2}kx^2$. This can be verified from Eq. 8–6 because $F = -dU/dx$ with this choice of U. Hence, for the undeformed solid ($x = 0$) the potential energy is a minimum and $x = 0$ is a position of stable equilibrium.

If the solid is deformed beyond a certain point, called its *elastic limit*, it will remain permanently deformed; that is, its structure is permanently altered so that its new undeformed shape is changed (Fig. 15–2). It turns out that Hooke's law holds almost up to the elastic limit. Beyond the elastic limit, the forces can no longer be specified by a potential energy function, because the forces then depend on many factors including the speed of deformation and the previous history of the solid.

Notice that the restoring force and potential energy function of the harmonic oscillator are the same as that of a solid deformed in one dimension below the elastic limit. If the deformed solid is released, it will vibrate, just as the harmonic oscillator does. Therefore, as long as the amplitude of the vibration is small enough, that is, as long as the deformation does not exceed the elastic limit, mechanical vibrations behave exactly like harmonic oscillators. It is easy to generalize this discussion to show that any problem involving mechanical vibrations of small amplitude in three dimensions reduces to a combination of simple harmonic oscillators.

The vibrating string or membrane, sound vibrations, electrical oscillations in a cavity or transmission line, and some aspects of the quantum theory of the atom can all be described in a form which is identical math-

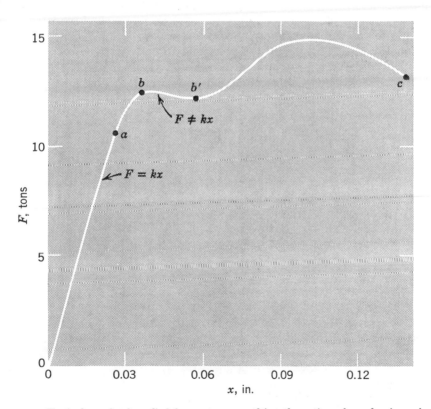

Fig. 15–2 Typical graph of applied force versus resulting elongation of an aluminum bar under tension. The sample was a foot long and a square inch in cross section. Notice that we may write $F = kx$ only for the portion Oa, since beyond this point the slope is no longer constant but varies in a complicated way with x. Point a is called the *elastic limit*. Between b and b' the elongation increases, even though the force is held constant; the material flows like a viscous fluid. At c, the sample can be stretched no farther; any increase in elongation results in the sample's breaking in two.

ematically to a system of harmonic oscillators. The analogy, in fact, enables us to solve problems in one area by using the techniques developed in other areas.

We shall develop the theory of oscillations in this chapter. Application of the ideas and techniques used here to other areas of physics will be made throughout the text.

15–3 Simple Harmonic Motion

Let us now solve the equation of motion of the simple harmonic oscillator,

$$m \frac{d^2x}{dt^2} + kx = 0. \tag{15–3}$$

Recall that any system of mass m upon which a force $F = -kx$ acts will be governed by this equation. In the case of a spring, the proportionality constant k is the force constant of the spring, determined by the stiffness of the spring. In other oscillating systems the proportionality constant k may be related to other physical features of the system, as we shall see later. We can use the oscillating spring as our prototype.

Equation 15–3 is a differential equation. It gives a relation between a function of the time, $x(t)$, and its second time derivative d^2x/dt^2. To find the position of the particle as a function of the time, we must find a function $x(t)$ which satisfies this relation.

We can rewrite Eq. 15–3 as

$$\frac{d^2x}{dt^2} = -\frac{k}{m} x. \tag{15–4}$$

Equation 15–4 then requires that $x(t)$ be some function whose second derivative is the negative of the function itself, except for a constant factor k/m. We know from the calculus, however, that the sine function or the cosine function has this property.* For example,

$$\frac{d}{dt} \cos t = -\sin t \quad \text{and} \quad \frac{d^2}{dt^2} \cos t = -\frac{d}{dt} \sin t = -\cos t.$$

This property is not affected if we multiply the cosine function by a constant A. We can allow for the fact that the sine function will do as well, and for the fact that Eq. 15–4 contains a constant factor, by writing as a tentative solution of Eq. 15–4,

$$x = A \cos (\omega t + \delta). \tag{15–5}$$

Here since

$$\cos (\theta + \delta) = \cos \delta \cos \theta - \sin \delta \sin \theta = a \cos \theta + b \sin \theta,$$

the constant δ allows for any combination of sine and cosine solutions. Hence,

---

* The motion is not only periodic but also bounded. Only the sine and cosine functions (or combinations of them) have both these properties.

with the (as yet) unknown constants A, ω, and δ, we have written as general a solution to Eq. 15–4 as we can. In order to determine these constants such that Eq. 15–5 is actually the solution of Eq. 15–4, we differentiate Eq. 15–5 twice with respect to the time. We have

$$\frac{dx}{dt} = -\omega A \sin (\omega t + \delta)$$

and

$$\frac{d^2x}{dt^2} = -\omega^2 A \cos (\omega t + \delta).$$

Putting this into Eq. 15–4 we obtain

$$-\omega^2 A \cos (\omega t + \delta) = -\frac{k}{m} A \cos (\omega t + \delta).$$

Therefore, if we choose the constant ω such that

$$\omega^2 = \frac{k}{m}, \tag{15–6}$$

then

$$x = A \cos (\omega t + \delta)$$

is in fact a solution of the equation of a simple harmonic oscillator.

The constants A and δ are still undetermined and, therefore, still completely arbitrary. This means that any choice of A and δ whatsoever will satisfy Eq. 15–4, so that a large variety of motions is possible for the oscillator. Actually, this is characteristic of a differential equation of motion, for such an equation does not describe just one single motion but a group or family of possible motions which have some features in common but differ in other ways. In this case ω is common to all the allowed motions, but A and δ may differ among them. We shall see later that A and δ are determined for a particular harmonic motion by how the motion is started.

Let us determine the *physical* significance of the constant ω. If the time t in Eq. 15–5 is increased by $2\pi/\omega$, the function becomes

$$x = A \cos [\omega(t + 2\pi/\omega) + \delta],$$

$$= A \cos (\omega t + 2\pi + \delta),$$

$$= A \cos (\omega t + \delta).$$

That is, the function merely repeats itself after a time $2\pi/\omega$. Therefore, $2\pi/\omega$ is the *period* of the motion, T. Since $\omega^2 = k/m$, we have

$$T = \frac{2\pi}{\omega} = 2\pi \sqrt{\frac{m}{k}}. \tag{15–7}$$

Hence, all motions given by Eq. 15–4 have the same period of oscillation, and this is determined only by the mass m of the vibrating particle and the force constant k. The *frequency* f of the oscillator is the number of complete vibrations per unit time and is given by

$$f = \frac{1}{T} = \frac{\omega}{2\pi} = \frac{1}{2\pi}\sqrt{\frac{k}{m}}. \qquad (15\text{-}8)$$

Hence,
$$\omega = 2\pi f = \frac{2\pi}{T}. \qquad (15\text{-}9)$$

The quantity ω is often called the *angular frequency*, being 2π times the frequency f. It has the dimensions of angular speed, being $2\pi/T$. Its units are radians/sec. In Section 15–6 we shall give a geometric meaning to this angular frequency.

The constant A has a simple physical meaning. The cosine function takes on values from -1 to 1. The *displacement* x from the central equilibrium position $x = 0$, therefore, has a maximum value of A. Hence, A ($= x_{\max}$) is the *amplitude* of the motion. Since A is not fixed by our differential equation, motions of various amplitudes are possible, but all have the same frequency and period. *The period of a simple harmonic motion is independent of the amplitude of the motion.*

The quantity $(\omega t + \delta)$ is called the *phase* of the motion. The constant δ is called the *phase constant*. Two motions may have the same amplitude and frequency but differ in phase. If $\delta = -\pi/2$, for example,

$$x = A\cos(\omega t + \delta) = A\cos(\omega t - 90°)$$

$$= A\sin\omega t,$$

so that the displacement is zero at the time $t = 0$. When $\delta = 0$, the displacement $x = A\cos\omega t$ is a maximum at the time $t = 0$. Other phase constants give other initial displacements.

The amplitude A and the phase constant δ of the oscillation are determined by the initial position and speed of the particle. These two initial conditions will specify A and δ exactly. Once the motion has started, however, the particle will continue to oscillate with a constant amplitude and phase constant at a fixed frequency, unless other forces disturb the system.

In Fig. 15–3 we plot the displacement x versus the time t for various simple harmonic motions. Three comparisons are made. In Fig. 15–3a Case I and Case II have the same amplitude and frequency but differ in phase by $\delta = \pi/4$ or 45°. In Fig. 15–3b Case I and Case III have the same frequency and phase but differ in amplitude by a factor of 2. In Fig. 15–3c Case I and Case IV have the same amplitude and phase but differ in frequency by a factor $\frac{1}{2}$ or in period by a factor 2.

One should study these curves carefully to become familiar with the terminology used in simple harmonic motion.

Another distinctive feature of simple harmonic motion is the relation between the displacement, the velocity, and the acceleration of the oscillating particle. Let us compare these quantities for the particular motion of Case I,

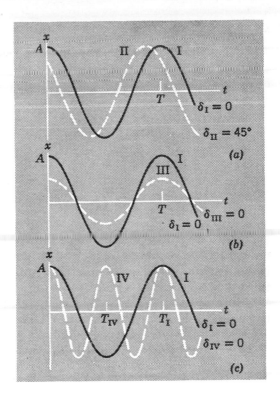

Fig. 15–3 Various solutions of the harmonic oscillator equation. (a) Both solutions have the same amplitude and period but differ in phase by 45°. (b) Both have the same period and phase but differ in amplitude by a factor of 2. (c) Both have the same phase constant and amplitude but differ in period by a factor of 2.

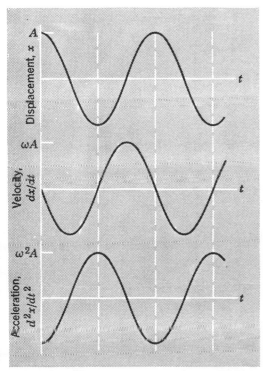

Fig. 15–4 The relations between displacement, velocity, and acceleration in simple harmonic motion. The phase constant δ is zero since the displacement is maximum at $t = 0$.

which is typical. In Fig. 15–4 we plot separately the displacement x versus the time t, the velocity $v = dx/dt$ versus the time t, and the acceleration $a = d^2x/dt^2$ versus the time t. The mathematical relations corresponding to these curves are

$$x = A \cos (\omega t + \delta),$$

$$v = \frac{dx}{dt} = -A\omega \sin (\omega t + \delta), \qquad (15\text{--}10)$$

$$a = \frac{d^2x}{dt^2} = -A\omega^2 \cos (\omega t + \delta).$$

For the case plotted we have taken $\delta = 0$. The units and scale of displacement, velocity, and acceleration are omitted for simplicity of comparison. Notice that the maximum displacement is A, the maximum speed is ωA, and the maximum acceleration is $\omega^2 A$.

When the displacement is a maximum in either direction, the speed is zero because the velocity must now change its direction. The acceleration at this

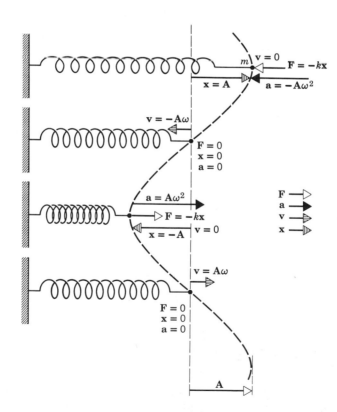

Fig. 15–5 Force, acceleration, velocity, and displacement of a mass m undergoing simple harmonic motion. This figure should be carefully compared with Fig. 15–4.

instant, like the restoring force, has a maximum value but is directed opposite to the displacement.

When the displacement is zero, the speed of the particle is a maximum and the acceleration is zero, corresponding to a zero restoring force.

The speed increases as the particle moves toward the equilibrium position and then decreases as it moves out to the maximum displacement, just as for a pendulum bob.

In Fig. 15-5 we show the instantaneous values of x, v, and a at four instants in the motion of a mass particle oscillating at the end of a spring.

15-4   Energy Considerations in Simple Harmonic Motion

The simple harmonic oscillator is a conservative system, since the force is derivable from the potential energy function $U = \frac{1}{2}kx^2$. Thus, $F = -dU/dx = -kx$. No dissipative forces act on the system so that the total mechanical energy is conserved. Naturally the kinetic energy and the potential energy vary during oscillation. Their sum is conserved, however (see Section 8-3), as we shall now show directly.

The kinetic energy K at any instant is $\frac{1}{2}mv^2$. Using the relations

$$v = \frac{dx}{dt} = -A\omega \sin (\omega t + \delta)$$

and

$$\omega^2 = \frac{k}{m},$$

we obtain

$$K = \frac{1}{2}mv^2,$$
$$= \frac{1}{2}m\omega^2 A^2 \sin^2 (\omega t + \delta),$$
$$= \frac{1}{2}kA^2 \sin^2 (\omega t + \delta). \tag{15-11}$$

The kinetic energy, therefore, has a maximum value of $\frac{1}{2}kA^2$ or $\frac{1}{2}m(\omega A)^2$, in agreement with the maximum speed ωA noted earlier. During the motion the kinetic energy varies between zero and this maximum value as shown by the curves in Fig. 15-6a and 15-6b.

The potential energy at any instant is $U = \frac{1}{2}kx^2$. But

$$x = A \cos (\omega t + \delta),$$

so that

$$U = \frac{1}{2}kA^2 \cos^2 (\omega t + \delta). \tag{15-12}$$

The potential energy also has a maximum value of $\frac{1}{2}kA^2$. During the motion the potential energy varies between zero and this maximum value, as shown by the curves in Fig. 15-6a and 15-6b.

The total mechanical energy is the sum of the kinetic and the potential energy. Using Eqs. 15-11 and 15-12 we obtain

$$E = K + U = \frac{1}{2}kA^2 \sin^2 (\omega t + \delta) + \frac{1}{2}kA^2 \cos^2 (\omega t + \delta) = \frac{1}{2}kA^2. \tag{15-13}$$

We see that the total mechanical energy is constant and has the value $\frac{1}{2}kA^2$

At the maximum displacement the kinetic energy is zero but the potential energy has the value $\frac{1}{2}kA^2$. At the equilibrium position the potential energy is zero but the kinetic energy has the value $\frac{1}{2}kA^2$. At other positions the kinetic and potential energies each contribute energy whose sum is always $\frac{1}{2}kA^2$. This constant total energy is shown in Fig. 15–6a and 15–6b. *The total energy of a particle executing simple harmonic motion is proportional to*

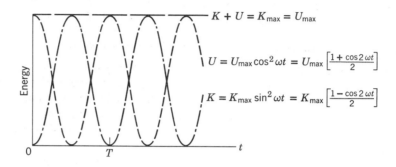

$$K + U = K_{max} = U_{max}$$

$$U = U_{max}\cos^2\omega t = U_{max}\left[\frac{1+\cos 2\omega t}{2}\right]$$

$$K = K_{max}\sin^2\omega t = K_{max}\left[\frac{1-\cos 2\omega t}{2}\right]$$

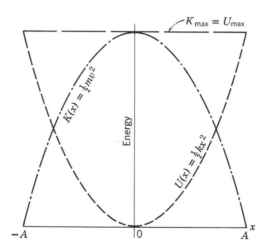

Fig. 15–6 Energies of a simple harmonic oscillator. Top, potential energy $\frac{1}{2}kx^2$ (– – – –), kinetic energy $\frac{1}{2}mv^2$ (—·—·—·—), and total energy (——————) plotted as a function of time. Bottom, potential, kinetic, and total energy plotted as a function of displacement from the equilibrium position. (Compare with Fig. 8–3.)

the square of the amplitude of the motion. It is clear from Fig. 15–6a that the *average* kinetic energy for the motion during one period is exactly equal to the *average* potential energy and that each of these average quantities is $\frac{1}{4}kA^2$.

Equation 15–13 can be written quite generally as

$$K + U = \tfrac{1}{2}mv^2 + \tfrac{1}{2}kx^2 = \tfrac{1}{2}kA^2. \tag{15 14}$$

From this relation we obtain $v^2 = (k/m)(A^2 - x^2)$ or

$$v = \frac{dx}{dt} = \pm \sqrt{\frac{k}{m}(A^2 - x^2)}. \tag{15-15}$$

This relation shows rather clearly that the speed is a maximum at the equilibrium position $x = 0$ and zero at the maximum displacement $x = A$. In fact, we can start from the conservation of energy principle, Eq. 15–14 (in which $\frac{1}{2}kA^2 = E$), and by integration of Eq. 15–15 obtain the displacement as a function of time. The results are identical with Eq. 15–10 which we deduced from the differential equation of the motion, Eq. 15–3. (See Problem 14.)

The effect of dissipative forces will be discussed in Section 15–8.

▶ **Example 1.** The horizontal coiled spring of Fig. 15–5 is found to be stretched 3.0 in. from its equilibrium position when a force of 0.75 lb acts on it. Then a 1.5-lb body is attached to the end of the spring and is pulled 4.0 in. along a horizontal frictionless table from the equilibrium position. The body is then released and executes simple harmonic motion.

(a) What is the force constant of the spring?

A force of 0.75 lb on the spring produces a displacement of 0.25 ft. Hence,

$$k = \frac{F}{x} = \frac{0.75 \text{ lb}}{0.25 \text{ ft}} = 3.0 \text{ lb/ft}.$$

Why didn't we use $k = -F/x$ here?

(b) What is the force exerted by the spring on the 1.5-lb body just before it is released?

The spring is stretched 4.0 in. or $\frac{1}{3}$ ft. Hence, the force exerted by the spring is

$$F = -kx = -(3.0 \text{ lb/ft})(\tfrac{1}{3} \text{ ft}) = -1.0 \text{ lb}.$$

The minus sign indicates that the force is directed opposite to the displacement.

(c) What is the period of oscillation after release?

$$T = 2\pi \sqrt{\frac{m}{k}} = 2\pi \sqrt{\frac{1.5/32}{3.0}} \text{ sec} = \frac{\pi}{4} \text{ sec} = 0.79 \text{ sec}.$$

(d) What is the amplitude of the motion?

The maximum displacement corresponds to zero kinetic energy and a maximum potential energy. This is the initial condition before release, so that the amplitude is the initial displacement of 4.0 in. Hence, $A = \frac{1}{3}$ ft.

(e) What is the maximum speed of the vibrating body?

From Eq. 15–10, $v_{max} = A\omega = A2\pi/T$,

$$v_{max} = (\tfrac{1}{3} \text{ ft}) \left(\frac{2\pi}{\pi/4} \text{ sec}^{-1} \right) = 2.7 \text{ ft/sec}.$$

The maximum speed occurs at the equilibrium position, where $x = 0$. This value is achieved twice in each period, the velocity being -2.7 ft/sec when the body passes through $x = 0$ first after release and $+2.7$ ft/sec when the body passes through $x = 0$ on the return trip.

(f) What is the maximum acceleration of the body?

From Eq. 15–10, $a_{max} = A\omega^2 = Ak/m$,

$$a_{max} = \left(\frac{1}{3} \right) \left(\frac{3.0}{1.5/32} \right) \text{ ft/sec}^2 = 21 \text{ ft/sec}^2.$$

The maximum acceleration occurs at the ends of the path where $x = \pm A$ and $v = 0$. Hence, $a = -21$ ft/sec^2 at $x = +A$ and $a = +21$ ft/sec^2 at $x = -A$, the acceleration and displacement being oppositely directed.

(g) Compute the velocity, the acceleration, and the kinetic and potential energies of the body when it has moved in halfway from its initial position toward the center of motion.

At this point, $$x = \frac{A}{2} = \tfrac{1}{6} \text{ ft,}$$

so that from Eq. 15-15,

$$v = -\frac{2\pi}{T} \sqrt{A^2 - x^2}$$

$$= -\frac{2\pi}{\pi/4} \sqrt{\left(\frac{1}{3}\right)^2 - \left(\frac{1}{6}\right)^2} \text{ ft/sec} = \frac{4}{\sqrt{3}} \text{ ft/sec} = 2.3 \text{ ft/sec,}$$

$$a = -\frac{k}{m} x = \frac{-3.0}{1.5/32} \left(\frac{1}{6}\right) \text{ ft/sec}^2 = 11 \text{ ft/sec}^2,$$

$$K = \tfrac{1}{2} mv^2 = \left(\frac{1}{2}\right) \left(\frac{1.5}{32}\right) \left(\frac{4}{\sqrt{3}}\right)^2 \text{ ft-lb} = \tfrac{1}{8} \text{ ft-lb,}$$

$$U = \tfrac{1}{2} kx^2 = \left(\frac{1}{2}\right) (3) \left(\frac{1}{6}\right)^2 \text{ ft-lb} = \tfrac{1}{24} \text{ ft-lb.}$$

(h) Compute the total energy of the oscillating system.

Since the total energy is conserved, we can compute it at any stage of the motion. Using previous results, we obtain

$$E = K + U = \tfrac{1}{8} + \tfrac{1}{24} = \tfrac{1}{6} \text{ ft-lb,} \qquad \left(\text{particle at } x = \frac{A}{2}\right)$$

$$E = U_{\max} = \tfrac{1}{2} kx_{\max}^2 = \left(\frac{1}{2}\right) (3) \left(\frac{1}{3}\right)^2 \text{ ft-lb} = \tfrac{1}{6} \text{ ft-lb,} \qquad (\text{particle at } x = A)$$

$$E = K_{\max} = \tfrac{1}{2} mv_{\max}^2 = \left(\frac{1}{2}\right) \left(\frac{1.5}{32}\right) \left(\frac{8}{3}\right)^2 \text{ ft-lb} = \tfrac{1}{6} \text{ ft-lb,} \qquad (\text{particle at } x = 0)$$

(i) What is the equation of motion of the body?

In general, we have

$$x = A \cos (\omega t + \delta).$$

We have already found that $A = \tfrac{1}{3}$ ft. We must now determine ω and δ. We obtain

$$\omega = \frac{2\pi}{T} = \frac{2\pi}{\pi/4} = 8 \text{ radians/sec,}$$

so that, with our particular units,

$$x = \tfrac{1}{3} \cos (8t + \delta).$$

At the time $t = 0$, $x = \tfrac{1}{3}$ ft, so that at that instant

$$x = \tfrac{1}{3} \cos \delta = \tfrac{1}{3}$$

or $$\delta = 0 \text{ radian.}$$

Therefore, with $A = \tfrac{1}{3}$ ft, $\omega = 8$ radians/sec, and $\delta = 0$ radian, we obtain

$$x = \tfrac{1}{3} \cos 8t.$$

This gives the equation of motion of the body, where x is in feet, t is in seconds, and the angle $8t$ is in radians. ◀

15–5   Applications of Simple Harmonic Motion

A fow physical systems that move with simple harmonic motion are considered here. Others will be discussed from time to time throughout the rest of the text.

The Simple Pendulum. A simple pendulum is an idealized body consisting of a point mass, suspended by a light inextensible cord. When pulled to one side of its equilibrium position and released, the pendulum swings in a vertical plane under the influence of gravity. The motion is periodic and oscillatory. We wish to determine the period of the motion.

Figure 15–7 shows a pendulum of length l, particle mass m, making an angle θ with the vertical. The forces acting on m are $m\mathbf{g}$, the gravitational force acting down, and $\mathbf{T}$, the tension in the cord. Choose axes tangent to the circle of motion and along the radius. Resolve $m\mathbf{g}$ into a radial component, $mg \cos \theta$, and a tangential component, $mg \sin \theta$. The radial components of the forces supply the necessary centripetal acceleration to keep the particle moving on a circular arc. The tangential component is the restoring force acting on m tending to return it to the equilibrium position. Hence, the restoring force is

$$F = -mg \sin \theta.$$

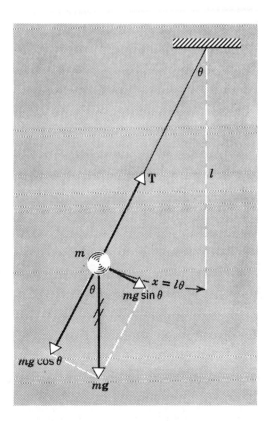

Fig. 15–7 The forces acting on a simple pendulum are the tension **T** in the string and the weight $m\mathbf{g}$ of mass m.

Notice that the restoring force is not proportional to the angular displacement θ but to sin θ instead. The resulting motion is, therefore, not simple harmonic. However, *if the angle θ is small*, sin θ is very nearly equal to θ in radians.* The displacement along the arc is $x = l\theta$, and for small angles this is nearly straight-line motion. Hence, assuming

$$\sin \theta \cong \theta,$$

we obtain
$$F = -mg\theta = -mg\frac{x}{l} = -\frac{mg}{l}x.$$

For *small displacements*, therefore, the restoring force is proportional to the displacement and is oppositely directed. This is exactly the criterion for simple harmonic motion. The constant mg/l represents the constant k in $F = -kx$. Check the dimensions of k and mg/l. The period of a simple pendulum when its amplitude is small is

$$T = 2\pi \sqrt{\frac{m}{k}} = 2\pi \sqrt{\frac{m}{mg/l}} \quad \text{or} \quad T = 2\pi \sqrt{\frac{l}{g}}. \quad (15\text{–}16)$$

Notice that the period is independent of the mass of the suspended point particle.

When the amplitude of the oscillation is not small, the general equation for the time of a complete oscillation can be shown to be

$$T = 2\pi \sqrt{\frac{l}{g}}\left(1 + \frac{1}{2^2}\cdot\sin^2\frac{\Phi}{2} + \frac{1}{2^2}\cdot\frac{3^2}{4^2}\cdot\sin^4\frac{\Phi}{2} + \cdots\right). \quad (15\text{–}17)$$

Here Φ is the maximum angular displacement and the succeeding terms become smaller and smaller. The period can then be computed to any desired degree of accuracy by taking enough terms in the infinite series. When $\Phi = 15°$, corresponding to a total to-and-fro angular displacement of 30°, the true period differs from that given by Eq. 15–16 by less than 0.5%. Figure 15–8 is a graph showing the ratio of the actual period of Eq. 15–17 and the approximate period of Eq. 15–16 as a function of Φ.

Because the period of a simple pendulum is practically independent of the amplitude, the pendulum is useful as a timekeeper. As damping forces reduce the amplitude of swing, the period remains very nearly unchanged. In a pendulum clock energy is supplied automatically by an escapement mechanism to compensate for frictional loss. The pendulum clock with escapement was invented by Christian Huygens (1629–1695). Huygens also conceived of the cycloidal pendulum, a device for keeping the period of a pendulum *completely* independent of its amplitude (Fig. 15–9).

---

* For example,

		Difference, %
$\theta = \ \ 0° =$ 0.0000 radian	$\sin \theta = 0.0000$	0
$\theta = \ \ 2° =$ 0.0349 radian	$\sin \theta = 0.0349$	0.00
$\theta = \ \ 5° =$ 0.0873 radian	$\sin \theta = 0.0872$	0.11
$\theta = 10° =$ 0.1745 radian	$\sin \theta = 0.1736$	0.51
$\theta = 15° =$ 0.2618 radian	$\sin \theta = 0.2588$	1.14

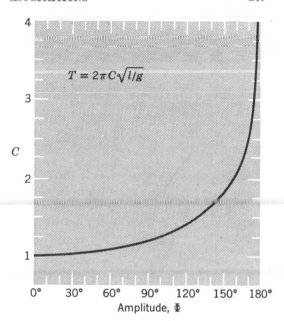

Fig. 15–8 How the period T of a simple pendulum increases as its amplitude Φ is increased. (The weight is to be thought of as being at the end of a weightless rigid rod, rather than at the end of a string.) Note that the period approaches infinite values as the amplitude approaches $180°$. (Is this reasonable?) The factor C is the sum in parentheses in Eq. 15–17.

$$T = 2\pi C\sqrt{l/g}$$

The simple pendulum also provides a convenient method for measuring the value of g, the acceleration due to gravity. We need not perform a free-fall experiment here, but instead we merely measure l and T. More complicated pendulums are used extensively in geophysics. Ore and oil deposits whose densities differ from those of their surroundings cause variations in the total value of g. Precision measurements of g over the prospected region can give useful information about the nature of the underlying deposits.

The Torsional Pendulum. In Fig. 15–10 we show a disk suspended by a wire attached to the center of mass of the disk. The wire is securely fixed to a solid support and to the disk. At the equilibrium position of the disk a radial line is drawn from its center to P, as shown. If the disk is rotated in a horizontal plane to the radial position Q, the wire will be twisted. The twisted wire will exert a torque on the disk tending to return it to the position P. This is a restoring torque. The restoring torque is found to be pro-

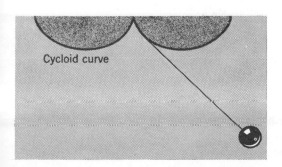

Cycloid curve

Fig. 15–9 A method invented by Huygens to make a pendulum isochronous, that is, its period independent of its amplitude. Advanced study of mechanics shows that if the pendulum bob moves along a cycloid curve, its motion will be isochronous. It can be shown that if cycloidal cheeks are placed against the top of the string as shown, the bob itself will describe a cycloid.

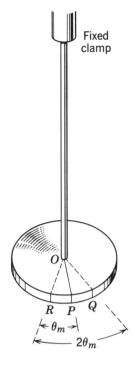

Fig. 15–10 The torsional pendulum. The line drawn from the center to P oscillates between Q and R, sweeping out an angle $2\theta_m$ where θ_m is the (angular) amplitude of the pendulum.

portional to the amount of twist, or the angular displacement (from Hooke's law), so that

$$\tau = -\kappa\theta. \tag{15–18}$$

Here κ is a constant that depends on the properties of the wire and is called the *torsional* constant. The minus sign shows that the torque is directed opposite to the angular displacement θ. Equation 15–18 is the condition for *angular simple harmonic motion*.

The equation of motion for such a system is

$$\tau = I\alpha = I\frac{d^2\theta}{dt^2},$$

so that, on using Eq. 15–18, we obtain

$$-\kappa\theta = I\frac{d^2\theta}{dt^2}$$

or

$$\frac{d^2\theta}{dt^2} = -\left(\frac{\kappa}{I}\right)\theta. \tag{15–19}$$

Notice the similarity between Eq. 15–19 for simple angular harmonic motion and Eq. 15–4 for simple linear harmonic motion. In fact, the equations are identical mathematically. We have simply substituted angular displacement θ for linear displacement x, rotational inertia I for mass m, and torsional constant κ for force constant k. The solution of Eq. 15–19 is, therefore, a simple harmonic oscillation in the angle coordinate θ, namely

$$\theta = \theta_m \cos (\omega t + \delta). \tag{15–20}$$

Here, θ_m is the maximum angular displacement, that is, the amplitude of the angular oscillation. In Fig. 15–10 the disk oscillates about the equilibrium position $\theta = 0$ (line OP), the total angular range being $2\theta_m$ (from OQ to OR).

The period of the oscillation by analogy with Eq. 15–7 is

$$T = 2\pi \sqrt{\frac{I}{\kappa}}. \tag{15–21}$$

If κ is known and T is measured, the rotational inertia I of any oscillating rigid body can be determined. If I is known and T is measured, the torsional constant κ of any sample of wire can be determined.

Many laboratory instruments involve torsional oscillations, notably the galvanometer. The Cavendish balance is a torsional pendulum (Chapter 16). The balance wheel of a watch is another example of angular harmonic motion, the restoring torque here being supplied by a spiral hairspring.

▶ **Example 2.** A thin rod of mass 0.10 kg and length 0.10 meter is suspended by a wire which passes through its center and is perpendicular to its length. The wire is twisted and the rod set oscillating. The period is found to be 2.0 sec. When a flat body in the shape of an equilateral triangle is suspended similarly through its center of mass, the period is found to be 6.0 sec. Find the rotational inertia of the triangle about this axis.

The rotational inertia of the rod is $Ml^2/12$ (see Table 12–1). Hence,

$$I_{\text{rod}} = \frac{(0.10 \text{ kg})(0.10 \text{ meter})^2}{12} = 8.3 \times 10^{-5} \text{ kg-m}^2.$$

From Eq. 15–21,

$$\frac{T_{\text{rod}}}{T_{\text{triangle}}} = \left(\frac{I_{\text{rod}}}{I_{\text{triangle}}}\right)^{\frac{1}{2}} \quad \text{or} \quad I_{\text{triangle}} = I_{\text{rod}} \left(\frac{T_t}{T_r}\right)^2,$$

so that

$$I_{\text{triangle}} = (8.3 \times 10^{-5} \text{ kg-m}^2) \left(\frac{6.0 \text{ sec}}{2.0 \text{ sec}}\right)^2 = 7.5 \times 10^{-4} \text{ kg-m}^2.$$

Does the amplitude of the oscillation affect the period in these cases?   ◀

The Physical Pendulum. Any rigid body mounted so that it can swing in a vertical plane about some axis passing through it is called a physical pendulum. This is a generalization of the simple pendulum in which a weightless cord holds a single particle. Actually all real pendulums are physical pendulums.

In Fig. 15–11 a body of irregular shape is pivoted about a horizontal frictionless axis P and displaced from the equilibrium position by an angle θ. The equilibrium position is that in which the center of mass of the body, C, lies vertically below P. The distance from pivot to center of mass is d, the rotational inertia of the body about an axis through the pivot is I, and

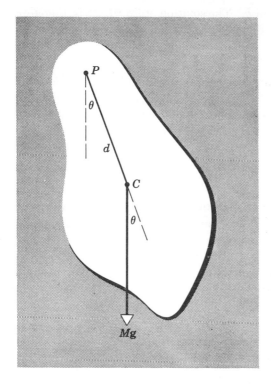

Fig. 15–11 The physical pendulum, with center of mass C, is shown pivoted at P and displaced an angle θ from its equilibrium position (when C hangs directly below P). Its weight $M\mathbf{g}$ supplies a restoring torque.

the mass of the body is M. The restoring torque for an angular displacement θ is

$$\tau = -Mgd \sin \theta$$

and is due to the tangential component of the force of gravity. Since τ is proportional to $\sin \theta$, rather than θ, the condition for simple angular harmonic motion does not, in general, hold here. For small angular displacements, however, the relation $\sin \theta = \theta$ is, as before, an excellent approximation, so that for *small amplitudes*,

$$\tau = -Mgd\theta$$

or

$$\tau = -\kappa\theta,$$

where

$$\kappa = Mgd.$$

But

$$\tau = I \frac{d^2\theta}{dt^2} = I\alpha,$$

so that

$$\frac{d^2\theta}{dt^2} = \frac{\tau}{I} = \frac{-\kappa}{I}\theta.$$

Hence, the period of a physical pendulum oscillating with small amplitude is

$$T = 2\pi \sqrt{\frac{I}{\kappa}} = 2\pi \sqrt{\frac{I}{Mgd}}. \qquad (15\text{--}22)$$

At larger amplitudes the physical pendulum still has a periodic motion, but not a simple harmonic one,

Notice that this treatment applies to an object of any shape and that the pivot can be located anywhere. As a special case consider a point mass m suspended at the end of a weightless string of length l. Here

$$I = ml^2, \qquad M = m, \qquad d = l,$$

so that

$$T = 2\pi \sqrt{\frac{I}{Mgd}} = 2\pi \sqrt{\frac{l}{g}},$$

which is the period of a simple pendulum with small amplitude.

The physical pendulum rather than the simple pendulum is used for accurate determinations of g and for geophysical prospecting.

Equation 15–22 can be solved for the rotational inertia I, giving

$$I = \frac{T^2 Mgd}{4\pi^2}. \tag{15–23}$$

The quantities on the right are all directly measurable. The center of mass can be determined by suspension as was shown in Fig. 14–4. Hence, the rotational inertia of a body of any shape can be determined by suspending the body as a physical pendulum from the axis of rotation.

▶ **Example 3.** Find the length of a simple pendulum whose period is equal to that of a particular physical pendulum.

Equating the period of a simple pendulum to that of a physical pendulum, we obtain

$$T = 2\pi \sqrt{\frac{l}{g}} = 2\pi \sqrt{\frac{I}{Mgd}}$$

or

$$l = \frac{I}{Md}. \tag{15–24}$$

Hence, as far as its period of oscillation is concerned, the mass of a physical pendulum may be considered to be concentrated at a point whose distance from the pivot is $l = I/Md$. This point is called the *center of oscillation* of the physical pendulum. Notice that it depends on the location of the pivot for any given body.

Huygens originally developed this concept in his study of time-keeping devices.

Example 4. A disk is pivoted at its rim (Fig. 15–12). Find its period for small oscillations and the length of the equivalent simple pendulum.

The rotational inertia of a disk about an axis through its center is $\frac{1}{2}Mr^2$, where r is the radius and M is the mass of the disk. The rotational inertia about the pivot at the rim is

$$\tfrac{1}{2}Mr^2 + Mr^2 \qquad \text{or} \qquad I = \tfrac{3}{2}Mr^2.$$

The period then, with $d = r$, is

$$T = 2\pi \sqrt{\frac{I}{Mgr}} = 2\pi \sqrt{\frac{3}{2}\frac{Mr^2}{Mgr}} = 2\pi \sqrt{\frac{3}{2}\frac{r}{g}},$$

independent of the mass of the disk.

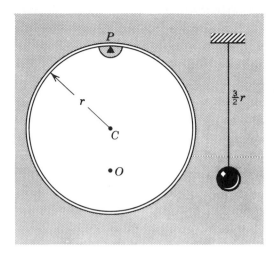

Fig. 15–12 Example 4. A physical pendulum consisting of a disk pivoted at the edge (P), along with a simple pendulum having the same period. O is the center of oscillation.

The simple pendulum having the same period has a length

$$l = \frac{I}{Mr} = \tfrac{3}{2}r$$

or three-fourths the diameter of the disk. The center of oscillation of the disk pivoted at P is, therefore, at O, a distance $\tfrac{3}{2}r$ below the point of support. What is the required mass of the equivalent simple pendulum?

If we pivot the disk at a point midway between the rim and the center, as at O, we find that

$$I = \tfrac{3}{4}Mr^2, \qquad d = \tfrac{1}{2}r, \qquad T = 2\pi\sqrt{\tfrac{3}{2}r/g}$$

just as before. This illustrates a general property of the center of oscillation O and the point of support P, namely, if the pendulum is pivoted about a new axis through O, its period is unchanged and P becomes the new center of oscillation.

If the disk were pivoted at the center, what would be its period of oscillation?

Example 5. The period of a disk of radius 4.00 in. executing small oscillations about a pivot at its rim is measured to be 0.784 sec. Find the value of g, the acceleration due to gravity at that location.

From $T = 2\pi\sqrt{\tfrac{3}{2}r/g}$, we obtain

$$g = \frac{6\pi^2 r}{T^2}.$$

With $T = 0.784$ sec and $r = \tfrac{1}{3}$ ft, we obtain

$$g = \frac{6\pi^2 \cdot \tfrac{1}{3}}{(0.784)^2} \text{ ft/sec}^2 = 32.1 \text{ ft/sec}^2. \qquad \blacktriangleleft$$

15–6 Relation between Simple Harmonic Motion and Uniform Circular Motion

It is instructive to consider the relation between simple harmonic motion along a line and uniform circular motion. This relation is useful in describing many features of simple harmonic motion. It also gives a simple geometric meaning to the angular frequency ω and the phase constant δ.

Uniform circular motion is also an example of a combination of simple harmonic motions, a phenomenon we deal with rather often in wave motion.

In Fig. 15–13 Q is the point moving along a circle of radius A with a constant angular speed of ω radians/sec. The point P is the perpendicular projection of Q on the horizontal diameter, along the x-axis. Let us call Q the *reference point* and the circle on which it moves the *reference circle*. As the reference point revolves, the projected point P moves back and forth along the horizontal diameter. The x coordinate of Q is always the same as the coordinate of P; the x component of the velocity of Q is always the same as the velocity of P; and the x component of the acceleration of Q is always the same as the acceleration of P.

Let the angle between the radius OQ and the x-axis at the time $t = 0$ be called δ. At any later time t, the angle between OQ and the x-axis is $(\omega t + \delta)$,

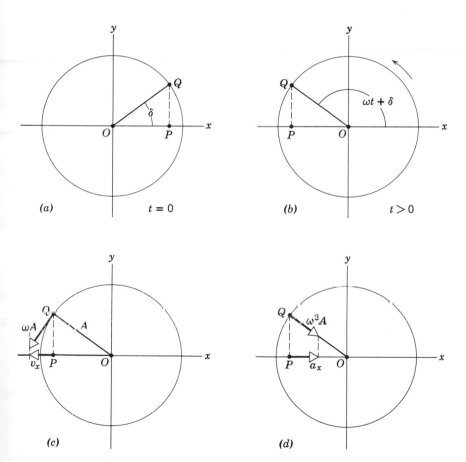

Fig. 15–13 The relation of simple harmonic motion to uniform circular motion. Q moves in uniform circular motion and P in simple harmonic motion. Q has angular speed ω, P angular frequency ω. (*a, b*) The x component of Q's displacement is always equal to P's displacement. (*c*) The x component of Q's velocity is always equal to P's velocity. (*d*) The x component of Q's acceleration is always equal to P's acceleration.

the point Q moving with constant angular speed. The x coordinate of Q at any time is, therefore,

$$x = A \cos (\omega t + \delta). \qquad (15\text{--}25)$$

Hence, the projected point P moves with simple harmonic motion along the x-axis. Therefore, *simple harmonic motion can be described as the projection along a diameter of uniform motion in a circle.*

The angular frequency ω of simple harmonic motion is the same as the angular speed of the reference point. The frequency of the simple harmonic motion is the same as the number of revolutions per unit time of the reference point. Hence, $f = \omega/2\pi$ or $\omega = 2\pi f$. The time for a complete revolution of the reference point is the same as the period T of the simple harmonic motion. Hence, $T = 2\pi/\omega$ or $\omega = 2\pi/T$. The phase of the simple harmonic motion, $\omega t + \delta$, is the angle xOQ that OQ makes with the x-axis at any time t (Fig. 15–13b). The angle that OQ makes with the x-axis at the time $t = 0$ (Fig. 15–13a) is δ, the phase constant or initial phase of the motion. The amplitude of the simple harmonic motion is the same as the radius of the reference circle.

The tangential velocity of the reference point Q is simply ωA. Hence, the x component of this velocity (Fig. 15–13c) is

$$v_x = -\omega A \sin (\omega t + \delta).$$

The minus sign gives a negative v_x when Q and P are moving to the left and a positive v_x when Q and P are to the right. Notice that v_x is zero at the end points of the simple harmonic motion, where $\omega t + \delta$ is zero and π, as required.

The acceleration of point Q in uniform circular motion is directed radially inward and has a magnitude of $\omega^2 A$. The acceleration of the projected point P is the x component of the acceleration of the reference point Q (Fig. 15–13c). Hence,

$$a_x = -\omega^2 A \cos (\omega t + \delta)$$

gives the acceleration of the point executing simple harmonic motion. Notice that a_x is zero at the midpoint of the simple harmonic motion, where $\omega t + \delta = \pi/2$ or $3\pi/2$, as required.

These results are all identical with those of simple harmonic motion along the x-axis.

If we had taken the perpendicular projection of the reference point onto the y-axis, instead, we would have obtained for the motion of the y-projected point

$$y = A \sin (\omega t + \delta). \qquad (15\text{--}26)$$

This is again a simple harmonic motion. It differs only in phase from Eq. 15–25, for if we replace δ by $\delta - \pi/2$, then $\cos (\omega t + \delta)$ becomes $\sin (\omega t + \delta)$. It is clear that the projection for uniform circular motion along *any* diameter gives a simple harmonic motion.

Conversely, uniform circular motion can be described as a combination of two simple harmonic motions. It is that combination of two simple harmonic motions, occurring along perpendicular lines, which have the same amplitude and frequency but differ in phase by 90°. When one component is at the maximum displacement, the other component is at the equilibrium point. If we combine these components (Eqs. 15–25 and 15–26), we obtain at once the relation

$$r = \sqrt{x^2 + y^2} = A.$$

By writing the relations for v_y and a_y (the student should do this) and combining corresponding quantities, we obtain also the relations

$$v = \sqrt{v_x^2 + v_y^2} = \omega A,$$

$$a = \sqrt{a_x^2 + a_y^2} = \omega^2 A.$$

These relations correspond respectively to the magnitudes of the displacement, the velocity, and the acceleration in uniform circular motion.

It will be possible for us to analyze many complicated motions as combinations of individual simple harmonic motions. Circular motion is a particularly simple combination. In the next section we shall consider other combinations of simple harmonic motions.

▶ **Example 6.** In the example of Section 15–4 we considered a body executing a horizontal simple harmonic motion. The equation of that motion (units?) was

$$x = \tfrac{1}{3} \cos 8t.$$

This motion can also be represented as the projection of uniform circular motion along a horizontal diameter.

(a) Give the properties of the corresponding uniform circular motion.

The x component of the circular motion is given by

$$x = A \cos (\omega t + \delta).$$

Therefore, the reference circle must have a radius $A = \tfrac{1}{3}$ ft, the initial phase or phase constant must be $\delta = 0$, and the angular velocity must be $\omega = 8$ radians/sec, in order to obtain the equation $x = \tfrac{1}{3} \cos 8t$ for the horizontal projection.

(b) From the motion of the reference point determine the time required for the body to come halfway in toward the center of motion from its initial position.

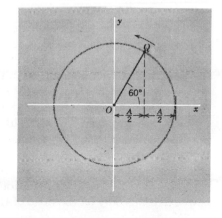

Fig. 15–14 Example 6. The body is shown for $\omega t = 60°$. Since ω is known, t may be found.

As the body moves halfway in, the reference point moves through an angle of $\omega t = 60°$ (Fig. 15–14). The angular velocity is constant at 8 radians/sec so that the time required to move through 60° is

$$t = \frac{60°}{\omega} = \frac{\pi/3 \text{ radians}}{8 \text{ radians/sec}} = \frac{\pi}{24} \text{ sec} = 0.13 \text{ sec.}$$

The time may also be computed directly from the equation of motion. Thus,

$$x = \tfrac{1}{3} \cos 8t \qquad \text{and} \qquad x = \frac{A}{2} = \tfrac{1}{6},$$

Hence, $$\tfrac{1}{6} = \tfrac{1}{3} \cos 8t \quad \text{or} \quad 8t = \cos^{-1}(\tfrac{1}{2}) = \frac{\pi}{3}.$$

Therefore, $$t = \frac{\pi}{24} \text{ sec} = 0.13 \text{ sec.} \qquad \blacktriangleleft$$

15–7 Combinations of Harmonic Motions

In physics there are many instances in which two linear simple harmonic motions *at right angles* are combined. The resulting motion is the sum of two independent oscillations. Consider first the case in which the *frequencies* of the vibrations *are the same*, such as

$$x = A_x \cos (\omega t + \delta),$$
$$y = A_y \cos (\omega t + \alpha). \tag{15–27}$$

The x and y motions have different amplitudes and different phases, however.

If the phases are the same so that $\delta = \alpha$, the resulting motion is a straight line. This can be shown analytically, for on eliminating t from the equations

$$x = A_x \cos (\omega t + \delta) \qquad y = A_y \cos (\omega t + \delta),$$

we obtain $$y = (A_y/A_x)x.$$

This is the equation of a straight line, whose slope is A_y/A_x. In Fig. 15–15a and b we show the resultant motion for two cases, $A_y/A_x = 1$ and $A_y/A_x = 2$. In these cases both the x and y displacements reach a maximum at the same time and reach a minimum at the same time. They are in phase.

If the phases are different, the resulting motion will not be a straight line. For example, if the phases differ by $\pi/2$, the maximum x displacement occurs when the y displacement is zero and vice versa. When the amplitudes are equal, the resulting motion is circular; when the amplitudes are unequal, the resulting motion is elliptical. Two cases, $A_y/A_x = 1$ and $A_y/A_x = 2$, are shown in Fig. 15–15c and d, for $\delta = \alpha + \pi/2$. The cases $A_y/A_x = 1$ and $A_y/A_x = 2$, for $\delta = \alpha - \pi/4$, are shown in Fig. 15–15e and f.

Since the circle and the straight line are special cases of an ellipse, all possible combinations of two simple harmonic motions at right angles having the same frequency correspond to *elliptical* paths. This can be shown analytically by combining Eq. 15–27 and eliminating the time; the student can show that the resulting equation is that of an ellipse. The shape of the ellipse depends only on the ratio of the amplitudes, A_y/A_x, and the *difference*

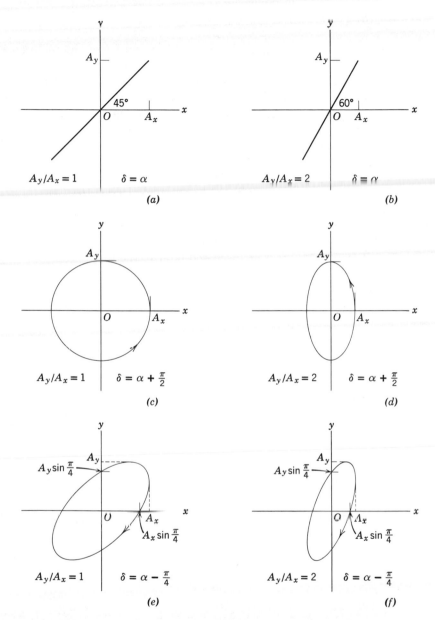

Fig. 15–15 Simple harmonic motion in two dimensions. (*a*) The amplitudes of x and y (namely A_x and A_y) are the same, as are their phase constants. (*b*) y's amplitude is twice x's, but their phases are the same. (*c*) Their amplitudes are equal, but x leads y in phase by 90°. (*d*) Same as (*c*) except that y's amplitude is twice x's. (*e*) Equal amplitudes, but x lags y in phase by 45°. (*f*) Same as (*e*) except that y's amplitude is twice x's.

in phase between the two oscillations, $\delta - \alpha$. The actual motion can be either clockwise or counterclockwise, depending on which component leads in phase.

The simplest way to produce such patterns is by means of an oscilloscope (Chapter 27). In this, electrons are deflected by each of two electric fields at right angles to one another. The field strengths alternate sinusoidally with the same frequency, but their phases and amplitudes can be varied. In this way the electrons can be made to trace out the various patterns discussed above on a fluorescent screen. We can also produce these patterns mechanically by means of a simple pendulum swinging with small amplitude but not confined to one vertical plane. Such combinations of two simple harmonic motions at right angles having the same frequency are particularly important in the study of polarized light and alternating current circuits.

Combinations of simple harmonic motions of the same frequency in the *same direction*, but with different amplitudes and phases, are of special interest in the study of diffraction and interference of light, sound, and electromagnetic radiation. This will be discussed later in the text.

If two oscillations of *different frequencies* are combined at right angles, the resulting motion is more complicated. The motion is not even periodic unless the two component frequencies ω_1 and ω_2 are the ratio of two integers. Oscillations of different frequencies in the same direction may also be combined. The treatment of this motion is particularly important in the case of sound vibrations and will be discussed in Chapter 20.

15–8 Damped Harmonic Motion

Up to this point we have assumed that no frictional forces act on our oscillator. If this were so, a pendulum or a weight on a spring would oscillate indefinitely. Actually, the amplitude of the oscillation gradually decreases to zero, as a result of friction. The motion is said to be damped by friction and is called *damped harmonic motion*. Often the friction arises from air resistance or internal forces. The magnitude of the frictional force usually depends on the speed. In most cases of interest the frictional force is proportional to the velocity of the body but directed opposite to it. An example of a damped oscillator is shown in Fig. 15–16.

The equation of motion of the damped simple harmonic oscillator is given by the second law of motion, $F = ma$, in which F is the sum of the restoring force $-kx$, and the damping force $-b\,dx/dt$. Here b is a positive constant. We obtain

$$F = ma,$$

or

$$-kx - b\frac{dx}{dt} = m\frac{d^2x}{dt^2}$$

or

$$m\frac{d^2x}{dt^2} + b\frac{dx}{dt} + kx = 0. \tag{15–28}$$

If b is small, the solution of this equation (given without proof) * is

$$x = Ae^{-bt/2m}\cos(\omega't + \delta), \tag{15–29}$$

where

$$\omega' = \sqrt{\frac{k}{m} - \left(\frac{b}{2m}\right)^2}. \tag{15–30}$$

---

* See, for example, H. W. Reddick and F. H. Miller, *Advanced Mathematics for Engineers*, third edition, John Wiley & Sons, pp. 76–78.

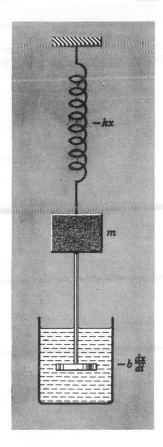

Fig. 15–16 An example of a damped oscillator. A disk is attached to the mass and immersed in a fluid which exerts a damping force $-b \, dx/dt$. The elastic restoring force is $-kx$.

In Fig. 15–17 we plot the displacement x as a function of the time t for oscillatory motion with small damping.

We can interpret the solution as follows. First of all, the frequency is smaller and the period is longer when friction is present. Friction slows down the motion, as might be expected. If no friction were present, b would equal zero and ω' would equal $\sqrt{k/m}$ or ω, which is the angular frequency of undamped motion. When friction is present, ω' is less than ω, as shown by Eq. 15–30. Secondly, the amplitude of the

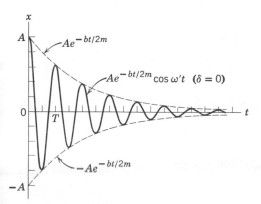

Fig. 15–17 Damped harmonic motion plotted versus time. The motion is oscillation with ever-decreasing amplitude. The amplitude is also plotted against time (– – –) and is seen to start with value A and decay exponentially to zero when $t = \infty$.

motion gradually decreases to zero. The amplitude factor is $Ae^{-bt/2m}$. Once again, if there were no friction present, b would equal zero and the amplitude would have the constant value A as time went on.

If the force of friction is great enough, b becomes so large that Eq. 15–29 is no longer a valid solution of the equation of motion.* Then the motion will not be periodic at all. The body merely returns to its equilibrium position when released from its initial displacement A.

In damped harmonic motion the energy of the oscillator is gradually dissipated by friction and falls to zero in time.

15–9   Forced Oscillations and Resonance

Thus far we have discussed only the natural oscillations of a body, that is, the oscillations that occur when the body is displaced and then released. For a mass attached to a spring the natural frequency is

$$\omega = \sqrt{\frac{k}{m}}$$

in the absence of friction and

$$\omega' = \sqrt{\frac{k}{m} - \left(\frac{b}{2m}\right)^2},$$

in the presence of a small frictional force bv.

A different situation arises, however, when the body is subject to an oscillatory external force. As examples, a bridge vibrates under the influence of marching soldiers, the housing of a motor vibrates owing to periodic impulses from an irregularity in the shaft, and a tuning fork vibrates when exposed to the periodic force of a sound wave. The oscillations that result are called *forced* oscillations. These forced oscillations have the frequency of the *external force* and not that of the natural frequency of the body. However, the response of the body depends on the relation between the forced and the natural frequency. A succession of small impulses properly timed can produce an oscillation of large amplitude. A child using a swing learns that by pumping at proper time intervals he can make the swing move with a large amplitude. The problem of forced oscillations is a very general one. Its solution is useful in acoustic systems, alternating current circuits, and atomic physics as well as in mechanics.

The equation of motion of a forced oscillator follows from the second law of motion. In addition to the restoring force $-kx$ and the damping force $-b\,dx/dt$, we have an applied oscillating external force. For simplicity let this external force be given by $F_m \cos \omega''t$. Here F_m is the maximum value of the external force and ω'' is its angular frequency. We can imagine such a force applied directly to the suspended mass of Fig. 15–16, if we wish, for concreteness.

From $$F = ma,$$

we obtain $$-kx - b\frac{dx}{dt} + F_m \cos \omega''t = m\frac{d^2x}{dt^2}$$

or $$m\frac{d^2x}{dt^2} + b\frac{dx}{dt} + kx = F_m \cos \omega''t. \tag{15–31}$$

The solution of this equation (given without proof) * is

$$x = \frac{F_m}{G} \sin (\omega''t - \alpha), \tag{15–32}$$

---

* Ibid., pp. 80–83.

where $\qquad G - \sqrt{(m\omega''^2 \quad k)^2 + b^2\omega''^2} = \sqrt{m^2(\omega''^2 - \omega^2)^2 + b^2\omega''^2},$ $\qquad$ (15–33)

and $\qquad\qquad\qquad\qquad \alpha - \cos^{-1}\dfrac{b\omega''}{G}.$ $\qquad\qquad\qquad\qquad$ (15–34)

Let us consider the resulting motion in a qualitative way.

Notice (Eq. 15–32) that the system vibrates with the frequency of the driving force, ω'', rather than of its natural frequency ω, and that the motion is undamped harmonic motion.

The factor G is large when the frequency of the driving force ω'' is very different from the natural undamped frequency of the system ω. This means that the amplitude of the resulting motion, F_m/G, is small. As the driving frequency approaches the naturally undamped frequency, G becomes smaller and the amplitude increases. The amplitude reaches a maximum value when the driving frequency and the natural frequency are nearly equal. The phenomenon is called resonance; the frequency ω'', which gives the maximum amplitude for the forced vibration of the system, is called the resonant frequency.

The amplitude of the forced vibration depends on the frictional force as well as on the driving frequency. The greater the friction, the larger G is, and the smaller the amplitude. In Fig. 15–18 we have drawn five curves giving the amplitude of the forced vibration as a function of the ratio of the driving frequency ω'' to the undamped natural frequency ω. Each of the five curves corresponds to a different value of the damping constant b. Curve (a) shows the amplitude when $b = 0$, that is, when there is no damping. In this case, the amplitude becomes infinite at $\omega'' = \omega$ because energy is being fed into the system continuously by the applied force and none of it is

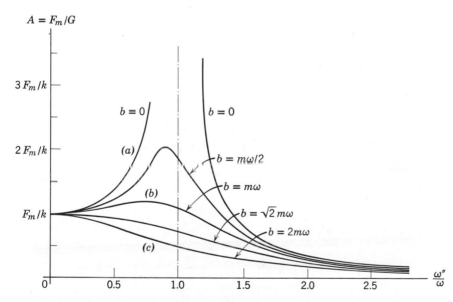

Fig. 15–18 The amplitude of a driven harmonic oscillator is plotted versus the ratio of the driving frequency to the undamped natural frequency. Curves for five different degrees of damping are shown; curve (a) shows no damping and curve (c) high damping. We notice that the resonant peak moves nearer and nearer the dotted line as b becomes smaller and smaller. This diagram can be considered as a three-dimensional graph if the curves are thought of as contour lines.

Fig. 15–19 On July 1, 1940, the Tacoma Narrows Bridge at Puget Sound, Washington, was completed and opened to traffic. It was then the third longest span in the world. Just four months later a mild gale set the bridge oscillating until the main span broke up, ripping loose from the cables and crashing into the water below. The steady wind produced a fluctuating resultant force in resonance with a natural frequency of the structure. This caused a steady increase in amplitude until the bridge was destroyed. Many other bridges were later redesigned to make them aerodynamically stable.

dissipated. In practice, some friction is always present, so the amplitude reaches a large, but finite, value. Of course, when the amplitude gets so large that Hooke's law no longer holds and the elastic limit is exceeded, the system is no longer governed by Eq. 15–31. Often the system breaks, as in the Tacoma Bridge disaster (Fig. 15–19). Curves (b) and (c) give the amplitude of forced vibration for two cases of finite (increasing) damping. The natural damped frequency ω' is less than the natural undamped frequency ω of the system.

Notice that the resonant frequency is not quite equal to either the natural frequency or the natural damped frequency but is somewhat smaller than either of these. In the case of small damping the differences are rather small so that the resonant frequency can be taken to be the same as the natural frequency with small error.

The displacement caused by a constant force F_m applied to a system with a force constant k is simply F_m/k. Notice (Fig. 15–18) that the amplitude of the forced vibrations is rather large compared to this static displacement. A column of soldiers marching in step across a bridge can set it vibrating with a destructively large amplitude if the frequency of their steps happens to be some natural frequency of the bridge. This is the reason why soldiers break step when crossing a bridge. The resonating principle is put to constructive use in many electrical, acoustic, and atomic devices, as we shall see later.

QUESTIONS

1. Give some examples in nature of motions that are approximately simple harmonic. Why are motions that are exactly simple harmonic rare?

2. A spring has a force constant k, and a mass m is suspended from it. The spring is cut in half and the same mass is suspended from one of the halves. Is the frequency of vibration the same before and after the spring is cut? How are the frequencies related?

3. Any real spring has mass. If this mass is taken into account, explain qualitatively how this will change our expressions for the period of oscillation of a spring-and-mass system. (See Problem 30.)

4. Suppose we have a block of unknown mass and a spring of unknown stiffness constant. Show how we can predict the period of oscillation of this block-spring system simply by measuring the extension of the spring produced by attaching the block to it.

5. Explain how the masses of bodies can be compared by observing their frequencies of oscillation when supported by a spring.

6. What is the purpose of the balance wheel in a watch or the pendulum of a grandfather's clock?

7. Could we ever construct a simple pendulum?

8. The following problem was proposed and solved by Galileo. A wire hangs in a tall dark tower, so that the upper end is not visible or accessible but the lower end is. How can we determine the length of the wire?

9. Predict by qualitative arguments whether a pendulum oscillating with large amplitude will have a period longer or shorter than the period for oscillations with small amplitude. (Consider extreme cases.)

10. How can a pendulum be used so as to trace out a sinusoidal curve?

11. What component simple harmonic motions would give a figure 8 as the resultant motion?

12. A vertical spring-and-mass system executes simple harmonic motion. How, if at all, does *gravitational* potential energy enter into the expression for the conservation of energy of such a system? How, if at all, does the weight of the mass enter into the expression for the force on the mass?

13. Why are damping devices often used on machinery? Give an example.

14. Give some examples of common phenomena in which resonance plays an important role.

PROBLEMS

1. A 4-kg block extends a spring 16 cm from its unstretched position. The block is removed and a 0.50-kg body is hung from the same spring. If the spring is then stretched and released, what is its period of motion?

2. A 2.0-kg mass hangs from a spring. A 300-gm body hung below the mass stretches the spring 2.0 cm farther. If the 300-gm body is removed and the mass set into oscillation, find the period of motion.

3. A body oscillates with simple harmonic motion according to the equation

$$x = 6.0 \cos \left(3\pi t + \frac{\pi}{3} \right) \text{ meters.}$$

What is (a) the displacement, (b) the velocity, and (c) the acceleration at the time $t = 2$ sec. Find also (d) the phase angle, (e) the angular frequency, and (f) the period of the motion.

4. Two particles execute simple harmonic motion of the same amplitude and frequency along the same straight line. They pass one another when going in opposite directions each time their displacement is half their amplitude. What is the phase difference between them?

5. A block is on a horizontal surface which is moving horizontally with a simple harmonic motion of frequency two oscillations per second. The coefficient of static friction between block and plane is 0.50. How great can the amplitude be if the block does not slip along the surface?

6. A block is on a piston which is moving vertically with a simple harmonic motion of period 1 sec. (a) At what amplitude of motion will the block and piston separate? (b) If the piston has an amplitude of 5 cm, what is the maximum frequency for which the block and piston will be in contact continuously?

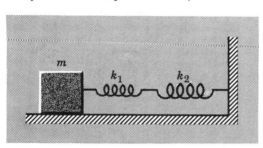

7. Two springs are joined and connected to a mass m as shown in Fig. 15–20. The surfaces are frictionless. If the springs separately have force constants k_1 and k_2, show that the frequency of oscillation of m is

$$f = \frac{1}{2\pi} \sqrt{\frac{k_1 k_2}{(k_1 + k_2)m}}.$$

Fig. 15–20

(The electrical analog of this system is a parallel connection of two capacitors.)

8. The springs are now attached to m and to fixed supports as shown in Fig. 15–21. Show that the frequency of oscillation in this case is

$$f = \frac{1}{2\pi} \sqrt{\frac{k_1 + k_2}{m}}.$$

(The electrical analog of this system is a series combination of two capacitors.)

9. The vibration frequencies of atoms in solids at normal temperatures are of the order 10^{13}/sec. Imagine the atoms to be connected

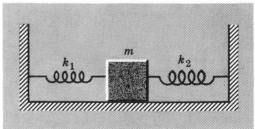

Fig. 15–21

to one another by springs. Suppose that a single silver atom vibrates with this frequency and that all the other atoms are at rest. Then compute the force constant of a single spring. One mole of silver has a mass of 108 gm and contains 6.02 × 10²³ atoms.

10. The end of one of the prongs of a tuning fork which executes simple harmonic motion of frequency 1000 per second has an amplitude of 0.40 mm. Neglect damping and find (a) the maximum acceleration and maximum speed of the end of the prong, and (b) the speed and acceleration of the end of the prong when it has a displacement 0.20 mm.

11. A spring of force constant 19.6 nt/meters hangs vertically. A body of mass 0.2 kg is attached to its free end and then released. Assume that the spring was unstretched before the body was released and find how far below the initial position the body descends. Find also the frequency and amplitude of the resulting simple harmonic motion.

12. An automobile can be considered to be mounted on a spring as far as vertical oscillations are concerned. The springs of a certain car are adjusted so that the vibrations have a frequency of 3.0 per second. What is the spring's force constant if the car weighs 3200 lb? What will the vibration frequency be if five passengers, averaging 100 lb each, ride in the car?

13. The scale of a spring balance reading from 0 to 32 lb is 4 in. long. A package suspended from the balance is found to oscillate vertically with a frequency of 2.0 oscillations per second. How much does the package weigh?

14. Start from Eq. 15–14 for the conservation of energy (with $\frac{1}{2}kA^2 = E$) and obtain the displacement as a function of the time by integration of Eq. 15–15. Compare with Eq. 15–10.

15. When the displacement is one-half the amplitude, what fraction of the total energy is kinetic and what fraction is potential in simple harmonic motion? At what displacement is the energy half kinetic and half potential?

16. (a) Prove that in simple harmonic motion the average potential energy equals the average kinetic energy when the average is taken with respect to time over one period of the motion, and that each average equals $\frac{1}{4}kA^2$. (See Fig. 15–6a.) (b) Prove that when the average is taken with respect to position over one cycle, the average potential energy equals $\frac{1}{6}kA^2$ and the average kinetic energy equals $\frac{1}{3}kA^2$. (See Fig. 15–6b.) (c) Explain physically why the two results above (a and b) are different.

17. (a) Show that the general relation for the period or frequency of any simple harmonic motion is

$$T = 2\pi \sqrt{\frac{x}{a}} \qquad f = \frac{1}{2\pi} \sqrt{-\frac{a}{x}}.$$

(b) Show that the general relation for the period or frequency of any simple angular harmonic motion is

$$T = 2\pi \sqrt{-\frac{\theta}{\alpha}} \qquad f = \frac{1}{2\pi} \sqrt{-\frac{\alpha}{\theta}}.$$

18. A simple pendulum of length 1.00 meter makes 100 complete oscillations in 204 sec at a certain location. What is the value of the acceleration of gravity at this point?

19. What is the length of a simple pendulum whose period is exactly 1 sec at a point where $g = 32.2$ ft/sec²?

20. Show that the maximum tension in the string of a simple pendulum, when the amplitude θ_m is small, is $mg(1 + \theta_m^2)$. At what position of the pendulum is the tension a maximum?

21. (a) What is the frequency of a simple pendulum 2 meters long? (b) Assuming small amplitudes, what would its frequency be in an elevator accelerating upward at a rate of 2.0 meters/sec²? (c) What would its frequency be in free fall?

22. A uniform board of length L is balanced on a fixed horizontal cylinder of radius a, such that the length of board is perpendicular to the cylinder axis. The plank is set rocking without slipping. (a) Show that the motion is simple harmonic if the amplitude is small. (b) Find the period of motion.

23. What is the period of a pendulum formed by pivoting a meter stick so that it is free to rotate about a horizontal axis passing through its end? Through the 75-cm mark? Through the 60-cm mark?

24. Show that if a uniform stick of length l is mounted so as to rotate about a horizontal axis perpendicular to the stick and at a distance d from the center of mass, the period has a *minimum* value when $d = l/\sqrt{12} = 0.289l$.

25. When a man stands on the end of a diving board, the equilibrium position of the end is lowered a distance h. Neglect the mass of the board compared to the man and show that when the board oscillates with the man on its end, its frequency will be equal to that of a simple pendulum of length h.

26. Electrons in an oscilloscope are deflected by two mutually perpendicular electric fields in such a way that at any time t the displacement is given by

$$x = A \cos \omega t, \qquad y = A \cos (\omega t + \alpha).$$

(a) Describe the path of the electrons and determine its equation when $\alpha = 0°$. (b) When $\alpha = 30°$. (c) When $\alpha = 90°$.

27. A circular hoop of radius 2.0 ft and weight 8.0 lb is suspended on a horizontal nail. (a) What is its frequency of oscillation for small displacements from equilibrium? (b) What is the length of the equivalent simple pendulum?

28. The balance wheel of a watch vibrates with an angular amplitude of π radians and a period of 0.5 sec. Find (a) the maximum angular speed of the wheel, (b) the angular speed of the wheel when its displacement is $\pi/2$ radians, and (c) the angular acceleration of the wheel when its displacement is $\pi/4$ radians.

29. A solid sphere of mass 2.0 kg and diameter 0.3 meter is suspended on a wire. Find the period of angular oscillation for small displacements if the torque required to twist the wire is 6.0×10^{-3} nt-m/radian.

30. If the mass of a spring m_s is not negligible compared to the mass m of the object suspended from it, the period of motion is approximately

$$T = 2\pi \sqrt{\left(m + \frac{m_s}{3}\right) \Big/ k}.$$

Derive this result. Notice that different parts of the spring take part in the motion to different degrees, but the effect is the same as if one-third the mass of the spring were added to the suspended object and the spring then considered massless. Make the approximation that the spring stretches uniformly along its length as it vibrates, just as a massless spring does.

Gravitation

CHAPTER 16

16-1 Historical Introduction

Until the seventeenth century the tendency of a body to fall toward the earth, that is, its weight, was regarded as an inherent property of all bodies needing no further explanation. That the weight of a body should be regarded as a force of attraction between the earth and that body was an idea that occurred to Newton and some of his contemporaries, notably Robert Hooke.

The laws governing celestial motions were regarded as quite different from those governing the motions of bodies on the earth. The motion of the heavenly bodies, particularly the planets and the sun, was a subject of much active interest at this time. This subject was discussed by students of natural philosophy at Cambridge in 1664. In 1665, the plague broke out. School was suspended and the students were sent home. One of them was Isaac Newton, then a 23-year-old "scholar of the college."

At home in Woolsthorpe, Newton continued to think about these questions. Apparently he was inspired as he saw an apple fall to the earth in the orchard.* It occurred to him that the same force of gravitation which attracts the apple to the earth might also attract the moon to the earth. Newton thought that the centripetal acceleration of the moon in its orbit and the downward acceleration of a body on the earth might have the same origin

---

* In a biography of Newton written in 1752 by his friend Stukeley, the author writes of having tea with Newton in a garden under some apple trees, when Newton said that the setting was the same as when he got the idea of gravitation. "It was occasioned by the fall of an apple, as he sat in a contemplative mood . . . ," writes Stukeley.

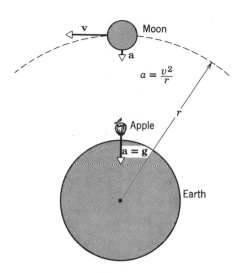

Fig. 16-1 Both the moon and the apple are accelerated toward the center of the earth under the influence of gravity. The difference in their motions arises because the moon has a tangential velocity **v** whereas the apple does not.

(Fig. 16–1). The very idea that celestial motions and terrestrial motions were subject to similar laws was a break with tradition.

The acceleration of the moon toward the earth can be computed from its period of revolution and the radius of its orbit. We obtain 0.00894 ft/sec^2 (see Example 4, Chapter 4). This value is about 3600 times smaller than g, the acceleration due to gravity on the surface of the earth. Newton sought to account for this difference by assuming that the acceleration of a falling body is inversely proportional to the square of its distance from the earth.

The question of what we mean by "distance from the earth" arises immediately. Newton regarded every particle of the earth as contributing to the gravitational attraction it had on other bodies. The distance and direction of particles of the earth from some object are different for each particle. Newton made the daring assumption that the earth could be treated for such purposes as if all the mass were concentrated at its center.

We could treat the earth as a particle with respect to the sun, for example. It is not obvious at all, however, that we could safely treat the earth as a particle with respect to an apple located only a few feet above its surface. On this assumption, however, a falling body near the earth's surface is a distance of one earth radius from the center of the earth, or 4000 miles. The moon is about 240,000 miles away. The inverse square of the ratio of these distances is $(4000/240,000)^2 = 1/3600$, in agreement with the ratio of the accelerations of the moon and apple.

It is believed that Newton made these calculations in 1666. To quote him,

And in the same year (1666) I began to think of gravity extending to the orb of the moon. . . . I deduced that the forces which keep the planets in their Orbs must [be] reciprocally as the squares of their distances from the centers about which they revolve: and thereby compared the force requisite to keep the Moon in her Orb with the force of gravity at the surface of the earth and found them answer pretty nearly.

His results were not published until 1687, however, when his *Principia Mathematica* appeared. The reason is thought to be that he was not satisfied at first that he could prove his basic assumption about the earth's acting as a mass particle for objects outside it.* Before he could solve this problem exactly, Newton had to invent calculus. His proof will be given in Section 16–6.

The *force* on the moon and on the apple depends on the mass of the moon and the mass of the apple, respectively, as well as on that of the earth. Hence, Newton assumed that a gravitational force depended on the masses of the attracting bodies as well as inversely on the square of their distance of separation. He then generalized his concept of gravitational attraction into a law of universal gravitation. He thought that all bodies, no matter where they were located, exerted forces of gravitational attraction upon one another. In order to discover the exact nature of this attractive force, he had to consider bodies of various different masses at significantly different distances from one another. He could not change the distance between the center of the earth and a body on the earth very appreciably, however. It was for this reason that he first compared the motion of the moon and a body on earth. The force between different macroscopic bodies on the earth was so small that it had not yet been detected. Newton apparently realized that this force was small and easily masked by frictional or other forces. Hence, he next turned his attention to the motion of the planets in an attempt to confirm his ideas.

The earliest scientific attempts to understand the solar system were made by the Greeks. A detailed description of the conclusions of Greek astronomy was given by Ptolemy (second century). His system is known as the Ptolemaic, or geocentric, theory. It assumes that the earth is stationary at the center of the universe, with the sun, moon, planets, and stars all revolving about the earth in complex orbits. This theory was accepted for almost fifteen centuries and greatly influenced philosophy and literature as well as science. However, the theory was quite complex and could not quantitatively account for an increasing number of observations. In the sixteenth century Copernicus suggested that a simpler description of celestial motions could be given by assuming that the sun was at rest at the center of the universe. In the Copernican or heliocentric theory, the earth was a planet rotating on its axis and revolving about the sun, and the other planets had similar motions (Fig. 16–2).

The growing controversy over the two theories stimulated astronomers to obtain more accurate observational data. Such data were compiled by Tycho Brahe (1546–1601), who was the last great astronomer to make ob-

---

* Some students of history believe that he merely wished to avoid controversy. The publication of his *Theory of Light and Colors* had involved him in bitter arguments. Newton was a shy and introspective man. Bertrand Russell writes of Newton, "If he had encountered the sort of opposition with which Galileo had to contend, it is probable that he would never have published a line." It was Halley, a devoted friend with a great interest in celestial mechanics, who persuaded Newton to publish the *Principia*.

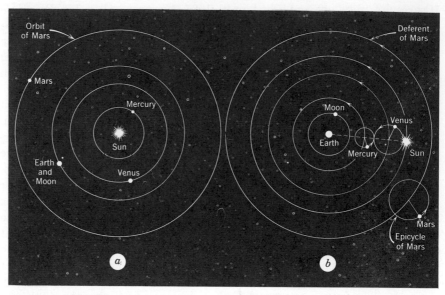

Fig. 16–2 (a) The Copernican view of the solar system is illustrated. The planets move in concentric orbits with the sun at the center. (b) Ptolemaic view of the solar system. Each planet undergoes two simultaneous circular motions. For example, Mars travels about an epicycle while the center of the epicycle travels along a deferent. The earth is at the center of the system. Only the moon and sun have no epicycles. Contrast the simplicity of the Copernican system with the complexity of the Ptolemaic.

servations without the use of a telescope.* His data on planetary motions were analyzed and interpreted for about twenty years by Johannes Kepler (1571–1630), who had been Brahe's assistant. Kepler found important regularities in the motion of the planets. These regularities are known as *Kepler's three laws of planetary motion*.

1. All planets move in elliptical orbits having the sun as one focus (the law of orbits).

2. A line joining any planet to the sun sweeps out equal areas in equal times (the law of areas).

3. The square of the period of any planet about the sun is proportional to the cube of the planet's mean distance from the sun (the law of periods).

Kepler's laws lent strong support to the Copernican theory. They showed the great simplicity with which planetary motions could be described when the sun was taken as the reference body. However, these laws were empirical; they simply described the observed motion of the planets without any theoretical interpretation. Kepler had no concept of force as a cause of

---

* A telescope was invented in 1609 by Galileo. With it he later discovered the moons of Jupiter and the phases of Venus. Galileo was a strong advocate of the Copernican theory and used his observations to argue in its behalf. Newton, incidentally, also invented a telescope, the reflecting type.

such regularities. In fact, the concept of force was not yet clearly formulated. It was, therefore, a great triumph for Newton's ideas that he could *derive* Kepler's laws from his laws of motion and his law of gravitation. Newton's law of gravitation in this case required each planet to be attracted toward the sun with a force proportional to the mass of the planet and inversely proportional to the square of its distance from the sun.

In this way Newton was able to account for the motion of the planets in the solar system and of bodies falling near the surface of the earth with one common concept. He thereby synthesized into one theory the previously separate sciences of terrestrial mechanics and celestial mechanics. The real scientific significance of Copernicus' work lies in the fact that the heliocentric theory opened the way for this synthesis.* Subsequently, on the assumption that the earth rotates and revolves about the sun, it became possible to explain such diverse phenomena as the daily and the annual apparent motion of the stars, the flattening of the earth from a spherical shape, the behavior of the tradewinds, and many other things that could not have been tied together so simply in a geocentric theory.

In the following sections we consider the exact nature of the law of universal gravitation and its consequences.

16–2   The Law of Universal Gravitation

The force between any two mass particles having masses m_1 and m_2 separated by a distance r is an attraction acting along the line joining the particles and has the magnitude

$$F = G\frac{m_1 m_2}{r^2},$$

(16–1)

where G is a universal constant having the same value for all pairs of particles.

This is Newton's law of universal gravitation. It is important to stress at once many features of this law in order that we understand it clearly.

First of all, the gravitational forces between two particles are an action-reaction pair. The first particle exerts a force on the second particle that is directed toward the first particle along the line joining the two. Likewise, the second particle exerts a force on the first particle that is directed toward the second particle along the line joining the two. These forces are equal in magnitude but oppositely directed.

The universal constant G must not be confused with the **g** which is the acceleration of a body arising from the earth's gravitational pull on it. The constant G has the dimensions $(L^3)/(MT^2)$ and is a number; **g** has the dimensions $(L)/(T^2)$, is a vector, and is neither universal nor constant.

Notice that Newton's law of universal gravitation is not a defining equation for any of the physical quantities (force, mass, or length) contained in it.

---

* Newton would have been the first to insist that his work was the culmination of the work of others. He once said in a letter to Robert Hooke, "If I have seen further [than you] it is by standing upon the shoulders of Giants." Among these giants we must certainly include Galileo and Kepler.

The concept of force is defined in developing the second law. How the actual force in any particular situation depends on other measurable quantities is determined by physical laws deduced from observation. The law of universal gravitation is such a law. The constant G must be determined from experiment. Once G is determined for a given pair of bodies, we can use that value in the law of gravitation to determine the gravitational forces between any other pair of bodies.

Notice also that Eq. 16–1 expresses the force between mass *particles*. If we want to determine the force between real extended bodies, as for example the earth and the moon, we must regard each body as decomposed into particles. Then the interaction between all particles must be computed. Integral calculus makes such a calculation possible. Newton's motive in developing the calculus arose in part from a desire to solve such problems. In general, it is incorrect to assume that all the mass of a body can be concentrated at its center of mass for gravitational purposes. This assumption is correct for uniform spheres, however, a result that we shall use often and prove in Section 16–6.

Implicit in the law of universal gravitation is the idea that the gravitational force between two particles is completely independent of the presence of other bodies or the properties of the intervening space. The correctness of this idea depends on the correctness of the deductions using it and has so far been borne out. This fact has been used by some to rule out "gravity screens."

16–3   The Constant of Universal Gravitation, G

To determine the value of G it is necessary to measure the force of attraction between two known masses. The first accurate measurement was made by Lord Cavendish in 1798. Significant improvements were made by Poynting and Boys in the nineteenth century. The present accepted value of G was obtained by P. R. Heyl and P. Chizanowski at the U. S. National Bureau of Standards in 1942. This value is

$$G = 6.673 \times 10^{-11}\,\text{nt-m}^2/\text{kg}^2,$$

accurate to within 0.003×10^{-11} nt-m^2/kg^2. In the British engineering system this value is 3.436×10^{-8} lb-ft^2/slug^2.

The constant G can be determined by the maximum deflection method illustrated in Fig. 16–3. Two small balls, each of mass m, are attached to the ends of a light rod. This rigid "dumbbell" is suspended in a horizontal position by a fine vertical fiber. Two large balls each of mass M are placed near the ends of the dumbbell on opposite sides. When the large masses are in the positions A and B, the small masses are attracted by the law of gravitation, and a torque is exerted on the dumbbell rotating it counterclockwise. When the large masses are in the positions A' and B', the dumbbell rotates clockwise. The fiber opposes these torques as it is twisted. The angle θ

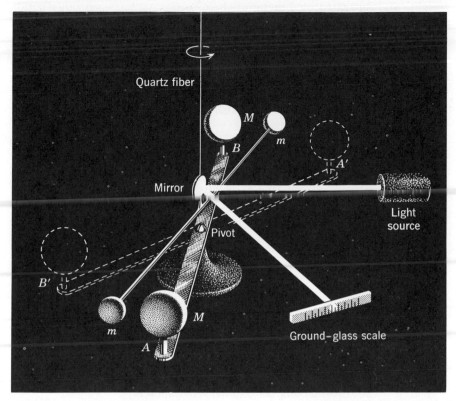

Fig. 16-3 The Cavendish balance, used for experimental verification of Newton's law of universal gravitation. Masses m,m are suspended from a fiber. Masses M,M can rotate on a stationary support. An image of the lamp filament is reflected by the mirror attached to m,m onto the scale so that any rotation of m,m can be measured.

through which the fiber is twisted when the balls are moved from one position to the other is measured by observing the deflection of a beam of light reflected from the small mirror attached to it. If the masses and their distances of separation and the torsion constant of the fiber are known, we can calculate G from the measured angle of twist. The force of attraction is very small so that the fiber must have an extremely small torsion constant if we are to obtain a detectable twist. In Example 1 at the end of this section some data are given from which G can be calculated.

The masses in the Cavendish balance of Fig. 16-3 are, of course, not particles but extended objects. Since they are uniform spheres, however, they act gravitationally as though all their mass were concentrated at their centers (Section 16-6).

Because G is so small, the gravitational forces between bodies on the earth's surface are extremely small and can be neglected for ordinary purposes. For example, two spherical objects each having a mass of 100 kg (about 220-lb weight) and separated by 1 meter at their centers attract each other with a force

$$F = \frac{Gm_1m_2}{r^2} = \frac{(6.67 \times 10^{-11}) \times (10^2) \times (10^2)}{(1)^2} \text{ nt}$$

$$= 6.67 \times 10^{-7} \text{ nt}$$

or about 1.5×10^{-7} lb! The Cavendish experiment must be a very delicate one indeed.

The large gravitational force which the earth exerts on all bodies near its surface is due to the extremely large mass of the earth. In fact, we can determine the mass of the earth from the law of universal gravitation and the value of G calculated from the Cavendish experiment. For this reason Cavendish is said to have been the first person to "weigh" the earth. Consider the earth, mass M_e, and an object on its surface of mass m. The force of attraction is given either by

$$F = mg$$

or by

$$F = \frac{GmM_e}{R_e^2}.$$

Here R_e is the radius of the earth, which is the separation of the two bodies, and g is the acceleration due to gravity at the earth's surface. Combining these equations we obtain

$$M_e = \frac{g}{G} R_e^2 = \frac{(9.80 \text{ meters/sec}^2)\,(6.37 \times 10^6 \text{ meters})^2}{6.67 \times 10^{-11} \text{ nt-m}^2/\text{kg}^2} = 5.97 \times 10^{24} \text{ kg}$$

or 6.6×10^{21} tons   "weight."

If we were to divide the total mass of the earth by its total volume, we would obtain the average density of the earth. This turns out to be 5.5 gm/cm^3, or about 5.5 times the density of water. The average density of the rock on the earth's surface is much less than this value. We can conclude that the interior of the earth contains material of density greater than 5.5 gm/cm^3. From the Cavendish experiment we have obtained information about the nature of the earth's core! (See Question 6 and Problem 28.)

▶ **Example 1.** Let the small spheres of Fig. 16–3 each have a mass of 10.0 gm and let the light rod be 50.0 cm long. The period of torsional oscillation of this system is found to be 769 sec. Then two large fixed spheres each of mass 10.0 kg are placed near each suspended sphere so as to produce the maximum torsion. The angular deflection of the suspended rod is then 4.00×10^{-3} radian and the distance between centers of the large and small spheres is 10.0 cm. Calculate the universal constant of gravitation G from these data.

The period of torsional oscillation is given by Eq. 15–21,

$$T = 2\pi \sqrt{\frac{I}{\kappa}}.$$

For the rigid dumbbell, neglecting the contribution of the light rod,

$$I = \Sigma \, mr^2 = (10.0 \text{ gm})(25.0 \text{ cm})^2 + (10.0 \text{ gm})(25.0 \text{ cm})^2$$

or

$$I = 1.25 \times 10^{-3} \text{ kg-m}^2.$$

With $T = 769$ sec, we can obtain the torsional constant κ as

$$\kappa = \frac{4\pi^2 I}{T^2} = \frac{(4\pi^2)(1.25 \times 10^{-3} \text{ kg-m}^2)}{(769 \text{ sec})^2} = 8.34 \times 10^{-8} \text{ kg-m}^2/\text{sec}^2.$$

The relation between the applied torque and the angle of twist is $\tau = \kappa\theta$. We now know κ and the value of θ at maximum deflection.

The torque arises from the gravitational forces exerted by the large spheres on the small ones. This torque will be a maximum for a given separation when the line joining the centers of these spheres is at right angles to the rod. The force on *each* small sphere is

$$F = \frac{GMm}{r^2},$$

and the moment arm for each force is half the length of the rod ($l/2$). Then,

$$\text{torque} = \text{force} \times \text{moment arm}$$

or

$$\tau = 2 \, \frac{GMm}{r^2} \frac{l}{2}.$$

Combining this with

$$\tau = \kappa\theta,$$

we obtain

$$G = \frac{\kappa\theta r^2}{Mml} = \frac{(8.34 \times 10^{-8} \text{ kg-m}^2/\text{sec}^2)(4.00 \times 10^{-3} \text{ radian})(0.100 \text{ meter})^2}{(10.0 \text{ kg})(0.0100 \text{ kg})(0.500 \text{ meter})}$$

$$= 6.67 \times 10^{-11} \text{ nt-m}^2/\text{kg}^2.$$

Notice that we have neglected the interaction of each large sphere with the small sphere farthest from it. Does this affect our calculation? ◀

16-4   Inertial and Gravitational Mass

The gravitational force on a body is proportional to its mass. This proportionality between gravitational force and mass is the reason we ordinarily consider the theory of gravitation to be a branch of mechanics, whereas theories of other kinds of force (electromagnetic, nuclear, etc.) may not be.

An important consequence of this proportionality is that we can measure a mass by measuring the gravitational force on it. This can be done by the use of a spring balance or by comparing the gravitational force on one mass with that on a standard mass, as in a balance; in other words we can determine the mass of a body by weighing it. This gives us a more practical and more convenient method of measuring mass than is given by our original definition of mass (Section 5-4).

The question arises whether these two methods really measure the same property. The word mass has been used in two quite different experimental situations. For example, if we try to push a block of ice from rest along a horizontal frictionless surface, we notice that it requires some effort. The block seems to be inert and tends to stay at rest, or if it is moving it tends to keep moving. Gravity does not enter here at all. It would take the same effort to accelerate the block of ice in gravity-free space. It is the mass of the block which makes it necessary to exert a force to change its motion. This is the mass occurring in $\mathbf{F} = m\mathbf{a}$ in our original experiments in dynamics. We call this mass m the *inertial mass*. Now there is a different situation which involves the mass of the block. For example, it requires effort just to hold the block up in the air at rest above the earth. If we do not support it, the block will fall to the earth with accelerated motion. The force required to hold up the block is equal in magnitude to the force of gravitational attraction between it and the earth. Here inertia plays no role whatever; the property of material bodies, that they are attracted to other objects such as the earth, does play a role. The force is given by

$$F = G\frac{m'M_e}{R_e{}^2},$$

where m' is the *gravitational mass* of the block. *Are the gravitational mass m' and the inertial mass m of the block really the same?* Let us look more carefully at this.

Consider two particles A and B of gravitational masses m_A' and m_B' acted on by a third particle C of gravitational mass m_C'. Let the third particle be an equal distance r from the other two. Then, the gravitational force exerted on A by C is

$$F_{AC} = G\frac{m_A'm_C'}{r^2},$$

and the gravitational force exerted on B by C is

$$F_{BC} = G\frac{m_B'm_C'}{r^2}.$$

The ratio of the gravitational forces on A and B is the ratio of their gravitational masses; that is,

$$\frac{F_{AC}}{F_{BC}} = \frac{m_A'}{m_B'}.$$

Now suppose that the third body C is the earth. Then F_{AC} and F_{BC} are what we have called the *weights* of bodies A and B. Hence,

$$\frac{W_A}{W_B} = \frac{m_A'}{m_B'}.$$

Therefore, the law of universal gravitation contains within it the result that the weights of various bodies, at the same place on the earth, are exactly proportional to their *gravitational masses*.

Now suppose we measure the inertial masses m_A and m_B of the particles A and B by dynamical experiments. Having done this, we then let these particles fall to the earth from a given place and measure their accelerations. We find experimentally that objects of different *inertial masses* all fall with the same acceleration g arising from the earth's gravitational pull. But the earth's gravitational pull on these bodies are their weights, so that using the second law of motion we obtain

$$W_A = m_A g,$$

$$W_B = m_B g$$

or

$$\frac{W_A}{W_B} = \frac{m_A}{m_B}.$$

In other words the weights of bodies at the same place on the earth are exactly proportional to their *inertial masses*, as well. Hence, inertial mass and gravitational mass are at least proportional to one another. In fact, they appear to be identical.

Newton devised an experiment to test directly the apparent equivalence of inertial and gravitational mass. If we go back (Section 15–5) and look up the derivation of the period of a simple pendulum, we find that the period (for small angles) was given by

$$T = 2\pi \sqrt{\frac{ml}{m'g}},$$

where m in the numerator refers to the inertial mass of the pendulum bob and m' in the denominator is the gravitational mass of the pendulum bob, such that $m'g$ gives the gravitational pull on the bob. Only if we assume that m equals m', as we did there, do we obtain the expression

$$T = 2\pi \sqrt{\frac{l}{g}}$$

for the period. Newton made a pendulum bob in the form of a thin shell. Into this hollow bob he put different substances, being careful always to have the same *weight* of substance as determined by a balance. Hence, in all cases the force on the pendulum was the same at the same angle. Because the external shape of the bob was always the same, even the air resistance on the moving pendulum was the same. As one substance replaced another inside the bob, any difference in acceleration could only be due to a difference in the *inertial* mass. Such a difference would show up by a change in the period of the pendulum. But in all cases Newton found the period of the pendulum to be the same, always given by $T = 2\pi\sqrt{l/g}$. Hence, he concluded that $m = m'$ and that inertial and gravitational masses are equivalent.

In 1909, Eötvös devised an apparatus which could detect a difference of 1 part in 100 million in gravitational force. He found that equal inertial masses always experienced equal gravitational forces within the accuracy of his apparatus.

In classical physics the equivalence of gravitational and inertial mass was looked upon as a remarkable accident having no deep significance. But in modern physics this equivalence is regarded as a clue leading to a deeper understanding of gravitation. This was, in fact, an important clue leading to the development of the general theory of relativity.

16-5 Variations in Acceleration Due to Gravity

Up to this point we have taken the acceleration due to gravity, g, as a constant. From Newton's law of gravitation, however, it is apparent that g will vary with altitude, that is, with distance from the center of the earth. We have already pointed this out specifically in the moon-apple discussion. Let us compute the change in g that occurs as we proceed outward from the earth's surface. From Eq. 16-1,

$$F = G\frac{m_1 m_2}{r^2},$$

we obtain, on differentiating with respect to r,

$$dF = -2\frac{Gm_1 m_2}{r^3}\,dr.$$

Combining these two equations, we obtain

$$\frac{dF}{F} = -2\frac{dr}{r}.$$

Therefore, the fractional change in F is twice the fractional change in r. The minus sign indicates that the force decreases as the separation distance increases. If we let m_1 be the earth's mass and m_2 the object's mass, the gravitational force on the object attributable to the earth is

$$F = m_2 g$$

directed toward the earth. If we differentiate this expression, we obtain

$$dF = m_2 dg,$$

and on dividing this equation by the previous one we find that

$$\frac{dF}{F} = \frac{dg}{g} = -2\frac{dr}{r}. \tag{16-2}$$

For example, in going up 10 miles from the earth's surface, r changes from about 4000 miles to 4010 miles, a relative increase of $1/400$. Therefore,* g must change by about $-1/200$ over this distance, or from about 980 cm/sec^2 to about 975 cm/sec^2. Hence, g is really very nearly constant near the earth's surface. Its variation with altitude at 45° latitude is shown in Table 16–1.

Table 16–1

VARIATION OF g WITH ALTITUDE AT 45° LATITUDE

Altitude, ft	g, ft/sec^2	Altitude, meter	g, meters/sec^2
0	32.174	0	9.806
1,000	32.170	1,000	9.803
4,000	32.161	4,000	9.794
16,000	32.124	8,000	9.782
60,000	31.988	16,000	9.757
100,000	31.865	32,000	9.708
500,000	30.631	100,000	9.598

Because the earth is actually slightly ellipsoidal, rather than spherical, there is also a small gradual change in g with latitude. The distance from sea level to the center of the earth becomes less as we proceed from the equator to the poles. The variation of g with latitude at sea level is shown in Table 16–2.

---

* Equation 16–2 is a differential expression which is valid to a good approximation, even when dr is replaced by a finite change Δr, provided only that $\Delta r/r$ is very small.

Table 16-2

VARIATION OF g WITH LATITUDE AT SEA LEVEL

Latitude	Ft/sec²	Meters/sec²
0°	32.0878	9.78039
10°	32.0929	9.78195
20°	32.1076	9.78641
30°	32.1302	9.79329
40°	32.1578	9.80171
50°	32.1873	9.81071
60°	32.2151	9.81918
70°	32.2377	9.82608
80°	32.2525	9.83059
90°	32.2577	9.83217

Actually the values of g given in Tables 16-1 and 16-2 are only mean values because there are local variations of small magnitude owing to the varying nature of the underlying earth at different locations of a given latitude. These variations are used in the petroleum industry to help locate oil deposits.

The rotation of the earth really accounts for a large part of the variation in the apparent value of g with latitude. This is discussed in the following example.

▶ **Example 2.** Figure 16-4 is a schematic view of the earth looking down on the North Pole. In it we show an enlarged view of a body of mass m hanging from a spring balance at the equator. The forces on this body are the upward pull of the spring balance, w, which is the apparent weight of the body, and the downward pull of the earth's gravitational attraction, $F = GmM_e/R_e^2$. This body is not in equilibrium because it experiences a centripetal acceleration a_R as it rotates with the earth. There must, therefore, be a net force acting on the body toward the center of the earth. Consequently, the force F of gravitational attraction (the true weight of the body) must exceed the upward pull of the balance w (the apparent weight of the body).

From the second law of motion we obtain

$$F - w = ma_R,$$

$$\frac{GM_em}{R_e^2} - mg = ma_R,$$

$$g = \frac{GM_e}{R_e^2} - a_R \qquad \text{at the equator.}$$

At the poles $a_R = 0$ so that

$$g = \frac{GM_e}{R_e^2} \qquad \text{at the poles.}$$

This is the value of g we would obtain anywhere were the rotation of the earth to be neglected.

(a) *(b)*

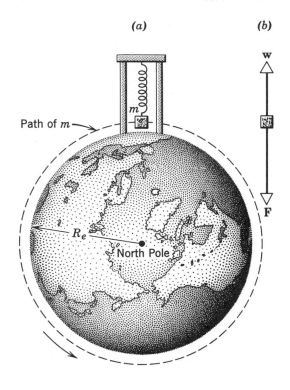

Path of m

Fig. 16-4 Example 2. Effect of the earth's rotation on the weight of a body as measured by a spring balance.

R_e

North Pole

Actually the centripetal acceleration is not directed in toward the center of the earth other than at the equator. It is directed perpendicularly in toward the earth's axis of rotation at any given latitude. The detailed analysis is, therefore, really a two-dimensional one. However, the extreme case is at the equator. Then

$$a_R = \omega^2 R_e = \left(\frac{2\pi}{T}\right)^2 R_e = \frac{4\pi^2 R_e}{T^2},$$

in which ω is the angular speed of the earth's rotation, T is the period, and R is the radius of the earth. Using the values

$$R_e = 6.37 \times 10^6 \text{ meters},$$

$$T = 8.64 \times 10^4 \text{ sec},$$

we obtain $\qquad a_R = 0.0336 \text{ meters/sec}^2.$

Referring to Table 16-2, we see that this effect is enough to account for more than half the difference between the observed values of g at low and high latitudes. ◄

16-6 Gravitational Effect of a Spherical Distribution of Mass

We have already used the fact that a large sphere attracts particles outside it, just as though the mass of the sphere were concentrated at its center. Let us now prove this result.

Consider a uniformly dense spherical shell whose thickness t is small compared to its radius r (Fig. 16-5). We seek the gravitational force it exerts on an external particle P of mass m.

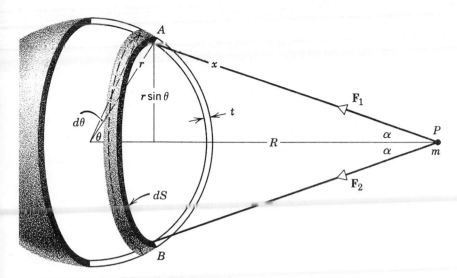

Fig. 16–5 Gravitational attraction of a section dS of a spherical shell of matter on m.

We assume that each small part (particle) of the shell exerts on P a force which is proportional to the mass of the small part, inversely proportional to the square of the distance between that part of the shell and P, and directed along the line joining them. We must then obtain the resultant force on P attributable to all parts of the spherical shell.

The small part of the shell at A attracts m with a force $\mathbf{F}_1$. A small part of equal mass at B attracts m with a force $\mathbf{F}_2$. The resultant of these two forces on m is $\mathbf{F}_1 + \mathbf{F}_2$. Notice, however, that the vertical components of these two forces cancel one another and that the horizontal components, $F_1 \cos \alpha$ and $F_2 \cos \alpha$, are equal. By dividing the spherical shell into pairs of particles like these, we can see at once that all transverse forces on m cancel in pairs. A small mass in the upper hemisphere exerts a force having an upward component on m that will annul the downward component of force exerted on m by an equal symmetrically located mass in the lower hemisphere of the shell. To find the resultant force on m arising from the shell, we need consider only horizontal components.

Let us take as our element of mass of the shell a circular strip labeled dS in the figure. Its length is $2\pi (r \sin \theta)$, its width is $r\, d\theta$, and its thickness is t. Hence, it has a volume

$$dV = 2\pi t r^2 \sin \theta \, d\theta.$$

Let us call the density ρ, so that the mass within the strip is

$$dM = \rho \, dV = 2\pi t \rho r^2 \sin \theta \, d\theta.$$

The force exerted by dM on the particle of mass m at P is horizontal and has the value

$$dF = G \frac{m \, dM}{x^2} \cos \alpha$$

$$= 2\pi G t \rho m r^2 \frac{\sin \theta \, d\theta}{x^2} \cos \alpha.$$

(16–3)

The variables x, α, and θ are related. From the figure we see that

$$\cos \alpha = \frac{R - r \cos \theta}{x}. \tag{16-4}$$

Since, by the law of cosines,

$$x^2 = R^2 + r^2 - 2Rr \cos \theta, \tag{16-5}$$

then

$$r \cos \theta = \frac{R^2 + r^2 - x^2}{2R}. \tag{16-6}$$

On differentiating Eq. 16–5, we obtain

$$2x \, dx = 2Rr \sin \theta \, d\theta$$

or

$$\sin \theta \, d\theta = \frac{x}{Rr} \, dx. \tag{16-7}$$

We now put Eq. 16–6 into Eq. 16–4 and then put Eqs. 16–4 and 16–7 into Eq. 16–3. As a result we eliminate θ and α and obtain

$$dF = \frac{\pi G t \rho m r}{R^2} \left(\frac{R^2 - r^2}{x^2} + 1 \right) dx.$$

This is the force exerted by the circular strip dS on the particle m.

We must now consider every element of mass in the shell and sum up over all the circular strips in the entire shell. This operation is an integration over the shell with respect to the variable x. But x ranges from a minimum value of $R - r$ to a maximum value $R + r$.

Since

$$\int_{R-r}^{R+r} \left(\frac{R^2 - r^2}{x^2} + 1 \right) dx = 4r,$$

we obtain the resultant force

$$F = \int_{R-r}^{R+r} dF = G \frac{(4\pi r^2 \rho t) m}{R^2} = G \frac{Mm}{R^2}, \tag{16-8}$$

where

$$M = 4\pi r^2 t \rho$$

is the total mass of the shell. This is exactly the same result we would obtain for the force between *particles* of mass M and m separated a distance R. We have proved, therefore, that *a uniformly dense spherical shell attracts an external mass point as if all its mass were concentrated at its center.*

A solid sphere can be regarded as composed of a large number of concentric shells. If each spherical shell has a uniform density, even though different shells may have different densities, the same result applies to the solid sphere. Hence, a body like the earth, the moon, or the sun, to the extent that they are such spheres, may be regarded gravitationally as point particles to bodies outside them.

Notice that our proof applies only to spheres and then only when the density is constant over the sphere or a function of radius alone.

An interesting result of some significance is the force exerted by a spherical shell on a particle *inside* it. This force is *zero*. To prove this we refer to Fig. 16–6, where m is shown inside the shell. Notice that R is now smaller than r. The limits of our integration over x are now $r - R$ to $R + r$. But

$$\int_{r-R}^{R+r} \left(\frac{R^2 - r^2}{x^2} + 1 \right) dx = 0,$$

so that $F = 0$.

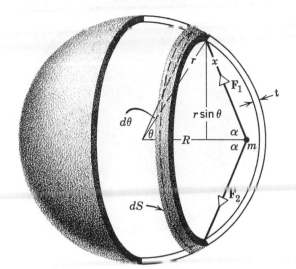

Fig. 16–6 Gravitational attraction of a section dS of a spherical shell of matter on m. Here m is inside the shell.

This result, although not at first obvious, is plausible because the mass elements of the shell on opposite sides of m now exert forces of opposite directions on m inside. The total annulment depends on the fact that the force varies precisely as an inverse square of the separation distance of two particles. (See Problem 8.) Important consequences of this result will be discussed in the chapters on electricity. There we shall see that the electrical force between charged particles also depends inversely on the square of the distance between them. A consequence of interest in gravitation is that the gravitational force exerted by the earth on a particle decreases as the particle goes deeper into the earth, *assuming a constant density for the earth,* for the portions of matter in shells external to the position of the particle exert no force on it, the force becoming zero at the center of the earth. Hence, g would be a maximum at the earth's surface and decrease both outward and inward from that point *if the earth had constant density.* Can you imagine a spherically symmetric distribution of the earth's mass which would not give this result? (See Problem 28.)

▶ **Example 3.** Suppose a tunnel could be dug through the earth from one side to the other along a diameter, as shown in Fig. 16–7.

(a) Show that the motion of a particle dropped into the tunnel is simple harmonic motion. Neglect all frictional forces and assume that the earth has a uniform density.

The gravitational attraction of the earth for the particle at a distance r from the center of the earth arises entirely from that portion of matter of the earth in shells internal to the position of the particle. The external shells exert no force on the particle. Let us assume that the earth's density is uniform at the value ρ. Then the mass inside a sphere of radius r is

$$M' = \rho V' = \rho \frac{4\pi r^3}{3}.$$

This mass can be treated as though it were concentrated at the center of the earth for gravitational purposes. Hence, the force on the particle of mass m is

$$F = \frac{-GM'm}{r^2}.$$

The minus sign indicates that the force is attractive and directed toward the center of the earth.

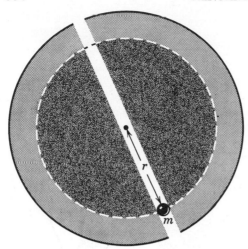

Fig. 16–7 Example 3. Particle moving in a tunnel through the earth.

Substituting for M', we obtain

$$F = -G\frac{(\rho 4\pi r^3)m}{3r^2} = -\left(G\rho\frac{4\pi m}{3}\right)r = -kr.$$

Here $G\rho 4\pi m/3$ is a constant, which we have called k. The force is, therefore, proportional to the displacement r but oppositely directed. This is exactly the criterion for simple harmonic motion.

(b) If mail were delivered through this chute, how much time would elapse between deposit at one end and delivery at the other end?

The period of this simple harmonic motion is

$$T = 2\pi\sqrt{\frac{m}{k}} = 2\pi\sqrt{\frac{3m}{G\rho 4\pi m}} = \sqrt{\frac{3\pi}{G\rho}}.$$

Let us take $\rho = 5.51 \times 10^3$ kg/meter^3 and $G = 6.67 \times 10^{-11}$ nt-m^2/kg. This gives

$$T = \sqrt{\frac{3\pi}{G\rho}} = \sqrt{\frac{3\pi}{(5.51 \times 10^3)(6.67 \times 10^{-11})}} \text{ sec} = 5050 \text{ sec} = 84.2 \text{ min}.$$

The time for delivery is one-half period, or about 42 min. Notice that this time is independent of the mass of the mail.

The earth does not really have a uniform density. Suppose ρ were some function of r, rather than a constant. What effect would this have on our problem? ◀

16–7 The Motion of Planets and Satellites

The motions of the bodies in the solar system can be deduced from the laws of motion and the law of universal gravitation. Let us consider a simplified picture which gives us good approximate answers. Let us assume that the orbits of the sun and planets are circles, rather than ellipses, and neglect the forces between planets, considering only the interaction between the sun and a given planet. This procedure will apply equally well to the motion of a satellite about a planet.

Consider two spherical bodies of masses M and m moving in circular orbits under the influence of each other's gravitational attraction. The center of mass of this system of two bodies lies along the line joining them at a point C such that $mr = MR$ (Fig. 16–8). If there are no external forces acting on this system, the center of mass has no acceleration. In this case we choose C to be the origin of our coordinate system. The large body of mass M moves in an orbit of constant radius R and the small body of mass m in an orbit of constant radius r, both having the same angular velocity ω. In order for this to happen, the gravitational force acting on each body must provide the necessary centripetal acceleration. Since these gravitational forces are simply an action-reaction pair, the centripetal forces must be equal but oppositely directed. That is, $m\omega^2 r$ (the magnitude of the centripetal force of M on m) must equal $M\omega^2 R$ (the magnitude of the centripetal force of m on M). That this is so follows at once, for $mr = MR$ so that $m\omega^2 r = M\omega^2 R$. The specific requirement, then, is that the gravitational force on either body must equal the centripetal force needed to keep it moving in its circular orbit, that is,

$$\frac{GMm}{(R + r)^2} = m\omega^2 r. \tag{16–9}$$

If one body has a much greater mass than the other, as in the case of the sun and a planet, its distance from the center of mass is much smaller than that of the other body. Let us therefore assume that R is negligible compared to r. Equation 16–9 then becomes

$$GM_s = \omega^2 r^3,$$

where M_s is the mass of the sun. If we express the angular velocity in terms

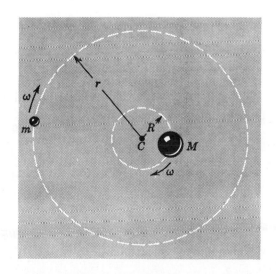

Fig. 16–8 Two bodies moving in circular orbits under the influence of each other's gravitational attraction. They both have the same angular velocity ω.

of the period of the revolution, $\omega = 2\pi/T$, we obtain

$$GM_s = \frac{4\pi^2 r^3}{T^2}.$$ (16-10)

This can be considered as the basic (approximate) equation of planetary motion. Let us consider some of its consequences.

One immediate consequence of Eq. 16–10 is that it predicts Kepler's third law of planetary motion, in the special case of circular orbits. For we can express Eq. 16–10 as

$$T^2 = \frac{4\pi^2}{GM_s} r^3.$$

Notice that the mass of the planet is not involved in this expression. Here, $4\pi^2/GM_s$ is a constant, the same for all planets.

When the period T and radius r of revolution are known for any planet, Eq. 16–10 can be used to determine the mass of the sun. For example, the earth's period is

$$T = 365 \text{ days} = 3.15 \times 10^7 \text{ sec},$$

and its orbital radius is

$$r = 93 \text{ million miles} = 1.5 \times 10^{11} \text{ meters}.$$

Hence,

$$M_s - \frac{4\pi^2 r^3}{GT^2} = \frac{(4\pi^2)(1.5 \times 10^{11} \text{ meters})^3}{(6.67 \times 10^{-11} \text{ nt-m}^2/\text{kg}^2)(3.15 \times 10^7 \text{ sec})^2} \cong 2.0 \times 10^{30} \text{ kg}.$$

The mass of the sun is thus about 300,000 times the mass of the earth. The error made in neglecting R compared to r is seen to be trivial, for

$$R = \frac{m}{M} r = \frac{1}{300,000} r \cong 300 \text{ miles}; \qquad \frac{R}{r} 100\% \cong \frac{1}{3000} \text{ of } 1\%.$$

In a similar manner we can determine the mass of the earth from the period and radius of the moon's orbit about the earth. (See Problem 16.)

If we know the mass of the sun M_s and the period of revolution T of any planet about it, we can determine the radius of the planet's orbit r from Eq. 16–10. Since the period is easily obtained from astronomical observations, this method of determining a planet's distance from the sun is fairly reliable.

Currently there is much work going into the construction and launching of artificial satellites of the earth. The relation between the period of revolution of such a satellite and its distance from the earth is given by Eq. 16–10 in which the mass of the earth M_e is substituted for M_s. (See Fig. 16–9.)

Kepler's second law of planetary motion must, of course, hold for circular orbits. In such orbits both ω and r are constant so that equal areas are

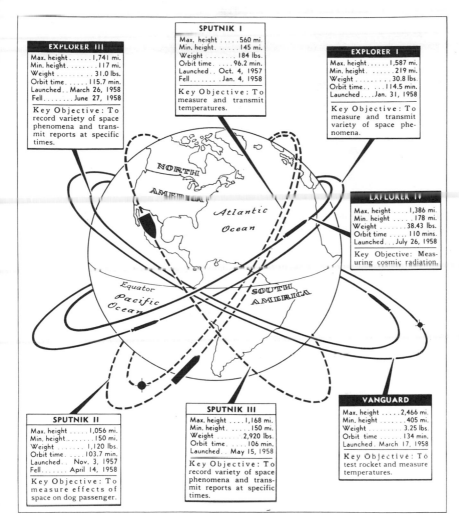

EXPLORER III

Max. height . . . . . 1,741 mi.
Min. height . . . . 117 mi.
Weight . . . . 31.0 lbs.
Orbit time . . . . . 115.7 min.
Launched . March 26, 1958
Fell . . . . June 27, 1958

Key Objective: To record variety of space phenomena and transmit reports at specific times.

SPUTNIK I

Max. height . . . . . 560 mi
Min. height . . . . . 145 mi.
Weight . . . . 184 lbs.
Orbit time . . . . . 96.2 min.
Launched . . Oct. 4, 1957
Fell . . . . Jan. 4, 1958

Key Objective: To measure and transmit temperatures.

EXPLORER I

Max. height . . . . . . 1,587 mi.
Min. height . . . . . . 219 mi.
Weight . . . . 30.8 lbs.
Orbit time . . . . 114.5 min.
Launched . . . . Jan. 31, 1958

Key Objective: To measure and transmit variety of space phenomena.

EXPLORER IV

Max. height . . . . 1,386 mi.
Min. height . . . . 178 mi.
Weight . . . . 38.43 lbs.
Orbit time . . . . . 110 mins.
Launched . . . July 26, 1958

Key Objective: Measuring cosmic radiation.

SPUTNIK II

Max. height . . . . . 1,056 mi.
Min. height . . . . 150 mi.
Weight . . . . 1,120 lbs.
Orbit time . . . . . 103.7 min.
Launched . . Nov. 3, 1957
Fell . . . . April 14, 1958

Key Objective: To measure effects of space on dog passenger.

SPUTNIK III

Max. height . . . . 1,168 mi.
Min. height . . . . . 150 mi.
Weight . . . . 2,920 lbs.
Orbit time . . . . 106 min.
Launched . . May 15, 1958

Key Objective: To record variety of space phenomena and transmit reports at specific times.

VANGUARD

Max. height . . . . . 2,466 mi.
Min. height . . . . 405 mi.
Weight . . . . 3.25 lbs.
Orbit time . . . . 134 min.
Launched . March 17, 1958

Key Objective: To test rocket and measure temperatures.

Fig. 16–9 Data on the first seven earth satellites. Maximum and minimum heights as well as the period are as of immediately after launching. (From *The New York Times*, August 3, 1958.)

swept out in equal times by the line joining a planet and the sun. For the exact elliptical orbits, however, or for any orbit in general, both r and ω will vary. Let us consider this case.

Figure 16–10 shows a particle revolving about C along some arbitrary path. The area swept out by the radius vector in a very short time interval Δt is shown shaded in the figure. This area, neglecting the small triangular region at the end, is one-half the base times the altitude or approximately $\frac{1}{2}(r\omega \, \Delta t) \cdot r$. This expression becomes more exact in the limit as $\Delta t \to 0$, the small triangle going to zero more rapidly than the large one. The rate at which area

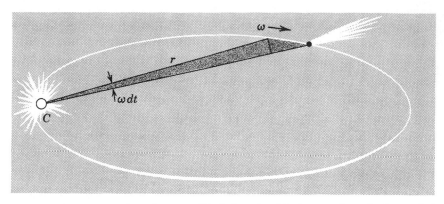

Fig. 16–10 A comet moving along an elliptical path with the sun C at the focus of the ellipse. In time dt the comet sweeps out an angle $d\theta = \omega\, dt$.

is being swept out instantaneously is, therefore,

$$\lim_{\Delta t \to 0} \frac{\frac{1}{2}(r\omega\, \Delta t)(r)}{\Delta t} = \frac{1}{2}\omega r^2.$$

But $m\omega r^2$ is simply the angular momentum of the particle about C. Hence, Kepler's second law, which requires that the rate of sweeping out of area, $\frac{1}{2}\omega r^2$, be constant, is entirely equivalent to the statement that *the angular momentum of any planet about the sun remains constant*. The angular momentum of the particle about C cannot be changed by a force on it directed toward C. Kepler's second law would, therefore, be valid for any *central force*, that is, any force directed toward the sun. The exact nature of this force—how it depends on distance of separation or other properties of the bodies—is not revealed by this law.

It is Kepler's first law that requires the gravitational force to depend exactly on the inverse square of the distance between two bodies, that is, on $1/r^2$. Only such a force, it turns out, can yield planetary orbits which are elliptical with the sun at one focus.

Newton's laws of motion and his law of universal gravitation are in almost complete agreement with astronomical observations.* In our calculation we considered the motion of a planet about the sun as a "two-body" problem. However, we saw that the motion of the sun could be neglected while retaining a high degree of accuracy because of the large ratio of solar mass to planetary mass. This reduced the problem to that of motion of one body about a center of force. If we had required greater accuracy, we would have had to include the sun's motion in our problem. In fact, for an exact treatment we would have to take into account the effect of other planets and satel-

---

* The major axis of the elliptical orbit of Mercury rotates slightly more than that predicted by Newtonian mechanics when the perturbing influence of other planets is included. This effect is accounted for in the theory of relativity.

lites on the motion of sun and planet. This "many-body" problem is quite formidable, but it can be solved by approximation methods to a high degree of accuracy. The results of such calculations are in excellent agreement with astronomical observations.

16–8   The Gravitational Field

A basic fact of gravitation is that two masses exert forces on one another. We can think of this as a direct interaction between the two mass particles, if we wish. This point of view is called *action-at-a-distance*, the particles interacting even though they are not in contact. Another point of view is the *field* concept which regards a mass particle as modifying the space around it in some way and setting up a *gravitational field*. This field then acts on any other mass particle in it, exerting the force of gravitational attraction on it. The field, therefore, plays an intermediate role in our thinking about the forces between mass particles. According to this view we have two separate parts to our problem. First, we must determine the field established by a given distribution of mass particles; and secondly, we must calculate the force that this field exerts on another mass particle placed in it.

For example, consider the earth as an isolated mass. If a body is now brought in the vicinity of the earth, a force is exerted on it. This force has a definite direction and magnitude at each point in space. The direction is radially in toward the center of the earth and the magnitude is mg. We can, therefore, associate with each point near the earth a vector $\mathbf{g}$ which is the acceleration that a body would experience if it were released at this point. We call $\mathbf{g}$ the *gravitational field strength* at the point in question. Since

$$\mathbf{g} = \frac{\mathbf{F}}{m}, \qquad (16\text{–}11)$$

we could define gravitational field strength at any point just as well as the gravitational force per unit mass at that point. We can calculate the force from the field simply by multiplying $\mathbf{g}$ by the mass m of the particle placed at any point.

The gravitational field is an example of a *vector field*, each point in this field having a vector associated with it. There are also scalar fields, such as the temperature field in a heat-conducting solid. The gravitational field is also an example of a *stationary field*, because the value of the field at a given point does not change with time.

The field concept is particularly useful, in fact indispensible, for understanding electromagnetic forces between moving electric charges. It has distinct advantages, both conceptually and in practice, over the action-at-a-distance concept. The field concept was not used in Newton's day. It was developed much later by Faraday for electromagnetism and only then applied to gravitation. Subsequently, this point of view was adopted for gravitation in the general theory of relativity. The chief purpose of introducing it here is to give the student an early familiarity with a concept that proves to be basic to all physical theory.

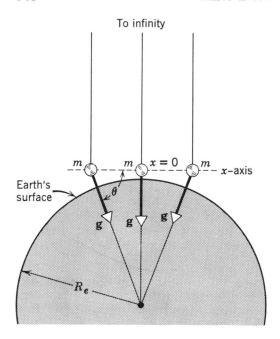

Fig. 16–11 Example 4. A simple pendulum m suspended at infinity.

▶ **Example 4.** In Chapter 15 we derived the formula for the period of a simple pendulum, $T = 2\pi \sqrt{l/g}$. Keeping in mind that the earth's gravitational field is not uniform over large distances, as was assumed for small distances, what is the longest period a simple pendulum could have in the vicinity of the earth's surface?

The formula $T = 2\pi \sqrt{l/g}$, although not applicable when g varies over the pendulum's path, suggests that we increase the length of the pendulum. Let us make the length infinite. The pendulum bob would then travel along the arc of a circle of infinite radius, that is, along a straight line, as shown in Fig. 16–11. The direction of the earth's gravitational field is everywhere radially in toward the center of the earth, so that its direction changes along the arc. Let us assume that the bob of mass m has an amplitude that is small compared to the radius of the earth. Then the bob is always a distance R_e, the earth's radius, from the center of the earth, to a good approximation. Then the force F on m is

$$F = \frac{GM_e m}{R_e^2} = mg,$$

where M_e is the mass of the earth. This force is directed toward the earth's center as shown. The component of this vector force along x, the line of motion of the bob, is

$$F_x = F \cos \theta = -F \frac{x}{R_e} = -\frac{GM_e m}{R_e^3} x,$$

where the minus sign indicates that the force is directed opposite to the displacement from $x = 0$. We can write this as

$$F_x = -kx,$$

where $k = GM_e m/R_e^3$, a constant.

The formula for the period of a simple harmonic oscillator is $T = 2\pi \sqrt{m/k}$. Hence,

$$T = 2\pi \sqrt{\frac{m}{k}} = 2\pi \sqrt{\frac{m}{GM_e m/R_e^3}} = 2\pi \sqrt{\frac{R_e}{GM_e/R_e^2}} = 2\pi \sqrt{\frac{R_e}{g}},$$

because g at the earth's surface equals GM_e/R_e^2. Putting in $R_e = 6.37 \times 10^6$ meters and $g = 9.80$ meters/sec^2, we obtain $T = 84$ min as the longest period of a simple pendulum in the vicinity of the earth's surface. (See Problem 10.) ◀

16-9   Gravitational Potential Energy

To calculate the gravitational potential energy of a particle we must compute the work done against the force of gravity in displacing the particle from a reference position to its given position. The reference position is arbitrary and was taken before (Section 8-3) to be the surface of the earth. This choice proved convenient when we assumed that gravity exerted a constant force on our particle. We have seen, however, that the force of gravity actually varies with position. In such cases the reference position is most conveniently taken as the force-free position. For example, in the motion of a particle on a horizontal spring (Section 8-3), the reference position for elastic potential energy was taken to be the force-free equilibrium position. In the gravitational case the force-free position is an infinite distance from the attracting center. Hence, *the gravitational potential energy of a particle will be taken to be zero when the particle is an infinite distance from the center of attraction.*

To determine the potential energy of a particle, $U(r)$, at some distance r from the center of attraction, we must compute the work done by some outside agent against gravity, $W_{\infty r}$, in bringing the particle in along a radial line from infinity to that point. The student should recall that the potential energy is taken as zero at infinity and that the difference in the potential energy at two points is simply the work done in moving a body from one point to the other (Section 8 3). Hence,

$$U(r) = W_{\infty r} = \int_{\infty}^{r} F \, dr,$$

$$= \int_{\infty}^{r} \frac{GMm}{r^2} \, dr = GMm \left[-\frac{1}{r} \right]_{\infty}^{r} = -\frac{GMm}{r}. \qquad (16\text{-}12)$$

The minus sign indicates that the potential energy is negative at any finite distance. This corresponds to the fact that the force is attractive: it takes positive work to separate bodies against attractive forces; these attractive forces do work on the bodies in drawing them closer together. To put it another way, the potential energy decreases (from zero) as the particle is brought in (from infinity); it increases from some negative value as the particle is moved out (to some less negative value).

The path taken by the particle is actually irrelevant. If instead of bringing the particle in from infinity along a radial line we choose some arbitrary path, the same result holds as long as the end points of the paths coincide.

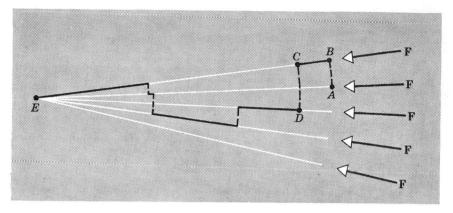

Fig. 16–12 Work done in taking a mass from A to E is independent of the path.

For we can decompose any path into infinitesimal step-like portions, which are drawn alternately along the radius and perpendicular to it (Fig. 16–12). No work is done along perpendicular segments, like AB, because along them the force is perpendicular to the displacement. But the work done along the radial parts of the path, such as BC, adds up to the work done in going directly along a radial path, such as AE. The work done in moving the particle between two points in a gravitational field is, therefore, independent of the actual path connecting these points. Hence, the gravitational force is a *conservative* force.

The gravitational force is derivable from the potential energy. The relation for spherically symmetric potential energy functions is $F = -dU/dr$; see Eq. 8–6. This relation is the converse of Eq. 16–12. From it we obtain

$$F = -\frac{dU}{dr} = -\frac{d}{dr}\left(-\frac{GMm}{r}\right) = -\frac{GMm}{r^2}. \qquad (16\text{–}13)$$

The minus sign here coincides with the fact that the force is an attractive one, directed inward along a radius opposite to the radial displacement vector.

We can, if we wish, associate a scalar field with gravitation. We first define the *gravitational potential V* as the *gravitational potential energy per unit mass* of a body in a gravitational field. Then,

$$V = \frac{U(r)}{m} = -\frac{GM}{r}. \qquad (16\text{–}14)$$

Associated with every point in the space around a mass M we then have a number, the gravitational potential. This gives us a *scalar field*, potential being a scalar quantity. To determine the force exerted by this field on a mass particle m placed in it, we simply compute $-dV/dr$ at the point in question and multiply by m. The force has a magnitude $-m\,dV/dr$ and a direction radially in toward the center of force M.

The gravitational potential energy of a particle of mass m at the surface of the earth is obtained directly as (Eq. 16–12) $U(R) = -GM_em/R_e$. The amount of work required to move a body from the surface of the earth to infinity is GM_em/R_e, or about 6×10^7 joules/kg. If we could give a projectile more than this energy at the surface of the earth, then, neglecting the resistance of the earth's atmosphere, it would escape from the earth never to return. As it proceeds outward its kinetic energy decreases and its potential energy increases, but its speed is never reduced to zero. The critical initial speed, called the escape speed, v_0, such that the projectile does not return, is given by

$$\tfrac{1}{2}mv_0^2 = \frac{GM_em}{R_e}$$

or $$v_0 = \sqrt{2\frac{GM_e}{R_e}} = 6.96 \text{ miles/sec} = 25{,}000 \text{ miles/hr.}$$

Should a projectile, such as a rocket, be given this initial speed, it would escape from the earth. For initial speeds less than this the projectile will return. Its kinetic energy becomes zero before infinity is reached and the projectile falls back to earth.

The lighter molecules in the earth's upper atmosphere can attain high enough speeds by thermal agitation to escape into outer space. Hydrogen gas, which must have been present in the earth's atmosphere a long time ago, has now disappeared from it. Helium gas escapes at a steady rate, much of it resupplied by radioactive decay from the earth's crust. The escape speed for the sun is much too great to allow hydrogen to escape from its atmosphere. On the other hand, the speed of escape on the moon is so small that it can hardly keep any atmosphere at all. (See Problem 17.)

We have seen that the potential energy of a body of mass m in a gravitational field of a body of mass M is

$$U(r) = -\frac{GMm}{r}.$$

Notice that this is also the potential energy of a body of mass M in a gravitational field of a body of mass m. The potential energy is, therefore, a property of the *system* of particles, rather than of either particle alone. The potential energy changes whether M or m is moved. The potential energy is the work done in assembling the system by bringing it together from infinite separation. The potential energy, $-GMm/r$, is associated with the *pair* of bodies M and m, and it is meaningless to say that part belongs to M and part to m. When we speak of the potential energy of a planet near the sun or of a block lifted above the earth, the only justification for speaking as though the potential energy belongs to the planet or to the block alone is this: When the potential energy of a system of two bodies changes into kinetic energy, the lighter body gets most of the kinetic energy. The sun is so much more massive than a planet that the sun receives hardly any of the kinetic energy; and the same is true for the earth in the earth-block system.

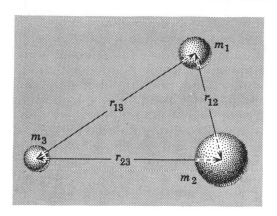

The joint nature of potential energy is brought out strikingly when more than two bodies are involved. In such cases the potential energy concept is especially useful because potential energy is a *scalar* quantity. The following example will illustrate these points.

Consider three bodies of masses m_1, m_2, and m_3. Let them initially be infinitely far from one another. The problem is to compute the work required to bring them into the positions shown in Fig. 16–13. We can proceed as follows. Let us first bring m_2 in toward m_1 from an infinite separation to the separation $\mathbf{r}_{12}$. The work done against the gravitational force exerted by m_1 on m_2 is $-Gm_1m_2/r_{12}$. Now let us bring m_3 in from infinity to the separation $\mathbf{r}_{13}$ from m_1 and $\mathbf{r}_{23}$ from m_2. The work done against the gravitational force exerted by m_1 on m_3 is $-Gm_1m_3/r_{13}$ and that against the gravitational force exerted by m_2 on m_3 is $-Gm_2m_3/r_{23}$. The total work done in assembling this system is the total potential energy of the system,

$$-\left(\frac{Gm_1m_2}{r_{12}} + \frac{Gm_1m_3}{r_{13}} + \frac{Gm_2m_3}{r_{23}}\right).$$

Notice that no vector operations are needed in this procedure.

No matter how we assemble the system, that is, regardless of which bodies are moved or which paths are taken, we always find this same amount of work required to bring the bodies into the configuration of Fig. 16–13 from an initial infinite separation. The potential energy must, therefore, be associated with the system rather than with any one or two bodies. If we wanted to separate the system into three isolated masses once again, we would have to supply an amount of energy

$$+\left(\frac{Gm_1m_2}{r_{12}} + \frac{Gm_1m_3}{r_{13}} + \frac{Gm_2m_3}{r_{23}}\right).$$

This energy may be regarded as a sort of binding energy holding the mass particles together in the configuration shown.

Just as we can associate elastic potential energy with the compressed or stretched configuration of a spring holding a mass particle, so we can associate gravitational potential energy with the configuration of a system of mass particles held together by gravitational forces. Similarly, if we want to think of the elastic potential energy of a particle as being stored in the spring, so we can think of the gravitational potential energy as being stored in the gravitational field of the system of particles. A change in either configuration results in a change of potential energy.

These concepts occur again when we meet forces of electric or magnetic origin, or, in fact, of nuclear origin. Their application is rather broad in physics. The advantage of the energy method over the dynamical method is derived from the fact that the energy method uses scalar quantities and scalar operations rather than vector quantities and vector operations. When the actual forces are not known, as is often the case in nuclear physics, the energy method is essential.

▶ **Example 5.** What is the binding energy of the earth-sun system? Neglect the presence of other planets or satellites.

For simplicity assume that the earth's orbit about the sun is circular at a radius r_{es}. The work done against the gravitational force to bring the earth and sun from an infinite separation to a separation r_{es} is

$$-G \frac{M_s M_e}{r_{es}} \cong -5 \times 10^{33} \text{ joules},$$

where we take $M_s \cong 300,000 M_e$, $M_e = 6 \times 10^{24}$ kg, $r_{es} = 150 \times 10^9$ meters. The minus sign indicates that the force is attractive so that work is done by the gravitational force. It would take an equivalent amount of work by an outside agent to separate these bodies completely so that the binding energy is 5×10^{33} joules.

What effect does the presence of the moon and other planets have on the energy binding the earth to the solar system?

How would the kinetic energy of the earth's orbital motion enter the problem? ◀

16–10   Energy Considerations in Planetary Motion

Consider again the motion of a planet of mass m_p about the sun of mass M_s. We shall consider the sun to be at rest at the origin of coordinates with the planet moving about it in a circular orbit. The potential energy of the system is

$$U(r) = -\frac{GM_s m_p}{r},$$

where r is the radius of the planet's circular orbit. The kinetic energy of the system is

$$K = \tfrac{1}{2} m_p \omega^2 r^2$$

the sun being at rest. From the equation preceding Eq. 16–10 we obtain

$$\omega^2 r^2 = \frac{GM_s}{r},$$

so that

$$K = \frac{1}{2} \frac{GM_s m_p}{r}.$$

The total energy is

$$E = K + U = \frac{1}{2} \frac{GM_s m_p}{r} - \frac{GM_s m_p}{r} = -\frac{GM_s m_p}{2r}. \qquad (16\text{--}15)$$

This energy is constant and is negative. Now the kinetic energy can never be negative, but from Eq. 16–15 we see that it must go to zero as the separation goes to infinity. The potential energy is always negative, except for its zero value at infinite separation. The meaning of the total negative energy, then, is that the system is a closed one, the planet always being bound to the attracting solar center and never escaping from it (Fig. 16–14).

Even when we consider elliptical orbits, in which r and ω vary, the total energy is negative. It is also constant, corresponding to the fact that gravitational forces are conservative. Hence, both the total energy and the total angular momentum are constant in planetary motion. These quantities are often called *constants of the motion*. We obtain the actual orbit of a planet with respect to the sun by starting with these conservation relations and eliminating the time variable by use of the laws of dynamics and gravitation. The result is that planetary orbits are elliptical.

In the earlier theories of the atom, as in the Bohr theory of the hydrogen atom, these identical mechanical relations are used in describing the motion of an electron about an attracting nuclear center. These same relations are

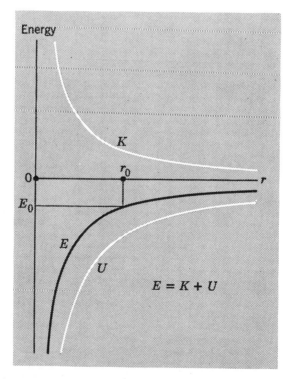

Fig. 16–14 Kinetic energy K, potential energy U, and total energy $E = U + K$ of a body in circular planetary motion. A planet with total energy $E_0 < 0$ will remain in an orbit of radius r_0. The farther the planet is from the sun, the greater its (constant) total energy E. To escape from the center of force and still have kinetic energy at infinity, it would need positive total energy.

used for open orbits (total energy positive) as in the experiments of Rutherford on the scattering of charged nuclear particles by other charged nuclear particles. Central forces, and particularly inverse square forces, will be encountered often in physical systems.

16–11   The Earth as a Frame of Reference

In describing the experiments which were fundamental to our definitions of force and mass, we had to assume some reference frame relative to which accelerations could be measured. If the reference frame itself were erratically accelerated, we would not observe any regularity in our measured accelerations. As a matter of fact, our laboratory experiments are performed in a coordinate system which is fixed to the earth. We have already discussed the effect that the rotation of the earth about its own axis has on our measurements. What effect does the motion of the earth as a whole about the sun, or some other cosmic body, have?

The acceleration of the earth with respect to the sun is $\omega^2 r$ or about 6×10^{-3} meters/sec^2. It would seem at first that this acceleration, small as it is, might prove disturbing in experiments involving small forces. That this is not the case, however, follows from the universality of the law of gravitation. Not only the earth but also the masses we use in our laboratory apparatus are accelerated toward the sun at practically the same rate.

Let us compute the error made in neglecting the earth's orbital acceleration. The acceleration of the earth toward the sun is k/r^2 where r is the distance from the center of the sun and the center of the earth and k is GM_s. Consider now a body on that side of the earth most distant from the sun. We can imagine that we are weighing it on a spring scale, for example. Then, the part of its acceleration toward the sun which is due to the gravitational attraction of the sun itself is

$$\frac{k}{(r + r_0)^2} = \frac{k}{r^2}\left(1 - \frac{2r_0}{r} + \cdots + \text{much smaller terms}\right),$$

where r_0 is the radius of the earth. The *difference* between the acceleration of the earth due to the sun's attraction (that is, k/r^2) and the acceleration of the apparatus due to the sun's attraction (the expression above) would be less than $(k/r^2)(2r_0/r)$. But $2r_0/r$ is about 10^{-4}. The difference, then, would be less than 10^{-4} of the earth's acceleration, or less than 10^{-6} meter/sec^2. The relative acceleration of the body and the earth due to the sun's attraction is about one-ten-millionth as strong as the gravitational acceleration of the body due to the earth. The moon has a similar effect of comparable magnitude on the body. Hence, only if we were measuring to one part in a million would we need to consider seriously the accelerating nature of a reference frame attached to the earth. For almost all practical purposes the earth is good enough as a frame of reference.

16–12   Inertial Guidance

In order to navigate an airplane over great distances when the earth's surface is hidden or in order to guide a rocket or instrument an artificial satellite, it is important to know the *vertical* direction at all times. The true vertical is the direction to the center of the earth. A pilot cannot reliably use his muscular sense or the position of his body for this because they merely indicate the direction of the resultant of his weight and the centrifugal force, not the true vertical. And rockets and satellites do not as yet have human pilots anyhow.

A person at rest on the earth uses a plumb bob as a vertical indicator. At first glance it seems absurd to expect a pendulum to indicate the true vertical inside an accelerating vehicle. (See Problems 5–19 and 6–20.) And yet a properly designed physical pendulum can do just that. An explanation follows.

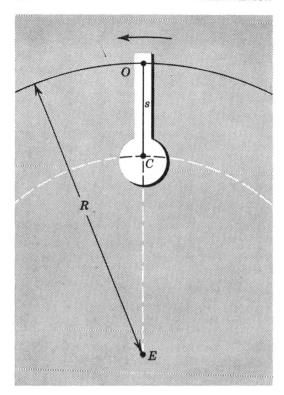

Fig. 16–15 In an inertial guidance mechanism, a physical pendulum moves in such a way that its center line OC always points to the center of the earth.

Any acceleration of the motion of a vehicle can be resolved into a vertical component and a horizontal one. Vertical accelerations merely accelerate the point of suspension of the pendulum without affecting the average orientation of the pendulum. In fact, if the only accelerations were vertical, the mean position of the pendulum would always indicate the vertical. Hence, we need consider only the horizontal component of the acceleration. A horizontal motion is a motion parallel to the surface of the earth; it is *not* straight-line motion but is instead a *circular* motion about the center of the earth. Horizontal motion is motion in a line parallel to a great circle of the earth. These statements are true whether the earth is rotating on its axis or not.

The problem then is to design a physical pendulum whose axis from point of support to center of mass always lies along a radial line to the center of the earth, regardless of the horizontal acceleration of the point of support. The situation is shown in Fig. 16–15.

Let us assume that we have already constructed the desired physical pendulum so that the line OC, from point of support to center of mass, always points along a radial line from the center of the earth, E, to O. What property does this pendulum have?

The point C moves along a great circle at a distance $(R - s)$ from E. The angular acceleration of O or C is α. The translational motion of the center of mass can be found by assuming that the external force acts at the center of mass with all the mass M concentrated at that point. Hence, the external force is

$$f_{\text{ext}} = Ma_{\text{cm}}$$

$$- M(R - s)\alpha.$$

This external force actually acts on the pendulum at the point of support O. This force gives rise to a torque about an axis through the center of mass. It is this torque which rotates the system about C in such a way that OC is always radial. The angular acceleration about C is exactly α in that case. Using the relations

$$\tau_{cm} = I_c \alpha$$

and
$$\tau_{cm} = f_{ext}s = M(R - s)\alpha s,$$

where s is the distance from O to C, we obtain

$$M(R - s)\alpha s = I_c \alpha$$

or
$$I_c = M(R - s)s.$$

But the rotational inertia of the pendulum about O, I_o, is related to its rotational inertia about a parallel axis through C, I_c, by

$$I_o = I_c + Ms^2,$$

(see Eq. 12–8) so that the *required condition on the pendulum is*

$$I_o = M(R - s)s + Ms^2 - MRo. \tag{16–16}$$

What period would such a physical pendulum have on the earth's surface? Using the relation

$$T = 2\pi \sqrt{I_0/Mgs}, \tag{15–22}$$

we obtain
$$T = 2\pi \sqrt{R/g} = 84 \text{ min.}$$

Hence, the physical pendulum which indicates the vertical in accelerated vehicles has the same period as a simple pendulum whose length is the radius of the earth in a uniform field **g**. This period is the same (see Example 4) as that of an infinitely long simple pendulum in the earth's real gravitational field.

To illustrate the difficulty of actually constructing such a pendulum, assume it has the shape of a disk of radius a. Then

$$I_o = \frac{Ma^2}{2}$$

and
$$I_0 = \frac{Ma^2}{2} + Ms^2 = MRs$$

or
$$\frac{Ma^2}{2} - Ms(R \quad s).$$

If R is taken to be the radius of the earth, we can neglect s compared to R, so that

$$\frac{Ma^2}{2} = MRs$$

or
$$s = \frac{a^2}{2R}.$$

If a equals 1 ft, for example, then s, the distance from point of support to center of mass, must be 2.4×10^{-8} ft!

In practice, we must construct a physical pendulum of period $T = 84$ min and set the initial orientation of the pendulum correctly to achieve the theoretical result. If R varies appreciably from the radius of the earth, then s must be treated as a variable quantity, thereby further complicating the actual realization of such a device.

QUESTIONS

1. If the force of gravity acts on all bodies in proportion to their masses, why doesn't a heavy body fall faster than a light body?

2. Modern observational astronomy and navigation procedures make use of the geocentric (or Ptolemaic) point of view (by using the rotating "celestial sphere"). Is this wrong? If not, then what criterion determines the system (the Copernican or Ptolemaic) we use? When would we use the heliocentric (or Copernican) system?

3. Give examples of the fact that gravitational attraction between two bodies is not affected by the presence of matter between them.

4. How does the weight of a body vary en route from the earth to the moon? Would its mass change?

5. Would we have more sugar to the pound at the pole or the equator?

6. Does the concentration of the earth's mass near its center change the variation of g with height compared with a homogeneous sphere? How?

7. Because the earth bulges near the equator, the source of the Mississippi River, although high above sea level, is nearer to the center of the earth than is its mouth. How can the river flow "uphill"?

8. One clock is based on an oscillating spring, the other on a pendulum. Both are taken to Mars. Will they keep the same time there that they kept on Earth? Will they agree with each other? Explain. Mars has a mass 0.1 that of Earth and a radius half as great.

9. What measurements must an astronomer make to determine the mass of another planet, such as Saturn?

10. Under what conditions would Kepler's second law become invalid?

11. The gravitational attraction of the sun and the moon on the earth produces tides. The sun's effect is about half as great as the moon's. Under what circumstances will the resultant effect be a maximum? A minimum?

12. The direct pull of the sun on the earth is about 175 times that of the moon. Why is it then that the moon causes the larger tides?

13. If tides slow down the rotation of the earth (owing to friction), the angular momentum of the earth decreases. What happens to the motion of the moon as a consequence of the conservation of angular momentum? Does the sun (and solar tides) play a role here?

14. Would you expect the total energy of the solar system to be constant? The total angular momentum? Explain your answers.

15. Does a rocket really need the escape speed of 25,000 miles/hr initially to escape from the earth?

16. Neglecting air friction and technical difficulties, can a satellite be put into an orbit by being fired from a huge cannon at the earth's surface? Explain.

17. Can a satellite move in a stable orbit in a plane not passing through the earth's center? Explain.

18. An artificial satellite of the earth releases a bomb. Neglecting the effects of air resistance, does the bomb ever strike the earth?

19. After Sputnik I was put into orbit we were told that it would not return to earth but would burn up in its *descent*. Considering the fact that it did not burn up in its *ascent*, how is this possible?

20. Show that a satellite may speed down; that is, show that if frictional forces cause a satellite to lose total energy, it will move into an orbit closer to the earth and may have increased kinetic energy.

21. Popular reports of artificial earth satellites refer to them as "free from the earth's gravitational pull." Is this true? Explain.

22. Inside a space ship what difficulties would you encounter in walking? In jumping? In drinking?

23. If a planet of given density were made larger, its force of attraction for an object on its surface would increase because of the planet's greater mass but would decrease because

of the greater distance from the object to the center of the planet. Which effect predominates?

24. Consider a hollow spherical shell. How does the gravitational potential inside compare with that on the surface? What is the gravitational field strength inside?

PROBLEMS

1. At what altitude above the earth's surface would the acceleration of gravity be about 16 ft/sec²?

2. The distinction between mass and weight drew attention when Jean Richer in 1672 took a pendulum clock from Paris to Cayenne, French Guiana, for use in astronomical observations and found that it lost 2.5 min each day. It was already known from Huygens' work that the period of a pendulum of given length was proportional to $1/\sqrt{g}$. If $g =$ 980.9 cm/sec² in Paris, what is g in Cayenne?

3. What is the period of a "seconds pendulum" (period = 2 sec on earth) on the surface of the moon?

4. How far from the earth must a body be along a line toward the sun so that the sun's gravitational pull balances the earth's? The sun is 9.3×10^7 miles away and its mass is $3.24 \times 10^5 M_e$.

5. A body is suspended on a spring balance in a ship sailing along the equator with a speed v. Show that the scale reading will be very close to $W_0(1 \pm 2\omega v/g)$, where ω is the angular speed of the earth and W_0 is the scale reading when the ship is at rest. Explain the plus or minus.

6. With what speed would mail pass through the center of the earth if it were delivered by the chute of Example 3?

7. (a) Show that in a chute dug through the earth along any chord line, rather than along a diameter, the motion of an object will be simple harmonic. (b) Find the period of the motion. (c) Will the object attain the same speed along the chord line as it does along a diameter?

8. Consider a mass particle at a point P anywhere inside a spherical shell of matter. Assume the shell is of uniform thickness and density. Construct a narrow double cone with apex at P intercepting areas A_1 and A_2 on the shell (Fig. 16–16). (a) Show that the resultant gravitational force exerted on the particle at P by the intercepted mass elements is zero. (b) Show then that the resultant gravitational force of the entire shell on an internal particle is zero everywhere.

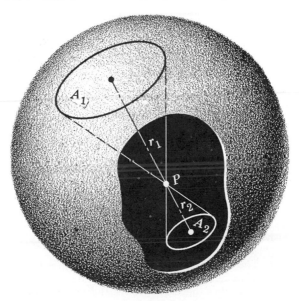

Fig. 16–16

9. (a) With what horizontal speed must a satellite be projected at 100 miles above the surface of the earth so that it will have a circular orbit about the earth? Take the earth's radius as 4000 miles. (b) What will be the period of rotation?

10. Use qualitative arguments to explain why the following four periods are equal (all are 84 min): (a) time of revolution of a satellite just above the earth's surface; (b) period of oscillation of mail in a tunnel through the earth; (c) period of simple pendulum having a length equal to the earth's radius in a uniform field 9.8 nt/kg; (d) period of an infinite simple pendulum in the earth's real gravitational field.

11. A projectile is fired vertically from the earth's surface with an initial speed of 10 km/sec. Neglecting atmospheric retardation, how far above the surface of the earth would it go? Take the earth's radius as 6400 km.

12. Does it take more energy to get a satellite up to 2000 miles above the earth than to put it in orbit there? 4000 miles? 6000 miles? Take the earth's radius to be 4000 miles.

13. Two earth satellites, A and B, each of mass m, are to be launched into (nearly) circular orbits about the earth's center. Satellite A is to orbit at an altitude of 4000 miles. Satellite B is to orbit at an altitude of 12,000 miles. The radius of the earth R_e is 4000 miles (Fig. 16–17). (a) What is the ratio of the potential energy of satellite B to that of

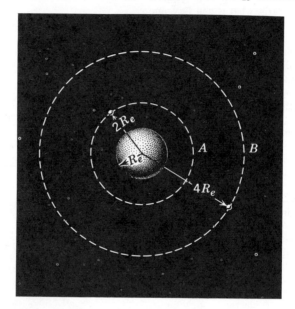

Fig. 16–17

satellite A, in orbit? (Explain the result in terms of the work required to get each satellite from its orbit to infinity.) (b) What is the ratio of the kinetic energy of satellite B to that of satellite A, in orbit? (c) Which satellite has the greater total energy if each has a mass of 1 slug? By how much?

14. (a) Can a satellite be sent out to a distance where it will revolve about the earth with an angular velocity equal to that at which the earth rotates, so that it remains always above the same point on the earth? (b) Must the plane of its orbit be an equatorial plane? (c) What would be the radius of such an orbit?

15. The mean distance of Mars from the sun is 1.524 times that of Earth from the sun. Find the number of years required for Mars to make one revolution about the sun.

16. Determine the mass of the earth from the period T and the radius r of the moon's orbit about the earth; $T = 27.3$ days and $r = 2.39 \times 10^5$ miles.

17. (a) Show that to escape from the atmosphere of a planet a necessary condition for a molecule is that it have a speed such that $v^2 > 2GM/r$, where M is the mass of the planet and r is the distance of the molecule from the center of the planet. (b) Determine the escape speed from the earth for an atmospheric particle 1000 km above the earth's surface. (c) Do the same for the moon and the sun.

18. Mars has a mean diameter of 4200 miles, Earth one of 7900 miles. The mass of Mars is $0.107 M_e$. (a) How does the mean density of Mars compare with that of Earth? (b) What is the value of g on Mars? (c) What is the escape velocity on Mars?

19. In a double star, two stars of mass 3×10^{30} kg each rotate about their common center of mass, 10^{17} meters away. (a) What is their common angular speed? (b) Suppose that a meteorite passes through this center of mass moving at right angles to the line joining the stars. What must its speed be if it is to escape from the gravitational field of the double star?

20. If the earth should keep its total energy but lose half its angular momentum by a change in the direction of its velocity, (a) how near would it approach the sun and (b) what would its period be? (Assume the orbit is circular initially and elliptical finally. Use conservation of energy and the fact that the velocity is perpendicular to the radius at the extremities of the earth's elliptical orbit.)

21. Two particles of mass m and M are initially at rest an infinite distance apart. Show that at any instant their relative velocity of approach attributable to gravitational attraction is $\sqrt{2G(M + m)/d}$, where d is their separation at that instant.

22. A particle of mass m is subject to an attractive central force of magnitude k/r^2, k being a constant. If at the instant when the particle is at an extreme position in its closed orbit, at a distance a from the center of force, its speed is $\sqrt{k/2ma}$, find the other extreme position.

23. What is the percentage change in the acceleration of the earth toward the sun from a total eclipse of the sun to the point where the moon is on a side of the earth directly opposite the sun?

24. An 800-kg mass and a 600-kg mass are separated by 0.25 meter. (a) What is the gravitational field strength due to these masses at a point 0.20 meter from the 800-kg mass and 0.15 meter from the 600-kg mass? (b) What is the gravitational potential at this point due to these same masses?

25. Masses of 200 and 800 gm are 12 cm apart. (a) Find the gravitational force on a unit mass at a point on the line joining the masses 4 cm from the 200-gm mass. (b) Find the potential energy per unit mass at that point. (c) How much work is needed to move this unit mass to a point 4 cm from the 800-gm mass along the line of centers?

26. (a) Write an expression for the potential energy of a body of mass m in the gravitational field of the earth and moon. Let M_e be the earth's mass, M_μ the moon's mass (where $M_e = 81 M_\mu$), R the distance from the earth's center, and r the distance from the moon's center. The distance between earth and moon is about 240,000 miles. (b) At what point or points will the gravitational field strength attributable to the earth and moon be zero? (c) What will the potential energy and field strength be for m when it is on the earth's surface? The moon's surface? Are these answers unique?

27. A sphere of matter, radius a, has a concentric cavity, radius b, as shown in cross section in Fig. 16–18. (a) Sketch the gravitational force F exerted by the sphere on a particle of mass m, located a distance r from the center of the sphere, as a function of r in the range $0 \le r \le \infty$. Consider points $r = 0$, b, a, and ∞ in particular. (b) Sketch the corresponding curve for the potential energy $U(r)$ of the system. (c) From these graphs,

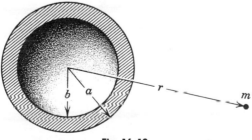

Fig. 16–18

how would you obtain graphs of the gravitational field strength and the gravitational potential due to the sphere?

28. The variation of g in the earth's interior is given in the accompanying table. The earth's radius is 6400 km.

Depth, km	g, meters/sec^2	Depth, km	g, meters/sec^2
0	9.82	1400	9.88
33	9.85	1600	9.86
100	9.89	1800	9.85
200	9.92	2000	9.86
300	9.95	2200	9.90
413	9.98	2400	9.98
600	10.01	2600	10.09
800	9.99	2800	10.26
1000	9.95	2900	10.37
1200	9.91	4000	8.00

Within the earth's central core (below 2900 km) the values of g diminish monotonically (not linearly) from 10.37 meters/sec^2 to zero. The actual variation of g below 4000 km is uncertain. (*a*) Plot qualitatively g versus r (where r *is the distance from the earth's center*) from 0 to 6400 km. (*b*) Explain carefully how the earth's density must vary as we proceed from its surface to its center in order to account for this variation of g. (*c*) Take $\rho = 1$ at the surface (its average value is actually 3.0 gm/cm^3), and plot qualitatively ρ versus r. Assume throughout that ρ and g are spherically symmetrical.

Fluid Statics

CHAPTER 17

17-1 Fluids

It is convenient in mechanics to classify matter into solids and fluids. A *fluid* is a substance that can *flow*. Hence, the term fluid includes liquids and gases. Because a solid body has definite size and shape, the mechanics of solids is the mechanics of a rigid body, modified by the laws of elasticity for bodies that cannot be considered perfectly rigid. Fluids change their shape readily, however, and their mechanical behavior cannot be described in this way. Of course, there are marked differences between gases and liquids; for example, gases are easily compressed whereas liquids are nearly incompressible; and a liquid has definite size but a gas expands to fill any closed vessel containing it. However, in discussing the mechanical behavior of fluids we use only the properties of liquids and gases that are connected with their ability to flow. Therefore, the same basic laws control the static and dynamic behavior of both liquids and gases.

17-2 Pressure and Density

There is a difference in the way a force acts on a fluid and on a solid. A force can be applied to a single point of a solid and be sustained by it; but a force can only be applied to and sustained by a *surface* of an enclosed fluid. Furthermore, in a fluid at rest such a force is always directed at right angles to the surface. For a fluid at rest cannot sustain a tangential force; the fluid layers would simply slide over one another when subjected to such a force. It is convenient, therefore, to describe the force acting on a fluid by specifying the *pressure p*, which is defined as the magnitude of the normal force per unit surface area.   Pressure is a scalar quantity.   Some common units of pressure are lb/in.^{2}, lb/ft^2, and nt/meter^2.

A fluid under pressure exerts a force on any surface in contact with it.   Consider a closed surface containing a fluid (Fig. 17–1).   An element of the surface can be represented by a vector $\Delta \mathbf{S}$ whose magnitude gives the area of the element and whose

Fig. 17–1   An element of surface ΔS can be represented by a vector $\Delta \mathbf{S}$, equal to it in magnitude and normal to it in direction.

direction is taken to be the outward normal to the surface of the element.   (See Problem 2–21.)   Then the force $\Delta \mathbf{F}$ exerted by the fluid against this surface element is

$$\Delta \mathbf{F} = p \, \Delta \mathbf{S}.$$

Since $\Delta \mathbf{F}$ and $\Delta \mathbf{S}$ have the same direction, the pressure p can be written as

$$p = \frac{\Delta F}{\Delta S}.$$

The pressure may vary from point to point on the surface.   Then we take a small element of surface containing the point and consider this quotient as the element shrinks to the point.   Then the pressure at the point is given as

$$p = \lim_{\Delta S \to 0} \frac{\Delta F}{\Delta S}.$$

The *density* ρ of a homogeneous fluid (its mass divided by its volume) may depend on many factors, such as its temperature and the pressure to which it is subjected.   For liquids the density varies very little over wide ranges in pressure and temperature, and we can safely treat it as a constant for our present purposes.   The density of a gas, however, is very sensitive to changes in temperature and pressure.   The fact that ρ is a variable for a gas complicates the treatment of gas mechanics.

For convenient reference we list in Table 17–1 the densities of some common gases, liquids, and solids.

Table 17–1

DENSITIES (IN KG/METER^3) AT $0°C$ AND 1-ATM PRESSURE

Gases		Solids	
Air	1.293	Aluminum	2.70×10^3
Carbon dioxide (CO$_2$)	1.977	Brass (approx.)	$8.5 \ \times 10^3$
Helium (He)	0.1785	Copper	$8.9 \ \times 10^3$
Hydrogen (H$_2$)	0.0899	Cork (approx.)	0.24×10^3
Oxygen (O$_2$)	1.429	Gold	$19.3 \ \times 10^3$
Nitrogen (N$_2$)	1.251	Ice	0.92×10^3
		Iron (approx.)	$7.6 \ \times 10^3$
Liquids		Lead	$11.3 \ \times 10^0$
Ether	0.73×10^3	Platinum	$21.4 \ \times 10^3$
Ethyl alcohol	0.81×10^3	Silver	$10.5 \ \times 10^3$
Mercury	$13.6 \ \times 10^3$	Wood, elm (approx.)	0.57×10^3
Olive oil	0.92×10^3	Wood, white pine	0.42×10^3
Sea water	1.03×10^3	Zinc	$7.1 \ \times 10^3$
Water	1.00×10^3		

17–3   The Variation of Pressure in a Fluid at Rest

If a fluid is in equilibrium, every portion of the fluid is in equilibrium. Let us consider a small element of fluid volume submerged within the body of the fluid. Let this element have the shape of a thin disk and be a distance y above some reference level, as shown in Fig. 17–2a. The thickness of the disk is dy and each face has an area A. The mass of this element is $\rho A \, dy$ and its weight is $\rho g A \, dy$. The forces exerted on the element by the surrounding fluid are perpendicular to its surface at each point (Fig. 17–2b).

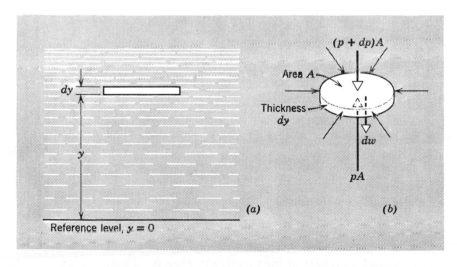

(a)   (b)

Fig. 17–2   (a) A small volume element of fluid at rest.   (b) The forces on the element.

The resultant horizontal force is zero, for the element has no horizontal acceleration. The horizontal forces are due only to the pressure of the fluid, and by symmetry the pressure must be the same at all points within a horizontal plane at y.

The fluid element is also unaccelerated in the vertical direction, so that the resultant vertical force on it must be zero. However, the vertical forces are due not only to the pressure of the fluid on its faces but also to the weight of the element. If we let p be the pressure on the lower face and $p + dp$ the pressure on its upper face, the upward force is pA (exerted on the lower face) and the downward force is $(p + dp)A$ (exerted on the upper face) plus the weight of the element dw. Hence, for vertical equilibrium

$$pA = (p + dp)A + dw$$

$$= (p + dp)A + \rho gA \, dy,$$

and
$$\frac{dp}{dy} = -\rho g. \tag{17-1}$$

This equation tells us how the pressure varies with elevation above some reference level in a fluid in static equilibrium. As the elevation increases (dy positive), the pressure decreases (dp negative). The cause of this pressure variation is the weight per unit cross-sectional area of the layers of fluid lying between the points whose pressure difference is being measured.

The quantity ρg is often called the *weight density* of the fluid; it is the weight per unit volume of the fluid. For water, for example, the weight density is 62.4 lb/ft^3.

If p_1 is the pressure at elevation y_1 and p_2 the pressure at elevation y_2 above some reference level, integration of Eq. 17–1 gives

$$\int_{p_1}^{p_2} dp = -\int_{y_1}^{y_2} \rho g \, dy$$

or
$$p_2 - p_1 = -\int_{y_1}^{y_2} \rho g \, dy. \tag{17-2}$$

For liquids ρ is practically constant because liquids are nearly incompressible; and differences in level are rarely so great that any change in g need be considered. Hence, taking ρ and g as constants, we obtain

$$p_2 - p_1 = -\rho g(y_2 - y_1) \tag{17-3}$$

for a homogeneous liquid.

If a liquid has a free surface, this is the natural level from which to measure distances. To change our reference level to the top surface, we take y_2 to be the elevation of the surface, at which point the pressure p_2 acting on the fluid is that exerted by the earth's atmosphere p_0. We take y_1 to be at any level and we represent the pressure there as p. Then,

$$p_0 - p = -\rho g(y_2 - y_1).$$

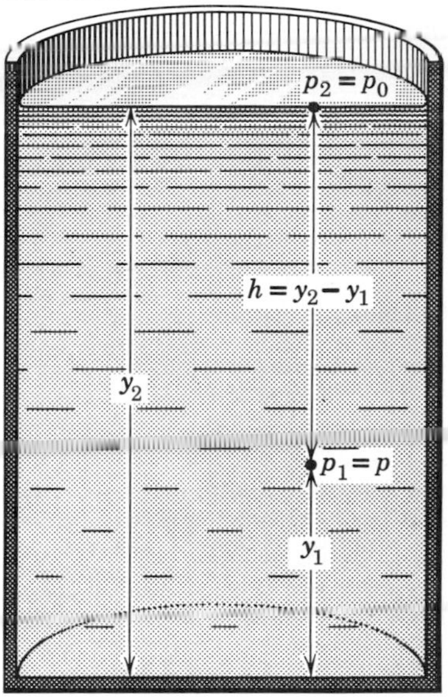

Fig. 17–3 A liquid whose top surface is open to the atmosphere.

But $y_2 - y_1$ is the depth h below the surface at which the pressure is p (see Fig. 17–3), so that

$$p = p_0 + \rho g h. \tag{17–4}$$

This shows clearly that the pressure is the same at all points at the same depth.

For gases ρ is comparatively small and the difference in pressure at two points is usually negligible (see Eq. 17–3). Thus, in a vessel containing a gas the pressure can be taken as the same everywhere. However, this is not the case if $y_2 - y_1$ is very great. The pressure of the air varies greatly as we ascend to great heights in the atmosphere or descend to great depths in a mine. In fact, in such cases the density ρ varies with altitude and ρ must be known as a function of y before we can integrate Eq. 17–2.

▶ **Example 1.** We can get a reasonable idea of the variation of pressure with altitude in the earth's atmosphere if we assume that the density ρ is proportional to the pressure. This would be exactly true if the temperature of the air remained the same at all altitudes. Using this assumption, find the pressure p at an altitude y above sea level.

From Eq. 17–1 we have

$$\frac{dp}{dy} = -\rho g.$$

Since ρ is proportional to p, we have

$$\frac{\rho}{\rho_0} = \frac{p}{p_0},$$

where ρ_0 and p_0 are the known values of density and pressure at sea level. Then,

$$\frac{dp}{dy} = -g\rho_0 \frac{p}{p_0},$$

so that

$$\frac{dp}{p} = -\frac{g\rho_0}{p_0} dy.$$

Integrating this from the value p_0 at the point $y = 0$ (sea level) to the value p at the point y (above sea level), we obtain

$$\ln \frac{p}{p_0} = -\frac{g\rho_0}{p_0} y$$

or

$$p = p_0 e^{-g(\rho_0/p_0)y}.$$

However,

$$g = 9.80 \text{ meters/sec}^2, \quad \rho_0 = 1.20 \text{ kg/meters}^3 \text{ (at 20°C)}, \quad p_0 = 1.01 \times 10^5 \text{ nt/meter}^2,$$

so that

$$g\frac{\rho_0}{p_0} = 1.16 \times 10^{-4} \text{ meter}^{-1} = 0.116 \text{ km}^{-1}.$$

Hence,

$$p = p_0 e^{-ay}.$$

where $a = 0.116 \text{ km}^{-1}$.

We have seen that because liquids are almost incompressible the lower layers are not noticeably compressed by the weight of the upper layers superimposed on them and the density ρ is practically constant at all levels. For gases at uniform temperature the density ρ of any layer is proportional to the pressure p at that layer. The variation of pressure with distance above the bottom of the fluid for a gas is different from that for a liquid. Figure 17–4 shows the pressure distribution in water and in air. ◀

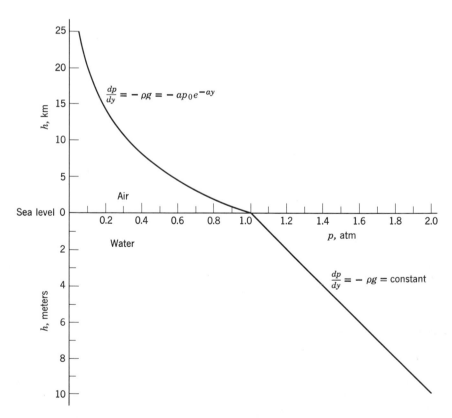

Fig. 17–4 Example 1. Variation of pressure with altitude in air and with depth in water. Note that the scales for altitude and depth are different.

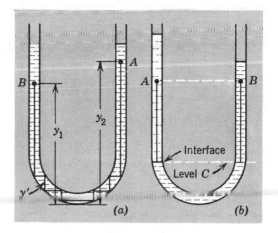

Fig. 17-5 (a) The difference in pressure between two points A and B depends only on their difference in elevation $y_2 - y_1$. (b) Two points A and B at the same elevation can be at different pressures if the fluid densities there differ.

Equation 17-3 gives the relation between the pressures at any two points in a fluid, regardless of the shape of the containing vessel. For no matter what the shape of the containing vessel, two points in the fluid can be connected by a path made up of vertical and horizontal steps. For example, consider points A and B in the homogeneous fluid contained in the U-tube of Fig. 17-5a. Along the zigzag path from A to B there is a difference in pressure $\rho g y'$ for each vertical segment of length y', whereas along each horizontal segment there is no change in pressure. Hence, the difference in pressure between A and B is ρg times the algebraic sum of the vertical segments from A to B, or $\rho g(y_1 - y_2)$.

If the U-tube contains different liquids, say a dense liquid in the right tube and a less dense one in the left tube, as shown in Fig. 17-5b, the pressure can be different at the same level on different sides. In the figure the liquid surface is higher in the left tube than in the right. The pressure at A will be greater than at B. The pressure at C is the same on both sides, but the pressure falls less from C to A than from C to B, for a column of fluid of unit cross-sectional area connecting A and C will weigh less than a corresponding column connecting B and C.

▶ **Example 2.** A U-tube is partly filled with water. Another liquid, which does not mix with water, is poured into one side until it stands a distance d above the water level on the other side, which has meanwhile risen a distance l (Fig. 17-6). Find the density of the liquid relative to that of water.

In Fig. 17-6 points C are at the same pressure. Hence, the pressure drop from C to each surface is the same, for each surface is at atmospheric pressure.

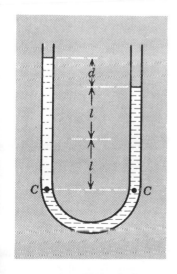

Fig. 17-6 Example 2.

The pressure drop on the water side is $\rho_w g 2l$; the $2l$ comes from the fact that the water column has risen a distance l on one side and fallen a distance l on the other side, from its initial position. The pressure drop on the other side is $\rho g(d + 2l)$, where ρ is the density of the unknown liquid. Hence,

$$\rho_w g 2l = \rho g(d + 2l)$$

and

$$\frac{\rho}{\rho_w} = \frac{2l}{(2l + d)}.$$

The ratio of the density of a substance to the density of water is called the *relative density* of that substance.   ◄

17–4 Pascal's Principle and Archimedes' Principle

When a fluid is at rest, the difference of pressure between two points depends only on the difference of level and density (Eq. 17–2). Hence, if the pressure at any point is increased, there will be an equal increase of pressure at every point, provided the density does not change. In addition to the pressure attributable to its weight, a confined fluid may be subjected to an additional pressure by the application of an external force (Fig. 17–7). When the atmospheric pressure p_0 increases on the free surface of a liquid, the pressure at any depth must increase by the same amount (Eq. 17–4). The same result holds if we cover the top surface with a piston and press down on it. This result was stated by the French scientist Blaise Pascal (1623–1662) and is called *Pascal's principle*. It is usually given as follows: Pressure applied to an enclosed fluid is transmitted undiminished to every portion of the fluid and the walls of the containing vessel. This result is a necessary consequence of the laws of fluid mechanics, rather than an independent principle.

If the fluid is incompressible, a change in pressure in one portion of the fluid is transmitted instantaneously to all other parts. In a compressible fluid the pressure change in one part propagates through the fluid as a

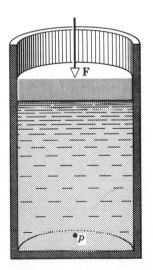

Fig. 17–7 A fluid in a cylinder fitted with a movable piston. The pressure at p is due not only to the weight of the fluid above p but also to the force exerted by the piston.

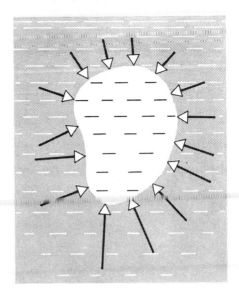

Fig. 17-8 Archimedes' principle.

wave at the speed of sound in that fluid. Once the disturbance has died out and equilibrium is re-established, it is found that Pascal's principle is valid for a compressible fluid also. Changes in temperature accompany changes in pressure in a compressible fluid.

Archimedes' principle is also a necessary consequence of the laws of fluid statics. When a body is wholly or partly immersed in a fluid at rest, the fluid exerts pressure on every part of the body's surface in contact with the fluid. The pressure is greater on the parts immersed more deeply. The resultant of all the forces is an upward force called the *buoyancy* of the immersed body. We can determine the magnitude and direction of this resultant force quite simply as follows.

The pressure on each part of the surface of the body certainly does not depend on the material the body is made of. Let us suppose, then, that the body, or as much of it as is immersed, is replaced by fluid like the surroundings. This fluid will experience the pressures that acted on the immersed body (Fig. 17-8) and will be at rest. Hence, the resultant upward force on it will equal its weight and will act vertically upward through its center of gravity. From this follows *Archimedes' principle*, namely, that a body wholly or partly immersed in a fluid is buoyed up with a force equal to the weight of the fluid displaced by the body. We have seen that the force acts vertically up through the center of gravity of the fluid before its displacement. The corresponding point in the immersed body is called its *center of buoyancy*.

▶ **Example 3.** What fraction of the total volume of an iceberg is exposed? The density of ice (Table 17-1) is $\rho_i = 0.92$ gm/cm^3 and that of sea water is $\rho_w = 1.03$ gm/cm^3. The weight of the iceberg is

$$W_i = \rho_i V_i g,$$

where V_i is the volume of the iceberg; the weight of the volume V_w of sea water displaced is the buoyant force

$$B = \rho_w V_w g.$$

But B equals W_i, for the iceberg is in equilibrium, so that

$$\rho_w V_w g = \rho_i V_i g,$$

and

$$\frac{V_w}{V_i} = \frac{\rho_i}{\rho_w} = \frac{0.92}{1.03} = 89\%.$$

The volume of water displaced V_w is the volume of the submerged portion of the iceberg, so that 11% of the iceberg is exposed. ◀

17–5 Measurement of Pressure

Evangelista Torricelli (1608–1647) devised a method for measuring the pressure of the atmosphere by his invention of the mercury barometer in 1643. The mercury barometer is a long glass tube that has been filled with mercury and then inverted in a dish of mercury, as in Fig. 17–9. The space above the mercury column contains only mercury vapor whose pressure is so small at ordinary temperatures that it can be neglected. It is easily shown (see Eq. 17–3) that the atmospheric pressure p_0 is

$$p_0 = \rho g h.$$

Most pressure gauges use atmospheric pressure as a reference level and measure the difference between the actual pressure and atmospheric pressure, called the *gauge pressure*. The actual pressure at a point in a fluid is called the *absolute pressure*. Gauge pressure is given either above or below atmospheric pressure. A gauge that reads pressures below atmospheric is usually called a vacuum gauge.

The pressure of the atmosphere at any point is numerically equal to the weight of a column of air of unit cross-sectional area extending from that point to the top of the atmosphere. The atmospheric pressure at a point, therefore, decreases with altitude. There are variations in atmospheric pressure from day to day since the atmosphere is not static. The mercury column in the barometer will have a height of about 76 cm at sea level, varying with the atmospheric pressure. A pressure equivalent to that exerted by exactly 76 cm of mercury at 0°C under standard gravity, $g = 32.174$ ft/sec$^2 = 980.665$ cm/sec^2, is called *one standard atmosphere* (1 atm). The density of mercury at this temperature is 13.5950 gm/cm^3. Hence, one standard atmosphere is equivalent to

$$1 \text{ atm} = (13.5950 \text{ gm/cm}^3)(980.665 \text{ cm/sec}^2)(76.00 \text{ cm})$$

$$= 1.013 \times 10^5 \text{ nt/meter}^2$$

$$= 2116 \text{ lb/ft}^2$$

$$= 14.70 \text{ lb/in.}^2$$

Often pressures are specified by giving the height of mercury column, at 0°C under standard gravity, which exerts the same pressure. This is the

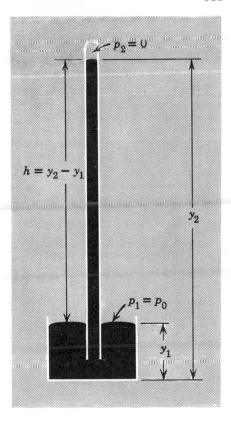

$p_2 = 0$

$h = y_2 - y_1$

y_2

$p_1 = p_0$

y_1

Fig. 17-2 The Torricelli barometer.

origin of the expression "centimeters of mercury" or "inches of mercury" pressure. Pressure is the ratio of force to area, however, and not a length.

Torricelli was Galileo's successor as professor of mathematics at the Accademia in Florence. He described his experiments with the mercury barometer in two letters of 1644 to his friend M. A. Ricci in Rome. In them he says that the aim of his investigation was "not simply to produce a vacuum, but to make an instrument which shows the mutations of the air, now heavier and dense, and now lighter and thin." On hearing of the Italian experiments, Blaise Pascal, in France, reasoned that if the mercury column was held up simply by the pressure of the air, the column ought to be shorter at a high altitude. He tried it on a church steeple in Paris, but desiring more decisive results, he wrote to his brother-in-law to try the experiment on the Puy de Dôme, a high mountain in Auvergne. There was a difference of 3 inches in the height of the mercury, "which ravished us with admiration and astonishment." Pascal himself repeated the experiment using red wine and a glass tube 46 feet long.

The chief significance of these experiments at the time was the realization it brought that an evacuated space could be created. Aristotle believed that a vacuum could not exist, and as late a writer as Descartes held the same view. For two thousand years philosophers spoke of the horror that nature had for empty space—the *horror vacui*. Because of this horror nature was said to prevent the formation of a vacuum by laying hold of anything nearby and with it instantly filling up any vacuated space. Hence, the mercury or wine should fill up the inverted tube because "nature abhorred a vacuum." The experiments of Torricelli and Pascal showed that there were limitations to nature's ability to prevent a vacuum. They created a sensation at the time. The goal of producing a vacuum became more of a practical reality through the development of pumps by Otto von Guericke in Germany around 1650 and by Robert Boyle in England around 1660. Even though these pumps were relatively crude, they did provide a tool for experimentation. With a pump and a glass jar, an experimental space could be provided in which to study how the properties of heat, light, sound, and later electricity and magnetism, are affected by an increasingly rarefied atmosphere. Although even today we cannot completely remove every trace of gas from a closed vessel, these seventeenth-century experimenters freed science from the bugaboo of *horror vacui* and spurred efforts to create highly evacuated systems.

Except for the telescope, no scientific discovery of the seventeenth century excited wonder and curiosity to a greater degree than did the experiments with the barometer and the air pump.

The open-tube manometer (Fig. 17–10) measures gauge pressure. It consists of a U-shaped tube containing a liquid, one end of the tube being open to the atmosphere and the other end being connected to the system whose pressure p we want to measure. From Eq. 17–4 we obtain

$$p - p_0 = \rho g h.$$

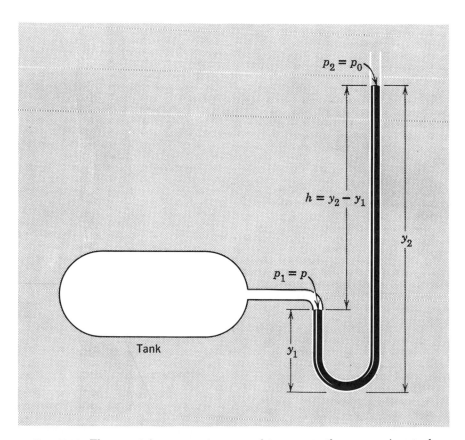

Fig. 17–10 The open-tube manometer, as used to measure the pressure in a tank.

Thus the gauge pressure, $p - p_0$, is proportional to the difference in height of the liquid columns in the U-tube. If the vessel contains gas under high pressure, a dense liquid like mercury is used in the tube; water can be used when low gas pressures are involved.

▶ **Example 4.** An open-tube mercury manometer (Fig. 17–10) is connected to a gas tank. The mercury is 39.0 cm higher on the right side than on the left when a barometer nearby reads 75.0 cm of Hg. What is the absolute pressure of the gas? Express the answer in centimeters of Hg, atm, and lb/in.^{2}.

The gas pressure is the pressure at the top of the left mercury column. This is the same as the pressure at the same horizontal level in the right column. The pressure at this level is the atmospheric pressure (75.0 cm of Hg) plus the pressure exerted by the extra 39.0-cm column of Hg, or a total of 114 cm of Hg. Therefore, the absolute pressure of the gas is

$$114 \text{ cm of Hg} = \tfrac{114}{76} \text{ atm} = 1.50 \text{ atm} = (1.50)(14.7) \text{ lb/in.}^2$$
$$= 22.1 \text{ lb/in.}^2.$$

What is the gauge pressure of the gas?   ◀

QUESTIONS

1. Two bodies have the same shape and size but one is denser than the other. Assuming the air resistance to be the same on each, show that when they are released simultaneously from the same height the heavier body will get to the ground first.

2. Water is poured to the same level in each of the three vessels shown, all of the same base area (Fig. 17–11). If the pressure is the same at the bottom of each vessel, the force experienced by the base of each vessel is the same. Why then do the three vessels have different weights when put on a scale? This apparently contradictory result is commonly known as the "hydrostatic paradox."

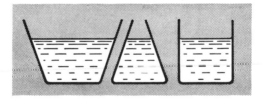

3. Does Archimedes' law hold in a vessel in free fall? In a satellite moving in a circular orbit? Explain.

Fig. 17–11

4. An ice cube is floating in a glass of water. When the ice melts, will the water level rise? Explain.

5. A spherical bob made of cork floats half submerged in a pot of tea at rest on the earth. Will the cork float or sink aboard a spaceship coasting in free space? On the surface of Mars?

6. A ball floats on the surface of water in a container exposed to the atmosphere. Will the ball remain immersed at its former depth or will it sink or rise somewhat if (a) the container is covered and the air is removed, (b) the container is covered and the air is compressed?

7. Explain why an inflated balloon will rise to a definite height once it starts to rise, whereas a submarine will always sink to the bottom of the ocean once it starts to sink, if no changes are made. How then can a submarine stay at a definite level under the water?

8. An open bucket of water is on a smooth plane inclined at an angle α to the horizontal. Find the equilibrium inclination to the horizontal of the free surface of the water when (a) the bucket is held at rest, $a = 0$ and $v = 0$; (b) the bucket is allowed to slide down at constant speed, $a = 0$, $v = $ constant; (c) the bucket slides down without restraint, $a = $ constant. If the plane is curved so that $a \neq$ constant, what will happen?

9. A barge filled with scrap iron is in a canal lock. If the iron is thrown overboard, what happens to the water level in the lock?

10. A bucket of water is suspended from a spring balance. Does the balance reading change when a piece of iron suspended from a string is immersed in the water? When a piece of cork is put in the water?

11. A solid cylinder is placed in a container in contact with the base. When liquid is poured into the container, none of it goes beneath the solid which remains closely in contact with the base. Is there a buoyant force on the solid? Explain.

12. Estimate with some care the buoyant force exerted by the atmosphere on you.

13. An open-tube manometer has one tube twice the diameter of the other. Explain how this would affect the operation of the manometer. Does it matter which end is connected to the chamber whose pressure is to be measured?

PROBLEMS

1. (a) Find the pressure, in $lb/in.^2$, 500 ft below the surface of the ocean. The relative density of sea water is 1.03. (b) Find the pressure in the atmosphere 10 miles above sea level.

2. A simple U-tube contains mercury. When 13.6 cm of water is poured into the right arm, how high does the mercury rise in the left arm from its initial level?

3. In 1654 Otto von Guericke, burgomaster of Magdeburg and inventor of the air pump,

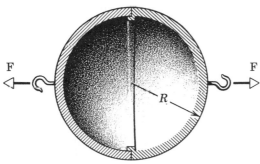

Fig. 17–12

gave a demonstration before the Imperial Diet in which two teams of eight horses could not pull apart two evacuated brass hemispheres. (a) Show that the force F required to pull apart the hemispheres is $F = \pi R^2 P$ where R is the (outside) radius of the hemispheres and P is the difference in pressure outside and inside the sphere (Fig. 17–12). (b) Taking R equal to 1 ft and the inside pressure as 0.1 atm, what force would the team of horses have had to exert to pull apart the hemispheres? (c) Why were two teams of horses used? Would not one team prove the point just as well?

4. The height at which the pressure in the atmosphere is just $1/e$ that at sea level is called the *scale height* of the atmosphere at sea level. (a) Show that the scale height H at sea level is also the height of an atmosphere that has the same density everywhere as at sea level and that will exert the same pressure at sea level as the actual infinite atmosphere does. (b) Show that the scale height at sea level is 8.6 km.

5. Water stands at a depth D behind the vertical upstream face of a dam, as shown in Fig. 17–13. Let W be the width of the dam. (a) Find the resultant force exerted on the dam by the water and the torque exerted about O by this force. (b) What is the line of action of the equivalent resultant force?

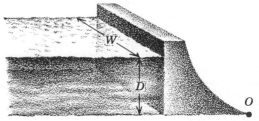

Fig. 17–13

6. A swimming pool has the dimensions 80 ft × 30 ft × 8 ft. When it is filled with water, what is the force on the bottom? On the ends? On the sides?

7. A U-tube is filled with a single homogeneous liquid. The liquid is temporarily depressed in one side by a piston. The piston is removed and the level of the liquid in each side oscillates. Show that the period of oscillation is $\pi\sqrt{2L/g}$ where L is the total length of the liquid in the tube.

8. The surface of contact of two fluids of different densities that are at rest and do not mix is horizontal. Prove this general result (a) from the fact that the potential energy of a system must be a minimum in stable equilibrium; (b) from the fact that at any two points in a horizontal plane in either fluid the pressures are equal.

9. (a) Consider a container of fluid subject to a *vertical upward* acceleration a. Show that the pressure variation with depth in the fluid is given by

$$p = \rho h(g + a),$$

where h is the depth and ρ is the density. (b) Show also that if the fluid as a whole undergoes a *vertical downward* acceleration a, the pressure at a depth h is given by

$$p = \rho h(g - a).$$

(c) What is the state of affairs in free fall?

10. (a) Consider the horizontal acceleration of a mass of liquid in an open container. Acceleration of this kind causes the liquid surface to drop at the front of the tank and to rise at the rear. Show that the liquid surface slopes at an angle θ with the horizontal, where $\tan \theta = a/g$, a being the horizontal acceleration. (b) How does the pressure vary with depth?

11. (a) A fluid mass is rotating at constant angular velocity ω about the central vertical axis of a cylindrical container. Show that the variation of pressure in the radial direction is given by

$$\frac{dp}{dr} = \rho\omega^2 r.$$

(b) Take $p = p_c$ at the axis of rotation ($r = 0$) and show that the pressure p at any point r is

$$p = p_c + \tfrac{1}{2}\rho\omega^2 r^2.$$

(c) Show that the liquid surface is of paraboloidal form (Fig. 17–14); that is, a vertical cross section of

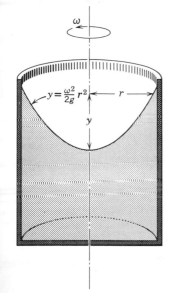

Fig. 17–14

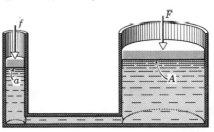

Fig. 17–15

the surface is the curve $y = \omega^2 r^2/2g$. (d) Show that the variation of pressure with depth is $dp = \rho g\,dh$.

12. A piston of small cross-sectional area a is used in the hydraulic press to exert a small force f on the enclosed liquid. A connecting pipe leads to a larger piston of cross-sectional area A (Fig. 17–15). (a) What force F will the larger piston sustain? (b) If the small piston

has a diameter of 1.5 in. and the large piston one of 21 in., what weight on the small piston will support 2 tons on the large piston?

13. What is the minimum area of a block of ice 1.0 ft thick floating on water that will hold up an automobile weighing 2500 lb? Does it matter where the car is placed on the block of ice?

14. An iron casting weighs 60 lb in air and 40 lb in water. What is the volume of cavities in the casting?

15. A hollow spherical iron shell floats almost completely submerged in water. If the outer diameter is 2.0 ft and the relative density of iron is 7.8, find the inner diameter.

16. A block of wood floats in water with two-thirds of its volume submerged. In oil it has 0.9 of its volume submerged. Find the density of the wood and the oil.

17. Assume the density of brass weights to be 8 gm/cm^3 and that of air to be 0.0012 gm/cm^3. What per cent error e arises from neglecting the buoyancy of air in weighing an object of m gm and relative density ρ on a beam balance?

Fluid Dynamics

CHAPTER 18

18-1 General Concepts of Fluid Flow

One way of describing the motion of a fluid would be to try the formidable task of following the motion of each individual particle in the fluid. We would give coordinates x, y, z to each fluid particle and specify these as functions of the time t. The coordinates x, y, z at the time t of the fluid particle which was at x_0, y_0, z_0 at the time t_0 would be determined by functions $x(x_0, y_0, z_0, t_0, t)$, $y(x_0, y_0, z_0, t_0, t)$, $z(x_0, y_0, z_0, t_0, t)$, which then describe the motion of the fluid. This procedure is a direct generalization of the concepts of particle mechanics and was first developed by Joseph-Louis Lagrange (1736–1813).

There is a treatment, developed by Leonard Euler (1707–1783), which is more convenient for most purposes. In it we give up the attempt to specify the history of each fluid particle and instead specify the density and the velocity of the fluid at each point in space at each instant of time. This is the method we shall follow here. We describe the motion of the fluid by specifying the density $\rho(x, y, z, t)$ and the velocity $\mathbf{v}(x, y, z, t)$ at the point (x, y, z) at the time t. We thus focus our attention on what is happening at a particular point in space at a particular time, rather than on what is happening to a particular fluid particle. Any quantity used in describing the state of the fluid, for example the pressure p, will have a definite value at each point in space and at each instant of time. Although this description of fluid motion focuses attention on a point in space rather than on a fluid particle, we cannot avoid following the fluid particles themselves, at least for short time intervals dt. For it is the particles, after all, and not the space points, to which the laws of mechanics apply.

In order to understand the nature of the simplifications we shall make, let us consider first some general characteristics of fluid flow.

Fluid flow can be *steady* or *nonsteady*. When the fluid velocity **v** at any given point is constant in time, the fluid motion is said to be steady. That is, at any given point in a steady flow the velocity of each passing fluid particle is always the same. At some other point a particle may travel with a different velocity, but every other particle which passes this second point behaves there just as this particle did when it passed this point. These conditions can be achieved at low flow speeds. In nonsteady flow the velocities **v** *are* a function of the time. In the case of turbulent flow the velocities vary erratically from point to point as well as from time to time.

Fluid flow can be *rotational* or *irrotational*. If the element of fluid at each point has no net angular velocity about that point, the fluid flow is irrotational. We can imagine a small paddle wheel immersed in the moving fluid (Fig. 18–1). If the wheel moves without rotating, the motion is irrotational; otherwise it is rotational. Irrotational flow is important chiefly because it yields fairly simple mathematical problems. Angular momentum will play

Fig. 18–1 A small paddle wheel placed in a flowing liquid rotates in rotational flow and does not rotate in irrotational flow.

no role here and **v** is relatively simple. Rotational flow includes vortex motion, such as whirlpools or eddies, and motion in which the velocity vector varies in the transverse direction.

Fluid flow can be *compressible* or *incompressible*. Liquids can usually be considered as flowing incompressibly. But even a highly compressible gas may sometimes undergo unimportant changes in density. Its flow is then practically incompressible. In flight, at speeds much lower than the speed of sound in air, the motion of the air relative to the wings is one of nearly incompressible flow. Ordinary subsonic aerodynamics is an example of incompressible flow. In such cases the density ρ is a constant, independent of x, y, z, and t, and the mathematical treatment of fluid flow is thereby greatly simplified.

Finally, fluid flow can be *viscous* or *nonviscous*. Viscosity in fluid motion is the analog of friction in the motion of solids. In some cases, such as in lubrication problems, it is extremely important. Often, however, it is negligible. When it is present, viscosity introduces tangential forces between layers of fluid in relative motion and results in dissipation of mechanical energy.

Fig. 18–2 A particle passing
through points P, Q, and R
traces out a streamline. Any
other particle passing through
P must be traveling along the
same streamline in steady flow.

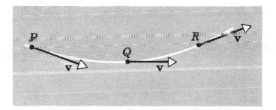

We shall confine our discussion of fluid dynamics for the most part to
steady, irrotational, incompressible, nonviscous flow. The mathematical simplifications resulting should be obvious. Nevertheless, this restricted analysis
has wide application in practice, as we shall see.

18–2 Streamline Flow

In steady flow the velocity **v** at a given point is constant in time. Consider
the point P (Fig. 18–2) within the fluid. Since **v** at P does not change in
time, every particle arriving at P will pass on with the same speed in the same
direction. The same is true about the points Q and R. Hence, if we trace
out the path of the particle, as is done in the figure, that curve will be the
path of every particle arriving at P. This curve is called a *streamline*. A
streamline is parallel to the velocity of the fluid particles at every point. No
two streamlines can ever cross one another, for if they did, an oncoming
fluid particle could go either one way or the other, and the flow could not be
steady.

In principle we can draw a streamline through every point in the fluid.
Let us select a finite number of streamlines to form a bundle, like the streamline pattern of Fig. 18–3. This tubular region is called a *tube of flow*. The
boundary of such a tube consists of streamlines and is always parallel to the
velocity of the fluid particles. Hence, *no fluid can cross the boundaries of a
tube of flow* and the tube behaves somewhat like a pipe of the same shape.

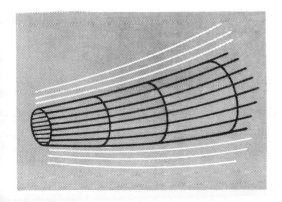

Fig. 18–3 A tube of flow made up
of a bundle of streamlines.

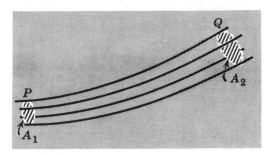

Fig. 18–4 A tube of flow used in proving the equation of continuity.

The fluid that enters at one end must leave at the other. In steady flow the pattern of streamlines in the fluid is stationary in time.*

18–3   The Equation of Continuity

In Fig. 18–4 we have drawn a thin tube of flow. The velocity of the fluid inside, although parallel to the tube at any point, may have different magnitudes at different points. Let the speed be v_1 for fluid particles at P and v_2 for fluid particles at Q. Let A_1 and A_2 be the cross-sectional areas of the tubes perpendicular to the streamlines at the points P and Q, respectively. In the time interval Δt a fluid element travels approximately the distance $v\,\Delta t$. Then the mass of fluid Δm crossing A_1 in the time interval Δt is approximately

$$\Delta m_1 = \rho_1 A_1 v_1\,\Delta t$$

or the *mass flux* $\Delta m_1/\Delta t$ is approximately

$$\frac{\Delta m_1}{\Delta t} = \rho_1 A_1 v_1.$$

We must take Δt small enough so that in this time interval neither v nor A varies appreciably over the distance the fluid travels. In the limit as $\Delta t \to 0$, we obtain the precise result

$$\frac{dm_1}{dt} = \rho_1 A_1 v_1 \qquad \text{at } P.$$

Now at Q the mass flux is correspondingly

$$\frac{dm_2}{dt} = \rho_2 A_2 v_2 \qquad \text{at } Q,$$

where ρ_1 and ρ_2 are the fluid densities at P and Q respectively. Since no

---

* The path or line of motion and the streamline coincide only for steady flow. The streamline gives the *instantaneous* direction of the velocity of all the fluid particles along that line. In nonsteady flow the path traced out by a *given* fluid particle *as time goes on* does not coincide with the streamline for a given instant. The streamline changes as time goes on in nonsteady flow, so that the streamline and the line of motion touch each other at the point where the fluid particle is located at the instant in question. Steady flow is clearly a simpler case to visualize and analyze.

fluid can leave through the walls of the tube and there are no "sources" or "sinks" wherein fluid can be created or destroyed in the tube, the mass crossing each section of the tube per unit time must be the same. Hence,

$$\frac{dm_1}{dt} = \frac{dm_2}{dt}$$

or

$$\rho_1 A_1 v_1 = \rho_2 A_2 v_2, \tag{18-1}$$

and

$$\rho A v = \text{constant}.$$

This result (Eq. 18-1) is called the *equation of continuity* of mass flow. It expresses the law of conservation of mass in fluid dynamics.

Would you expect Eq. 18-1 to hold when the flow is viscous? When it is rotational?

In the more general case in which sources or sinks are present and in which the density varies with time as well as position, the equation of continuity can easily be constructed. It is only necessary that the mass be conserved. For the special case in which the fluid velocity **v** has only an x component, v_x, we obtain *

$$\frac{d(\rho v_x)}{dx} + \frac{d\rho}{dt} = Q. \tag{18-2}$$

In this expression the first term $d(\rho v_x)/dx$ gives the increase in mass flux per unit cross-sectional area per unit distance along x, the second term gives the increase in fluid density per unit time, and the third term gives the mass of fluid appearing per unit time per unit volume from a source. For example, if there is no source or sink, then Q is neither positive nor negative but is zero. Suppose that in this case the mass flux per unit cross-sectional area decreases as we proceed along x. Then $d(\rho v_x)/dx$ is negative. Hence, $d\rho/dt$ must be positive, in fact, equal to $-d(\rho v_x)/dx$, corresponding to the fact that in such a case the density must be increasing with time as the fluid "piles up" during its flow. The student can easily construct other situations to test Eq. 18-2. Is Eq. 18-2 dimensionally correct?

If the fluid is incompressible, as we shall henceforth assume, then $\rho_1 = \rho_2$ and Eq. 18-1 takes on the simpler form

$$Av = \text{constant}$$

or

$$A_1 v_1 = A_2 v_2. \tag{18-3}$$

The product Av gives the *volume flux* or flow rate, as it is often called. Notice that it predicts that in steady incompressible flow the speed of flow varies inversely with the cross-sectional area, being larger in narrower parts of the tube. The fact that the product Av remains constant along a tube of flow allows us to interpret the streamline picture somewhat. In a narrow part of the tube the streamlines must crowd closer together than in a wide part. Hence, as the distance between streamlines decreases, the fluid speed must increase. Therefore, we conclude that widely spaced streamlines indicate regions of low speed and closely spaced streamlines indicate regions of high speed.

---

* Strictly speaking we should write the derivatives as partial derivatives, since v and ρ are functions of several variables.

We can obtain another interesting result by applying the second law of motion to the flow of fluid between P and Q. A fluid particle at P with speed v_1 must be decelerated in the forward direction in acquiring the smaller forward speed v_2 at Q. Hence, the fluid is decelerated in going from P to Q. The deceleration can come about from a difference in pressure acting on the fluid particle flowing from P to Q or from the force of gravity. In a horizontal tube of flow the gravitational force does not change. Hence, we can conclude that in steady horizontal flow the pressure is greatest where the speed is least.

Were you ever in a crowd when it started to push its way through a small opened door? Outside in the back of the crowd the cross-sectional area was large, the pressure was great, but the speed of advance rather small. Through the door of small cross section the pressure was relieved and the speed of advance gratifyingly increased. This particular "human fluid" is compressible and viscous, of course, and the flow is sometimes turbulent and rotational.

18–4 Bernoulli's Equation

A fundamental equation of fluid dynamics is Bernoulli's equation. It is essentially a statement of the work-energy theorem for fluid flow.

Consider the nonviscous, steady, incompressible flow of a fluid through the pipeline or tube of flow in Fig. 18–5. The portion of pipe shown in the figure

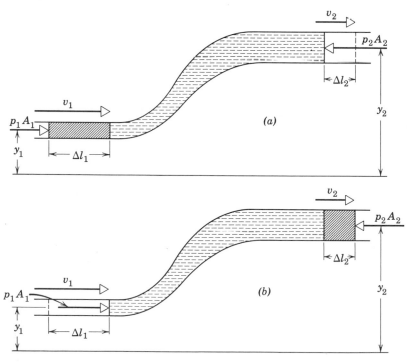

Fig. 18–5 A portion of fluid (cross-shading *and* horizontal shading) moves through a section of pipeline from position (*a*) to position (*b*).

has a uniform cross section A_1 at the left. It is horizontal there at an elevation y_1 above some reference level. It gradually widens and rises and then at the right has a uniform cross section A_2. It is horizontal there at an elevation y_2. Let us concentrate our attention on the portion of fluid represented by both cross-shading and horizontal shading and call this fluid the "system." Consider then the motion of the system from the position shown in (a) to that in (b).

At all points in the narrow part of the pipe, the pressure is p_1 and the speed v_1. At all points in the wide part the pressure is p_2 and the speed v_2. The left portion of the system (cross-shading, Fig. 18-5a) advances a distance Δl_1, parallel to an external force $p_1 A_1$ supplied by the fluid to its left, so that the work done *on* the system is $p_1 A_1 \, \Delta l_1$. The right portion of the system (cross-shading, Fig. 18-5b) advances a distance Δl_2 against an oppositely directed force $p_2 A_2$ supplied by the fluid beyond, so that the work done *by* the system is $p_2 A_2 \, \Delta l_2$. Hence, to move the system from position (a) to position (b), a net amount of work must be done on the system by the pressures applied to it equal to

$$p_1 A_1 \, \Delta l_1 - p_2 A_2 \, \Delta l_2.$$

Now $A_1 \, \Delta l_1$ and $A_2 \, \Delta l_2$ are the volumes of the two cross-shaded regions. These volumes are equal because the fluid is incompressible. In fact, if we let m be the mass of either cross-shaded region and take the fluid density to be ρ, then

$$A_1 \, \Delta l_1 = A_2 \, \Delta l_2 = \frac{m}{\rho},$$

and $\qquad\qquad (p_1 - p_2)\dfrac{m}{\rho} = \text{net work done on system.}$

If our pipe has a continuously variable cross section, this analysis can be made exact by considering the process in the limit as Δl_1, Δl_2, and Δt shrink to zero at the points 1 and 2. The result is the same as before.

If the flow is nonviscous, the net work done on the system by pressure must equal the net gain in mechanical energy. The horizontal shaded portion of the fluid does not change at all in either kinetic or potential energy during the flow from (a) to (b). Only the cross-shaded portions contribute to changes in mechanical energy. In fact,

$$\tfrac{1}{2}mv_2{}^2 - \tfrac{1}{2}mv_1{}^2 = \text{net change of kinetic energy,}$$

and $\qquad mgy_2 - mgy_1 = \text{net change in gravitational potential energy,}$

where m is the mass in either cross-shaded region. Hence,

$$(p_1 - p_2)\frac{m}{\rho} = (\tfrac{1}{2}mv_2{}^2 - \tfrac{1}{2}mv_1{}^2) + (mgy_2 - mgy_1) \qquad (18\text{-}4)$$

or on rearranging terms,

$$p_1 + \tfrac{1}{2}\rho v_1{}^2 + \rho g y_1 = p_2 + \tfrac{1}{2}\rho v_2{}^2 + \rho g y_2. \qquad (18\text{-}5)$$

Since the subscripts 1 and 2 refer to *any* two locations along the pipeline, we can drop the subscripts and write

$$p + \tfrac{1}{2}\rho v^2 + \rho g y = \text{constant.} \tag{18-6}$$

Either Eq. 18–5 or Eq. 18–6 is called *Bernoulli's equation* for steady, non-viscous, incompressible flow. It was first presented by Daniel Bernoulli (1700–1782) in his *Hydrodynamica* in 1738.

Bernoulli's equation is strictly applicable only to steady flow. The quantities involved must be evaluated along the same streamline; hence, the constant in Eq. 18–6 is not the same for all streamlines. In our figure the streamline used is along the central portion of the tube of flow or pipeline.

In a nonviscous incompressible fluid we cannot change the temperature of the fluid by mechanical means. Hence, Bernoulli's equation, as stated above, refers to isothermal (constant temperature) processes. It is possible, however, to change the temperature of a nonviscous compressible fluid by mechanical means. We can generalize this equation to include a compressible fluid by adding to the left of Eq. 18–6 a term u, which represents the *internal energy* per unit volume of the fluid. This term (and the pressure p) will have a value that depends on the temperature.

If the flow is viscous, forces of a frictional nature act on the fluid. Some of the work done by pressure, computed for the incompressible case, goes into heat energy rather than into an increase in mechanical energy. Then, of course, the change in mechanical energy is less than the work done by pressure, and Eq. 18–4 can be written as

$$(p_1 - p_2)\frac{m}{\rho} = (\tfrac{1}{2}mv_2{}^2 - \tfrac{1}{2}mv_1{}^2) + (mgy_2 - mgy_1) + Q,$$

where Q represents the heat energy generated in the viscous flow from point 1 to point 2. In practice Bernoulli's equation can be modified accordingly by use of empirical corrections for conversion of mechanical energy to heat energy. However, if the pipe is smooth and the diameter is large compared to the length, and if the fluid flows slowly and has a small viscosity, the heat generated is negligible.

Just as the statics of a particle is a special case of particle dynamics, so fluid statics is a special case of fluid dynamics. It should come as no surprise, therefore, that the law of pressure change with height in a fluid at rest is included in Bernoulli's equation as a special case. For let the fluid be at rest; then $v_1 = 0 = v_2$ and Eq. 18–5 becomes

$$p_1 + \rho g y_1 = p_2 + \rho g y_2$$

or
$$p_2 - p_1 = -\rho g(y_2 - y_1),$$

which is the same as Eq. 17–3.

In Eq. 18–6 all terms have the dimension of a pressure (check this). The pressure $p + \rho g h$, which would be present even if there were no flow, is denoted as the *static pressure;* the term $\tfrac{1}{2}\rho v^2$ is called *dynamic pressure*.

18–5   Applications of Bernoulli's Equation and the Equation of Continuity

In general, Bernoulli's equation is used to determine fluid velocities by means of pressure measurements. The principle generally used in such measuring devices is the following: The equation of continuity requires that the speed of the fluid at a constriction increase; Bernoulli's equation then shows that the pressure must fall there. That is, for a horizontal pipe $\frac{1}{2}\rho v^2 + p$

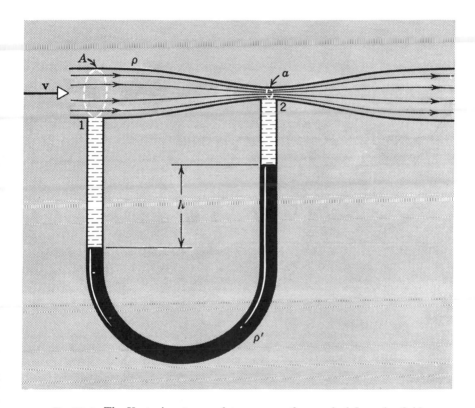

Fig. 18–6   The Venturi meter, used to measure the speed of flow of a fluid.

equals a constant; if v increases and the fluid is incompressible, p must decrease. This result was also deduced from dynamic considerations in Section 18–3.

1. The *Venturi meter* (Fig. 18–6) is a gauge put in the flow pipe to measure the flow speed of a liquid. A liquid of density ρ flows through a pipe of cross sectional area A. At the throat the area is reduced to a and a manometer tube is attached, as shown. Let the manometer liquid, such as mercury, have a density ρ'. By applying Bernoulli's equation and the equation of

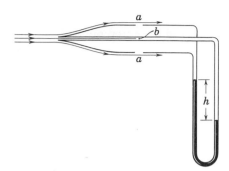

Fig. 18-7   Cross-sectional diagram of a Pitot tube.

continuity at points 1 and 2, the student can show that the speed of flow at A is

$$v = a \sqrt{\frac{2(\rho' - \rho)gh}{\rho(A^2 - a^2)}}.$$

If we want the volume flux or flow rate Q, which is the volume of liquid transported past any point per second, we simply compute

$$Q = vA.$$

2. The *Pitot tube* (Fig. 18-7) is used to measure the flow speed of a gas. Consider the gas, say air, flowing past the openings at a. These openings are parallel to the direction of flow and are set far enough back so that the velocity and pressure outside the openings have the free-stream values. The pressure in the left arm of the manometer, which is connected to these openings, is then the static pressure in the gas stream, p_a. The opening of the right arm of the manometer is at right angles to the stream. The velocity is reduced to zero at b and the gas is stagnant at that point. The pressure at b is the full ram pressure, p_b. Applying Bernoulli's equation to points a and b, we obtain

$$p_a + \tfrac{1}{2}\rho v^2 = p_b,$$

where, as shown in the figure, p_b is greater than p_a. If h is the difference in height of the liquid in the manometer arms and ρ' is the density of the manometer liquid, then

$$p_a + \rho'gh = p_b.$$

Comparing these two equations, we find

$$\tfrac{1}{2}\rho v^2 = \rho'gh$$

or

$$v = \sqrt{\frac{2gh\rho'}{\rho}},$$

which gives the gas speed. This device can be calibrated to read v directly and is then known as an air-speed indicator.

3. Let us consider the *lift on an airplane wing*. Figure 18-8 shows the steady flow pattern past an airfoil, the cross section of an airplane wing, in

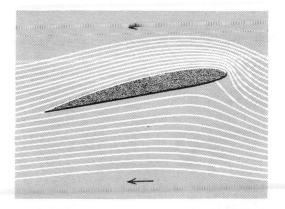

Fig. 18–8 Streamlines about an airfoil.

a wind tunnel. Airfoils characteristically have a sharp trailing edge and greater curvature on the upper surface than on the lower. This shape results in a greater flow speed past the upper surface than past the lower, which can be seen from the streamline pattern in the figure. The crowding of the streamlines above the airfoil shows that the air speed there is greater than the free-stream speed. The pressure on the top of the wing, therefore, drops below the free-stream pressure, by Bernoulli's law. On the bottom of the wing the flow speed is generally lower than the free-stream speed and the pressure is greater than the free-stream pressure. The pressure difference between the bottom and top surfaces results in an upward force, or lift.

If the angle between the flow direction and the airfoil is increased enough, the flow may cease to be steady and turbulence sets in. Then Bernoulli's equation no longer holds. In fact, the pressure above the wing rises, the lift decreases, and the airplane may stall.

4. As our final example let us compute the *thrust on a rocket* produced by the escape of its exhaust gases. Consider a chamber (Fig. 18–9) of cross-sectional area A filled with a gas of density ρ at a pressure p. Let there be a small orifice of cross-sectional area A_0 at the bottom of the chamber. We wish to find the speed v_0 with which the gas escapes through the orifice.

Let us write Bernoulli's equation (Eq. 18–5) as

$$p_1 - p_2 = \rho g(y_2 - y_1) + \tfrac{1}{2}\rho(v_2{}^2 - v_1{}^2).$$

For a gas the density is so small that we can neglect the variation in pressure with height in a chamber (see Section 17–3). Hence, if p represents the pressure p_1 in the chamber and p_0 represents the atmospheric pressure p_2 just outside the orifice, we have

$$p - p_0 = \tfrac{1}{2}\rho(v_0{}^2 - v^2)$$

or $$v_0{}^2 = \frac{2(p - p_0)}{\rho} + v^2 \qquad (18\text{–}7)$$

where v is the speed of the flowing gas inside the chamber and v_0 is the *speed of efflux* of the gas through the orifice. Although a gas is compressible and

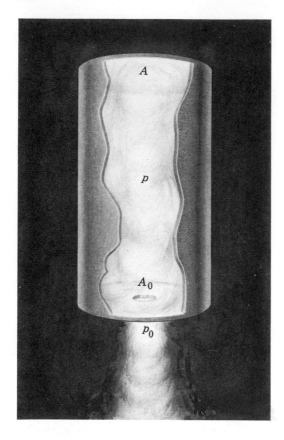

Fig. 18-9 Fluid streaming out of a chamber.

the flow may become turbulent, we can treat the flow as steady and incompressible for pressure and efflux speeds that are not too high.

Now let us assume continuity of mass flow (in a rocket engine this is achieved when the mass of escaping gas equals the mass of gas created by burning the fuel), so that (for an assumed constant density)

$$Av = A_0 v_0.$$

If the orifice is very small so that $A_0 \ll A$, then $v_0 \gg v$, and we can neglect v^2 compared to v_0^2 in Eq. 18–7. Hence, the speed of efflux is

$$v_0 = \sqrt{\frac{2(p - p_0)}{\rho}}. \tag{18–8}$$

If our chamber is the exhaust chamber of a rocket, the thrust on the rocket (Section 9–6) is $v_0 \, dM/dt$. But the mass of gas flowing out in time dt is $dM = \rho A_0 v_0 \, dt$, so that

$$v_0 \frac{dM}{dt} = v_0 \rho A_0 v_0 = \rho A_0 v_0{}^2,$$

and from Eq. 18–8 the thrust is

$$2A_0(p - p_0).$$

18-6　Other Conservation Laws in Fluid Mechanics

In Newtonian particle mechanics the derivation of the laws of conservation of linear momentum and angular momentum makes explicit use of Newton's third law of motion. The internal forces and torques in a mechanical system cancel one another because of this third law, leaving only the external forces and torques to contribute to the momenta. In the case of a fluid the internal forces are represented by the pressure within the fluid. But the very concept of pressure itself contains Newton's third law implicitly. The force produced by pressure exerted in one direction across any surface element is equal and opposite to the force exerted in the opposite direction across the same surface element. Also, each of these two forces is applied at the same place, namely at the surface element. Both forces must have the same line of action. Hence, in the equations for the time rate of change of linear momentum or of angular momentum of a fluid, the internal pressures will cancel out. We can conclude then that the time rate of change of the total linear momentum in a volume V of moving fluid is equal to the total *external force* acting on it. Likewise, the time rate of change of the total angular momentum in a volume V of moving fluid is equal to the total *external torque* acting on it. The conservation laws of linear and angular momentum follow.

The vortices formed when a liquid flows out through a small hole in the bottom of a container are due to the law of conservation of angular momentum. The only external force is gravity, which exerts no torque about the hole. Hence, the angular momentum of the fluid remains constant. If a fluid element has any angular momentum at all initially, when it is some distance from the hole, its angular velocity will have to increase as it approaches the hole in order for its angular momentum to remain constant.

18-7　Fields of Flow

In the chapter on gravitation we saw how to summarize the physical state of affairs near masses by use of a field. Each point in the field can be regarded as having a vector associated with it, namely **g**, the gravitational force per unit mass at that point. Or, alternately, we can associate a scalar quantity with each point in space, namely the gravitational potential V. We can then draw a surface, called an equipotential surface, through all points that have the same potential. We draw several such surfaces, the potential on one differing by a constant amount from that on the next one, etc. The gravitational force at any point is then directed along a line passing through this point perpendicular to these surfaces, and its magnitude is determined from the rate of change of potential with distance in this direction, as indicated by the spacing and orientation of the equipotential surfaces. By drawing in lines of force we can picture vividly how space is affected by the presence of mass.

Likewise, in fluid dynamics we can summarize the physical state of affairs within a moving fluid by means of a field of flow. In general, the field of flow is a *vector* field. We associate a vector quantity with each point in space, namely the flow velocity **v** at that point. For a steady flow the field of flow is stationary. Of course, even in this case a particular fluid particle may still have a variable velocity as it moves from point to point in the field. The field gives the properties of the space from which we deduce the behavior of particles in that space. If the flow is irrotational, as well as steady, we call it *potential flow*. Then the flow velocity **v** can be related to a velocity potential ψ, just as in gravitation $\mathbf{g}$ can be related to the gravitational potential V. If we draw in surfaces of equal velocity potential, as we drew in surfaces of equal gravitational potential, we can deduce $\mathbf{v}$ from the equipotential flow surfaces just as $\mathbf{g}$ is deduced from the equipotential gravitational surfaces. Hence, a field for potential flow is analogous to a conservative force field.

A flowing fluid mass can always be divided into tubes of flow. When the flow is steady, the tubes remain unchanged in shape and the fluid that is at one instant in a tube remains inside this tube thereafter. We have seen that the flow velocity inside a tube of flow is parallel to the tube and has a magnitude inversely proportional to the area of the cross section (Eq. 18–1). Let us assign such cross sections to the tubes that the constant of proportionality is the same for all of them; if possible we take this constant to be unity. That is, the volume flux is the same for all tubes, namely unit flux. Then the magnitude of the flow velocity can be determined from the areas of the cross sections of the tubes of flow. There is another procedure equivalent to this which consists of setting up a unit area perpendicular to the direction of flow and drawing through it just as many streamlines as the number of units of magnitude of the velocity at that point.

Let us consider some examples of fields of flow. For drawing purposes we consider only *two-dimensional* examples. In these the flow velocity is the same at all points on a line perpendicular to the plane at any point.

In Fig. 18–10 we have drawn a *homogeneous field of flow*. Here all the streamlines are parallel and the flow velocity $\mathbf{v}$ is the same at all points. We have seen that there are two equivalent ways of deriving the relative magnitudes of the flow velocities from such fields of flow: (a) from the widths of the tubes of flow and (b) from the distances between lines of equal velocity potential. The latter method applies to steady irrotational flow only. For such flows we draw in the lines of equal velocity potential as dashed lines.

In Fig. 18–11 we show the field for a *uniform rotation* (see Problem 11, Chapter 17). Here v is proportional to r. In Fig. 18–12 we draw the field of flow of a *vortex*. In this case v is proportional to $1/r$ (see Problem 19). These are examples of rotational flow. Notice that both uniform rotation and vortex motion are represented by circular streamlines but are entirely different kinds of flow. Obviously the *shapes* of the streamlines give only limited information; their spacing is needed too.

Figure 18–13 represents the field of flow for a *source*. All streamlines are directed radially outward. The source is a line through O perpendicular to the paper emitting a fixed mass per unit time Q. The field of flow around a linear *sink* is shown in Fig. 18–14 and is the same as the source except for the sign of the flow.

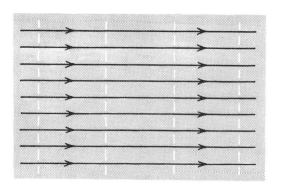

Fig. 18–10 Streamlines (———) and surfaces of equal velocity potential (– – –) for a homogeneous field of flow.

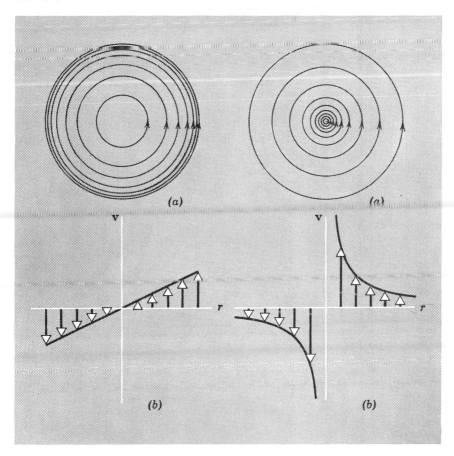

Fig. 18-11 (a) Uniform rotational field of flow. (b) Variation of fluid velocity from the center.

Fig. 18-12 (a) Vortical field of flow. (b) Variation of fluid velocity from the center.

For a linear source and linear sink which have the same strengths, Q and −Q, and are slightly separated, we obtain the combined field called *linear dipole flow*, shown in Fig. 18-15.

As we shall see later the electrostatic field, the magnetic field, and the field of flow for an electric current are also vector fields. In this connection, the homogeneous field (Fig. 18-10) corresponds to the electric field of a plane capacitor, the source field and sink field (Figs. 18-13 and 18-14) correspond to the electric field of a cylindrical capacitor or straight wire of positive and negative charge respectively, and the linear dipole field (Fig. 18-15) corresponds to the electric field of two oppositely charged wires. In all these the field of flow is potential flow and the electric fields are conservative.

The homogeneous field of Fig. 18-10 also represents the magnetic field inside a solenoid. The vortex field of Fig. 18-12 represents the magnetic field around a straight current-carrying wire. This last is an example of a rotational field.

Because of these analogies between fluid and electromagnetic fields, we can often determine a field of flow, which is impossible to calculate by present mathematical methods, by experimental measurements on appropriate electrical devices.

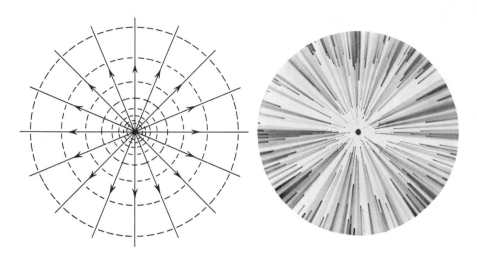

Fig. 18–13 Left, flow from a linear point source.   Right, fluid flow map of the same.   The maps in this figure and Fig. 18–14 are made by allowing water to flow between a horizontal layer of plate glass and a horizontal layer of plaster.   In the right diagram the water comes up through a hole in the center of the plaster and flows out toward the edges.   The direction of the flow is made visible by sprinkling the plaster with potassium permanganate crystals which dissolve and color the water a deep red.   (The fluid flow maps were made and photographed by Professor A. D. Moore at the University of Michigan, and are taken from *Introduction to Electric Fields*, by W. E. Rogers, McGraw-Hill Book Co., 1954.)

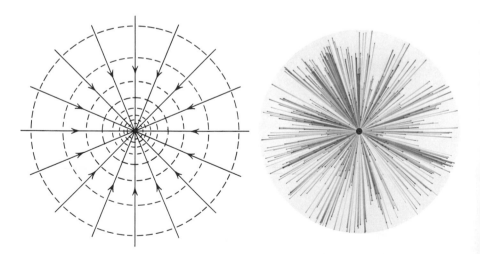

Fig. 18–14 Left, flow into a linear point sink.   Right, a fluid flow map of the same.

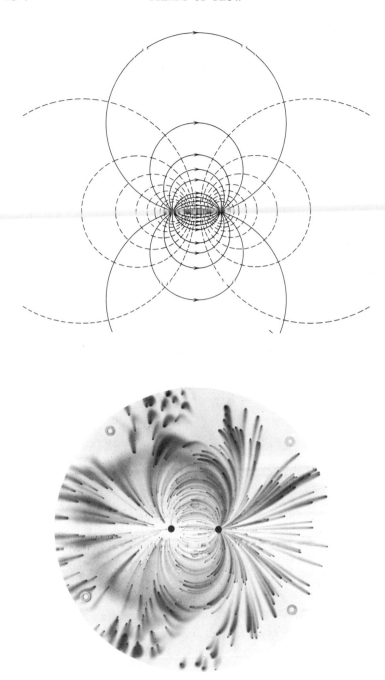

Fig. 18-15   Top, linear dipole flow.   The source is on the left, the sink on the right.   Bottom, a fluid flow map of the same.   (The fluid flow maps were made and photographed by Professor A. D. Moore at the University of Michigan, and are taken from *Introduction to Electric Fields*, by W. E. Rogers, McGraw-Hill Book Co., 1954.)

As we have seen throughout this chapter, the basic field ideas and conservation principles find application in many areas of physics. We shall encounter them many times again.

QUESTIONS

1. Can you assign a coefficient of static friction between two surfaces, one of which is a fluid surface?

2. Describe the forces acting on an element of fluid as it flows through a pipe of nonuniform cross section.

3. The height of the liquid in the standpipes indicates that the pressure drops along the channel, even though the channel has a uniform cross section and the flowing liquid is incompressible (Fig. 18–16). Explain.

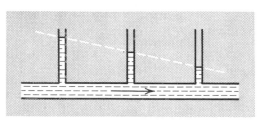

Fig. 18–16

4. (a) Explain how a pitcher can make a baseball curve to his right or left. Justify your answer by drawing a diagram of the streamlines and applying Bernoulli's equation. (b) Why is it easier to throw a curve with a tennis ball than with a baseball?

5. Two rowboats moving parallel to one another in the same direction are pulled toward one another. Two automobiles moving parallel are pulled in the same direction. Explain such phenomena on the basis of Bernoulli's equation.

6. Can the action of a parachute in retarding free fall be explained by Bernoulli's equation?

7. Liquid is flowing inside a horizontal pipe which has a constriction along its length. Vertical tube manometers are attached at both the wide portion and the narrow portion of the pipe. If a stopcock at the exit end is closed, will the liquid in the manometer tubes rise or fall? Explain.

8. Can you explain why water flows in a continuous stream down a vertical pipe, whereas it breaks into drops when falling freely?

9. Can you explain why an object falling from a great height reaches a steady terminal speed?

10. Does the difference in pressure between the lower and upper surfaces of an airplane wing depend on the altitude of the moving plane? Explain.

11. The accumulation of ice on an airplane wing may change its shape in such a way that its lift is greatly reduced. Explain.

12. Use the criterion of the paddle wheel (Fig. 18–1) to determine which flow fields (Figs. 18–10 through 18–15) are rotational.

PROBLEMS

1. A garden hose having an internal diameter of 0.75 in. is connected to a lawn sprinkler that consists merely of an enclosure with 24 holes, each 0.05 in. in diameter. If the water in the hose has a speed of 3.0 ft/sec, at what speed does it leave the sprinkler holes?

2. Models of torpedoes are sometimes tested in a pipe of flowing water, much as a wind tunnel is used to test model airplanes. Consider a circular pipe of internal diameter 10.0 in. and a torpedo model, aligned along the axis of the pipe, with a diameter of 2.0 in. The torpedo is to be tested with water flowing past it at 8.0 ft/sec. (a) With what speed must the water flow in the unconstricted part of the pipe? (b) What will the pressure difference be between the constricted and unconstricted parts of the pipe?

3. How much work is done by pressure in forcing 50 ft³ of water through a 0.5-in. pipe if the difference in pressure at the two ends of the pipe is 15 lb/in.²?

4. Water falls from a height of 60 ft at the rate of 500 ft³/min and drives a water turbine. What is the maximum power that can be developed by this turbine?

5. By applying Bernoulli's equation and the equation of continuity to points 1 and 2 of Fig. 18–6, show that the speed of flow at the entrance is

$$v = a \sqrt{\frac{2(\rho' - \rho)gh}{\rho(A^2 - a^2)}}.$$

6. A Venturi meter has a pipe diameter of 10.0 in. and a throat diameter of 5.0 in. If the water pressure in the pipe is 8.0 lb/in.² and in the throat is 6.0 lb/in.², determine the rate of flow of water in ft³/sec (volume flux).

7. Consider the Venturi tube of Fig. 18–6 without the manometer. Let A equal $5a$. Suppose the pressure at A is 2.0 atm. Compute the values of v at A and v' at a that would make the pressure p' at a equal to zero. Compute the corresponding volume flow rate if the diameter at A is 5.0 cm. The phenomenon at a when p' falls to nearly zero is known as *cavitation*. The water vaporizes into small bubbles. This phenomenon is of great theoretical and practical interest.

8. In a horizontal oil pipeline of constant cross-sectional area the pressure decrease between two points 1000 ft apart is 5 lb/in.². What is the energy loss per cubic foot of oil per unit distance?

9. Castle Geyser at Yellowstone National Park shoots water 250 ft into the air. What is the minimum gauge pressure at the base?

10. Figure 18–17 shows liquid discharging from an orifice in a large tank at a distance h below the water level. (a) Apply Bernoulli's equation to a streamline connecting points 1, 2, and 3, and show that the speed of efflux is

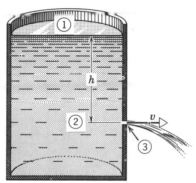

Fig. 18–17

$$v = \sqrt{2gh}.$$

This is known as Torricelli's law. (b) If the orifice were curved directly upward, how high would the liquid stream rise?

11. A tank is filled with water to a height H. A hole is punched in one of the walls at a depth h below the water surface (Fig. 18–18). (a) Find the distance x from the foot of the wall at which the stream strikes the floor. (b) Could a hole be punched at another depth so that this second stream would have the same range? If so, at what depth?

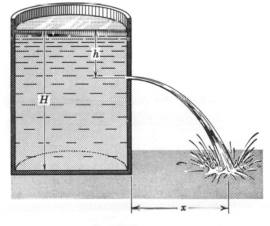

Fig. 18–18

12. The upper surface of water in a standpipe is a height H above level ground. At what depth h should a small hole be put to make the emerging horizontal water stream strike the ground at the maximum distance from the base of the standpipe? What is this maximum distance?

13. Calculate the speed of efflux of a liquid from an opening in a tank, taking into account the velocity of the top surface of the liquid, as follows. (a) Show that

$$v_0^2 = \frac{2gh}{1 - v^2/v_0^2} \qquad \text{from Bernoulli's equation,}$$

where v is the speed of the top surface. (b) Then consider the flow as one big tube of flow and obtain v/v_0 from the equation of continuity, so that

$$v_0 = \sqrt{2gh} \sqrt{\frac{1}{1 - (A_0/A)^2}},$$

where A is the tube cross section at the top and A_0 is the tube cross section at the opening. (c) Then show that if the hole is small compared to the area of the surface,

$$v_0 \cong \sqrt{2gh} \, [1 + \tfrac{1}{2}(A_0/A)^2].$$

14. A Pitot tube is mounted on an airplane wing to determine the speed of the plane relative to the air. The tube contains alcohol and indicates a level difference of 4.9 in. What is the plane's speed in miles/hr relative to the air?

15. Air streams horizontally past an airplane wing of area 36 ft^2 weighing 540 lb. The speed over the top surface is 200 ft/sec and 150 ft/sec under the bottom surface. What is the lift on the wing? The net force on it?

16. If the speed of flow past the lower surface of a wing is 350 ft/sec, what speed of flow over the upper surface will give a lift of 20 lb/ft^2?

17. (a) Consider the stagnant air at the front edge of a wing and the air rushing over the wing surface at a speed v. Find the greatest value possible for v in streamline flow, assuming air is incompressible and using Bernoulli's equation. Take the density of air to be 1.2×10^{-3} gm/cm^3. (b) How does this compare with the speed of sound of 770 miles/hr? Can you explain the difference? Why should there be any connection between these quantities?

18. A hollow tube has a disk DD attached to its end. When air is blown through the tube, the disk attracts the card CC. Let the area of the card be A and let v be the average

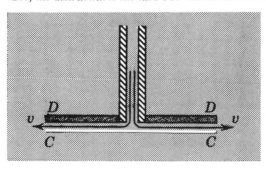

Fig. 18–19

airspeed between CC and DD (Fig. 18–19); calculate the resultant upward force on CC. Neglect the card's weight.

19. Before Newton proposed his theory of gravitation, a model of planetary motion proposed by René Descartes was widely accepted. In Descartes' model the planets were caught in and dragged along by a whirlpool of ether particles centered around the sun. Newton showed that this vortex scheme contradicted observations, for: (a) The speed of an ether particle in the vortex varies inversely as its distance from the sun. (b) The period of revolution of such a particle varies directly as the square of its distance from the sun. (c) This result contradicts Kepler's third law. Prove (a), (b), and (c).

20. A force field is conservative if $\oint \mathbf{F} \cdot d\mathbf{s} = 0$. The circle on the integration sign means that the integration is to be taken along a closed curve (a round trip) in the field. A flow is a potential flow (hence irrotational) if $\oint \mathbf{v} \cdot d\mathbf{s} = 0$ for every closed path in the field.

Using this criterion, show that the fields of Figs. 18–10, 18–13, and 18–14 are fields of potential flow.

21. The so-called Poiseuille field of flow is shown in Fig. 18–20. The spacing of the streamlines indicates that although the motion is rectilinear, there is a velocity gradient in the transverse direction. Show that such a flow is rotational.

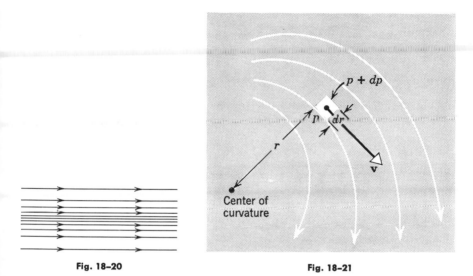

Fig. 18–20   Fig. 18–21

22. In flows that are sharply curved centrifugal effects are appreciable. Consider an element of fluid which is moving with speed v along a streamline of a curved flow in a horizontal plane (Fig. 18–21).

(a) Show that $dp/dr = \rho v^2 / r$, so that the pressure increases by an amount $\rho v^2 / r$ per unit distance perpendicular to the streamline as we go from the concave to the convex side of the streamline.

(b) Then use Bernoulli's equation and this result to show that vr equals a constant, so that speeds increase toward the center of curvature. Hence, streamlines that are uniformly spaced in a straight pipe will be crowded toward the inner wall of a curved passage and widely spaced toward the outer wall. This problem should be compared to Problem 17–11 in which the curved motion is produced by rotating a container. There the speed varied directly with r, but here it varies inversely.

(c) Show that this flow is irrotational.

Waves in Elastic Media

CHAPTER 19

19-1 Mechanical Waves

The phenomenon of wave motion appears in almost every branch of physics. We are all familiar with water waves, since they are so easily observed. There are also sound waves, light waves, radio waves, and other electromagnetic waves. In fact, one formulation of the mechanics of atoms and subatomic particles is called wave mechanics. Clearly, then, the properties and behavior of waves are of great importance in physics.

In this chapter and the next we confine our attention to waves in deformable or elastic media. These waves might be called *mechanical waves*. They originate in the displacement of some portion of an elastic medium from its normal position, causing it to oscillate about an equilibrium position. Because of the elastic properties of the medium, the disturbance is transmitted from one layer to the next. This disturbance, or wave, consequently progresses through the medium. It is important to note that the medium itself does not move as a whole along with the wave motion; the various parts of the medium oscillate only in limited paths. For example, in water waves small floating objects like corks show that the actual motion of various parts of the water is slightly up and down and back and forth. Yet the water waves move steadily along the water. As they reach floating objects they set them in motion, thus transferring energy to them. Energy can be transmitted over considerable distances by wave motion. The energy in the waves is the kinetic and potential energy of the matter, but the transmission of the energy comes about by its being passed along from one part of the matter to the next, not by any long-range motion of the matter itself. Mechanical waves are characterized by the transport of energy through matter by steady, regular motion of a disturbance in that matter without any corresponding bulk motion of the matter itself.

It is necessary to have a medium for the transmission of mechanical waves. No medium is required for the transmission of electromagnetic waves, light passing freely, for example, through the vacuum of outer space from the stars. The medium transmitting a mechanical wave must have inertia and elasticity. Most of us are familiar with the waves in a rope or in a spring, as well as with water waves. In each case the medium has inertia and also elasticity. It is the elasticity which gives rise to restoring forces on any part of the medium displaced from the equilibrium position. In the example of a block suspended from a spring and undergoing simple harmonic motion both inertia and elasticity are present. This oscillatory motion is not a wave motion, however, because there is no energy transported along the spring. Here the elasticity and inertia are entirely separate. Recall that the inertia was assumed to reside entirely in the block and the elasticity (or restoring force) entirely in the spring (Chapter 15). In mechanical wave motion the elasticity and inertia are distributed in some manner throughout the medium. If a spring itself has inertia, as any real spring has, waves can be produced in it and energy transported along it. Hence, oscillatory motion may or may not involve wave motion.

19–2   Types of Waves

In listing water waves, light waves, and sound waves as examples of wave motion, we are classifying waves according to their broad physical properties. Waves can be classified in many other ways.

We can distinguish different kinds of waves by considering how the motions of the particles of matter are related to the direction of propagation of the waves themselves. If the motions of the matter particles conveying the wave are perpendicular to the direction of propagation of the wave itself, we then have a *transverse* wave. For example, when a horizontal rope under tension is set oscillating up and down at one end, a transverse wave travels down the rope; the disturbance moves along the rope, but the rope particles vibrate at right angles to the direction of propagation of the disturbance (Fig. 19–1).

Light waves are not mechanical waves. The disturbance that travels along is not a motion of matter but an electromagnetic field (Chapter 42). But because the electric and magnetic fields are perpendicular to the direction of propagation, light waves are transverse waves.

If, however, the motion of the particles conveying a mechanical wave is back and forth along the direction of propagation, we then have a *longitudinal wave*. For example, when a vertical spring under tension is set oscillating up and down at one end, a longitudinal wave travels along the spring; the coils vibrate back and forth in the direction in which the disturbance travels along the spring (Fig. 19–2). Sound waves are longitudinal waves. We shall discuss them in greater detail in Chapter 20.

Some waves are neither purely longitudinal nor purely transverse. For

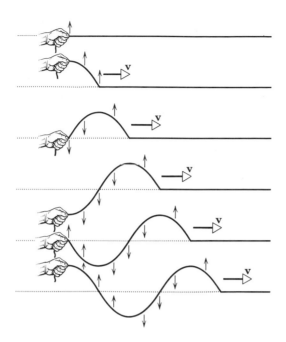

Fig. 19-1 In a transverse wave the particles of the medium (rope) vibrate at right angles to the direction in which the wave itself is propagated.

example, in waves on the surface of water the particles of water move both up and down and back and forth, tracing out elliptical paths as the water waves move by.

Waves can also be classified as one-, two-, and three-dimensional waves, according to the number of dimensions in which they propagate energy. Waves moving along the horizontal string or the vertical spring are one-dimensional. Surface waves or ripples on water are two-dimensional. Sound waves and light waves are three-dimensional.

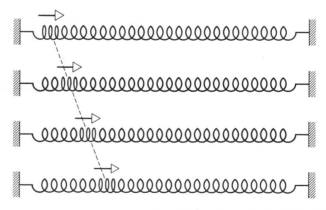

Fig. 19-2 In a longitudinal wave the particles of the medium (spring) vibrate in the same direction as that in which the wave itself is propagated. Note the compressional pulse moving to the right with uniform velocity.

Waves may be classified further according to the behavior of a particle of the matter conveying the wave during the course of time the wave propagates. For example, we can produce a *pulse* or a *single wave* traveling down a taut rope by applying a single sidewise movement at its end. Each particle remains at rest until the pulse reaches it, then it moves during a short time, and then it again remains at rest. If we continue to move the end of the rope back and forth (Fig. 19-1), we produce a *train of waves* traveling along the rope. If our motion is periodic, we produce a *periodic train of waves* in which each particle of the rope has a periodic motion. The simplest special case of a periodic wave is a *simple harmonic wave* which gives each particle a simple harmonic motion.

Consider for a moment a three-dimensional pulse. We can draw a surface through all points undergoing a similar disturbance at a given instant. As time goes on, this surface moves along showing how the pulse propagates. We can draw similar surfaces for subsequent pulses. For a periodic wave we can generalize the idea by drawing in surfaces, all of whose points are in the same phase of motion. These surfaces are called *wavefronts*. If the medium is homogeneous and isotropic, the direction of propagation is always at right angles to the wave front. A line normal to the wavefronts, indicating the direction of motion of the waves, is called a *ray*.

Wavefronts can have many shapes. If the disturbances are propagated in a single direction, the waves are called *plane waves*. At a given instant conditions are the same everywhere on any plane perpendicular to the direction of propagation. The wavefronts are plane and the rays are parallel straight lines (Fig. 19-3). Another simple case is that of *spherical waves*. Here the disturbance is propagated out in all directions from a point source of waves. The wavefronts are spheres and the rays are radial lines leaving the point source in all directions (Fig. 19-4). Far from the source the spherical wavefronts have very small curvature, and over a limited region they can often be regarded as plane. Of course, there are many other possible

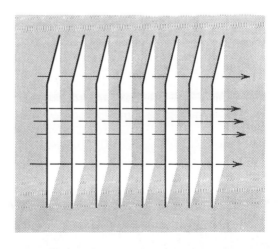

Fig. 19-3 A plane wave. The planes represent wavefronts spaced a wavelength apart, and the arrows represent rays.

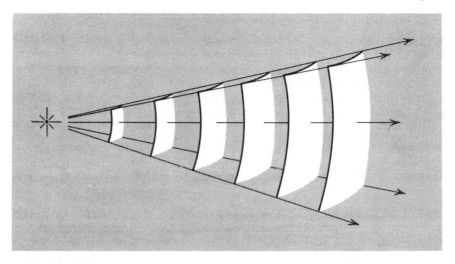

Fig. 19–4 A spherical wave. The rays are radial and the wavefronts, spaced a wavelength apart, form spherical shells. Far out from the source, however, small portions of the wavefronts become nearly plane.

shapes for wavefronts. Each one in a sense can be considered as defining a class of waves.

We shall refer to all these wave types as we progress through the wave phenomena of physics. In this chapter we often use the transverse wave in a string to illustrate the general properties of waves. In the next chapter we shall see the consequences of these properties for sound, a longitudinal mechanical wave. Later in the text the properties of nonmechanical waves such as light and matter waves will be discussed.

19–3 Traveling Waves

Let us consider a long string stretched in the x direction along which a transverse wave is traveling. At some instant of time, say $t = 0$, the shape of the string can be represented * by

$$y = f(x) \qquad t = 0, \tag{19–1}$$

where y is the transverse displacement of the string at the position x. In Fig. 19–5a we show a possible waveform (a pulse) on the string at $t = 0$. Experiment shows that as time goes on such a wave travels along the string without changing its form. At some time t later the wave has traveled a distance vt to the right, where v is magnitude of the wave velocity, assumed constant. The equation of the curve at the time t is, therefore,

$$y = f(x - vt) \qquad t = t. \tag{19–2}$$

This gives us the same waveform about the point $x = vt$ at time t as we had about $x = 0$ at the time $t = 0$ (Fig. 19–5b). Equation 19–2 is the general

---

* The symbol f here means "a function of." It should not be confused with the frequency f.

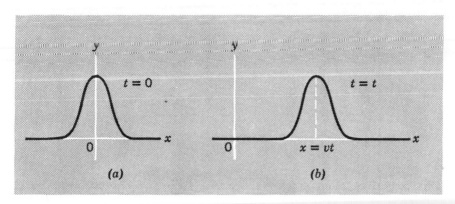

Fig. 19–5 (a) The shape of a string (in this case a pulse) at $t = 0$. (b) At time $t > 0$, the pulse has traveled to the right a distance $x = vt$.

equation representing a wave of *any shape traveling to the right*. To obtain a particular shape we must specify exactly what the function f is.*

Let us look more carefully at this equation. If we wish to follow a particular part (or phase) of the wave as time goes on, then in the equation we look at a particular value of y (say, the top of the pulse just described). Mathematically this means we look at how x changes with t when $(x - vt)$ has some particular fixed value. We see at once that as t increases x must increase in order to keep $(x - vt)$ fixed. Hence, Eq. 19–2 does in fact represent a wave traveling to the right (increasing x as time goes on). Clearly if we wished to represent a wave *traveling to the left* we would write

$$y = f(x + vt), \tag{19–3}$$

for here the position x of some fixed phase $(x + vt)$ of the wave decreases as time goes on. The velocity of a particular phase of the wave is easily obtained. For a particular phase we require that

$$x - vt = \text{constant.}$$

Then differentiation gives

$$dx - v\,dt = 0$$

or

$$\frac{dx}{dt} = v, \tag{19–4}$$

so that v is really the *phase velocity* of the wave. For a wave traveling to the left we obtain $-v$, in the same way, as its phase velocity.†

---

* When we say that "y is a function of $(x - vt)$," we mean that the variables x and t occur only in the combination $x - vt$. For example, $\sin k(x - vt)$, $\log (x - vt)$, and $(x - vt)^0$ are functions of $x - vt$, but $x^2 - vt^2$ is not.

† In disturbances that can be represented as a group of waves, the energy is transported with a velocity different from the phase velocity of any individual wave. This group velocity will be considered in Chapter 39 in connection with electromagnetic waves. Until then whenever we use the term wave velocity we mean the phase velocity of the wave.

The general equation of a wave can be interpreted further. Note that for any fixed value of the time t the equation gives y as a function of x. This defines a curve, and this curve represents the actual shape of the string at this chosen time. It gives us a snapshot of the wave at this time. Suppose we wish to focus our attention on one point of the string, that is, a fixed value of x. Then the equation gives us y as a function of the time t. This describes how the transverse position of this point on the string changes with time.

The entire argument just presented holds for longitudinal waves as well as for transverse waves. The analogous longitudinal example is that of a long straight tube of gas whose axis is taken as the x-axis, and the wave or pulse is a pressure change traveling along the tube. Then the same reasoning leads us to an equation, having the form of Eqs. 19–2 and 19–3, which gives the pressure variations with time at all points of the tube. (See Section 20–3.)

Let us now consider a particular waveform, whose importance will soon become clear. Suppose that at the time $t = 0$ we have a wavetrain along the string given by

$$ y = y_m \sin 2\pi \frac{x}{\lambda}. \tag{19-5} $$

The wave shape is a sine curve (Fig. 19–6). The maximum displacement y_m is the *amplitude* of the sine curve. The value of the transverse displacement y is the same at x as it is at $x + \lambda$, $x + 2\lambda$, etc. The symbol λ is called the *wavelength* of the wavetrain and represents the distance between two adjacent points in the wave having the same phase. As time goes on let the wave travel to the right with a phase velocity v. Hence, the equation of the wave at the time t is

$$ y = y_m \sin \frac{2\pi}{\lambda} (x - vt). \tag{19-6} $$

Notice that this has the form required for a traveling wave (Eq. 19–2).

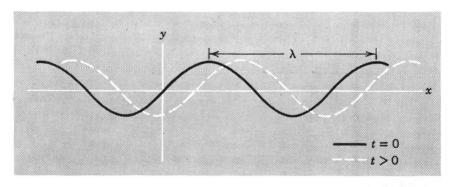

Fig. 19–6 At $t = 0$, the string has a shape $y = y_m \sin 2\pi x/\lambda$ (solid line). At a later time, the sine wave has moved to the right a distance $x = vt$, and the string has a shape given by $y = y_m \sin 2\pi(x - vt)/\lambda$.

The *period* T is the time required for the wave to travel a distance of one wavelength λ, so that

$$\lambda = vT. \tag{19–7}$$

Putting this relation into the equation of the wave, we obtain

$$y = y_m \sin 2\pi \left(\frac{x}{\lambda} - \frac{t}{T} \right). \tag{19–8}$$

From this form it is clear that y has the same value at $x + \lambda$, $x + 2\lambda$, etc., as it does at x at any given time, and that y has the same value at the time $t + T$, $t + 2T$, etc., as it does at the time t at any given position.

To reduce Eq. 19–8 to a more compact form, we define two quantities, the *wave number* k and the *angular frequency* ω (see Eq. 15–9). They are given by

$$k = \frac{2\pi}{\lambda} \quad \text{and} \quad \omega = \frac{2\pi}{T}. \tag{19–9}$$

In terms of these quantities, the equation of a sine wave traveling to the right is

$$y = y_m \sin (kx - \omega t). \tag{19–10a}$$

For a sine wave traveling to the left, we have

$$y = y_m \sin (kx + \omega t). \tag{19–10b}$$

Comparing Eqs. 19–7 and 19–9, we see that the phase velocity v of the wave is given by

$$v = \frac{\lambda}{T} = \frac{\omega}{k}. \tag{19–11}$$

In the traveling waves of Eqs. 19–10a and 19–10b we have assumed that the displacement y is zero at the position $x = 0$ at the time $t = 0$. This, of course, need not be the case. The general expression for a sinusoidal wavetrain traveling to the right is actually

$$y = y_m \sin (kx - \omega t - \phi),$$

where ϕ is called the phase angle. For example, if $\phi = -90°$, the displacement y at $x = 0$ and $t = 0$ is y_m. Obviously this particular example is

$$y = y_m \cos (kx - \omega t),$$

for the cosine function is displaced by 90° from the sine function.

If we fix our attention on a given point of the string, say $x = \pi/k$, the displacement y at that point can be written * as

$$y = y_m \sin (\omega t + \phi).$$

This is similar to Eq. 15–26 for simple harmonic motion. Hence, any particular element of the string undergoes simple harmonic motion about its equilibrium position as this wavetrain travels along the string.

---

* Using the fact that $\sin (\pi - \theta) = \sin \theta$.

19–4 The Superposition Principle

It is an experimental fact that for many kinds of waves *two or more waves can traverse the same space independently of one another*. With light, for example, we see objects clearly, even though the light reaching our eyes from a particular object travels in a space through which a great many other light waves are traveling in many different directions. Likewise, in sound we can distinguish the notes of particular instruments playing in an orchestra.

The fact that waves act independently of one another means that the displacement of any particle at a given time is simply the sum of the displacements that the individual waves alone would give it. This process of vector addition of the displacements of a particle is called *superposition*. For waves in deformable media the superposition principle holds whenever the mathematical relation between the deformation and the restoring force is one of simple proportionality. Such a relation is expressed mathematically by a linear equation. For electromagnetic waves the superposition principle holds because the mathematical relations between the electric and magnetic fields are linear.

Actually, the superposition principle seems so obvious that it is worthwhile to point out that it does not hold in every case. Superposition fails when the equations governing wave motion are not linear. Physically this happens when the wave disturbance is very large and the ordinary linear laws of mechanical action no longer hold. For example, beyond the elastic limit Hooke's law no longer holds and the linear relation $F = -kx$ can no longer be used.

As for sound, violent explosions create shock waves. Although shock waves are longitudinal elastic waves in air, they behave differently from ordinary sound waves. The equation governing their propagation is quadratic, and superposition does not hold. With two very loud notes the ear hears something more than just the two individual notes. Those familiar with high-fidelity apparatus will know that "intermodulation distortion" between two tones arises when the system fails to combine the tones linearly, and that this distortion is more apparent when the amplitude of the tones is high. A more obvious physical example is water waves. Ripples cannot travel independently across breakers as they can across gentle swells.

The importance of the superposition principle physically is that it makes it possible to analyze a complicated wave motion as a combination of simple waves. In fact, as was shown by the French mathematician J. Fourier (1768–1830), all that we need to build up the most general form of periodic wave are simple harmonic waves.* Fourier showed that any periodic motion of a particle can be represented as a combination of simple harmonic motions. For example, if $y(t)$ represents the motion of a source of waves having a period T, we can analyze $y(t)$ as follows:

$$y(t) = A_0 + A_1 \sin \omega t + A_2 \sin 2\omega t + A_3 \sin 3\omega t + \cdots$$

$$+ B_1 \cos \omega t + B_2 \cos 2\omega t + B_3 \cos 3\omega t + \cdots,$$

---

* See, for example, Thomas, *Calculus and Analytic Geometry*, Addison-Wesley, second edition, 1953, pp. 596–599.

where $\omega = 2\pi/T$. This expression is called a Fourier series. The A's and B's are constants which have definite values for any particular periodic motion $y(t)$. (See Fig. 19–7, for example.) If the motion is not periodic, as a pulse, the sum is replaced by an integral, the so-called Fourier integral. Hence, any motion of a source of waves can be represented in terms of simple harmonic motions. Since the motion of the source creates the waves, it should come as no surprise that the waves themselves can be analyzed as

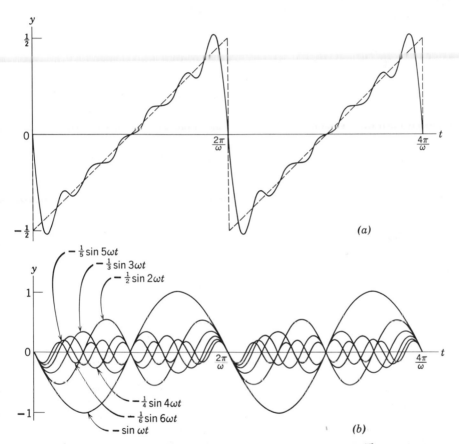

Fig. 19–7 (a) The dotted line is a sawtooth "wave" commonly encountered in cathode-ray oscilloscopes. It can be written $y(t) = \dfrac{\omega}{2\pi}t - \frac{1}{2}$ for $0 < t < \dfrac{2\pi}{\omega}$, as $y(t) = \dfrac{\omega}{2\pi}t - \dfrac{3}{2}$ for $\dfrac{2\pi}{\omega} < t < \dfrac{4\pi}{\omega}$, etc. The Fourier series for this function is $y(t) = -\sin \omega t - \frac{1}{2}\sin 2\omega t - \frac{1}{3}\sin 3\omega t - \cdots$. The solid line is the sum of the first six terms of this series and can be seen to approximate the sawtooth quite closely, except for overshooting near the discontinuities. As more terms of the series are included, the approximation becomes better and better.

(b) Here are shown the first six terms of the Fourier series which, when added together, yield the solid curve in (a).

combinations of simple harmonic waves. Herein lies the importance of simple harmonic motion and simple harmonic waves.

19–5 Wave Velocity

In the general equation for a wave

$$y = f(x - vt),$$

v is the constant velocity with which the wave propagates through the medium. Let us again consider a transverse wave in a string.

It can easily be shown experimentally that the wave velocity depends only on the tension or force F exerted on the string and the mass per unit length μ of the string. Assuming, then, that the wave velocity v depends only on F and μ, we can use dimensional analysis to find how v depends on these quantities. In terms of mass (M), length (L), and time (T), the dimensions of F are (MLT^{-2}) and the dimensions of μ are (ML^{-1}). The only way these dimensions can be combined to get a velocity [which has the dimensions (LT^{-1})] is to take the square root of F/μ. That is, F/μ has the dimensions (L^2T^{-2}) and $\sqrt{F/\mu}$ has the dimensions (LT^{-1}) of a velocity. Dimensional analysis cannot account for any dimensionless quantities, so that the result

$$v = \sqrt{\frac{F}{\mu}} \tag{19–12}$$

may or may not be exact. The most we can say is that the wave velocity is equal to a constant times $\sqrt{F/\mu}$. The value of the constant can be obtained from a mechanical analysis of the problem or from experiment. These methods show that the constant is equal to unity and that Eq. 19–12 is correct as it stands.

Now let us *derive* the velocity of a pulse in a stretched string by a mechanical analysis. In Fig. 19–8 we show a wave pulse proceeding from right to left in the string with a speed v. We can imagine the entire string to be moved from left to right with this same speed so that the wave pulse remains fixed in space, whereas the particles composing the string successively pass through the pulse. Such a stationary pulse can be produced in practice on a string loosely wrapped around two rotating pulleys.

Therefore, instead of taking our system of reference to be the walls between which the string is stretched, we choose a reference system which is in uniform motion with respect to that one. Because Newton's laws involve only accelerations, which are the same in both systems, we can use them in either system. We just happen to choose a more convenient system.

We consider a small section of the pulse of length Δl to form an arc of a circle of radius R, as shown in the diagram. If μ is the mass per unit length of the string, the

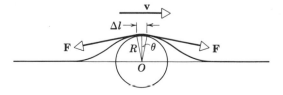

Fig. 19–8 Derivation of wave velocity by considering the forces on a section of string of length Δl.

so-called linear density, then $\mu \, \Delta l$ is the mass of this element. The tension F in the string is a tangential pull at each end of this small segment of the string. The horizontal components cancel and the vertical components are each equal to $F \sin \theta$. Hence, the total vertical force is $2F \sin \theta$. Since θ is small, we can take $\sin \theta = \theta$ and

$$2F \sin \theta = 2F\theta = 2F \frac{\Delta l}{2R} = F \frac{\Delta l}{R}.$$

This gives the force supplying the centripetal acceleration of the string particles directed toward O. Now the centripetal force acting on a mass $\mu \, \Delta l$ moving in a circle of radius R with speed v is $\mu \, \Delta l v^2 / R$. Notice that the tangential velocity v of this mass element along the top of the arc is horizontal and is the same as the pulse phase velocity. Combining the equivalent expressions just given we obtain

$$F \frac{\Delta l}{R} = \frac{\mu \, \Delta l \, v^2}{R}$$

or

$$v = \sqrt{\frac{F}{\mu}}.$$

If the amplitude of the pulse were very large compared to the length of the string, we would not have been able to use the approximation $\sin \theta = \theta$. Furthermore, the tension F in the string would be changed by the presence of the pulse, whereas we assumed F to be unchanged from the original tension in the stretched string. Therefore, our result, like superposition, holds only for relatively small transverse displacements of the string—which case, however, is widely applicable in practice. Notice also that the wave velocity is independent of the shape of the wave, for no particular assumption about the actual shape of the pulse was used in the proof.

The frequency of a wave is naturally determined by the frequency of the source. The speed with which the wave travels through a medium is determined by the properties of the medium, as illustrated before. Once the frequency f and speed v of the wave are determined, the wavelength λ is fixed. In fact, from Eq. 19–7 using the fact that $f = 1/T$, we have

$$\lambda = \frac{v}{f}. \tag{19–13}$$

▶ **Example 1.** A transverse sinusoidal wave is generated at one end of a long horizontal rope by a bar which moves the end up and down through a distance of $\frac{1}{2}$ ft. The motion is continuous and is repeated regularly twice each second. (a) If the string has a linear density of 0.0050 slug/ft and is kept under a tension of 2.0 lb, find the velocity, amplitude, frequency, and wavelength of the wave motion.

The end moves $\frac{1}{4}$ ft away from the equilibrium position, first above it, then below it, for a total displacement of $\frac{1}{2}$ ft. Therefore, the amplitude y_m is $\frac{1}{4}$ ft.

The entire motion is repeated twice each second so that the frequency is 2 vibrations per second.

The wave velocity is given by $v = \sqrt{F/\mu}$. But $F = 2.0$ lb and $\mu = 0.0050$ slug/ft, so that

$$v = \sqrt{\frac{2.0 \text{ lb}}{0.0050 \text{ slug/ft}}} = 20 \text{ ft/sec}.$$

The wavelength is given by $\lambda = v/f$, so that

$$\lambda = \frac{20 \text{ ft/sec}}{2 \text{ vib/sec}} = 10 \text{ ft}.$$

(b) Assuming the wave moves from left to right, and taking the starting point as $x = 0$ and $t = 0$, write the equation of the wave.

The general expression for a transverse sinusoidal wave moving from left to right is

$$y = y_m \sin (kx - \omega t - \phi).$$

At the start, t equals zero and the end of the string at $x = 0$ is in the equilibrium position $y = 0$. On inserting these values for y, x, and t,

$$0 = y_m \sin (-\phi),$$

we find that ϕ, the phase angle, must be zero. Hence, for this wave

$$y = y_m \sin (kx - \omega t),$$

and with the values just found,

$$y_m = \tfrac{1}{4} \text{ ft} = 0.25 \text{ ft},$$

$$\lambda = 10 \text{ ft} \quad \text{or} \quad k = \frac{2\pi}{\lambda} = \frac{\pi}{5} \text{ ft}^{-1},$$

$$v = 20 \text{ ft/sec} \quad \text{or} \quad \omega = vk = 4\pi \text{ sec}^{-1},$$

we obtain as the equation for the wave

$$y = 0.25 \sin (0.2\pi x - 4\pi t),$$

where x and y are in feet and t is in seconds.

Example 2. As this wave passes along the string, each particle of the string moves up and down at right angles to the direction of the wave motion. Find the velocity and acceleration of a particle 10 ft from the end.

The general form of this wave is

$$y = y_m \sin (kx - \omega t) = y_m \sin k(x - vt).$$

The v in this equation is the constant horizontal velocity of the wavetrain. What we are after now is the velocity of a particle in the string through which this wave moves; this particle velocity is neither horizontal nor constant. In fact, each particle moves vertically, that is, in the y direction. In order to determine the particle velocity, which we shall designate by the symbol u, let us fix our attention on a particle at a particular position x—that is, x is now a constant in this equation—and ask how the particle displacement y changes with time. With x constant we obtain

$$u = \frac{dy}{dt} = -y_m \omega \cos (kx - \omega t).$$

The acceleration a of the particle at x is

$$a = \frac{d^2 y}{dt^2} = \frac{du}{dt} = -y_m \omega^2 \sin (kx - \omega t) = -\omega^2 y.$$

This shows that for each particle through which this tranverse sinusoidal wave passes we have precisely SHM (simple harmonic motion), for the acceleration a is proportional to the displacement y, but oppositely directed.

For a particle at $x = 10$ ft with the wave of Example 1, in which

$$y_m = 0.25 \text{ ft}, \quad k = \frac{\pi}{5} \text{ ft}^{-1}, \quad \omega = 4\pi \text{ sec}^{-1},$$

we obtain

$$u = -y_m \omega \cos (kx - \omega t)$$

or $\quad u = -(0.25) \left[4\pi \cos \left(\dfrac{10\pi}{5} - 4\pi t \right) \right]$ ft/sec $= -\pi \cos (2\pi - 4\pi t)$ ft/sec,

and $\qquad\qquad\qquad\qquad a = -\omega^2 y$

or $\quad a = -(4\pi)^2 0.25 \sin (0.2\pi x - 4\pi t)$ ft/sec$^2 = -4\pi^2 \sin (2\pi - 4\pi t)$ ft/sec^2,

where t is expressed in seconds.

Can you describe the motion of this particle at the time $t = 4$ sec? ◀

19–6   Power and Intensity in Wave Motion

In Fig. 19–9 we draw an element of the stretched string at some position x. The *transverse* component of the tension in the string exerted *by* the element to the left of x *on* the element to the right of x is

$$F_{\text{trans}} = -F \frac{dy}{dx}.$$

F is the tension in the string; dy/dx gives the tangent of the angle made by the direction of **F** with the horizontal and, because we assume small displacements, this can be taken equal also to the sine of the angle. The transverse force is in the direction of increasing y; in the figure the slope is negative, so the transverse force is positive. The transverse velocity of the particle at x is dy/dt, which may be positive or negative. The power being expended by the force at x, or the energy passing through the particle at x per unit time in the positive x direction (see Section 7–4), is

$$P = \left(-F \frac{dy}{dx} \right) \frac{dy}{dt}.$$

Suppose that the wave on the string is the simple sine wave,

$$y = y_m \sin (kx - \omega t).$$

Then the magnitude of the slope at x is

$$\frac{dy}{dx} = k y_m \cos (kx - \omega t), \qquad t = \text{constant},$$

and the transverse force is

$$-F \frac{dy}{dx} = -F k y_m \cos (kx - \omega t).$$

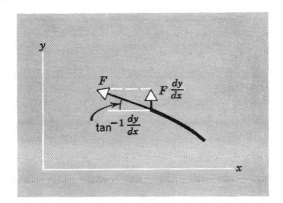

Fig. 19–9 The transverse (vertical) component of the tension in the string at each point y is $F \dfrac{dy}{dx}$.

The transverse velocity of a particle of the string at x is

$$u = \frac{dy}{dt} = -\omega y_m \cos (kx - \omega t), \qquad x = \text{constant}.$$

Hence, the power transmitted is

$$P = (-Fky_m)(-\omega y_m) \cos^2 (kx - \omega t),$$

$$= y_m{}^2 k\omega F \cos^2 (kx - \omega t).$$

Notice that the power or rate of flow of energy is not constant. The power is not constant because the power input oscillates. As the energy is passed along the string, it is stored alternately in each element of string as kinetic energy of motion and potential energy of deformation. The situation is much like that in an alternating current circuit; there energy is alternately stored in the inductor and in the capacitor and the power input oscillates. For a string the power is absorbed by internal friction and viscous effects and appears as heat; in the circuit the power is expended in the resistor and appears as heat or radiation. The power input to the string or the circuit is often taken to be the *average* over one period of motion. The average power delivered is

$$\bar{P} = \frac{1}{T} \int_t^{t+T} P \, dt,$$

where T is the period. Using the fact that the average value of $\sin^2 x$ or $\cos^2 x$ over one cycle is $\frac{1}{2}$, we obtain for the string

$$P = \tfrac{1}{2} y_m{}^2 k\omega F = 2\pi^2 y_m{}^2 f^2 \frac{F}{v},$$

a result which does not depend on x or t. For the string, however, $v = \sqrt{F/\mu}$, so that

$$\bar{P} = 2\pi^2 y_m{}^2 f^2 \mu v.$$

The fact that the rate of transfer of energy depends on the square of the wave amplitude and square of the wave frequency is true in general, holding for all types of waves.

The student should confirm the fact that, if we had picked a wave traveling in the negative x direction, we would have obtained the negative of this result. That is, the wave delivers power in the direction of wave propagation.

In a space wave, such as a light wave or a sound wave, it is more significant to speak of the *intensity* of the wave. Intensity is defined as the power transmitted across a unit area normal to the direction in which the wave is traveling. Just as with power in the wave in a string, the intensity of a space wave is always proportional to the square of the amplitude.

As a wave progresses through space, its energy may be absorbed. For example, in a viscous medium, such as syrup or lead, mechanical waves would rapidly decay in amplitude and disappear, owing to absorption of energy by internal friction. In most cases of interest to us, however, absorption will be negligible. Throughout this chapter we have assumed that there is no loss of energy in a given wave, no matter how far it travels.

▶ **Example 3.** Spherical waves (as in Fig. 19–4) travel through an isotropic medium from a source of waves whose power output is P. Find how the wave intensity depends on the distance from the source.

The intensity of a space wave is the power transmitted across a unit area normal to the direction of propagation. As the wavefront expands from a distance r_1 from the source at the center to a distance r_2, its surface area increases from $4\pi r_1{}^2$ to $4\pi r_2{}^2$.

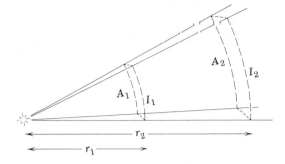

Fig. 19–10   Example 3.

Assuming no absorption of energy, the total energy transported per second by the wave remains constant at the value P, so that

$$P = 4\pi r_1{}^2 I_1 = 4\pi r_2{}^2 I_2,$$

where I_1 and I_2 are the wave intensities at r_1 and r_2 respectively. Hence,

$$\frac{I_1}{I_2} = \frac{r_2{}^2}{r_1{}^2},$$

and the wave intensity varies inversely as the square of its distance from the source (see Fig. 19–10). Since the intensity is proportional to the square of the amplitude, the amplitude of the wave must vary inversely as the distance from the source. ◀

19–7   Interference of Waves

Interference is a technical term referring to the physical effects of super-imposing two or more wave trains.

Let us consider two waves of equal frequency and amplitude traveling with the same speed in the same direction $(+x)$ but with a phase difference ϕ between them. The equations of the two waves will be

$$y_1 = y_m \sin (kx - \omega t - \phi) \tag{19–14}$$

and
$$y_2 = y_m \sin (kx - \omega t). \tag{19–15}$$

We can rewrite the first equation in two equivalent forms

$$y_1 = y_m \sin \left[k \left(x - \frac{\phi}{k} \right) - \omega t \right] \tag{19–14a}$$

or
$$y_1 = y_m \sin \left[kx - \omega \left(t + \frac{\phi}{\omega} \right) \right]. \tag{19–14b}$$

Equations 19–14a and 19–15 suggest that if we take a "snapshot" of the two waves at any time t, we will find them displaced from one another along the x-axis by the constant distance ϕ/k. Equations 19–14b and 19–15 suggest that if we station ourselves at any position x (say, π/k), the two waves will give rise to two simple harmonic motions having a constant time difference ϕ/ω. This gives some insight into the meaning of the phase difference ϕ.

Now let us find the resultant wave, which is the sum of Eqs. 19–14 and 19–15 or

$$y = y_1 + y_2 = y_m \left[\sin (kx - \omega t - \phi) + \sin (kx - \omega t) \right].$$

From the trigonometric equation for the sum of the sines of two angles

$$\sin B + \sin C = 2 \sin \tfrac{1}{2}(B + C) \cos \tfrac{1}{2}(C - B), \qquad (19\text{--}16)$$

we obtain
$$y = y_m \left[2 \sin \left(kx - \omega t - \frac{\phi}{2} \right) \cos \frac{\phi}{2} \right],$$

$$= \left(2y_m \cos \frac{\phi}{2} \right) \sin \left(kx - \omega t - \frac{\phi}{2} \right). \qquad (19\text{--}17)$$

This resultant wave corresponds to a new wave having the same frequency but with an amplitude $2y_m \cos (\phi/2)$. If ϕ is *very small* (compared to 180°), the resultant amplitude will be *nearly* $2y_m$. That is, when ϕ is very small, $\cos (\phi/2) \cong \cos 0° = 1$. When ϕ is *zero*, the two waves have the same phase everywhere. The crest of one corresponds to the crest of the other and likewise for the troughs. The waves are then said to interfere constructively. The resultant amplitude is just twice that of either wave alone. If ϕ is *near* 180°, the resultant amplitude will be *nearly* zero. That is, when $\phi \cong 180°$, $\cos (\phi/2) \cong \cos 90° = 0$. When ϕ is *exactly* 180°, the crest of one wave corresponds exactly to the trough of the other. The waves are then said to interfere destructively. The resultant amplitude is zero.

In Fig. 19–11a we show the superposition of two wavetrains almost in phase (ϕ small) and in Fig. 19–11b the superposition of two wavetrains almost 180° out of phase ($\phi \approx 180°$). Notice that in these figures the algebraic sum of the ordinates of the thin (component) curves at any value of x equals the ordinate of the thick (resultant) curve. The sum of two waves can, therefore, have different values, depending on their phase relations.

The resultant wave will be a sine wave, even when the amplitudes of the component sine waves are unequal. Figure 19–12, for example, illustrates the addition of two sine waves of the same frequency and velocity but different amplitudes. The resultant amplitude depends on the phase difference, which is taken as zero in this figure. The result for other phase differences could be obtained by shifting one of the component waves sideways with respect to the other and would give a smaller resultant amplitude. The smallest resultant amplitude would be the difference in the amplitudes of the components, obtained when the phases differ by 180°. However, the resultant is always a sine wave. The addition of any number of sine waves having the same frequency and velocity gives a similar result. The resultant waveform will always have a constant amplitude because the component waves (and their resultant) all move with the same velocity and maintain the same relative position. The actual state of affairs can be pictured by having all the waves in Figs. 19–11 and 19–12 move toward the right with the same speed.

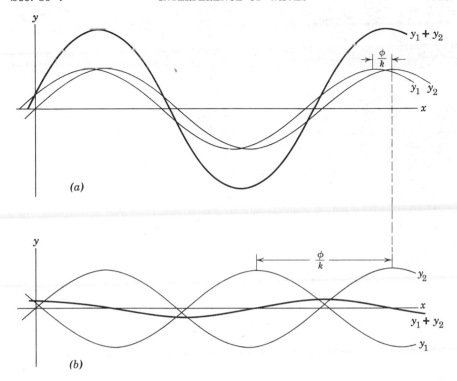

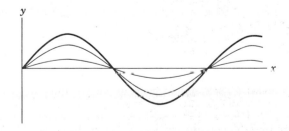

Fig. 19–11 (*a*) The superposition of two waves of equal frequency and amplitude that are almost in phase results in a wave of almost twice the amplitude of either component. (*b*) The superposition of two waves of equal frequency and amplitude and almost 180° out of phase results in a wave whose amplitude is nearly zero. Note that in both the resultant frequency is unchanged. (The drawings depict the instant $t = 0$.)

In practice interference effects are obtained from wavetrains originating in the same source or else in sources kept in phase with each other but separated in space. The phase difference between the waves at a point can be calculated by finding the difference between the paths traversed by them from the source to the point of interference. The path difference is ϕ/k or $(\phi/2\pi)\lambda$. When the path difference is 0, λ, 2λ, 3λ, etc., or very near these values so that $\phi = 0$, 2π, 4π, etc., the two waves interfere constructively. For path differences of, or near, $\frac{1}{2}\lambda$, $\frac{3}{2}\lambda$, $\frac{5}{2}\lambda$, etc., ϕ is π, 3π, 5π, etc., and the

Fig. 19–12 The addition of two waves of same frequency and phase but differing amplitudes (light lines) yields a third wave of the same frequency and phase (heavy line).

waves interfere destructively. We shall return to these matters later in more detail. Chapter 43 is devoted to interference effects with light waves. With sound waves the principal interference effects are beats and standing waves. We shall discuss these at length in Sections 20–4 and 20–6.

19–8   Complex Waves

The waves we have considered so far have been of the simple harmonic type, in which the displacements at any time are represented by a sine curve. We have seen that superposition of any number of such waves having the same frequency and velocity, but arbitrary amplitudes and phases, still gives rise to a resultant wave of this simple type. If, however, we superimpose waves that have *different frequencies*, the resulting wave is *complex*. In a complex wave the motion of a particle is no longer simple harmonic motion, and the wave shape is no longer a sine curve. In this section we consider only the qualitative aspects of complex waves. The analytical treatment of such waves will be given when we encounter physical situations described

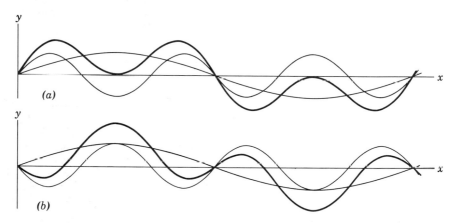

Fig. 19–13 The addition of two waves with frequency ratio 3:1 (light lines) yields a wave whose shape (heavy line) depends on the phase relationship of the components. Compare (*a*) and (*b*).

by them. We will look at the results of adding graphically two or more waves traveling with the same speed in the same direction but having various relative frequencies, amplitudes, and phases.

In Figs. 19–13*a* and 19–13*b* we add two waves having the same amplitude but having frequencies in the ratio 3 to 1; the phase difference is changed from *a* to *b* and we see how changing the phase difference may produce a resultant of very different form. If these represent sound waves, our eardrums will vibrate in a way represented by the resultant in each case, but we will hear and interpret these as the two original frequencies, regardless of their phase difference. If the resultant waves represent visible light, our eyes will receive the same sensation of a mixture of two colors, regardless of the phase difference of the components.

In Fig. 19–14 three waves of different frequencies, amplitudes, and phases are added. The resultant complex wave is quite different from a simple periodic wave and resembles waveforms generated by musical instruments.

In Fig. 19–15 a wave of very high frequency is added to one of very low frequency. Each component frequency is clearly discernible in the resultant. In communication

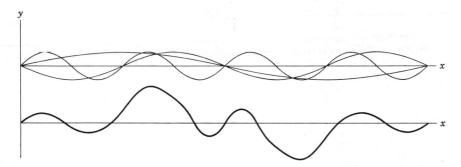

Fig. 19–14 The addition of three waves (top) of differing frequencies yields a complex wave-form (bottom).

systems information represented by smaller frequencies is carried on a much higher frequency signal which can travel longer distances. In such a case, however, the resultant looks quite different from Fig. 19–15, for a product of waves, rather than a sum, is involved.

Fig. 19–15 The addition (heavy line) of two waves of widely differing frequency (light lines).

In Fig. 19–16 two waves of nearly the same frequency are added. The resultant wave consists of groups which, in the case of sound, produce the familiar phenomenon of beats.

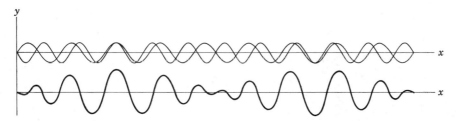

Fig. 19–16 The addition (bottom) of two waves with nearly the same frequency (top), illustrating the phenomenon of beats. (See Chapter 20.)

In all of these figures the resultant wave is obtained from the principle of super-position by simply adding the displacements caused by the individual waves at every point. Because all the component waves travel with the same velocity, the resultant waveform moves with this same velocity and the wave shape is unchanged.

The cathode-ray oscilloscope (Chapter 28) gives the simplest way of observing how complex waves can be synthesized and analyzed in terms of simple harmonic waves.

19–9 Standing Waves

In finite bodies traveling waves are reflected from the boundaries of the bodies and give rise to waves traveling in the opposite direction. These add to the original waves according to the principle of superposition.

Consider two wave trains of the same frequency, speed, and amplitude which are traveling in *opposite directions* along a string. Two such waves may be represented by the equations

$$y_1 = y_m \sin (kx - \omega t),$$

$$y_2 = y_m \sin (kx + \omega t).$$

Hence, the resultant may be written as

$$y = y_1 + y_2 = y_m \sin (kx - \omega t) + y_m \sin (kx + \omega t) \qquad (19\text{–}18a)$$

or, using the trigonometric relation of Eq. 19–16,

$$y = 2y_m \sin kx \cos \omega t. \qquad (19\text{–}18b)$$

Equation 19–18b is the equation of a *standing* wave. Notice that a particle at any particular point x executes simple harmonic motion as time goes on, and that all particles vibrate with the same frequency. In a traveling wave each particle of the string vibrates with the same amplitude. Characteristic of a standing wave, however, is the fact that the amplitude is not the same for different particles but varies with the location x of the particle. In fact, the amplitude, $2y_m \sin kx$, has a *maximum* value of $2y_m$ at positions where

$$kx = \frac{\pi}{2}, \frac{3\pi}{2}, \frac{5\pi}{2}, \text{ etc.}$$

or

$$x = \frac{\lambda}{4}, \frac{3\lambda}{4}, \frac{5\lambda}{4}, \text{ etc.}$$

These points are called *antinodes* and are spaced one-half wavelength apart. The amplitude has a *minimum* value of zero at positions where

$$kx = \pi, 2\pi, 3\pi, \text{ etc.}$$

or

$$x = \frac{\lambda}{2}, \lambda, \frac{3\lambda}{2}, 2\lambda, \text{ etc.}$$

These points are called *nodes* and are spaced one-half wavelength apart. The separation between a node and an adjacent antinode is one-quarter wavelength.

It is clear that energy is not transported along the string to the right or to the left, for energy cannot flow past the nodal points in the string which are permanently at rest. Hence, the energy remains "standing" in the string, although it alternates between vibrational kinetic energy and elastic potential energy. In fact, the only justification for calling this a wave motion at all is that we can think of the motion as a superposition of waves traveling in opposite directions (Eq. 19–18a). We can equally well regard the motion as an oscillation of the string as a whole (Eq. 19–18b), each particle oscillating with SHM of angular frequency ω and with an amplitude that depends on its location. Each small part of the string has inertia and elasticity, and the string as a whole can be thought of as a collection of coupled oscillators. Hence, the vibrating string is the same in principle * as a spring-mass system, except that a spring-mass system has only one natural frequency, and a vibrating string has a large number of natural frequencies (Section 19–10).

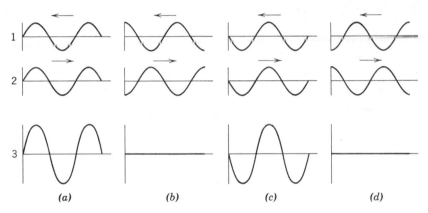

Fig. 19–17 Standing waves as the superposition of left- and right-going waves; 1 and 2 are the components, 3 the resultant.

In Fig. 19–17, in (a), (b), (c), and (d), we show a standing wave pattern separately at intervals of one-quarter of a period in the lower figures, 3. The traveling waves, one moving toward $+x$ and the other moving toward $-x$, whose superposition can be considered to give rise to the standing wave, are shown for the same times, 1 and 2.

In Fig. 19–18 we show the envelope of a portion of a standing wave in a string corresponding to a time exposure of the motion. The pattern of nodes and antinodes is clear, and the interchange of energy in a segment of string between two nodes from potential energy deformation to kinetic energy of motion suggests itself. Often the string vibrates so rapidly that only this envelope of the motion is apparent. The string then looks like a blur with no motion and a fixed stationary form. Standing waves can be produced with light waves and with sound waves (Chapter 20) as well.

---

* For a general discussion see "On the Teaching of 'Standing Waves,'" J. Rekveld, *American Journal of Physics*, March 1958, p. 159.

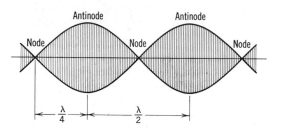

Fig. 19–18 The envelope of a standing wave, corresponding to a time exposure of the motion.

We have seen that the superposition of a traveling wave and a reflected wave will give rise to a standing wave. We shall now consider the process of reflection of a wave more closely. Suppose a pulse travels down a stretched string which is fixed at one end, as shown in Fig. 19–19. When the pulse arrives at that end, it exerts an upward force on the support. The support is rigid, however, and does not move. By Newton's third law the support exerts an equal but oppositely directed force on the string. This reaction force generates a pulse at the support, which travels back along the string in a direction opposite to that of the incident pulse. We say that the incident pulse has been *reflected* at the fixed end point of the string. Notice that the reflected pulse returns with its transverse displacement reversed.

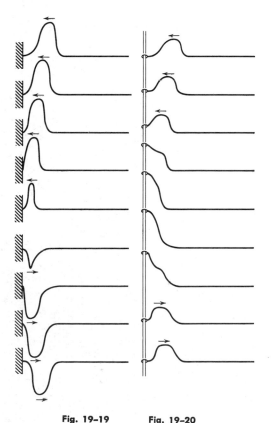

Fig. 19–19 Reflection of a pulse at the fixed end of a string. The drawings are spaced uniformly in time. The phase is changed by 180° on reflection.

Fig. 19–20 Reflection of a pulse at an end free to move in a transverse direction. (The string is attached to a ring which slides vertically without friction.) The phase is unchanged on reflection.

Fig. 19–19   **Fig. 19–20**

If a wavetrain is incident on the fixed end point, a reflected wavetrain is generated at that point in the same way. The displacement of any point along the rope is the sum of the displacements caused by the incident and reflected wave. Since the end point is fixed, these two waves must always interfere destructively at that point so as to give zero displacement there. Hence, the reflected wave is always 180° out of phase with the incident wave at a fixed boundary. We say that *on reflection from a fixed end a wave undergoes a phase change of 180°.*

Let us now consider the reflection of a pulse at a free end of a stretched string, that is, at an end that is free to move transversely. This can be achieved by attaching the end to a pin set in a frictionless transverse slot, or (see later) to a long and very much lighter string. When the pulse arrives at the free end, it exerts a force on the element of string there. This element is accelerated and its inertia carries it past the equilibrium point; it "overshoots" and exerts a reaction force on the string. This generates a pulse which travels back along the string in a direction opposite to that of the incident pulse. Once again we get reflection, but now at a free end. The free end will obviously suffer the maximum displacement of the particles on the string; an incident and a reflected wavetrain must interfere constructively at that point if we are to have a maximum there. Hence, the reflected wave is always in phase with the incident wave at that point (see Fig. 19–20). We say that *at a free end a wave is reflected without change of phase.*

Hence, when we have a standing wave in a string, there will be a node at a fixed end and an antinode at a free end. These ideas will be applied to sound waves and electromagnetic waves in subsequent chapters.

In the treatment just given we have assumed that there is total reflection at the boundary. In general, at a boundary there is partial reflection and partial transmission. For example, suppose that instead of being attached to a rigid wall the string is attached to another string. At the boundary joining the strings the incident wave will be partly reflected and partly transmitted. The amplitude of the reflected wave will be less than that of the incident wave because a transmitted wave continues along the second string and carries away some of the incident energy. If the second string has a greater linear density than the first, the wave reflected back into the first will still suffer a phase shift of 180° on reflection. But because its amplitude is less than the incident wave, the boundary point will not be a node and will move. Thus a net energy transfer occurs along the first string into the second. If the second string has a smaller linear density than the first, partial reflection occurs without change of phase, but once again energy is transmitted to the second string. In practice the best way to realize a "free end" for a string is to attach it to a long and very much lighter string. The energy transmitted is negligible, and the second string serves to maintain the tension in the first one.

It is of interest to note that the transmitted wave travels with a different velocity than the incident and reflected waves. The wave velocity is determined by the relation $v = \sqrt{F/\mu}$; the tension is the same in both strings, but their densities are different. Hence, the wave travels more slowly in the denser string. If the string does not break at the boundary, the frequency of the transmitted wave is the same as that of the incident and reflected waves. Waves having the same frequency but traveling with different velocities have different wavelengths. Hence, from the relation $\lambda = v/f$ we conclude that in the denser string, where v is less, the wavelength is shorter. This phenomenon of change of wavelength as a wave passes from one medium to another will be encountered frequently in our study of light waves.

19–10 Resonance

In general, whenever a system capable of oscillating is acted on by a periodic series of impulses having a frequency equal or nearly equal to one of the natural frequencies of oscillation of the system, the system is set into oscillation with a relatively large amplitude. This phenomenon is called *resonance*, and the system is said to resonate with the applied impulses.

Consider a string fixed at both ends. Oscillations or standing waves can be established in the string. The only requirement we have to satisfy is that the end points be nodes. There may be any number of nodes in between or none at all, so that the wavelength associated with the standing waves can take on many different values. The distance between adjacent nodes is $\lambda/2$, so that in a string of length l there must be exactly an integral number n of half wavelengths, $\lambda/2$. That is,

$$\frac{n\lambda}{2} = l$$

or
$$\lambda = \frac{2l}{n}, \qquad n = 1, 2, 3, \cdots.$$

But $\lambda = v/f$ and $v = \sqrt{F/\mu}$, so that the natural frequencies of oscillation of the system are

$$f = \frac{n}{2l}\sqrt{\frac{F}{\mu}}, \qquad n - 1, 2, 3, \cdots. \tag{19–19}$$

If the string is set vibrating and left to itself, the oscillations gradually die out. The motion is damped by dissipation of energy through the elastic supports at the ends and by the resistance of the air to the motion. We can pump energy into the system by applying a driving force. If the driving frequency is near that of any natural frequency of the string, the string will vibrate at that frequency with a large amplitude. Because the string has a large number of natural frequencies, resonance can occur at many different frequencies. This is in contrast to the spring-mass system where there is only one resonant frequency.

This effect is often demonstrated by attaching a string to a fixed end, by means of a weight attached to it over a pulley, and connecting the other end to a vibrator, as shown in Fig. 19–21. The transverse oscillations of the vibrator set up a traveling wave in the string which is reflected back from the fixed end. The frequency of the waves is that of the vibrator, and the wavelength is determined by $\lambda = v/f$. The fixed end P is a node, but the end Q vibrates and is not. If we now vary the tension in the string by changing the hanging weight, for example, we can change the wavelength. Changing the tension changes the wave velocity, and the wavelength changes in proportion to the velocity, the frequency being constant. Whenever the wave-

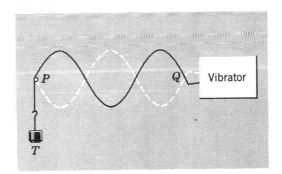

Fig. 19-21 Standing waves in a driven string when the natural and driving frequencies are very nearly equal.

length becomes nearly equal to $2l/n$, where l is the length of the string, we obtain standing waves of great amplitude. The string now vibrates in one of its natural modes and resonates with the vibrator. The vibrator does work on the string to maintain these oscillations against the losses due to damping. The amplitude builds up only to the point at which the vibrator expends all its energy input against damping losses. The point Q is almost a node because the amplitude of the vibrator is small compared to that of the string.

Hence, with damping, the resonant frequency is almost, but not quite, a natural frequency of the string. One end point is a node, the other almost a node. In between there are points that are almost nodes, points at which the amplitude is very small. These points cannot be true nodes, for energy must flow along the string past them from the vibrator. This situation is analogous to the resonance condition for a damped harmonic oscillator with driving force, discussed in Section 15-9. There, too, the resonant frequency was almost the same as the natural frequency of the system, and the amplitude was large but not infinite. If no damping were present, the resonant frequency would be exactly a natural frequency. Then the amplitude would build up to infinity as the energy is pumped in. In practice, the system would cease to obey Hooke's law, or the small-oscillations condition, as the amplitude becomes large and the system would break. This happens even with damping, when the damping is small or the driving force is large (as in the Tacoma Bridge disaster, Fig. 15-19).

If the frequency of the vibrator is much different from a natural frequency of the system, as given by Eq. 19-19, the wave reflected at P on returning to Q may be much out of phase with the vibrator, and it can do work on the vibrator. That is, the string can give up some energy to the vibrator just as well as receive energy from it. The "standing" wave pattern is not fixed in form but wiggles about. On the average the amplitude is small and not much different from that of the vibrator. This situation is analogous to the erratic motion of a swing being pushed periodically with a frequency other than its natural one. The displacement of the swing is rather small.

Hence, the string absorbs peak energy from the vibrator at resonance. Tuning a radio is an analogous process. By tuning a dial the natural frequency of an alternating current in the receiving circuit is made equal to the frequency of the waves broadcast by the station desired. The circuit resonates with the transmitted signals and absorbs peak energy from the signal. We shall encounter resonance conditions again in sound, in electromagnetism, in optics, and in atomic and nuclear physics. In these areas, as in mechanics, the system will absorb peak energy from the source at resonance and relatively little energy off resonance.

▶ **Example 4.** In a demonstration with the apparatus just described, the vibrator has a frequency $f = 20$ cycles/sec, and the string has a linear density $\mu = 1.56 \times 10^{-4}$ slug/ft and a length $l = 24$ ft. The tension F is varied by pulling down on the end of the string over the pulley. If the demonstrator wants to show resonance, starting with one loop and then with two, three, and four loops, what force must he exert on the string?

At resonance,

$$f = \frac{n}{2l} \sqrt{\frac{F}{\mu}}.$$

Hence, the tension F is given by

$$F = \frac{4l^2 f^2 \mu}{n^2}.$$

For one loop, $n = 1$, so that

$$F_1 = 4l^2 f^2 \mu = 4(24 \text{ ft})^2 (20 \text{ sec}^{-1})^2 (1.56 \times 10^{-4} \text{ slug/ft}) = 144 \text{ lb}.$$

For two loops, $n = 2$, and

$$F_2 = \frac{4l^2 f^2 \mu^2}{4} = \frac{F_1}{4} = 36 \text{ lb}.$$

Likewise, for three and four loops

$$F_3 = \frac{F_1}{(3)^2} = 16 \text{ lb},$$

$$F_4 = \frac{F_1}{(4)^2} = 9 \text{ lb}.$$

Hence, the demonstrator gradually relaxes the tension to obtain resonance with an increasing number of loops. Although the resonant frequency is always the same under these circumstances, the speed of propagation and the wavelength at resonance decrease proportionately.

Taking damping into account, are the tensions given exactly correct?

If the tension were kept fixed, giving a definite wave speed, would we obtain more than one resonance condition by varying the frequency of the vibrator? ◀

QUESTIONS

1. How could you prove experimentally that energy is associated with a wave?

2. Energy can be transferred by particles as well as by waves. How can we distinguish experimentally between these methods of energy transfer?

3. Can a wave motion be generated in which the particles of the medium vibrate with angular simple harmonic motion? If so, explain how and describe the wave.

4. Are torsional waves transverse or longitudinal? Can they be considered as a superposition of two waves, which are either transverse or longitudinal?

5. How can one create plane waves? Spherical waves?

6. The following functions in which A is a constant are of the form $f(x \pm vt)$:

$$y = A(x - vt) \qquad y = A(x + vt)^2$$

$$y = A \sqrt{x - vt} \qquad y = A \ln (x + vt).$$

Explain why these functions are not useful in wave motion.

7. How do the amplitude and the intensity of surface water waves vary with the distance from the source?

8. The inverse square law does not apply exactly to the decrease in intensity of sounds with distance. Why not?

9. When two waves interfere, does one alter the progress of the other?

10. When waves interfere, is there a loss of energy? Explain your answer.

11. Why don't we observe interference effects between the light beams emitted from two flashlights or between the sound waves emitted by the violins in a violin section of an orchestra?

12. If two waves differ only in amplitude and are propagated in opposite directions through a medium, will they produce standing waves? Is energy transported? Are there any nodes?

13. Consider the standing waves in a string to be a superposition of traveling waves and explain, using superposition ideas, why there are no true nodes in the resonating string of Fig. 19–21, even at the "fixed" end. (Hint: Consider damping effects.)

PROBLEMS

1. Show that $y = y_m \sin (kx - \omega t)$ may be written in the alternative forms

$$y = y_m \sin k(x - vt) \qquad y = y_m \sin 2\pi \left(\frac{x}{\lambda} - ft \right)$$

$$y = y_m \sin \omega \left(\frac{x}{v} - t \right) \qquad y = y_m \sin 2\pi \left(\frac{x}{\lambda} - \frac{t}{T} \right).$$

2. The speed of electromagnetic waves in vacuum is 3×10^8 meters/sec. (a) Wavelengths in the visible part of the spectrum (light) range from about 4×10^{-7} meter in the violet to about 7×10^{-7} in the red. What is the range of frequencies of light waves? (b) The range of frequencies for shortwave radio (for example, FM radio and VHF television) is 1.5 megacycles/sec to 300 megacycles/sec. What is the corresponding wavelength range? (c) X-rays are also electromagnetic. Their wavelength range extends from about 5×10^{-9} meter to 1.0×10^{-11} meter. What is the frequency range for X-rays?

3. The equation of a transverse wave traveling in a rope is given by

$$y = 10 \sin \pi(0.01x - 2.00t),$$

where y and x are expressed in centimeters and t in seconds. (a) Find the amplitude, frequency, velocity, and wavelength of the wave. (b) Find the maximum transverse speed of a particle in the rope.

4. Write the equation for a wave traveling in the negative direction along the x-axis and having an amplitude 0.01 meter, a frequency 550 vib/sec, and a speed 330 meters/sec.

5. A wave of frequency 500 cycles/sec has a phase velocity of 350 meters/sec. (a) How far apart are two points $60°$ out of phase? (b) What is the phase difference between two displacements at a certain point at times 10^{-3} sec apart?

6. (a) A continuous sinusoidal longitudinal wave is sent along a coil spring from a vibrating source attached to it. The frequency of the source is 25 vib/sec, and the distance between successive rarefactions in the spring is 24 cm. Find the wave speed. (b) If the maximum longitudinal displacement of a particle in the spring is 3.0 cm and the wave

moves in the $-x$ direction, write the equation for the wave. Let the source be at $x = 0$ and the displacement at $x = 0$ and $t = 0$ be zero.

7. What is the speed of a transverse wave in a rope of length 2.0 meters and mass 0.06 kg under a tension of 500 nt?

8. Prove that the slope of a string at any point x is numerically equal to the ratio of the particle speed to the wave speed at that point.

9. (a) From Example 2 show that the *maximum* speed of a particle in a string through which a sinusoidal wave is passing is $u = y_m \omega$. (b) In Example 2 we saw that the particles in the string oscillate with simple harmonic motion. The mechanical energy of each particle is the sum of its potential and kinetic energies and is always equal to the *maximum* value of its kinetic energy. Consider an element of string of mass $\mu \, \Delta x$ and show that the energy *per unit length* of the string is given by

$$E_l = 2\pi^2 \mu f^2 y_m{}^2.$$

(c) Show finally that the average power or average rate of transfer of energy is the product of the energy per unit length and the wave speed. (d) Do these results hold only for a sinusoidal wave?

10. Spherical waves are emitted from a 1.0-watt source in an isotropic nonabsorbing medium. What is the wave intensity 1.0 meter from the source?

11. (a) Show that the intensity I (the energy crossing unit area per unit time) is the product of the energy per unit volume e and the speed of propagation v of a wave disturbance. (b) Radio waves travel at a speed of 3×10^8 meters/sec. Find the energy density in a radio wave 300 miles from a 50,000-watt source, assuming the waves to be spherical.

12. A line source emits a cylindrical expanding wave. Assuming the medium absorbs no energy, find how the amplitude and intensity of the wave depend on the distance from the source.

13. Determine the amplitude of the resultant motion when two sinusoidal motions having the same frequency and traveling in the same line are combined, if their amplitudes are 3.0 cm and 4.0 cm and they differ in phase by $\pi/2$ radians.

14. A source S and a detector D of high-frequency waves are a distance d apart on the ground. The direct wave from S is found to be in phase at D with the wave from S that is reflected from a horizontal layer at an altitude H (Fig. 19–22). The incident and reflected rays make the same angle with the reflecting layer. When the layer rises a distance h, no signal is detected at D. Neglect absorption in the atmosphere and find the relation between d, h, H, and the wavelength λ of the waves.

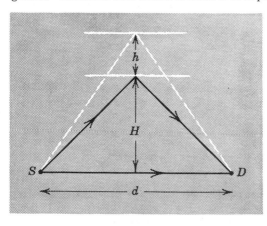

Fig. 19–22

15. Three component sinusoidal waves have the same period, but their amplitudes are in the ratio 1, 1/2, and 1/3 and their phase angles are 0, $\pi/2$, and π respectively. Plot the resultant waveform and discuss its nature.

16. Four component sine waves have frequencies in the ratio 1, 2, 3, and 4 and amplitudes in the ratio 1, 1/2, 1/3, and 1/4, respectively. The first and third components are 180° out of phase with the second and fourth components. Plot the resultant waveform and discuss its nature.

17. A string vibrates according to the equation

$$y = 5 \sin \frac{\pi x}{3} \cos 40\pi t,$$

where x and y are in centimeters and t is in seconds. (a) What are the amplitude and velocity of the component waves whose superposition can give rise to this vibration? (b) What is the distance between nodes? (c) What is the velocity of a particle of the string at the position $x = 1.5$ cm when $t = 9/8$ sec?

18. Two transverse sinusoidal waves travel in opposite directions along a string. Each has an amplitude of 3.0 cm and a wavelength of 6.0 cm. The speed of a transverse wave in the string is 0.5 cm/sec. Plot the shape of the string at each of the following times: $t = 0$ (arbitrary), $t = 3$, $t = 6$, and $t = 9$ sec.

19. In a laboratory experiment on standing waves a string 3.0 ft long is attached to the prong of an electrically driven tuning fork which vibrates perpendicular to the length of the string at a frequency of 60 vib/sec. The weight of the string is 0.096 lb. (a) What tension must the string be under (weights are attached to the other end) if it is to vibrate in four loops? (b) What would happen if the tuning fork is turned so as to vibrate parallel to the length of the string?

20. A wave travels out uniformly in all directions from a point source. Justify the following expression for the displacement y of the medium at any distance r from the source:

$$y = \frac{y_m}{r} \sin k(r - vt).$$

Consider the speed, direction of propagation, periodicity, and intensity of the wave.

Sound Waves

CHAPTER 20

20–1   Audible, Ultrasonic, and Infrasonic Waves

Sound waves are longitudinal mechanical waves. They can be propagated in solids, liquids, and gases. The material particles transmitting such a wave oscillate in the direction of propagation of the wave itself. Actually, there is a large range of frequencies within which longitudinal mechanical waves can be generated. Sound waves are confined to the frequency range which can stimulate the human ear and brain to the sensation of hearing. This frequency range spreads from about 20 cycles/sec to about 20,000 cycles/sec and is called the *audible* range. A longitudinal mechanical wave whose frequency is below the audible range is called an *infrasonic* wave, and one whose frequency is above the audible range is called an *ultrasonic* wave.

Infrasonic waves of interest are usually generated by large sources, earthquake waves being an example. The high frequencies associated with ultrasonic waves may be produced by elastic vibrations of a quartz crystal induced by resonance with an applied alternating electric field (piezoelectric effect). It is possible to produce ultrasonic frequencies as high as 6×10^8 cycles/sec in this way; the corresponding wavelength in air is about 5×10^{-5} cm, the same as the length of visible light waves.

Audible waves originate in vibrating strings (for example, violin, human vocal cords), vibrating air columns (for example, organ, clarinet), and vibrating plates and membranes (for example, drum, loudspeaker, xylophone). These vibrating elements alternately compress the surrounding air on a forward movement and rarefy the air on a backward movement. The air transmits these disturbances outward from the source as a wave. Upon entering the ear, these waves produce the sensation of sound. Waveforms which are approximately periodic or consist of a small number of approximately periodic components give rise to a pleasant sensation, as for example musical sounds. Sound whose waveform is very irregular is heard as noise. Noise can be represented as a superposition of periodic waves, but the number of components is very large.

In this chapter we deal with the properties of longitudinal mechanical waves, using sound waves as the prototype.

20-2   Propagation and Speed of Longitudinal Waves

Sound waves, if unimpeded, will spread out in all directions from a source. It is simpler to deal with one-dimensional propagation, however, than with three-dimensional propagation. For this purpose we consider first the transmission of longitudinal waves in a tube.

Figure 20-1 shows a piston at one end of a long tube filled with a compressible medium. The vertical lines represent certain layers of molecules which

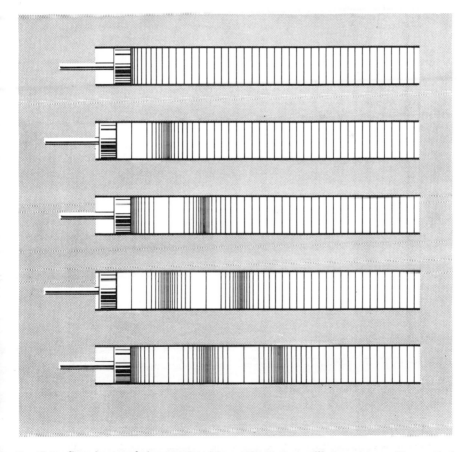

Fig. 20-1 Sound waves being generated in a tube by an oscillating piston. The vertical lines divide the compressible medium in the tube into layers.

are equally spaced when the medium, such as a fluid, is at rest. In our discussion we shall ignore the random thermal motion of the molecules for the time being at least. If we push the piston forward, the layers of fluid in front of it are compressed. These layers will in turn compress layers farther along the tube, and a compressional pulse travels down the tube. If we then quickly withdraw the piston, the layers of fluid in front of it expand and a pulse of rarefaction travels down the tube from layer to layer. These pulses are similar to transverse pulses traveling along a string, except that the particles of the medium are displaced along the direction of propagation (longitudinal) instead of at right angles to this direction (transverse). If the piston oscillates back and forth, a continuous train of compressions and rarefactions will travel along the tube (Fig. 20–1).

For the moment, let us assume that the tube is very long so that we can ignore reflections from the other end. We wish to determine the speed of propagation.

Consider a portion of the tube (Fig. 20–2) in which a longitudinal wave is moving toward the right. Rarefactions are shown at R and R' and compressions at C and C'. At the point Q just ahead of the foremost compression the fluid is not yet disturbed by the wave. In a compression the vibrating particles move in the same direction as the wave. Hence, the particle at C has some speed u toward the right when that at Q is at rest with respect to the tube. This is shown at the top of the figure.

Now let us imagine that the fluid as a whole is moving to the left with the same speed v at which the wave is moving to the right within it. In such a case the compressions and rarefactions are stationary with respect to the tube. This is shown at the bottom of the figure. Consider the conditions at C and at Q. The pressure at C is greater than that at Q because C is in a compression. Let Δt be the time during which a fluid element flows from Q to C. Then during this time interval a mass m of fluid passes Q at a speed v, and an equal mass passes C at a reduced speed, namely $v - u$. The reduction of speed can be called $-\Delta v$. The fluid element, therefore, experiences an average negative acceleration of $-\Delta v/\Delta t$ during this interval. The decrease in speed is due to the fact that the pressure at C, p_C is greater than at Q, p_Q. Hence, the backward force acting on the fluid at C, $p_C A$ is larger than the forward

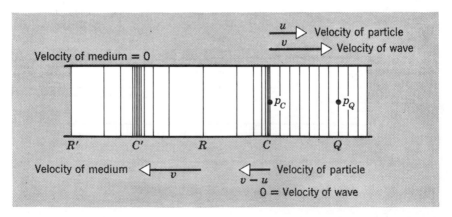

Fig. 20–2 A longitudinal wave moving to the right through a compressible medium enclosed in a tube. The medium is compressed at C, C', rarefied at R, R', but undisturbed at Q.

force at Q, $p_Q A$. Here A is the cross-sectional area of the interior of the tube. The resultant force acting on the fluid mass under consideration is

$$F = p_C A - p_Q A = A(p_C - p_Q) = A \, \Delta p,$$

so that from Newton's second law,

$$F = ma,$$

$$A \, \Delta p = m\left(-\frac{\Delta v}{\Delta t}\right).$$

We can determine the mass m by considering the fluid passing through a cross section at the point Q, where the density of the undisturbed fluid is ρ_0. The volume of fluid passing through in the time interval Δt (Eq. 18–3) is $Av \, \Delta t$, so that its mass is

$$m = \rho_0 A v \, \Delta t.$$

Substituting this into the previous equation, we obtain

$$A \, \Delta p = \rho_0 A v \, \Delta t\left(-\frac{\Delta v}{\Delta t}\right),$$

so that $\rho_0 v = -\dfrac{\Delta p}{\Delta v}$ or $\rho_0 v^2 = \dfrac{-\Delta p}{\Delta v/v}.$

Now the fluid that would occupy a volume $V = Av \, \Delta t$ at Q is compressed by an amount $A \, \Delta t(-\Delta v) = -\Delta V$ on reaching C. Hence,

$$\frac{-\Delta v}{v} = \frac{A \, \Delta t(-\Delta v)}{A \, \Delta t \, v} = \frac{-\Delta V}{V},$$

and we obtain $\rho_0 v^2 = \dfrac{-\Delta p}{\Delta V/V}.$

The ratio of the change in pressure on a body, Δp, to the fractional change in volume resulting, $-\Delta V/V$, is called the bulk modulus of elasticity B of the body. That is, $B = -V \, \Delta p/\Delta V$. B is positive because an increase in pressure causes a decrease in volume. In terms of B, the speed of the longitudinal wave in the medium is

$$v = \sqrt{\frac{B}{\rho_0}}. \tag{20–1}$$

Notice that the speed of the wave is determined by the properties of the medium through which it propagates, and that an elastic property (B) and an inertial property (ρ) are involved. In Table 20–1 values are given for the speed of longitudinal (sound) waves in various media.

If the medium is a gas, such as air, it is possible to express B in terms of the undisturbed gas pressure p_0. For a sound wave in a gas we obtain

$$v = \sqrt{\frac{\gamma p_0}{\rho_0}},$$

where γ is a constant called the ratio of specific heats for the gas (Chapter 23).

If the medium is a solid, for a thin rod the bulk modulus is replaced by a stretch modulus (called Young's modulus). If the solid is extended, we must allow for the

for a solid $v = \sqrt{\dfrac{E}{\rho}}$ $v = 16,900$ fps

for steel, $E = 30 \times 10^6$ psi, $\rho = 490 \, \text{#}/\text{ft}^3$

Table 20–1

SPEED OF SOUND

Medium	Tempera-ture, °C	Speed	
		Meters/sec	Ft/sec
Air	0	331.3	1,087
Hydrogen	0	1,286	4,220
Oxygen	0	317.2	1,041
Water	15	1,450	4,760
Lead	20	1,230	4,030
Aluminum	20	5,100	16,700
Copper	20	3,560	11,700
Iron	20	5,130	16,800
Extreme values			
Granite		6,000	19,700
Vulcanized rubber	0	54	177

fact that, unlike a fluid, a solid offers elastic resistance to tangential or shearing forces and the speed of longitudinal waves will depend on the shear modulus as well as the bulk modulus.

20–3   Traveling Longitudinal Waves

Consider again the continuous train of compressions and rarefactions traveling down the tube of Fig. 20–1. As the wave advances along the tube, a particle of fluid oscillates about its equilibrium position. The displacement is to the right or left along the x direction of propagation of the wave. For convenience let us *represent the displacement* of any particle (or layer) from its equilibrium position at x *by the letter* y, just as we did for a transverse wave in a string. It is to be understood that the displacement y is along the direction of propagation for a longitudinal wave, whereas for a transverse wave it is at right angles to the direction of propagation. Then the equation of a longitudinal wave traveling to the right may be written as

$$y = f(x - vt).$$

For the particular case of a simple harmonic oscillation we may have

$$y = y_m \cos \frac{2\pi}{\lambda} (x - vt).$$

In this equation v is the speed of the longitudinal wave, y_m is its amplitude, and λ is its wavelength; y gives the displacement of a particle at time t from its equilibrium position at x. As before, we may write this more compactly as

$$y = y_m \cos (kx - \omega t). \qquad (20\text{-}2)$$

It is usually more convenient to deal with pressure variations in a sound wave than with the actual displacements of the particles conveying the wave. Let us, therefore, write the equation of the wave in terms of the pressure variation rather than in terms of the displacement.

From the relation

$$B = - \frac{\Delta p}{\Delta V / V},$$

we have

$$\Delta p = -B \frac{\Delta V}{V}.$$

Just as we let y represent the displacement from the equilibrium position x, so we now let p represent the *change* from the undisturbed pressure p_0. Then p replaces Δp, and

$$p = -B \frac{\Delta V}{V}.$$

If a layer of fluid at pressure p_0 has a length Δx and cross-sectional area A, its volume is $V = A \, \Delta x$. When the pressure changes, its volume will change by $A \, \Delta y$, where Δy is the amount by which the length of the layer changes during compression or rarefaction. Hence,

$$p = -B \frac{\Delta V}{V} = -B \frac{A \, \Delta y}{A \, \Delta x}.$$

As we let $\Delta x \to 0$ so as to shrink to a line in the fluid, we obtain

$$p = -B \frac{dy}{dx}. \qquad (20\text{-}3)$$

If the particle displacement is simple harmonic, then, from Eq. 20-2, we obtain

$$\frac{dy}{dx} = -k y_m \sin (kx - \omega t),$$

and from Eq. 20-3 $\qquad p = B k y_m \sin (kx - \omega t). \qquad (20\text{-}4)$

Hence, the pressure variation is also simple harmonic.

Since $v = \sqrt{B/\rho_0}$, we can write Eq. 20-4 more conveniently as

$$p = [k \rho_0 v^2 y_m] \sin (kx - \omega t).$$

Recall that p represents the change from standard pressure p_0. If p_0 were atmospheric pressure, then p would represent the gauge pressure. The term in brackets represents the maximum change in pressure and is called the *pressure amplitude.* If we denote this by P, then

$$p = P \sin (kx - \omega t), \tag{20-5}$$

where $$P = k\rho_0 v^2 y_m. \tag{20-6}$$

Hence, a sound wave may be considered either as a displacement wave or as a pressure wave. If the former is written as a cosine function, the latter will be a sine function and vice versa. The displacement wave is 90° out of phase with the pressure wave. That is, when the displacement from equilibrium at a point is a maximum or a minimum, the excess pressure there is zero; when the displacement at a point is zero, the excess or deficiency of pressure there is a maximum. Equation 20–6 gives the relation between the pressure amplitude (maximum variation of pressure from equilibrium) and the displacement amplitude (maximum variation of position from equilibrium). The student should check the dimensions of each side of Eq. 20–6 for consistency. What units may the pressure amplitude have?

In Chapter 19 we proved that the intensity of a wave is proportional to the square of the displacement amplitude of the wave. We have just shown that for sound waves the pressure amplitude is proportional to the displacement amplitude. Hence, the intensity of a sound wave is proportional to the square of the pressure amplitude. The greater the pressure variations, the louder or more intense the sound wave. In fact, when the intensity is expressed in terms of the pressure amplitude, the frequency does not appear explicitly in the expression (see Problem 9). Hence, by measuring pressure changes, the intensities of sounds having *different* frequencies can be compared directly. For this reason instruments that measure pressure changes are preferred to those that measure displacement amplitude. As we shall see in Example 1, the displacement amplitudes would be difficult to measure in any case.

▶ **Example 1.** (*a*) The maximum pressure variation P that the ear can tolerate in loud sounds is about 28 nt/meter². Normal atmospheric pressure is about 100,000 nt/meter². Find the corresponding maximum displacement for a sound wave in air having a frequency of 1000 cycles/sec.

From Eq. 20–6 we have

$$y_m = \frac{P}{k\rho_0 v^2}.$$

From Table 20–1, $v = 331$ meters/sec so that

$$k = \frac{2\pi}{\lambda} = \frac{2\pi f}{v} = \frac{2\pi \times 10^3}{331} \text{ meter}^{-1} = 19.0 \text{ meter}^{-1}.$$

The density of air ρ_0 is

$$1.22 \text{ kg/meter}^3.$$

Hence, for $P = 28$ nt/meter² we obtain

$$y_m = \frac{28}{(19.0)(1.22)(331)^2} \text{ meter} = 1.1 \times 10^{-5} \text{ meter}.$$

The displacement amplitudes for the *loudest* sounds are about 10^{-5} meter, a very small value indeed.

(*b*) In the faintest sound that can be heard at 1000 cycles/sec the pressure amplitude is about 2.0×10^{-5} nt/meter². Find the corresponding displacement amplitude.

From $y_m = P/k\rho_0 v^2$, using these values for k, v, and ρ_0, we obtain, with $P = 2.0 \times 10^{-5}$ nt/meter^2,

$$y_m \simeq 8 \times 10^{-12} \text{ meter} \simeq 10^{-11} \text{ meter}.$$

This compares to the radius of an atom, which is about 10^{-10} meter. How can it be that the ear responds to such a small displacement?   ◀

In our analysis we have ignored the molecular structure of matter and treated the fluid as a continuous medium. In gases, however, the spaces between molecules are large compared to the diameters of the molecules. The molecules move about at random. The oscillations produced by a sound wave passing through are superimposed on this random thermal motion. An impulse given to one molecule is passed on to another molecule only after the first one has moved through the empty space between them and collided with the second. From this brief discussion, would you ever expect the speed of sound to exceed the average molecular speed in a fluid?

20–4   Standing Longitudinal Waves

Longitudinal waves traveling along a tube are reflected at the ends of the tube, just as transverse waves in a string are reflected at its ends. Interference between the waves traveling in opposite directions gives rise to standing longitudinal waves.

If the end of the tube is closed, the reflected wave is 180° out of phase with the incident wave. This result is a necessary consequence of the fact that the displacement of the particles at a closed end must always be zero. Hence, a closed end is a displacement *node*. If the end of the tube is open, the particles there are free to move. However, the nature of the reflection there depends on whether the tube is wide or narrow compared to the wavelength. If the tube is narrow compared to the wavelength, as in most musical instruments, the reflected wave has nearly the same phase as the incident wave. Then the open end is almost a displacement *antinode*. The exact antinode is usually somewhere near the opening, but the effective length of the air columns of a wind instrument, for example, is not as definite as the length of a string fixed at both ends.

Standing longitudinal waves in a gas column can be dramatically demonstrated by means of the apparatus shown in Fig. 20–3. A source of longitudinal waves, such as the speaker of an audio oscillator at S, sets up vibrations in a flexible diaphragm at one end of the tube. Gas fills the tube from the inlet and passes slowly out through regularly spaced small openings

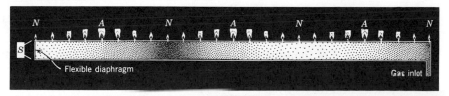

Fig. 20–3 Flames indicating the presence of standing waves in a tube filled with illuminating gas.

along the top. The escaping gas is lit, giving a series of flames. When a frequency is found at which the gas column is in resonance, the amplitude of the standing longitudinal waves becomes rather large and we can see a wave-like variation in the height and width of the gas flames along the tube. It is as though standing longitudinal waves are transformed into a stationary transverse wave pattern. The interval between nodes or antinodes is clearly visible. By varying the frequency we can pass from one resonance condition to another. The natural modes of oscillation of the gas column are determined by the effective length of the column and the wave speed. The wavelength, λ, at resonance can be taken to be twice the distance between adjacent nodes (or antinodes), and knowing the frequency f of the source at resonance, we can determine the wave speed in the gas under these conditions from $v = f\lambda$. This apparatus is not actually used for such measurements. There are more flexible and accurate ways to measure the speed of sound in gases. (See Problem 16 and Example 2.)

In Fig. 20–3 the nodes and antinodes, N and A, refer to the particle *displacements* in the standing wave. At a displacement node, the pressure variations (above and below the average) are a maximum. Hence, a displacement node corresponds to a pressure antinode. At a displacement antinode there are no pressure variations. Hence, a displacement antinode corresponds to a pressure node.

This can be understood physically by realizing that two small elements of gas on opposite sides of a displacement node are vibrating in *opposite phase*. Hence, when they approach each other, the pressure at this node is a maximum, and when they recede from each other, the pressure at this node is a minimum. Two small elements of gas which are on opposite sides of a displacement antinode vibrate *in phase* and, therefore, give rise to no pressure variations at the antinode.

20–5 Vibrating Systems and Sources of Sound

If a string fixed at both ends is bowed, transverse vibrations travel along the string; these disturbances are reflected at the fixed ends, and a standing wave pattern is formed. The maximum energy goes into the natural modes of vibration of the string. These vibrations give rise to longitudinal waves in the surrounding air which transmits them to our ears as a musical sound.

We have seen (Section 19–10) that a particular string of length l can resonate at a number of different frequencies,

$$ f_n = \frac{n}{2l} v = \frac{n}{2l} \sqrt{\frac{F}{\mu}}, \qquad n = 1, 2, 3, \cdots. \tag{20-7} $$

Here v is the speed of the transverse waves in the string whose superposition can be thought of as giving rise to the vibrations; the speed v is the same for all frequencies and for a string $v = \sqrt{F/\mu}$. At any one of these frequencies the string will contain a whole number n of loops between its ends, and the condition that the ends be nodes is met (Fig. 20–4).

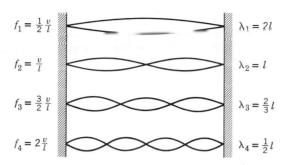

Fig. 20–4 The first four modes of vibration of a string fixed at both ends. Note that $f_n \lambda_n = v = \sqrt{F/\mu}$.

The lowest frequency, $\sqrt{F/\mu}/2l$, is called the *fundamental* frequency f_1 and the others are called *overtones*. Overtones whose frequencies are integral multiples of the fundamental are said to form a harmonic series. The fundamental is the first harmonic. The frequency $2f_1$ is the first overtone or the second harmonic, the frequency $3f_1$ is the second overtone or the third harmonic, and so on.

If the string is initially distorted so that its shape is the same as *any one* of the possible harmonics, it will vibrate at the frequency of that particular harmonic, when released. The initial conditions usually arise from striking or bowing the string, however, and in such cases not only the fundamental but many of the overtones are present in the resulting vibration. We have a superposition of many natural modes of oscillation. The actual displacement is the sum of the many harmonics with various different amplitudes. (See Fig. 19–14.) The impulses that are sent through the air to the ear and brain give rise to one net effect which is characteristic of the particular stringed instrument. The quality of the sound of a particular note (fundamental frequency) played by an instrument is determined by the number of overtones present and their respective intensities. In Fig. 20–5 the sound spectra and corresponding waveforms for the violin and piano are shown.

An organ pipe is the simplest example of sound originating in a vibrating air column and is characteristic of all wind instruments. If one end of a pipe is open and a stream of air is directed against an edge, standing longitudinal waves can be set up in the tube. The air column will then resonate at its natural frequencies of vibration, given by

$$f_n = \frac{n}{2l} v, \qquad n = 1, 2, 3, \cdots.$$

Here v is the speed of the longitudinal waves in the column whose superposition can be thought of as giving rise to the vibrations, and n is the number of half wavelengths in the length l of the column. As with the plucked or bowed string, the fundamental and overtones are excited at the same time.

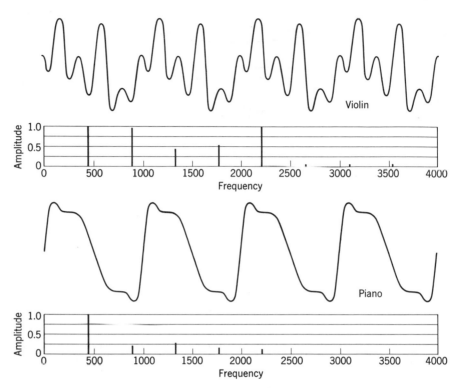

Fig. 20-5 Waveform and sound spectrum for two stringed instruments, the violin and the piano. The fundamental frequency in both cases is 440 cycles/sec (concert A). The wave shown in each diagram extends over four cycles. The sound spectrum shows the relative amplitude of the various harmonic components of the wave. Notice the presence of loud higher harmonics (especially the fifth) in the violin spectrum.

In an open pipe the fundamental frequency corresponds (approximately) to a displacement antinode at each end and a displacement node in the middle, as shown in Fig. 20–6. The succeeding drawings of Fig. 20–6 show three of the overtones, the second, third, and fourth harmonics. Hence, in an open pipe the fundamental frequency is $v/2l$ and *all* harmonics are present.

In a closed pipe the closed end is a displacement node. Figure 20–7 shows the modes of vibration of a closed pipe. The fundamental frequency is $v/4l$ (approximately), which is one-half that of an open pipe of the same length. The only overtones present are those that give a displacement node at the closed end and an antinode (approximately) at the open end. Hence, as is shown in Fig. 20–7, the second, fourth, etc., harmonics are missing. In a closed pipe the fundamental frequency is $v/4l$, and only the *odd* harmonics are present. The quality of the sounds from an open pipe is, therefore, different from that from a closed pipe.

Vibrating rods, plates, and stretched membranes also give rise to sound waves. Consider a stretched flexible membrane, such as a drumhead. If it is struck a blow, a two-dimensional pulse travels outward from the struck point and is reflected again and again at the boundary of the membrane. If some point of the membrane is forced to vibrate periodically, continuous trains of waves travel out along the membrane. Just as in the one-dimensional case of the string, so here too standing waves can be set up in the two-dimensional membrane. Each of these standing waves has a certain frequency natural to (or characteristic of) the membrane. Again the lowest frequency is called the fundamental and the others are overtones. Generally, a number of overtones are present along with the fundamental when the membrane is vibrating. These vibrations may excite sound waves of the same frequency.

The nodes of a vibrating membrane are lines rather than points. Since the boundary of the membrane is fixed, it must be a nodal line. For a circular membrane fixed at its edge, possible modes of vibration along with their nodal lines are shown in Fig. 20–8. The natural frequency of each mode is given in terms of the fundamental f_1. Notice that the frequencies of the overtones are *not* harmonics, that is, they are not integral multiples of f_1. Vibrating rods also have a nonharmonic set of natural frequencies. Rods and plates have limited use as musical instruments for this reason.

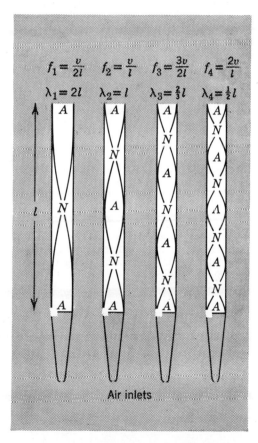

Fig. 20–6 The first four modes of vibration of an open organ pipe. The distance from the center of the pipe to the light lines drawn inside the pipe indicate the displacement amplitude at each place. N and A mark the locations of the nodes and antinodes. Note that *both* ends of the pipe are open.

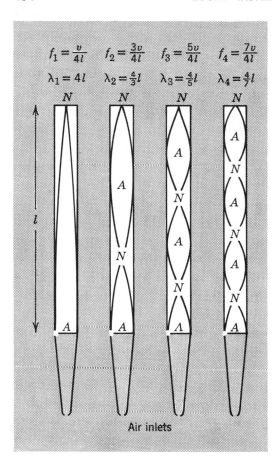

$$f_1 = \frac{v}{4l} \quad f_2 = \frac{3v}{4l} \quad f_3 = \frac{5v}{4l} \quad f_4 = \frac{7v}{4l}$$

$$\lambda_1 = 4l \quad \lambda_2 = \frac{4}{3}l \quad \lambda_3 = \frac{4}{5}l \quad \lambda_4 = \frac{4}{7}l$$

Air inlets

Fig. 20–7 The first four modes of vibration of a closed organ pipe. Notice that the even-numbered harmonics are absent and the upper end of the pipe is closed.

In general, we find that all elastic bodies will vibrate freely with a definite set of frequencies for a given set of boundary or end conditions. These frequencies are called proper frequencies, characteristic frequencies, or *eigen* * frequencies of the system. In general, the eigen frequencies do *not* form a harmonic series, although some of them may be related as the ratio of whole numbers. In all these cases we have standing waves, and certain regions of the bodies stay at rest all the time. These nodes are curves in two-dimensional bodies and surfaces in three-dimensional bodies.

Recall that for a vibrating string the equation describing a standing wave (Eq. 19–18b) is of the type

$$y = 2y_m \cos 2\pi ft \sin \frac{2\pi x}{\lambda}.$$

This holds for a string fixed at both ends ($y = 0$ at $x = 0$ or $x = n\lambda/2$). The picture of the string at any time is determined by the equation

$$y = C \sin \frac{2\pi x}{\lambda} = C \sin \frac{n\pi x}{l} \qquad (t = \text{constant}),$$

where C is a constant, l is the length of the string, and n is a whole number specifying the mode of vibration (the harmonic). This function $\sin 2\pi x/\lambda$ (or $\cos 2\pi x/\lambda$) fixes the

---

* *Eigen*—from the German—**meaning** *own, individual, characteristic.*

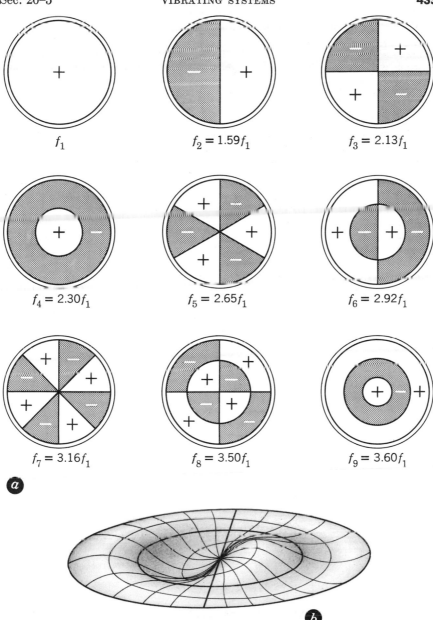

Fig. 20–8 (*a*) The first nine modes of vibration of a circular drumhead clamped around its periphery. The lines represent nodes, the circumference being a node in every case. The + and − signs represent opposite displacements; at an instant when the + areas are raised, the − areas will be depressed. Note that the frequency of each mode is not an integral multiple of the fundamental f_1 as is the ones for strings and tubes. (*b*) A sketch of a drumhead vibrating in mode f_6. The displacement shown here is exaggerated for clarity.

position of the nodes and is called the proper function, characteristic function, or *eigen function* of the string.

Likewise, the nodes of any vibrating elastic body are fixed by certain functions of position which are called the eigen functions of the problem. In general, these functions are *not* sinusoidal functions but are functions that become zero for certain values of the coordinates. The determination of these functions and the corresponding values of the eigen frequencies is an exceedingly important problem in atomic, nuclear, and solid-state physics. They characterize the behavior of such systems. It is in quantum mechanics that the procedure has been successfully worked out for microscopic systems. However, the results bear a striking analogy to the results of classical vibration and wave theory, as applied to macroscopic systems.

▶ **Example 2.** Figure 20–9 shows a simple piece of apparatus that can be used to measure the speed of sound in air by resonance methods. A vibrating tuning fork of frequency f is held near the open end of a tube. The tube is partly filled with water. The length of air column can be varied by changing the water level. It is found that the sound intensity is a maximum when the water level is gradually lowered from the top of the tube a distance a. Thereafter, the intensity reaches a maximum again at distances s, $2s$, $3s$, etc., below the level at a. Find the speed of sound in air.

The sound intensity reaches a maximum when the air column resonates with the tuning fork. The air column acts like a closed tube. The standing wave pattern consists of a node at the water surface and an antinode near the open end. Since the frequency of the source is fixed and the speed of sound in the air column has a definite value, resonance occurs at one specific wavelength,

$$\lambda = \frac{v}{f}.$$

The distance s between successive resonance positions is, therefore, the distance between adjacent nodes. (See Fig. 20–9.) Hence,

$$s = \frac{\lambda}{2} \quad \text{or} \quad \lambda = 2s.$$

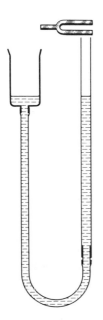

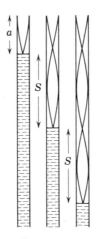

Fig. 20–9 Example 2. Measuring the speed of sound in air. The water level in the tube can be adjusted by raising or lowering the reservoir on the left which is connected to the tube by a rubber hose.

Combining equations we find

$$2s = \frac{v}{f}$$

and

$$v = 2sf.$$

In an experiment using a fork of frequency $f = 1080$ cycles/sec, s is found to be 15.3 cm. Hence,

$$\lambda = 2s = 30.6 \text{ cm}$$

and

$$v = f\lambda = (1080)(0.306) \text{ meters/sec} = 330 \text{ meters/sec}.$$

What significance does the distance a have?
Could gases other than air be used conveniently in this apparatus?

20–6 Beats

When two wavetrains of the *same* amplitude and *frequency* travel through the same region in opposite directions, standing waves are formed. This is one example of interference. Another type of interference results when two wavetrains of equal amplitude but slightly *different frequency* travel through the same region. With sound such a condition exists when, for example, two adjacent piano keys are struck simultaneously.

Consider some one point in space through which the waves are passing. In Fig. 20–10a we plot the displacements produced by the two waves separately as a function of time. The resultant vibration at that point as a

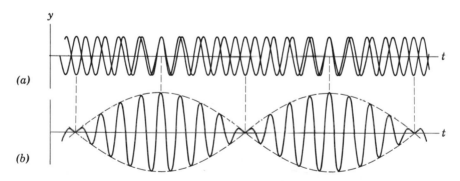

Fig. 20–10 The beat phenomenon. Two waves of slightly different frequencies, shown in (a), combine in (b) to give a wave whose amplitude (dashed line) varies periodically.

function of time is the sum of the individual vibrations and is plotted in Fig. 20–10b. We see that the *amplitude* of the resultant wave is not constant but *varies in time*. In the case of sound the varying amplitude gives rise to variations in loudness which are called *beats*. Two strings may be tuned to the same frequency by tightening one of them while sounding both until the beats disappear.

Let us represent the displacement at the point produced by one wave as

$$y_1 = y_m \cos 2\pi f_1 t,$$

and the displacement at the point produced by the other wave of equal amplitude as

$$y_2 = y_m \cos 2\pi f_2 t.$$

By the superposition principle, the resultant displacement is

$$y = y_1 + y_2 = y_m(\cos 2\pi f_1 t + \cos 2\pi f_2 t),$$

and since $\qquad \cos a + \cos b = \left[2 \cos \dfrac{a - b}{2} \cos \dfrac{a + b}{2} \right],$

this can be written as

$$y = \left[2y_m \cos 2\pi \left(\frac{f_1 - f_2}{2}\right) t \right] \cos 2\pi \left(\frac{f_1 + f_2}{2}\right) t. \qquad (20\text{-}8)$$

The resulting vibration may then be considered to have a frequency

$$\bar{f} = \frac{f_1 + f_2}{2},$$

which is the average frequency of the two waves, and an amplitude given by the expression in brackets. Hence, the amplitude varies with time with a frequency:

$$\delta = \frac{f_1 - f_2}{2}.$$

If f_1 and f_2 are nearly equal, this term is small and the amplitude fluctuates slowly. This phenomenon is a form of amplitude modulation which has a counterpart in radio receivers (side bands in AM radio).

A beat, that is, a maximum of amplitude, will occur whenever

$$\left| \cos 2\pi \left(\frac{f_1 - f_2}{2}\right) t \right|$$

equals 1 or -1. Since *each* of these values occurs once in each cycle (see Fig. 19–16), the number of beats per second is twice the frequency δ or $f_1 - f_2$. Hence, the number of beats per second equals the difference of the frequencies of the component waves. Beats between two tones can be detected by the ear up to a frequency of about seven per second. At higher frequencies individual beats cannot be distinguished in the sound produced.

There are many phenomena in physics similar to beats, that is, there are many phenomena wherein the difference in frequency of two superposed waves can be detected. These occur when a detector is nonlinear, that is, when the stimulus and the response are not related linearly. The ear is a nonlinear detector; so is a vacuum tube. In the case of light the photoelectric effect provides a nonlinear detector. This has been used to produce difference frequencies or beats between two light waves.

20-7   The Doppler Effect

When a listener is in motion toward a stationary source of sound, the pitch (frequency) of the sound heard is higher than when he is at rest. If the listener is in motion away from the stationary source, he hears a lower pitch than when he is at rest. We obtain similar results when the source is in motion toward or away from a stationary listener. The pitch of the whistle of the locomotive is higher when the source is approaching the hearer than when it has passed and is receding.

Christian Johann Doppler (1803–1853), an Austrian, in a paper of 1842, called attention to the fact that the color of a luminous body, just as the pitch of a sounding body, must be changed by relative motion of the body and the observer. This *Doppler effect*, as it is called, applies to waves in general. Let us apply it now to sound waves. We consider only the special case in which the source and observer move along the line joining them.

When an observer is in motion *toward* a stationary source, he receives more waves in each unit of time than when he is at rest (see Fig. 20–11). The additional waves received in unit time are those that occupy the distance he travels in a unit of time. The distance traveled per unit time is the speed v_o of the observer. If λ is the wavelength, there are v_0/λ such additional waves. If v is the speed of sound transmitted through the intervening medium and f is the frequency of the source, the wavelength is $\lambda = v/f$. The frequency heard by the observer f' is the ordinary frequency f heard at rest plus the increase $f(v_o/v)$ arising from the motion of the observer or

$$f' = f\left(1 + \frac{v_o}{v}\right) = f\left(\frac{v + v_o}{v}\right). \tag{20-9a}$$

When the observer is in motion *away* from the stationary source, there is a *decrease* in frequency $f(v_o/v)$ corresponding to the waves that do not reach the observer each unit of time because of his receding motion. Then

$$f' = f\left(1 - \frac{v_o}{v}\right) = f\left(\frac{v - v_o}{v}\right).$$

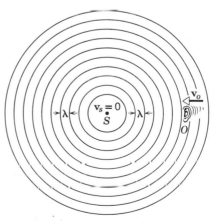

Fig. 20–11   The Doppler effect due to motion of the observer (ear). The source is at rest.

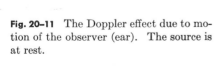

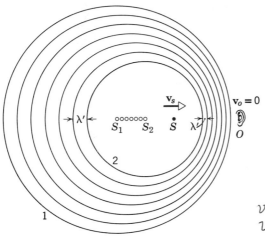

Fig. 20-12 The Doppler effect due to motion of the source. The observer is at rest. Wavefront 1 was emitted by the source when it was at S_1, wavefront 2 was emitted when it was at S_2, etc. At the instant the "snapshot" was taken, the source was at S.

v = speed of sound
v_o = velocity of observer
   "   "   source
v_s =

Hence, the general relation holding when the *source is at rest* with respect to the medium but the *observer is moving* through it is

$$f' = f\left(\frac{v \pm v_o}{v}\right),$$
(20-9)

where the *plus* sign holds for motion *toward* the source and the *minus* sign holds for motion *away* from the source. Notice that the cause of the change here is the fact that the observer intercepts more or fewer waves each second because of his motion through the medium.

When the *source* is in motion *toward* a stationary observer, the effect is a shortening of the wavelength (see Fig. 20-12), for the source is following after the approaching waves and the crests, therefore, come closer together. If the frequency of the source is f and its speed is v_s, then during each vibration it travels a distance v_s/f and each wavelength is shortened by this amount. Hence, the wavelength of the sound arriving at the observer is not $\lambda = v/f$ but $\lambda' = v/f - v_s/f$. Hence, the frequency of the sound heard by the observer is *increased*, being

$$f' = \frac{v}{\lambda'} = \frac{v}{(v - v_s)/f} = f\left(\frac{v}{v - v_s}\right).$$
(20-10a)

If the source moves *away* from the observer, the wavelength emitted is v_s/f greater than λ, so that the observer hears a *decreased* frequency, namely

$$f' = \frac{v}{(v + v_s)/f} = f\left(\frac{v}{v + v_s}\right).$$

Hence, the general relation holding when the *observer is at rest* with respect to the medium but the *source is moving* through it is

$$f' = f\left(\frac{v}{v \mp v_s}\right),$$
(20-10)

change in frequency = $\Delta f = \dfrac{2 v_s f v}{(v^2 - v_s^2)}$
= frequency shift.

where the *minus* sign holds for motion *toward* the observer and the *plus* sign holds for motion *away* from the observer. Notice that the cause of the change here is the fact that the motion of the source through the medium shortens or lengthens the wave transmitted through the medium.

If both source *and* observer move through the transmitting medium, the student should be able to show that the observer hears a frequency

$$f' = f\left(\frac{v \pm v_o}{v \mp v_s}\right) \qquad (20\text{–}11)$$

where the upper signs ($+$ numerator, $-$ denominator) correspond to the source and observer moving along the line joining the two in the direction *toward* the other, and the lower signs in the direction *away* from the other. Notice that Eq. 20–11 reduces to Eq. 20–9 when $v_s = 0$ and to Eq. 20–10 when $v_o = 0$, as it must.

If a vibrating tuning fork on its resonating box is moved rapidly toward a wall, the observer will hear two notes of different frequency. One is the note heard directly from the receding fork and is lowered in pitch by the motion. The other note is due to the waves reflected from the wall, and this is raised in pitch. The interference of these two wave trains produces beats.

The Doppler effect is very important in light. The speed of light is so great that only astronomical or atomic sources, which have high velocities compared to terrestrial macroscopic sources, show pronounced Doppler effects. The astronomical effect consists of a shift in the wavelength observed from light emitted by elements on moving astronomical bodies compared to the wavelength observed from these same elements on earth. (See Chapter 40.) An easily observed consequence of the Doppler effect is the broadening (or spread in frequency) of the radiation emitted from hot gases. This broadening results from the fact that the emitting atoms or molecules move in all directions and with varying speeds relative to the observing instruments, so that a spread of frequencies is detected. (See Section 24–3.)

There are differences, however, in the exact Doppler effect formula for light and for sound. In sound it is not just the relative motion of source and observer that determines the frequency change. In fact, as we have seen, even when the relative motion is the same (v_o in Eq. 20–9a equals v_s in Eq. 20–10a), we obtain different quantitative results, depending on whether the source or the observer is moving. This difference occurs because v_o and v_s are measured relative to the medium in which the sound wave is propagated and because this medium determines the wave speed. Light, however, does not require a material medium for its transmission, and the speed of light relative to the source or the observer is always the same value c, regardless of the motion of these bodies relative to each other. This is a basic postulate of the special theory of relativity. Hence, for light only the relative motion of source and observer can lead to physical changes, there being no material medium to use as a reference frame. Although the Doppler formula for light (Chapter 40) differs from that for sound, the effects are qualitatively the same. We can use Eq. 20–10 as a good approximation if v_s is taken to mean the *relative* velocity of source and observer and if v_s is very small compared to the velocity of light.

▶ **Example 3.** Show that Eqs. 20–9 and 20–10 become practically identical when the speed of the sources and the observer are small compared to the speed of sound in the medium.

Let $v_o = v_s = u$. That is, let u represent the speed of observer *or* source. Then Eq. 20–9 becomes

$$f' = f\left(1 \pm \frac{u}{v}\right).$$

We must show then that Eq. 20–10,

$$f' = f\left(\frac{v}{v \mp u}\right),$$

reduces to the previous form when $u/v \ll 1$.

We can rewrite Eq. 20–10 as

$$f' = f\left(\frac{1}{1 \mp u/v}\right).$$

Now by the binomial expansion

$$\left(\frac{1}{1 \mp u/v}\right) = \left(1 \mp \frac{u}{v}\right)^{-1} = 1 \pm \frac{u}{v} + \left(\frac{u}{v}\right)^2 \pm \cdots.$$

But if $u/v \ll 1$, we can certainly neglect $(u/v)^2$ and higher powers so that

$$\left(\frac{1}{1 \mp u/v}\right) = 1 \pm \frac{u}{v},$$

and Eq. 20–10 becomes $\qquad f' = f\left(1 \pm \frac{u}{v}\right),$

the same as Eq. 20–9.

As a numerical example take $u = 73.0$ miles/hr. The speed of sound in air is about 730 miles/hr. Then if the source has a speed $v_s = u = 73.0$ miles/hr toward the stationary observer, the frequency heard by the observer is Eq. 20–10,

$$f' = f\left(\frac{v}{v - v_s}\right) = f\left(\frac{730}{730 - 73.0}\right)$$

or $\qquad\qquad \dfrac{f'}{f} = 1.11.$

If the observer has a speed $v_0 = u = 73.0$ miles/hr toward the stationary source, the frequency heard by the observer is Eq. 20–9,

$$f' = f\left(\frac{v + v_o}{v}\right) = f\left(\frac{730 + 73.0}{730}\right)$$

or $\qquad\qquad \dfrac{f'}{f} = 1.10.$

Hence, when $u/v = 73.0/730 = 1/10$, the percentage difference in the frequency heard between that for the moving observer and that for the moving source, the relative motion being the same, is only 1%. ◀

When v_o or v_s becomes comparable in magnitude to v, the formulas just given for the Doppler effect must be modified. The modification is required because the linear relation between restoring force and displacement assumed up until now no longer holds in the medium. The speed of wave propagation is no longer the normal phase velocity, and the wave shapes change in time. Components of the motion at right angles to the line joining source and observer also contribute to the Doppler effect at these high speeds. When v_o or v_s exceeds v, the Doppler formula clearly has no meaning.

There are many instances in which the source moves through a medium at a speed greater than the phase velocity of the wave in that medium. In such cases the wavefront takes the shape of a cone with the moving body at its apex. Some examples are the bow wave from a speedboat on the water and the "shock wave" from an airplane or projectile moving through the air at a speed greater than the velocity of sound in that medium (supersonic speeds). The Cerenkov radiation consists of light waves emitted by charged particles which move through a medium with a speed greater than the phase velocity of light in that medium.

In Fig. 20–13 we show the present positions of the spherical waves which originated at various positions of the source during its motion. The radius of each sphere at this

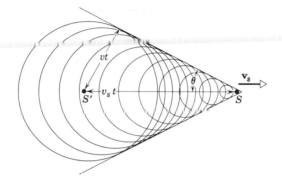

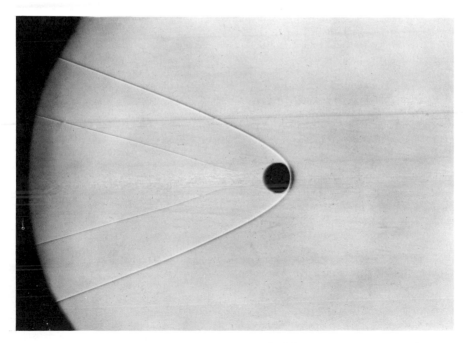

Fig. 20 13 Above, a group of wavefronts associated with a projectile moving with supersonic speed. The wavefronts are spherical and their envelope is a cone. The student should see the relation between this figure and the previous one. Below, a spark photograph of a projectile undergoing this motion. (U. S. Navy Photograph.)

time is the product of the wave speed v and the time t which has elapsed since the source was at its center. The envelope of these waves is a cone whose surface makes an angle θ with the direction of motion of the source. From the figure we obtain the result

$$\sin \theta = \frac{v}{v_s}.$$

For water waves the cone reduces to a pair of intersecting lines. In aerodynamics the ratio v_s/v is called the Mach number.

QUESTIONS

1. List some sources of infrasonic waves.

2. What experimental evidence is there for assuming that the speed of sound is the same for all wavelengths?

3. What quantity, if any, for transverse waves in a string corresponds to the pressure amplitude for longitudinal waves in a tube?

4. A bell is rung for a short time in a school. After a while its sound is inaudible. Trace the sound waves and the energy they transfer from the time of emission until they become inaudible.

5. How can we experimentally locate the positions of nodes and antinodes in a string? In an air column? On a vibrating surface?

6. Explain how a stringed instrument is "tuned."

7. The bugle has no valves. How then can we sound different notes on it? To what notes is the bugler limited? Why?

8. Would a plucked violin string oscillate for a longer or a shorter time if the violin had no sounding board? Explain.

9. Two ships with steam whistles of the same pitch sound off in the harbor. Would you expect this to produce an interference pattern with regions of high and low intensity?

10. Is there a Doppler effect for sound when the observer or the source moves at right angles to the line joining them? How then can we determine the Doppler effect when the motion has a component at right angles to this line?

11. What effect does the wind velocity have on the Doppler effect for sound?

12. Two identical tuning forks emit notes of the same frequency. Explain how you might hear beats between them.

PROBLEMS

1. The lowest pitch detectable as sound by the average human ear consists of about 20 vib/sec and the highest of about 20,000 vib/sec. What is the wavelength of each in air?

2. A sound wave has a frequency of 440 vib/sec. What is the wavelength of this sound in air? In water?

3. Bats emit ultrasonic waves. The shortest wavelength emitted in air by a bat is about 0.13 in. What is the highest frequency a bat can emit?

4. (a) A loudspeaker has a diameter of 6.0 in. At what frequency will the wavelength of the sound it emits in air be equal to its diameter? Be ten times its diameter? Be one-tenth its diameter? (b) Make the same calculations for a speaker of diameter 12.0 in. If the wavelength is large compared to the diameter of the speaker, the sound waves spread out almost uniformly in all directions from the speaker, but when the wavelength is small compared to the diameter of the speaker, the wave energy is propagated mostly in the forward direction.

5. A rule for finding your distance from a lightning flash is to count seconds from the time you see the flash until you hear the thunder and then divide the count by five. The

result is supposed to give the distance in miles. Explain this rule and determine the per cent error in it at standard conditions.

6. A stone is dropped into a well. The sound of the splash is heard at a time t later. What is the depth d of the well? Find d when $t = 3.0$ sec.

7. (a) The speed of sound in a certain metal is V. One end of a pipe of that metal of length l is struck a blow. A listener at the other end hears two sounds, one from the wave that has traveled along the pipe and the other from the wave that has traveled through the air. If v is the speed of sound in air, what time interval t elapses between the two sounds? (b) Suppose $t = 1.4$ sec and the metal is iron. Find the length l.

8. The pressure in a traveling sound wave is given by the equation

$$p = 1.5 \sin \pi(x - 330t),$$

where x is in meters, t in seconds, and p in nt/meter^2. Find the pressure amplitude, frequency, wavelength, and velocity of the wave.

9. Show that the intensity of a sound wave, (a) when expressed in terms of the pressure amplitude P, is given by

$$I = \frac{P^2}{2\rho_0 v},$$

where v is the speed of the wave and ρ_0 is the standard density of air, and, (b) when expressed in terms of the displacement amplitude y_m, is given by

$$I = 2\pi^2 \rho_0 v y_m^2 f^2,$$

where f is the frequency of the wave.

10. (a) If two sound waves, one in air and one in water, are equal in intensity, what is the ratio of the pressure amplitude of the wave in water to that of the wave in air? (b) If the pressure amplitudes are equal instead, what is the ratio of the intensities of the waves?

11. A note of frequency 300 vib/sec has an intensity of 1 microwatt/meter^2. What is the amplitude of the air vibrations caused by this sound?

12. Two waves give rise to pressure variations at a certain point in space given by

$$p_1 = P \sin 2\pi ft,$$

$$p_2 = P \sin 2\pi(ft - \delta).$$

What is the amplitude of the resultant wave at this point when $\delta = 0$, $\delta = \frac{1}{4}$, $\delta = \frac{1}{6}$, $\delta = \frac{1}{8}$?

13. In Fig. 20–14 we show an acoustic interferometer, used to demonstrate the interference of sound waves. S is a diaphragm that vibrates under the influence of an electromagnet. D is a sound detector, such as the ear or a microphone. Path SBD can be varied in length, but path SAD is fixed.

The interferometer contains air, and it is found that the sound intensity has a minimum value of 100 units at one position of B and continuously climbs to a maximum value of 900 units at a second position 1.65 cm back of the first. Find (a) the frequency of the sound emitted from the source, and (b) the relative amplitudes of the two

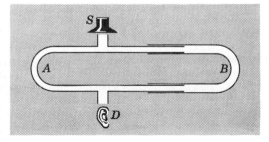

Fig. 20–14

waves arriving at the detector. (c) How can it happen that these waves have different amplitudes, considering that they originate at the same source?

14. Two loudspeakers, S_1 and S_2, each emit sound of frequency 200 vib/sec uniformly in all directions. S_1 has an acoustic output of 1.2×10^{-3} watt and S_2 one of 1.8×10^{-3} watt. S_1 and S_2 vibrate in phase. Consider a point P which is 4 meters from S_1 and 3 meters from S_2. (a) How are the phases of the two waves arriving at P related? (b) What is the intensity of sound at P with both S_1 and S_2 on? (c) What is the intensity of sound at P if S_1 is turned off (S_2 on)? (d) What is the intensity of sound at P if S_2 is turned off (S_1 on)?

15. The water level in a vertical glass tube 1.0 meter long can be adjusted to any position in the tube. A tuning fork vibrating at 660 vib/sec is held just over the open top end of the tube. At what positions of the water level will there be resonance?

16. In Fig. 20–15 a rod R is clamped at its center and a disk D at its end projects into a glass tube, which has cork filings spread over its interior. A plunger P is provided at the

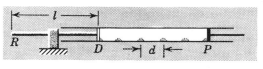

Fig. 20–15

other end of the tube. The rod is set into longitudinal vibration and the plunger is moved until the filings form a pattern of nodes and antinodes (the filings form well-defined ridges at the antinodes). If we know the frequency f of the longitudinal vibrations in the rod, a measurement of the average distance d between successive antinodes determines the speed of sound v in the gas in the tube. Show that

$$v = 2fd.$$

This is Kundt's method for determining the speed of sound in various gases.

17. A tube 1.0 meter long is closed at one end. A stretched wire is placed near the open end. The wire is 0.30 meter long and has a mass of 0.010 kg. It is held fixed at both ends and vibrates in its fundamental mode. It sets the air column in the tube into vibration at its fundamental frequency by resonance. Find (a) the frequency of oscillation of the air column and (b) the tension in the wire.

18. A tube can act like an acoustic filter, discriminating against the passage through it of sound of frequencies different from the natural frequencies of the tube. The muffler of an automobile is an example. (a) Explain how such a filter works. (b) How can we determine the cut-off frequency, below which frequency sound is not transmitted?

19. An open organ pipe has a fundamental frequency of 300 vib/sec. The first overtone of a closed organ pipe has the same frequency as the first overtone of the open pipe. How long is each pipe?

20. The strings of a cello have a length L. By what length l must they be shortened by fingering to change the pitch by a frequency ratio r? Find l, if $L = 0.80$ meters and $r = 6/5, \cdots, r = 3/2$.

21. Two identical piano wires have a fundamental frequency of 600 vib/sec when kept under the same tension. What fractional increase in the tension of one wire will lead to the occurrence of six beats per second when both wires vibrate simultaneously?

22. A tuning fork of unknown frequency makes three beats per second with a standard fork of frequency 384 vib/sec. The beat frequency decreases when a small piece of wax is put on a prong of the first fork. What is the frequency of this fork?

23. Could you go through a red light fast enough to have it appear green? Would you get a ticket for speeding? Take $\lambda = 6200 \times 10^{-8}$ cm for red light, $\lambda = 5400 \times 10^{-8}$ cm for green light, and $c = 3 \times 10^{10}$ cm/sec as the speed of light.

24. A whistle of frequency 540 vib/sec rotates in a circle of radius 2.0 ft at an angular speed of 15 radians/sec. What is the lowest and the highest frequency heard by a listener a long distance away at rest with respect to the center of the circle?

25. A siren emitting a sound of frequency 1000 vib/sec moves away from you toward a cliff at a speed of 10 meters/sec. (a) What is the frequency of the sound you hear coming directly from the siren? (b) What is the frequency of the sound you hear reflected off the

cliff? (c) What beat frequency would you hear? Take the speed of sound in air as 330 meters/sec.

26. A source of sound waves of frequency 1080 vib/sec moves to the right with a speed of 108 ft/sec relative to the ground. To its right is a reflecting surface moving to the left with a speed of 216 ft/sec relative to the ground. Take the speed of sound in air to be 1080 ft/sec and find (a) the wavelength of the sound emitted in air by the source, (b) the number of waves per second arriving at the reflecting surface, (c) the speed of the reflected waves, (d) the wavelength of the reflected waves.

27. A bullet is fired with a speed of 2200 ft/sec. Find the angle made by the shock wave with the line of motion of the bullet.

28. The speed of light in water is about three-fourths the speed of light in vacuum. A beam of high-speed electrons from a betatron emits Cerenkov radiation in water, the wavefront being a cone of angle 60°. Find the speed of the electrons in the water.

29. Calculate the speed of the projectile illustrated in the photograph in Fig. 20–13. Assume the speed of sound in the medium through which the projectile is travelling to be 380 meters/sec.

Temperature

CHAPTER 21

21-1 Macroscopic and Microscopic Descriptions

In analyzing physical situations we usually focus our attention on some portion of matter which we separate, in our minds, from the environment external to it. Such a portion is called the *system*. Everything outside the system which has a direct bearing on its behavior is called the *environment*. We then seek to determine the behavior of the system by finding how it interacts with its environment. For example, a ball can be the system and the environment can be the air and the earth. In free fall we seek to find how the air and the earth affect the motion of the ball. Or the gas in a container can be the system, and a movable piston and a Bunsen burner can be the environment. We seek to find how the behavior and properties of the gas are affected by the action of the piston and burner. In all such cases we must choose certain quantities to describe the behavior of the system. In choosing such quantities, however, we can adopt either of two points of view, the *macroscopic* or the *microscopic*.

In the case of processes involving heat phenomena, the macroscopic point of view is given by thermodynamics and the microscopic one by the atomic theory of heat. In the macroscopic approach, which we adopted in mechanics, we describe the gross characteristics of a system, specifying a few of its measurable properties which are suggested more or less directly by our sense perceptions. For example, for a gas in a container the volume, pressure, and temperature are all macroscopic quantities, things which our senses perceive directly. In the microscopic approach we describe the detailed characteristics of a system by specifying many quantities that are not directly measurable and are generally not suggested directly by our sense perceptions. For the gas in a container, for example, we specify the number of molecules, their speeds or energies, their interactions, etc. Of course, the microscopic picture must lead us ultimately to values and properties of the directly measurable macroscopic quantities. When applied to the same system, these different points of view must be compatible.

These different approaches are related to one another by the fact that the few directly measurable macroscopic properties are simply averages over a period of time of a large number of microscopic characteristics. For example, the pressure in a gas is the average rate of change of momentum due to all the collisions made per unit area by the molecules in a gas. The temperature in a gas is related to the average kinetic energy of translation of the molecules. Even in mechanics we sometimes looked at the microscopic variables whose averages were macroscopic or directly measurable quantities. The coefficient of friction, for example, was a gross macroscopic characteristic related to detailed microscopic quantities.

We begin our examination of heat phenomena in this chapter with a study of temperature. As we progress through this and subsequent chapters we shall try to gain a deeper understanding of these phenomena by interweaving the microscopic and the macroscopic description—atomic heat theory and thermodynamics. The interweaving of the microscopic and the macroscopic points of view is characteristic of modern physics.

21-2 Thermal Equilibrium—The Zeroth Law of Thermodynamics

The sense of touch is the first and simplest way to distinguish hot bodies from cold bodies. By touch we can roughly arrange bodies in the order of their hotness, deciding that A is hotter than B, B than C, etc. We speak of this as our *temperature* sense. This is a very subjective and qualitative procedure for determining the temperature of a body and certainly not very useful for purposes of science. An old and simple experiment, suggested in 1690 by John Locke, shows the unreliability of this method. Let two hands be immersed, one in hot water, the other in cold. Then let both hands be placed in water of intermediate hotness. This will seem cooler to the first hand and warmer to the second hand. Our judgment of temperature can be rather misleading. Furthermore, the range of our temperature sense is limited. What we need is an objective, and preferably numerical, measure of temperature.

To begin with, we should try to understand the meaning of temperature. Let an object A which feels cold to the hand and an identical object B which feels hot be placed in contact with each other. After a sufficient length of time, A and B give rise to the same temperature sensation. Then A and B are said to be in *thermal equilibrium* with each other. We can generalize the expression "two bodies are in thermal equilibrium" to mean that the two bodies are in states such that, if the two *were* connected, the combined systems would be in thermal equilibrium. The logical and operational test for thermal equilibrium is to use a third or test body, such as a thermometer. This is summarized in a postulate often called *the zeroth law of thermodynam-*

ics: If A and B are in thermal equilibrium with a third body C, then A and B are in thermal equilibrium with each other.

This discussion expresses the fundamental idea that the temperature of a system is a property which eventually attains the same value as that of other systems when all these systems are put in contact. This concept is in accord with the everyday idea of temperature as the measure of the hotness or coldness of a system, because as far as our temperature sense can be trusted, the hotness of all objects becomes the same after they have been in contact long enough. It should be emphasized that the idea contained in the zeroth law, although simple, can hardly be called obvious. For example, Jones and Smith each know Green, but they may or may not know each other. Two pieces of iron, A and B, attract a magnet C, but they may or may not attract each other. Hence, it is necessary to express this idea concretely so that we can set up a rational procedure for measuring temperature.

21–3 Measurement of Temperature

There are many physical properties which change with temperature. Among these are the volume of a liquid, the length of a rod, the electrical resistance of a wire, the pressure of a gas kept at constant volume, the volume of a gas kept at constant pressure, and the color of a lamp filament. Any of these properties can be used in the construction of a thermometer. A thermometer is specified by choosing a particular *thermometric substance* and a particular *thermometric property* of this substance, which we assume to change continuously and monotonically with temperature. For example, the thermometric substance may be a liquid in a glass capillary tube and the thermometric property can be the length of the liquid column; or the thermometric substance may be a gas kept in a container at constant volume and the thermometric property can be the pressure of the gas; and so forth.

Now let X stand for *any one* of the thermometric properties we may care to use. We arbitrarily choose the following linear function of the property X as the temperature T which the thermometer, and any system in thermal equilibrium with it, has:

$$T(X) = aX. \tag{21-1}$$

In this expression a is a constant which we must still evaluate. By choosing this linear form for $T(X)$ we have fixed it so that *equal temperature differences,* or temperature intervals, *correspond to equal changes in* X. This means, for example, that every time the mercury column in the mercury-in-glass thermometer changes in length by one unit, the temperature changes by a definite fixed amount, no matter what the starting temperature. It also follows that two temperatures are in the same ratio as their corresponding X's, that is

$$\frac{T(X_1)}{T(X_2)} = \frac{X_1}{X_2}.$$

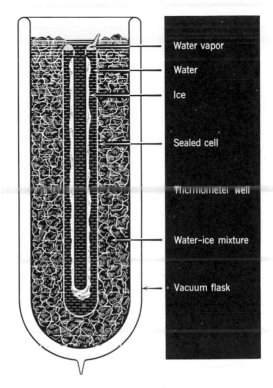

Fig. 21-1 The National Bureau of Standards triple-point cell. The cell contains pure water and is sealed permanently after all air has been removed. It is then immersed in a water-ice bath. The system is at the triple point when ice, water, and vapor are all present inside the cell. The thermometer to be calibrated is immersed in the central well.

Water vapor

Water

Ice

Sealed cell

Thermometer well

Water-ice mixture

Vacuum flask

To determine the constant a, and hence to calibrate the thermometer, we specify a *standard fixed point* at which all thermometers must give the same reading for temperature T. This fixed point is chosen to be that at which ice, liquid water, and water vapor coexist in equilibrium and is called the *triple point of water*. This state can be achieved only at a definite pressure and is unique (Fig. 21-1). The water vapor pressure at the triple point is 4.58 mm Hg. The temperature at this standard fixed point is arbitrarily * set at 273.16 degrees Kelvin and is abbreviated as 273.16°K. The Kelvin degree is a unit temperature interval. We shall discuss specific scales and units in Section 21-6.

If we indicate values at the triple point by the subscript 0, then

$$\frac{T(X)}{T(X_0)} = \frac{X}{X_0}$$

where

$$T(X_0) = 273.16°K,$$

so that

$$T(X) = 273.16°K \, \frac{X}{X_0}. \qquad (21-2)$$

Hence, when the thermometric property has the value X, the temperature

___

* Adopted in 1954 at the Tenth Conference on Weights and Measures in **Paris.**

T is given in °K by $T(X)$, when the value of X and X_0 are inserted on the right-hand side of this equation.

We can now apply Eq. 21–2 to any particular thermometer. For a liquid-in glass thermometer X is L, the length of the liquid column, and

$$T(L) = 273.16°\text{K} \frac{L}{L_0}.$$

For a gas at constant pressure, X is V, the volume of the gas, and

$$T(V) = 273.16°\text{K} \frac{V}{V_0} \qquad (\text{constant } P).$$

For a gas at constant volume, X is P, the gas pressure, and

$$T(P) = 273.16°\text{K} \frac{P}{P_0} \qquad (\text{constant } V).$$

For a platinum-resistance thermometer, X is R, the electrical resistance, and

$$T(R) = 273.16°\text{K} \frac{R}{R_0},$$

and likewise for other thermometric substances and thermometric properties.

The question now arises whether the value we obtain for the temperature of a system depends on the choice of the thermometer we use to measure it. We have insured by definition that all the different kinds of thermometers will agree at the standard fixed point, but what happens at other points? We can imagine a series of tests in which the temperature of a given system is measured simultaneously with each of many different thermometers. Results of such tests show that there are differences among the readings of the various kinds of thermometers. Even when different thermometers of the same kind are used, such as constant-volume gas thermometers using different gases, we obtain different temperature readings for a given system in a given state.

Hence, to obtain a completely definite scale of temperature, we must select one particular kind of thermometer as the standard. The arbitrary choice of a particular kind of thermometer provides a definite basis for experimental investigations. Because the smallest variation in readings is found among different constant-volume gas thermometers, a gas is chosen as the standard thermometric substance. It turns out that as the amount of gas used in such a thermometer, and therefore its pressure, is reduced, the variation in readings between gas thermometers using different kinds of gas is reduced also. Hence, there seems to be something fundamental about the behavior of a thermometer containing a gas at low pressure.

▶ **Example 1.** The mercury column in a mercury-in-glass thermometer has a length of 6.0 cm at the triple point. What is the length of the column when the scale indicates a temperature of 300°K?

We have $L_0 = 6.0$ cm and $T(L) = 300°K$. Then from

$$T(L) = 273.16°K \, \frac{L}{L_0}$$

we obtain
$$300°K = 273.16°K \, \frac{L}{6.0 \text{ cm}}$$

or
$$L = 6.6 \text{ cm.}$$

Such a thermometer actually makes use of the change with temperature of the difference in volume of the mercury and the glass container. Is it correct then to regard the length as the thermometric property? (See Problem 18.)   ◀

21–4   The Gas Thermometer

At any temperature the pressure of a gas depends on its volume. If the volume is kept constant, the pressure depends on the temperature and increases steadily with rising temperature. The constant-volume gas thermometer uses the pressure at constant volume as the thermometric property.

The thermometer is shown diagrammatically in Fig. 21–2. It consists basically of a bulb of glass, glazed porcelain, fused quartz, platinum or

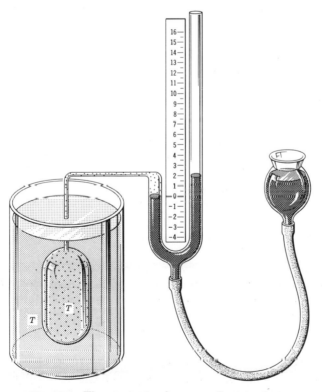

Fig. 21–2 The constant-volume gas thermometer.

platinum-iridium (depending on the temperature range over which it is to be used), connected by a capillary tube to a mercury pressure gauge, such as an open manometer. The bulb containing some gas is put into the bath or environment whose temperature is to be measured; the height of the reservoir is adjusted so that the mercury in the left branch of the U-tube is at a fixed reference mark to keep the confined gas at a constant volume. Then we read the height of the mercury in the right branch. The pressure of the confined gas is the difference of the heights of the mercury columns (times ρg) plus the atmospheric pressure (as indicated by the barometer reading). In practice we must make corrections to allow for the small volume change owing to slight contraction or expansion of the bulb and make allowance for the fact that not all the confined gas (such as that in the capillary) has been immersed in the bath. Assume that these corrections and any other necessary ones have been made, and let P be the corrected value of the pressure at the temperature of the bath. Then the temperature is given by

$$T(P) = 273.16°\text{K}\,\frac{P}{P_0} \qquad \text{(constant } V\text{).} \qquad (21\text{--}3)$$

The constant-pressure gas thermometer is more difficult to operate than the constant-volume one, and its construction and the corrections to its readings are more complicated. The constant-volume thermometer is therefore the gas thermometer which is used almost universally in scientific work today.

21–5   Ideal Gas Temperature

Let a certain amount of gas be put into the bulb of a constant-volume gas thermometer so that when the bulb is surrounded by water at the triple point the pressure P_0 is equal to a definite value, say 80.0 cm Hg. Now surround the bulb with steam condensing at 1-atm pressure and, with the volume kept constant at its previous value, measure the gas pressure in this case, P_s. Then calculate the temperature from $T(P_s) = 273.16°\text{K}$ $(P_s/80.0$ cm Hg). Next remove some of the gas so that P_0 has a smaller value, say 40.0 cm Hg. Then measure the new value of P_s and calculate the temperature from $T(P_s) = 273.16°\text{K}$ $(P_s/40.0$ cm Hg). Continue with this same procedure, reducing the amount of gas in the bulb again, and at this new lower value of P_0 calculating the temperature at the steam point $T(P_s)$. If we plot the values $T(P_s)$ against P_0 and have enough data, we can extrapolate the resulting curve to the intersection with the axis where $P_0 = 0$.

In Fig. 21–3, we plot curves obtained from such a procedure for constant-volume thermometers of some different gases. These curves show that the temperature readings of a constant-volume gas thermometer depend on the gas used at ordinary values of the reference pressure. However, as the reference pressure is decreased, the temperature readings of constant-volume gas thermometers using different gases approach the same value. Therefore, *the extrapolated value of the temperature depends only on the general properties*

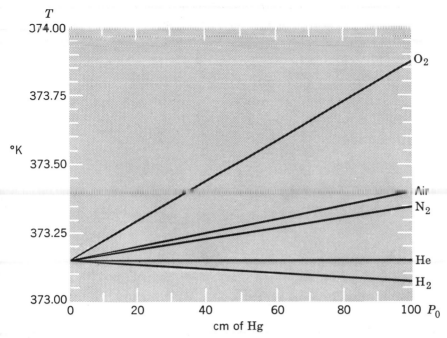

Fig. 21-3 Variation of T with P_0 for various gases. Note that at a given P_0 the values of T given by different gas thermometers differ. The discrepancy is small, although measurable, being about 0.2 per cent in the most extreme cases shown (O_2 and H_2 at 100 cm Hg). Helium gives nearly the same T at all pressures (the curve is almost horizontal) so that its behaviour is the most similar to that of an ideal gas over the entire range shown.

of gases and not on any particular gas. We therefore define an *ideal gas temperature* by the relation

$$T = 273.16°K \lim_{P_0 \to 0} \left(\frac{P}{P_0}\right) \qquad \text{(constant } V\text{)}. \qquad (21\text{–}4)$$

Our standard thermometer is therefore chosen to be a constant-volume gas thermometer using a temperature scale defined by Eq. 21–4.

We should remember that although our temperature scale is independent of the properties of any one particular gas, it does depend on the properties of gases in general (that is, on the properties of an ideal gas). Therefore, to measure a temperature, a gas must be used at that temperature. The lowest temperature that can be measured with any gas thermometer is about $T = 1°K$. To obtain this low temperature we must use low-pressure helium, for helium becomes a liquid at a temperature lower than any other gas. We see then that we cannot yet give any meaning to a temperature of $T = 0°K$, called the absolute zero.

To define absolute zero, we need a temperature scale which is *independent of the properties of any particular substance.* We shall show in Chapter 25 that the *thermodynamic temperature scale*—called the Kelvin scale—is such a scale, so that it is possible to give definite meaning to temperatures in all regions, independent of any thermometric substance. We shall then be able to define absolute zero in a physically sound way. We shall show also that *the ideal gas scale and the Kelvin thermodynamic scale are identical in the range of temperatures in which a gas thermometer may be used.* For this reason we can write °K after an ideal gas temperature, as we have already done.

The student should not think of absolute zero as some state of zero energy and no motion. The common conception that all molecular action ceases at absolute zero is incorrect. Actually this notion assumes that the purely macroscopic concept of temperature is strictly connected to the microscopic concept of molecular motion. When we try to make such a connection we find in fact that the molecules of a substance at absolute zero have a finite amount of kinetic energy, the so-called zero-point energy. The molecular energy is a minimum, but not zero, at absolute zero.

21–6   The Celsius and Fahrenheit Scales

Two temperature scales in common use today are the Celsius temperature scale, formerly * called centigrade, and the Fahrenheit temperature scale. These can be defined in terms of the absolute thermodynamic Kelvin scale, which is the fundamental temperature scale in science.

The Celsius temperature scale uses a degree (the unit of temperature) which has the same magnitude as the Kelvin (or ideal gas) scale. If we let t represent the Celsius temperature, then

$$t = T - 273.15° \tag{21-5}$$

relates the Celsius temperature t°C and the Kelvin temperature T°K. We see that the triple point of water corresponds to 0.01°C. The zero point on the Celsius scale is the temperature at which ice and air-saturated water are in equilibrium at atmospheric pressure, the so-called ice point. To obtain the Celsius temperature at which steam condenses at 1-atm pressure, we write

$$t_s = T_s - 273.15°,$$

and with $T_s = 373.15$°K, from Fig. 21–3, we obtain

$$t_s = 100.00°C.$$

Hence, in ordinary laboratory practice the Celsius degree is taken as the change in temperature that produces one-hundredth the change in the thermometric property that occurs when the thermometer is heated from the ice point to the steam point.

The Fahrenheit scale, still in common use in English-speaking countries, has no scientific status. It is perhaps simplest to say that it is based on a

---

* In 1948 the Ninth General Conference on Weights and Measures decided that the name "centigrade" should be abandoned and "Celsius" be used instead. This scale was originally invented by a Swede named Celsius in 1742.

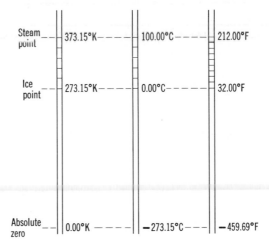

Fig. 21–4 Comparison of the Kelvin, Celsius, and Fahrenheit temperature scales.

scale of two fixed points, the ice point, which is set at 32°F, and the steam point, which is set at 212°F. Then clearly one Fahrenheit degree is 5/9 as large as one Celsius degree, and the relation between t_C (temperature on Celsius scale) and t_F (temperature on Fahrenheit scale) is

$$t_C = \tfrac{5}{9}(t_F - 32).$$

In Fig. 21–4 we compare the Kelvin, Celsius, and Fahrenheit scales.

21–7   The International Temperature Scale

Let us now summarize the key ideas of the last few sections. The standard fixed point in thermometry is the triple point of water which is arbitrarily assigned a value 273.16°K. The constant-volume gas thermometer is the standard thermometer. The extrapolated gas scale is used and the ideal gas temperature is obtained from $T = 273.16°K \lim_{P_0 \to 0} (P/P_0)$. This scale can be shown to be identical with the absolute thermodynamic Kelvin scale in the range in which a gas thermometer can be used.

By using the standard thermometer in this way, we can experimentally determine other reference points for temperature measurements, called fixed points. The basic fixed points adopted for experimental reference are listed in Table 21–1 and apply at standard atmospheric pressure. The temperatures can be expressed on the Celsius scale, with the use of Eq. 21–5, once the Kelvin temperature is determined.

Determination of such temperatures is a painstaking and time-consuming job. It would not make sense to use this procedure to determine temperatures for all work. Hence, an International temperature scale was adopted in 1927 (revised in 1948) to provide a scale that could be used easily and rapidly for practical purposes, such as for calibration of industrial or scientific instruments. This scale consists of a set of methods for providing in practice the best possible approximations to the Kelvin scale. A set of fixed points,

Table 21-1

Fixed Points of the International Temperature Scale

Fixed Points	Substance	Designation	Temperature, °C	Temperature, °K
Standard	Water	Triple Point	0.01	273.16
Basic	Oxygen	Normal boiling point	−182.97	90.18
	Ice	Normal melting point	0.00	273.15
	Water	Normal boiling point	100.00	373.15
	Sulphur	Normal boiling point	444.60	717.75
	Antimony	Normal melting point	630.50	903.65
	Silver	Normal melting point	960.80	1233.95
	Gold	Normal melting point	1063.00	1336.15

the basic points in Table 21–1, is adopted, and a set of instruments is specified to be used in interpolating between these fixed points. Formulas are specified for correcting the basic temperatures according to the actual barometer reading. The International scale departs from the Celsius scale at temperatures between the fixed points, but the difference is usually negligible. The International temperature scale has become the legal standard in nearly all countries.

21–8　Temperature Expansion

The most common effects of temperature changes are changes in size and changes of state of materials. Changes of state will be discussed briefly later. Let us now consider changes of sizes which occur without changes of state.

Consider a simple model of a solid. The atoms in a solid are held together in a regular array of forces of electrical origin. The forces between atoms are like those that would be exerted by a set of springs connecting the atoms, so that we can visualize the solid body as a sort of microscopic bedspring (Fig. 21–5). These "springs" are very stiff, and there are about 10^{23} of them per cubic centimeter. At any temperature the atoms of the solid are vibrating. The amplitude of vibration is about 10^{-9} cm and the frequency about 10^{13} vib/sec.

When the temperature is increased, the amplitude of the atomic vibrations increases, in general, and the average distance between atoms increases. This leads to an expansion of the whole solid body as the temperature is increased. The change in *any* linear dimension of the solid, such as its length, width, or height, is called a linear expansion. If the length of this linear dimension is l, the change in length, arising from a change in

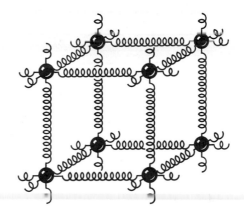

Fig. 21-5 A solid can be visualized diagrammatically as a sort of microscopic bedspring in which the molecules are held together by elastic forces.

temperature ΔT, can be called Δl. We find from experiment that this change in length Δl is proportional to the temperature change ΔT and, of course, to the original length l. Hence, we can write

$$\Delta l = \alpha l \, \Delta T$$

where α is called the *coefficient of linear expansion*. Naturally this coefficient has different values for different materials. Rewriting this formula we obtain

$$\alpha = \frac{1}{l} \frac{\Delta l}{\Delta T},$$

so that α has the meaning of a fractional change in length per degree temperature change.

Strictly speaking, the value of α depends on the actual temperature and the reference temperature chosen to determine l (see Problem 13). However, its variation is quite small and usually negligible compared to the accuracy with which engineering measurements need be made. We can safely take it as a constant for a given material, independent of the temperature. In Table 21-2 we list the experimentally determined values for the average coefficient of linear expansion of several common solids in the temperature

Table 21-2

Substance	$\bar{\alpha}$ (per C°)	Substance	$\bar{\alpha}$ (per C°)
Aluminum	23×10^{-6}	Hard rubber	80×10^{-6}
Brass	19×10^{-6}	Ice	51×10^{-6}
Copper	17×10^{-6}	Invar	0.7×10^{-6}
Glass (ordinary)	9×10^{-6}	Lead	29×10^{-6}
Glass (pyrex)	3.2×10^{-6}	Steel	11×10^{-6}

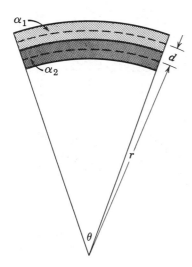

Fig. 21-6 Example 2. Radius of curvature of a bimetallic strip.

range 0°C to 100°C (except for ice, for which the range is -10°C to 0°C). For all the substances listed there, the change in size consists of an expansion as the temperature rises, for α is positive. The order of magnitude of the expansion is about 1 millimeter per meter length per 100 Celsius degree.*

▶ **Example 2.** Two metal strips, each of length l_0 and thickness d at temperature T_0, are riveted together so that their ends coincide. One strip is made of a metal having a linear coefficient of expansion α_1 and the other of metal with a coefficient α_2, where $\alpha_1 > \alpha_2$. When this bimetallic strip is heated to a temperature $T_0 + \Delta T$, one strip becomes longer than the other and the bimetallic strip bends into the arc of a circle. Determine the radius of curvature r of the strip.

There will be tensions and compressions in the strip. Roughly speaking, the central line of each strip will be free of such forces and will expand as if the whole strip were free. Let l_1 represent the expanded length of the upper strip and l_2 that of the lower strip (Fig. 21–6).

The separation of these lines is d. Assume that d is very small compared to r. Then

$$l_2 = r\theta$$

$$l_1 = (r + d)\theta,$$

so that

$$\frac{l_1}{l_2} = 1 + \frac{d}{r}.$$

But

$$\frac{l_1}{l_2} = \frac{l_0(1 + \alpha_1\,\Delta T)}{l_0(1 + \alpha_2\,\Delta T)} = \frac{1 + \alpha_1\,\Delta T}{1 + \alpha_2\,\Delta T} \cong 1 + (\alpha_1 - \alpha_2)\,\Delta T.$$

Hence,

$$1 + \frac{d}{r} = 1 + (\alpha_1 - \alpha_2)\,\Delta T$$

or

$$r = \frac{d}{(\alpha_1 - \alpha_2)\,\Delta T}.$$

---

* One Celsius degree (1 C°) is a temperature *interval* (ΔT) of one unit measured on a Celsius scale. One degree Celsius (1 °C) is a specific temperature reading (T) on that scale.

Notice that if $\alpha_1 - \alpha_2$, or if $\Delta T - 0$, then $r - \infty$, so that the bimetallic strip stays straight in these instances.

The bimetallic strip is the control element in the common thermostat. Could it be used as a thermometer? ◄

If a solid is isotropic, the per cent change in length for a given temperature change is the same for all lines in the solid. The distance between every two points changes in the ratio α per degree temperature change. The expansion is analogous to a photographic enlargement, except that a solid is three-dimensional. Thus, if you have a flat plate with a hole punched in it, $\Delta l/l$ for a given ΔT is the same for the length, the thickness, the face diagonal, the body diagonal, and the hole diameter. Every line, whether straight or curved, lengthens in the ratio α per degree temperature rise. If you scratch your name on the plate, the line representing your name has the same fractional change in length as any other line. The analogy to a photographic enlargement is shown in Fig. 21–7.

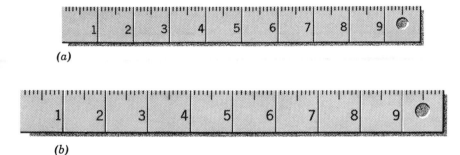

(a)

(b)

Fig. 21–7 The same steel rule at two different temperatures. Note that upon expansion every dimension is increased by the same proportion: the scale, the numbers, the hole, and the thickness are all increased by the same factor. (The expansion shown, from (a) to (b), corresponds to a temperature rise of about 100,000 C°!)

With these ideas in mind, the student should be able to show (see Problems 14 and 15) that to a high degree of accuracy the fractional change in area A per degree temperature change for an isotropic solid is 2α, that is,

$$\Delta A = 2\alpha A \, \Delta T,$$

and the fractional change in volume V per degree temperature change for an isotropic solid is 3α, that is,

$$\Delta V = 3\alpha V \, \Delta T.$$

As for fluids, because the shape of a fluid is not definite, only the change in *volume* with temperature is significant. Gases respond strongly to temperature or pressure changes, whereas the change in volume of liquids with

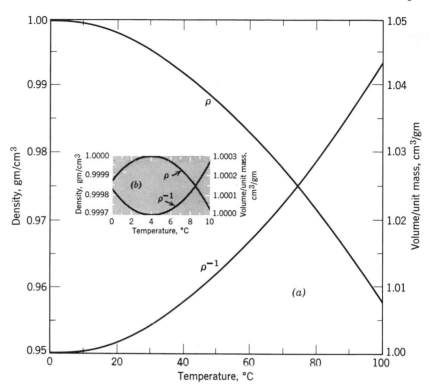

Fig. 21-8 (a) The variation with temperature of density and its reciprocal (that is, the volume occupied by 1 gm) of water under atmospheric pressure. The insert (b) shows the variation between 0 and 10° in more detail.

changes in temperature or pressure is very small. If we let β represent the coefficient of volume expansion for a liquid, that is,

$$\beta = \frac{1}{V}\frac{\Delta V}{\Delta T},$$

we find that β is relatively independent of the temperature. Liquids typically expand with increasing temperature, their volume expansion being generally about ten times greater than that of solids.

However, the most common liquid, water, does not behave like other liquids. In Fig. 21–8 we show the expansion curve for water. Notice that above 4°C water expands as the temperature rises, although not linearly. The peculiarity of water, however, lies in its behavior between 0 and 4°C. As the temperature is lowered from 4 to 0°C, water expands instead of contracting. Such an expansion with decreasing temperature is not observed in any other common liquid or for any common solid, except for rubber-like substances. The density of water is a maximum at 4°C, where its value * is 1.0000 gm/cm^3 or 1000 kg/meter^3. At all other temperatures its density is less. This behavior of water is the reason why lakes freeze first at their upper surface.

QUESTIONS

1. Would you call a phenomenon which can be seen only with the aid of a microscope microscopic or macroscopic?

2. Is temperature a microscopic or macroscopic concept?

3. Does our "temperature sense" have a built-in sense of direction; that is, does hotter necessarily mean higher temperature, or is this just an arbitrary convention? Celsius, by the way, originally chose the steam point as $0°C$ and the ice point as $100°C$.

4. How would you suggest going about measuring the temperature of (a) the sun, (b) the earth's upper atmosphere, (c) a tiny insect, (d) the moon, (e) the ocean floor, and (f) liquid helium?

5. Is one gas any better than another for purposes of a standard constant-volume gas thermometer? What properties are desirable in a gas for such purposes?

6. State some objections to using water in glass as a thermometer. Is mercury in glass an improvement?

7. Can you explain why the column of mercury first descends and then rises when a mercury-in-glass thermometer is put in a flame?

8. What are the dimensions of α, the coefficient of linear expansion? Does the value of α depend on the unit of length used? When $F°$ are used instead of $C°$ as a unit of temperature change, does the numerical value of α change? If so, how?

9. Can you give a plausible explanation for the fact that some substances contract with rising temperature?

10. Explain how the period of a pendulum clock can be kept constant with temperature by attaching tubes of mercury to the bottom of the pendulum. (See Problem 9.)

11. Explain why the apparent expansion of a liquid in a bulb does not give the true expansion of the liquid.

12. Explain why lakes freeze first at the surface.

PROBLEMS

1. If the ideal gas temperature at the steam point is $373.15°K$, what is the limiting value of the ratio of the pressures of a gas at the steam point and at the triple point of water when the gas is kept at constant volume?

2. At what temperature do the Fahrenheit and Celsius scales give the same reading? The Fahrenheit and the Kelvin scales?

3. (a) The temperature of the surface of the sun is about $6000°K$. Express this temperature on the Fahrenheit scale. (b) Express normal human body temperature, $98.6°F$, on the Celsius scale. (c) Express the pasteurization temperature, $165°F$, on the Celsius scale. (d) Excluding Hawaii and Alaska, the highest recorded temperature in the United States is $134°F$ (in the shade) at Death Valley, California, and the lowest is $-70°$ at Rogers Pass, Montana. Express these extremes on the Celsius scale. (e) Express the normal boiling point of oxygen, $-183°C$, on the Fahrenheit scale.

---

* It is to this value of *unit* maximum density of water, in gm/cm^3, that the relative sizes of the kilogram and meter were originally supposed to correspond. Accurate measurements show, however, that the international standards of mass and length do not correspond exactly to this value. The maximum density of water is actually 0.999973 gm/cm^3 at $3.98°C$. (See Fig. 21–8b.)

4. In the interval between 0 and 660°C, a platinum resistance thermometer of definite specifications is used for interpolating temperatures on the International Temperature Scale. The temperature t is given by a formula for the variation of resistance with temperature:

$$R = R_0(1 + At + Bt^2).$$

R_0, A, and B are constants determined by measurements at the ice point, the steam point, and the sulphur point. (a) If R equals 10.000 ohms at the ice point, 13.946 ohms at the steam point, and 24.817 ohms at the sulphur point, find R_0, A, and B. (b) Plot R versus t in the temperature range from 0 to 660°C.

5. A steel metric scale is to be ruled so that the millimeter intervals are accurate to within 0.001 mm at a certain temperature. Determine the maximum temperature variation allowable during the ruling.

6. A clock pendulum made of Invar is calibrated to have a period of 0.5 sec at 20°C. If the clock is used in a climate where the temperature averages 30°C, what correction (approximately) is necessary at the end of 30 days to the time given by the clock?

7. The Pyrex glass mirror in the telescope at Palomar Observatory has a diameter of 200 in. The temperature ranges from −10 to 50°C on Mount Palomar. Determine the maximum change in the diameter of the mirror.

8. The distance between the towers at the ends of the main span of the Golden Gate Bridge at San Francisco is 4200 ft. The sag of the cable halfway between the towers at 50°F is 470 ft. Take $\bar{a} = 6.5 \times 10^{-6}$ per F° for the cable and compute the change in length of the cable between the towers and the change in sag midway between for a temperature change from −20 to 110°F.

9. A glass tube nearly filled with mercury is attached to the bottom of an iron pendulum rod 100 cm long. How high must the mercury be in the glass tube so that the center of mass of this pendulum will not rise or fall with changes in temperature?

10. A steel rod is 3.000 cm in diameter at 25°C. A brass ring has an interior diameter of 2.992 cm at 25°C. At what common temperature will the ring just slide onto the rod?

11. A circular hole in an aluminum plate is 1.000 in. in diameter at 0°C. What is its diameter when the temperature of the plate is raised to 100°C?

12. (a) In a bimetallic strip, $d = 0.1$ cm, and the metals are steel and zinc. Find the radius of curvature r of the strip if it rises 20 F° from the temperature at which $r = \infty$. For zinc, $\bar{a} = 25 \times 10^{-6}$ per C°. (b) If the strip was 10 cm long, estimate the sidewise deflection of the tip.

13. Show that if α is treated as a variable, dependent on the temperature T, then

$$L = L_0 \left[1 + \int_{T_0}^{T} \alpha(T) \, dT \right]$$

where L_0 is the length at a reference temperature T_0.

14. The area A of a rectangular plate is ab. Its coefficient of linear expansion is α. After a temperature rise ΔT, side a is longer by Δa and side b is longer by Δb. Show

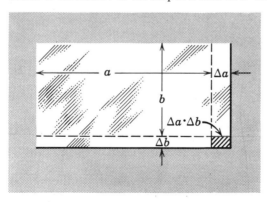

Fig. 21-9

that if we neglect the small area $\Delta a \cdot \Delta b$, shown cross-hatched and greatly exaggerated in size in Fig. 21-9, then $\Delta A = 2\alpha A \, \Delta T$.

15. Prove that, neglecting extremely small quantities, the change in volume of a solid on expansion through a temperature rise ΔT is given by $\Delta V = 3\alpha V \, \Delta T$ where α is the coefficient of linear expansion.

16. Density is mass per unit volume. If the volume V is temperature dependent, so is the density ρ. Show that the change in density $\Delta\rho$ with change in temperature ΔT is given by

$$\Delta\rho = -\beta\rho\,\Delta T$$

where β is the volume coefficient of expansion. Explain the minus sign.

17. Find the change in volume of an aluminum sphere of 10.0-cm radius when it is heated from 0 to 100°C.

18. Consider a mercury-in-glass thermometer. Assume that the cross section of the capillary is constant at A_0, and that V_0 is the volume of the bulb of mercury at 0°C. If the mercury just fills the bulb at 0°C, show that the length of the mercury column in the capillary at a temperature t°C is

$$l = \frac{V_0}{A_0}(\beta - 3\alpha)t,$$

that is, proportional to the temperature, where β is the volume coefficient of expansion of mercury and α is the linear coefficient of expansion of glass.

19. (a) Prove that the change in rotational inertia I with temperature of a solid object is given by $\Delta I = 2\alpha I\,\Delta T$. (b) Prove that the change in period t of a physical pendulum with temperature is given by $\Delta t = \frac{1}{2}\alpha t\,\Delta T$.

20. Show that when the temperature of a liquid in a barometer changes by ΔT, and the pressure is constant, the height h changes by $\Delta h = \beta h\,\Delta T$ where β is the coefficient of volume expansion.

21. Two vertical glass tubes filled with a liquid are connected at their lower ends by a horizontal capillary tube. One tube is surrounded by a bath containing ice and water in

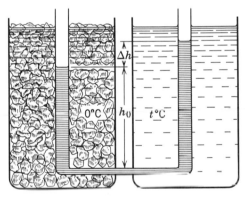

Fig. 21–10

equilibrium (0°C), the other by a hot-water bath (t°C). The difference in height of the liquids in the two columns is Δh, and h_0 is the height of the column at 0°C. Show how this apparatus (Fig. 21–10), first used in 1816 by Dulong and Petit, can be used to measure the true coefficient of volume expansion β of a liquid (rather than the differential expansion between glass and liquid). Determine β if $t = 16.0$°C, $h_0 = 126$ cm, and $\Delta h = 1.50$ cm.

Heat and the First Law
of Thermodynamics

CHAPTER 22

22-1 Heat, a Form of Energy

When two systems at different temperatures are placed together, the final temperature reached by both systems is somewhere between the two starting temperatures. This is a rather common experience. We used this observation in fact, in Chapter 21, to define in an operational way what is meant by temperature.

Man has long sought for a deeper understanding of such phenomena. Up to the beginning of the nineteenth century, they were explained by postulating the existence of a substance, *caloric*, in every body. It was believed that a body at high temperature contained much caloric and one at a low temperature just a little caloric. When the two bodies were put together, the body rich in caloric lost some to the other until both bodies reached the same temperature. Actually, the caloric theory was able to describe some processes, such as heat conduction or the mixing of substances in a calorimeter, in a satisfactory way. The concept of heat as a substance, whose total amount remained constant, eventually could not stand the test of experiment. Nevertheless, even today we describe many common temperature changes as the transfer of "something" from one body at a higher temperature to one at the lower, and this "something" we call heat. A suitable, but nonoperational definition, might be that *heat is that which is transferred between a system and its surroundings as a result of temperature differences only.*

It was many years after the inception of the caloric theory before it became generally understood that heat is a form of energy rather than a substance. The first really conclusive evidence that heat could not be a substance was given by Benjamin Thompson (1753–1814), an American from

Woburn, Massachusetts, who later became Count Rumford of Bavaria. In a paper read before the Royal Society * in 1798 he wrote,

I . . . am persuaded, that a habit of keeping the eyes open to everything that is going on in the ordinary course of the business of life has oftener led, as it were by accident, or in the playful excursions of the imagination . . . to useful doubts and sensible schemes for investigation and improvement, than all the more intense meditations of philosophers, in the hours expressly set apart for study. It was by accident that I was led to make the Experiments of which I am about to give an account.

Rumford made his discovery while supervising the boring of cannon for the Bavarian government. To prevent overheating, the bore of the cannon was kept full of water. The water was constantly replenished as it boiled away during the boring process. It was accepted that caloric had to be supplied to water to boil it. The continuous production of caloric was explained by the hypothesis that when a substance was more finely subdivided, as in boring, its capacity for retaining caloric became smaller, and that the caloric released in this way was what caused the water to boil. Rumford noticed, however, that the water boiled away even when his boring tools became so dull that they were no longer cutting or subdividing matter.

He writes, after ruling out by experiment all possible caloric interpretations,

. . . in reasoning on this subject, we must not forget to consider that most remarkable circumstance, that the source of Heat generated by friction, in these Experiments, appeared evidently to be *inexhaustible* . . . it appears to me to be extremely difficult, if not quite impossible, to form any distinct idea of any thing capable of being excited and communicated in the manner the Heat was excited and communicated in these Experiments, except it be *MOTION*.

Here we have the germ of the idea that the mechanical work expended in the boring process was responsible for the creation of heat. The idea was not clearly put until much later, by others. Instead of the continuous disappearance of mechanical energy and the continuous creation of heat, each process separately violating any conservation principle, the whole process was viewed as merely a transformation of energy from one form to another, the total energy being conserved.

Although the concept of energy and its conservation seems self-evident today, it was a rather novel idea just one hundred years ago. It had eluded such men as Galileo and Newton and was not really accepted until late in the nineteenth century. Throughout the subsequent history of physics this conservation idea has led men to deeper probing and to new discoveries in nature. Its early history was remarkable, too, in many ways. Several thinkers arrived at this great truth at about the same time; and, at first, all of them either met with a very cold reception or were completely ignored. The principle of the conservation of energy was established by Julius Robert von Mayer (1814–1878) of Heilbronn, and again independently by James

---

* Rumford, an American, was founder of the *Royal Institution* in London for the diffusion of knowledge in applied science. On the other hand, the Smithsonian Institution in Washington owes its origin to an Englishman.

Prescott Joule (1818–1889) in England, Hermann von Helmholtz (1821–1894) in Germany, and L. A. Colding (1815–1888) in Denmark.*

It was Joule who showed by experiment that, whenever a given quantity of mechanical energy was converted to heat, the same quantity of heat was always developed. Thus, the equivalence of heat and mechanical work as two forms of energy was definitely established.

It was Helmholtz who first expressed clearly the idea that not only heat and mechanical energy but all forms of energy are equivalent, and that a given amount of one form cannot disappear without an equal amount appearing in some of the other forms.

22–2 Quantity of Heat and Specific Heat

The quantity of heat involved in a physical process is measured by some change which occurs with the process. To be more specific, a unit of heat is defined as the heat necessary to produce some standard change. This leads to an operational definition of heat.† There are three units commonly used, the calorie, the kilocalorie, and the British thermal unit (Btu).

One calorie (cal) is the quantity of heat needed to raise the temperature of 1 gram of water from 14.5 to 15.5°C.

One kilocalorie (kcal) is the quantity of heat needed to raise the temperature of 1 kilogram of water from 14.5 to 15.5°C.

One Btu is the quantity of heat needed to raise the temperature of a standard pound (about $\frac{1}{32}$ slug) of water from 63 to 64°F.

The reference temperatures are stated because there is a slight variation in heat needed for a one-degree temperature rise with the temperature interval chosen. We shall neglect this variation for most purposes. We represent quantity of heat symbolically by the letter Q. The units are related as follows:

$$1 \text{ Btu} = 252 \text{ cal} = 0.252 \text{ kcal}.$$

Substances differ from one another in the quantity of heat needed to produce a given rise of temperature in a given mass. The ratio of the quantity of heat ΔQ supplied to a body to its corresponding temperature rise ΔT is called the heat capacity of the body; that is,

$$C = \text{heat capacity} = \frac{\Delta Q}{\Delta T}.$$

---

* From the posthumous publication of *Reflections* (1872) of the French engineer Sadi Carnot (1796–1832), it is evident that he had clearly arrived at the conservation of energy principle before all the others. It will give the student some food for thought to realize that of the five men who were the first to grasp the full import of the conservation of energy principle, all were young men and all were professionally outside the field of physics at the time of their contributions. Mayer was a physician, age 28; Helmholtz, a physiologist, age 32; Colding, an engineer, age 27; Joule, an industrialist, age 25; and Carnot, an engineer, age 34. Rumford was an old man, age 45, by comparison, although his American origin adds to the international flavor of the birth of this scientific idea.

† The definition can be put in operational form as follows: let 1 gm of water be put in thermal equilibrium with a body at 14.5°C; let the body temperature, and thus the water temperature, be raised to 15.5°C; we then say that 1 cal of heat has been absorbed by the water.

The heat capacity of a body is numerically equal to the quantity of heat needed to increase its temperature by one degree. The *heat capacity per unit mass*, called *specific heat*, is characteristic of the material of which the body is composed:

$$c = \frac{\text{heat capacity}}{\text{mass}} = \frac{\Delta Q/\Delta T}{m} = \frac{\Delta Q}{m\,\Delta T}.$$ (22-1)

The specific heat capacity of a material is numerically equal to the quantity of heat that must be supplied to a *unit mass* of the material to raise its temperature by one degree.

Strictly speaking, neither the heat capacity of a body nor the specific heat of a material is constant but depends on the location of the temperature interval. Hence, the previous equations give only average values for these quantities in the temperature range of ΔT. The specific heat c of a material at any temperature is defined precisely by

$$c = \frac{1}{m}\frac{dQ}{dT}.$$ (22-2)

Hence, the heat that must be given to a body of mass m, whose material has a specific heat capacity c, to increase its temperature from T_1 to T_2, is

$$Q = m \int_{T_1}^{T_2} c\,dT$$ (22-3)

where c is a function of the temperature. At ordinary temperatures and over ordinary temperature intervals, specific heats can be considered to be constants. In Fig. 22-1 the variation in the specific heat of water with temperature is shown. Information of this sort is obtained by using an electrical heating coil to supply heat at a rate that can be accurately determined. It is clear from the graph that the specific heat of water varies less than 1% from its value of 1.00 at 15°C.

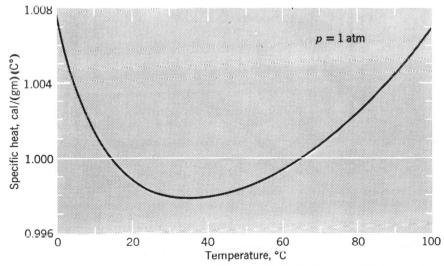

Fig. 22-1 The variation with temperature of the specific heat of water held at a pressure of 1 atm.

The specific heat of a material does not have a unique value. It may have many different values, depending on the conditions under which the heat is added. For a given m and ΔT, ΔQ may have many values. For example, if a gas is heated at constant volume, it takes less heat to raise its temperature one degree than if it is heated at constant pressure. Hence, we obtain a unique value for c only when we specify the conditions, such as specific heat at constant pressure c_p, or specific heat at constant volume c_V, etc.

In Table 22–1 we list the average specific heat capacities at constant pressure c_p of some solids. The units* are cal/(gm)(C°) or Btu/(lb)(F°). The

Table 22–1

Substance	Specific Heat, cal/(gm)(C°) or Btu/(lb)(F°)	Temperature, °C
Aluminum	0.219	15 to 185
Aluminum	0.0093	−240
Brass	0.094	15 to 100
Copper	0.093	10 to 100
Copper	0.0035	−250
Glass	0.118	10 to 100
Ice	0.55	−10 to 0
Ice	0.45	−30
Iron	0.119	20 to 100
Lead	0.0310	20 to 100
Lead	0.0150	−250
Mercury	0.033	0 to 100
Silver	0.056	0 to 100
Wood	0.42	0

student should be able to show that 1 cal/(gm)(C°) is exactly equal to 1 Btu/(lb)(F°).

Notice that the specific heat of water, made equal to one by the choice of the unit of heat, is very large compared to that of most other substances. The value for ice indicates that change of phase of a substance from liquid to solid may be accompanied by a large change in specific heat. Notice, too, that specific heat depends on the temperature and that at extremely low temperatures specific heats drop considerably from their values at ordinary temperatures. The specific heats of gases will be considered separately in Chapter 23.

---

* The lb symbol here means the *mass* of a standard pound. This departure from our previous convention is a concession to engineering usage in the interest of saving the engineering student from possible confusion in later courses.

The specific heat capacities of solids seem to vary widely from one material to another. If, however, we look at the heat capacity per mole, called the *molar heat capacity*, rather than the heat capacity per unit mass, we find that in the temperature range above 0°C nearly all solids have a molar heat capacity of about 6 cal/(mole)(C°). The number of molecules is the same for a mole of any substance, so we can conclude that the amount of heat required *per molecule* to raise the temperature of a solid a given amount is very nearly the same for all solids. Hence, the amount of heat required to raise the temperature of a solid depends on how many molecules there are in the solid sample rather than on the mass of an individual molecule. In Chapter 23, in which the molar heat capacity of gases is discussed, we consider the classical explanation of this remarkable fact. The variation of molar heat capacity with temperature, however, cannot be explained classically. One of the triumphs of quantum physics is that it gives a detailed theory of specific heats in excellent agreement with experimental observations.

▶ **Example 1.** A 75-gm block of copper, taken from a furnace, is dropped into a 300-gm glass beaker containing 200-gm of cold water. The temperature of the water rises from 12 to 27°C. What was the temperature of the furnace, approximately?

This is an example of two systems originally at different temperatures reaching thermal equilibrium after contact. No mechanical energy is involved, only heat exchange. Hence, we have

heat lost by copper = heat gained by (beaker + water),

$$m_C c_C (T_C - T_e) = (m_G c_G + m_W c_W)(T_e - T_W).$$

The subscript C stands for copper, G for glass, and W for water. The initial copper temperature is T_C, the initial beaker water temperature is T_W, and T_e is the final equilibrium temperature. Substituting the given values, with $c_C = 0.093$, $c_G = 0.118$, and $c_W = 1$ (see Table 22–1), we obtain

$$(75 \text{ gm})[0.093 \text{ cal/(gm)(C°)}](T_C - 27°C) = \{(300 \text{ gm})[0.118 \text{ cal/(gm)(C°)}]$$

$$+ (200 \text{ gm})[1 \text{ cal/(gm)(C°)}]\} (27°C - 12°C)$$

or, solving for T_C,　　　　　　　　$T_C = 532°C.$

The student should try to list all the approximations, both experimental and theoretical, that were used implicitly to arrive at this answer.　　　　◀

22–3　Heat Conduction

When two parts of a substance are kept at different temperatures, experiment shows that there is a continuous distribution of temperature in between. The transfer of energy arising from the temperature difference between adjacent parts of the substance is called *heat conduction*.

Consider a slab of material of cross-sectional area A and thickness Δx, whose faces are kept at different temperatures. We measure the heat Q that flows perpendicular to the faces for a time t. Experiment shows that Q is proportional to the time t and to the cross-sectional area A for a given temperature difference ΔT, and that Q is proportional to $\Delta T/\Delta x$ for a given t and A, providing both ΔT and Δx are small. That is,

$$\frac{Q}{t} \propto A \frac{\Delta T}{\Delta x} \qquad \text{approximately.}$$

In the limit of a slab of infinitesimal thickness dx, across which there is a temperature difference dT, we obtain the fundamental law of heat conduction

$$\frac{dQ}{dt} = -kA\,\frac{dT}{dx}. \tag{22-4}$$

Here dQ/dt is the time rate of heat transfer, dT/dx is called the *temperature gradient*, and k is a constant of proportionality called the *thermal conductivity*. We choose the direction of heat flow to be the direction in which x increases; since heat flows in the direction of decreasing T, we introduce a minus sign in Eq. 22-4 (that is, dQ/dt is plus when dT/dx is minus).

A substance with a large thermal conductivity k is a good heat conductor; one with a small thermal conductivity k is a poor heat conductor, or a good insulator. The value of k depends on the temperature, increasing slightly with increasing temperature, but k can be taken to be practically constant throughout a substance if the temperature difference is not too great between its parts. In Table 22-2 we list values of k for various substances;

Table 22-2

THERMAL CONDUCTIVITIES, $(\text{KCAL}/\text{SEC})/(\text{METER}^2)(\text{C}°/\text{METER})$

(Gases at 0°C; others at about room temperature)

Metals		Hydrogen	3.3×10^{-5}
Aluminum	4.9×10^{-2}	Oxygen	5.6×10^{-6}
Brass	2.6×10^{-2}	Others	
Copper	9.2×10^{-2}	Asbestos	2×10^{-5}
Lead	8.3×10^{-3}	Concrete	2×10^{-4}
Silver	9.9×10^{-2}	Cork	4×10^{-5}
Steel	1.1×10^{-2}	Glass	2×10^{-4}
Gases		Ice	4×10^{-4}
Air	5.7×10^{-6}	Wood	2×10^{-5}

we see that metals as a group are better heat conductors than nonmetals, and that gases are very poor heat conductors.

Let us apply Eq. 22-4 to a rod of length L and constant cross-sectional area A once a steady state has been reached (Fig. 22-2). In a steady state the temperature at each point is constant in time. Hence, dQ/dt is the same at all cross sections. (Why?) But $dQ/dt = -kA(dT/dx)$, so that, for a constant k and A, the temperature gradient dT/dx is the same at all cross sections. Hence, T decreases linearly along the rod and $dT/dx = (T_2 - T_1)/L$. Therefore, the heat Q transferred in time t is given by

$$\frac{Q}{t} = -kA\,\frac{T_2 - T_1}{L}. \tag{22-5}$$

The phenomenon of heat conduction also shows clearly that the concepts of heat and temperature, although related, are distinctly different.

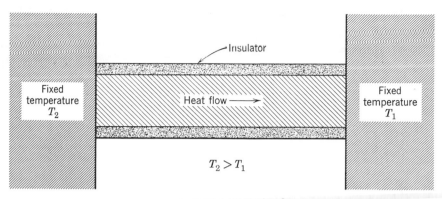

Fig. 22-1 Conduction of heat through an insulated conducting bar.

The flow of heat through a rod is not the same thing as the temperature difference between its ends. Different rods, having the same temperature difference, may transfer entirely different quantities of heat in the same time.

▶ **Example 2.** Consider a compound slab, consisting of two materials having different thicknesses, L_1 and L_2, and different thermal conductivities, k_1 and k_2. If the temperatures of the outer surfaces are T_2 and T_1, find the rate of heat transfer through the compound slab (Fig. 22-3) in a steady state.

Let T_x be the temperature at the interface between the two materials. Then

$$\frac{Q_2}{t} = \frac{k_2 A (T_2 - T_x)}{L_2}$$

and

$$\frac{Q_1}{t} = \frac{k_1 A (T_x - T_1)}{L_1}.$$

In a steady state $Q_1/t = Q_2/t$, so that

$$\frac{k_2 A (T_2 - T_x)}{L_2} = \frac{k_1 A (T_x - T_1)}{L_1}.$$

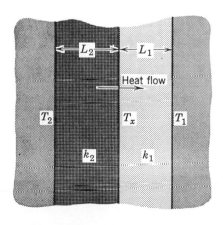

Fig. 22-3 Example 2. Conduction of heat through two layers of matter with differing conductivities.

Let Q/t be the rate of heat transfer (the same for all sections). Then, solving for T_x and substituting into either of these equations, we obtain

$$\frac{Q}{t} = \frac{A(T_2 - T_1)}{(L_1/k_1) + (L_2/k_2)}.$$

The extension to any number of sections in series is obviously

$$\frac{Q}{t} = \frac{A(T_2 - T_1)}{\Sigma(L_i/k_i)}.$$

◀

22–4   The Mechanical Equivalent of Heat

If heat is just another form of energy, any unit of energy could be a heat unit. The calorie and Btu originated before it was generally accepted that heat is energy. It was Joule who first carefully measured the mechanical energy equivalent of heat energy, that is, the number of joules equivalent to 1 calorie, or the number of foot-pounds equivalent to 1 Btu.

The relative size of the "heat units" and the "mechanical units" can be found from experiments in which a measured quantity of mechanical energy is completely converted into a measured quantity of heat. Joule originally used an apparatus in which falling weights rotated a set of paddles in a water container (Fig. 22–4). The loss of mechanical energy was computed from a knowledge of the weights and the heights through which they fell and the gain in heat energy by determining the equivalent mass of water and its rise in temperature. Joule wanted to show that the same amount of heat energy would be obtained from a given expenditure of work, regardless of the method used to produce the work. So he produced heat by stirring mercury, by rubbing together iron rings in a mercury bath, by converting electrical energy into heat in a wire immersed in water, and in other ways. Always the constant of proportionality between heat produced and work performed agreed within his experimental error of 5%. Joule did not have at his disposal the accurately standardized thermometers of today, nor could he make such reliable corrections for heat losses from the system as are

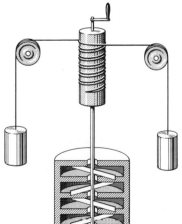

Fig. 22–4 Joule's arrangement for the determination of the mechanical equivalent of heat. The falling weights turn paddles which stir the water in the container, thus raising its temperature.

possible now. His pioneer experiments are noteworthy not only for the skill and ingenuity he showed but also for the influence they had in convincing scientists everywhere of the correctness of the mechanical theory of heat.

Using precision methods * today, the accepted results are

$$778 \text{ ft-lb} = 1 \text{ Btu},$$

$$4.186 \text{ joules} = 1 \text{ cal},$$

$$4186 \text{ joules} = 1 \text{ kcal}.$$

That is, 4.186 joules of mechanical energy, when converted to heat, will raise the temperature of 1 gm of water by 1 C°, etc. Hence, energy of any kind, as, for example, the kinetic energy of a moving bullet or the elastic potential energy stored in a compressed spring, can be expressed in units like calories just as well as in units like joules.

22-5 Heat and Work

We have seen that *heat is energy that flows from one body to another because of a temperature difference between them.* The idea that heat is something *in* a body, as the caloric theory assumed, contradicts many experimental facts. It is only as it flows, because of a temperature difference, that the energy is called heat energy. If heat were a substance, or a definite kind of energy that kept its identity while contained in a system, it would not be possible to remove heat indefinitely from a system which does not change. Yet Rumford showed that this was possible. In fact, by continually performing mechanical work in Joule's apparatus, we can obtain an indefinite amount of heat out of the water, by connecting it to a cooler system, for example, without changing the condition of the water.

Now in the same way work is not something of which a system contains a definite amount. We can put an indefinite amount of work into a system without changing its condition, as Joule's apparatus again illustrates. Work, like heat, involves a transfer of energy. In mechanics, work was involved in energy transfers in which temperature played no role. If heat energy is transmitted by temperature differences, we can distinguish heat and work by defining *work as energy that is transmitted from one system to another in such a way that a difference of temperature is not directly involved.* This definition is consistent with our previous use of the term. That is, in the expression $dW = F\,dx$, the force F can arise from electrical, magnetic, gravitational, and other sources. The term work includes all these energy transfer processes, but it specifically excludes energy transfer arising from temperature differences.

---

* It is of interest to note that Henry A. Rowland, in 1879, carried out an elaborate and painstaking research on determining the mechanical equivalent of heat which, to this day, remains a model of careful experimentation. His result, in which he expressed great confidence, differs from the accepted value today by only 1 part in 2000. Rowland graduated from Rensselaer Polytechnic Institute in 1870 and in 1876 became the first Professor of Physics at the then newly established Johns Hopkins University, where he conducted this experiment. See "The Education of an American Scientist, Henry A. Rowland" by Samuel Rezneck, *American Journal of Physics*, February 1960.

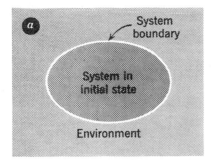

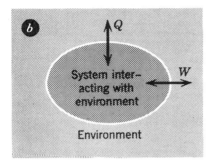

Fig. 22–5 (*a*) A system is initially in equilibrium with its environment. (*b*) During a thermodynamic process it interacts with the environment, exchanging heat *Q* and/or work *W*. (*c*) After the process is complete, the system is again in equilibrium.

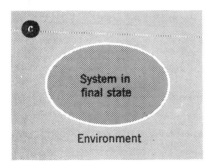

Consider another simple example, that of rubbing your hands together or rubbing two surfaces together. There is no limit to the amount of heat that can be removed from the system or to the amount of work that can be put into it, so that there is no definite meaning to phrases such as "the heat in the system" or "the work in the system." The quantities Q and W are not associated with the system but are instead associated with the process of *interaction* of the system with its environment. It is only through the interaction that we can give definite meaning to heat and work. We can then definitely identify Q with the heat transferred to or from the system and W with the work done on or by the system in the interaction. In many processes there is a flow of heat and a performance of work. The study of such interactions and of the changes in energy involved in the performance of work and the flow of heat is the subject matter of *thermodynamics*.

In Fig. 22–5 we consider a general thermodynamic process. We must first state definitely what the system is and what the environment is. In the figure we draw a specific closed surface surrounding the system to clearly define it. In (a) the system is in its initial state in equilibrium with the environment external to it. In (b) the system interacts with its environment through some specific process. During this process, heat and/or work may go into or out of the system. Arrows representing the flow of Q or W must pierce the surface enclosing the system. In (c) the system has reached its final state, again in equilibrium with the environment external to it.

Consider now a specific example. In Fig. 22–6 we show diagrammatically a falling weight which turns a generator which in turn sends an electric current through a resistor immersed in a water container. Let us choose the system to be the electric circuit, the water, and its container. Then the system interacts with its environment, which here is the falling weight. The state of the system will change, and the cause of the change is the external work done on the system by the falling weight. Differences in temperature are not directly involved in this transfer of energy from environment to system. Now suppose instead that we chose as the system only the water and container, so that the environment or surroundings are the electric circuit as well as the falling weight. Then because of the temperature difference between the resistor and the water, there is a flow of heat from environment to system; here work is not done directly on the system. Hence, it is clear that we must first state definitely what the system is and what the environment is before we can decide whether the change in the state of the system is due to the flow of heat or to the performance of work or both. There will be a transfer of heat between system and environment

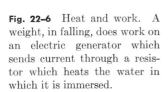

Fig. 22–6 Heat and work. A weight, in falling, does work on an electric generator which sends current through a resistor which heats the water in which it is immersed.

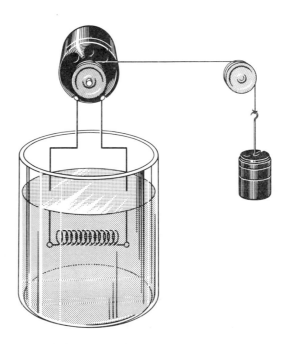

only when a temperature difference exists, and if no temperature difference exists, the energy transfer involves work.

Suppose we now try to compute Q or W for a specific thermodynamic process. Consider a gas in a cylindrical container with a movable piston. Let the gas be the system. Initially it is in equilibrium with the environment external to it and has a pressure p_i and a volume V_i. We can think of the containing walls as the system boundary. Heat can flow into the system or out of it through the walls, and work can be done on the system by having the piston compress it, or work can be done by the system by expanding against the piston. Consider some process whereby the system interacts with its environment and reaches a final equilibrium state characterized by a pressure p_f and a volume V_f.

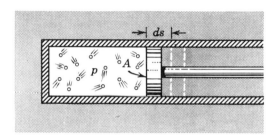

Fig. 22–7   Gas at pressure p does work dW on a piston of surface area A by exerting a force pA and producing a displacement ds.

In Fig. 22–7 we show the gas expanding against the piston. The work done by the gas in displacing the piston through an infinitesimal distance ds is

$$dW = F\,ds = pA\,ds = p\,dV$$

where dV is the differential increase in the volume of the gas. In general, the pressure will not be constant during a displacement. To obtain the total work W done on the piston by the gas in a large displacement, we must know how p varies with the displacement. Then we compute the integral

$$W = \int dW = \int_{V_i}^{V_f} p\,dV$$

over the range in volume. This integral can be evaluated graphically as the area under the curve in a p–V diagram, as shown for a special case in Fig. 22–8.

However, there are many different ways in which the system can be taken from the initial state i to the final state f. For example (Fig. 22–9), the pressure may be kept constant from i to a and then the volume kept constant from a to f. Then the work done by the expanding gas is equal to the area under the line ia. Another possibility is the path ibf, in which case the

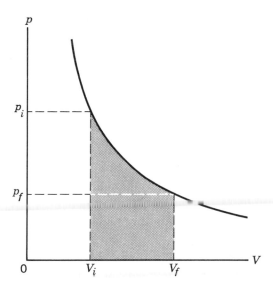

Fig. 22-8 The work done by a gas is equal to the area under a p-V curve.

work done by the gas is the area under the line bf. The continuous curve from i to f is another possible path in which the work done by the gas is still different from the previous two paths. We can see, therefore, that *the work done by a system depends not only on the initial and final states but also on the intermediate states, that is, on the path.*

Exactly the same result follows if we try to compute the flow of heat during the process. State i is characterized by a temperature T_i and state f by a temperature T_f. The heat flowing into the system, say, depends on how the system is heated. We can heat it at a constant pressure p_i, for example, until we reach the temperature T_f, and then change the pressure at constant temperature to the final value p_f. Or we can first lower the pressure to p_f and then heat it at that pressure to the final temperature T_f. Or we can

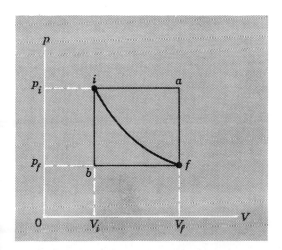

Fig. 22-9 The work done by a system depends not only on the initial state (i) and the final state (f) but on the intermediate path as well.

follow many other paths. Each path gives a different result for the heat flowing into the system. Hence, *the heat lost or gained by a system depends not only on the initial and final states but also on the intermediate states, that is, on the path.* This is an experimental fact.

Both heat and work "depend on the path" taken; neither one is independent of the path, and neither one can be conserved alone.

22–6 The First Law of Thermodynamics

We can now tie all these ideas together. Let a system have its state changed from state i to state f, say, in a definite way, so that the heat absorbed by the system is Q and the work done by the system is W. Then, using heat units or mechanical units of energy, we compute the difference $Q - W$. Now we start over and change the state of the system from the same state i to the same state f, but this time in another way by a different path. We do this over and over again, using different paths each time. We find that in every case the quantity $Q - W$ *is the same.* That is, although Q and W separately depend on the path taken, $Q - W$ does not depend at all on how we took the system from state i to state f but only on the initial and final state.

The student will recall from mechanics that when an object is moved from an initial point i to a final point f in a gravitational field in the absence of friction, the work done depends only on the positions of the two points and not at all on the path through which the body is moved. From this it was concluded that there is a function of the space coordinates of the body whose final value minus its initial value equals the work done in displacing the body. We called this function the potential energy function. Now in thermodynamics we find that when a system has its state changed from state i to state f, the quantity $Q - W$ depends only on the initial and final coordinates and not at all on the path taken between these end points. We conclude that there is a function of the thermodynamic coordinates whose final value minus its initial value equals the change $Q - W$ in the process. We call this function the *internal energy function.*

Now Q is the energy added to the system by the transfer of heat and W is the energy given up by the system in performing work, so that $Q - W$ *must represent the internal energy change of the system.* Let us represent the internal energy function by the letter U. Then the internal energy of the system in state f, U_f, minus the internal energy of the system in state i, U_i, is simply *the change in internal energy of the system,* and this quantity *has a definite value independent of how the system went from state i to state f.* We have

$$U_f - U_i = Q - W.$$

Just as for potential energy, so for internal energy too it is the change that matters. If some arbitrary value is chosen for the internal energy in some standard reference state, its value in any other state can be given a definite value.

This relation may also be written as

$$Q = (U_f - U_i) + W \tag{22-0}$$

and is known as the *first law of thermodynamics*. In applying Eq. 22–6 we must remember that Q is considered positive when heat enters the system and W is positive when work is done by the system.

If our system undergoes only an infinitesimal change in state, only an infinitesimal amount of heat dQ is absorbed and only an infinitesimal amount of work dW is done, so that the internal energy change dU is also infinitesimal. In such a case, the first law is written in *differential * form* as

$$dQ = dU + dW. \tag{22-7}$$

The first law of thermodynamics is thought to apply to every process in nature. Of course, because of its generality, the information it gives is far from complete, although exact and correct. There are some very general questions which it cannot answer. For example, although it tells us that energy is conserved in every process, it does not tell us whether any particular process can actually occur. An entirely different generalization, called the second law of thermodynamics, gives us this information, and much of the subject matter of thermodynamics depends on this second law (Chapter 25).

22–7 Some Applications of the First Law of Thermodynamics

We have seen that when a gas expands the work it does on its environment is

$$W = \int p \, dV,$$

where p is the pressure exerted on or by the gas and dV is the differential change in volume of the gas. Let us consider a special case in which the pressure remains constant while the volume changes by a finite amount, say from V_1 to V_2. Then

$$W = \int_{V_1}^{V_2} p \, dV = p \int_{V_1}^{V_2} dV = p(V_2 - V_1) \qquad \text{(constant pressure).}$$

A process taking place at constant pressure is called an *isobaric* process. For example, water is heated in the boiler of a steam engine up to its boiling point and is vaporized to steam; then the steam is superheated, all processes proceeding at a constant pressure.

In Fig. 22–10 we show a simple diagram of an isobaric process. The sys-

---

* W and Q are not actual functions of the state of a system, that is, they do not depend on the values of the system's coordinates. Hence, dW and dQ are not exact differentials as the term is used in mathematics. All they mean here is a very small quantity. More advanced books write them as $đQ$ and $đW$ to indicate their inexact nature. However, dU *is* an exact differential, for U is an exact function of the system's coordinates.

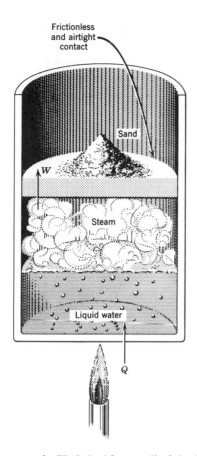

Frictionless
and airtight
contact

Sand

W

Steam

Liquid water

Q

Fig. 22-10 Water boiling at constant pressure (isobarically). The pressure is kept constant by the weight of the sand and the piston.

tem is H_2O inside a cylindrical container. A frictionless airtight piston is loaded with a pile of sand to produce the desired pressure on the H_2O and to maintain it automatically. Heat can be transferred from the environment to the system by means of a Bunsen burner. If the process continues long enough, the water boils and some is converted to steam. The system may expand and do work on the piston, but the pressure it exerts on the piston is automatically always the same, for this pressure must be equal to the constant pressure which the piston exerts on the system. If we wedged the piston so that it could not move, or if we added or took away some sand during the heating process, the process would not be isobaric.

Let us consider the boiling process. We know from high school physics or chemistry that substances will change their phase from liquid to vapor, for example, at a definite combination of values of pressure and temperature. Water will vaporize at 100°C and atmospheric pressure, for example. For a system to undergo a change of phase heat must be added to it, or taken from it, quite apart from the heat necessary to bring its temperature to the required value. Consider the change of phase of a mass m of liquid to a vapor occurring at constant temperature and pressure. Let V_L be the volume of liquid and V_V the volume of vapor. The work done by this substance in expanding from V_L to V_V at constant pressure is

$$W = p(V_V - V_L).$$

Let L represent the heat of vaporization, that is, the heat needed per unit mass to change a substance from liquid to vapor at constant temperature and pressure. Then the heat absorbed by the mass m during the change of state is

$$Q = mL.$$

From the first law of thermodynamics, we have

$$Q = (U_2 - U_1) + W,$$

so that $$mL = (U_V - U_L) + p(V_V - V_L)$$

for this process.

▶ **Example 3.** At atmospheric pressure 1 gm of water, having a volume of 1.000 cm³, becomes 1671 cm³ of steam when boiled. The heat of vaporization of water is 539 cal/gm at 1 atm. Hence, if $m = 1$ gm,

$$Q = mL = 539 \text{ cal} \quad \text{(heat energy added to the system)},$$

$$W = p(V_V - V_L) = (1.013 \times 10^5 \text{ nt/meter}^2)[(1671 - 1) \times 10^{-6} \text{ meter}^3]$$

$$= 169.5 \text{ joules} \quad \text{(external work done by the system in expanding against its surroundings)}.$$

Since 1 cal equals 4.186 joules, $W = 41$ cal. Then,

$$U_V - U_L = mL - p(V_V - V_L) = (539 - 41) \text{ cal}$$

$$= 498 \text{ cal} \quad \text{(increase in internal energy of the system)}.$$

Hence, of the 539 cal needed to boil 1 gm of water (at 100°C and 1 atm), 41 cal go into external work of expansion and 498 cal go into internal energy added to the system. This energy represents the internal work done in overcoming the strong attraction of H_2O molecules for one another in the liquid state.

How would you expect the 80 cal that are needed to melt 1 gm of ice to water (at 0°C and 1 atm) to be shared by the external work and the internal energy? ◀

A process that takes place in such a way that no heat flows into or out of the system is called an *adiabatic process*. Experimentally such processes are achieved either by sealing the system off from its surroundings with heat insulating material or by performing the process quickly. Because the flow of heat is somewhat slow, any process can be made practically adiabatic if it is performed quickly enough.

For an adiabatic process Q equals zero, so that from the first law we obtain

$$U_f - U_i = -W.$$

Hence, the internal energy of a system increases exactly by the amount of work done *on* the system in an adiabatic process. If work is done *by* the system in an adiabatic process, the internal energy of the system decreases

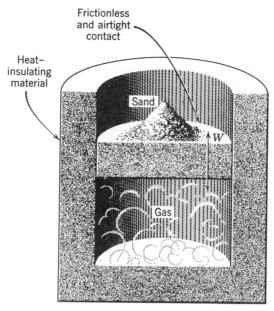

Fig. 22–11 In an adiabatic process there is no flow of heat to or from the system. Here the walls are insulated and, as sand is removed or added, the volume of the gas changes adiabatically.

by exactly the amount of external work it performs. An increase of internal energy usually raises the system's temperature, and a decrease of internal energy usually lowers the system's temperature. A gas that expands adiabatically does external work and its internal energy decreases; such a process is used to attain low temperatures. The increase of temperature during an adiabatic compression of air is well known from the heating of a bicycle pump.

In Fig. 22–11 we show a diagram of a simple adiabatic process. The system is a gas inside a cylinder made of heat-insulating material. Heat cannot enter the system from its environment or leave the system to the environment. Again we have a pile of sand on a frictionless airtight piston. The only interaction permitted between system and environment is through the performance of work. Such a process can occur when sand is added or removed from the piston, so that the gas can be compressed or can expand against the piston.

Among the many engineering examples of adiabatic processes are the expansion of steam in the cylinder of a steam engine, the expansion of hot gases in an internal combustion engine, and the compression of air in a Diesel engine or in an air compressor. These processes all take place rapidly enough so that only a very small amount of heat can enter or leave the system through its walls during that short time. The compressions and rarefactions in a sound wave are so rapid that the behavior of the transmitting gas is adiabatic (Example 5, Chapter 23).

The most important reason for studying adiabatic processes, however, is that ideal engines use processes that are exactly adiabatic. These ideal engines determine the theoretical limits to the operation and capabilities of real engines. We shall look further into this in Chapter 25.

A process of much theoretical interest is that of *free expansion*. This is an adiabatic process in which no work is performed on or by the system. Something like this can be achieved by connecting one vessel which contains a gas to another evacuated vessel with a stopcock connection, the whole system being enclosed with thermal insulation (Fig. 22–12). If the stopcock is suddenly opened, the gas rushes into the vacuum and expands freely. Because of the heat insulation this process is adiabatic, and because the walls of the vessels are rigid no external work is done. Hence, in the first law we have $Q = 0$ and $W = 0$, so that $U_i = U_f$ for this process. The initial and final internal energies are equal in free expansion.

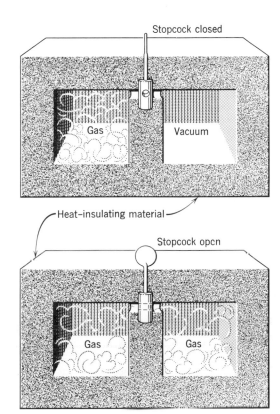

Fig. 22–12 Free expansion. There is no change of internal energy U since there is no flow of heat Q and no external work W is done.

QUESTIONS

1. Give examples to distinguish clearly between temperature and heat.

2. (*a*) Show how heat conduction and calorimetry could be explained by the caloric theory. (*b*) List some heat phenomena that cannot be explained by the caloric theory.

3. Can heat be considered a form of stored (or potential) energy? Would such an interpretation contradict the concept of heat as energy in process of transfer because of a temperature difference?

4. Can heat be added to a substance without causing the temperature of the substance to rise? If so, does this contradict the concept of heat as energy in process of transfer because of a temperature difference?

5. Give an example of a process in which no heat is transferred to or from the system but the temperature of the system changes.

6. Both heat conduction and wave propagation involve the transfer of energy. Is there any difference in principle between these two phenomena?

7. In what way is steady-state heat flow analogous to the flow of an incompressible fluid?

8. On a winter day the temperature of the inside surface of a wall is much lower than room temperature and that of the outside surface is much higher than the outdoor temperature. Explain.

9. What connection is there between an object's feeling hot or cold and its heat capacity? Between this and its thermal conductivity?

10. What requirements for thermal conductivity, specific heat capacity, and coefficient of expansion would you want a material to be used as a cooking utensil to satisfy?

11. Is the mechanical equivalent of heat, J, a physical quantity or merely a conversion factor for converting energy from heat units to mechanical units and vice versa?

12. Discuss the process of the freezing of water from the point of view of the first law of thermodynamics. Remember that ice occupies a greater volume than an equal mass of water.

13. Does a gas do any work when it expands adiabatically? If so, what is the source of the energy needed to do this work?

14. A gas is kept at a constant temperature as it expands. It does external work. Does the internal energy of the gas change during this process? If not, what is the source of the energy needed to do the work?

PROBLEMS

1. In a Joule experiment, a mass of 6.00 kg falls through a height of 50.0 meters and rotates a paddle wheel which stirs 0.600 kg of water. The water is initially at 15°C. By how much does its temperature rise?

2. Compute the possible increase in temperature for water going over Niagara Falls, 162 ft high. What factors would tend to prevent this possible rise?

3. An energetic athlete dissipates all the energy in a diet of 4000 kcal per day. If he were to release this heat at a steady rate, how would his heat output compare with that of a 100-watt bulb? Assume the bulb's output to be entirely heat.

4. Show that the specific heat of a substance has the same numerical value whether expressed in cal/(gm)(C°) or Btu/(lb)(F°).

5. Calculate the specific heat of a metal from the following data. A container made of the metal weighs 8.0 lb and contains in addition 30 lb of water. A 4.0-lb piece of the metal initially at a temperature of 350°F is dropped into the water. The water and container initially have a temperature of 60°F and the final temperature of the entire system is 65°F.

6. A thermometer of mass 0.055 kg and of specific heat 0.20 kcal/(kg)(C°) reads 15.0°C. It is then inserted into 0.300 kg of water and it comes to the same final temperature of the

water. If the thermometer reads 44.4 °C and is accurate, what was the temperature of the water before insertion of the thermometer, neglecting other heat losses?

7. Count Rumford weighed a metal object at low temperature and then at high temperature to see whether its "caloric content" increased. He concluded that (for gold) the "caloric" did not weigh more than 10^{-6} the weight of the sample. (a) Should the mass of a sample increase when heated, according to modern theories? (b) If so, by what order of magnitude? (c) Was Rumford safe in rejecting the caloric theory on this basis, in retrospect?

8. Take the average specific heat of copper to be 0.090 cal/(gm)(C°) in the temperature range 0 to 1000°C. If 1 kg of copper is heated from 0 to 1000°C, by how much does its mass increase?

9. A "flow calorimeter" is used to measure the specific heat of a liquid. Heat is added at a known rate to a stream of the liquid as it passes through the calorimeter at a known rate. Then a measurement of the resulting temperature difference between the inflow and the outflow points of the liquid stream enables us to compute the specific heat of the liquid.

A liquid of density 0.85 gm/cm³ flows through a calorimeter at the rate of 8.0 cm³/sec. Heat is added by means of a 250-watt electric heating coil, and a temperature difference of 15 C° is established in steady-state conditions between the inflow and outflow points. Find the specific heat of the liquid.

10. By means of a heating coil energy is transferred at a *constant* rate to a substance in a *thermally insulated* container. The temperature of the substance is measured as a function of the time. Show how we can deduce the way in which the heat capacity of the body depends on the temperature from this information.

11. Suppose the specific heat of a substance is found to vary with temperature in a parabolic fashion, that is

$$c = A + BT^2,$$

where A and B are constants and T is Celsius temperature. Compare the *mean* specific heat of the substance in a temperature range $T = 0°C$ to $T = t°C$ to the specific heat at the midpoint $T = (t/2)°C$.

12. Power is supplied at the rate of 0.40 hp for 2.0 min in drilling a hole in a 1.0-lb brass block. (a) How much heat is generated? (b) What is the rise in temperature of the brass if 75% of the heat generated warms the brass? (c) What happens to the other 25%?

13. A 2.0-gm lead bullet moving at a speed of 200 meters/sec becomes embedded in a 2.0-kg wooden block of a ballistic pendulum. Calculate the rise in temperature of the bullet, assuming that all the heat generated raises the bullet's temperature.

14. Consider the rod shown in Fig. 22-2. Suppose $L = 25$ cm, $A = 1.0$ cm², and the material is copper. If $T_2 = 125°C$, $T_1 = 0°C$, and a steady state is reached, find (a) the temperature gradient, (b) the rate of heat transfer, and (c) the temperature at a point in the rod 10 cm from the high-temperature end.

15. Show that in a compound slab the temperature gradient in each portion is inversely proportional to the thermal conductivity.

16. Assuming k is constant, show that the radial flow of heat in a substance between two concentric spheres is given by

$$T_1 - T_2 = \frac{Q}{4\pi kt}\left(\frac{1}{r_1} - \frac{1}{r_2}\right)$$

where the inner sphere has a radius r_1 and temperature T_1, and the outer sphere has a radius r_2 and temperature T_2.

17. Heat generated by radioactivity within the earth is conducted outward through the oceans. For purposes of approximate calculation, assume the average temperature gradient within the solid earth beneath the ocean to be 0.07 C°/meter and the average thermal conductivity to be 2×10^{-4} kcal/(meter)(sec)(C°), and determine the rate of heat transfer per square meter. Assume that this is approximately the rate for the entire surface of the earth, and determine how much heat is thereby transferred through the earth's surface each day.

18. Assuming k is constant, show that the radial flow of heat in a substance between two coaxial cylinders is given by

$$T_1 - T_2 = \frac{Q}{2\pi Lkt} \ln \frac{r_2}{r_1}$$

where the inner cylinder has a radius r_1 and temperature T_1, and the outer cylinder has a radius r_2 and temperature T_2, each cylinder having a length L.

19. Determine the value of J, the mechanical equivalent of heat, from the following data: 2000 cal of heat are supplied to a system; the system does 3350 joules of external work during that time; the increase in internal energy during the process is 5030 joules.

20. When a system is taken from state i to state f along the path iaf, it is found that $Q = 50$ cal and $W = 20$ cal. Along the path ibf, $Q = 36$ cal (Fig. 22–13). (a) What is W

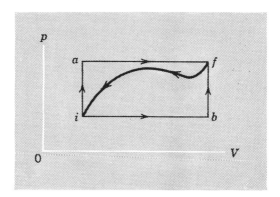

Fig. 22–13

along the path ibf? (b) If $W = -13$ cal for the curved return path fi, what is Q for this path? (c) Take $U_i = 10$ cal. What is U_f? (d) If $U_b = 22$ cal, what is Q for the process ib? For the process bf?

21. A thermos bottle contains coffee. The thermos bottle is vigorously shaken. Consider the coffee as the system. (a) Does its temperature rise? (b) Has heat been added to it? (c) Has work been done on it? (d) Has its internal energy changed?

22. Consider a block sliding down an inclined plane. First take the block alone as the system. (a) Does its temperature rise? (b) Has heat been added to it? (c) Has work been done on it? (d) Has its internal energy changed?

Now take the block and inclined plane as the system. (a) Does its temperature rise? (b) Has heat been added to it? (c) Has work been done on it? (d) Has its internal energy changed?

23. In Fig. 22–12, suppose that one side contains gas at a temperature T_1 and a pressure p_1 and the other side a gas at a temperature T_2 and a pressure $p_2 > p_1$. What happens when the stopcock is opened, from the point of view of the first law of thermodynamics if (a) $p_2 > p_1$ and $T_2 > T_1$; (b) $p_2 > p_1$ and $T_2 < T_1$?

Kinetic Theory of Gases—I

CHAPTER 23

23-1 Historical Introduction

The problem of the structure of matter was a subject of philosophy even in ancient times. The Greek philosopher Leucippus and his pupil Democritus (c.460–c.370 B.C.), are considered the founders of the atomic theory of matter. They hypothesized that all matter consisted of identical, indivisible particles, atoms (from *atomos*, Greek for indivisible), separated by empty space. Of course, these ideas were speculative, not being worked out in detail or related to experimentation. But they were taken up again after the Renaissance, over two thousand years later, when experimentation began to play a role in natural philosophy. In the 1600's, Gassendi and Boyle tried to explain the observed properties of gases in terms of their smallest constituent particles, which they called "molecules." There were differing opinions as to the size, properties, and nature of these molecules, however.

It was Daniel Bernoulli (1700–1782) who was the first to give a theoretical explanation of the gas laws discovered by Boyle and to relate temperature and molecular motion directly. He calculated the pressure of a gas from the collisions of the molecules with the wall and inferred that the velocities of the molecules increase when the temperature is raised. Joule greatly clarified and extended Bernoulli's work, relating the molecular kinetic energy of a gas to its temperature in a quantitative way. A. Kronig (1822–1879) and Rudolph Clausius (1822–1888) refined and extended these ideas into virtually the present form of the so-called kinetic theory of gases. Clerk Maxwell (1831–1879) in England, Ludwig Boltzmann (1844–1906) in Austria, and J. Willard Gibbs (1839–1903) in America completed the theory.

In the kinetic theory of gases Newtonian mechanics is extended down to the atomic scale. Here we have a microscopic theory which predicts correctly a great many macroscopically observed quantities. Of course, in applying Newtonian ideas we could not hope to obtain useful results by trying to specify the position and velocity of every particle in a gas. Instead, we use a statistical method and deduce mean values of various quantities. For it is the mean values, rather than the individual values of the gas particles' properties, which we observe and measure experimentally.

23–2 Equation of State of an Ideal Gas

It is found from experiment that all gases behave essentially in the same way provided their densities are not too high. That is, if the temperatures are not too low and the pressures are not too high, all real gases show the same simple behavior. This suggests the concept of an *ideal gas*, one that will have this simple behavior under *all* conditions. Let us first deduce the ideal gas law. We shall then seek to interpret it on a microscopic scale with the aid of the kinetic theory of gases.

Methods exist for measuring the pressure p, the volume V, the temperature T, and the mass m of a gas. We call V/m the specific volume. Consider now experiments carried out on a gas at low density. Such experiments lead to the result that at a constant temperature the pressure of a gas is inversely proportional to its specific volume (Boyle's law); and that the product of the pressure and the specific volume is directly proportional to the temperature (Charles' law). These experimental results can be summarized by the relation

$$p\,\frac{V}{m} = rT \tag{23-1}$$

where r is a constant of proportionality whose value depends on the specific gas being investigated.

When we compare the values of r for various gases, we find from experiment that r is inversely proportional to the molecular weight M of the gas. That is, we find that $r = R/M$, where R is a constant of proportionality, the *same* for all gases. Hence, R is not specific to a particular gas but is a *universal* constant. We can therefore rewrite Eq. 23–1 as

$$p\,\frac{V}{m} = \frac{R}{M}\,T$$

or

$$pV = \frac{m}{M}\,RT.$$

It must be pointed out that the molecular weight M has no dimension but is only a number. From elementary chemistry we know that the molecular weight of a molecule is the ratio of the mass of that molecule to $\frac{1}{16}$ the mass of an oxygen atom. In this respect, molecular weight is a misnomer.

In chemistry it is convenient to define a new unit of mass. One "gram molecule" or "mole" is defined as the mass of that number of grams to which the molecular weight is numerically equal, that is, M grams. Hence, the number of grams contained in 1 mole is adapted individually to each substance. The mass in moles is commonly expressed as n so that if m is the mass of a gas in grams, then n (moles) equals m (grams)$/M$.

Hence, our previous formula takes on the familiar form

$$pV = nRT \tag{23–2}$$

when the mass of the gas is expressed as n moles. The numerical value of the universal gas constant R is found to be

$$R = 8.314 \text{ joule/(mole)(K°)} = 1.986 \text{ cal/(mole)(K°)}$$

We see that the volume per mole of a gas depends only on the pressure and temperature (that is, $V/n = RT/p$) and not on the nature of the gas. Under standard conditions ($p = 1$ atm and $T = 273°$K) the volume occupied by 1 mole of any gas is 22.4 liters.

The behavior of real gases conforms closely to Eq. 23–2 under a wide range of conditions and begins to deviate from it only as gas densities become higher. We shall consider this effect in Chapter 24. However, an ideal gas is assumed to behave according to Eq. 23–2 under all circumstances. Therefore, the relation

$$pV = nRT$$

is called the *equation of state* of an ideal gas and can be taken as the definition of an ideal gas on the macroscopic scale.

▶ **Example 1.** A cylinder contains oxygen gas at a temperature of 20°C and a pressure of 15 atm in a volume of 100 liters. A fitted piston is lowered into the cylinder, decreasing the volume occupied by the gas to 80 liters and raising the temperature to 25°C. What then is the gas pressure?

We can write Eq. 23–2 as

$$p\frac{V}{T} = nR.$$

Since the amount of gas is unchanged, nR is constant and we have

$$\frac{p_1 V_1}{T_1} = \frac{p_2 V_2}{T_2}.$$

Our initial conditions are

$$p_1 = 15 \text{ atm}, \qquad T_1 = 293°\text{K}, \qquad V_1 = 100 \text{ liters}.$$

Our final conditions are

$$p_2 = ?, \qquad T_2 = 298°\text{K}, \qquad V_2 = 80 \text{ liters}.$$

Hence,

$$p_2 = \left(\frac{T_2}{V_2}\right)\left(\frac{p_1 V_1}{T_1}\right) = \left(\frac{298°\text{K}}{80 \text{ liters}}\right)\left(\frac{15 \text{ atm} \times 100 \text{ liters}}{293°\text{K}}\right) = 19 \text{ atm}.$$

Example 2. Calculate the work done by 1 mole of an ideal gas which expands isothermally, that is, at constant temperature, from an initial volume V_i to a final volume V_f.

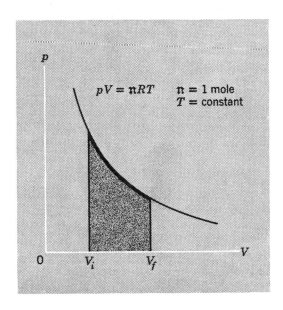

Fig. 23-1   Example 2.   The shaded area represents the work done by 1 mole of gas in expanding from V_i to V_f with the temperature held fixed.

The work done may be represented as

$$W = \int_{V_i}^{V_f} p \, dV.$$

From the ideal gas law, with $n = 1$ mole, we have

$$P = \frac{RT}{V},$$

so that

$$W = \int_{V_i}^{V_f} \frac{RT}{V} \, dV.$$

The temperature is constant so that

$$W = RT \int_{V_i}^{V_f} \frac{dV}{V} = RT \ln\left(\frac{V_f}{V_i}\right)$$

is the work done by 1 mole of an ideal gas in an isothermal expansion at temperature T from an initial volume V_i to a final volume V_f.

Notice that when the gas expands, so that $V_f > V_i$, the work done by the gas is positive; when the gas is compressed, so that $V_f < V_i$, the work done by the gas is negative. This is consistent with the sign convention adopted for W in the first law of thermodynamics. The work done is shown as the shaded area in Fig. 23-1. The solid line is an isotherm, that is, a curve giving the relation of p to V at a constant temperature.

In practice, how can we keep an expanding or contracting gas at constant temperature?   ◄

23-3   Kinetic Theory Model of a Gas

Let us now consider the microscopic model of a gas. The assumptions we make in constructing this model must ultimately be justified by agreement between the macroscopic results they predict and experiment.

We now summarize the assumptions made in the kinetic theory model of a gas.

A gas consists of particles called molecules.   Depending on the particular gas being considered, each molecule will consist of one atom or a group of atoms.   If the gas is a pure element or a compound and is in a stable state, all its molecules are considered to be identical.

The molecules are in random motion and obey Newton's laws of motion.   The molecules of a gas move in all directions and with various speeds.   In computing the properties of the motion, we assume that Newtonian mechanics is valid in this microscopic domain.   As is true for all our assumptions, this one will hold or prove untrue depending on the validity of the experimental facts it predicts.

The total number of molecules is large.   The direction and speed of motion of any one molecule may change abruptly on collision with the wall or another molecule.   Any particular molecule will follow a zigzag path owing to these collisions.   However, because there are so many molecules we assume that the resulting large number of collisions maintains the over-all distribution of molecular velocities.   The randomness of the motion is maintained so that, for example, the number of molecules moving in any one direction is, on the average, the same as that moving in any other direction.

The volume of the molecules themselves is a negligibly small fraction of the volume occupied by the gas.   Even though we have many molecules, they are extremely small.   We know that the volume occupied by a gas can be changed through a large range of values with no difficulty, and that when a gas condenses the volume occupied by the resulting liquid is many thousands of times smaller than that of the gas.   Hence, our assumption is plausible.   In later sections we shall investigate the actual size of molecules and see whether this assumption needs to be modified or not.

No appreciable forces act on the molecules except during a collision.   Hence, between collisions a molecule moves with uniform speed in a straight line. Because the molecules have been assumed to be so small, the average distance between molecules is large compared to the size of a molecule.   Hence, we assume that the range of molecular forces (which determines the collision cross section) is comparable to the molecular size.

Collisions are perfectly elastic and are of negligible duration.   Collisions between molecules and with the walls of the container conserve kinetic energy and momentum.   Because the collision time is negligible compared to the time spent by a molecule between collisions, the kinetic energy which is converted to potential energy of deformation during the collision is available again as kinetic energy after such a brief time that we can ignore this exchange entirely.

The statements given in italics can be taken as the assumptions of the kinetic theory of gases.   Obviously we can examine each assumption more carefully, as is done in the exact advanced theory.   These investigations lead us to the limits beyond which our model will not apply or will apply only approximately.   Some of these limitations will become apparent when we broaden the region of application of the theory in subsequent sections. However, the success of kinetic theory in accounting for the experimental facts has been so impressive that there is no doubt of its approximate correctness for real gases. We assume then that an *ideal* gas behaves microscopically as though all these assumptions are correct.

23–4 Kinetic Calculation of the Pressure

Let us now calculate the pressure of an ideal gas. To simplify matters, we consider a gas in a cubical vessel whose walls are perfectly elastic. Let each edge be of length l. Call the faces normal to the x-axis (Fig. 23–2) A_1 and A_2, each of area l^2. Consider a particular molecule which has a velocity **v**. We can resolve **v** into components v_x, v_y, and v_z in the directions of the edges. If this particle collides with the side A_1, it will rebound with its x component of velocity reversed. There will be no effect on v_y or v_z, so that the change Δp in the particle's momentum will be

$$\Delta p = p_f - p_i = -mv_x - (mv_x) = -2mv_x,$$

normal to A_1. Hence, the momentum imparted to A_1 will be $2mv_x$, since the total momentum is conserved.

Suppose now that this same particle reaches A_2 without striking any other particle on the way. The time required to cross the cube will be l/v_x. At A_2 it will again have its x component of velocity reversed and will return to A_1 again. Assuming no collisions in between, the round trip will take a time $2l/v_x$. Hence, the number of collisions per unit time this particle makes with A_1 is $v_x/2l$, so that the momentum it transfers to A_1 per unit time is

$$2mv_x \frac{v_x}{2l} = \frac{mv_x^2}{l}.$$

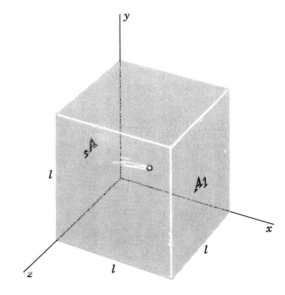

Fig. 23–2 A perfectly elastic cubical box of side l, containing an ideal gas. A molecule is shown progressing toward A_1.

Now to obtain the total force on A_1, that is, the momentum imparted to it per unit time by all the gas molecules, we must sum up mv_x^2/l for all the particles. Then, to find the pressure, we divide this force by the area of A_1, namely l^2.

Assume that we have a chemically homogeneous gas, and that m is the mass of each molecule. Then

$$p = \frac{m}{l^3}\left(v_{x1}^2 + v_{x2}^2 + \cdots\right),$$

where v_{x1} is the x component of the velocity of particle 1, v_{x2} is that of particle 2, etc. If N is the total number of particles in the container and n is the number per unit volume, then $N/l^3 = n$ or $l^3 = N/n$. Hence,

$$p = mn\left(\frac{v_{x1}^2 + v_{x2}^2 + \cdots}{N}\right).$$

But mn is simply the mass of the particles per unit volume, that is, the density ρ. The quantity $(v_{x1}^2 + v_{x2}^2 + \cdots)/N$ is the average value of v_x^2 for all the particles in the container. Let us call this $\overline{v_x^2}$. Then

$$p = \rho\overline{v_x^2}.$$

For any particular particle $v^2 = v_x^2 + v_y^2 + v_z^2$. Because we have a large number of particles and because they are moving entirely at random, the average values of v_x^2, v_y^2, and v_z^2 are all equal. The value of each is therefore exactly one-third the average value of v^2. There is no preference among the molecules for motion along any one of the three axes. Hence, $\overline{v_x^2} = \frac{1}{3}\overline{v^2}$, so that

$$p = \rho\overline{v_x^2} = \tfrac{1}{3}\rho\overline{v^2} = \tfrac{1}{3}mn\overline{v^2}. \tag{23-3}$$

Although we arrived at this result by neglecting collisions between particles, our previous discussion explains why the result is true even when collisions are accounted for. Because of the exchange of velocities in an elastic collision between identical particles, there will always be some one molecule that will collide with side A_2 with momentum mv_x corresponding to the one that left A_1 with this momentum. Also, the time spent during collisions is negligible compared to the time spent between collisions. Hence, our neglect of collisions is merely a convenient device for calculation. Likewise, we could have chosen a container of any shape—the cube merely simplifies the calculation.

Although we have calculated the pressure exerted only on the side A_1, it follows from Pascal's law that the pressure is the same on all sides and everywhere in the interior.* This result can also be proved directly from kinetic theory.

---

* We neglect the weight of the gas, a negligible effect. (See Section 17-3 and Problem 12, this chapter.)

The square root of $\overline{v^2}$ is called the *root-mean-square* speed of the molecules and is a kind of average or typical molecular speed.* Using Eq. 23–3, we can calculate this root-mean-square speed from measured values of the pressure and density of the gas. Thus,

$$v_{rms} = \sqrt{\overline{v^2}} = \sqrt{\frac{3p}{\rho}}. \qquad (23\text{–}4)$$

It seems worthwhile to point out two features used in the kinetic theory already given that are new. One feature is that we have used statistical methods and arguments to obtain an answer. However, at the bottom of our statistics lies Newtonian mechanics, governing each individual action. The kinetic theory of gases is important historically for the impetus it gave to statistical mechanics. In recent times the statistical approach to physics has become dominant because of the development of quantum physics, a statistical scheme whose basis is not Newtonian at all.

Another feature, somewhat connected to the first, is that we have related the macroscopic quantities (such as pressure) to average values of microscopic quantities (such as $\overline{v^2}$). But averages can be taken over short times or over long times, over small regions of space or large regions of space. The average computed in a small region for a short time might depend on the time or region chosen, so that the values obtained in this way may fluctuate. This could easily happen in a gas of very low density, for example. Not only are there fluctuations in these "average" values in an exact theory, but there are some cases in which these fluctuations are important. (See Section 24–4.) Fluctuations can be ignored for most purposes, however, because they are negligible when the total number of particles in the system is large.

▶ **Example 3.** Calculate the root-mean-square speed of hydrogen molecules at 0°C and 1-atm pressure, assuming it to be an ideal gas. Under these standard conditions hydrogen has a density of 8.99×10^{-2} kg/meter³. Then

$$p = 1 \text{ atm} = 1.013 \times 10^5 \text{ nt/meter}^2,$$

$$\rho = 8.99 \times 10^{-2} \text{ kg/meter}^3,$$

$$v_{rms} = \sqrt{\frac{3p}{\rho}} = 1838 \text{ meter/sec}.$$

This is of the order of a mile per second, or 3600 miles/hr.   ◀

In Table 23–1 we give the results of similar calculations for a number of common gases at 0°C. As a preview to the next section, we also list the kinetic energy per mole of gas at 0°C. Notice that although the average speeds of different gases varies considerably at the same temperature, *the kinetic energy per mole is nearly the same for all gases at the same temperature.*

An interesting observation is that these molecular speeds are of the same order of magnitude as the speed of propagation of sound at the same pressure and temperature. For example, in air at 0°C and 1-atm pressure, $v_{rms} = 485$ meters/sec and the speed of sound is 331 meters/sec; in hydrogen $v_{rms} = 1838$ meters/sec and sound travels at 1286 meters/sec; in oxygen $v_{rms} = 461$ meters/sec and sound travels at 317 meters/sec. These results

---

* This will be considered in greater detail in Section 24–2 in which the molecular distribution of speeds is discussed.

Table 23–1

Gas	v_{rms}, meters/sec	Molecular Weight	Kinetic Energy per mole, $\frac{1}{2}Mv^2$ (joules/per mole)
O_2	461	32	3400
N_2	493	28	3390
Air	485	28.8	3280
CO	492	20	3390
H_2	1838	2.02	3370
He	1311	4.0	3430
CO_2	393	44	3400
H_2O	615	18	3400
Ne	584	20.1	3420

are to be expected in terms of our model of a gas. (See Problem 23.) We visualize the propagation of sound waves as a directional motion of the molecules as a whole superimposed on their random motion. Hence, the energy of the sound wave is carried as kinetic energy from one gas molecule to the next one with which it collides. The molecules themselves, in spite of their high speeds, do not move very far during any reasonable time; they are contained within a relatively small space by multiple collisions.* But the energy of the sound wave *is* communicated from one molecule to the next with that high speed. We do not expect the speed of sound to be exactly as great as v_{rms} (see Example 5), and in fact the numerical difference is predicted from the exact theory of sound.

▶ **Example 4.** Assume that the speed of sound in a gas is the same as the root-mean-square speed of the molecules, and show how the speed of sound depends on the absolute temperature.

From the relation

$$v_{rms} = \sqrt{\frac{3p}{\rho}}$$

and the ideal gas law

$$p\frac{V}{m} = \frac{RT}{M} \quad \text{or} \quad \frac{p}{\rho} = \frac{RT}{M},$$

we obtain

$$v_{rms} = \sqrt{\frac{3RT}{M}},$$

---

* This explains why there is a time lag between opening an ammonia bottle at one end of the room and smelling it at the other end. Although molecular speeds are high, the multiple collisions restrain the advance of the ammonia molecules. They diffuse through the air at a speed that is rather small compared to molecular speeds.

so that the speed of sound v_1 at a temperature T_1 is related to the speed of sound v_2 at a temperature T_2 by

$$\frac{v_1}{v_2} = \sqrt{\frac{T_1}{T_2}}.$$

For example, if the speed of sound at 273°K is 332 meters/sec in air, its speed at 300°K will be

$$\sqrt{\tfrac{300}{273}} \times 332 \text{ meters/sec} = 348 \text{ meters/sec}.$$

Would our result change if the speed of sound were proportional to, rather than equal to, the root-mean-square speed of the molecules of a gas?   ◀

23–5   Kinetic Interpretation of Temperature

Let $\mathfrak{M}$ be the total mass of the gas in our container. Then $\mathfrak{M} = Nm$. Using the fact that $n = N/V$, we can rewrite Eq. 23–3 as

$$p = \tfrac{1}{3}mn\overline{v^2} = \frac{1}{3}\frac{mN}{V}\overline{v^2} = \frac{1}{3}\frac{\mathfrak{M}\overline{v^2}}{V},$$

$$pV = \tfrac{1}{3}\mathfrak{M}\overline{v^2}.$$

The quantity $\tfrac{1}{3}\mathfrak{M}\overline{v^2}$ is two-thirds the total kinetic energy of translation of the molecules,* that is, $\tfrac{2}{3}(\tfrac{1}{2}\mathfrak{M}\overline{v^2})$. We write our relation then as

$$pV = \tfrac{2}{3}(\tfrac{1}{2}\mathfrak{M}\overline{v^2}). \tag{23–5}$$

For simplicity, let us assume that we have 1 mole of gas ($\mathfrak{n} = 1$ mole) so that $\mathfrak{M}$ can be replaced by M, the gram-molecular weight. For 1 mole of an ideal gas the equation of state is

$$pV = RT. \tag{23–6}$$

Comparing these two expressions, we obtain

$$\tfrac{1}{2}M\overline{v^2} = \tfrac{3}{2}RT. \tag{23–7}$$

That is, *the total translational kinetic energy of the molecules of a gas is directly proportional to the absolute temperature.* We may say that this result, Eq. 23–7, is necessary to fit the kinetic theory to the gas law. Or we can consider Eq. 23–7 as a definition of gas temperature on a kinetic theory or microscopic basis. In either case, we gain some insight into the meaning of temperature for gases.

The average kinetic energy per molecule is $\tfrac{1}{2}m\overline{v^2}$. We have already concluded that the total molecular kinetic energy is proportional to the temperature. Let us write the expression corresponding to Eq. 23–7 for *one* molecule as

$$\tfrac{2}{3}(\tfrac{1}{2}m\overline{v^2}) = kT, \tag{23–8}$$

---

* For, $\tfrac{1}{2}mv_1^2 + \tfrac{1}{2}mv_2^2 + \cdots = \tfrac{1}{2}mN\left(\dfrac{v_1^2 + v_2^2 + \cdots}{N}\right) = \tfrac{1}{2}\mathfrak{M}\overline{v^2}$.

where k is a universal constant, known as Boltzmann's constant. It follows from Eq. 23–5 that

$$pV = \tfrac{2}{3}(\tfrac{1}{2}\mathfrak{M}\overline{v^2}) - \tfrac{2}{3}N(\tfrac{1}{2}m\overline{v^2}) = \tfrac{2}{3}N(\tfrac{3}{2}kT)$$

or
$$pV = NkT. \tag{23–9}$$

Comparing Eq. 23–9 with the equation of state of an ideal gas

$$pV = \mathfrak{n}RT,$$

we obtain
$$k = \frac{R}{N/\mathfrak{n}}.$$

But the ratio of the number of molecules N to the number of moles $\mathfrak{n}$ is the number of molecules per mole, or Avogadro's number N_0. That is,

$$k = \frac{R}{N_0}.$$

Avogadro's number can be measured by at least fourteen interdependent methods involving many phenomena in chemistry and physics, all of about the same accuracy. The current value (to four significant figures) is

$$N_0 = 6.023 \times 10^{23} \text{ molecules/mole.}$$

Hence, Boltzmann's constant is

$$k = \frac{R}{N_0} = \frac{8.31 \text{ joule/mole } °K}{6.023 \times 10^{23} \text{ molecules/mole}} = 1.38 \times 10^{-23} \text{ joule/molecule } °K.$$

We shall return to Boltzmann's constant in Chapter 24.

Equation 23–7 predicts directly the experimental observation made in the previous section that the kinetic energy per mole is (nearly) the same for all gases at the same temperature. From Eq. 23–8 we can conclude that at the same temperature T the ratio of the rms speeds of molecules of two different gases is equal to the square root of the inverse ratio of their masses. That is,

$$T = \frac{2}{3k} \frac{m_1 \overline{v_1}^2}{2} = \frac{2}{3k} \frac{m_2 \overline{v_2}^2}{2}$$

or
$$\frac{v_{1\,\mathrm{rms}}}{v_{2\,\mathrm{rms}}} = \sqrt{\frac{m_2}{m_1}}. \tag{23–10}$$

An application of Eq. 23–10 is found in the diffusion of two different gases in a container with porous walls placed in an evacuated space. The lighter gas will escape faster than the heavier one. The ratio of the *number* of molecules which find their way through the porous walls for a short time interval will also be $\sqrt{m_2/m_1}$. This diffusion process is used as one method of separating (fissionable) U^{235} (0.7%) from a normal sample of uranium containing mostly (nonfissionable) U^{238} (99.3%). To quote from the Smyth report,[*]

* *A General Account of the Development of Methods of Using Atomic Energy for Military Purposes* . . ., H. D. Smyth, U. S. Government Printing Office, 1945.

"As long ago as 1896 Lord Rayleigh showed that a mixture of gases of different atomic weight could be partly separated by allowing some of it to diffuse through a porous barrier into an evacuated space. Because of their higher average speed the molecules of the light gas diffuse through the barrier faster so that the gas which has passed through the barrier (i.e., the 'diffusate') is enriched in the lighter constituent and the residual gas which has not passed through the barrier is impoverished in the lighter constituent. The gas most highly enriched in the lighter constituent is the so-called 'instantaneous diffusate'; it is the part that diffuses before the impoverishment of the residue has become appreciable. If the diffusion process is continued until nearly all the gas has passed through the barrier, the average enrichment of the diffusate naturally diminishes. . . . On the assumption that the diffusion rates are inversely proportional to the square roots of the molecular weights the separation factor for the instantaneous diffusate, called the 'ideal separation factor' α, is given by

$$\alpha = \sqrt{\frac{M_2}{M_1}},$$

where M_1 is the molecular weight of the lighter gas and M_2 that of the heavier. Applying this formula to the case of uranium will illustrate the magnitude of the separation problem. Since uranium itself is not a gas, some gaseous compound of uranium must be used. The only one obviously suitable is uranium hexafluoride, UF_6. . . . Since fluorine has only one isotope, the two important uranium hexafluorides are $U^{235}F_6$ and $U^{238}F_6$; their molecular weights are 349 and 352. Thus if a small fraction of a quantity of uranium hexafluoride is allowed to diffuse through a porous barrier, the diffusate will be enriched in $U^{235}F_6$ by a factor

$$\alpha = \sqrt{\tfrac{352}{349}} = 1.0043. \ . \ . \ .$$

To separate the uranium isotopes, many successive diffusion stages (i.e., a cascade) must be used. . . . Studies by Cohen and others show that the best flow arrangement for the successive stages is that in which half the gas pumped into each stage diffused through the barrier, the other (impoverished) half being returned to the feed of the next lower stage. . . . If one desires to produce 99 per cent pure $U^{235}F_6$, and if one uses a cascade in which each stage has a reasonable overall enrichment factor, then it turns out that roughly 4000 stages are required. . . . Most of the material that eventually emerges from the cascade has been recycled many times. Calculation shows that for an actual uranium-separation plant it may be necessary to force through the barriers of the first stage 100,000 times the volume of gas that comes out the top of the cascade (i.e., as desired product $U^{235}F_6$)."

23-6 Intermolecular Forces

Forces between molecules are known to be of electric and magnetic origin. All molecules contain electric charges in motion. These molecules are electrically neutral in the sense that the negative charge of the electrons is equal and opposite to the charge of the nuclei. This does not mean, however, that molecules do not interact electrically. For example, when two molecules approach each other, the charges on each are disturbed and depart slightly from their usual positions in such a way that the average distance between opposite charges in the two molecules is a little smaller than that between like charges. Hence, an attractive intermolecular force results. This internal rearrangement takes place only when molecules are fairly close together, so that these forces act only over short distances; they are short-range forces. If the molecules come very close together, so that their outer charges begin to overlap, the intermolecular force becomes repulsive. The molecules repel each other because there is no way for a molecule to rearrange itself internally to prevent repulsion of the adjacent external electrons. It is this repulsion on contact that accounts for the

Fig. 23-3 (*a*) The mutual potential energy of two molecules versus their separation. (*b*) The mutual force, $-dU/dr$, corresponding to this potential energy. Notice that $F = 0$ at $r = r_0$ where U is a minimum, whereas F is a minimum where U goes through an inflection point.

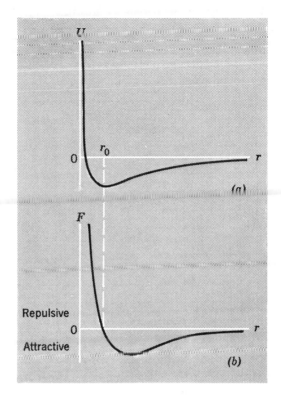

billiard ball character of molecular collisions in gases. If it were not for this repulsion, molecules would move right through each other instead of rebounding on collision.

Let us assume that molecules are approximately spherically symmetrical. Then we can describe intermolecular forces graphically by plotting the mutual potential energy of two molecules, U, as a function of distance r between their centers. The force F acting on each molecule is related to the potential energy U by $F = -dU/dr$ (see Example 4, Chapter 8). In Fig. 23–3a we plot a typical $U(r)$. Here we can imagine one molecule to be fixed at O. Then the other molecule will be repelled from O when the slope of U is negative and will be attracted to O when the slope is positive. At r_0 no force acts between the molecules; the slope is zero there. In Fig. 23–3b we plot the mutual force $F(r)$ corresponding to this potential energy function. The separation distance between two identical molecules at which the mutual potential energy is zero is often taken as the approximate distance of closest approach in a collision and hence as the diameter of the molecule. For simple molecules the diameter is about 2.5×10^{-10} meter. The forces between molecules practically cease at about 10^{-9} meter or 4 diameters apart, so that molecular forces are very short-range ones. The distance r_0 at which the potential is a minimum (the equilibrium point) is about 3.5×10^{-10} meter for simple molecules. Of course, different molecules have different sizes and internal arrangement of charges so that intermolecular forces vary from one molecule to another. However, they always show the qualitative behavior indicated in the figures.

Consider a given species of molecule. In the solid state these molecules vibrate about the equilibrium position r_0, not having enough energy to escape from the potential valley (that is, from the attractive binding force). The centers of vibration O are more or less fixed in a solid. In a liquid the molecules have greater vibrational energy about centers which are free to move but which remain about the same distance from one another. These molecules have their greatest kinetic energy in the gaseous state. In a gas the average distance between the molecules is considerably greater than the effective range of intermolecular forces, and the molecules move in straight lines between collisions. Clerk Maxwell discusses the relation between the kinetic theory model of a gas and the intermolecular forces as follows: "Instead of saying that the particles are hard, spherical, and elastic, we may if we please say that the particles are centers of force, of which the action is insensible except at a certain small distance, when it suddenly appears as a repulsive force of very great intensity. It is evident that either assumption will lead to the same results."

It is interesting to compare the measured intermolecular forces with the gravitational force of attraction between molecules. If we choose a separation distance of 4×10^{-10} meter, for example, the force between two helium atoms is about 6×10^{-13} nt. The computed gravitational force at that separation is about 7×10^{-42} nt, smaller than the intermolecular force by a factor of 10^{29}! This is a typical result and shows that gravitational forces are negligible in comparison with intermolecular forces. Although the intermolecular forces appear to be small by ordinary standards, we must remember that the mass of a molecule is so small (about 10^{-26} kg) that these forces can impart instantaneous accelerations of about 10^{15} meters/sec^2 ($10^{14}g$). Of course, these accelerations may last for only a very short time because one molecule can very quickly move out of the range of influence of the other.

23–7 Specific Heats of an Ideal Gas

The molecules in an ideal gas were pictured as hard elastic spheres. There are no forces between the molecules except during collisions, and the molecules are not deformed as a result of collisions. Hence, there is no internal potential energy. The internal energy of an ideal gas is therefore entirely kinetic. We have already found that the average kinetic energy per molecule is $\frac{3}{2}kT$, so that the internal energy U of an ideal gas containing N molecules is

$$U = \tfrac{3}{2}NkT = \tfrac{3}{2}\text{n}RT. \tag{23–11}$$

This is an important theoretical result, for it says that *the internal energy of an ideal gas* is proportional to the Kelvin temperature and *depends only on the temperature*, being independent of pressure and volume.* With this result we can now obtain information about the specific heats of an ideal gas.

The specific heat of a substance is the heat per unit mass required to raise its temperature by one degree. For gases a convenient unit of mass is the mole. The corresponding specific heat is called the molar heat capacity and is represented by C. Only two specific heat capacities are of practical use for gases, namely, the molar specific heat at constant volume, C_v, and the molar specific heat at constant pressure, C_p.

---

* The result that the internal energy of an ideal gas depends only on the temperature can be shown to be a necessary consequence of the equation of state of an ideal gas. We need to use the first and second laws of thermodynamics to prove this on a macroscopic scale. In our case we have used a specific microscopic model of a gas, one designed to correspond to the equation of state of an ideal gas, to arrive at this general result. The specific relation of Eq. 23–11 is of very restricted validity, however, for our model has so far ignored the rotational, vibrational, and dissociation energies of real molecules (see Section 23–8).

Fig. 23–4 (a) Heat dQ is transferred to a gas contained in a vessel of constant volume; the resulting rise in the internal energy of the gas, $dU = C_v dT$, is evidenced by a rise in the temperature. (b) Heat dQ is transferred to a gas in a cylinder fitted with a frictionless piston, the pressure being maintained by the weight of the piston and sand. Here both work, $dW = p dV$, is done *and* a change in internal energy, $dU = dQ - dW$, is effected.

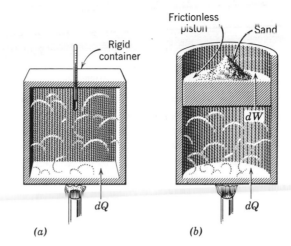

(a)   (b)

If we have n moles of an ideal gas with a molar specific heat at constant volume C_v and we raise its temperature at constant volume by an amount dT, the heat transferred is $nC_v dT$ and the external work done is zero (Fig. 23–4a). From the first law of thermodynamics

$$dQ = dU + p dV.$$

But $dQ = nC_v dT$ and $dW = p dV = 0$, so that

$$nC_v dT = dU. \tag{23–12}$$

If the same amount of gas were heated at constant pressure p until the temperature changed by the same amount, the heat transferred would be $nC_p dT$. In this case, however, the gas would expand and external work $p dV$ would be done (Fig. 23–4b). From the first law for this process we obtain

$$nC_p dT = dU + p dV. \tag{23–13}$$

The temperature change is the same in both cases. Since U depends only on the temperature for an ideal gas, the internal energy change dU is therefore the same in both processes. Then, combining Eqs. 23–12 and 23–13,

$$nC_v dT = nC_p dT - p dV$$

or

$$n(C_p - C_v) dT = p dV. \tag{23–14}$$

The quantity $p dV$ is the work done during an expansion at constant pressure. If, in the equation of state $pV = nRT$ we keep p constant and differentiate both sides, we obtain

$$p dV = nR dT,$$

so that Eq. 23–14 becomes

$$n(C_p - C_v) dT = nR dT$$

or

$$C_p - C_v = R. \tag{23–15}$$

This result shows that the molar heat capacity of an ideal gas at constant pressure is always larger than that at constant volume by an amount equal to the universal gas constant R. But $R = 8.31$ joules/mole K° or 1.99 cal/mole K°, so that the difference is very nearly 2 cal/mole K°. Although Eq. 23–15 is exact only for an ideal gas, it is very nearly true for real gases at moderate pressure (see Table 23–2). Notice that in obtaining this result we did not use the specific relation $U = \frac{3}{2}nRT$, but we have used the fact that U depends only on the temperature.

If now we have some way of computing C_v, Eq. 23–15 will give us C_p and vice versa. We *can* obtain C_v by combining Eq. 23–12 with the specific kinetic theory result for the internal energy of an ideal gas, $U - \frac{3}{2}nRT$ (Eq. 23–11). Thus

$$C_v = \frac{1}{n}\frac{dU}{dT} = \frac{1}{n}\frac{d}{dT}\left(\tfrac{3}{2}nRT\right) = \tfrac{3}{2}R.$$

This result (about 3 cal/mole K°) turns out to be rather good for monatomic gases. However, it is in serious disagreement with values obtained for diatomic and polyatomic gases (see Table 23–2, p. 508). This suggests that Eq. 23–11 is not generally correct. Since that relation followed directly from the kinetic theory model, we are forced to the conclusion that the model must be modified if the kinetic theory is to survive as a useful approximation to the behavior of real gases. We shall look into the modified theory in the next section.

▶ **Example 5.** The processes of compression and rarefaction in a sound wave are practically adiabatic at audio frequencies. Show that in this case the speed of sound in an ideal gas is given by

$$v = \sqrt{\frac{\gamma p}{\rho}},$$

where $\gamma = C_p/C_v$.

The speed of sound waves in a fluid was shown in Chapter 20 to be $v = \sqrt{B/\rho}$, where ρ is the fluid density and B is the bulk modulus of the fluid, $B = -V\,\Delta p/\Delta V$.

An adiabatic process is one in which no heat enters or leaves the system. Hence, $\Delta Q = 0$.

For an ideal gas, the change in internal energy in a process in which the temperature changes by ΔT is given by $nC_v\,\Delta T$ (Eq. 23–12). Hence, from the first law of thermodynamics,

$$\Delta Q = \Delta U + p\,\Delta V,$$

we obtain for this process

$$0 = nC_v\,\Delta T + p\,\Delta V$$

or

$$\Delta T = -p\frac{\Delta V}{nC_v}.$$

The ideal gas law is $pV = nRT$, so that if p, V, and T are permitted to take on small variations, we obtain

$$p\,\Delta V + V\,\Delta p = nR\,\Delta T$$

by taking differentials. But from Eq. 23–15,

$$R = C_p - C_v.$$

On substituting for R and ΔT in our differential expression, we obtain

$$p\,\Delta V + V\,\Delta p = -(C_p - C_v)\frac{p\,\Delta V}{C_v} = -(\gamma - 1)p\,\Delta V$$

where $\gamma = C_p/C_v$ is called the ratio of specific heats. On transposing and dividing this equation by pV, we find

$$\frac{\Delta p}{p} + \gamma\frac{\Delta V}{V} = 0.$$

Hence, $$B = -\frac{V\,\Delta p}{\Delta V} = \gamma p$$

for adiabatic processes.

Therefore, the speed of sound in an ideal gas under adiabatic conditions is

$$v = \sqrt{\frac{B}{\rho}} = \sqrt{\frac{\gamma p}{\rho}}.$$

Does this result modify the result obtained in Example 4? Can you guess now why the speed of sound in a gas is not the same as the root-mean-square speed of the gas molecules?

Example 6. Show that for an ideal gas undergoing an adiabatic process pV^γ equals a constant. In Example 5, we found that

$$\frac{\Delta p}{p} + \gamma\frac{\Delta V}{V} = 0$$

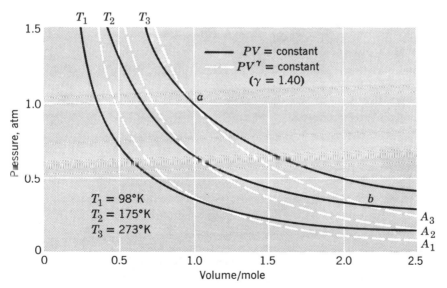

Fig. 23–5 T_1, T_2, and T_3 show how the pressure of an ideal gas changes as its volume is changed, the temperature being held constant (isothermal process). A_1, A_2, and A_3 show how the pressure of an ideal gas changes as its volume is changed, no heat being allowed to flow to or from the gas (adiabatic process). It is clear that an adiabatic *increase* in volume (for example going from a to b along A_3) is always accompanied by a decrease in temperature, since at a, $T = 273°$K, whereas at b, $T = 175°$K.

for an ideal gas undergoing an adiabatic change. In the limit of small increments, we can replace Δ by d, so that

$$\frac{dp}{p} + \gamma \frac{dV}{V} = 0.$$

Integrating, we obtain

$$\ln p + \gamma \ln V = \text{constant}$$

or

$$pV^\gamma = \text{constant}. \tag{23-16}$$

The value of the constant is determined by the quantity of gas present, so that Eq. 23-16 may be used to describe the relation between the pressure and the volume of any quantity of gas undergoing an adiabatic change. In Fig. 23–5 we compare the isothermal and adiabatic behaviors of an ideal gas.   ◄

23–8   Equipartition of Energy

A modification of the kinetic theory model designed to explain the specific heats of gases was first suggested by Clausius in 1857. Recall that in our model a molecule was assumed to behave like a hard elastic sphere and that we treated its kinetic energy as purely translational. The specific heat result was satisfactory for a monatomic molecule and suggests that this picture is a good one for monatomic molecules. Further, because of the great success of this simple model in other respects in predicting the correct behavior of gases of all kinds over wide temperature ranges, we are confident that it is the average kinetic energy of translation alone which determines what we measure as the temperature of a gas.

However, in the case of specific heats we are concerned not only with temperature changes but also with a heat (energy) exchange process, and we must ask whether or not a molecule can store energy internally, that is, in a form other than kinetic energy of translation. This would certainly be so if we pictured a molecule not as a rigid particle but as an object having internal structure. For then a molecule would be capable of rotational and vibrational motion as well as translational motion. In collisions, the rotational and vibrational modes of motion can be excited, and this would contribute to the internal energy of the gas. Here then is a model which enables us to modify the kinetic theory formula for the internal energy of a gas.

Let us now find the total energy of a system containing a large number of molecules, where each molecule is thought of as an object having internal structure. The energy will consist of kinetic energy of translation of individual molecules, with terms like $\frac{1}{2}mv_x^2$; of kinetic energy of rotation of individual molecules, with terms like $\frac{1}{2}I\omega_x^2$; of kinetic energy of vibration of the atoms in a molecule, with terms like $\frac{1}{2}\mu v^2$, and of potential energy of vibration of the atoms in a molecule, with terms like $\frac{1}{2}kx^2$. Although other kinds of energy contributions exist, such as magnetic, for gases and even for simple compounds and crystals of metals, the total energy can be given quite accurately by terms such as those mentioned. Although physically these various terms have different origins, notice that they all have the same mathematical form, namely, a positive constant times the square of a quantity which can take on negative or positive values. We can show from a statistical analysis that *when the number of particles is large and Newtonian mechanics holds, all these terms have the same average value, and this average value depends only on the temperature.* In other words, the available energy depends only on the temperature and distributes itself in equal shares to each of the independent ways in which the molecules can absorb energy. This theorem, stated here without proof, is called the *equipartition of energy* and was deduced by Clerk Maxwell in his mathematical theory of statistical mechanics. Each such independent mode of energy absorption is called a *degree of freedom*.

From Eq. 23–7 we know that the kinetic energy of translation of a mole of gaseous molecules is $\frac{3}{2}RT$. The kinetic energy of translation is the sum of three terms, however, namely $\frac{1}{2}M\overline{v_x^2}$, $\frac{1}{2}M\overline{v_y^2}$, and $\frac{1}{2}M\overline{v_z^2}$. The theorem of equipartition requires that each such term contribute the same amount to the total energy, or an amount $\frac{1}{2}RT$ per degree of freedom.

For *monatomic gases* the molecules have only translational motion (no internal structure in kinetic theory), so that $U = \frac{3}{2}RT$ for a mole. It follows from Eq. 23–12 that $C_v = \frac{3}{2}R \cong 3$ cal/(mole)(K°) as we have seen. Then from Eq. 23–14, $C_p = \frac{5}{2}R$, and the ratio of specific heats is

$$\gamma = \frac{C_p}{C_v} = \frac{5}{3} = 1.67.$$

For a *diatomic gas* we can think of each molecule as having a dumbbell shape (two spheres joined by a rigid rod). Such a molecule can rotate about any one of three mutually perpendicular axes. However, the rotational inertia about an axis along the rigid rod should be negligible compared to that about axes perpendicular to the rod, so that the rotational energy should consist of only two terms,* such as $\frac{1}{2}I\omega_y^2$ and $\frac{1}{2}I\omega_z^2$. Each rotational degree of freedom is required by equipartition to contribute the same energy as each translational degree, so that for a diatomic gas having both rotational and translational motion,

$$U = 3(\tfrac{1}{2}RT) + 2(\tfrac{1}{2}RT) = \tfrac{5}{2}RT \text{ per mole,}$$

$$C_v = \tfrac{5}{2}R \cong 5 \text{ cal/(mole)(K°),}$$

$$C_p = C_v + R = \tfrac{7}{2}R,$$

$$\gamma = \frac{C_p}{C_v} = \frac{7}{5} = 1.40.$$

For *polyatomic gases*, each molecule contains three or more spheres (atoms) joined together by rods in our model, so that the molecule is capable

---

* We have already ruled out the possibility that a monatomic molecule could rotate. Actually it could spin about any one of three mutually perpendicular axes if it had any extent, such as a finite sphere. Implicitly, therefore, we have adopted a point mass as our model of the atom. Hence, in a diatomic molecule we are rid of one rotational degree of freedom, for point masses joined by a rigid line have no motion about an axis along that line.

of rotating energetically about each of three mutually perpendicular axes. Hence, for a polyatomic gas having both rotational and translational motion,

$$U = 3(\tfrac{1}{2}RT) + 3(\tfrac{1}{2}RT) - 3RT,$$

$$C_v = 3R = 6 \text{ cal/(mole)(K°)},$$

$$C_p = 4R,$$

$$\gamma = \frac{C_p}{C_v} = 1.33.$$

Let us now turn to experimental data to test these ideas. In Table 23–2 we list the molar specific heats—for common gases at 20°C and 1 atm.

Table 23–2

Type of Gas	Gas	C_p, cal/(mole)(K°)	C_v, cal/(mole)(K°)	$C_p - C_v$	$\gamma = C_p/C_v$
Monatomic	He	4.97	2.98	1.99	1.67
	A	4.97	2.98	1.99	1.67
Diatomic	H_2	6.87	4.88	1.99	1.41
	O_2	7.03	5.03	2.00	1.40
	N_2	6.95	4.96	1.99	1.40
	Cl_2	8.29	6.15	2.14	1.35
Polyatomic	CO_2	8.83	6.80	2.03	1.30
	SO_2	9.65	7.50	2.15	1.29
	C_2H_6	12.35	10.30	2.05	1.20
	NH_3	8.80	6.65	2.15	1.31

Notice that for monatomic and diatomic gases the values of C_v, C_p, and γ are close to the ideal gas results for most types of molecules. In some diatomic gases, like chlorine, and in most polyatomic gases the specific heats are larger than our predicted values. Even γ shows no simple regularity for polyatomic gases. All this suggests that our model is not yet close enough to the actual structure of molecules.

Of course, we have not yet considered energy contributions from vibrating motion of the atoms in diatomic and polyatomic molecules. That is, we can modify the dumbbell model and join the spheres instead by springs. This new model will greatly improve our results in some of the cases already cited. Notice, however, that instead of having a theoretical model for all gases, we are now reduced to an empirical model which differs from gas to gas. We can obtain a reasonably good picture of molecular behavior this way and the empirical model is therefore useful; however it ceases to be fundamental.

To see this more clearly, let us consider the experimental fact that the specific heats of gases depend on the temperature. In Fig. 23–6 we show the

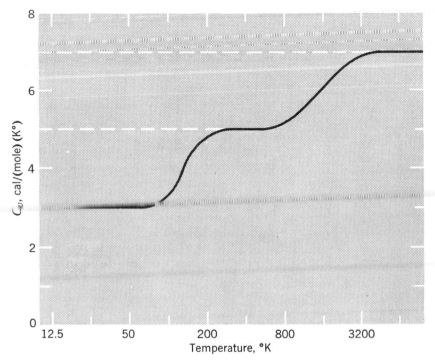

Fig. 23-6 Variation of the molar heat C_v of hydrogen with temperature. (Note that T is drawn on a logarithmic scale.)

variation of the molar heat of hydrogen with temperature. Notice that the value of 5 cal/(mole)(K°), which is required for diatomic molecules by our model, is characteristic of hydrogen only in the temperature range from about 250 to 750°K. Above 750°K, C_v increases steadily to 7 cal/(mole)(K°), and below 250°K, C_v decreases rapidly to 3 cal/(mole)(K°). Other gases show similar variations of specific heat with temperature.

The previous discussion provides us with a possible explanation. At low temperatures the hydrogen molecule has translational energy only and cannot rotate. As the temperature rises rotation becomes possible so that at ordinary temperatures a hydrogen molecule acts like our dumbbell model. At very high temperatures the very energetic collisions between molecules cause the atoms in the molecule to vibrate and the molecule ceases to behave as a rigid body. Different gases, because of their different molecular structure, may show these effects at different temperatures. Thus a chlorine molecule appears to be capable of vibratory motion at room temperature.

Although this description turns out to be essentially correct, and we have obtained much insight into the behavior of molecules, this behavior is in direct contradiction to the kinetic theory. For kinetic theory is based on Newtonian mechanics applied to a large collection of particles, and the equipartition of energy is a necessary consequence of this classical statistical mechanics. But *if equipartition of energy holds, then, no matter what happens to the total internal energy as the temperature changes, each part of the energy* —translational, rotational, and vibrational—*must share equally in the change.* There is no possible classical mechanism for changing one mode of mechanical energy at a time in such a system. Kinetic theory requires that the specific heats of gases be independent of the temperature.

Hence, we have come to the limit of validity of classical mechanics when we seek to explain the structure of the atom (or molecule). Just as Newtonian principles break down in the region of very high speeds (near the speed of light), so here in the region of very small dimensions they also break down. Relativity theory modifies Newtonian ideas to account for the behavior of physical systems in the region of high speeds. It is quantum physics that modifies Newtonian ideas to account for the behavior of physical systems in the region of small dimensions. Both relativity theory and quantum mechanics are generalizations of classical theory in the sense that they give the (correct) Newtonian results in the regions in which Newtonian physics has accurately described experimental observations. In the following two chapters we shall confine our attention to the very fruitful application of thermodynamics and the kinetic theory to "classical" systems.

QUESTIONS

1. State how an ideal gas is defined on a macroscopic level. On a microscopic level.

2. In kinetic theory we assume that there are a large number of molecules present in a gas. Real gases behave like an ideal gas at low densities. Are these statements contradictory? If not, what conclusion can you draw from them?

3. We have assumed that the walls of the container are elastic for molecular collisions. Actually, the walls may be inelastic. In practice this makes no difference as long as the walls are at the same temperature as the gas. Explain.

4. In large-scale inelastic collisions mechanical energy is lost through internal friction resulting in a rise in temperature owing to increased internal molecular agitation. Is there a loss of mechanical energy to heat in an inelastic collision between molecules?

5. What justification is there in neglecting the change in gravitational potential energy of molecules in a gas?

6. We have assumed that the force exerted by molecules on the wall of a container is steady in time. How is this justified?

7. The average velocity of the molecules in a gas must be zero if the gas as a whole and the container are not in translational motion. Explain how it can be that the average speed is not zero.

8. If a container of gas is moving with respect to a coordinate system, the average velocity of the molecules with respect to that system is increased over the stationary case. Does the temperature therefore increase?

9. The gas kinetic temperature in the upper atmosphere is of the order of 1000°K. It is quite cold up there. Explain away this paradox.

10. Why must the time allowed for diffusion separation be relatively short?

11. Suppose we wanted to obtain U^{238} instead of U^{235} as the end product of a diffusion process. Would we use the same process in either case? If not, explain how the separation process would have to be modified.

12. Can you describe a centrifugal device for gaseous separation? Is a centrifuge better than a diffusion chamber for separation of gases?

13. Would you expect real molecules to be spherically symmetrical? If not, how would the potential energy function of Fig. 23–3 change?

14. Explain how we might keep a gas at a constant temperature during a thermodynamic process.

15. Explain why the temperature of a gas drops in an adiabatic expansion.

16. Explain in words why the specific heat at constant pressure is greater than the specific heat at constant volume.

PROBLEMS

1. An air bubble of 20 cm³ volume is at the bottom of a lake 40 meters deep where the temperature is 4°C. The bubble rises to the surface which is at a temperature of 20°C. Take the temperature to be the same as that of the surrounding water and find its volume just before it reaches the surface.

2. One mole of an ideal gas undergoes an isothermal expansion. Find the heat flow into the gas in terms of the initial and final volumes and the temperature.

3. Calculate the work done in compressing 1 mole of oxygen from a volume of 22.4 liters at 0°C and 1-atm pressure to 16.8 liters at the same temperature.

4. Oxygen gas having a volume of 1.0 liter at 40°C and a pressure of 76 cm Hg expands until its volume is 1.5 liters and its pressure is 80 cm Hg. Find the number of moles of oxygen in the system and its final temperature.

5. An automobile tire has a volume of 1000 in.³ and contains air at a gauge pressure of 24 lb/in.² when the temperature is 0°C. What is the gauge pressure of the air in the tires when its temperature rises to 27°C and its volume increases to 1020 in.³?

6. The mass of the H_2 molecule is 3.32×10^{-24} gm. If 10^{23} hydrogen molecules per second strike 2.0 cm² of wall at an angle of 45° with the normal when moving with a speed of 10^5 cm/sec, what pressure do they exert on the wall?

7. (a) Determine the average value of the kinetic energy of the molecules of an ideal gas at 0°C and at 100°C. (b) What is the kinetic energy of a mole of ideal gas at these temperatures?

8. (a) Compute the root-mean-square speed of an argon atom at room temperature (20°C). (b) At what temperature will the root-mean-square speed be half that value? Twice that value?

9. (a) Compute the temperature at which the root-mean-square speed is equal to the speed of escape from the surface of the earth for hydrogen. For oxygen. (b) Do the same for the moon, assuming gravity on its surface to be $0.164g$. (c) The temperature high in the earth's upper atmosphere is about 1000°K. Would you expect to find much hydrogen there? Much oxygen?

10. Show how to find the root-mean-square speeds of helium and argon molecules at 40°C from that of oxygen molecules (460 meters/sec at 0°C). The molecular weight of oxygen is 32, of argon 40, of helium 4.

11. Compute the number of molecules in a gas contained in a volume of 1 cm³ at a pressure of 10^{-3} atm and a temperature of 200°K.

12. Oxygen gas at 273°K and 1-atm pressure is confined to a cubical container 10 cm on a side. (a) How long does it take a typical molecule to cross the container? (b) Compare the change in gravitational potential energy of an oxygen molecule falling the height of the box with its mean kinetic energy.

13. (a) Consider an ideal gas at 273°K and 1-atm pressure. Imagine that the molecules are for the most part evenly spaced at the centers of identical cubes. Using Avogadro's number and taking the diameter of a molecule to be 3.0×10^{-8} cm, find the length of an edge of such a cube and compare this length to the diameter of a molecule. (b) Now consider a mole of water having a volume of 18 cm³. Again imagine the molecules to be evenly spaced at the centers of identical cubes. Find the length of an edge of such a cube and compare this length to the diameter of a molecule.

14. Avogadro's law states that under the same condition of temperature and pressure equal volumes of gas contain equal numbers of molecules. Derive this law from kinetic theory using Eq. 23–3 and the equipartition of energy assumption.

15. Dalton's law states that when mixtures of gases having no chemical interaction are present together in a vessel, the pressure exerted by each constituent at a given temperature is the same as it would exert if it alone filled the whole vessel, and that the total pressure is equal to the sum of the partial pressures of each gas. Derive this law from kinetic theory, using Eq. 23–3.

16. The mass of a gas molecule can be computed from the value of the specific heat at constant volume. Take $C_v = 0.075$ kcal/(kg)(C°) for argon and calculate (a) the mass of an argon atom and (b) the atomic weight of argon.

17. Take the mass of a helium atom to be 6.66×10^{-27} kg. Compute the specific heat at constant volume for helium gas.

18. Calculate the mechanical equivalent of heat from the value of R and the values of C_v and γ for oxygen from Table 23–2.

19. Ten grams of oxygen are heated at constant atmospheric pressure from 27 to 127°C. How much heat is transferred to the oxygen? What fraction of the heat is used to raise the internal energy of the oxygen?

20. How would you explain physically the observed value of $C_v = 7.50$ cal/(mole)(K°) for gaseous SO_2 at 15°C and 1 atm?

21. Show that the speed of sound in a gas is independent of the pressure and density.

22. Show that the velocity of sound in air increases approximately 2 ft/sec for each Celsius degree rise in temperature.

23. The speed of sound in different gases at the same temperature depends on the molecular weight of the gas. Show specifically that $v_1/v_2 = \sqrt{M_2/M_1}$ (constant T) where v_1 is the speed of sound in the gas of molecular weight M_1 and v_2 is the speed of sound in the gas of molecular weight M_2.

24. Air at 0°C and 1-atm pressure has a density of 1.293×10^{-3} gm/cm³ and the speed of sound in air is 332 meters/sec at that temperature. Compute the ratio of specific heats of air from these data.

25. (a) A monatomic ideal gas initially at 17°C is suddenly compressed to one-tenth its original volume. What is its temperature after compression? (b) Make the same calculation for a diatomic gas.

26. The atomic weight of iodine is 127. A standing wave in iodine gas at 400°K has nodes that are 6.77 cm apart when the frequency is 1000 vib/sec. Is iodine gas monatomic or diatomic?

27. A mass of gas occupies a volume of 4.0 liters at a pressure of 1.0 atm and a temperature of 300°K. It is compressed adiabatically to a volume of 1.0 liter. Determine (a) the final pressure and (b) the final temperature, assuming it to be an ideal gas for which $\gamma = 1.5$.

28. One mole of an ideal gas expands adiabatically from an initial temperature T_1 to a final temperature T_2. Prove that the work done by the gas is $C_v(T_1 - T_2)$.

29. (a) A liter of gas with $\gamma = 1.3$ is at 273°K and 1-atm pressure. It is suddenly compressed to half its original volume. Find its final pressure and temperature. (b) The gas is now cooled back to 0°C at constant pressure. What is its final volume?

30. (a) Show that the variation in pressure in the earth's atmosphere, assumed to be isothermal, is given by $p = p_0 e^{-Mgy/RT}$ where M is the molecular weight of the gas. (See Example 1, Chapter 17.) (b) Show also that $n = n_0 e^{-Mgy/RT}$ where n is the number of molecules per unit volume.

Kinetic Theory of Gases—II

CHAPTER 24

24–1   Mean Free Path

The path traversed by a molecule between two successive collisions with other molecules is called a *free path*. During a free path the molecule moves with constant speed along a straight line. The average distance between collisions is called the *mean free path* (Fig. 24–1).

If molecules were points, they would not collide with one another at all and the mean free path would be infinite. Molecules, however, do have a finite extent and hence they collide with one another. If they were so large or so numerous that they completely filled the space available to them, leaving no free space for translational motion, the mean free path would be zero. Clearly then the mean free path is related to molecular size and the density of matter.

To compute the mean free path simply, we can consider molecules to be spheres of diameter d. The cross section for a contact collision is simply πd^2. That is, a collision will take place when the centers of two molecules approach within a distance d of one another. An equivalent description of collisions made by any one molecule is to regard that one molecule as having a diameter $2d$ and all other molecules as point particles. In Fig. 24–2 we illustrate these equivalent points of view.

If we follow a single molecule of equivalent diameter $2d$ as it moves through a gas of point particles, we find that in time t it will sweep out a cylinder of cross-sectional area πd^2 and of length vt where v is the molecular speed. In the time t this molecule will make a collision with every other molecule whose center lies in this cylindrical volume (Fig. 24–3). If there are n molecules per unit volume, the number of collisions in time t is the number of other molecules in the cylinder, $\pi d^2 n v t$.

Fig. 24-1 A molecule traveling through a gas, colliding with other molecules in its path. Of course, all the other molecules comprising the gas are moving in a similar fashion.

Fig. 24-2 If a collision occurs whenever two molecules come within a distance d of each other, (a), the process can be treated equivalently by thinking of one molecule as having an effective diameter $2d$ and the other as being a point mass, (b).

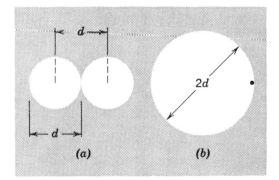

(a) (b)

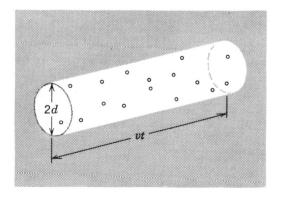

Fig. 24-3 A molecule of equivalent diameter $2d$ traveling with speed v sweeps out a cylinder of base πd^2 and height vt in a time t. It suffers a collision with every other molecule whose center lies within this cylinder.

The mean free path $\bar{l}$ is simply the average distance between collisions. Hence, $\bar{l}$ is the total distance vt covered in time t divided by the number of collisions that take place in this time, or

$$\bar{l} = \frac{vt}{\pi d^2 nvt} = \frac{1}{\pi nd^2}.$$

This equation is based on the picture of a molecule hitting stationary targets. Actually the molecule hits moving targets. The collision frequency is increased as a result * and the mean free path is reduced to

$$\bar{l} = \frac{1}{\pi \sqrt{2}\, nd^2}. \tag{24-1}$$

▶ **Example 1.** To get an idea of the magnitude of the mean free path and the collision frequency, let us use typical data from Chapter 23. We take 2.5×10^{-8} cm as a typical molecular diameter d. At standard conditions the root-mean-square speed is about 10^5 cm/sec and there are about 3×10^{19} atoms/cm^3 in a gas. Then the number of collisions per unit time, or the collision frequency, is

$$\pi d^2 n \sqrt{2}\, v = \pi (2.5 \times 10^{-8} \text{ cm})^2 (3 \times 10^{19} \text{ cm}^{-3})(1.4)(10^5 \text{ cm/sec})$$

$$\cong 8 \times 10^9 \text{ sec}^{-1},$$

or eight billion collisions per second! The corresponding mean free path at *standard conditions* is

$$\bar{l} = \frac{1}{\pi \sqrt{2}\, nd^2} = \frac{v}{8 \times 10^9 \text{ sec}^{-1}} = \frac{10^5 \text{ cm/sec}}{8 \times 10^9 \text{ sec}^{-1}} = 1.2 \times 10^{-5} \text{ cm}.$$

This is about 500 molecular diameters. ◀

The mean free path of molecules in a gas is a true measure of the degree of vacuum attained in the gas, for it measures the mean path over which no collisions occur. A perfect vacuum would correspond to an infinite mean free path. Since the mean free path depends on molecular size, and on pressure and temperature (which determine the density), a statement of pressure alone is a less meaningful description of the degree of evacuation than is the mean free path. In the earth's atmosphere the mean free path of air molecules at sea level (760 mm Hg) is about 10^{-5} cm. At 100 km above the earth (10^{-3} mm Hg) the mean free path is 1 meter. At 300 km (10^{-6} mm Hg) it is already 10 km or 6 miles on the average between collisions, and yet there are about 10^8 particles per cubic centimeter in this region. This emphasizes the fact that molecules are small. The density drops to 1 molecule per cubic centimeter at about 2500 km above the earth's surface. What would you expect the mean free path to be out there?

---

* The two v's in the original equation are different in this case. The one in the numerator is the mean molecular speed measured with respect to the container. The one in the denominator is the mean *relative* speed of the molecule with respect to other molecules. It is this relative speed that determines the number of collisions. These two speeds are not equal but, indeed, are in the ratio $1/\sqrt{2}$.

24–2 Distribution of Molecular Speeds

In the previous chapter we discussed the root-mean-square (rms) speed of the molecules of a gas. We would expect the velocities of the molecules to vary, however, over a wide range of magnitude and over all directions. We have already seen that at room temperature and atmospheric pressure there are about 10^9 collisions per second between molecules in a gas. The speed of a molecule may change as a result of a collision. At any given time some molecules will have speeds exceeding the root-mean-square value and others will have speeds below that value. A molecule is likely to encounter successive collisions of all different kinds. Extreme values, such as speeds near zero or speeds that are orders of magnitude larger than the root-mean-square value, are not very likely because this would require a large number of preferential collisions. Most molecules will have speeds near some average value.

Clerk Maxwell solved mathematically the problem of the most probable distribution of speeds in a large number of molecules of a gas. Maxwell assumed complete randomness of molecular motions and obtained the following result: *

$$N_v \, dv = 4\pi N \left(\frac{m}{2\pi kT}\right)^{3/2} v^2 e^{-(mv^2/2kT)} \, dv. \qquad (24\text{–}2)$$

In this equation $N_v \, dv$ represents the number of molecules having a speed between v and $v + dv$. Here N is the total number of molecules, T is the absolute temperature, k is Boltzmann's constant, and m is the mass of a molecule. Notice that for a given gas the distribution depends only on the temperature.

In Fig. 24–4 we plot the Maxwellian distribution of speeds of a given number of molecules of a gas for two different temperatures. The number of molecules having a speed between v and $v + \Delta v$ equals the area under the curve between the vertical lines at v and at $v + \Delta v$. Notice that at any given temperature the number of molecules in a definite speed interval † Δv increases as the speed increases up to a maximum at the most probable speed and then decreases asymptotically toward zero at high speeds. The distribution curve is *not* symmetrical about the most probable value, v_p, for the lowest speed must be zero, whereas there is no classical limit necessarily to the upper speed a molecule can attain. In this case the average value of all speeds, $\bar{v}$, is somewhat larger than the most probable value. The root-

---

* See Leigh Page, *Introduction to Theoretical Physics*, D. Van Nostrand Company, 1935, Chapter 9, for example.

† The student should note that we cannot simply plot the "number of particles having speed v" against v, for there are a finite number of particles and strictly an infinite number of possible speeds. Hence, the probability that a particle has a precisely stated speed is zero. However, we can divide the whole range of speeds into a finite number of intervals and the probability that a particle has a speed somewhere in that interval is a definite nonzero value. These ideas are consistent with the fact that the area under the curve in an interval of width Δv goes to zero as Δv goes to zero.

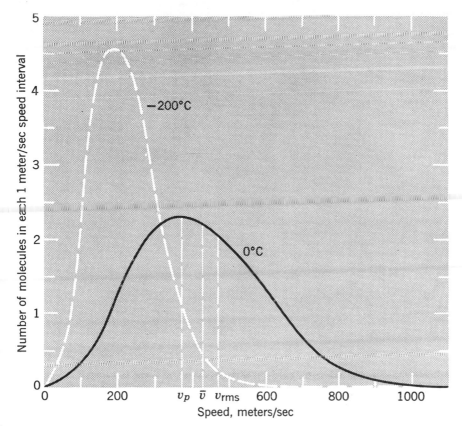

Fig. 24–4 The Maxwellian distribution of speeds of 1000 oxygen molecules at two different temperatures. The number of molecules within a certain range of speeds (say, 600 to 800 meters/sec) is the area under this section of the curve.

mean-square value, v_{rms}, being the square root of the sum of the squares of the speeds, is still larger.

At a higher temperature the most probable speed increases, in accordance with the meaning of temperature on the microscopic scale. However, the range in speeds is greater and the fraction of molecules within Δv of the most probable speed declines. This change is accompanied by an increase in the number of molecules which have speeds greater than a given speed. This effect explains many observed phenomena, such as the increase in the rates of chemical reactions with rising temperature.

Although the probability of finding molecules having extreme speeds is small, it is not zero. A few molecules can be found at any time and any temperature which have enormous speeds, whereas a few others are practically at rest. The distribution of speeds of molecules in a liquid resembles the curves of Fig. 24–4. This explains why some molecules in a liquid at low temperatures can escape through the surface (evaporate). Only the fastest molecules can overcome the attraction of the molecules in the surface and escape by evaporation. The average kinetic energy of the remaining molecules drops correspondingly, leaving the liquid at a lower temperature. This is why we refer to evaporation as a cooling process.

From Eq. 24–2 we see that the distribution of molecular speeds depends on the mass of the molecule, as well as on the temperature. The smaller the mass, the larger the proportion of high-speed molecules at any given temperature. Hence, hydrogen gas is more likely to escape from the earth's atmosphere at high altitudes than oxygen or nitrogen. Recent investigations indicate that the moon may have a tenuous atmosphere. For the molecules in this atmosphere not to have a great probability of escaping from the weak gravitational pull of the moon, even at the low temperatures there, we would expect them to be molecules or atoms of the heavier elements. In fact, evidence seems to point to the heavy inert gases, such as krypton and xenon, which were produced largely by radioactive decay early in the moon's history. The atmospheric pressure on the moon is believed to be about one ten-million-millionth (10^{-13}) of the earth's atmospheric pressure.

▶ **Example 2.** The speeds of ten particles in meters/sec are 0, 1.0, 2.0, 3.0, 3.0, 3.0, 4.0, 4.0, 5.0, and 6.0. Find (a) the average speed, (b) the root-mean-square speed, and (c) the most probable speed of these particles.

(a) The average speed is simply

$$\bar{v} = \frac{0 + 1.0 + 2.0 + 3.0 + 3.0 + 3.0 + 4.0 + 4.0 + 5.0 + 6.0}{10} = 3.1 \text{ meters/sec.}$$

(b) The mean-square speed is

$$\overline{v^2} = \frac{0 + (1.0)^2 + (2.0)^2 + (3.0)^2 + (3.0)^2 + (3.0)^2 + (4.0)^2 + (4.0)^2 + (5.0)^2 + (6.0)^2}{10}$$

$$= 12.5 \text{ meters}^2/\text{sec}^2$$

and the root-mean-square speed is

$$v_{\text{rms}} = \sqrt{12.5 \text{ meters}^2/\text{sec}^2} = 3.5 \text{ meters/sec.}$$

(c) Of the ten particles three have speeds of 3.0 meters/sec, two have speeds of 4.0 meters/sec, and the other five each have a different speed. Hence, the most probable speed of a particle v_p is

$$v_p = 3.0 \text{ meters/sec.}$$

Example 3. Use Eq. 24–2 to determine the average speed $\bar{v}$, the root-mean-square speed v_{rms}, and the most probable speed v_p of the molecules in a gas in terms of the gas parameters.

$N_v \, dv$ represents the number of molecules having a speed between v and $v + dv$. With $\lambda = m/2kT$, Maxwell's distribution law, Eq. 24–2, can be written as

$$N_v \, dv = 4\pi N \left(\frac{\lambda}{\pi}\right)^{3/2} v^2 e^{-\lambda v^2} \, dv. \tag{24–3}$$

The average speed $\bar{v}$ is obtained by the usual method of obtaining an average value; we multiply each speed interval by the number of particles in that speed interval, sum of these quantities over all speeds, and then divide by the total number of particles. The summation process can be treated as an integral here because the speeds vary practically continuously from zero to infinity; the total number of particles can also be written as an integral, namely $N = \int_0^\infty N_v \, dv$ Therefore,

$$\bar{v} = \frac{\int_0^\infty N_v v \, dv}{\int_0^\infty N_v \, dv}.$$

Substituting Eq. (24–3) for $N_v \, dv$ and integrating * we obtain

$$\bar{v} = \frac{2}{\sqrt{\pi\lambda}} = \frac{2}{\sqrt{m\pi/2kT}} = \sqrt{\frac{8}{\pi}\frac{kT}{m}} \cong 1.6 \sqrt{\frac{kT}{m}} \qquad (average\ speed). \qquad (24\text{–}4)$$

Likewise, the mean-square speed is given by

$$\overline{v^2} = \frac{\int_0^\infty N_v v^2 \, dv}{\int_0^\infty N_v \, dv} = \frac{3}{2\lambda},$$

$$v_{\text{rms}} \equiv \sqrt{\overline{v^2}} = \sqrt{\frac{6kT}{2m}} = 1.7 \sqrt{\frac{kT}{m}} \qquad (root\text{-}mean\text{-}square\ speed). \qquad (24\text{–}5)$$

Finally, the most probable speed can be obtained by finding the speed at which the function N_v has a maximum value. It is given by the equation

$$\frac{dN_v}{dv} = 0.$$

From Eq. 24–3 we obtain

$$4\pi N \left(\frac{\lambda}{\pi}\right)^{3/2} \frac{d}{dv} \left(v^2 e^{-\lambda v^2}\right) = 0$$

or

$$\frac{d}{dv}\left(v^2 e^{-\lambda v^2}\right) = 0.$$

This gives

$$2v e^{-\lambda v^2}(1 - \lambda v^2) = 0.$$

Hence, $$v_p = \frac{1}{\sqrt{\lambda}} = \sqrt{\frac{2kT}{m}} = 1.4 \sqrt{\frac{kT}{m}} \qquad (most\ probable\ speed). \qquad (24\text{–}6)$$

In Fig. 24–4 the three values v_p, $\bar{v}$, and v_{rms} are shown in correct order and approximately proper positions.

Notice that all these quantities increase with the temperature T, and all of them increase as the molecular weight decreases. This is reasonable, for the higher the temperature of a gas, the higher the mean kinetic energy of the molecules. Also, molecules of different gases at the same temperature have the same mean kinetic energy so that the lighter molecules have larger speeds on the average.   ◀

---

* From tables of integrals,

$$\int_0^\infty v^2 e^{-\lambda v^2} \, dv = \frac{1}{4}\sqrt{\frac{\pi}{\lambda^3}}\,; \qquad \int_0^\infty v^3 e^{-\lambda v^2} \, dv = \frac{1}{2\lambda^2}\,; \qquad \int_0^\infty v^4 e^{-\lambda v^2} \, dv = \frac{3}{8}\sqrt{\frac{\pi}{\lambda^5}}.$$

24–3   Experimental Confirmation of the Maxwellian Distribution

The development of the technique of atomic and molecular beams has made it possible to verify directly the various theoretical conclusions drawn from the Maxwellian distribution of molecular speeds. The most striking success of the atomic and molecular beam method in kinetic theory was to determine experimentally the actual distribution of speeds. This was done by Stern in 1926, by Eldridge in 1927, and by Lammert in 1929 in a way quite analogous to the toothed-wheel method used by Fizeau to measure the speed of light (Problem 14, Chapter 11; Chapter 40). Stern's method is shown in Fig. 24–5. Mercury is heated in a small furnace A. The atoms have a distribution of speeds which depends on the temperature. A vertical

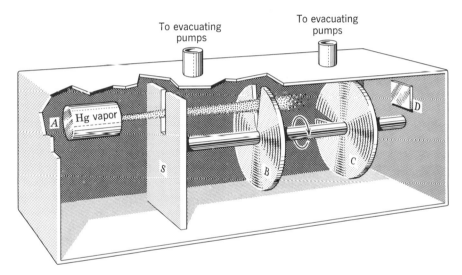

Fig. 24–5 Stern's experiment to determine the distribution of speeds of molecules in a beam.

slit is placed in front of a small opening in the furnace. Those atoms moving in the proper direction emerge from the slit system as a beam parallel to an axis which supports two rotating disks, B and C. The whole system is highly evacuated to reduce collisions with molecules of residual gases. Each of the disks has a radial wedge-like slit, the second one being offset by a few degrees from the first. For a particular constant rotational speed of the disks, only those atoms having speeds in a narrow range can pass through both slits and strike the detecting plate D. For another constant rotational speed only atoms in a different range of speeds can get through. Hence, the system acts as a velocity selector. By observing the relative numbers of atoms deposited on D as a function of disk speed, we can calculate the distribution of speeds in the furnace (see Question 10). In Fig. 24–6 we show Lammert's results, obtained by refining Stern's technique. The relative intensities are calculated from the measured intensity of the image as a function of rotational speed and are plotted along with the theoretical intensity distribution for Hg vapor at 100°C. These, and other, experimental results are in excellent agreement with the theory.

Another example of the Maxwell distribution is provided by observations of the light emitted by radiating atoms. When an atom in motion with respect to the detector emits light, the frequency and wavelength of the detected radiation are changed by the Doppler effect (Chapters 20 and 40). The frequency may be greater or less than that emitted by an atom at rest, depending on whether the atom is moving toward or away from the detector. Hence, when observing radiation of a characteristic frequency emitted by atoms in a gas discharge tube we should actually find a

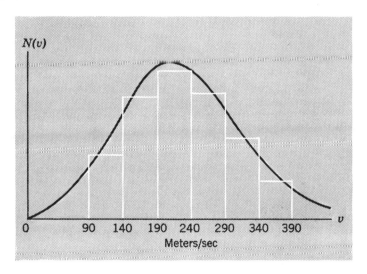

Fig. 24–6 Lammert's results using Stern's method. The data are for mercury vapor at 100°C.

spread of frequencies, the amount of spread and relative intensities of the different frequencies being determined by the velocity distribution of the atoms in the source. The first measurements of this Doppler broadening were made by A. A. Michelson (1895). He found that the broadening in seventeen different elements from hydrogen to bismuth varied with the temperature of the source and the atomic mass exactly as predicted by the Maxwell distribution of velocities and the Doppler formula for light. Michelson also computed the root-mean-square velocities of the atoms from his data and found good agreement with predicted kinetic theory values.

Although the Maxwell speed distribution for gases agrees remarkably well with observations under ordinary conditions, it fails at extremely low temperatures and high densities, where the basic assumptions of the classical kinetic theory are known to fail. In these regions it is necessary to use distributions founded on the principles of quantum physics, the Fermi-Dirac distribution and the Bose-Einstein distribution. These quantum distributions agree closely with the Maxwellian distribution in the classical region and show agreement with experiment where the classical distribution fails. Hence, there are definite limits to the applicability of the Maxwellian distribution, as in fact there are to any theory.

24–4 The Brownian Movement

The great prominence given to atomic and molecular theory during the last quarter of the nineteenth century was deplored by many able scientists. In spite of the many quantitative agreements between the kinetic theory and the behavior of gases, no proof of the separate existence of atoms and molecules had been obtained, nor had any observation been made that could really demonstrate the continuous motions of the molecules. Ernst Mach (1838–1916) saw no point to "thinking of the world as a mosaic, since we cannot examine its individual pieces of stone." It had been established rather early in the development of kinetic theory that an atom should be about 10^{-7} cm or 10^{-8} cm in diameter. No one actually expected to see an atom or detect the effect of a single atom.

The leader of the opposition to the atomic theory was Wilhelm Ostwald. He was a champion of the principle of the conservation of energy and regarded energy as the ultimate reality. Ostwald argued that with a thermodynamical treatment of a process we know all that it is essential to know about the process and that further mechanical assumptions about the mechanism of the reactions are unproved hypotheses. He abandoned the atomic and molecular theories and fought to free science "from hypothetical conception which lead to no immediate experimentally verifiable conclusions." Other prominent physicists were reluctant to admit the atom as an established scientific fact.

Ludwig Boltzmann felt compelled to protest this attitude in an article in 1897, stressing the indispensability of atomism in natural science. The progress of science is often guided by the analogies of nature's processes which occur in the minds of investigators. Kinetic theory was such a mechanical analogy. As with most analogies it suggests experiments to test the validity of our mental pictures and leads to further investigations and clearer knowledge.

As is always true in such controversies in science, the decision rests with experiment. The earliest and most direct experimental evidence for the reality of atoms was the proof of the atomic kinetic theory provided by the quantitative studies of the Brownian movement. These observations convinced both Mach and Ostwald of the validity of the kinetic theory and the atomic description of matter on which it rests. The atomic theory gained unquestioned acceptance in subsequent years when diverse experiments based on different physical principles all led to the same values of the fundamental atomic constants.

The Brownian movement is named after the English botanist Robert Brown who discovered in 1827 that pollen suspended in water shows a continuous random motion when viewed under a microscope. At first these motions were considered a form of life, but it was soon found that small inorganic particles behave similarly. There was no quantitative explanation of this phenomenon until the development of kinetic theory. Then, in 1905, Albert Einstein developed a theory of the Brownian movement.* In his *Autobiographical Notes*, Einstein writes, "My major aim in this was to find facts which would guarantee as much as possible the existence of atoms of definite size. In the midst of this I discovered that, according to atomistic theory, there would have to be a movement of suspended microscopic particles open to observation, without knowing that observations concerning the Brownian motion were already long familiar."

The basic assumption made by Einstein is that particles which are suspended in a liquid or a gas share in the thermal motions of the medium and that on the average the kinetic energy of each particle is $\frac{3}{2}kT$, in accordance with the principle of equipartition of energy. In this view the Brownian motions result from impacts by molecules of the fluid, and the suspended particles acquire the same mean kinetic energy as the molecules of the fluid.

We can draw the following picture of this phenomenon. The suspended particles are extremely large compared to the molecules of the fluid and are being continually bombarded on all sides by them. If the particles are sufficiently large or the number of molecules is sufficiently great, equal numbers of molecules strike the particles on all sides each instant. For smaller particles or fewer molecules the number of molecules striking various sides of the particle at any instant, being just a matter of chance, may not be equal. Hence, the particle at each instant suffers an unbalanced force causing it to move this way or that. The particles therefore act just like very large molecules in the fluid, and their motions should be exactly analogous to the motions of the fluid molecules. Notice that if Avogadro's number were infinite there would be no statistical unbalance and no Brownian motion. If Avogadro's number were very small, the Brownian motion would be very large. Hence, Avogadro's number should be deducible from observations of the Brownian motion. Deeply ingrained in this whole picture is the idea of molecular motion and the smallness of molecules, as well. The Brownian motion therefore offers a striking experimental test of the kinetic theory hypotheses.

Notice that the Brownian movement also demonstrates the occurrence of fluctuations. For, on the average over a long time, the forces exerted by molecules striking a suspended particle from different directions should be in equilibrium. In a short time interval, however, it may happen that the impacts from one direction may be larger and more numerous than those from the opposite direction, so that the particle is accelerated. Because this unbalance is merely a matter of chance, it will not persist, so the particle is first driven in one direction, then in another.

The suspended particles are under the influence of gravity and would settle to the bottom were it not for the molecular bombardment opposing

---

* Einstein's theory appeared as an article in the same issue of the *Annalen der Physik* which contained his famous paper on the restricted theory of relativity and his paper on the theory of the photoelectric effect (Chapter 47). It was for his work on the photoelectric effect that he won the Nobel prize in 1921.

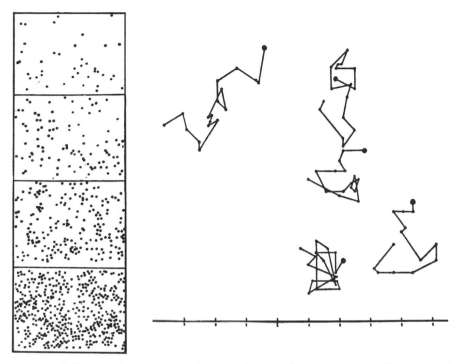

Fig. 24–7 Left, a gamboge (gum resin) suspension contained in a glass vessel was viewed in a microscope by Perrin. At first the distribution of particles was uniform, but in time they settled to the distribution shown. The particles have a diameter of 0.6×10^{-3} cm and the horizontal lines are 10×10^{-3} cm apart. (From J. Perrin, *Bulletin des Séances de la Société Francaise de Physique*, p. 170, 1909.)

Right, sketch made by V. Henri from his cinematographic study of Brownian movement. Henri used a microscope with a motion-picture camera which ran 20 frames/sec, each exposure being $\frac{1}{320}$ sec. The zigzag lines show the position of five rubber particles as recorded by successive frames. (Of course, the lines must not be construed as representing the actual motion of the particles.) The scale at the bottom is divided into microns (10^{-3} cm). (From V. Henri, *ibid.*, p. 45*, 1908.)

this tendency. The net effect in time is a variation in the density of suspended particles with height in a fluid. Exact equations can be derived for this variation in density. (See Problem 9.) Jean Perrin, a French physical chemist, confirmed the equations in 1908 by determining the numbers of small particles of gum resin suspended at different heights in a liquid drop (Fig. 24–7, left). From his data he deduced a value of Avogadro's number $N_0 = 6 \times 10^{23}$ particles/mole. Perrin also made measurements of the displacements of Brownian particles during many equal time intervals and found that they have the statistical distribution required by kinetic theory and the root-mean-square displacement predicted by Einstein (Fig. 24–7, right).

Among the many subsequent experiments was that of E. Kappler, in 1931, who observed the Brownian movement of a very small mirror (area 0.7 mm²), mounted on a fine torsion fiber with light reflected from the mirror to a moving photographic film. The mirror is mounted in a chamber with gas at low pressure (10^{-2} mm Hg); the record on the moving film yields the function $\theta(t)$ (angular displacement as a function of time). This shows clearly the rotational Brownian movement of the mirror which consists of a series of angular displacements produced by impacts from the molecules. As the gas pressure is lowered, there is a gradual decrease in the motion. From the photographic record we can obtain values of the angular displacement θ and the angular velocity ω. Then the equipartition of energy principle requires that

$$\tfrac{1}{2}I\overline{\omega^2} = \tfrac{1}{2}kT$$

and that

$$\tfrac{1}{2}\kappa\overline{\theta^2} = \tfrac{1}{2}kT,$$

for $\tfrac{1}{2}I\overline{\omega^2}$ is the average rotational kinetic energy of the system and $\tfrac{1}{2}\kappa\overline{\theta^2}$ is the average potential energy of the system. Here I is the rotational inertia of the system and κ the torsion constant of the fiber. From his observations Kappler could calculate Boltzmann's constant k and from the relation $N_0 = R/k$ he could obtain Avogadro's number. His values were $k = 1.36 \times 10^{-23}$ joule/K° $\pm 3\%$ (the accepted value today of 1.380×10^{-23} joule/K° being within the limits of error) and $N_0 = 6.1 \times 10^{23}$ particles/mole.

It is not necessary at this point to cite other experiments on the Brownian motion and subsequent atomic experiments. The overwhelming mass of data obtained from the most diverse experimental sources is unanimous in yielding the same value for Avogadro's number, within the accuracy of measurement. The concept of the atomic and molecular structure of matter is now established beyond question.

24–5   The van der Waals Equation of a Gas

In the previous chapter we discussed the behavior of an ideal gas. On the macroscopic scale the fundamental relationship which characterizes an ideal gas is the equation of state

$$pV = nRT.$$

A consequence of this equation and the principles of thermodynamics is the requirement that the internal energy U of a gas depends only on the temperature. Real gases are found to obey these relations fairly well at low densities, but their behavior may become markedly different as the density increases. These deviations from ideal behavior cannot be neglected in accurate scientific work because they are often of great importance. For example, to establish an absolute thermodynamic scale in the laboratory we must know how to make the necessary corrections to the scale of a gas thermometer. We must therefore know the behavior of real gases rather accurately. Of even greater importance, perhaps, is the fact that the behavior of real gases gives us information on the nature of intermolecular forces and the structure of molecules.

Kinetic theory provides the microscopic description of the behavior of an ideal gas. We have already suggested how the assumptions of kinetic theory could become invalid. Under some conditions we may not be justified in neglecting the fact that the molecules occupy a fraction of the volume available to the gas and that the range of molecular forces is greater than the size of the molecule. At high densities these effects are no longer negligible.

J. D. van der Waals (1837–1923) deduced a modified equation of state which takes these factors into account in a simple way. Let us follow his reasoning. Let us first imagine the molecules to be hard spheres of diameter d. The diameter of such a sphere would correspond to the distance between the centers of molecules at which strong collision forces come into play. During its motion the center of a molecule cannot approach within a distance $d/2$ from a wall or a distance d from the center of another molecule. Hence, the actual volume available to a molecule is smaller than the volume of the containing vessel. Just how much smaller depends on how many molecules there are. Let us represent the volume per mole, V/n, by v. Then the "free volume" per mole would be less than this by the "covolume" b. Hence, we modify the equation of state from the ideal relation $pv = RT$ to

$$p(v - b) = RT$$

to allow for this. Because of the reduced volume, the number of impacts on the wall increases, thereby increasing the pressure.

We can also allow for the effect of attractive forces between molecules in a simple way. Imagine a plane passed through a gas and consider, at any instant, the intermolecular forces which act across it. Each molecule on the left, say, will attract and be attracted by some small number n of those on the right. Now compare this situation with another similar in every way except that the number of molecules per unit volume is doubled. Here any particular molecule on the left will interact on the average with $2n$ of those on the right, for the range of the molecular force is the same, and twice as many molecules now fall into this range. Since there also are twice as many molecules on the left as before which attract in this way, it is clear that the number of attractive bonds across the plane has increased fourfold. Therefore, the effect of these forces varies as the square of the number of particles per unit volume or inversely as the square of the volume per mole, that is, as $(1/v)^2$. Because of these intermolecular-force bonds, the gas should, for a given externally applied pressure, occupy a volume less than the volume it would occupy as an ideal gas. Or, equivalently, the gas acts as though it is subject to a pressure in excess of the externally applied pressure. This excess pressure is proportional to $(1/v)^2$, or equal to a/v^2 where a is a constant. Hence, we obtain the *van der Waals equation* of a gas,

$$\left(p + \frac{a}{v^2}\right)(v - b) = RT. \tag{24-7}$$

The actual values of a and b are to be determined from experiments on the particular gas under consideration, and in this respect the equation is empirical. We must realize that these corrections to the ideal gas law are of the simplest kind, and that failure of the van der Waals equation in any particular case is evidence that the model is oversimplified for that case. No one simple formula is known which applies to all gases under all conditions.

We have seen that real gases do not follow the ideal gas law exactly. Our discussion suggests also that for real gases the internal-energy function depends on the volume as well as on the temperature. For if there are (long range) attractive forces between molecules, the potential energy increases as the average distance between molecules increases. Hence, we would expect the internal energy of most real gases to increase slightly with the volume at ordinary temperatures, and this is found to be the case. Of course, collisions can be regarded as arising from repulsive forces. If the molecules move rapidly so as to make many collisions, the potential energy of the (short range) repulsive forces may be more important than that of the attractive forces and the internal energy could decrease as the volume increases. This is true for hydrogen and helium at ordinary temperatures. In either case, however, the internal energy U is not a function of temperature alone but depends also on the volume. The dependence of the internal energy of a gas on the volume can be deduced readily from the observed results of the free expansion experiment, discussed in Chapter 22.

▶ **Example 4.** On a pressure-volume diagram compare the behavior of an ideal gas at constant temperature to that of a real (van der Waals) gas.

In Fig. 24–8 we draw the isotherms (curves of constant T) according to the law $pv = RT$ as dashed lines, and the isotherms according to the law $(p + a/v^2)(v - b) = RT$ as solid lines. The ideal gas isotherms are each one branch of a rectangular hyperbola, $pv = $ constant. For the real gas the pressure varies with volume as

$$p = \frac{RT}{(v - b)} - \frac{a}{v^2}. \tag{24-8}$$

As the volume per mole decreases from large values, the pressure rises but the a/v^2 term, which diminishes the pressure, climbs rapidly so that the pressure passes through a maximum at A. As the volume is further decreased, the $RT/(v - b)$ term climbs more rapidly so that the pressure goes through a minimum at B and then rises rapidly to infinity as v tends to the value b. As the temperature rises, the maxima and minima are less pronounced. At the so-called critical temperature ($T = T'_2$), they coincide in a horizontal inflection point called the critical point. At still higher temperatures this inflection point gradually disappears ($T = T_3$). For air the critical temperature is about $-140°C$ and the pressure at the critical point is about 37 atm.

We can obtain the pressure p_{cr}, the molar volume v_{ci}, and the temperature T_{cr} of the critical point quite generally from the conditions that the tangent to the isotherm is horizontal, $dp/dv = 0$ when $T = $ constant, and that the point is an inflection point, $d^2p/dv^2 = 0$ when $T = $ constant. We obtain

$$\frac{dp}{dv} = -\frac{RT}{(v - b)^2} + \frac{2a}{v^3} = 0 \qquad T = \text{constant},$$

$$\frac{d^2p}{dv^2} = \frac{2RT}{(v - b)^3} - \frac{6a}{v^4} = 0 \qquad T = \text{constant}.$$

This gives us

$$v_{cr} = 3b$$

$$T_{cr} = \frac{8a}{27bR}$$

and, putting these in Eq. 24–8, we obtain

$$p_{cr} = \frac{a}{27b^2}.$$

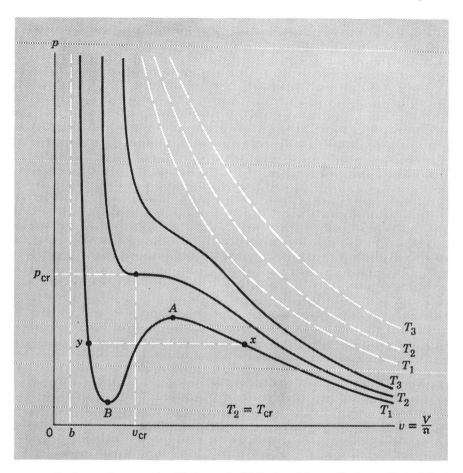

Fig. 24–8 Isotherms for a van der Waals gas (solid line) and for an ideal gas (dashed line) for three different temperatures. The critical point occurs at T_2.

The isotherms as a whole are suggestive of the actual experimental behavior of liquids and gases. The maxima and minima of the isotherms below the critical temperature are not usually observed experimentally. At some point x the gas begins to condense. As the volume is decreased, the pressure remains constant (dotted line) until at y all the gas has been transformed into liquid. Beyond y, as we decrease the volume, we are compressing a liquid, with the consequent sharp rise in pressure needed to make even small volume changes. Actually the portions xA and By of the isotherms can be obtained experimentally by using very pure gases and liquids. We call these supersaturated vapors and supercooled liquids, and they are in meta-stable states. The portion AB cannot be reproduced experimentally and is unstable. ◄

The constants a and b in van der Waals' equation can be calculated from the experimental values of the critical quantities. The term a/v^2 is called an internal pressure. Some values for air are of interest. For air at 0°C and external pressure p of 1 atm, the internal pressure is 0.0028 atm; at 0°C and external pressure p at 100 atm, the internal pressure is 26.0 atm. For air at −75°C the corresponding values of the internal pressure are 0.0056 atm and 84.5 atm. When a gas expands under pressure and does work against outside compressing forces, it must also do work against these internal forces. For air at −79°C and 100 atm, the work done against internal forces is nearly as great as that done against external forces. There is an important distinction between internal and external work, however. In the case of external work, energy is transferred from the body to an outside body; in the case of internal work, there is merely a transfer from one kind of energy to another within the body, as from potential to kinetic. The constant b varies from gas to gas but is usually of the order of 30 cm³/mole. Hence, the covolume is about 0.15% of the free volume available to a gas at standard conditions.

Although the van der Waals formula is a good qualitative guide, the quantitative experimental data cannot be matched everywhere with constant values for a and b. The reason is that even this model is oversimplified. Instead of assuming that the molecules always have a well-defined diameter, for example, we must use the actual intermolecular force (Fig. 23–3). In this way a more accurate correction to the ideal gas law can be made. Van der Waals himself knew this would be necessary for accurate quantitative work. In fact, it is research of this sort which helps to determine the actual shape of the intermolecular-force curves.

QUESTIONS

1. Consider the case in which the mean free path is greater than the longest straight line in a vessel. Is this a perfect vacuum for a molecule in this vessel?

2. Give a qualitative explanation of the connection between the mean free path of ammonia molecules in air and the time it takes to smell the ammonia when a bottle is opened across the room.

3. The two opposite walls of a container of gas are kept at different temperatures. Describe the mechanism of heat conduction through the gas.

4. If molecules are not spherical, what meaning can we give to d in Eq. 24–1 for the mean free path? In which gases would the molecules act the most nearly as rigid spheres?

5. Suppose we dispense with the hypothesis of elastic collisions in kinetic theory and consider the molecules as centers of force acting at a distance. Does the concept of mean free path have any meaning under these circumstances?

6. Since the actual force between molecules depends on the distance between them, forces can cause deflections even when molecules are far from "contact" with one another. Furthermore, the deflection caused should depend on how long a time these forces act and hence on the relative speed of the molecules. (a) Would you then expect the measured mean free path to depend on temperature, even though the density remains constant? (b) If so, would you expect l to increase or decrease with temperature? (c) How does this dependence enter into Eq. 24–1?

7. Justify qualitatively the statement that, in a mixture of molecules of different kinds in complete equilibrium, each kind of molecule has the same Maxwellian distribution in speed that it would have if the other kinds were not present.

8. The Maxwellian distribution of speeds among molecules in a gas is shown in Fig. 24–4.

How would you expect the Maxwellian distribution of *velocities* to look? What would the average velocity be?

9. The slit system in Fig. 24–5 selects only those molecules moving in the $+x$ direction. Does this destroy the validity of the experiment as a measure of the distribution of speeds of molecules moving in all directions?

10. In Stern's method (Fig. 24–5) explain how we can calculate the distribution of speeds of the atoms in the furnace from the distribution of speeds among the atoms in the beam. Are these distributions different? (Hint: Assuming an equal number of atoms in each speed interval in the furnace, those of high speed escape in greater numbers in proportion to their speed.)

11. What determines the upper limit to the pressure that can be tolerated in the Stern experiment?

12. List examples of the Brownian motion in physical phenomena.

13. Show that as the volume per mole of a gas increases, the van der Waals equation tends to the equation of state of an ideal gas.

14. The covolume b in van der Waals' equation is often taken to be four times the actual volume of the gas molecules themselves. What factors would have to be taken into account to obtain such a result?

PROBLEMS

1. The mean free path of nitrogen molecules at 0°C and 1 atm is 0.80×10^{-5} cm. At this temperature and pressure there are 2.7×10^{19} molecules/cm³. What is the molecular diameter?

2. The best vacuum attained so far in the laboratory is 10^{-10} mm of Hg. How many molecules of gas remain per cubic centimeter at 20°C in this "vacuum"?

3. In the cosmotron at the Brookhaven National Laboratory the protons travel around a circular path of diameter 75 ft in a chamber of 10^{-6} mm Hg pressure.

(a) Estimate the number of gas molecules per cubic centimeter at this pressure.

(b) What is the mean free path of the gas molecules under these conditions if the molecular diameter is 2.0×10^{-8} cm?

4. At what frequency would the wavelength of sound be of the order of the mean free path in oxygen at 1-atm pressure and 0°C? Take the diameter of the oxygen molecule to be 3.00×10^{-8} cm.

5. A molecule of hydrogen (diameter 10^{-8} cm) escapes from a furnace ($T = 4000°K$) with the root-mean-square speed into a chamber containing atoms of cold argon (diameter 3×10^{-8} cm) at a density of 4×10^{19} atoms/cm³. (a) What is the speed of the hydrogen molecule? (b) On a collision between the molecule and an argon atom, what is the closest distance between their centers, considering each as spherical? (c) What is the initial number of collisions per unit time experienced by the hydrogen molecule?

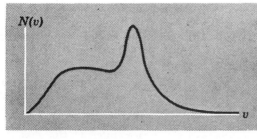

Fig. 24–9

6. Consider the distribution of speeds shown in Fig. 24–9. (a) List v_{rms}, $\bar{v}$, and v_p in the order of increasing speed. (b) How does this compare with the Maxwellian distribution?

7. Calculate the root-mean-square speed of smoke particles of mass 5.0×10^{-14} gm in air at 0°C and 1-atm pressure.

8. Particles of mass 6.2×10^{-14} gm are suspended in a liquid at 27°C and are observed to have a root-mean-square speed of 1.4 cm/sec. Calculate Avogadro's number from the equipartition theorem and these data.

9. Colloidal particles in solution are buoyed up by the liquid in which they are suspended. Let ρ' be the density of liquid and ρ the density of the particles. If V is the volume of a particle, show that the number of particles per unit volume in the liquid varies with height as

$$n = n_0 \exp \left[- \frac{N_0}{RT} V(\rho - \rho')gh \right].$$

This equation was tested by Perrin in his Brownian motion studies.

10. The average speed of hydrogen molecules at 0°C is 1694 meters/sec. Compute the average speed of colloidal particles of "molecular weight" 3.2×10^6 gm/mole.

11. Calculate the work done per mole in an isothermal expansion of a van der Waals gas from volume V_i to V_f.

12. The constant a in van der Waals' equation is 0.37 nt-m^4/mole^2 for CO_2 and 0.025 nt-m^4/mole^2 for hydrogen. Compute the internal pressures for these gases and the ratio of the internal to the external pressure for values of v/v_0 (where $v_0 = 22.4$ liters/mole) of 1, 0.01, and 0.001.

13. (a) The constant b in van der Waals' equation is 43 cm^3/mole for CO_2. Using the value for a in the previous problem, compute the pressure at 0°C for a specific volume of 0.55 liter/mole, assuming van der Waals' equation to be strictly true. (b) What is the pressure under these same conditions, assuming CO_2 behaves as an ideal gas?

14. Van der Waals' b for oxygen is 32 cm^3/mole. Assume b is four times the actual volume of a mole of "billiard-ball" O_2 molecules and compute the diameter of an O_2 molecule.

15. The constants a and b in the van der Waals equation are different for different substances. Show, however, that if we take v_c, p_c, and T_c as the units of specific volume, pressure, and temperature, the van der Waals equation becomes identical for all substances.

Entropy and the Second
Law of Thermodynamics

CHAPTER 25

25–1   Introduction

The essential content of the first law of thermodynamics is that energy is conserved. However, we can construct in our imaginations a great many thermodynamical processes which conserve energy but which actually never occur. For example, when a hot body and a cold body are put into contact, it simply does not happen that the hot body gets hotter and the cold body colder. Or again, a pond does not suddenly freeze on a hot summer day by liberating heat to its environment. And yet such processes do not violate the first law of thermodynamics. Similarly, the first law does not put any restriction on our ability to convert work into heat or heat into work, except that energy be conserved in the process. And yet in practice, although we can convert a given quantity of work completely into heat, we have never been able to devise a scheme that converts a given amount of heat energy completely into work.

It is through the concept of entropy and the formulation of the second law of thermodynamics that we have come to understand these limitations and have been able to express them in fundamental terms. Although the ideas are sometimes subtle and the theory may at times seem abstract, in application this is one of the most practical and fruitful areas of physics.

25–2   Reversible and Irreversible Processes

Let us first consider a system in thermodynamic equilibrium. A system will be in *thermodynamic equilibrium* when it meets the following requirements. (a) The system is in a state of mechanical equilibrium—there is no unbalanced force in the interior of the system and no unbalanced force between the system and its surroundings. (b) The system is in thermal equilibrium—all parts of the system are at the same temperature and this temperature is the same as that of the environment. (c) The system is in chemical equilibrium—it does not tend to undergo a spontaneous change of internal structure. A system in thermodynamic equilibrium can be specified macroscopically by giving the values of only a few quantities, such as pressure, volume, temperature, and quantity of a particular substance.

Now suppose that we change the state of the system. A change in state must involve some departure from thermodynamic equilibrium. For example, suppose that we change a system from one state to another having just half the volume. Imagine that we do this by quickly pushing down a piston. The system will not be in thermodynamic equilibrium. There will be relative motion of its parts owing to unbalanced forces; temperature differences may set in because the heating effects of the compression may affect different portions of the system in different ways; there may be chemical changes or changes in phase, such as condensation. Of course, eventually, if left to itself, the system may reach a new state of thermodynamic equilibrium. During the process of change, however, thermodynamic equilibrium does not exist.

Most processes of interest can be thought of as beginning in an equilibrium state, passing through nonequilibrium states, and ending in another equilibrium state. Thermodynamics seeks to understand such processes. But rather than concerning itself with the details of the highly complex processes whereby nonequilibrium states approach equilibrium, thermodynamics seeks instead to obtain simple and general information about such processes by comparing their behavior to that of an ideal process, called a reversible process. In a reversible process we change the state of a system by a continuous succession of equilibrium states.

For example, suppose we try to reduce the volume of a system to half its original value by a succession of small changes. We first increase the force on the piston by a very small amount. This will reduce the volume of the system a little; the system will depart from equilibrium, but only slightly. In a short time the system will reach a new equilibrium state. Then we increase the force on the piston again by a very small amount, reducing the volume further. Again we wait for a new equilibrium state to be established, and so forth. Hence, by many repetitions of this procedure we finally achieve the required change in volume. During this entire process the system is never in a state differing much from an equilibrium state. If we imagine carrying out this procedure with still smaller successive increases in pressure, the intermediate states will depart from equilibrium even less. By indefinitely increasing the number of changes and correspondingly decreasing the size of each change, we arrive at an ideal process in which the system passes through a continuous succession of equilibrium states. Such an ideal process is called a *reversible process*. In practice, we can approximate ideal reversible processes very closely by changing the conditions external to the system very slowly.

In an isothermal process the temperature of a system remains constant throughout the process. The temperature of a system as a whole has a definite value only in an equilibrium state, however, so that an isothermal process must involve only equilibrium states. Therefore, an isothermal process is a reversible process. In practice, the ideal isothermal process is approximated by changing the pressure and volume very slowly while keeping the system immersed in a bath at the required constant temperature.

In an adiabatic process no heat is allowed to enter or leave the system. Hence, an adiabatic process may be reversible or irreversible—the definition does not exclude either. In practice, we cannot obtain a perfect heat insulator. An adiabatic process would have to be carried out rapidly enough so that the system does not lose or gain a significant amount of heat. But a reversible process would have to be carried out slowly enough so that at each stage the system has enough time to come very near to equilibrium. A process that is both adiabatic and reversible is nevertheless achievable because the time required for equalization of pressure or for other processes to reach equilibrium is short compared to the rate at which heat is conducted.

We shall now seek exact quantitative information about reversible processes. This in turn will give us important qualitative information about irreversible processes. Because most natural processes are irreversible, we shall thereby have obtained a deeper understanding of how nature works.

25–3 The Carnot Cycle

A series of processes that returns a system to its original condition is called a cycle. If the cycle involves reversible processes only, it is a *reversible cycle*. Let us represent such a cycle for a gas on a p-V diagram (Fig. 25–1). The succession of equilibrium states is represented by the points on a closed curve. Along the curve abc the system is expanding and the area under this

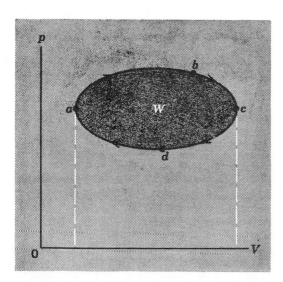

Fig. 25–1 A p–V diagram of a gas undergoing a reversible cycle. Since the process returns the gas to its original state, it is called a cycle. Since it is made up of a succession of equilibrium states, it is called reversible. The shaded area W represents the net work done by the gas in the cycle.

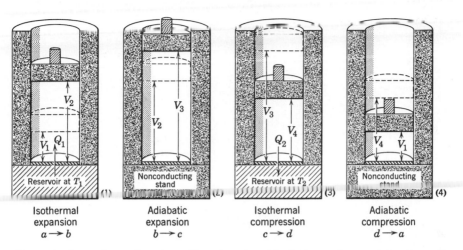

| Isothermal expansion $a \rightarrow b$ | Adiabatic expansion $b \rightarrow c$ | Isothermal compression $c \rightarrow d$ | Adiabatic compression $d \rightarrow a$ |

Fig. 25–2 An engine undergoing a Carnot cycle. The letters a, b, c, and d, refer to the corresponding points in Fig. 25–3.

curve represents the work done *by* the system during the expansion. Along the curve *cda*, which returns the system to its original state, the system is contracting and the area under this curve represents the work done *on* the system during the compression. Hence, the *net work* done *by* the system is represented by the area enclosed by the curve and is positive. If the cycle were traversed in the opposite sense, that is, expanding along *adc* and contracting along *cba*, the *net work* done *by* the system would be the negative of that of the previous case.

A theoretically important reversible cycle is the *Carnot cycle*, introduced by Sadi Carnot in 1824. We shall see later that this cycle will determine the limit of our ability to convert heat into work. The system consists of a single homogeneous "working substance," such as a gas, and the cycle is made up of two isothermal and two adiabatic reversible processes. The working substance, which we can think of as an ideal gas for concreteness, is contained in a cylinder with a heat-conducting base and nonconducting walls and piston. The environment will consist of a heat reservoir in the form of a body of very large heat capacity at a temperature T_1, another reservoir of very large heat capacity at a temperature T_2, and two nonconducting stands. The Carnot cycle is carried out in four steps, as shown in Fig. 25–2. The cycle is shown on the p-V diagram of Fig. 25–3, where an ideal gas is taken as the working substance.

Step 1. The gas is in an initial condition represented by p_1, V_1, T_1 (a, Fig. 25–3). The cylinder is put on the heat reservoir at temperature T_1, and the gas is allowed to expand very slowly to p_2, V_2, T_1 (b, Fig. 25–3). During the process an amount of heat Q_1 is absorbed by the gas by conduction through the base. The expansion is isothermal at T_1 and the gas does work in raising the piston.

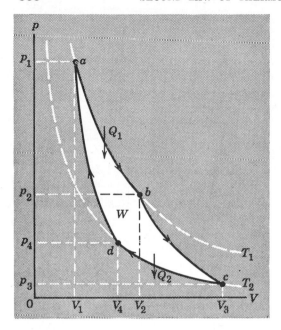

Fig. 25–3 The Carnot cycle illustrated in the previous figure, plotted on a p-V diagram for an ideal gas.

Step 2. The cylinder is put on the nonconducting stand and the gas is allowed to expand very slowly to p_3, V_3, T_2 (*c*, Fig. 25–3). The expansion is adiabatic because no heat can enter or leave the system. The gas does work in raising the piston and its temperature falls to T_2.

Step 3. The cylinder is put on the (colder) heat reservoir at T_2 and the gas is compressed very slowly to p_4, V_4, T_2 (*d*, Fig. 25–3). During the process an amount of heat Q_2 is transferred from the gas to the reservoir by conduction through the base. The compression is isothermal at T_2 and work is done *on* the gas by the piston.

Step 4. The cylinder is put on a nonconducting stand and the gas is compressed very slowly to the initial condition p_1, V_1, T_1. The compression is adiabatic because no heat can enter or leave the system. Work is done on the gas and its temperature rises to T_1.

The net work W done by the system during the cycle is represented by the area enclosed by path *abcd* of Fig. 25–3. The net amount of heat received by the system in the cycle is $Q_1 - Q_2$, where Q_1 is the heat absorbed in Step 1 and Q_2 is the heat given up in Step 3. The initial and final states are the same so that there is no net change in the internal energy U of the system. Hence, from the first law of thermodynamics,

$$W = Q_1 - Q_2 \tag{25–1}$$

for the cycle. The result of the cycle is that heat has been converted into work by the system. Any required amount of work can be obtained by simply repeating the cycle. Hence, the system acts like a *heat engine*.

We have used an ideal gas as an example of a working substance. The working substance can be anything at all, however. Of course, the p-V diagrams for other substances would be different. Common heat engines use steam or a mixture of fuel and air, or fuel and oxygen as their working substance. The high-temperature reservoir is called the source and the low-temperature reservoir is called the exhaust. In most practical cases, heat is obtained from the combustion of a fuel such as gasoline or coal. Recently, power plants have been constructed which obtain heat for their engines from the annihilation of mass in nuclear fission or fusion processes. Although real heat engines do not operate on a reversible cycle, the Carnot cycle, which is reversible, gives useful information about the behavior of any heat engine.

The efficiency e of a heat engine is defined as the ratio of the net work done by the engine during one cycle to the heat taken in from the high temperature source in one cycle. Hence,

$$e = \frac{W}{Q_1} = \frac{Q_1 - Q_2}{Q_1} = 1 - \frac{Q_2}{Q_1}. \tag{25-2}$$

Equation 25-2 shows that the efficiency of a heat engine is less than one (a hundred per cent) so long as the heat Q_2 delivered to the exhaust is not zero. Experience shows that every heat engine rejects some heat during the exhaust stroke. This represents the heat absorbed by the engine that is not converted to work in the process.

We may perform the Carnot cycle in reverse. Then an amount of heat Q_2 is removed from the lower temperature reservoir at T_2, and an amount of heat Q_1 is delivered to the higher temperature reservoir at T_1; work must be done *on* the system by an outside agency. The result of the reverse cycle is that work is done on the system which extracts heat from the lower temperature reservoir. Any amount of heat can be removed from this reservoir by simply repeating the reverse cycle. Hence, the system acts like a *refrigerator*, transferring heat from a body at a lower temperature to one at a higher temperature by means of work supplied to it.

▶ **Example 1.** Show that the efficiency of a Carnot engine using an ideal gas as the working substance is $e = (T_1 - T_2)/T_1$.

Along the isothermal path ab, the temperature, and hence the internal energy of an ideal gas, remains constant. From the first law, the heat Q_1 absorbed by the gas in its expansion must be equal to the work W_1 done in this expansion. From Example 2, Chapter 23, we have, assuming one mole of working substance,

$$Q_1 = W_1 = RT_1 \ln \frac{V_2}{V_1}.$$

Likewise, in the isothermal compression along the path cd, we have

$$Q_2 = W_2 = RT_2 \ln \frac{V_3}{V_4}.$$

On dividing the first equation by the second, we obtain

$$\frac{Q_1}{Q_2} = \frac{T_1 \ln (V_2/V_1)}{T_2 \ln (V_3/V_4)}.$$

From the equation describing an isothermal process for an ideal gas we obtain for the paths ab and cd

$$p_1V_1 = p_2V_2,$$

$$p_3V_3 = p_4V_4.$$

From the equation describing an adiabatic process for an ideal gas we have for paths bc and da

$$p_2V_2{}^\gamma = p_3V_3{}^\gamma,$$

$$p_4V_4{}^\gamma = p_1V_1{}^\gamma.$$

Multiplying these four equations together and canceling the factor $p_1p_2p_3p_4$ appearing on both sides, we obtain

$$V_1V_2{}^\gamma V_3V_4{}^\gamma = V_2V_3{}^\gamma V_4V_1{}^\gamma,$$

from which

$$(V_2V_4)^{\gamma-1} = (V_3V_1)^{\gamma-1}$$

and

$$\frac{V_2}{V_1} = \frac{V_3}{V_4}.$$

Using this result in our expression for Q_1/Q_2, we see that

$$\frac{Q_1}{Q_2} = \frac{T_1}{T_2},$$

so that

$$e = \frac{Q_1 - Q_2}{Q_1} = \frac{T_1 - T_2}{T_1}.$$

The temperatures T_1 and T_2 are those measured on the ideal gas thermometer scale described in Chapter 21.   ◀

25–4 The Second Law of Thermodynamics

The first heat engines constructed were found to be extremely inefficient devices. Only a small fraction of the heat absorbed at the high-temperature source could be converted to useful work. Even as engineering design improved, a sizable fraction of the absorbed heat was discharged at the lower-temperature exhaust of the engine, remaining unconverted to mechanical energy. It remained a hope to be able to devise an engine that could take heat from an abundant reservoir, like the ocean, and convert it completely into useful work. Then it would not be necessary to go to all the expense of providing a source of heat at a higher temperature than the outside environment by burning fuels (Fig. 25–4). Likewise, we might hope to be able to devise a refrigerator that simply transfers heat from a cold body to a hot body, without requiring the expense of outside work (Fig. 25–5). *Neither of these hopeful ambitions violate the first law of thermodynamics.* In the case of the heat engine we would simply convert heat energy completely and directly into mechanical energy, the total energy being conserved in the process. In the case of the refrigerator, the heat energy would simply be transferred from cold body to hot body without any loss of energy in the

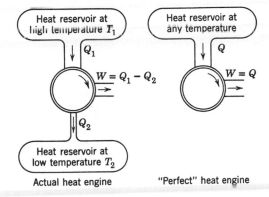

Fig. 25–4 In an actual heat engine, some of the heat Q_1 taken in by the engine is converted into work W, but the rest is rejected as heat Q_2. In a "perfect" heat engine all the heat input would be converted into work output.

process. Nevertheless *neither of these ambitions has ever been achieved*, and there is reason to believe they never will be. The impossibility of such devices is stated directly by *the second law of thermodynamics.*

There have been many different statements of the second law, each emphasizing another facet of the law, but all are logically equivalent to one another. For example, Rudolph Clausius stated it as follows: *It is impossible for any self-acting machine to convey heat continuously from one body to another at a higher temperature.*

This statement rules out our ambitious refrigerator, for it implies that to convey heat continuously from a cold to a hot object it is necessary to supply work by an outside agent. We know from experience that when two bodies are in contact, heat energy flows from the hot body to the cold body. The second law rules out the possibility of heat energy flowing from cold to hot

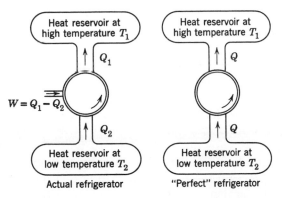

Fig. 25–5 In an actual refrigerator, work W is needed to transfer heat from a low-temperature to a high-temperature reservoir. In a "perfect" refrigerator, heat would flow from the low-temperature to the high-temperature reservoir without any work being done on the engine. Notice that in both the "perfect" machines (here and above), energy is conserved, that is, the first law is fulfilled. Their inattainability is predicted instead by the second law of thermodynamics.

body in such a case and so determines the direction of transfer of heat. The direction can be reversed only by an expenditure of work. The second law is a broad generalization inferred from experience.

Lord Kelvin stated the second law as follows: *A transformation whose only final result is to transform into work heat extracted from a source which is at the same temperature throughout is impossible.*

This statement rules out our ambitious heat engine, for it implies that we cannot produce mechanical work by extracting heat from a single reservoir without returning any heat to a reservoir at a lower temperature.

To show that the two statements are equivalent we need to show simply that, if either statement is false, the other statement must be false also. Suppose Clausius' statement were false so that we could have a refrigerator operating without needing a supply of fuel or work. Then we could use an ordinary engine to remove heat from the hot body, to do work and to return part of the heat to the cold body. But by connecting our desired refrigerator into the system, this heat would be returned to the hot body without expenditure of work and would become available again for use by the heat engine. Hence, the combination of an ordinary engine and the desired refrigerator would constitute a heat engine which violates Kelvin's statement. Or we can reverse the argument. If Kelvin's statement were incorrect, we could have a heat engine which simply takes heat from a source and converts it completely into work. By connecting this desired heat engine to an ordinary refrigerator, we could extract heat from the hot body, convert it completely to work, use this work to run the ordinary refrigerator, extract heat from the cold body, and deliver it plus the work converted to heat by the refrigerator to the hot body. The net result is a transfer of heat from cold to hot body without expenditure of work and this violates Clausius' statement.

The second law shows us that many processes actually are irreversible. For example, Clausius' statement specifically rules out a simple reversal of the process of heat transfer from hot body to cold body. Not only will some processes not run backward by themselves but no combination of processes can undo the effect of an irreversible process without causing another corresponding change elsewhere.

The second law of thermodynamics is a broad generalization from experience. It has far-reaching implications in all areas of science because in principle all heat transfer problems—whether in astronomy, biology, chemistry, geology, or physics—can be reduced to that of conversion of heat energy to mechanical energy by means of a heat engine. In subsequent sections we shall develop these ideas more fully and formulate the second law in quantitative fashion.

25-5   The Efficiency of Engines

It was Sadi Carnot (1796–1832), a French engineer, who first wrote scientifically on the theory of heat engines. In 1824 he published *Reflections on the Motive Power of Heat.* By then the steam engine was commonly used in industry but not much in transport. Carnot wrote:

In spite of labor of all sorts expended on the steam engine, and in spite of the perfection to which it has been brought, its theory is very little advanced. . . .

The production of motion in the steam engine is always accompanied by a circumstance which we should particularly notice. This circumstance is the passage of caloric from one body where the temperature is more or less elevated to another where it is lower. . . .

The motive power of heat is independent of the agents employed to develop it; its quantity is determined solely by the temperature of the bodies between which, in the final result, the transfer of the caloric occurs.

Hence, Carnot directed attention to the facts that the difference in temperature was the real source of "motive power," that the transfer of heat played a significant role, and that the choice of working substance was of no theoretical importance.

Carnot was led into some errors by his acceptance of the caloric theory of heat, but we should remember that the mechanical equivalent of heat and the conservation of energy principle were not known in 1824. Some years later Carnot became convinced of the falsity of the caloric theory. In some of his later papers, published posthumously in 1872, it became clear that Carnot had foreseen the principle of the conservation of energy and had made an accurate determination of the mechanical equivalent of heat. He had planned a program of research which included all the important developments in the field made by other investigators during the following several decades. However, he died during an epidemic of cholera in 1832 at the age of 36, leaving it to others to extend his work. It was William Thomson (later Lord Kelvin) who modified Carnot's reasoning to bring it into accord with the mechanical theory of heat, and who, together with Rudolph Clausius (1822–1888), successfully developed the science of thermodynamics.

Carnot developed the concept of a reversible engine and the reversible cycle named after him. He stated an important theorem in this connection: *The efficiency of all reversible engines operating between the same two temperatures is the same, and no irreversible engine working between the same two temperatures can have a greater efficiency than this.* Clausius and Kelvin showed that this theorem was a necessary consequence of the second law of thermodynamics. Notice that nothing is said about the working substance, so that the efficiency of a reversible engine is independent of the working substance and depends only on the temperatures. Furthermore, a reversible engine operates at the maximum efficiency possible for any engine working between the same two temperature limits. The proof of this theorem follows.

Let us call the two reversible engines H and H'. They operate between the temperatures T_1 and T_2, where $T_1 > T_2$. They may differ, say, in their working substance or in their initial pressures and length of stroke. H runs forward and H' backward. The forward running engine H takes in heat Q_1 at T_1 and gives out heat Q_2 at T_2. The backward running engine H' gives out heat Q_1' at T_1 and takes in heat Q_2' at T_2. We now connect the engines mechanically so that the work done by H is just suffi-

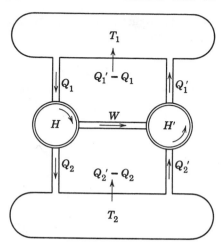

Fig. 25–6 Proof of Carnot's theorem.

cient to operate H' (Fig. 25–6). Suppose the efficiency e of H were greater than the efficiency e' of H'. Then

$$e > e',$$

$$\frac{Q_1 - Q_2}{Q_1} > \frac{Q_1' - Q_2'}{Q_1'}.$$

Since the work done by one engine equals the work done on the other engine,

$$W = W',$$

$$Q_1 - Q_2 = Q_1' - Q_2'.$$

Comparing these equations, we see that

$$\frac{1}{Q_1} > \frac{1}{Q_1'}$$

or $$Q_1 < Q_1'.$$

Hence (from the work equality), $$Q_2 < Q_2'.$$

Thus, the hot source gains heat $Q_1' - Q_1$ (positive) and the cool source loses heat $Q_2' - Q_2$ (positive). But no work is done in the process so that we have transferred heat from a body at one temperature to a body at a higher temperature without performing work—in direct contradiction to the second law. Hence, we conclude that e cannot be greater than e'. Likewise, by reversing the engines we can use the same reasoning to prove that e' cannot be greater than e. Hence,

$$e = e',$$

proving the first part of Carnot's theorem.

Now suppose that H is an irreversible engine. Then by the exact same procedure we can prove that e_{ir} cannot be greater than e'. But H cannot be reversed, so we cannot prove that e' cannot be greater than e_{ir}. Therefore, e_{ir} is either equal to or less than e'. Since $e' = e = e_{reversible}$, we have

$$e_{irreversible} \leqq e_{reversible},$$

thus proving the second part of Carnot's theorem.

Notice that from the second law we have obtained an important qualitative property of irreversible processes.

▶ **Example 2.** A steam engine takes steam from the boiler at 200°C (225 lb/in.² pressure) and exhausts directly into the air (14 lb/in.² pressure) at 100°C. What is its ideal efficiency?

$$e = \frac{T_1 - T_2}{T_1} = \frac{473°K - 373°K}{473°K} \times 100\% = 21.1\%.$$

Actual efficiencies of about 15% are usually realized. Energy is lost by friction, turbulence, and heat conduction. Lower exhaust temperatures on more complicated steam engines may raise the ideal efficiency to 35% and the actual efficiency to 20%. The efficiency of an ordinary automobile engine is about 22% and that of a large Diesel oil engine about 40%.   ◀

25–6   The Absolute Thermodynamic Temperature Scale

The efficiency of a reversible engine is independent of the working substance and depends only on the two temperatures between which the engine works. Since $e = 1 - Q_2/Q_1$, then Q_2/Q_1 can depend only on the temperatures. This led Lord Kelvin to suggest a new scale of temperature. If we let θ_1 and θ_2 represent these two temperatures, his defining equation is

$$\frac{\theta_1}{\theta_2} = \frac{Q_1}{Q_2}.$$

That is, two temperatures on this scale are to each other as the heats absorbed and rejected, respectively, by a Carnot engine operating between these temperatures. Because such a temperature scale is independent of the characteristics of any particular substance, it is called the *absolute thermodynamic temperature scale*.

To complete the definition of the absolute scale, we assign the arbitrary value of 273.16° Absolute to the temperature of the triple point of water. Hence, $\theta_0 = 273.16°$A. Then for a Carnot engine operating between reservoirs at the temperatures θ and θ_0 we have

$$\frac{\theta}{\theta_0} = \frac{Q}{Q_0}$$

$$\theta = 273.16°A \frac{Q}{Q_0}. \qquad (25\text{–}3)$$

If we compare this with the corresponding equation for the ideal gas temperature T, namely

$$T = 273.16°K \lim_{P_0 \to 0} \frac{P}{P_0}, \qquad (25\text{–}4)$$

we see that on the absolute scale Q plays the role of a thermometric property. However, Q does not depend on the characteristics of any substance because a Carnot engine is independent of the nature of the working substance. Therefore, we obtain a scale of temperature which is free of the objection we can raise to the ideal gas scale of Chapter 21, and in fact we arrive at a fundamental definition of temperature.

The definition of thermodynamic temperature enables us to rewrite the equation for the efficiency of a reversible engine as

$$e = \frac{Q_1 - Q_2}{Q_1} = \frac{\theta_1 - \theta_2}{\theta_1}. \qquad (25\text{–}5)$$

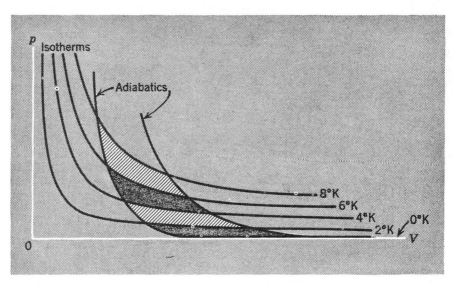

Fig. 25-7 A series of Carnot cycles tending toward absolute-zero temperature, as used in establishing the absolute thermodynamic scale of temperature. The difference in slope between isothermals and adiabatics has here been exaggerated for clarity.

But we have shown (Example 1) that the efficiency of a Carnot engine using an ideal gas as working substance is

$$e = \frac{Q_1 - Q_2}{Q_1} = \frac{T_1 - T_2}{T_1} \tag{25-6}$$

where T is the temperature given by the constant-volume thermometer containing the ideal gas. Hence, $Q_1/Q_2 = T_1/T_2$ and $Q_1/Q_2 = \theta_1/\theta_2$. Since $\theta_0 = T_0 = 273.16°$ and $\theta/\theta_0 = T/T_0$, it follows that $\theta = T$. Hence, *if an ideal gas were available for use in a constant-volume thermometer, the thermometer would give the absolute thermodynamic temperature.* We have seen that, although an ideal gas is not available, measurements made using the limiting process of Eq. 25-4 with real gases correspond to ideal gas behavior. Henceforth, we shall treat the ideal gas scale and the absolute thermodynamic scale as identical and signify both by $T°$K.

In practice, we cannot have a gas below 1°K. One of the methods used in measuring temperature below 1°K employs the absolute scale directly. The ratio of two absolute temperatures is the ratio of two heats transferred during two isothermal processes bounded by the same two adiabatics (Fig. 25-7). The location of the adiabatic boundaries (on the p-V diagram) can be found experimentally, and the heats transferred during two nearly reversible isothermal processes can be measured with great precision.

From the equations

$$T = 273.16°\text{K} \frac{Q}{Q_0} \qquad \text{or} \qquad \frac{T}{T_0} = \frac{Q}{Q_0}$$

it is clear that the heat Q transferred in an isothermal process between two given adiabatics decreases as the temperature T decreases. Conversely, the smaller Q is, the lower the corresponding temperature T is. Now the smallest possible value of Q is zero and the corresponding T is absolute zero. That is, *if a system undergoes a reversible isothermal process with no transfer of heat, the temperature at which this process takes place is the absolute zero.* Hence, at absolute zero, an isothermal process and an adiabatic process are identical (Fig. 25–7).

This definition of absolute zero applies to all substances and is independent of the properties of any one of them. Notice that no reference is made to molecules or molecular energy and that we have obtained a purely macroscopic definition of absolute zero.*

The efficiency of a Carnot engine is

$$e = 1 - \frac{T_2}{T_1},$$

which is the maximum possible efficiency any engine can have operating between temperatures T_1 and T_2. To obtain 100% efficiency, T_2 must be zero. Only when the low-temperature reservoir is at absolute zero will all the heat absorbed at the high-temperature reservoir be converted to work.

The fundamental feature of all cooling processes is that the lower the temperature, the more difficult it is to go still lower. This experience has led to the formulation of the *third law of thermodynamics*, which can be stated in one form as follows: *It is impossible by any procedure, no matter how idealized, to reduce any system to the absolute zero of temperature in a finite number of operations.* Hence, because we cannot obtain a reservoir at absolute zero, a heat engine with 100% efficiency is a practical impossibility.

25–7 Entropy

We wish to express the second law of thermodynamics in quantitative form. To do this we need a quantity which can measure the ability of a system to do work. Let us consider some examples in order to illustrate this need.

Perhaps the simplest example is the free expansion of an ideal gas. In such a process (shown in Fig. 22–12) an ideal gas expands against a vacuum, the gas being confined to rigid insulated enclosure. No work is done by the gas in such an expansion and no heat is transferred to or from the system during the process. The system is isolated. Hence, from the first law of thermodynamics, there is no change in the internal energy of the gas. That is, since $dQ = 0$ and $dW = 0$, dU must equal zero. For an ideal gas U depends only on the temperature so that there is no change in T in the process either. Nevertheless, to bring the gas back to its initial condition, we must do work on the gas by compressing it. Hence, as a result of free expansion the gas has lost some of its capacity for doing work. Notice that free expansion is an irreversible process.

Another simple example is that of heat conduction. If a hot body and a cold body are placed in contact, they ultimately reach thermal equilibrium. There has been no net loss of energy in the process. Nevertheless, the system as a whole has lost its capacity for doing work; for before being placed in contact the hot and cold bodies could do useful work by means of a heat

---

* The student may have heard of the concept of negative absolute temperatures. In a sense this name is misleading because negative temperatures are not "colder" than absolute zero but instead are "hotter" than infinite temperature. The existence of such "negative temperatures" does not alter the correctness of any statement in this chapter. For a discussion of this subject see an article by Norman F. Ramsey, *Physical Review*, **103**, 20, (1956).

engine, but after contact there is no temperature difference between them, so that they cannot do work. Heat conduction is also an irreversible process.

The physical quantity which describes the ability of a system to do work is called the *entropy*. The entropy is a measurable property. It is as important a concept as energy itself in thermodynamics. We shall define entropy quantitatively by means of a reversible process and then show how it can be applied to irreversible processes, as those already discussed.

We know that for isothermal processes taking place between the same two adiabatics

$$\frac{Q_1}{T_1} = \frac{Q_2}{T_2}.$$

Here Q represents the heat *absorbed* in an isothermal process at temperature T. In a Carnot cycle heat is absorbed at T_1 and rejected at T_2 so that for a (reversible) Carnot cycle (between two adiabatics) Q_2 is negative and

$$\frac{Q_1}{T_1} + \frac{Q_2}{T_2} = 0.$$

This equation states that the sum of the quantities Q/T is zero for a Carnot cycle.

Now let us consider a reversible cycle such as that shown in Fig. 25–8. Heat is absorbed and rejected isothermally at several different temperatures and the changes in temperature are produced by adiabatic processes, just as in the Carnot cycle. This cycle is equivalent to three Carnot cycles, for the cycle *abcdefghija* is equivalent to the three Carnot cycles *abija, bcghb, defgd* obtained by drawing in the adiabatic curves *bh* and *cg*. Hence, the sum of the quantities Q/T for the whole cycle is simply the sum of the quantities Q/T for the three Carnot cycles. For the whole cycle therefore

$$\sum \frac{Q}{T} = 0.$$

Any reversible cycle can be approximated in practice by the use of many isothermal and adiabatic processes in succession (Fig. 25–9), so that a general reversible cycle can be represented as the sum of many Carnot cycles. The

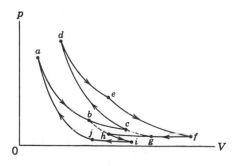

Fig. 25–8 A reversible cycle consisting of three Carnot cycles.

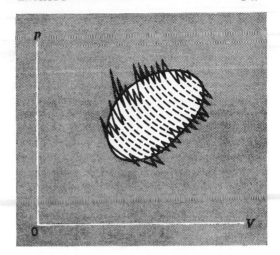

Fig. 25–9 Any reversible process can be approximated by a group of Carnot cycles. The cycle is approximated more closely as the number of successive adiabatic and isothermal steps increases.

larger the number of successive processes used, the smaller the isothermal and adiabatic steps become and the more accurate our approximation becomes. Since the integral is the limit of a sum, we find that for any reversible cycle

$$\oint \frac{dQ}{T} = 0, \tag{25–7}$$

where the symbol $\oint$ indicates that the integral is taken around the cycle. Here dQ is the infinitesimal heat absorbed at the absolute temperature T.

It follows from Eq. 25–7 that *the value of* $\int dQ/T$ *along a path from a state 1 to a state 2 will be the same no matter what reversible path we choose in going from 1 to 2.* (See Problem 12.) Notice that although $\int dQ$ is *not* independent of path, $\int dQ/T$ *is* independent of path. Hence, we again have found a property of a system, like the internal energy, whose value depends only on the state of the system and not on how it got there from a previous state. This property we call the *entropy* of the system and we denote it by S. Then if S_2 is the entropy of state 2 and S_1 is the entropy of state 1,

$$S_2 - S_1 = \int_1^2 \frac{dQ}{T} \tag{25–8}$$

gives the difference in entropy of a system in going from state 1 to state 2 along a reversible path. For an infinitesimal segment of a reversible path,

$$dS = \frac{dQ}{T} \tag{25–9}$$

gives the infinitesimal change in entropy. We can now state the result of

Eq. 25–7 in words, namely, *the change in the entropy in a reversible cycle is zero.*

The interpretation of entropy as a measure of the capacity of a system for doing work is consistent with the result that the change in entropy is zero for a reversible cycle, for a system carried through such a cycle loses no capacity for work.

Just as in the case of potential energy, and internal energy, it is the *differences* in entropy that are significant rather than the actual values of the entropy. If a particular value of S is assigned to one state of a system, the values for all other equilibrium states is definitely determined. Common units for entropy are calories per degree or joules per degree.

Now let us apply the entropy concept to *irreversible processes.* Consider first the free expansion of an ideal gas. The gas initially has a volume V_1, pressure p_1, temperature T, and entropy S_1. Suppose that the gas expands freely to a volume V_2, where $V_2 > V_1$. Its pressure drops so that $p_2 < p_1$, but the temperature remains the same. Since the gas is in a different state, its entropy may be different and we can call this S_2. Recall that free expansion is an irreversible process, and that the system is isolated (no interaction with environment).

Let us now return the gas to its initial state by a *reversible* process of slow compression in which we keep the temperature constant at T by removing an amount of heat Q. This reversible process brings the gas back to a pressure p_1, volume V_1, temperature T, and entropy S_1 and involves an interaction of the system with its environment. In this process the entropy of the gas changed from S_2 to S_1 in a measurable way; we removed a quantity of heat Q at the temperature T from the gas so that the entropy of the gas decreased by an amount Q/T from S_2 to S_1. Hence, *the entropy of the gas after free expansion is greater than its entropy before free expansion.*

Notice carefully that we measured the entropy increase in an irreversible process in an isolated system by computing the entropy change involved in a reversible process that brought the substance back to its initial state by interaction with the environment. The entropy has a definite value for a definite equilibrium state and can only be measured by a reversible process bringing the system back to a reference state. *If free expansion had been a reversible process, the entropy change would have been zero,* for $dQ = 0$ in such a process. Hence, the increase in entropy in an irreversible process can be thought of as a measure of the system's loss of capacity for doing work.

Consider now a second example of an irreversible process, the heat transfer taking place between two bodies in contact. Let bodies 1 and 2 be insulated from the environment but in contact with one another. If $T_1 > T_2$, an amount of heat dQ will be transferred from body 1 to body 2 in a short interval of time. During this time the entropy change is $+dQ/T_2$ for body 2 and $-dQ/T_1$ for body 1 so that the net change in entropy of the system is

$$\frac{dQ}{T_2} - \frac{dQ}{T_1}.$$

Because $T_1 > T_2$ this change in entropy is positive, that is, the entropy of the system increases. Actually we must measure the entropy change by a reversible process, such as transferring heat from the colder body to the hotter one. Clearly this will require an expenditure of work, showing that the system lost some capacity for work in the irreversible heat transfer process. The result is the same as before: Associated with a loss of capacity for work in an irreversible process is an increase in entropy for the system.

It can be shown in general that when a *system interacts with its environment* in going from state 1 to state 2, its entropy change is given by

$$S_2 - S_1 = \int_1^2 \frac{dQ}{T} \qquad \text{(reversible process)} \qquad (25\text{--}10a)$$

and

$$S_2 - S_1 > \int_1^2 \frac{dQ}{T} \qquad \text{(irreversible process)}. \qquad (25\text{--}10b)$$

If the system is completely *isolated*, then $dQ = 0$, and

$$S_2 = S_1 \qquad \text{(reversible process)}, \qquad (25\text{--}11a)$$

$$S_2 > S_1 \qquad \text{(irreversible process)}. \qquad (25\text{--}11b)$$

Hence, for any transformation occurring in an isolated system, the entropy of the final state can never be less than that of the initial state. Only if the transformation is reversible will the system undergo no change in entropy. It should be clearly understood that Eq. 25–11 applies only to isolated systems. It is possible, with the aid of an external system, to reduce the entropy of a body. The entropy of both systems taken together, however, cannot decrease.

We have now arrived at a statement of the second law of thermodynamics which is quantitative for reversible processes (Eqs. 25–10a, 25–11a), but only qualitative for irreversible processes (Eqs. 25–10b, 25–11b). These equations can be summarized by the statement that *a natural process always takes place in such a direction as to cause an increase in the entropy of the system plus environment. In the case of an isolated system it is the entropy of the system that tends to increase.*

Since all natural processes are irreversible and therefore involve increases in entropy, we can now understand Clausius' statement that the second law of thermodynamics is equivalent to the statement that the entropy of the universe is increasing, and that the first law of thermodynamics is equivalent to the statement that the total energy of the universe is constant.

The entropy of a system at absolute zero is called the zero-point entropy. In terms of entropy the third law of thermodynamics can be stated as follows: *It is impossible by any procedure, no matter how idealized, to reduce the entropy of a system to its zero-point value in a finite number of operations.*

▶ **Example 3.** Compute the entropy change when 1 kg of ice at 0°C melts to water at 0°C, taking the latent heat of melting of ice to be 79.6 cal/gm.

The temperature remains constant at $T = 273°K$. Therefore,

$$S_{water} - S_{ice} = \int_0^Q \frac{dQ}{T} = \frac{1}{T} \int_0^Q dQ = \frac{Q}{T}.$$

But $$Q = 10^3 \text{ gm} \times 79.6 \text{ cal/gm} = 7.96 \times 10^4 \text{ cal}$$

or $$S_{water} - S_{ice} = \frac{7.96 \times 10^4}{273} \text{ cal/°K} = 292 \text{ cal/°K}$$

$$= 1222 \text{ joules/°K}.$$

In the process of melting, the ice takes heat from the surroundings which must be at a temperature above 0°C. The heat conduction example shows that the gain in entropy of the ice exceeds the loss in entropy of the surroundings, so that the process as a whole involves an increase in the entropy. To reverse the process, that is, to freeze water, would require that heat be conducted from the water to a body at a temperature below 0°C. For such a system (water + cold body) the total entropy would again increase, as shown in the heat conduction example.

Example 4. Calculate the entropy change that n moles of an ideal gas undergoes in a reversible isothermal expansion from a volume V_i to a volume V_f.

From the first law

$$dU = dQ - p\, dV.$$

But $dU = 0$, since U depends only on temperature for an ideal gas and the temperature is constant. Hence,

$$dQ = p\, dV$$

and $$dS = \frac{dQ}{T} = \frac{p\, dV}{T}.$$

But $$pV = nRT,$$

so that $$dS = nR \frac{dV}{V}$$

and $$S_f - S_i = \int_{V_i}^{V_f} nR \frac{dV}{V} = nR \ln \frac{V_f}{V_i}. \tag{25-12}$$

Since $V_f > V_i$, $S_f > S_i$ and the *entropy of the gas increases*.

In order to carry out this process we must have a reservoir at temperature T which is in contact with the system and supplies the heat to the gas. Hence, the *entropy of the reservoir decreases* by $dQ/T[= nR \ln (V_f/V_i)]$, so that in this process the entropy of system + environment does not change. This is characteristic of a reversible process. ◀

25-8 Entropy and Disorder

Freeman J. Dyson, in a popular article * "What Is Heat?," writes:

Heat is disordered energy. So with two words the nature of heat is explained. . . . .

Energy can exist without disorder. For example, a flying rifle bullet or an atom of U^{235} carries ordered energy. The motion of the bullet is the kind we call kinetic. When the bullet hits a steel plate and is stopped, the energy of its motion is transferred to random motions of the atoms in the bullet and the plate. This disordered energy makes itself felt in the form of heat. . . . The energy dwelling in the uranium atom is the kind we call potential; it consists of the electric forces which tend to push the constituent protons apart. When the atom fissions, the energy of motion of the

* *Scientific American*, September 1954, page 58.

flying fragments is converted by collisions into random motions of the electrons and other atoms nearby in the surrounding matter—that is to say, into heat. This conversion of potential energy into heat is the working principle of nuclear reactors.

These two examples illustrate the general principle that energy becomes heat as soon as it is disordered. It is conversely true that disorder can exist without energy, and that disorder becomes heat as soon as it is energized. The atoms of U^{235} and U^{238} in a piece of ordinary uranium are mixed in a random way, but this disorder carries no energy. . . .

In order to go further it is necessary to talk quantitatively. We must measure heat precisely in terms of numbers. . . . First it is clear that to specify heat we must use at least two numbers: one to measure the quantity of energy, the other to measure the quantity of disorder. The quantity of energy is measured in terms of a practical unit called the calorie. . . . The quantity of disorder is measured in terms of the mathematical concept called entropy. . . .

Let us now investigate the connection between entropy and disorder. Work, for example, is a macroscopic concept. We describe work by changes in macroscopic coordinates, such as pressure and volume. Work involves orderly motion. The disordered motions of molecules do not constitute work. But when work is dissipated into internal energy, as in the case of friction, the disorderly motion of molecules is increased. Such a process involves an increase in disorder. The natural diffusion of one gas through another when they are mixed involves an increase in disorder—the disorder is greater after diffusion than it was when the gases were separated. *In all cases observed in nature there is a tendency for processes to proceed toward a state of greater disorder.* We have already seen that natural processes tend toward a state of greater entropy so that we expect a connection between the thermodynamic concept of entropy and the statistical concept of disorder.

It is shown by statistical mechanics that the connection is given by the relation

$$S = k \ln w. \tag{25-13}$$

Here, k is Boltzmann's constant, S is the entropy of the system, and w is the probability that the system will exist in the state it is in relative to all the possible states it could be in. Hence, Eq. 25–13 connects a thermodynamic or macroscopic quantity, the entropy, with a statistical or microscopic quantity, the probability.

Let us illustrate by computing the change in entropy of an ideal gas in an isothermal expansion. Here the number of molecules and the temperature do not change, but the volume does. The probability that a given molecule may be found in a region having a volume V is proportional to V; that is, the greater V is, the greater the chance of finding it in V. Hence, the probability of finding a *single* molecule in V is

$$w_1 = cV$$

where c is a constant. The probability of finding N molecules simultaneously in the volume V is the N-fold product of w_1. That is, the probability of a state consisting of N molecules in a volume V is

$$w = w_1{}^N = (cV)^N. \tag{25-14}$$

For example, if the probability of finding a single molecule in V is $\frac{1}{2}$ (that is, there is a 50% chance of it being in V and a 50% chance of it being outside V), the probability of finding two molecules in V is $\frac{1}{4}$. There are four equally probable states here (both in; both out; one in, the other out; one out, the other in), and only one of them is a state with both molecules in V.

If we now combine Eq. 25–13 and Eq. 25–14 we obtain

$$S = kN \, (\ln c + \ln V).$$

Hence, the difference in entropy between a state of volume V_f and a state of volume V_i (temperature and number of molecules remaining constant) is

$$S_f - S_i = kN \, (\ln c + \ln V_f) - kN \, (\ln c + \ln V_i)$$

$$= kN \ln \frac{V_f}{V_i} = \frac{RN}{N_0} \ln \frac{V_f}{V_i} = nR \ln \frac{V_f}{V_i}$$

in exact agreement with the strictly thermodynamic result of Eq. 25–12.

By means of the statistical definition of entropy, Eq. 25–13, we can give meaning to the entropy of a system in a nonequilibrium state. A nonequilibrium state has a definite entropy because it has a definite degree of disorder. Therefore, *the second law can be put on a statistical basis*, for the direction in which natural processes take place (toward higher entropy) is determined by the laws of probability (toward a more probable state). From this point of view a violation of the second law, strictly speaking, is not an impossibility. If we waited long enough, for example, we might find the water in a pond suddenly freezing on a hot summer day. Such an occurrence is possible, but the probability of it happening, when computed, turns out to be incredibly small; for this to happen once would take on the average a time of the order of 10^{10} times the age of the universe. Hence, the second law of thermodynamics shows us the most probable course of events, not the only possible ones. But its area of application is so broad and the chance of nature's contradicting it is so small that it occupies the distinction of being one of the most useful and most general laws in all science.

QUESTIONS

1. Can a given amount of mechanical energy be converted completely into heat energy? If so, give an example.

2. Can you suggest a reversible process whereby heat can be added to a system? Would adding heat by means of a Bunsen burner be a reversible process?

3. A block returns to its initial position after dissipating mechanical energy to heat through friction. Is this process reversible thermodynamically?

4. Give some examples of irreversible processes in nature.

5. Couldn't we just as well define the efficiency of an engine as $e = W/Q_2$ rather than as $e = W/Q_1$? Why don't we?

6. What factors reduce the efficiency of a heat engine from its ideal value?

7. In order to increase the efficiency of a Carnot engine most effectively, would you increase T_1, keeping T_2 constant, or would you decrease T_2, keeping T_1 constant?

8. Can a kitchen be cooled by leaving the door of an electric refrigerator open? Explain.

9. Is there a change in entropy in purely mechanical motions?

10. Two samples of a gas initially at the same temperature and pressure are compressed from a volume V to a volume $(V/2)$, one isothermally, the other adiabatically. In which sample is the final pressure greater? Does the entropy of the gas change in either process?

11. Suppose we had chosen to represent the state of a system by its entropy and its absolute temperature rather than by its pressure and volume. What would a Carnot cycle look like on a T-S diagram?

12. Show that the total entropy increases when work is converted into heat by friction between sliding surfaces. Describe the increase in disorder.

13. Comment on the statement "A heat engine converts disordered mechanical motion into organized mechanical motion."

14. Explain the statement "Cosmic rays continually *decrease the entropy of the earth* on which they fall." Does this contradict the second law of thermodynamics?

PROBLEMS

1. An ideal gas heat engine operates in a Carnot cycle between 227 and 127°C. It absorbs 6.0×10^4 cal at the higher temperature. How much work per cycle is this engine capable of performing?

2. In a two-stage heat engine a quantity of heat Q_1 is absorbed at a temperature T_1, work W_1 is done, and a quantity of heat Q_2 is expelled at a lower temperature T_2 by the first stage. The second stage absorbs the heat expelled by the first, does work W_2, and expels a quantity of heat Q_3 at a lower temperature T_3. Prove that the efficiency of the combination engine is $(T_1 - T_3)/T_1$.

3. A combination mercury-steam turbine takes saturated mercury vapor from a boiler at 876°F and exhausts it to heat a steam boiler at 460°F. The steam turbine receives steam at this temperature and exhausts it to a condenser at 100°F. What is the maximum efficiency of the combination?

4. (a) Plot an exact Carnot cycle on a p to V diagram for 1 mole of an ideal gas. Let point a correspond to $p = 1.0$ atm, $T = 300°K$, and let b correspond to $p = 0.5$ atm, $T = 300°K$; take the low temperature reservoir to be at $100°K$. Let $\gamma = 1.5$. (b) Compute graphically the work done in this cycle.

5. In a Carnot cycle, the isothermal expansion of the gas takes place at $400°K$ and the isothermal compression at $300°K$. During the expansion 500 cal of heat energy are transferred to the gas. Determine (a) the work performed by the gas during the isothermal expansion, (b) the heat rejected from the gas during the isothermal compression, (c) the work done on the gas during the isothermal compression.

6. (a) If the Carnot cycle is run backward, we have an ideal refrigerator. A quantity of heat Q_2 is taken in at the lower temperature T_2 and a quantity of heat Q_1 is given out at the higher temperature T_1. The difference is the work W that must be supplied to run the refrigerator. Show that

$$W = Q_2 \frac{T_1 - T_2}{T_2}.$$

(b) The *coefficient of performance* K of a refrigerator is defined as the ratio of the heat extracted from the cold source to the work needed to run the cycle. Show that ideally

$$K = \frac{T_2}{T_1 - T_2}.$$

In actual refrigerators K has a value of 5 or 6.

7. In a mechanical refrigerator the low-temperature coils are at a temperature of $-13°C$, and the compressed gas in the condenser has a temperature of $27°C$. What is the theoretical coefficient of performance?

8. How much work must be done to transfer 1 joule of heat from a reservoir at 7°C to one at 27°C by means of a refrigerator using a Carnot cycle? From one at $-73°C$ to one at 27°C? From one at $-173°C$ to one at 27°C? From one at $-223°C$ to one at 27°C?

9. How is the efficiency of a reversible heat engine related to the coefficient of performance of the reversible refrigerator obtained by running the engine backward?

10. In a heat pump, heat Q_2 is extracted from the outside atmosphere at T_2 and a larger quantity of heat Q_1 is delivered to the inside of the house at T_1, with the performance of work W. (a) Draw a schematic diagram of a heat pump. (b) How does it differ in principle from a refrigerator? In practical use? (c) How are Q_1, Q_2, and W related to one another? (d) Can a heat pump be reversed for use in summer? Explain. (e) What advantages does such a pump have over other heating devices?

11. In a heat pump, heat from the outdoors at $-5°C$ is transferred to a room at $17°C$, energy being supplied by an electric motor. How many joules of heat will be delivered to the room for each joule of electric energy consumed, ideally?

12. Show that no matter what reversible process is used to go from state 1 to state 2, the difference in entropy $S_2 - S_1$ has the same definite value. (Start with Eq. 25-7.)

13. Show that when a reversible but noncyclic process is performed, the total entropy remains unchanged. (Recall the criteria for reversibility and consider both system and environment.)

14. (a) Show that when a substance of mass m having a constant specific heat c is heated from T_1 to T_2 the entropy change is

$$S_2 - S_1 = mc \ln \frac{T_2}{T_1}.$$

(b) Does the entropy of the substance decrease on cooling? If so, does the total entropy decrease in such a process? Explain.

15. In a specific heat experiment 100 gm of lead [$c_p = 0.0345$ cal/(gm)(C°)] at $100°C$ is mixed with 200 gm of water at $20°C$. Find the difference in entropy of the system at the end from its value before mixing.

16. Heat can be removed from water at $0°C$ and atmospheric pressure without causing the water to freeze, if done with little disturbance of the water. Suppose the water is cooled to $-5.0°C$ before ice begins to form. What is the change in entropy per unit mass occurring during the sudden freezing that then takes place?

17. A brass rod is in contact thermally with a heat reservoir at $127°C$ at one end and a heat reservoir at $27°C$ at the other end. Compute the total change in the entropy arising from the process of conduction of 1200 cal of heat through the rod. Does the entropy of the rod change in the process?

18. A mole of a monatomic ideal gas is taken from an initial state of pressure p and volume V to a final state of pressure $2p$ and volume $2V$ by two different processes. (I) It expands isothermally until its volume is doubled, and then its pressure is increased at constant volume to the final state. (II) It is compressed isothermally until its pressure is doubled, and then its volume is increased at constant pressure to the final state.

Show the path of each process on a p-V diagram. For each process calculate (a) the heat absorbed by the gas in each part of the process; (b) the work done on the gas in each part of the process; (c) the change in internal energy of the gas $U_f - U_i$; (d) the change in entropy of the gas $S_f - S_i$.

PART II

Physics

For Students of Science
and Engineering

Charge and Matter

CHAPTER 26

26–1 Electromagnetism—A Preview

The science of electricity has its roots in the observation, known to Thales of Miletus in 600 B.C., that a rubbed piece of amber will attract bits of straw. The study of magnetism goes back to the observation that naturally occurring "stones" (that is, magnetite) will attract iron. These two sciences developed quite separately until 1820, when Hans Christian Oersted (1777–1851) observed a connection between them, namely, that an *electric* current in a wire can affect a *magnetic* compass needle (Section 33–1).

The new science of electromagnetism was developed further by many workers, of whom one of the most important was Michael Faraday (1791–1867). It fell to James Clerk Maxwell (1831–1879) to put the laws of electromagnetism in the form in which we know them today. These laws, often called *Maxwell's equations*, are displayed in Table 38–3, which the student may want to examine at this time. These laws play the same role in electromagnetism that Newton's laws of motion and of gravitation do in mechanics.

Although Maxwell's synthesis of electromagnetism rests heavily on the work of his predecessors, his own contribution is central and vital. Maxwell deduced that light is electromagnetic in nature and that its speed can be found by making purely electric and magnetic measurements. Thus the science of optics was intimately connected with those of electricity and of magnetism. The scope of Maxwell's equations is remarkable, including as it does the fundamental principles of all large-scale electromagnetic and optical devices such as motors, cyclotrons, electronic computers, radio, television, microwave radar, microscopes, and telescopes.

The development of classical electromagnetism did not end with Maxwell. The English physicist Oliver Heaviside (1850–1925) and especially the Dutch physicist H. A. Lorentz (1853–1928) contributed substantially to the clarification of Maxwell's theory. Heinrich Hertz (1857–1894) * took a great step forward when, more than twenty years after Maxwell set up his theory, he produced in the laboratory electromagnetic "Maxwellian waves" of a kind that we would now call short radio waves. It remained for Marconi and others to exploit this practical application of the electromagnetic waves of Maxwell and Hertz.

Present interest in electromagnetism takes two forms. At the level of engineering applications Maxwell's equations are used constantly and universally in the solution of a wide variety of practical problems. At the level of the foundations of the theory there is a continuing effort to extend its scope in such a way that electromagnetism is revealed as a special case of a more general theory. Such a theory would also include (say) the theories of gravitation and of quantum physics. This grand synthesis has not yet been achieved.

26–2 Electric Charge

The rest of this chapter deals with electric charge and its relationship to matter. We can show that there are *two kinds* of charge by rubbing a glass rod with silk and hanging it from a long silk thread as in Fig. 26–1. If a second glass rod is rubbed with silk and held near the rubbed end of the first rod, the rods will repel each other. On the other hand, a hard-rubber rod rubbed with fur will *attract* the glass rod. Two hard-rubber rods rubbed with fur will repel each other. We explain these facts by saying that rubbing a rod gives it an *electric charge* and that the charges on the two rods exert forces on each other. Clearly the charges on the glass and on the hard rubber must be different in nature.

Benjamin Franklin (1706–1790), who, among his other achievements, was the first American physicist, named the kind of electricity that appears on the glass *positive* and the kind that appears on the hard rubber *negative;* these names have remained to this day. We can sum up these experiments by saying that *like charges repel and unlike charges attract.*

Electric effects are not limited to glass rubbed with silk or to hard rubber rubbed with fur. Any substance rubbed with any other under suitable conditions will become charged to some extent; by comparing the unknown charge with a charged glass rod or a charged hard-rubber rod, it can be labeled as either positive or negative.

The modern view of bulk matter is that, in its normal or neutral state, it contains equal amounts of positive and negative electricity. If two bodies like glass and silk are rubbed together, a small amount of charge is transferred from one to the other, upsetting the electric neutrality of each. In this case the glass would become positive, the silk negative.

---

* "Heinrich Hertz," by P. and E. Morrison, *Scientific American*, December 1957.

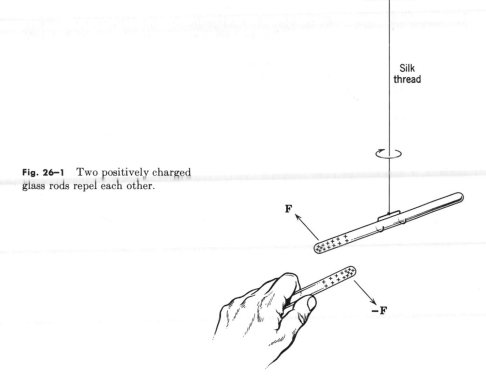

Fig. 26–1 Two positively charged
glass rods repel each other.

Silk
thread

F

−F

26–3 Conductors and Insulators

A metal rod held in the hand and rubbed with fur will not seem to develop
a charge. It is possible to charge such a rod, however, if it is furnished with
a glass or hard-rubber handle and if the metal is not touched with the hands
while rubbing it. The explanation is that metals, the human body, and the
earth are *conductors* of electricity and that glass, hard rubber, plastics, etc.,
are *insulators* (also called *dielectrics*).

In conductors electric charges are free to move through the material,
whereas in insulators they are not. Although there are no perfect insulators,
the insulating ability of fused quartz is about 10^{25} times as great as that of
copper, so that for many practical purposes some materials behave as if they
were perfect insulators.

In metals a fairly subtle experiment called the *Hall effect* (see Section 33–5)
shows that only negative charge is free to move. Positive charge is as im-
mobile as it is in glass or in any other dielectric. The actual charge carriers in
metals are the *free electrons*. When isolated atoms are combined to form a
metallic solid, the outer electrons of the atom do not remain attached to
individual atoms but become free to move throughout the volume of the
solid. For some conductors, such as electrolytes, both positive and negative
charges can move.

A class of materials called *semiconductors* is intermediate between conductors and insulators in its ability to conduct electricity. Among the elements, silicon and germanium are well-known examples. In semiconductors the electrical conductivity can often be greatly increased by adding very small amounts of other elements; traces of arsenic or boron are often added to silicon for this purpose. Semiconductors have many practical applications, among which is their use in the construction of transistors. The mode of action of semiconductors cannot be described adequately without some understanding of the basic principles of quantum physics.

26–4　Coulomb's Law

Charles Augustin de Coulomb (1736–1806) in 1785 first measured electrical attractions and repulsions quantitatively and deduced the law that governs them. His apparatus, shown in Fig. 26–2, resembles the hanging rod of Fig. 26–1, except that the charges in Fig. 26–2 are confined to small spheres a and b.

If a and b are charged, the electric force on a will tend to twist the suspension fiber. Coulomb canceled out this twisting effect by turning the suspension head through the angle θ needed to keep the two charges at the particular distance apart in which he was interested. The angle θ is then a relative measure of the electric force acting on charge a. The device of Fig. 26–2 is called a *torsion balance;* a similar arrangement was used later by Cavendish to measure gravitational attractions (Section 16–3).

Coulomb's first experimental results can be represented by

$$F \propto \frac{1}{r^2}.$$

F is the magnitude of the force that acts on each of the two charges a and b; r is their distance apart. These forces, as Newton's third law requires, act along the line joining the charges but point in opposite directions. Note that the magnitude of the force on each charge is the same, even though the charges may be different.

Coulomb also studied how the electrical force varied with the relative size of the charges on the spheres of his torsion balance. For example, if we touch a charged conducting sphere to an exactly similar but uncharged conducting sphere, the original charge must divide equally between the spheres. By such techniques Coulomb extended the inverse square relationship to

$$F \propto \frac{q_1 q_2}{r^2}, \tag{26–1}$$

where q_1 and q_2 are relative measures of the charges on spheres a and b. Equation 26–1, which is called *Coulomb's law*, holds only for charged objects whose sizes are much smaller than the distance between them. We often say that it holds only for *point charges*.

Coulomb's law resembles the inverse square law of gravitation which was already more than 100 years old at the time of Coulomb's experiments; q plays the role of m in that law. In gravity, however, the forces are always

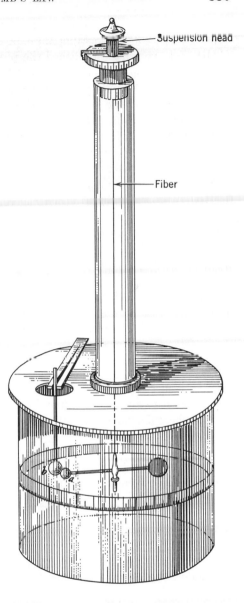

Suspension head

Fiber

Fig. 26–2 Coulomb's torsion balance from his 1785 memoir to the French Academy of Sciences.

attractive; this corresponds to the fact that there are two kinds of electricity but (apparently) only one kind of mass.

Our belief in Coulomb's law does not rest quantitatively on Coulomb's experiments. Torsion balance measurements are difficult to make to an accuracy of better than a few per cent. Such measurements could not, for example, convince us that the exponent in Eq. 26–1 is exactly 2 and not, say, 2.01. In Section 28–5 we show that Coulomb's law can also be deduced from an indirect experiment which shows that the exponent in Eq. 26–1 lies between the limits of approximately 2.000000002 and 1.999999998. Small wonder that we usually assume the exponent to be exactly 2.

Although we have established the physical concept of electric charge, we have not yet defined a unit in which it may be measured. It is possible to do so operationally by putting equal charges q on the spheres of a torsion balance and by measuring the magnitude F of the force that acts on each when the charges are a measured distance r apart. One could then define q to have a unit value if a unit force acts on each charge when the charges are separated by a unit distance and one can give a name to the unit of charge so defined.*

For practical reasons having to do with the accuracy of measurements, the unit of charge in the mks system is not defined using a torsion balance but is derived from the unit of electric current. If the ends of a long wire are connected to the terminals of a battery, it is common knowledge that an *electric current* i is set up in the wire. We visualize this current as a flow of _charge. The mks unit of current is the *ampere* (abbr. *amp*). In Section 34–4 we describe the operational procedures in terms of which the ampere is defined.

The mks unit of charge is the *coulomb* (abbr. *coul*). *A coulomb is defined as the amount of charge that flows through a given cross section of a wire in 1 second if there is a steady current of 1 ampere in the wire.* In symbols

$$q = it, \tag{26-2}$$

where q is in coulombs if i is in amperes and t is in seconds. Thus, if a wire is connected to an insulated metal sphere, a charge of 10^{-6} coul can be put on the sphere if a current of 1.0 amp exists in the wire for 10^{-6} sec.

▶ **Example 1.** A copper penny has a mass of 3.1 gm. Being electrically neutral, it contains equal amounts of positive and negative electricity. What is the magnitude q of these charges? A copper atom has a positive charge of 4.6×10^{-18} coul and a negative charge of equal magnitude.

The number N of copper atoms in a penny is found from the ratio

$$\frac{N}{N_0} = \frac{m}{M},$$

where N_0 is Avogadro's number, m the mass of the coin, and M the molecular weight of copper. This yields, solving for N,

$$N = \frac{(6.0 \times 10^{23} \text{ atoms/mole})(3.1 \text{ gm})}{64 \text{ gm/mole}} = 2.9 \times 10^{22} \text{ atoms}.$$

The charge q is

$$q = (4.6 \times 10^{-18} \text{ coul/atom})(2.9 \times 10^{22} \text{ atoms}) = 1.3 \times 10^5 \text{ coul}.$$

In a 100-watt, 110-volt light bulb the current is 0.91 amp. The student should verify that it would take 40 hr for a charge of this amount to pass through this bulb. ◀

---

* This scheme is the basis for the definition of the unit of charge called the *statcoulomb*. However, in this book we do not use this unit or the systems of units of which it is a part.

Equation 26–1 can be written as an equality by inserting a constant of proportionality. Instead of writing this simply as, say, k, it is usually written in a more complex way as $1/4\pi\epsilon_0$ or

$$F = \frac{1}{4\pi\epsilon_0}\frac{q_1 q_2}{r^2}. \qquad (26\text{–}3)$$

Certain equations that are derived from Eq. 26–3, but are used more often than it is, will be simpler in form if we do this.

In the mks system we can measure q_1, q_2, r, and F in Eq. 26–3 in ways that do not depend on Coulomb's law. Numbers with units can be assigned to them. There is no choice about the so-called *permittivity constant* ϵ_0; it must have that value which makes the right-hand side of Eq. 26–3 equal to the left-hand side. This (measured) value turns out to be *

$$\epsilon_0 = 8.85415 \times 10^{-12}\ \text{coul}^2/\text{nt-m}^2.$$

In this book the value $8.9 \times 10^{-12}\ \text{coul}^2/\text{nt-m}^2$ will be accurate enough for all problems. For direct application of Coulomb's law or in any problem in which the quantity $1/4\pi\epsilon_0$ occurs we may use, with sufficient accuracy for this book,

$$1/4\pi\epsilon_0 = 9.0 \times 10^9\ \text{nt-m}^2/\text{coul}^2.$$

▶ **Example 2.** Let the total positive and the total negative charges in a copper penny be separated to a distance such that their force of attraction is 1.0 lb ($= 4.5$ nt). How far apart must they be?

We have (Eq. 26–3)

$$F = \frac{1}{4\pi\epsilon_0}\frac{q_1 q_2}{r^2}.$$

Putting $q_1 q_2 = q^2$ (see Example 1) and solving for r yields

$$r = q\sqrt{\frac{1/4\pi\epsilon_0}{F}} = 1.3 \times 10^5\ \text{coul}\ \sqrt{\frac{9.0 \times 10^9\ \text{nt-m}^2/\text{coul}^2}{4.5\ \text{nt}}}$$

$$= 5.8 \times 10^9\ \text{meters} = 3.6 \times 10^6\ \text{miles}.$$

This suggests that it is not possible to upset the electrical neutrality of gross objects by any very large amount. What would be the force between the two charges if they were placed 1.0 meter apart? ◀

If more than two charges are present, Eq. 26–3 holds for every pair of charges. Let the charges be q_1, q_2, and q_3, etc.; we calculate the force exerted on any one (say q_1) by all the others from the vector equation

$$\mathbf{F}_1 = \mathbf{F}_{12} + \mathbf{F}_{13} + \mathbf{F}_{14} + \cdots, \qquad (26\text{–}4)$$

where $\mathbf{F}_{12}$, for example, is the force exerted on q_1 by q_2.

---

* For practical reasons this value is not actually measured by direct application of Eq. 26–3 but in an equivalent although more circuitous way that is described in Section 30–2.

▶ **Example 3.** Figure 26–3 shows three charges q_1, q_2, and q_3. What force acts on q_1? Assume that $q_1 = -1.0 \times 10^{-6}$ coul, $q_2 = +3.0 \times 10^{-6}$ coul, $q_3 = -2.0 \times 10^{-6}$ coul, $r_{12} = 15$ cm, $r_{13} = 10$ cm, and $\theta = 30°$.

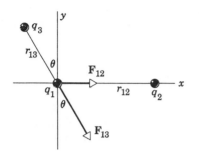

Fig. 263 Example 3. Showing the forces exerted on q_1 by q_2 and q_3.

From Eq. 26–3, ignoring the signs of the charges, since we are interested only in the magnitudes of the forces,

$$F_{12} = \frac{1}{4\pi\epsilon_0} \frac{q_1 q_2}{r_{12}^2}$$

$$= \frac{(9.0 \times 10^9 \text{ nt-m}^2/\text{coul}^2)(1.0 \times 10^{-6} \text{ coul})(3.0 \times 10^{-6} \text{ coul})}{(1.5 \times 10^{-1} \text{ meter})^2}$$

$$= 1.2 \text{ nt}$$

and $$F_{13} = \frac{(9.0 \times 10^9 \text{ nt-m}^2/\text{coul}^2)(1.0 \times 10^{-6} \text{ coul})(2.0 \times 10^{-6} \text{ coul})}{(1.0 \times 10^{-1} \text{ meter})^2}$$

$$= 1.8 \text{ nt.}$$

The directions of $\mathbf{F}_{12}$ and $\mathbf{F}_{13}$ are as shown in the figure.

The components of the resultant force $\mathbf{F}_1$ acting on q_1 (see Eq. 26–4) are

$$F_{1x} = F_{12x} + F_{13x} = F_{12} + F_{13} \sin\theta$$

$$= 1.2 \text{ nt} + (1.8 \text{ nt})(\sin 30°) = 2.1 \text{ nt}$$

and $$F_{1y} = F_{12y} + F_{13y} = 0 - F_{13} \cos\theta$$

$$= -(1.8 \text{ nt})(\cos 30°) = -1.6 \text{ nt.}$$

The student should find the magnitude of $\mathbf{F}_1$ and the angle it makes with the x-axis.
◀

26–5 Charge Is Quantized

In Franklin's day electric charge was thought of as a continuous fluid, an idea that was useful for many purposes. The atomic theory of matter, however, has shown that fluids themselves, such as water and air, are not continuous but are made up of atoms. Experiment shows that the "electric fluid" is not continuous either but that it is made up of integral multiples of a certain minimum electric charge. This fundamental charge, to which we give the symbol e, has the magnitude 1.60206×10^{-19} coul. Any physically existing charge q, no matter what its origin, can be written as ne where n is a positive or a negative integer.

When a physical property such as charge exists in discrete "packets" rather than in continuous amounts, the property is said to be *quantized*. Quantization is basic to modern physics. The existence of atoms and of particles like the electron and the proton indicates that *mass* is quantized also. Later the student will learn that several other properties prove to be quantized when suitably examined on the atomic scale; among them are energy and angular momentum.

The *quantum of charge e* is so small that the "graininess" of electricity does not show up in large-scale experiments, just as we do not realize that the air we breathe is made up of atoms. In an ordinary 110-volt, 100-watt light bulb, for example, 6×10^{18} elementary charges enter and leave the filament every second.

The classical theory of electromagnetism says nothing about the quantization of charge. In the same sense, Newton's laws of motion say nothing about the quantization of mass, that is, nothing about the existence of electrons, protons, atoms, etc. Both of these great theories are incomplete in that they do not correctly describe the behavior of charge and matter on the atomic scale. The classical theory of electromagnetism, for example, describes correctly what happens when a bar magnet is thrust through a closed copper loop; it fails, however, if we wish to explain the magnetism of the bar in terms of the atoms that make it up. The more detailed theories of quantum physics are needed for this and similar problems.

26–6   Charge and Matter

Matter as we ordinarily experience it can be regarded as composed of three kinds of elementary particles, the proton, the neutron, and the electron. Table 26–1 shows their masses and charges. Note that the masses of the neutron and the proton are approximately equal but that the electron is lighter by a factor of about 1840.

Atoms are made up of a dense, positively charged *nucleus*, surrounded by a

Table 26–1

PROPERTIES OF THE PROTON, THE NEUTRON, AND THE ELECTRON

Particle	Symbol	Charge	Mass
Proton	p	$+e$	1.67239×10^{-27} kg
Neutron	n	0	1.67470×10^{-27} kg
Electron	e^-	$-e$	9.1083×10^{-31} kg

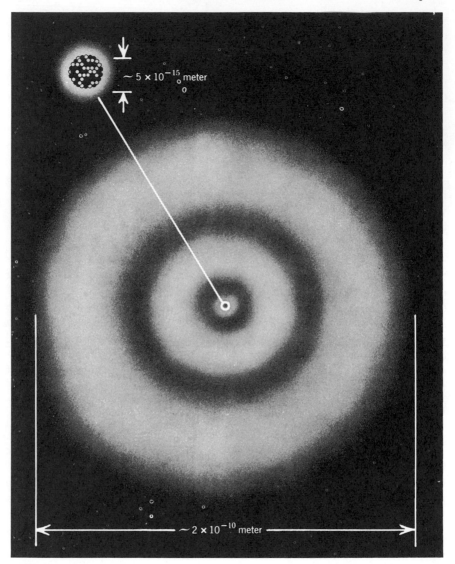

Fig. 26–4   An atom, suggesting the electron cloud and, above, an enlarged view of the nucleus.

cloud of electrons; see Fig. 26–4.   The nucleus varies in radius from about 1×10^{-15} meter for hydrogen to about 7×10^{-15} meter for the heaviest atoms.   The outer diameter of the electron cloud, that is, the diameter of the the atom, lies in the range $1\text{–}3 \times 10^{-10}$ meter, about 10^4 times larger than the nuclear diameter.

▶ **Example 4.**   The distance r between the electron and the proton in the hydrogen atom is about 5.3×10^{-11} meter.   What are the magnitudes of (a) the electrical force and (b) the gravitational force between these two particles?

From Coulomb's law,

$$F_o = \frac{1}{4\pi\epsilon_0} \frac{q_1 q_2}{r^2}$$

$$= \frac{(9.0 \times 10^9 \text{ nt-m}^2/\text{coul}^2)(1.6 \times 10^{-19} \text{ coul})^2}{(5.3 \times 10^{-11} \text{ meter})^2}$$

$$= 8.1 \times 10^{-8} \text{ nt.}$$

The gravitational force is given by Eq. 16–1, or

$$F_g = G \frac{m_1 m_2}{r^2}$$

$$= \frac{(6.7 \times 10^{-11} \text{ nt-m}^2/\text{kg}^2)(9.1 \times 10^{-31} \text{ kg})(1.7 \times 10^{-27} \text{ kg})}{(5.3 \times 10^{-11} \text{ meter})^2}$$

$$= 3.7 \times 10^{-47} \text{ nt.}$$

Thus the electrical force is about 10^{39} times stronger than the gravitational force. ◄

The significance of Coulomb's law goes far beyond the description of the forces acting between charged balls or rods. This law, when incorporated into the structure of quantum physics, correctly describes (a) the electric forces that bind the electrons of an atom to its nucleus, (b) the forces that bind atoms together to form molecules, and (c) the forces that bind atoms or molecules together to form solids or liquids. Thus most of the forces of our daily experience that are not gravitational in nature are electrical. A force transmitted by a steel cable is basically an electrical force because, if we pass an imaginary plane through the cable at right angles to it, it is only the attractive electrical interatomic forces acting between atoms on opposite sides of the plane that keep the cable from parting. We ourselves are an assembly of nuclei and electrons bound together in a stable configuration by Coulomb forces.

In the atomic *nucleus* we encounter a new force which is neither gravitational nor electrical in nature. This strong attractive force, which binds together the protons and neutrons that make up the nucleus, is called simply *the nuclear force*. If this force were not present, the nucleus would fly apart at once because of the strong Coulomb repulsion force that acts between its protons. The nature of the nuclear force is only partially understood today and forms the central problem of present-day researches in nuclear physics.

► **Example 5.**   What repulsive Coulomb force exists between two protons in a nucleus of iron? Assume a separation of 4.0×10^{-15} meter.

From Coulomb's law,

$$F = \frac{1}{4\pi\epsilon_0} \frac{q_1 q_2}{r^2}$$

$$= \frac{(9.0 \times 10^9 \text{ nt-m}^2/\text{coul}^2)(1.6 \times 10^{-19} \text{ coul})^2}{(4.0 \times 10^{-15} \text{ meter})^2}$$

$$= 14 \text{ nt.}$$

This enormous repulsive force must be more than compensated for by the strong attractive nuclear forces. This example, combined with Example 4, shows that nuclear binding forces are much stronger than atomic binding forces. Atomic binding forces are, in turn, much stronger than gravitational forces for the same particles separated by the same distance.   ◄

The repulsive Coulomb forces acting between the protons in a nucleus make the nucleus less stable than it otherwise would be. The spontaneous emission of alpha particles from heavy nuclei and the phenomenon of nuclear fission are evidences of this instability.

The fact that heavy nuclei contain significantly more neutrons than protons is still another effect of the Coulomb forces. Consider Fig. 26–5 in which a particular atomic species is represented by a circle, the coordinates being Z, the number of protons in the nucleus (that is, the *atomic number*), and N, the number of neutrons in the nucleus (that is, the *neutron number*). Stable nuclei are represented by filled circles and radioactive nuclei, that is, nuclei that disintegrate spontaneously, emitting electrons or α-particles, by open circles. Note that all elements (iron, for example, for which $Z = 26$; see arrow) exist in a number of different forms, called *isotopes*.

Figure 26–5 shows that light nuclei, for which the Coulomb forces are relatively unimportant,* lie on or close to the line labeled "$N = Z$" and thus have about equal numbers of neutrons and protons. The heavier nuclei have a pronounced neutron excess, U^{238} having 92 protons and $238 - 92$ or 146 neutrons.† In the absence of Coulomb forces we would assume, extending the $N = Z$ rule, that the most stable nucleus with 238 particles would have 119 protons and 119 neutrons. However, such a nucleus, if assembled, would fly apart at once because of Coulomb repulsion. Relative stability is found only if 27 of the protons are replaced by neutrons, thus diluting the total Coulomb repulsion. Even in U^{238} Coulomb repulsion is still very important because (a) this nucleus is radioactive and emits α-particles, and (b) it may break up into two large fragments (*fission*) if it absorbs a neutron; both processes result in separation of the nuclear charge and are Coulomb repulsion effects. Figure 26–5 shows that *all* nuclei with $Z > 83$ are unstable.

We have pointed out that matter, as we ordinarily experience it, is made up of electrons, neutrons, and protons. Nature exhibits much more variety than this, however. No fewer than 24 distinct elementary particles are now known, most of them having been discovered since 1940, either in the penetrating cosmic rays that come to us from beyond our atmosphere or in the reaction products of giant cyclotron-like devices.

Appendix F, which lists some properties of these particles, shows that, like the more familiar particles of Table 26–1, their charges are quantized, the quantum of charge again being e. An understanding of the nature of these particles and of their relationships to each other is perhaps the most significant research goal of modern physics.

---

* Coulomb forces are important in relation to the strong nuclear attractive forces only for large nuclei, because Coulomb repulsion occurs between *every pair* of protons in the nucleus but the attractive nuclear force does not. In U^{238}, for example, every proton exerts a force of repulsion on each of the other 91 protons. However, each proton (and neutron) exerts a nuclear attraction on only a small number of other neutrons and protons that happen to be near it. As we proceed to larger nuclei, the amount of energy associated with the repulsive Coulomb forces increases much faster than that associated with the attractive nuclear forces.

† The superscript in this notation is the *mass number A* ($= N + Z$). This is the total number of particles in the nucleus.

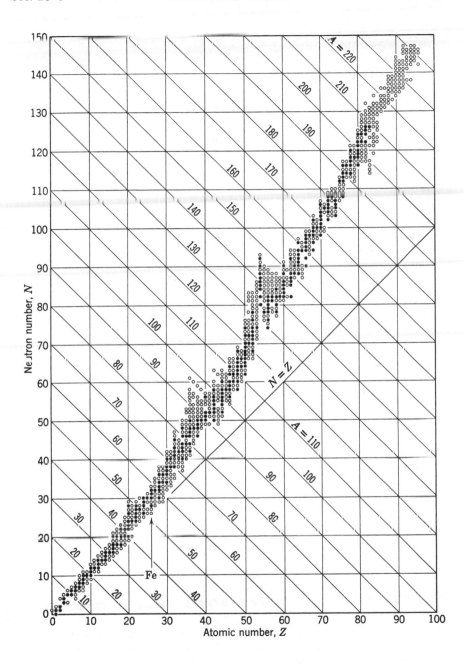

Fig. 26–5 The filled circles represent stable nuclei, the open ones radioactive nuclei. This figure does not show the more recently discovered radioactive nuclei, which appear throughout the chart, extending up to $Z = 103$.

26–7   Charge Is Conserved

When a glass rod is rubbed with silk, a positive charge appears on the rod. Measurement shows that a negative charge of equal magnitude appears on the silk. This suggests that rubbing does not create charge but merely transfers it from one object to another, disturbing slightly the electrical neutrality of each. This hypothesis of the *conservation of charge* has stood up under close experimental scrutiny both for large-scale events and at the atomic and nuclear level; no exceptions have ever been found.

An interesting example of charge conservation comes about when an electron (charge $= -e$) and a positron (charge $= +e$) are brought close to each other. The two particles may simply disappear, converting all their mass into energy according to the well-known $E = mc^2$ relationship; this *annihilation* process was described in Section 8–9. The energy appears in the form of two oppositely directed *gamma rays*, which are similar in character to X-rays. The net charge is zero both before and after the event so that charge is conserved. Mass is *not* conserved, being turned completely into energy.

Another example of charge conservation is found in radioactive decay, of which the following process is typical:

$$U^{238} \rightarrow Th^{234} + He^4. \tag{26-5}$$

The radioactive "parent" nucleus, U^{238}, contains 92 protons (that is, its atomic number $Z = 92$). It disintegrates spontaneously by emitting an α-particle (He^4; $Z = 2$) transmuting itself into the nucleus Th^{234}, with $Z = 90$. Thus the amount of charge present before disintegration ($+92e$) is the same as that present after the disintegration.

A final example of charge conservation is found in nuclear reactions, of which the bombardment of Ca^{44} with cyclotron-accelerated protons is typical. In a particular collision a neutron may emerge from the nucleus, leaving Sc^{44} as a "residual" nucleus:

$$Ca^{44} + p \rightarrow Sc^{44} + n.$$

The sum of the atomic numbers before the reaction $(20 + 1)$ is exactly equal to the sum of the atomic numbers after the reaction $(21 + 0)$. Again charge is conserved.

QUESTIONS

1. You are given two metal spheres mounted on portable insulating supports. Find a way to give them equal and opposite charges. You may use a glass rod rubbed with silk but may not touch it to the spheres. Do the spheres have to be of equal size for your method to work?

2. A charged rod attracts bits of dry cork dust which, after touching the rod, often jump violently away from it. Explain.

3. If a charged glass rod is held near one end of an insulated uncharged metal rod as in Fig. 26–6, electrons are drawn to one end, as shown. Why does the flow of electrons cease? There is an almost inexhaustible supply of them in the metal rod.

4. In Fig. 26–6 does any net electrical force act on the metal rod? Explain

5. An insulated rod is said to carry
an electric charge. How could you
verify this and determine the sign of
the charge?

6. Why do electrostatic experiments
not work well on humid days?

7. A person standing on an insulated stool touches a charged, insulated conductor. Is the conductor
discharged completely?

8. (a) A positively charged glass
rod attracts a suspended object. Can
we conclude that the object is neg-
atively charged? (b) A positively charged glass rod *repels* a suspended object. Can we
conclude that the object is *positively* charged?

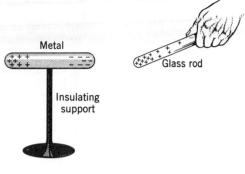

Fig. 26–6

9. Is the Coulomb force that one charge exerts on another changed if other charges
are brought nearby?

10. The quantum of charge is 1.60×10^{-19} coul. Is there a corresponding single quantum of mass?

11. Verify the fact that the decay schemes for the elementary particles in Appendix F
are consistent with charge conservation.

12. What does it mean to say that a physical quantity is (a) quantized or (b) conserved?
Give some examples.

13. A nucleus U^{238} splits into two equal halves. Are the nuclei so produced likely to
be stable or radioactive?

PROBLEMS

1. Protons in the cosmic rays strike the earth's upper atmosphere at a rate, averaged
over the earth's surface, of 0.15 protons/cm²-sec. What total current does the earth receive
from beyond its atmosphere in the form of incident cosmic ray protons? The earth's
radius is 6.4×10^6 meters.

2. A point charge of $+3.0 \times 10^{-6}$ coul is 12 cm distant from a second point charge of
-1.5×10^{-6} coul. Calculate the magnitude and direction of the force on each charge.

3. Two similar balls of mass m are hung from silk threads of
length l and carry similar charges q as in Fig. 26–7. Assume that
θ is so small that $\tan \theta$ can be replaced by its approximate equal,
$\sin \theta$. To this approximation show that

$$x = \left(\frac{q^2 l}{2\pi \epsilon_0 mg}\right)^{\frac{1}{3}}$$

where x is the separation between the balls. If $l = 120$ cm, $m =$
10 gm, and $x = 5.0$ cm, what is q?

4. Assume that each ball in Problem 3 is losing charge at the rate
of 1.0×10^{-9} coul/sec. At what instantaneous relative speed
$(= dx/dt)$ do the balls approach each other?

5. Three small balls, each of mass 10 gm, are suspended separately from a common point by silk threads, each 1.0 meter

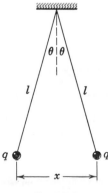

Fig. 26–7

long. The balls are identically charged and hang at the corners of an equilateral triangle 0.1 meter long on a side. What is the charge on each ball?

6. In Fig. 26–8 what is the resultant force on the charge in the lower left corner of the square? Assume that $q = 1.0 \times 10^{-7}$ coul and $a = 5.0$ cm.

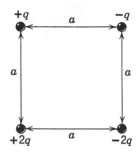

Fig. 26–8

7. A charge Q is placed at each of two opposite corners of a square. A charge q is placed at each of the other two corners. (a) If the resultant electrical force on Q is zero, how are Q and q related? (b) Could q be chosen to make the resultant force on *every* charge zero?

8. How far apart must two protons be if the electrical repulsive force acting on either one is equal to its weight?

9. (a) What equal positive charges would have to be placed on the earth and on the moon to neutralize their gravitational attraction? (b) Do you need to know the lunar distance to solve this problem? (c) How many pounds of hydrogen would be needed to provide the positive charge calculated in a?

10. A certain charge Q is to be divided into two parts, q and $Q - q$. What is the relationship of Q to q if the two parts, placed a given distance apart, are to have a maximum Coulomb repulsion?

11. Each of two small spheres is charged positively, the combined charge being 5.0×10^{-5} coul. If each sphere is repelled from the other by a force of 1.0 newton when the spheres are 2.0 meters apart, how is the total charge distributed between the spheres?

12. Two equal positive point charges are separated by a distance $2a$. A point test charge is located in a plane which is normal to the line joining these charges and midway between them. (a) Calculate the radius r of the circle of symmetry in this plane for which the force on the test charge has a maximum value. (b) What is the direction of this force, assuming a positive test charge.

13. A cube of edge a carries a point charge q at each corner. (a) Show that the magnitude of the resultant force on any one of the charges is

$$F = \frac{0.261q^2}{\epsilon_0 a^2}.$$

(b) What is the direction of **F** relative to the cube edges?

14. Estimate roughly the number of coulombs of positive charge in a glass of water.

15. (a) How many electrons would have to be removed from a penny to leave it with a charge of $+10^{-7}$ coul? (b) What fraction of the electrons in the penny does this correspond to?

16. The radius of a copper nucleus is about 1.9×10^{-13} cm. Calculate the density of the material that makes up the nucleus. Does your answer seem reasonable? (The atomic weight of copper is 64 gm/mole; ignore the mass of the electrons in comparison to that of the nucleus.)

17. In the radioactive decay of U^{238} (see Eq. 26–5) the center of the emerging α-particle is, at a certain instant, 9×10^{-15} meter from the center of the residual nucleus Th^{234}. At this instant (a) what is the force on the α-particle and (b) what is its acceleration?

The Electric Field

27-1   The Electric Field

With every point in space near the earth we can associate a *gravitational field strength* vector **g** (see Eq. 16–11).   This is the gravitational acceleration that a test body, placed at that point and released, would experience.   If m is the mass of the body and **F** the gravitational force acting on it, **g** is given by

$$\mathbf{g} = \mathbf{F}/m. \tag{27-1}$$

This is an example of a *vector field*.   For points near the surface of the earth the field is often taken as *uniform;* that is, **g** is the same for all points.

The flow of water in a river provides another example of a vector field, called a *flow field* (see Section 18–7).   Every point in the water has associated with it a vector quantity, the velocity **v** with which the water flows past the point.   If **g** and **v** do not change with time, the corresponding fields are described as *stationary*.   In the case of the river note that even though the water is moving the vector **v** at any point does not change with time for steady-flow conditions.

The space surrounding a charged rod seems to be affected by the rod, and we speak of an *electric field* in this space.   In the same way we speak of a *magnetic field* in the space around a bar magnet.   In the classical theory of electromagnetism the electric and magnetic fields are central concepts.

Before Faraday's time, the force acting between charged particles was thought of as a direct and instantaneous interaction between the two particles.   This *action-at-a-distance* view was also held for magnetic and for gravitational forces.   Today we prefer to think in terms of electric fields as follows:

1. Charge q_1 in Fig. 27–1 sets up an electric field in the space around itself. This field is suggested by the shading in the figure; later we shall show how to represent electric fields more concretely.

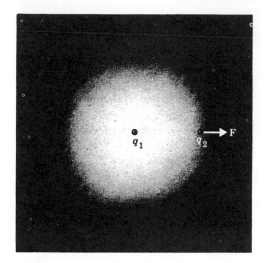

Fig. 27–1   Charge q_1 sets up a field that exerts a force **F** on charge q_2.

2. The field acts on charge q_2; this shows up in the force **F** that q_2 experiences.

The field plays an intermediary role in the forces between charges. There are two separate problems: (a) calculating the fields that are set up by given distributions of charge and (b) calculating the forces that given fields will exert on charges placed in them.   We think in terms of

$$\text{charge} \rightleftharpoons \text{field}$$

and not, as in the action-at-a-distance point of view, in terms of

$$\text{charge} \rightleftharpoons \text{charge}.$$

In Fig. 27–1 we can also imagine that q_2 sets up a field and that this field acts on q_1, producing a force $-\mathbf{F}$ on it.   The situation is completely symmetrical, each charge being immersed in a field associated with the other charge.

If the only problem in electromagnetism were that of the forces between stationary charges, the field and the action-at-a-distance points of view would be perfectly equivalent.   Suppose, however, that q_1 in Fig. 27–1 suddenly accelerates to the right.   How quickly does the charge q_2 learn that q_1 has moved and that the force which it (q_2) experiences must increase? Electromagnetic theory predicts that q_2 learns about q_1's motion by a *field disturbance* that emanates from q_1, traveling with the speed of light.   The action-at-a-distance point of view requires that information about q_1's acceleration be communicated *instantaneously* to q_2; this is not in accord with experiment.   Accelerating electrons in the antenna of a radio transmitter influence electrons in a distant receiving antenna only after a time l/c where l is the separation of the antennas and c is the speed of light.

27–2   The Electric Field Strength E

To define the electric field operationally, we place a small test body carrying a test charge q_0 (assumed positive for convenience) at the point in space that is to be examined, and we measure the electrical force $\mathbf{F}$ (if any) that acts on this body. The *electric field strength* $\mathbf{E}$ at the point is defined as *

$$\mathbf{E} = \mathbf{F}/q_0. \tag{27–2}$$

Here $\mathbf{E}$ is a vector because $\mathbf{F}$ is one, q_0 being a scalar. The direction of $\mathbf{E}$ is the direction of $\mathbf{F}$, that is, it is the direction in which a resting positive charge placed at the point would tend to move.

The definition of gravitational field strength $\mathbf{g}$ is much like that of electric field strength, except that the mass of the test body rather than its charge is the property of interest. Although the units of $\mathbf{g}$ are usually written as meters/sec², they could also be written as nt/kg (Eq. 27–1); those for $\mathbf{E}$ are nt/coul (Eq. 27–2). Thus both $\mathbf{g}$ and $\mathbf{E}$ are expressed as a force divided by a property (mass or charge) of the test body.

▶ **Example 1.** What is the magnitude of the electric field strength $\mathbf{E}$ such that an electron, placed in the field, would experience an electrical force equal to its weight? From Eq. 27–2, replacing q_0 by e and F by mg, where m is the electron mass, we have

$$E = \frac{F}{q_0} = \frac{mg}{e}$$

$$= \frac{(9.1 \times 10^{-31}\,\text{kg})(9.8\,\text{meters/sec}^2)}{1.6 \times 10^{-19}\,\text{coul}}$$

$$= 5.6 \times 10^{-11}\,\text{nt/coul.}$$

This is a very weak electric field. Which way will $\mathbf{E}$ have to point if the electric force is to cancel the gravitational force?   ◀

In applying Eq. 27–2 we must use a test charge as small as possible. A large test charge might disturb the primary charges that are responsible for the field, thus changing the very quantity that we are trying to measure. Equation 27–2 should, strictly, be replaced by

$$\mathbf{E} = \lim_{q_0 \to 0} \frac{\mathbf{F}}{q_0}. \tag{27–3}$$

This equation instructs us to use a smaller and smaller test charge q_0, evaluating the ratio $\mathbf{F}/q_0$ at every step. The electric field $\mathbf{E}$ is then the limit of this ratio as the size of the test charge approaches zero.

27–3   Lines of Force

The concept of the electric field as a vector was not appreciated by Michael Faraday, who always thought in terms of *lines of force*. The lines of force still form a convenient way of visualizing electric-field patterns. We shall use them for this purpose but we shall not employ them quantitatively.

---

* This definition of $\mathbf{E}$, though conceptually sound and quite appropriate to our present purpose, is rarely carried out in practice because of experimental difficulties. $\mathbf{E}$ is normally found by calculation from more readily measurable quantities such as the electric potential; see Section 29–7.

The relationship between the (imaginary) lines of force and the electric field strength vector is this:

1. The tangent to a line of force at any point gives the *direction* of **E** at that point.

2. The lines of force are drawn so that the number of lines per unit cross-sectional area is proportional to the *magnitude* of **E**. Where the lines are close together E is large and where they are far apart E is small.

It is not obvious that it is possible to draw a continuous set of lines to meet these requirements. Indeed, it turns out that if Coulomb's law were not true it would *not* be possible to do so; see Problem 4.

Figure 27–2 shows the lines of force for a uniform sheet of positive charge. We assume that the sheet is infinitely large, which, for a sheet of finite dimensions, is equivalent to considering only those points whose distance from the sheet is small compared to the distance to the nearest edge of the sheet. A positive test charge, released in front of such a sheet, would move away from the sheet along a perpendicular line. Thus the electric field strength vector at any point near the sheet must be at right angles to the sheet. The lines of force are uniformly spaced, which means that **E** has the same magnitude for all points near the sheet.

Figure 27–3 shows the lines of force for a negatively charged sphere. From symmetry, the lines must lie along radii. They point inward because a free positive charge would be accelerated in this direction. The electric field E is not constant but decreases with increasing distance from the charge. This is evident in the lines of force, which are farther apart at greater distances. From symmetry, E is the same for all points that lie a given distance from the center of the charge.

▶ **Example 2.** In Fig. 27–3 how does E vary with the distance r from the center of the charged sphere?

Suppose that N lines originate on the sphere. Draw an imaginary concentric sphere of radius r; the number of lines per unit cross-sectional area at every point on the sphere is $N/4\pi r^2$. Since E is proportional to this, we can write that

$$E \propto 1/r^2.$$

We derive an exact relationship in Section 27–4. How should E vary with distance from an infinitely long uniform cylinder of charge?   ◀

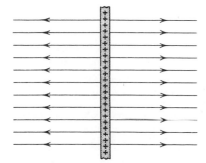

Fig. 27–2 Lines of force for a section of an infinitely large sheet of positive charge.

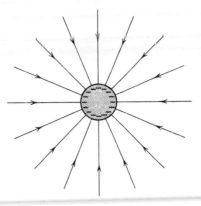

Fig. 27–3 Lines of force for a negatively charged sphere.

Figures 27–4 and 27–5 show the lines of force for two equal like charges and for two equal unlike charges, respectively. Michael Faraday, as we have said, used lines of force a great deal in his thinking. They were more real for him than they are for most scientists and engineers today. It is possible

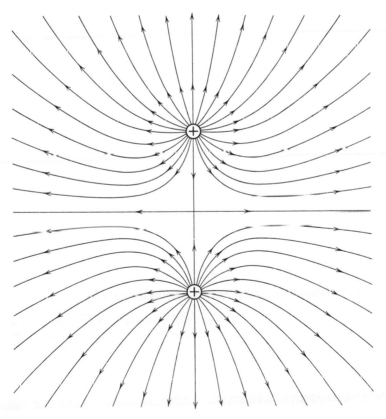

Fig. 27–4   Lines of force for two equal positive charges.

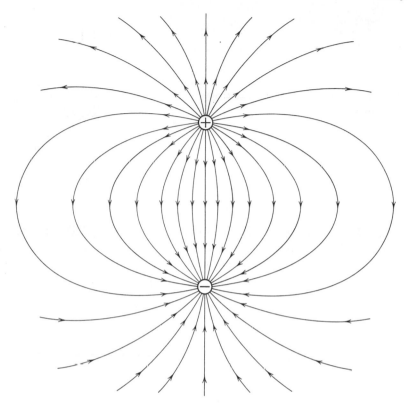

Fig. 27–5 Lines of force for equal but opposite charges.

to sympathize with Faraday's point of view. Can we not almost "see" the charges being pushed apart in Fig. 27–4 and pulled together in Fig. 27–5 by the lines of force? The student should compare Fig. 27–5 with Fig. 18–15, which represents a flow field. Figure 27–6 shows a representation of lines of force around charged conductors, using grass seeds suspended in an insulating liquid.

Lines of force give a vivid picture of the way E varies through a given region of space. However, the equations of electromagnetism (see Table 38–3) are written in terms of the electric field strength E and other field vectors and not in terms of the lines of force. The electric field E varies in a perfectly continuous way as any path in the field is traversed; see Fig. 27–7a. This kind of physical continuity, however, is different from the continuity of the lines of force, which has no real physical meaning. To illustrate this point we assert that the lines of force need not be continuous but can be drawn as in Fig. 27–7b. This figure agrees with the two properties of lines of force laid down at the beginning of this section. This point of view has been especially emphasized by Joseph Slepian.*

* See *American Journal of Physics*, **19**, 87 (1951).

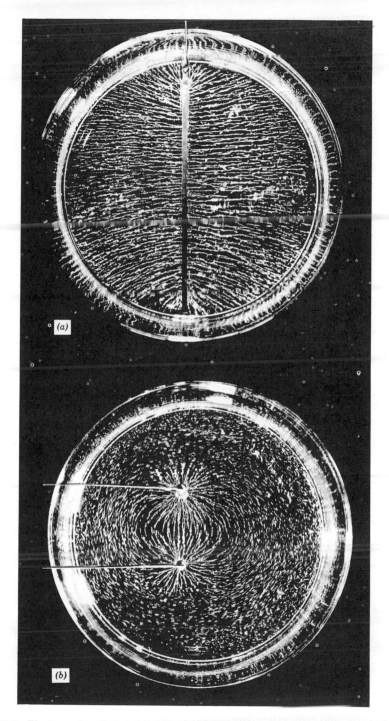

Fig. 27-6 Photographs of the patterns of electric lines of force around (a) a charged plate (compare Fig. 27-2), and (b) two rods with equal and opposite charges (compare Fig. 27-5). The patterns were made by suspending grass seed in an insulating liquid. (Courtesy Educational Services Incorporated, Watertown, Mass.)

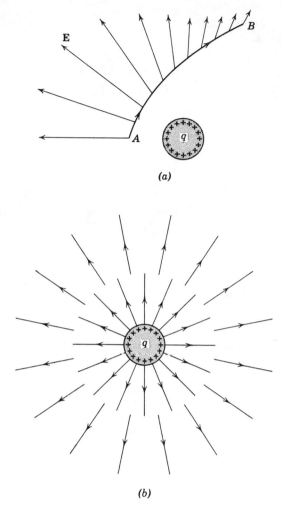

Fig. 27–7 (a) $\mathbf{E}$ varies continuously as we move along any path AB in the field set up by q. (b) Lines of force need not be continuous.

27–4 Calculation of E

Let a test charge q_0 be placed a distance r from a point charge q. The magnitude of the force acting on q_0 is given by Coulomb's law, or

$$F = \frac{1}{4\pi\epsilon_0}\frac{qq_0}{r^2}.$$

The electric field strength at the site of the test charge is given by Eq. 27–2, or

$$E = \frac{F}{q_0} = \frac{1}{4\pi\epsilon_0}\frac{q}{r^2}. \tag{27–4}$$

The direction of **E** is on a radial line from q, pointing outward if q is positive and inward if q is negative.

To find **E** for a group of point charges: (a) Calculate E_n due to each charge at the given point *as if it were the only charge present*. (b) Add these separately calculated fields vectorially to find the resultant field **E** at the point. In equation form,

$$\mathbf{E} = \mathbf{E}_1 + \mathbf{E}_2 + \mathbf{E}_3 + \cdots = \Sigma\mathbf{E}_n \qquad n = 1, 2, 3, \ldots . \qquad (27\text{-}5)$$

The sum is a vector sum, taken over all the charges.

If the charge distribution is a continuous one, the field it sets up at any point P can be computed by dividing the charge into infinitesimal elements dq. The field $d\mathbf{E}$ due to each element at the point in question is then calculated, treating the elements as point charges. The magnitude of $d\mathbf{E}$ (see Eq. 27–4) is given by

$$dE = \frac{1}{4\pi\epsilon_0}\frac{dq}{r^2}, \qquad (27\text{-}6)$$

where r is the distance from the charge element dq to the point P. The resultant field at P is then found by adding (that is, integrating) the field contributions due to all the charge elements, or,

$$\mathbf{E} = \int d\mathbf{E}. \qquad (27\text{-}7)$$

The integration, like the sum in Eq. 27–5, is a vector operation; in Example 5 we will see how such an integral is handled in a simple case.

▶ **Example 3.** *An electric dipole.* Figure 27–8 shows a positive and a negative charge of equal magnitude q placed a distance $2a$ apart, a configuration called an elec-

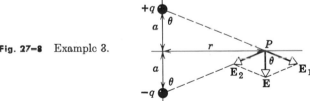

Fig. 27-8 Example 3.

tric dipole. The pattern of lines of force is that of Fig. 27–5, which also shows an electric dipole. What is the field **E** due to these charges at point P, a distance r along the perpendicular bisector of the line joining the charges? Assume $r \gg a$.

Equation 27–5 gives the vector equation

$$\mathbf{E} = \mathbf{E}_1 + \mathbf{E}_2,$$

where, from Eq. 27–4,*

$$E_1 = E_2 = \frac{1}{4\pi\epsilon_0}\frac{q}{a^2 + r^2}.$$

---

* Note that the r's in Eq. 27–4 and in this equation have different meanings.

The vector sum of $\mathbf{E}_1$ and $\mathbf{E}_2$ points vertically downward and has the magnitude

$$E = 2E_1 \cos \theta.$$

From the figure we see that

$$\cos \theta = \frac{a}{\sqrt{a^2 + r^2}}.$$

Substituting the expressions for E_1 and for $\cos \theta$ into that for E yields

$$E = \frac{2}{4\pi\epsilon_0} \frac{q}{(a^2 + r^2)} \frac{a}{\sqrt{a^2 + r^2}} = \frac{1}{4\pi\epsilon_0} \frac{2aq}{(a^2 + r^2)^{3/2}}.$$

If $r \gg a$, we can neglect a in the denominator; this equation then reduces to

$$E \cong \frac{1}{4\pi\epsilon_0} \frac{(2a)(q)}{r^3}. \qquad (27\text{-}8a)$$

The essential properties of the charge distribution in Fig. 27–8, the magnitude of the charge q and the separation $2a$ between the charges, enter Eq. 27–8a only as a product. This means that, if we measure $\mathbf{E}$ at various distances from the electric dipole (assuming $r \gg a$), we can never deduce q and $2a$ separately but only the product $2aq$; if q were doubled and a simultaneously cut in half, the electric field *at large distances from the dipole* would not change.

The product $2aq$ is called the *electric dipole moment p*. Thus we can rewrite this equation for E, *for distant points along the perpendicular bisector*, as

$$E = \frac{1}{4\pi\epsilon_0} \frac{p}{r^3}. \qquad (27\text{-}8b)$$

The result for distant points *along the dipole axis* (see Problem 10) and the general result for any distant point (see Problem 23) also contain the quantities $2a$ and q only as the product $2aq \;(= p)$. The variation of E with r in the general result for distant points is also as $1/r^3$, as in Eq. 27–8b.

The dipole of Fig. 27–8 is two equal and opposite charges placed close to each other so that their separate fields at distant points almost, but not quite, cancel. On this point of view it is easy to understand that $E(r)$ for a dipole varies as $1/r^3$ (Eq. 27–8b), whereas for a point charge $E(r)$ drops off more slowly, namely as $1/r^2$ (Eq. 27–4).

Example 4. Figure 27–9 shows a charge $q_1 \;(= +1.0 \times 10^{-6}$ coul) 10 cm from a charge $q_2 \;(= +2.0 \times 10^{-6}$ coul). At what point on the line joining the two charges is the electric field strength zero?

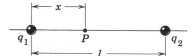

Fig. 27–9   Example 4.

The point must lie between the charges because only here do the forces exerted by q_1 and q_2 on a test charge oppose each other. If $\mathbf{E}_1$ is the electric field strength due to q_1 and $\mathbf{E}_2$ that due to q_2, we must have

$$E_1 = E_2$$

or (see Eq. 27–4) $\dfrac{1}{4\pi\epsilon_0} \dfrac{q_1}{x^2} = \dfrac{1}{4\pi\epsilon_0} \dfrac{q_2}{(l - x)^2}$

where x is the distance from q_1 and l equals 10 cm. Solving for x yields

$$x = \frac{l}{1 + \sqrt{q_2/q_1}} = \frac{10 \text{ cm}}{1 + \sqrt{2}} = 4.1 \text{ cm.}$$

The student should supply the missing steps. On what basis was the second root of the resulting quadratic equation discarded?

Example 5. Figure 27–10 shows a ring of charge q and of radius a. Calculate **E** for points on the axis of the ring a distance x from its center.

Consider a differential element of the ring of length ds, located at the top of the ring in Fig. 27–10. It contains an element of charge given by

$$dq = q\,\frac{ds}{2\pi a}$$

where $2\pi a$ is the circumference of the ring. This element sets up a differential electric field $d\mathbf{E}$ at point P.

The resultant field **E** at P is found by integrating the effects of all the elements that make up the ring. From symmetry this resultant field must lie along the ring axis. Thus only the component of $d\mathbf{E}$ parallel to this axis contributes to the final result. The component perpendicular to the axis is canceled out by an equal but opposite component established by the charge element on the opposite side of the ring.

Thus the general vector integral (Eq. 27–7)

$$\mathbf{E} = \int d\mathbf{E}$$

becomes a scalar integral $\qquad E = \int dE \cos\theta.$

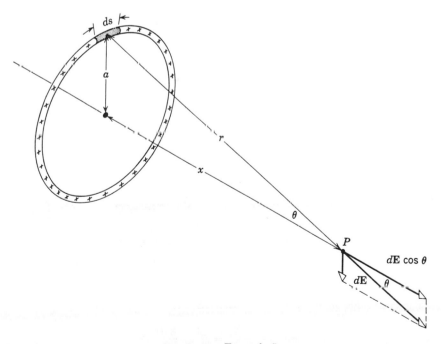

Fig. 27–10   Example 5

The quantity dE follows from Eq. 27–6, or

$$dE = \frac{1}{4\pi\epsilon_0} \frac{dq}{r^2} = \frac{1}{4\pi\epsilon_0} \left(\frac{q\,ds}{2\pi a}\right) \frac{1}{a^2 + x^2}.$$

From Fig. 27–10 we have $\cos\theta = \dfrac{x}{\sqrt{a^2 + x^2}}.$

Noting that, for a given point P, x has the same value for all charge elements and is not a variable, we obtain

$$E = \int dE \cos\theta = \int \frac{1}{4\pi\epsilon_0} \frac{q\,ds}{(2\pi a)(a^2 + x^2)} \frac{x}{\sqrt{a^2 + x^2}}$$

$$= \frac{1}{4\pi\epsilon_0} \frac{qx}{(2\pi a)(a^2 + x^2)^{3/2}} \int ds.$$

The integral is simply the circumference of the ring $(= 2\pi a)$, so that

$$E = \frac{1}{4\pi\epsilon_0} \frac{qx}{(a^2 + x^2)^{3/2}}.$$

Does this expression for E reduce to an expected result for $x = 0$?   For $x \gg a$ we can neglect a in the denominator of this equation, yielding

$$E \cong \frac{1}{4\pi\epsilon_0} \frac{q}{x^2}.$$

This is an expected result (compare Eq. 27–4) because at great enough distances the ring behaves like a point charge q.

Example 6.   *Line of charge.*   Figure 27–11 shows a section of an infinite line of charge whose linear charge density (that is, the charge per unit length, measured

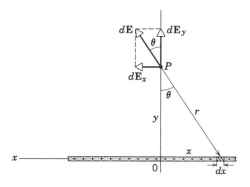

Fig. 27–11   Example 6.   A section of an infinite line of charge.

in coul/meter) has the constant value λ.   Calculate the field $\mathbf{E}$ a distance y from the line.

The magnitude of the field contribution dE due to charge element $dq \,(= \lambda\,dx)$ is given, using Eq. 27–6, by

$$dE = \frac{1}{4\pi\epsilon_0} \frac{dq}{r^2} = \frac{1}{4\pi\epsilon_0} \frac{\lambda\,dx}{y^2 + x^2}.$$

The vector $d\mathbf{E}$, as Fig. 27-11 shows, has the components

$$dE_x = -dE \sin\theta \quad \text{and} \quad dE_y = dE \cos\theta.$$

The minus sign in front of dE_x indicates that dE_x points in the negative x direction. The x and y components of the resultant vector $\mathbf{E}$ at point P are given by

$$E_x = \int dE_x = -\int_{x=-\infty}^{x=+\infty} \sin\theta \, dE \quad \text{and} \quad E_y = \int dE_y = \int_{x=-\infty}^{x=+\infty} \cos\theta \, dE.$$

E_x must be zero because every charge element on the right has a corresponding element on the left such that their field contributions in the x direction cancel. Thus $\mathbf{E}$ points entirely in the y direction. Because the contributions to E_y from the right- and left-hand halves of the rod are equal, we can write

$$E = E_y = 2\int_{x=0}^{x=+\infty} \cos\theta \, dE.$$

Note that we have changed the lower limit of integration and have introduced a factor of two.

Substituting the expression for dE into this equation gives

$$E = \frac{\lambda}{2\pi\epsilon_0} \int_{x=0}^{x=\infty} \cos\theta \, \frac{dx}{y^2 + x^2}.$$

From Fig. 27-11 we see that the quantities θ and x are not independent. We must eliminate one of them, say x. The relation between x and θ is (see figure)

$$x = y \tan\theta.$$

Differentiating, we obtain $dx = y \sec^2\theta \, d\theta.$

Substituting these two expressions leads finally to

$$E = \frac{\lambda}{2\pi\epsilon_0 y} \int_{\theta=0}^{\theta=\pi/2} \cos\theta \, d\theta.$$

The student should check this step carefully, noting that the limits must now be on θ and not on x. For example as $x \to +\infty$, $\theta \to \pi/2$, as Fig. 27-11 shows. This equation integrates readily to

$$E = \frac{\lambda}{2\pi\epsilon_0 y} \left| \sin\theta \right|_0^{\pi/2} = \frac{\lambda}{2\pi\epsilon_0 y}.$$

The student may wonder about the usefulness of solving a problem involving an infinite rod of charge when any actual rod must have a finite length (see Problem 15). However, for points close enough to finite rods and not near their ends, the equation that we have just derived yields results that are so close to the correct values that the difference can be ignored in many practical situations. It is usually unnecessary to solve exactly every geometry encountered in practical problems. Indeed, if idealizations or approximations are not made, the vast majority of significant problems of all kinds in physics and engineering cannot be solved at all.   ◀

27 5   A Point Charge In an Electric Field

An electric field will exert a force on a charged particle given by (Eq. 27-2)

$$\mathbf{F} = \mathbf{E}q.$$

This force will produce an acceleration

$$\mathbf{a} = \mathbf{F}/m,$$

where m is the mass of the particle. We will consider two examples of the acceleration of a charged particle in a uniform electric field. Such a field can be produced by connecting the terminals of a battery to two parallel metal plates which are otherwise insulated from each other. If the spacing between the plates is small compared with the dimensions of the plates, the field between them will be fairly uniform except near the edges. Note that in calculating the motion of a particle in a field set up by external charges the field due to the particle itself (that is, its *self-field*) is ignored. For example, the earth's gravitational field can have no effect on the earth itself but only on a second object, say a stone, placed in that field.

▶ **Example 7.** A particle of mass m and charge q is placed at rest in a uniform electric field (Fig. 27–12) and released. Describe its motion.

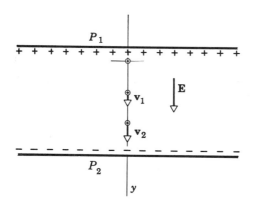

Fig. 27–12 A charge is released from rest in a uniform electric field set up between two oppositely charged metal plates P_1 and P_2.

The motion resembles that of a body falling in the earth's gravitational field. The (constant) acceleration is given by

$$a = \frac{F}{m} = \frac{qE}{m}.$$

The equations for uniformly accelerated motion (Section 3–7) then apply. With $v_0 = 0$, they are

$$v = at = \frac{qEt}{m},$$

$$y = \tfrac{1}{2}at^2 = \frac{qEt^2}{2m},$$

and

$$v^2 = 2ay = \frac{2qEy}{m}.$$

The kinetic energy attained after moving a distance y is found from

$$K = \tfrac{1}{2}mv^2 = \tfrac{1}{2}m\left(\frac{2qEy}{m}\right) = qEy.$$

This result also follows directly from the work-energy theorem because a constant force qE acts over a distance y.

Example 8. *Deflecting an electron beam.* Figure 27–13 shows an electron of mass m and charge e projected with speed v_0 at right angles to a uniform field **E**. Describe its motion.

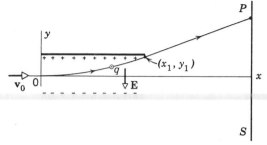

Fig. 27–13   Example 8. An electron is projected into a uniform electric field.

The motion is like that of a projectile fired horizontally in the earth's gravitational field. The considerations of Section 4–3 apply, the horizontal (x) and vertical (y) motions being given by

$$x = v_0 t$$

and

$$y = \tfrac{1}{2}at^2 = \frac{eE}{2m}t^2.$$

Eliminating t yields

$$y = \frac{eE}{2mv_0{}^2}x^2 \tag{27-9}$$

for the equation of the trajectory.

When the electron emerges from the plates in Fig. 27–13, it travels (neglecting gravity) in a straight line tangent to the parabola at the exit point. We can let it fall on a fluorescent screen S placed some distance beyond the plates. Together with other electrons following the same path, it will then make itself visible as a small luminous spot; this is the principle of the electrostatic *cathode-ray oscilloscope.*

Example 9. The electric field between the plates of a cathode-ray oscilloscope is 1.2×10^4 nt/coul. What deflection will an electron experience if it enters the field at right angles with a kinetic energy of 2000 ev ($= 3.2 \times 10^{-16}$ joule), a typical value? The deflecting assembly is 1.5 cm long.

Recalling that $K_0 = \tfrac{1}{2}mv_0{}^2$, we can rewrite Eq. 27–9 as

$$y = \frac{eEx^2}{4K_0}.$$

If x_1 is the horizontal position of the far edge of the plate, y_1 will be the corresponding deflection (see Fig. 27–13), or

$$y_1 = \frac{eEx_1{}^2}{4K_0}$$

$$= \frac{(1.6 \times 10^{-19}\ \text{coul})(1.2 \times 10^4\ \text{nt/coul})(1.5 \times 10^{-2}\ \text{meter})^2}{(4)(3.2 \times 10^{-16}\ \text{joule})}$$

$$= 3.4 \times 10^{-4}\ \text{meter} = 0.34\ \text{mm}.$$

The deflection measured, not at the deflecting plates but at the fluorescent screen, is much larger.

Example 10. A positive point test charge q_0 is placed halfway between two equal positive charges q. What force acts on it at or near this point P?

From symmetry the force *at* the point is zero so that the particle is in equilibrium; the nature of the equilibrium remains to be found. Figure 27–14 (compare Fig. 27–4)

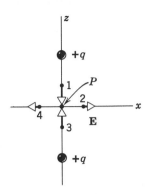

Fig. 27–14 Example 10. The electric field at four points near a point P which is centered between two equal positive charges.

shows the **E** vectors for four points near P. If the test charge is moved along the z axis, a *restoring* force is brought into play; however, the equilibrium is unstable for motion in the x-y plane. Thus we have the three-dimensional equivalent of *saddle point equilibrium;* see Fig. 14–8. What is the nature of the equilibrium for a negative test charge?   ◀

27–6   A Dipole in an Electric Field

An electric dipole moment can be regarded as a vector **p** whose magnitude p, for a dipole like that described in Example 3, is the product $2aq$ of the magnitude of either charge q and the distance $2a$ between the charges. The direction of **p** for such a dipole is from the negative to the positive charge. The vector nature of the electric dipole moment permits us to cast many expressions involving electric dipoles into concise form, as we shall see.

Figure 27–15a shows an electric dipole formed by placing two charges $+q$ and $-q$ a fixed distance $2a$ apart. The arrangement is placed in a uniform *external* electric field **E**, its dipole moment **p** making an angle θ with this field. Two equal and opposite forces **F** and $-$**F** act as shown, where

$$F = qE.$$

The net force is clearly zero, but there is a net torque about an axis through O (see Eq. 12–2) given by

$$\tau = 2F(a \sin \theta) = 2aF \sin \theta.$$

Combining these two equations and recalling that $p = (2a)(q)$, we obtain

$$\tau = 2aqE \sin \theta = pE \sin \theta. \tag{27–10}$$

Thus an electric dipole placed in an external electric field **E** experiences a torque tending to align it with the field. Equation 27–10 can be written in vector form as

$$\boldsymbol{\tau} = \mathbf{p} \times \mathbf{E}, \tag{27–11}$$

the appropriate vectors being shown in Fig. 27–15b.

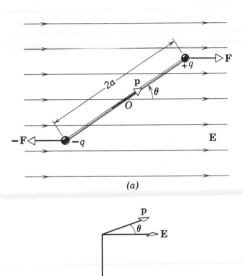

Fig. 27–15   (*a*) An electric dipole in a uniform external field.   (*b*) An oblique view, illustrating $\tau = \mathbf{p} \times \mathbf{E}$.

Work (positive or negative) must be done by an external agent to change the orientation of an electric dipole in an external field. This work is stored as potential energy U in the system consisting of the dipole and the arrangement used to set up the external field. If θ in Fig. 27–15*a* has the initial value θ_0, the work required to turn the dipole axis to an angle θ is given from Eq. 12–9 or

$$W = \int dW = \int_{\theta_0}^{\theta} \tau \, d\theta = U,$$

where τ is the torque exerted by the agent that does the work. Combining this equation with Eq. 27–10 yields

$$U = \int_{\theta_0}^{\theta} pE \sin \theta \, d\theta = pE \int_{\theta_0}^{\theta} \sin \theta \, d\theta$$

$$= pE \left| - \cos \theta \right|_{\theta_0}^{\theta}$$

Since we are interested only in *changes* in potential energy, we choose the reference orientation θ_0 to have any convenient value, in this case 90°. This gives

$$U = -pE \cos \theta \qquad (27\text{–}12)$$

or, in vector form,

$$U = -\mathbf{p} \cdot \mathbf{E}. \qquad (27\text{–}13)$$

▶ **Example 11.** An electric dipole consists of two opposite charges of magnitude $q = 1.0 \times 10^{-6}$ coul separated by $d = 2.0$ cm. The dipole is placed in an external field of 1.0×10^5 nt/coul.

(a) What maximum torque does the field exert on the dipole? The maximum torque is found by putting $\theta = 90°$ in Eq. 27–10 or

$$\tau = pE \sin \theta = qdE \sin \theta$$

$$= (1.0 \times 10^{-6} \text{ coul})(0.020 \text{ meter})(1.0 \times 10^5 \text{ nt/coul})(\sin 90°)$$

$$= 2.0 \times 10^{-3} \text{ nt-m}.$$

(b) How much work must an external agent do to turn the dipole end for end, starting from a position of alignment ($\theta = 0$)? The work is the difference in potential energy U between the positions $\theta = 180°$ and $\theta = 0$. From Eq. 27–12,

$$W = U_{180°} - U_{0°} = (-pE \cos 180°) - (-pE \cos 0)$$

$$= 2pE = 2qdE$$

$$= (2)(1.0 \times 10^{-6} \text{ coul})(0.020 \text{ meter})(1.0 \times 10^5 \text{ nt/coul})$$

$$= 4.0 \times 10^{-3} \text{ joule.} \qquad \blacktriangleleft$$

QUESTIONS

1. Name as many scalar fields and vector fields as you can.

2. (a) In the gravitational attraction between the earth and a stone, can we say that the earth lies in the gravitational field of the stone? (b) How is the gravitational field due to the stone related to that due to the earth?

3. A positively charged ball hangs from a long silk thread. We wish to measure $\mathbf{E}$ at a point in the same horizontal plane as that of the hanging charge. To do so, we put a positive test charge q_0 at the point and measure $\mathbf{F}/q_0$. Will F/q_0 be less than, equal to, or greater than E at the point in question?

4. Taking into account the quantization of electric charge (the single electron providing the basic charge unit), how can we justify the procedure suggested by Eq. 27–3?

5. In Fig. 27–5 the force on the lower charge points up and is finite. The crowding of the lines of force, however, suggests that E is infinitely great at the site of this (point) charge. A charge immersed in an infinitely great field should have an infinitely great force acting on it. What is the solution to this dilemma?

6. Electric lines of force never cross. Why?

7. In Fig. 27–4 why do the lines of force around the edge of the figure appear, when extended backwards, to radiate from the center of the figure?

8. Figure 27–2 shows that $\mathbf{E}$ has the same value for all points in front of an infinite uniformly charged sheet. Is this reasonable? One might think that the field should be stronger near the sheet because the charges are so much closer.

9. Two point charges of unknown magnitude and sign are a distance d apart. The electric field strength is zero at one point between them, on the line joining them. What can you conclude about the charges?

10. Compare the way E varies with r for (a) a point charge (Eq. 27–4), (b) a dipole (Eq. 27–8a), and (c) a quadrupole (Problem 18).

11. If a point charge q of mass m is released from rest in a nonuniform field, will it follow a line of force?

12. An electric dipole is placed in a *nonuniform* electric field. Is there a net force on it?

13. An electric dipole is placed at rest in a uniform external electric field, as in Fig. 27–15a, and released. Discuss its motion.

14. An electric dipole has its dipole moment **p** aligned with a uniform external electric field **E**. (a) Is the equilibrium stable or unstable? (b) Discuss the nature of the equilibrium if **p** and **E** point in opposite directions.

PROBLEMS

1. Sketch qualitatively the lines of force associated with a thin, circular, uniformly charged disk of radius R. (Hint: Consider as limiting cases points very close to the surface and points very far from it.) Show the lines only in a plane containing the axis of the disk.

2. (a) Sketch qualitatively the lines of force associated with three equal positive point charges placed at the corners of an equilateral triangle. Use symmetry arguments and limiting cases (see hint in Problem 1). Show the lines in the plane of the triangle only. (b) Discuss the nature of the equilibrium of a test charge placed at the center of the triangle.

3. In Fig. 27–4 consider any two lines of force leaving the upper charge. If the angle between their tangents for points near the charge is θ, it becomes $\theta/2$ at great distances. Verify this statement and explain it. (Hint: Consider how the lines must behave both close to either charge and far from the charges.)

4. Assume that the exponent in Coulomb's law is not "two" but n. Show that for $n \neq 2$ it is impossible to construct lines that will have the properties listed for lines of force in Section 27–3. For simplicity, treat an isolated point charge.

5. What is the magnitude of a point charge chosen so that the electric field 50 cm away has the magnitude 2.0 nt/coul?

6. Two equal and opposite charges of magnitude 2.0×10^{-7} coul are 15 cm apart. (a) What are the magnitude and direction of **E** at a point midway between the charges? (b) What force (magnitude and direction) would act on an electron placed there?

7. Two point charges are a distance d apart (Fig. 27–16). Plot $E(x)$, assuming $x = 0$ at the left-hand charge. Consider both positive and negative values of x. Plot E as positive if **E** points to the right and negative if **E** points to the left. Assume $q_1 = +1.0 \times 10^{-6}$ coul, $q_2 = +3.0 \times 10^{-6}$ coul, and $d = 10$ cm.

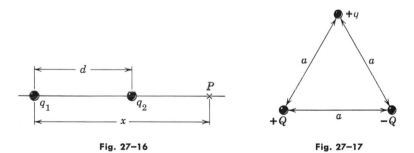

Fig. 27–16   Fig. 27–17

8. Three charges are arranged in an equilateral triangle as in Fig. 27–17. What is the direction of the force on $+q$?

9. Two point charges of magnitude $+2.0 \times 10^{-7}$ coul and $+8.5 \times 10^{-8}$ coul are 12 cm apart. (a) What electric field does each produce at the site of the other? (b) What force acts on each?

10. *Axial field due to an electric dipole.* In Fig. 27–8, consider a point a distance r from the center of the dipole *along its axis*. (a) Show that, at large values of r, the electric field is

$$E = \frac{1}{2\pi\epsilon_0} \frac{p}{r^3},$$

which is twice the value given for the conditions of Example 3.   (b) What is the direction of **E**?

11. In Fig. 27–8 assume that both charges are positive.   (a) Show that E at point P in that figure, assuming $r \gg a$, is given by

$$E = \frac{1}{4\pi\epsilon_0}\frac{2q}{r^2}.$$

(b) What is the direction of **E**?   (c) Is it reasonable that E should vary as r^{-2} here and as r^{-3} for the dipole of Fig. 27–8?

12. (a) In Fig. 27–18 locate the point (or points) at which the electric field strength is zero.   (b) Sketch qualitatively the lines of force.   Take $a = 50$ cm.

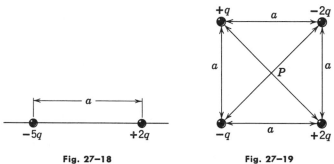

Fig. 27–18   Fig. 27–19

13. What is **E** in magnitude and direction at the center of the square of Fig. 27–19? Assume that $q = 1.0 \times 10^{-8}$ coul and $a = 5.0$ cm.

14. Two point charges of unknown magnitude and sign are placed a distance d apart. (a) If it is possible to have **E** = 0 at any point *not* between the charges but on the line joining them, what are the necessary conditions and where is the point located?   (b) Is it possible, for any arrangement of two point charges, to find *two* points (neither at infinity) at which **E** = 0; if so, under what conditions?

15. A thin nonconducting rod of finite length l carries a total charge q, spread uniformly along it.   Show that E at point P on the perpendicular bisector in Fig. 27–20 is given by

$$E = \frac{q}{2\pi\epsilon_0 y}\frac{1}{\sqrt{l^2 + 4y^2}}.$$

Show that as $l \rightarrow \infty$ this result approaches that of Example 6.

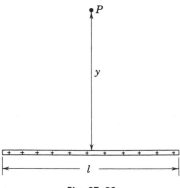

Fig. 27–20

16. A thin nonconducting rod is bent to form the arc of a circle of radius a and subtends an angle θ_0 at the center of the circle. A total charge q is spread uniformly along its length. Find the electric field strength at the center of the circle in terms of a, q, and θ_0.

17. A nonconducting hemispherical cup of inner radius a has a total charge q spread uniformly over its inner surface. Find the electric field at the center of curvature.

18. *Electric quadrupole.* Figure 27–21 shows a typical electric quadrupole. It consists of two dipoles whose effects at external points do not quite cancel. Show that the value of E on the axis of the quadrupole for points distant r from its center (assume $r \gg a$) is given by

$$E = \frac{3Q}{4\pi\epsilon_0 r^4}$$

where $Q \ (= 2qa^2)$ is called the *quadrupole moment* of the charge distribution.

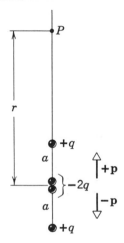

Fig. 27–21

19. An electron is constrained to move along the axis of the ring of charge in Example 5. Show that the electron can perform oscillations whose frequency is given by

$$\omega = \sqrt{\frac{eq}{4\pi\epsilon_0 m a^3}} \cdot$$

This formula holds only for small oscillations, that is, for $x \ll a$ in Fig. 27–10. (Hint: Show that the motion is simple harmonic and use Eq. 15–8.)

20. For the ring of charge in Example 5, show that the maximum value of E occurs at $x = a/\sqrt{2}$.

21. Consider the ring of charge of Example 5. Suppose that the charge q is not distributed uniformly over the ring but that charge q_1 is distributed uniformly over half the circumference and charge q_2 is distributed uniformly over the other half. Let $q_1 + q_2 = q$. (a) Find the *component* of the electric field at any point on the axis directed *along* the axis and compare with the uniform case of Example 5. (b) Find the *component* of the electric field at any point on the axis *perpendicular* to the axis and compare with the uniform case of Example 5.

22. A thin circular disk of radius a is charged uniformly so as to have a charge per unit area of σ. Find the electric field on the axis of the disk at a distance r from the disk.

23. *Field due to an electric dipole.* Show that the components of **E** due to a dipole are given, at distant points, by

$$E_x = \frac{1}{4\pi\epsilon_0} \frac{3pxy}{(x^2 + y^2)^{5/2}}$$

$$E_y = \frac{1}{4\pi\epsilon_0} \frac{p(2y^2 - x^2)}{(x^2 + y^2)^{5/2}},$$

where x and y are coordinates of a point in Fig. 27–22. Show that this general result includes the special results of Eq. 27–8b and of Problem 10.

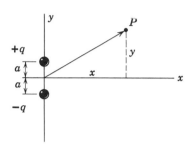

Fig. 27–22

24. What is the magnitude and direction of an electric field that will balance the weight of (a) an electron and (b) an alpha particle?

25. A particle having a charge of -2.0×10^{-9} coul is acted on by a downward electric force of 3.0×10^{-6} newton in a uniform electric field. (a) What is the strength of the electric field? (b) What is the magnitude and direction of the *electric* force exerted on a proton placed in this field? (c) What is the *gravitational* force on the proton? (d) What is the ratio of the electric to the gravitational forces in this case?

26. (a) What is the acceleration of an electron in a uniform electric field of 10^6 nt/coul? (b) How long would it take for the electron, starting from rest, to attain one-tenth the speed of light? (c) What considerations limit the applicability of Newtonian mechanics to such problems?

27. An electron moving with a speed of 5.0×10^8 cm/sec is shot parallel to an electric field of strength 1.0×10^3 nt/coul arranged so as to retard its motion. (a) How far will the electron travel in the field before coming (momentarily) to rest, and (b) how much time will elapse? (c) If the electric field ends abruptly after 0.8 cm, what fraction of its initial energy will the electron lose in traversing it?

28. An electron is projected as in Fig. 27–23 at a speed of 6.0×10^6 meters/sec and at an angle θ of $45°$; $E = 2.0 \times 10^3$ nt/coul (directed upward), $d = 2.0$ cm, and $l = 10.0$ cm (a) Will the electron strike either of the plates? (b) If it strikes a plate, where does it do so?

29. *Dipole in a nonuniform field.* Derive an expression for dE/dz at a point midway between two equal positive charges, where z is the distance from one of the charges, measured along the line joining them. Would there be a force on a small dipole placed at this point, its axis being aligned with the z axis? Recall that **E** = 0 at this point.

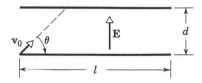

Fig. 27–23

30. *Oil drop experiment.* R. A. Millikan set up an apparatus (Fig. 27–24) in which a tiny, charged oil drop, placed in an electric field **E**, could be "balanced" by adjusting E until the electric force on the drop was equal and opposite to its weight. If the radius of the drop is 1.64×10^{-4} cm and E at balance is 1.92×10^5 nt/coul, (a) what charge is on the drop? (b) Why did Millikan not try to balance electrons in his apparatus instead of oil drops? The density of the oil is 0.851 gm/cm³. (Millikan first measured the electronic charge in this way. He measured the drop radius by observing the limiting speed that the drops attained when they fell in air with the electric field turned off. He charged the oil drops by irradiating them with bursts of X-rays.)

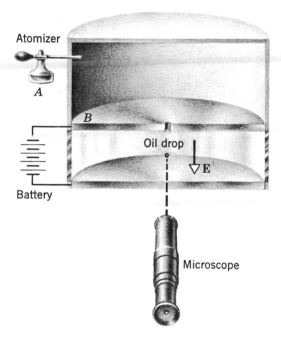

Fig. 27–24 Millikan's oil drop apparatus. Charged oil drops from atomizer A fall through the hole in plate B.

31. In a particular early run (1911), Millikan observed that the following measured charges, among others, appeared at different times on a single drop:

6.563×10^{-19} coul	13.13×10^{-19} coul	19.71×10^{-19} coul
8.204×10^{-19} coul	16.48×10^{-19} coul	22.89×10^{-19} coul
$11.50 \ \times 10^{-19}$ coul	18.08×10^{-19} coul	26.13×10^{-19} coul

What value for the elementary charge e can be deduced from these data?

32. An electric field **E** with an average magnitude of about 150 nt/coul points upward in the earth's atmosphere. We wish to "float" a sulfur sphere weighing 1.0 lb in this field by charging it. (a) What charge (sign and magnitude) must be used? (b) Why is the experiment not practical? Give a qualitative reason supported by a very rough numerical calculation to prove your point.

Gauss's Law

CHAPTER 28

28-1 Flux of the Electric Field

Flux (symbol Φ) is a property of any vector field; it refers to a hypothetical surface, which may be closed or open. For a *flow field* the flux (Φ_v) is measured by the number of streamlines that cut through the surface. For an *electric field* the flux (Φ_E) is measured by the number of lines of force that cut through the surface.

For closed surfaces we shall see that Φ_E is positive if the lines of force point outward everywhere and negative if they point inward. Figure 28–1 shows two equal and opposite charges and their lines of force. Curves S_1, S_2, S_3, and S_4 are the intersections with the plane of the figure of four hypothetical closed surfaces. From the statement just given, Φ_E is positive for surface S_1 and negative for S_2. The flux of the electric field is important because Gauss's law, one of the four basic equations of electromagnetism (see Table 38–3), is expressed in terms of it. Although the concept of flux may seem a little abstract at first, the student will soon see its value in solving problems.

To define Φ_E precisely, consider Fig. 28–2, which shows an arbitrary closed surface immersed in an electric field. Let the surface be divided into elementary squares ΔS, each of which is small enough so that it may be considered to be plane. Such an element of area can be represented as a vector $\Delta \mathbf{S}$, whose magnitude is the area ΔS; the direction of $\Delta \mathbf{S}$ is taken as the *outward-drawn normal* to the surface.

At every square in Fig. 28–2 we can also construct an electric field vector $\mathbf{E}$. Since the squares have been taken to be arbitrarily small, $\mathbf{E}$ may be taken as constant for all points in a given square.

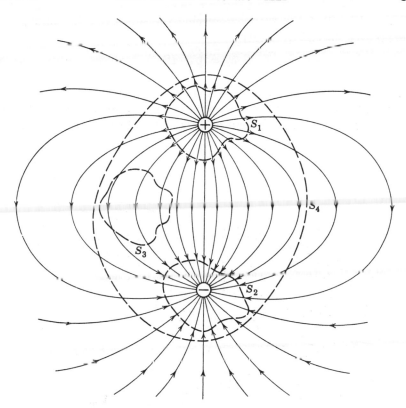

Fig. 28–1 Two equal and opposite charges. The dashed lines represent hypothetical closed surfaces.

The vectors $\mathbf{E}$ and $\Delta\mathbf{S}$ that characterize each square make an angle θ with each other. Figure 28–2b shows an enlarged view of the three squares on the surface of Fig. 28–2a marked x, y, and z. Note that at x, $\theta > 90°$; at y, $\theta = 90°$; and at z, $\theta < 90°$.

A semiquantitative definition of flux is

$$\Phi_E \cong \Sigma\mathbf{E}\cdot\Delta\mathbf{S}, \qquad\qquad (28\text{–}1)$$

which instructs us to add up the scalar quantity $\mathbf{E}\cdot\Delta\mathbf{S}$ for all elements of area into which the surface has been divided. For points such as x in Fig. 28–2 the contribution to the flux is negative; at y it is zero and at z it is positive. Thus if $\mathbf{E}$ is everywhere outward, $\theta < 90°$, $\mathbf{E}\cdot\Delta\mathbf{S}$ will be positive, and Φ_E for the entire surface will be positive; see Fig. 28–1, surface S_1. If $\mathbf{E}$ is everywhere inward, $\theta > 90°$, $\mathbf{E}\cdot\Delta\mathbf{S}$ will be negative, and Φ_E for the surface will be negative; see Fig. 28–1, surface S_2. From Eq. 28–1 we see that the appropriate mks unit for Φ_E is the newton-meter^2/coul.

The exact definition of the electric flux through a closed surface is the differential limit of Eq. 28–1. Replacing the sum over the surface by an integral over the surface yields

$$\Phi_E = \oint \mathbf{E} \cdot d\mathbf{S}. \tag{28–2}$$

This *surface integral* indicates that the surface in question is to be divided into infinitesimal elements of area $d\mathbf{S}$ and that the scalar quantity $\mathbf{E} \cdot d\mathbf{S}$ is to be evaluated for each element and the sum taken for the entire surface.

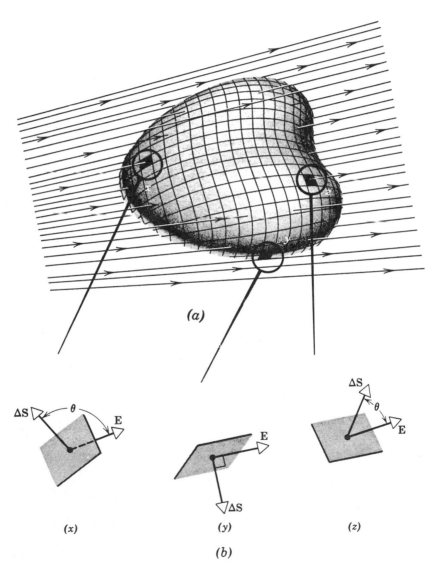

(a)

(x) *(y)* *(z)*

(b)

Fig. 28–2 *(a)* A hypothetical surface immersed in an electric field. *(b)* Three elements of area on this surface, shown enlarged.

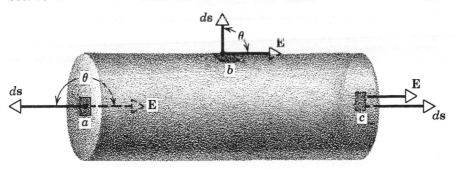

Fig. 28–3   Example 1. A cylindrical surface immersed in a uniform field **E** parallel to its axis.

The circle on the integral sign indicates that the surface of integration is a closed surface.*

▶ **Example 1.** Figure 28–3 shows a hypothetical cylinder of radius R immersed in a uniform electric field **E**, the cylinder axis being parallel to the field. What is Φ_E for this closed surface?

The flux Φ_E can be written as the sum of three terms, an integral over (a) the left cylinder cap, (b) the cylindrical surface, and (c) the right cap. Thus

$$\Phi_E = \oint \mathbf{E} \cdot d\mathbf{S}$$

$$= \int_{(a)} \mathbf{E} \cdot d\mathbf{S} + \int_{(b)} \mathbf{E} \cdot d\mathbf{S} + \int_{(c)} \mathbf{E} \cdot d\mathbf{S}.$$

For the left cap, the angle θ for all points is 180°, **E** has a constant value, and the vectors $d\mathbf{S}$ are all parallel. Thus

$$\int_{(a)} \mathbf{E} \cdot d\mathbf{S} = \int E \cos 180° \, dS$$

$$= -E \int dS = -ES,$$

where $S \, (= \pi R^2)$ is the cap area. Similarly, for the right cap,

$$\int_{(c)} \mathbf{E} \cdot d\mathbf{S} = +ES,$$

the angle θ for all points being zero here. Finally, for the cylinder wall,

$$\int_{(b)} \mathbf{E} \cdot d\mathbf{S} = 0,$$

because $\theta = 90°$, hence $\mathbf{E} \cdot d\mathbf{S} = 0$ for all points on the cylindrical surface. Thus

$$\Phi_E = -ES + 0 + ES = 0. \qquad \blacktriangleleft$$

---

* Similarly, a circle on a *line* integral sign indicates a closed *path*. It will be clear from the context and from the differential element ($d\mathbf{S}$ in this case) whether we are dealing with a surface integral or a line integral.

28-2   Gauss's Law

Gauss's law, which applies to any closed hypothetical surface (called a *Gaussian surface*), gives a connection between Φ_E for the surface and the net charge q enclosed by the surface.   It is

$$\epsilon_0 \Phi_E = q \qquad (28\text{-}3)$$

or, using Eq. 28-2,
$$\epsilon_0 \oint \mathbf{E} \cdot d\mathbf{S} = q. \qquad (28\text{-}4)$$

The fact that Φ_E proves to be zero in Example 1 is predicted by Gauss's law because no charge is enclosed by the Gaussian surface in Fig. 28-3 ($q = 0$).

Note that q in Eq. 28-3 (or in Eq. 28-4) is the *net* charge, taking its algebraic sign into account.   If a surface encloses equal and opposite charges, the flux Φ_E is zero.   Charge outside the surface makes no contribution to the value of q, nor does the exact location of the inside charges affect this value.

Gauss's law can be used to evaluate $\mathbf{E}$ if the charge distribution is so symmetric that by proper choice of a Gaussian surface we can easily evaluate the integral in Eq. 28-4.   Conversely, if $\mathbf{E}$ is known for all points on a given closed surface, Gauss's law can be used to compute the charge inside.   If $\mathbf{E}$ has an outward component for every point on a closed surface, Φ_E, as Eq. 28-2 shows, will be positive and, from Eq. 28-4, there must be a net positive charge within the surface (see Fig. 28-1, surface S_1).   If $\mathbf{E}$ has an inward component for every point on a closed surface, there must be a net negative charge within the surface (see Fig. 28-1, surface S_2).   Surface S_3 in Fig. 28-1 encloses no charge, so that Gauss's law predicts that $\Phi_E = 0$.   This is consistent with the fact that lines of $\mathbf{E}$ pass directly through surface S_3, the contribution to the integral on one side canceling that on the other.   What would be the value of Φ_E for surface S_4 in Fig. 28-1, which encloses both charges?

28-3   Gauss's Law and Coulomb's Law

Coulomb's law can be deduced from Gauss's law and symmetry considerations.   To do so, let us apply Gauss's law to an isolated point charge q as in Fig. 28-4.   Although Gauss's law holds for any surface whatever, information can most readily be extracted for a spherical surface of radius r centered

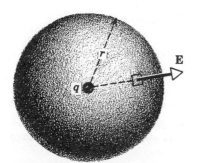

Fig. 28-4   A spherical Gaussian surface of radius r surrounding a point charge q.

on the charge. The advantage of this surface is that, from symmetry, $\mathbf{E}$ must be normal to it and must have the same (as yet unknown) magnitude for all points on the surface.

In Fig. 28-4 both $\mathbf{E}$ and $d\mathbf{S}$ at any point on the Gaussian surface are directed radially outward. The angle between them is zero and the quantity $\mathbf{E} \cdot d\mathbf{S}$ becomes simply $E\,dS$. Gauss's law (Eq. 28-4) thus reduces to

$$\epsilon_0 \oint \mathbf{E} \cdot d\mathbf{S} = \epsilon_0 \oint E\,dS = q.$$

Because E is constant for all points on the sphere, it can be factored from inside the integral sign, leaving

$$\epsilon_0 E \oint dS = q,$$

where the integral is simply the area of the sphere.* This equation gives

$$\epsilon_0 E(4\pi r^2) = q$$

or

$$E = \frac{1}{4\pi\epsilon_0}\frac{q}{r^2}. \tag{28-5}$$

Equation 28-5 gives the magnitude of the electric field strength $\mathbf{E}$ at any point a distance r from an isolated point charge q. The direction of $\mathbf{E}$ is already known from symmetry.

Let us put a second point charge q_0 at the point at which $\mathbf{E}$ is calculated. The magnitude of the force that acts on it (see Eq. 27-2) is

$$F = Eq_0.$$

Combining with Eq. 28-5 gives

$$F = \frac{1}{4\pi\epsilon_0}\frac{qq_0}{r^2},$$

which is precisely Coulomb's law. Thus we have deduced Coulomb's law from Gauss's law and considerations of symmetry.

Gauss's law is one of the fundamental equations of electromagnetic theory and is displayed in Table 38-3 as one of Maxwell's equations. Coulomb's law is not listed in that table because, as we have just proved, it can be deduced from Gauss's law and from simple assumptions about the symmetry of $\mathbf{E}$ due to a point charge.

It is interesting to note that writing the proportionality constant in Coulomb's law as $1/4\pi\epsilon_0$ (see Eq. 26-3) permits a particularly simple form for Gauss's law (Eq. 28-3). If we had written the Coulomb law constant simply as k, Gauss's law would have to be written as $(1/4\pi k)\Phi_E = q$. We prefer to leave the factor 4π in Coulomb's law so that it will not appear in Guass's law or in other much used relations that will be derived later.

---

* The usefulness of Gauss's law depends on our ability to find a surface over which, from symmetry, both E and θ (see Fig. 28-2) have constant values. Then $E\cos\theta$ can be factored out of the integral and E can be found simply, as in this example.

28–4 An Insulated Conductor

Gauss's law can be used to make an important prediction, namely: *An excess charge, placed on an insulated conductor, resides entirely on its outer surface.* This hypothesis was shown to be true by experiment (see Section 28–5) before either Gauss's law or Coulomb's law were advanced. Indeed, the experimental proof of the hypothesis is the experimental foundation upon which both laws rest: We have already pointed out that Coulomb's torsion balance experiments, although direct and convincing, are not capable of great accuracy. In showing that the italicized hypothesis is predicted by Gauss's law, we are simply reversing the historical situation.

Figure 28–5 is a cross section of an insulated conductor of arbitrary shape carrying an excess charge q. The dashed lines show a Gaussian surface that lies a small distance below the actual surface of the conductor. Although the Gaussian surface can be as close to the actual surface as we wish, it is important to keep in mind that the Gaussian surface is *inside* the conductor.

When an excess charge is placed at random on an insulated conductor, it will set up electric fields inside the conductor. These fields act on the charge carriers of the conductor and cause them to move, that is, they set up internal currents. These currents redistribute the excess charge in such a way that the internal electric fields are automatically reduced in magnitude. Eventually the electric fields inside the conductor become zero everywhere, the currents automatically stop, and electrostatic conditions prevail. This redistribution of charge normally takes place in a time that is negligible for most purposes. What can be said about the distribution of the excess charge when such electrostatic conditions have been achieved?

If, at electrostatic equilibrium, **E** is zero everywhere inside the conductor, it must be zero for every point on the Gaussian surface. This means that the flux Φ_E for this surface must be zero. Gauss's law then predicts (see Eq. 28–3) that there must be no net charge inside the Gaussian surface. If the excess charge q is not *inside* this surface, it can only be *outside* it, that is, *it must be on the actual surface of the conductor.*

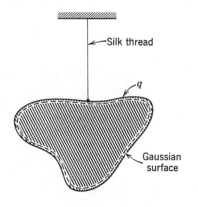

Silk thread

q

Gaussian surface

Fig. 28–5 An insulated conductor.

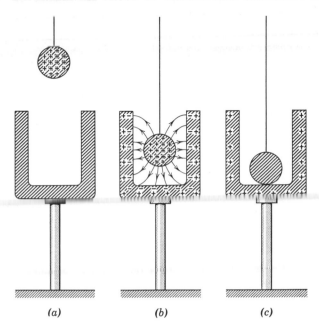

(a)   (b)   (c)

Fig. 28–6   The *entire* charge on the ball is transferred to the *outside* of the can. This state-ment and the discussion of the first paragraph of Section 28 5 are strictly correct only if the can is provided with a conducting lid which can be closed after the ball is inserted.

28–5   Experimental Proof of Gauss's and Coulomb's Laws

Let us turn to the experiments that prove that the hypothesis of Section 28–4. is true.   For a simple test, charge a metal ball and lower it with a silk thread deep into a metal can as in Fig. 28–6.   Touch the ball to the inside of the can; when the ball is removed from the can, all its charge will have vanished.   When the metal ball touches the can, the ball and can together form an "insulated conductor" to which the hypothesis of Section 28–4 applies.   That the charge moves entirely to the outside surface of the can can be shown by touching a small insulated metal object to the can; only on the *outside* of the can will it be possible to pick up a charge.

Benjamin Franklin seems to have been the first to notice that there can be no charge inside an insulated metal can.   In 1755 he wrote to a friend:

> I electrified a silver pint cann, on an electric stand, and then lowered into it a cork-ball, of about an inch diameter, hanging by a silk string, till the cork touched the bottom of the cann.   The cork was not attracted to the inside of the cann as it would have been to the outside, and though it touched the bottom, yet when drawn out, it was not found to be electrified by that touch, as it would have been by touch-ing the outside.   The fact is singular.   You require the reason; I do not know it. . . .

About ten years later Franklin recommended this "singular fact" to the attention of his friend Joseph Priestley (1733–1804).   In 1767 (about twenty years before Coulomb's experiments) Priestley checked Franklin's observation and, with remark-able insight, realized that the inverse square law of force followed from it.   Thus the indirect approach is not only more accurate than the direct approach of Section 26–4 but was carried out earlier.

Priestley, reasoning by analogy with gravitation, said that the fact that no electric force acted on Franklin's cork ball when it was surrounded by a deep metal can is similar to the fact (see Section 16–6) that no gravitational force acts on a mass inside a spherical shell of matter; if gravitation obeys an inverse square law, perhaps the electrical force does also. In Priestley's words:

> May we not infer from this [that is, Franklin's experiment] that the attraction of electricity is subject to the same laws with that of gravitation and is therefore according to the squares of the distances; since it is easily demonstrated that were the earth in the form of a shell, a body in the inside of it would not be attracted to one side more than another?

Michael Faraday also carried out experiments designed to show that excess charge resides on the outside surface of a conductor. In particular, he built a large metal-covered box which he mounted on insulating supports and charged with a powerful electrostatic generator. In Faraday's words:

> I went into the cube and lived in it, and using lighted candles, electrometers, and all other tests of electrical states, I could not find the least influence upon them . . . though all the time the outside of the cube was very powerfully charged, and large sparks and brushes were darting off from every part of its outer surface.

Henry Cavendish (1731–1810) carried out an improved version of the experiment of Fig. 28–6. With the instruments available to him, Cavendish proved experimentally that the exponent in the force law lay, with high probability, between 2.02 and 1.98. Cavendish, however, did not publish his results so that almost nobody knew about them at the time. Maxwell repeated Cavendish's experiment with more accuracy and set these limits as 2.00005 and 1.99995. In 1936 Plimpton and Lawton repeated the experiment again; they set the probability limits as 2.000000002 and 1.999999998.

Figure 28–7 is an idealized sketch of the apparatus of Plimpton and Lawton. It consists in principle of two concentric metal shells, A and B, the former being 5 ft in diameter. The inner shell contains a sensitive electrometer E connected so that it will indicate whether any charge moves between shells A and B.

By throwing switch S to the left, a substantial charge can be placed on the sphere assembly. If any of this charge moves to shell B, it will have to pass through the electrometer and will cause a deflection, which can be observed optically using telescope T, mirror M, and windows W.

However, when the switch S is thrown alternately from left to right, thus connecting the shell assembly either to the battery or to the ground, no effect is observed on the galvanometer. This is the strongest experimental evidence to date that the hypothesis of Section 28–4 is correct. Knowing the sensitivity of their electrometer, Plimpton and Lawton calculated that the exponent in Coulomb's law lies, with high probability, between the limits already stated.

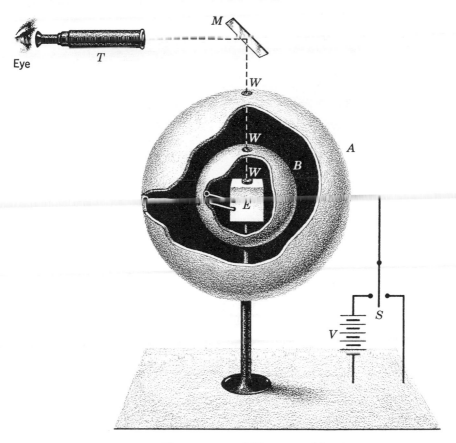

Fig. 28–7   The apparatus of Plimpton and Lawton.

28–6   Gauss's Law—Some Applications

Gauss's law can be used to calculate **E** if the symmetry of the charge distribution is high. One example of this, the calculation of **E** for a point charge, has already been discussed (Eq. 28–5). Here we present other examples.

▶ **Example 2.** *Spherically symmetric charge distribution.* Figure 28–8 shows a spherical distribution of charge of radius R. The *charge density* ρ (that is, the charge per unit volume, measured in coul/meter^3) at any point depends only on the distance of the point from the center and not on the direction, a condition called *spherical symmetry*. Find an expression for E for points (*a*) outside and (*b*) inside the charge distribution. Note that the object in Fig. 28–8 cannot be a conductor or, as we have seen, the excess charge will reside on its surface.

Applying Gauss's law to a spherical Gaussian surface of radius r in Fig. 28–8*a* (see Section 28–3) leads exactly to Eq. 28–5, or

$$E = \frac{1}{4\pi\epsilon_0}\frac{q}{r^2}, \tag{28–5}$$

where q is the total charge. Thus for points outside a spherically symmetric dis-

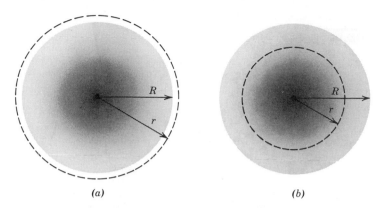

(a) (b)

Fig. 28–8 Example 2. A spherically symmetric charge distribution, showing two Gaussian surfaces. The density of charge, as the shading suggests, varies with distance from the center but not with direction.

tribution of charge, the electric field has the value that it would have if the charge were concentrated at its center. This reminds us that a sphere of mass m behaves gravitationally, for outside points, as if the mass were concentrated at its center. At the root of this similarity lies the fact that both Coulomb's law and the law of gravitation are inverse square laws. The gravitational case was proved in detail in Section 16 6; the proof using Gauss's law in the electrostatic case is certainly much simpler.

Figure 28–8b shows a spherical Gaussian surface of radius r drawn *inside* the charge distribution. Gauss's law (Eq. 28–4) gives

$$\epsilon_0 \oint \mathbf{E} \cdot d\mathbf{S} = \epsilon_0 E(4\pi r^2) = q'$$

or

$$E = \frac{1}{4\pi\epsilon_0} \frac{q'}{r^2},$$

in which q' is that part of q contained within the sphere of radius r. The part of q that lies outside this sphere makes no contribution to $\mathbf{E}$ at radius r. This corresponds, in the gravitational case (Section 16–6), to the fact that a spherical shell of matter exerts no gravitational force on a body inside it.

An interesting special case of a spherically symmetric charge distribution is a uniform sphere of charge. For such a sphere, which would be suggested by uniform shading in Fig. 28–8, the charge density ρ would have a constant value for all points within a sphere of radius R and would be zero for all points outside this sphere. For points inside such a uniform sphere of charge we can put

$$q' = q \frac{\frac{4}{3}\pi r^3}{\frac{4}{3}\pi R^3}$$

or

$$q' = q \left(\frac{r}{R}\right)^3,$$

where $\frac{4}{3}\pi R^3$ is the volume of the spherical charge distribution. The expression for E then becomes

$$E = \frac{1}{4\pi\epsilon_0} \frac{qr}{R^3}. \tag{28–6}$$

This equation becomes zero, as it should, for $r = 0$. Note that Eqs. 28–5 and 28–6 give the same result, as they must, for points on the surface of the charge distribution (that is, if $r = R$). Note that Eq. 28–6 does not apply to the charge distribution of Fig. 28–8b because the charge density, suggested by the shading, is *not* constant in that case.

Example 3. *The Thomson atom model.* At one time the positive charge in the atom was thought to be distributed uniformly throughout a sphere with a radius of about 1.0×10^{-10} meter, that is, throughout the entire atom. Calculate the electric field strength at the surface of a gold atom ($Z = 79$) on this assumption. Neglect the effect of the electrons.

The positive charge of the atom is Ze or $(79)(1.6 \times 10^{-19}$ coul$)$. Equation 28–5 yields, for E at the surface,

$$E = \frac{1}{4\pi\epsilon_0} \frac{q}{r^2}$$

$$= \frac{(9.0 \times 10^9 \text{ nt-m}^2/\text{coul}^2)(79)(1.6 \times 10^{-19} \text{ coul})}{(1.0 \times 10^{-10} \text{ meter})^2}$$

$$= 1.1 \times 10^{13} \text{ nt/coul}.$$

Figure 28–9 is a plot of E as a function of distance from the center of the atom, using Eqs. 28–5 and 28–6. We see that E has its maximum value on the surface and decreases linearly to zero at the center (see Eq. 28–6). Outside the sphere E decreases as the inverse square of the distance (see Eq. 28–5).

Example 4. *The Rutherford, or nuclear, atom.* We shall see in Section 28–7 that the positive charge of the atom is *not* spread uniformly throughout the atom (see Example 3) but is concentrated in a small region (the *nucleus*) at the center of the atom. For gold the radius of the nucleus is about 6.9×10^{-15} meter. What is the electric field strength at the nuclear surface? Again neglect effects associated with the atomic electrons.

The problem is the same as that of Example 3, except that the radius is much smaller. This will make the electric field strength at the surface larger, in proportion to the ratio of the squares of the radii. Thus

$$E = (1.1 \times 10^{13} \text{ nt/coul}) \frac{(1.0 \times 10^{-10} \text{ meter})^2}{(6.9 \times 10^{-15} \text{ meter})^2}$$

$$= 2.3 \times 10^{21} \text{ nt/coul}.$$

This is an enormous electric field, much stronger than could be produced and maintained in the laboratory. It is about 10^8 times as large as the field calculated in Example 3.

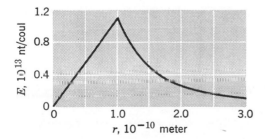

Fig. 28–9 Example 3. The electric field due to the positive charge in a gold atom, according to the Thomson model.

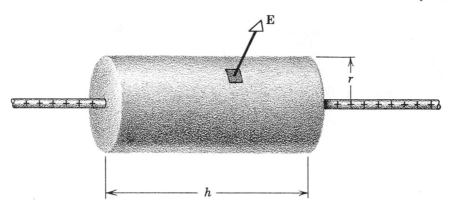

Fig. 28–10   Example 5.   An infinite rod of charge, showing a cylindrical Gaussian surface.

Example 5.   *Line of charge.*   Figure 28–10 shows a section of an infinite rod of charge, the *linear charge density* λ (that is, the charge per unit length, measured in coul/meter) being constant for all points on the line.   Find an expression for E at a distance r from the line.

From symmetry, **E** due to a uniform linear charge can only be radially directed. As a Gaussian surface we choose a circular cylinder of radius r and length h, closed at each end by plane caps normal to the axis. E is constant over the cylindrical surface and the flux of **E** through this surface is $E(2\pi rh)$ where $2\pi rh$ is the area of the surface. There is no flux through the circular caps because **E** here lies in the surface at every point.

The charge enclosed by the Gaussian surface of Fig. 28–10 is λh.   Gauss's law (Eq. 28–4),

$$\epsilon_0 \oint \mathbf{E} \cdot d\mathbf{S} = q,$$

then becomes

$$\epsilon_0 E(2\pi rh) = \lambda h,$$

whence

$$E = \frac{\lambda}{2\pi \epsilon_0 r}. \tag{28–7}$$

The direction of **E** is radially outward for a line of positive charge.

Note how much simpler the solution using Gauss's law is than that using integration methods, as in Example 6, Chapter 27.   Note too that the solution using Gauss's law is possible only if we choose our Gaussian surface to take full advantage of the radial symmetry of the electric field set up by a long line of charge.   We are free to choose any surface, such as a cube or a sphere, for a Gaussian surface.   Even though Gauss's law holds for all such surfaces, they are not all useful for the problem at hand; only the cylindrical surface of Fig. 28–10 is appropriate in this case.

Gauss's law has the property that it provides a useful technique for calculation only in problems that have a certain degree of symmetry, but in these problems the solutions are strikingly simple.

Example 6.   *A sheet of charge.*   Figure 28–11 shows a portion of a thin, *nonconducting*, infinite sheet of charge, the *surface charge density* σ (that is, the charge per unit area, measured in coul/meter²) being constant.   What is **E** at a distance r in front of the plane?

A convenient Gaussian surface is a "pill box" of cross-sectional area A and height $2r$, arranged to pierce the plane as shown.   From symmetry, **E** points at right angles

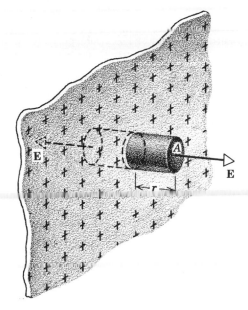

Fig. 28–11 Example 6. An infinite sheet of charge pierced by a cylindrical Gaussian surface. The cross section of the cylinder need not be circular, as shown, but can have an arbitrary shape.

to the end caps and away from the plane. Since **E** does not pierce the cylindrical surface, there is no contribution to the flux from this source. Thus Gauss's law,

$$\epsilon_0 \oint \mathbf{E} \cdot d\mathbf{S} = q$$

becomes $\epsilon_0(EA + EA) = \sigma A$

where σA is the enclosed charge. This gives

$$E = \frac{\sigma}{2\epsilon_0}. \qquad\qquad (28\text{–}8)$$

Note that E is the same for all points on each side of the plane; compare Fig. 27–2. Although an infinite sheet of charge cannot exist physically, this derivation is still useful in that Eq. 28–8 yields substantially correct results for real (not infinite) charge sheets if we consider only points not near the edges whose distance from the sheet is small compared to the dimensions of the sheet.

Example 7. *A charged conductor.* Figure 28–12 shows a *conductor* carrying on its surface a charge whose surface charge density at any point is σ; in general σ will vary from point to point. What is **E** for points a short distance above the surface?

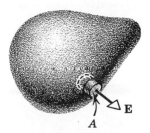

Fig. 28–12 Example 7. A charged insulated conductor, showing a Gaussian surface. The cross section of the surface need not be circular, as shown, but can have an arbitrary shape.

The direction of **E** *for points close to the surface* is at right angles to the surface, pointing away from the surface if the charge is positive. If **E** were *not* normal to the surface, it would have a component lying in the surface. Such a component would act on the charge carriers in the conductor and set up surface currents. Since there are no such currents under the assumed electrostatic conditions, **E** must be normal to the surface.

The magnitude of **E** can be found from Gauss's law using a small flat "pill box" of cross section A as a Gaussian surface. Since **E** equals zero everywhere inside the conductor (see Section 28–4), the only contribution to Φ_E is through the plane cap of area A that lies outside the conductor. Gauss's law

$$\epsilon_0 \oint \mathbf{E} \cdot d\mathbf{S} = q$$

becomes

$$\epsilon_0 (EA) = \sigma A$$

where σA is the net charge within the Gaussian surface. This yields

$$E = \frac{\sigma}{\epsilon_0}. \tag{28–9}$$

Comparison with Eq. 28–8 shows that the electric field is *twice as great* near a conductor carrying a charge whose surface charge density is σ as that near a nonconducting sheet with the same surface charge density. The student should compare the Gaussian surfaces in Figs. 28–11 and 28–12 carefully. In Fig. 28–11 lines of force leave the surface through *each* end cap, an electric field existing on *both* sides of the sheet. In Fig. 28–12 the lines of force leave only through the *outside* end cap, the inner end cap being inside the conductor where no electric field exists. If we assume the same surface charge density and cross-sectional area A for the two Gaussian surfaces, the enclosed charge $(= \sigma A)$ will be the same. Since, from Gauss's law, the flux Φ_E must then be the same in each case, it follows that $E (= \Phi_E/A)$ must be twice as large in Fig. 28–12 as in Fig. 28–11. It is helpful to note that in Fig. 28–11 half the flux emerges from one side of the surface and half from the other, whereas in Fig. 28–12 all the flux emerges from the outside surface. ◀

28–7   The Nuclear Model of the Atom

Ernest Rutherford (1871–1937) was first led, in 1911, to assume that the atomic nucleus existed when he tried to interpret some experiments carried out at the University of Manchester by his collaborators H. Geiger and E. Marsden.* The results of Examples 3 and 4 played an important part in Rutherford's analysis of these experiments.

These workers, at Rutherford's suggestion, allowed a beam of α-particles † to strike and be deflected by a thin film of a heavy element such as gold. They counted the number of particles deflected through various angles ϕ. Figure 28–13 shows the experimental setup schematically. Figure 28–14 shows the paths taken by typical α-particles as they scatter from a gold atom; the angles ϕ through which the α-particles are deflected range from 0 to 180° as the character of the collision varies from "grazing" to "head-on."

---

* See "The Birth of the Nuclear Atom," E. N. da C. Andrade, *Scientific American*, November 1956. See also Example 5, Chapter 10.

† α-Particles are helium nuclei that are emitted spontaneously by some radioactive materials such as radium. They move with speeds of the order of one-thirtieth that of light when so emitted.

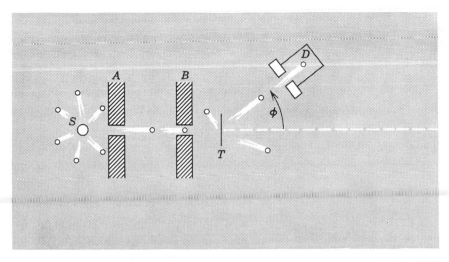

Fig. 20-13 Experimental arrangement for studying the scattering of α-particles. Particles from radioactive source S are allowed to fall on a thin metal "target" T; α-particles scattered by the target through an (adjustable) angle φ are counted by detector D.

The electrons in the gold atom, being so light, have almost no effect on the motion of an oncoming α-particle; the electrons are themselves strongly deflected, just as a swarm of insects would be by a stone hurled through them. Any deflection of the α-particle must be caused by the repulsive action of the positive charge of the gold atom, which is known to possess most of the mass of the atom.

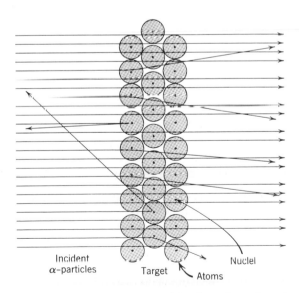

Incident
α-particles   Target   Atoms   Nuclei

Fig. 28-14 The deflection of the incident α-particles depends on the nature of the nuclear collision. (From Andrade, *Scientific American*, November 1956.)

At the time of these experiments most physicists believed in the so-called "plum pudding" model of the atom that had been suggested by J. J. Thomson (1856–1940). In this view (see Example 3) the positive charge of the atom was thought to be spread out through the whole atom, that is, through a spherical volume of radius about 10^{-10} meter. The electrons were thought to vibrate about fixed centers inside this sphere.

Rutherford showed that this model of the atom was not consistent with the α-scattering experiments and proposed instead the nuclear model of the atom that we now accept. Here the positive charge is confined to a very much smaller sphere whose radius is about 10^{-14} meter (the *nucleus*). The electrons move around this nucleus and occupy a roughly spherical volume of radius about 10^{-10} meter. This brilliant deduction by Rutherford laid the foundation for modern atomic and nuclear physics.

The feature of the α-scattering experiments that attracted Rutherford's attention at once was that a few α-particles are deflected through very large angles, up to 180°. To scientists accustomed to thinking in terms of the "plum pudding" model, this was a very surprising result. In Rutherford's words: "It was quite the most incredible event that ever happened to me in my life. It was almost as incredible as if you had fired a 15-inch shell at a piece of tissue paper and it came back and hit you."

The α-particle must pass through a region in which the electric field strength is very high indeed in order to be deflected so strongly.* Example 3 shows that, in Thomson's model, the maximum electric field strength is 1.1×10^{13} nt/coul. Compare this with the value calculated in Example 4 for a point on the surface of a gold nucleus (2.3×10^{21} nt/coul). Thus the deflecting force acting on an α-particle can be up to 10^8 times as great if the positive charge of the atom is compressed into a very small region (the nucleus) at the center of the atoms. Rutherford made his hypothesis about the existence of nuclei only after a much more detailed mathematical analysis than that given here.

QUESTIONS

1. A point charge is placed at the center of a spherical Gaussian surface. Is Φ_E changed (a) if the surface is replaced by a cube of the same volume, (b) if the sphere is replaced by a cube of one-tenth the volume, (c) if the charge is moved off-center in the original sphere, still remaining inside, (d) if the charge is moved just outside the original sphere, (e) if a second charge is placed near, and outside, the original sphere, and (f) if a second charge is placed inside the Gaussian surface?

2. By analogy with Φ_E, how would you define the flux Φ_g of a gravitational field? What is the flux of the earth's gravitational field through the boundaries of a room, assumed to contain no matter?

3. In Gauss's law,

$$\epsilon_0 \oint \mathbf{E} \cdot d\mathbf{S} = q,$$

is $\mathbf{E}$ the electric field intensity attributable to the charge q?

---

* The chance that a big deflection can result from the combined effects of many small deflections can be shown to be very small.

1. Show that Eq. 18–3 illustrates what might be called *Gauss's law for incompressible fluids*, or

$$\Phi_v = \oint \mathbf{v} \cdot d\mathbf{S} = 0.$$

5. A surface encloses an electric dipole. What can you say about Φ_E for this surface?

6. Suppose that a Gaussian surface encloses no net charge. Does Gauss's law require that $\mathbf{E}$ equal zero for all points on the surface? Is the converse of this statement true, that is, if $\mathbf{E}$ equals zero everywhere on the surface, does Gauss's law require that there be no net charge inside?

7. Would Gauss's law hold if the exponent in Coulomb's law were not exactly two?

8. Does Gauss's law, as applied in Section 28–4, require that all the conduction electrons in an insulated conductor reside on the surface?

9. In Section 28–4 we assumed that $\mathbf{E}$ equals zero everywhere inside a conductor. However, there are certainly very large electric fields inside the conductor, at points close to the electrons or to the nuclei. Does this invalidate the proof of Section 28–4?

10. It is sometimes said that excess charge resides entirely on the outer surface of a conductor because like charges repel and try to get as far away as possible from one another. Comment on this plausibility argument.

11. Is Gauss's law useful in calculating the field due to three equal charges located at the corners of an equilateral triangle? Explain.

12. The use of line, surface, and volume densities of charge to calculate the charge contained in an element of a charged object implies a continuous distribution of charge, whereas, in fact, charge on the microscopic scale is discontinuous. How, then, is this procedure justified?

13. Is $\mathbf{E}$ necessarily zero inside a charged rubber balloon if the balloon is (a) spherical or (b) sausage-shaped? For each shape assume the charge to be distributed uniformly over the surface.

14. A spherical rubber balloon carries a charge that is uniformly distributed over its surface. How does E vary for points (a) inside the balloon, (b) at the surface of the balloon, and (c) outside the balloon, as the balloon is blown up?

15. As you penetrate a uniform sphere of charge, E should decrease because less charge lies inside a sphere drawn through the observation point. On the other hand, E should increase because you are closer to the center of this charge. Which effect predominates and why?

16. Given a spherically symmetric charge distribution (not of uniform density of charge), is E necessarily a maximum at the surface? Comment on various possibilities.

17. An atom is normally *electrically neutral*. Why then should an α-particle be deflected by the atom under any circumstances?

18. If an α-particle, fired at a gold nucleus, is deflected through 135°, can you conclude (a) that any force has acted on the α-particle or (b) that any net work has been done on it?

PROBLEMS

1. Calculate Φ_E through a hemisphere of radius R. The field of $\mathbf{E}$ is uniform and is parallel to the axis of the hemisphere.

2. In Example 1 compute Φ_E for the cylinder if it is turned so that its axis is perpendicular to the electric field. Do not use Gauss's law.

3. A plane surface of area A is inclined so that its normal makes an angle θ with a uniform field of $\mathbf{E}$. Calculate Φ_E for this surface.

4. A point charge of 1.0×10^{-6} coul is at the center of a cubical Gaussian surface 0.50 meter on edge. What is Φ_E for the surface?

5. Charge on an originally uncharged insulated conductor is separated by holding a positively charged rod nearby, as in Fig. 28–15. What can you learn from Gauss's law about the flux for the five Gaussian surfaces shown? The induced negative charge on the conductor is equal to the positive charge on the rod.

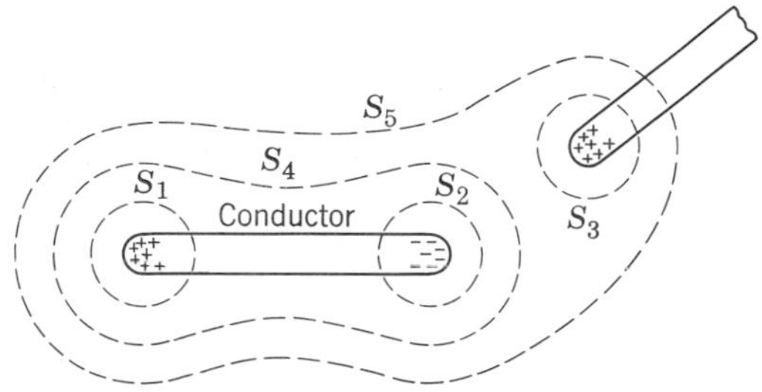

6. "Gauss's law for gravitation" is

$$\frac{1}{4\pi G} \Phi_g = \frac{1}{4\pi G} \oint \mathbf{g} \cdot d\mathbf{S} = m,$$

where m is the enclosed mass and G is the universal gravitation constant (Section 16–3). Derive Newton's law of gravitation from this.

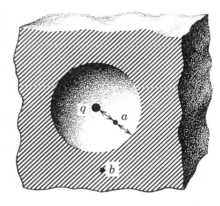

Fig. 28–15

7. Figure 28–16 shows a point charge of 1.0×10^{-7} coul at the center of a spherical cavity of radius 3.0 cm in a piece of metal. Use Gauss's law to find the electric field at point a, halfway from the center to the surface, and at point b.

8. An uncharged spherical thin metallic shell has a point charge q at its center. Give expressions for the electric field (a) inside the shell, and (b) outside the shell, using Gauss's law. (c) Has the shell any effect on the field due to q? (d) Has the presence of q any effect on the shell? (e) If a second point charge is held outside the shell, does this outside charge experience a force? (f) Does the inside charge experience a force? (g) Is there a contradiction with Newton's third law here?

9. Two large nonconducting sheets of positive charge face each other as in Fig. 28–17. What is **E** at points (a) to the left of the sheets, (b) between them, and (c) to the right of the sheets? Assume the same surface charge density σ for each sheet. Consider only points not near the edges whose distance from the sheets is small compared to the dimensions of the sheet. (Hint: **E** at any point is the vector sum of the separate electric field strengths set up by each sheet.)

Fig. 28–16

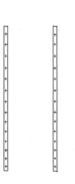

Fig. 28–17

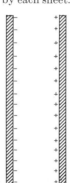

Fig. 28–18

10. Two large metal plates face each other as in Fig. 28–18 and carry charges with surface charge density $+\sigma$ and $-\sigma$, respectively, on their inner surfaces. What is E at points (a) to the left of the sheets, (b) between them, and (c) to the right of the sheets. Consider only points not near the edges whose distance from the sheets is small compared to the dimensions of the sheet.

11. Two large metal plates of area 1.0 meter² face each other. They are 5.0 cm apart and carry equal and opposite charges on their inner surfaces. If E between the plates is 55 nt/coul, what is the charge on the plates? Neglect edge effects. See Problem 10.

12. A thin-walled metal sphere has a radius of 25 cm and carries a charge of 2.0×10^{-7} coul. Find E for a point (a) inside the sphere, (b) just outside the sphere, and (c) 3.0 meters from the center of the sphere.

13. A 100-ev electron is fired directly toward a large metal plate that has a surface charge density of -2.0×10^{-6} coul/meter². From what distance must the electron be fired if it is to just fail to strike the plate?

14. Charge is distributed uniformly throughout an infinitely long cylinder of radius R. Show that E at a distance r from the cylinder axis ($r < R$) is given by

$$E = \frac{\rho r}{2\epsilon_0}$$

where ρ is the density of charge (coul/meter³). What result do you expect for $r > R$?

15. Figure 28–19 shows a spherical non-conducting shell of charge of uniform density ρ (coul/meter³). Plot E for distances r from the center of the shell ranging from zero to 30 cm. Assume that $\rho = 1.0 \times 10^{-6}$ coul/meter³, $a = 10$ cm, and $b = 20$ cm.

16. Figure 28–20 shows a section through a long, thin-walled metal tube of radius R, carrying a charge per unit length λ on its surface. Derive expressions for E for various distances r from the tube axis, considering both $r > R$ and $r < R$. Plot your re-

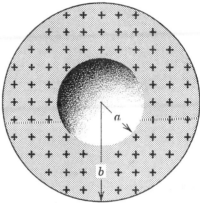

Fig. 28–19

sults for the range $r = 0$ to $r = 5$ cm, assuming that $\lambda = 2.0 \times 10^{-8}$ coul/meter and $R = 3.0$ cm.

17. Figure 28–21 shows a section through two long concentric cylinders of radii a and b. The cylinders carry equal and opposite charges per unit length λ. Using Gauss's law,

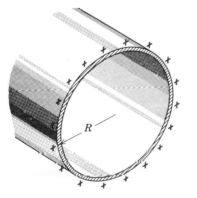

Fig. 28–20

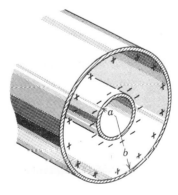

Fig. 28–21

prove (a) that $E = 0$ for $r > b$ and for $r < a$ and (b) that between the cylinders E is given by

$$E = \frac{1}{2\pi\epsilon_0}\frac{\lambda}{r}.$$

18. In Problem 17 an electron revolves in a circular path of radius r, between and concentric with the cylinders. What must be its kinetic energy K? Assume $a = 2.0$ cm, $b = 3.0$ cm, and $\lambda = 3.0 \times 10^{-8}$ coul/meter.

19. A long conducting cylinder carrying a total charge $+q$ is surrounded by a conducting cylindrical shell of total charge $-2q$, as shown in cross section in Fig. 28–22. Use Gauss's

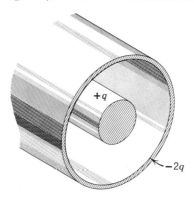

+q

−2q

Fig. 28–22

law to find (a) the electric field strength at points outside the conducting shell, (b) the distribution of the charge on the conducting shell, and (c) the electric field strength in the region between the cylinders. List the assumptions made in arriving at your answers.

20. A thin metallic spherical shell of radius a carries a charge q_a. Concentric with it is another thin metallic spherical shell of radius b ($b > a$) carrying a charge q_b. Use Gauss's law to find the electric field strength at radial points r where (a) $r < a$; (b) $a < r < b$; (c) $r > b$. (d) Discuss the criterion one would use to determine how the charges are distributed on the inner and outer surfaces of each shell.

21. A small sphere whose mass m is 1.0×10^{-3} gm carries a charge q of 2.0×10^{-8} coul. It hangs from a silk thread which makes an angle of $30°$ with a large, charged conducting sheet as in Fig. 28–23. Calculate the surface charge density σ for the sheet.

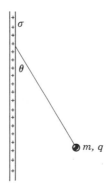

σ

θ

m, q

Fig. 28–23

22. Equation 28–9 ($E = \sigma/\epsilon_0$) gives the electric field at points near a charged conducting surface. Show that this equation leads to a familiar result when applied to a conducting sphere of radius r, carrying a charge q.

23. An α-particle, approaching the surface of a nucleus of gold, is a distance equal to one nuclear radius (6.9×10^{-15} meter) away from that surface. What are the forces on the α-particle and its acceleration at that point? The mass of the α-particle, which may be treated here as a point, is 6.7×10^{-27} kg.

24. A gold foil used in a Rutherford scattering experiment is 3×10^{-5} cm thick. (a) What fraction of its surface area is "blocked out" by gold nuclei, assuming a nuclear radius of 6.9×10^{-15} meter? Assume that no nucleus is screened by any other. (b) What fraction of the volume of the foil is occupied by the nuclei? (c) What fills all the rest of the space in the foil?

25. The electric field components in Fig. 28–24 are $E_x = bx^{\frac{1}{2}}$, $E_y = E_z = 0$, in which $b = 800$ nt/coul-m$^{\frac{1}{2}}$. Calculate (a) the flux Φ_F through the cube and (b) the charge within the cube. Assume that $a = 10$ cm.

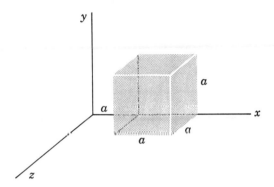

Fig. 28–24

Electric Potential

CHAPTER 29

29–1 Electric Potential

The electric field around a charged rod can be described not only by a (vector) electric field strength **E** but also by a scalar quantity, the *electric potential V*. These quantities are intimately related, and often it is only a matter of convenience which is used in a given problem.

To find the *electric potential difference* between two points A and B in an electric field, we move a test charge q_0 from A to B, always keeping it in equilibrium, and we measure the work W_{AB} that must be done by the agent moving the charge. The electric potential difference * is defined from

$$V_B - V_A = \frac{W_{AB}}{q_0}. \qquad (29–1)$$

The work W_{AB} may be (a) positive, (b) negative, or (c) zero. In these cases the electric potential at B will be (a) higher, (b) lower, or (c) the same as the electric potential at A.

The mks unit of potential difference that follows from Eq. 29–1 is the joule/coul. This combination occurs so often that a special unit, the *volt*, is used to represent it; that is,

$$1 \text{ volt} = 1 \text{ joule/coul.}$$

---

* This definition of potential difference, though conceptually sound and suitable for our present purpose, is rarely carried out in practice because of technical difficulties. Equivalent and more technically feasible methods are usually adopted.

Usually point A is chosen to be at a large (strictly an infinite) distance from all charges, and the electric potential V_A at this infinite distance is arbitrarily taken as zero. This allows us to define the *electric potential at a point*. Putting $V_A = 0$ in Eq. 29–1 and dropping the subscripts leads to

$$V = \frac{W}{q_0},\qquad (29\text{--}2)$$

where W is the work that an external agent must do to move the test charge q_0 from infinity to the point in question. The student should keep in mind that *potential differences* are of fundamental concern and that Eq. 29–2 depends on the arbitrary assignment of the value zero to the potential V_A at the reference position (infinity); this reference potential could equally well have been chosen as any other value, say -100 volts. Similarly any other agreed-upon point could be chosen as a reference position. In many circuit problems the *earth* is taken as a reference of potential and assigned the value zero.

Bearing in mind the assumptions made about the reference position, we see from Eq. 29–2 that V near an isolated positive charge is positive because positive work must be done by an outside agent to push a (positive) test charge in from infinity. Similarly, the potential near an isolated negative charge is negative because an outside agent must exert a restraining force on (that is, must do negative work on) a (positive) test charge as it comes in from infinity. Electric potential as defined in Eq. 29–2 is a scalar because W and q_0 in that equation are scalars.

Both W_{AB} and $V_B - V_A$ in Eq. 29–1 are independent of the path followed in moving the test charge from point A to point B. If this were not so, point B would not have a unique electric potential (with respect to point A as a defined reference position) and the concept of potential would have limited usefulness.

We can easily prove that potential differences are path-independent for the special case shown in Fig. 29–1. This figure illustrates the case in which the two points A and B are in a field set up by a spherical charge q; the two points are further chosen, for simplicity, to lie along a radial line. Although our

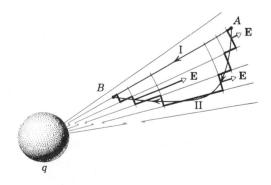

Fig. 29–1 A test charge q_0 is moved from A to B in the field of charge q along either of two paths. The open arrows show $\mathbf{E}$ at three points on path II.

path-independence proof applies only to this special case, it illustrates the general principles involved.

Point A in Fig. 29–1 may be taken as a defined reference point, and we imagine a positive test charge q_0 moved by an external agent from A to B. We consider two paths, path I being a radial line between A and B and path II being a completely arbitrary path between these two points. The open arrows on path II show the electric force per unit charge that would act at various points on a test charge q_0.

Path II may be approximated by a broken path made up of alternating elements of arc and of radius. Since these elements can be arbitrarily small, the broken path can be made arbitrarily close to the actual path. On path II the external agent does work *only along the radial segments* because along the arcs the force $\mathbf{F}$ and the displacement $d\mathbf{l}$ are at right angles, $\mathbf{F} \cdot d\mathbf{l}$ being zero in such cases. The sum of the work done on the radial segments that make up path II is the same as the work done on path I because each path has the same array of radial segments. Since path II is arbitrary, we have proved that the work done is the same for *all* paths connecting A and B. Although this proof holds only for the special case of Fig. 29–1, the potential difference is path-independent for *any* two points in *any* electrostatic field. We discussed path independence in Section 8–2 for the general class of *conservative forces;* electrostatic forces, like gravitational forces, are conservative.

The locus of points, all of which have the same electric potential, is called an *equipotential surface.* A family of equipotential surfaces, each surface corresponding to a different value of the potential, can be used to give a general description of the electric field in a certain region of space. We have seen earlier (Section 27–3) that electric lines of force can also be used for this purpose; in later sections (see, for example, Fig. 29–15) we explore the intimate connection between these two ways of describing the electric field.

No work is required to move a test charge between any two points on an equipotential surface. This follows from Eq. 29–1,

$$V_B - V_A = \frac{W_{AB}}{q_0},$$

because W_{AB} must be zero if $V_A = V_B$. This is true, because of the path independence of potential difference, even if the path connecting A and B does not lie entirely in the equipotential surface.

Figure 29–2 shows an arbitrary family of equipotential surfaces. The work to move a charge along paths I and II is zero because all these paths begin and end on the same equipotential surface. The work to move a charge along paths I$'$ and II$'$ is not zero but is the same for each path because the initial and the final potentials are identical; paths I$'$ and II$'$ connect the same pair of equipotential surfaces.

From symmetry, the equipotential surfaces for a spherical charge are a family of concentric spheres. For a uniform field they are a family of planes at right angles to the field. In all cases (including these two examples) the equipotential surfaces are at right angles to the lines of force and thus to $\mathbf{E}$

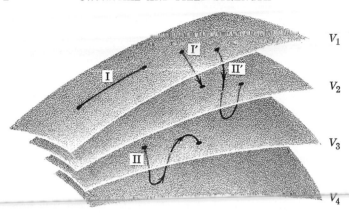

Fig. 29–2 Portions of four equipotential surfaces. The heavy lines show four paths along which a test charge is moved.

(see Fig. 29–15). If **E** were *not* at right angles to the equipotential surface, it would have a component lying in that surface. Then work would have to be done in moving a test charge about on the surface. Work cannot be done if the surface is an equipotential, so **E** must be at right angles to the surface.

There is a strong analogy between electrostatic forces and gravitational forces, based on the fact that their fundamental laws are inverse square laws (see Eqs. 26–3 and 16–1):

$$F_E = \frac{1}{4\pi\epsilon_0} \frac{q_1 q_2}{r^2} \quad \text{and} \quad F_g = G \frac{m_1 m_2}{r^2}.$$

Thus we can define the *gravitational potential* V_g (compare Eq. 29–2) from

$$V_g = \frac{W}{m},$$

where W is the work required to move a test body of mass m from infinity to the point in question. Gravitational equipotential surfaces can also be constructed; they prove to be everywhere at right angles to the gravitational field strength vector **g**. For a uniform gravitational field, such as that near the surface of the earth, these surfaces are horizontal planes. This correlates with the facts that (*a*) no net work is required to move a stone of mass m between two points with the same elevation and (*b*) the same net work is required to move a stone along any path starting on a given horizontal surface and ending on another.

29–2 Potential and Field Strength

Let A and B in Fig. 29–3 be two points in a uniform electric field **E**, set up by an arrangement of charges not shown, and let A be a distance d in the field direction from B. Assume that a positive test charge q_0 is moved, by an external agent and without acceleration, from A to B along the straight line connecting them.

The *electric* force on the charge is $q_0\mathbf{E}$ and points down. To move the charge in the way we have described we must counteract this force by applying an external force **F** of the same magnitude but directed upward. The work W done by the agent that supplies this force is

$$W_{AB} = Fd = q_0 Ed. \tag{29-3}$$

Substituting this into Eq. 29–1 yields

$$V_B - V_A = \frac{W_{AB}}{q_0} = Ed. \tag{29-4}$$

This equation shows the connection between potential difference and field strength for a simple special case. Note from this equation that another mks unit for **E** is the volt/meter. The student may wish to prove that a volt/meter is identical with a nt/coul; this latter unit is the one first presented for **E** in Section 27–2.

In Fig. 29–3 B has a higher potential than A. This is reasonable because an external agent would have to do positive work to push a positive test charge from A to B. Figure 29–3 could be used as it stands to illustrate the act of lifting a stone from A to B in the uniform gravitational field near the earth's surface.

What is the connection between V and E in the more general case in which the field is *not* uniform and in which the test body is moved along a path that is *not* straight, as in Fig. 29–4? The electric field exerts a force $q_0\mathbf{E}$ on the test charge, as shown. To keep the test charge from accelerating, an external agent must apply a force **F** chosen to be exactly equal to $-q_0\mathbf{E}$ for all positions of the test body.

If the external agent causes the test body to move through a displacement $d\mathbf{l}$ along the path from A to B, the element of work done by the external agent

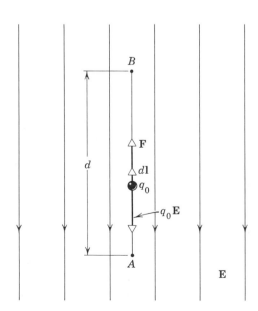

Fig. 29–3 A test charge q_0 is moved from A to B in a uniform electric field **E** by an external agent that exerts a force **F** on it.

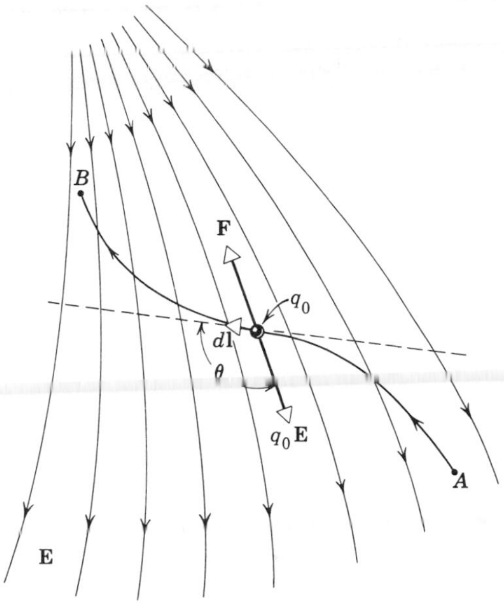

Fig. 29–4 A test charge q_0 is moved from A to B in a nonuniform electric field by an external agent that exerts a force **F** on it.

is $\mathbf{F} \cdot d\mathbf{l}$. To find the total work W_{AB} done by the external agent in moving the test charge from A to B, we add up (that is, integrate) the work contributions for all the infinitesimal segments into which the path is divided. This leads to

$$W_{AB} = \int_A^B \mathbf{F} \cdot d\mathbf{l} = -q_0 \int_A^B \mathbf{E} \cdot d\mathbf{l}.$$

Such an integral is called a *line integral*. Note that we have substituted $-q_0 \mathbf{E}$ for its equal, **F**.

Substituting this expression for W_{AB} into Eq. 29–1 leads to

$$V_B - V_A = \frac{W_{AB}}{q_0} = -\int_A^B \mathbf{E} \cdot d\mathbf{l}. \qquad (29\text{--}5)$$

If point A is taken to be infinitely distant and the potential V_A at infinity is taken to be zero, this equation gives the potential V at point B, or, dropping the subscript B,

$$V = -\int_\infty^B \mathbf{E} \cdot d\mathbf{l}. \qquad (29\text{--}6)$$

These two equations allow us to calculate the potential difference between any two points (or the potential at any point) if **E** is known at various points in the field

▶ **Example 1.** In Fig. 29–3 calculate $V_B - V_A$ using Eq. 29–5. Compare the result with that obtained by direct analysis of this special case (Eq. 29–4).

In moving the test charge the element of path $d\mathbf{l}$ always points in the direction of motion; this is upward in Fig. 29–3. The electric field **E** in this figure points down so that the angle θ between **E** and $d\mathbf{l}$ is 180°.

Equation 29–5 then becomes

$$V_B - V_A = -\int_A^B \mathbf{E} \cdot d\mathbf{l} = -\int_A^B E \cos 180° \, dl = \int_A^B E \, dl.$$

E is the constant for all parts of the path in this problem and can thus be taken outside the integral sign, giving

$$V_B - V_A = E \int_A^B dl = Ed,$$

which agrees with Eq. 29–4, as it must.

Example 2. In Fig. 29–5 let a test charge q_0 be moved without acceleration from A to B over the path shown. Compute the potential difference between A and B.

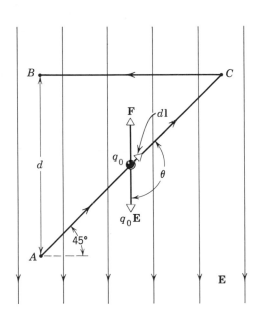

Fig. 29–5 Example 2. A test charge q_0 is moved along path ACB in a uniform electric field by an external agent.

For the path AC we have $\theta = 135°$ and, from Eq. 29–5,

$$V_C - V_A = -\int_A^C \mathbf{E} \cdot d\mathbf{l} = -\int_A^C E \cos 135° \, dl = \frac{E}{\sqrt{2}} \int_A^C dl.$$

The integral is the length of the line AC which is $\sqrt{2}d$. Thus

$$V_C - V_A = \frac{E}{\sqrt{2}} (\sqrt{2}d) = Ed.$$

Points B and C have the same potential because no work is done in moving a charge between them, **E** and $d\mathbf{l}$ being at right angles for all points on the line CB. In other words, B and C lie on the same equipotential surface at right angles to the lines of force. Thus

$$V_B - V_A = V_C - V_A = Ed.$$

This is the same value derived for a direct path connecting A and B, a result to be expected because the potential difference between two points is path independent. ◀

29–3   Potential Due to a Point Charge

Figure 29–6 shows two points A and B near an isolated point charge q. For simplicity we assume that A, B, and q lie on a straight line. Let us compute the potential difference between points A and B, assuming that a test charge q_0 is moved without acceleration along a radial line from A to B.

In Fig. 29–6 $\mathbf{E}$ points to the right and $d\mathbf{l}$, which is always in the direction of motion, points to the left. Therefore, in Eq. 29–5,

$$\mathbf{E}\cdot d\mathbf{l} = E \cos 180° \, dl = -E \, dl.$$

However, as we move a distance dl to the left, we are moving in the direction of decreasing r because r is measured from q as an origin. Thus

$$dl = -dr.$$

Combining yields
$$\mathbf{E}\cdot d\mathbf{l} = E \, dr.$$

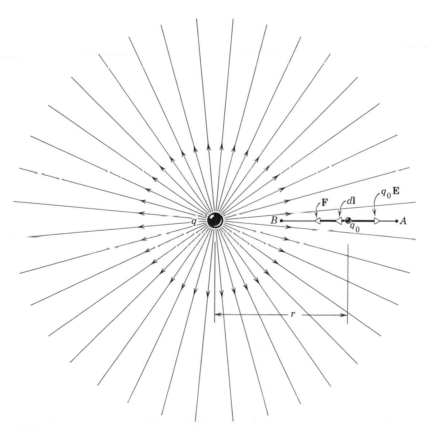

Fig. 29–6   A test charge q_0 is moved by an external agent from A to B in the field set up by a point charge q.

Substituting this into Eq. 29–5 gives

$$V_B - V_A = -\int_A^B \mathbf{E} \cdot d\mathbf{l} = -\int_{r_A}^{r_B} E \, dr.$$

Combining with Eq. 27–4,

$$E = \frac{1}{4\pi\epsilon_0} \frac{q}{r^2}$$

leads to $$V_B - V_A = -\frac{q}{4\pi\epsilon_0} \int_{r_A}^{r_B} \frac{dr}{r^2} = \frac{q}{4\pi\epsilon_0} \left(\frac{1}{r_B} - \frac{1}{r_A} \right). \qquad (29\text{--}7)$$

Choosing reference position A to be at infinity (that is, letting $r_A \to \infty$), choosing $V_A = 0$ at this position, and dropping the subscript B leads to

$$V = \frac{1}{4\pi\epsilon_0} \frac{q}{r}. \qquad (29\text{--}8)$$

This equation shows clearly that equipotential surfaces for an isolated point charge are spheres concentric with the point charge (see Fig. 29–15a). A study of the derivation will show that this relation also holds for points external to spherically symmetric charge distributions.

▶ **Example 3.** What must the magnitude of an isolated positive point charge be for the electric potential at 10 cm from the charge to be $+100$ volts?
Solving Eq. 29–8 for q yields

$$q = V4\pi\epsilon_0 r = (100 \text{ volts})(4\pi)(8.9 \times 10^{-12} \text{ coul}^2/\text{nt-m}^2)(0.10 \text{ meter})$$

$$= 1.1 \times 10^{-9} \text{ coul.}$$

This charge is comparable to charges that can be produced by friction.

Example 4. What is the electric potential at the surface of a gold nucleus? The radius is 6.6×10^{-15} meter and the atomic number $Z = 79$.
The nucleus, assumed spherically symmetrical, behaves electrically for external points as if it were a point charge. Thus we can use Eq. 29–8, or, recalling that the proton charge is 1.6×10^{-19} coul,

$$V = \frac{1}{4\pi\epsilon_0} \frac{q}{r} = \frac{(9.0 \times 10^{10} \text{ nt-m}^2/\text{coul}^2)(79)(1.6 \times 10^{-19} \text{ coul})}{6.6 \times 10^{-15} \text{ meter}}$$

$$= 1.7 \times 10^7 \text{ volts.} \qquad \blacktriangleleft$$

29–4   A Group of Point Charges

The potential at any point due to a group of point charges is found by (a) calculating the potential V_n due to each charge, as if the other charges were not present, and (b) adding the quantities so obtained, or (see Eq. 29–8)

$$V - \sum_n V_n = \frac{1}{4\pi\epsilon_0} \sum_n \frac{q_n}{r_n}, \qquad (29\text{--}9)$$

where q_n is the value of the nth charge and r_n is the distance of this charge from the point in question. The sum used to calculate V is an *algebraic sum* and not a vector sum like the one used to calculate $\mathbf{E}$ for a group of point charges (see Eq. 27–5). Herein lies an important computational advantage of potential over electric field strength.

If the charge distribution is continuous, rather than being a collection of points, the sum in Eq. 29–9 must be replaced by an integral, or

$$V = \int dV = \frac{1}{4\pi\epsilon_0} \int \frac{dq}{r}, \qquad (29\text{–}10)$$

where dq is a differential element of the charge distribution, r is its distance from the point at which V is to be calculated, and dV is the potential it establishes at that point.

▶ **Example 5.** What is the potential at the center of the square of Fig. 29–7? Assume that $q_1 = +1.0 \times 10^{-8}$ coul, $q_2 = -2.0 \times 10^{-8}$ coul, $q_3 = +3.0 \times 10^{-8}$ coul, $q_4 = +2.0 \times 10^{-8}$ coul, and $a = 1.0$ meter.

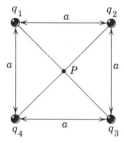

Fig. 29–7   Example 5

The distance r of each charge from P is $a/\sqrt{2}$ or 0.71 meter. From Eq. 29–9

$$V = \sum_n V_n = \frac{1}{4\pi\epsilon_0} \frac{q_1 + q_2 + q_3 + q_4}{r}$$

$$= \frac{(9.0 \times 10^{10}\ \text{nt-m}^2/\text{coul}^2)(1.0 - 2.0 + 3.0 + 2.0) \times 10^{-8}\ \text{coul}}{0.71\ \text{meter}}$$

$$= 500\ \text{volts}.$$

Is the potential constant within the square? Does any point inside have a negative potential? Can you sketch roughly the intersection of the plane of Fig. 29–7 with the equipotential surface corresponding to zero volts?

Example 6.   *A charged disk.* Find the electric potential for points on the axis of a uniformly charged circular disk whose surface charge density is σ (see Fig. 29–8).

Consider a charge element dq consisting of a flat circular strip of radius y and width dy. We have

$$dq = \sigma(2\pi y)(dy),$$

where $(2\pi y)(dy)$ is the area of the strip. All parts of this charge element are the same distance $r'\ (= \sqrt{y^2 + r^2})$ from axial point P so that their contribution dV to the

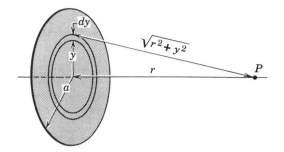

Fig. 29–8 Example 6. A point P on the axis of a uniformly charged circular disk of radius a.

electric potential at P is given by Eq. 29–8, or

$$dV = \frac{1}{4\pi\epsilon_0} \frac{dq}{r'} = \frac{1}{4\pi\epsilon_0} \frac{\sigma 2\pi y\, dy}{\sqrt{y^2 + r^2}}.$$

The potential V is found by integrating over all the strips into which the disk can be divided (Eq. 29–10) or

$$V = \int dV = \frac{\sigma}{2\epsilon_0} \int_0^a (y^2 + r^2)^{-\frac{1}{2}} y\, dy$$

$$= \frac{\sigma}{2\epsilon_0}(\sqrt{a^2 + r^2} - r).$$

This general result is valid for all values of r. In the special case of $r \gg a$ the quantity $\sqrt{a^2 + r^2}$ can be approximated as

$$\sqrt{a^2 + r^2} = r\left(1 + \frac{a^2}{r^2}\right)^{\frac{1}{2}} = r\left(1 + \frac{1}{2}\frac{a^2}{r^2} + \cdots\right) \cong r + \frac{a^2}{2r},$$

in which the quantity in parentheses in the second member of this equation has been expanded by the binomial theorem (see Appendix I). This equation means that V becomes

$$V \cong \frac{\sigma}{2\epsilon_0}\left(r + \frac{a^2}{2r} - r\right) = \frac{\sigma\pi a^2}{4\pi\epsilon_0 r} = \frac{1}{4\pi\epsilon_0}\frac{q}{r},$$

where q ($= \sigma\pi a^2$) is the total charge on the disk. This limiting result is expected because the disk behaves like a point charge for $r \gg a$. ◀

29–5　Potential Due to a Dipole

Two equal charges, q, of opposite sign, separated by a distance $2a$, constitute an electric dipole; see Example 3, Chapter 27. The electric dipole moment **p** has the magnitude $2aq$ and points from the negative charge to the positive charge. Here we derive an expression for the electric potential V at any point of space due to a dipole, provided only that the point is not too close to the dipole.

A point P is specified by giving the quantities r and θ in Fig. 29–9. From symmetry, it is clear that the potential will not change as point P rotates about the z axis, r and θ being fixed. Thus we need only find $V(r,\theta)$ for any plane containing this axis; the plane of Fig. 29–9 is such a plane. Applying

Eq. 29–9 gives

$$V = \sum_n V_n = V_1 + V_2 = \frac{1}{4\pi\epsilon_0}\left(\frac{q}{r_1} - \frac{q}{r_2}\right) = \frac{q}{4\pi\epsilon_0}\frac{r_2 - r_1}{r_1 r_2},$$

which is an exact relationship.

We now limit consideration to points such that $r \gg 2a$. These approximate relations then follow from Fig. 29–9:

$$r_2 - r_1 \cong 2a\cos\theta \qquad \text{and} \qquad r_1 r_2 \cong r^2,$$

and the potential reduces to

$$V = \frac{q}{4\pi\epsilon_0}\frac{2a\cos\theta}{r^2} = \frac{1}{4\pi\epsilon_0}\frac{p\cos\theta}{r^2}, \qquad (29\text{–}11)$$

in which $p \,(= 2aq)$ is the dipole moment. Note that V vanishes everywhere in the equatorial plane ($\theta = 90°$). This reflects the fact that it takes no work to bring a test charge in from infinity along the perpendicular bisector of the dipole. For a given radius, V has its greatest positive value for $\theta = 0$ and its greatest negative value for $\theta = 180°$. Note that the potential does not depend separately on q and $2a$ but only on their product p.

It is convenient to call *any* assembly of charges, for which V at distant points is given by Eq. 29–11, an *electric dipole*. Two point charges separated by a small distance behave this way, as we have just proved. However, other charge configurations also obey Eq. 29–11. Suppose that by measurement at points outside an imaginary box (Fig. 29–10) we find a pattern of lines of force that can be described quantitatively by Eq. 29–11. We then declare that the object inside the box is an *electric dipole*, that its axis is the line zz', and that its dipole moment **p** points vertically upward.

Many molecules have electric dipole moments. That for H_2O in its vapor state is 6.1×10^{-30} coul-m. Figure 29–11 is a representation of this molecule, showing the three nuclei and the surrounding electron cloud. The dipole moment **p** is represented

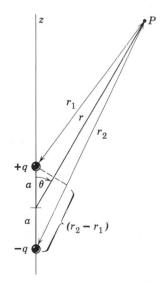

Fig. 29–9   A point P in the field of an electric dipole.

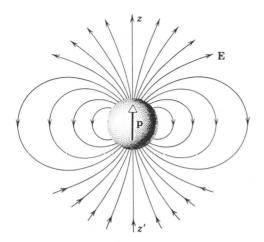

Fig. 29–10 If an object inside the spherical box sets up the electric field shown (described quantitatively by Eq. 29–11), it is an electric dipole.

by the arrow on the axis of symmetry of the molecule. In this molecule the effective center of positive charge does not coincide with the effective center of negative charge. It is precisely because of this separation that the dipole moment exists.

Atoms, and many molecules, do *not* have permanent dipole moments. However, dipole moments may be induced by placing any atom or molecule in an external electric field. The action of the field (Fig. 29–12) is to separate the centers of positive and of negative charge. We say that the atom becomes *polarized* and acquires an *induced electric dipole moment*. Induced dipole moments disappear when the electric field is removed.

Electric dipoles are important in situations other than atomic and molecular ones. Radio and radar antennas are often in the form of a metal wire or rod in which electrons surge back and forth periodically. At a certain time one end of the wire or rod will be negative and the other end positive. Half a cycle later the polarity of the ends is exactly reversed. This is an *oscillating* electric dipole. It is so named because its dipole moment changes in a periodic way with time.

Fig. 29–11 A schematic representation of a water molecule, showing the three nuclei, the electron cloud, and the orientation of the dipole moment.

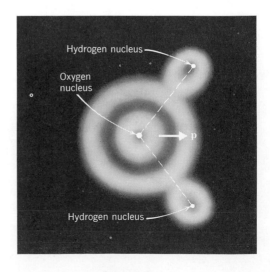

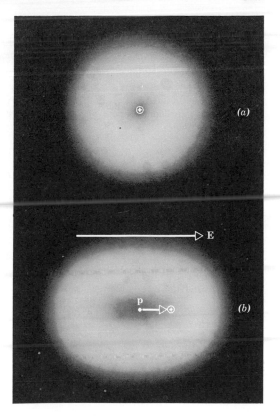

Fig. 29-12 (*a*) An atom, showing the nucleus and the electron cloud. The center of negative charge coincides with the center of positive charge, that is, with the nucleus. (*b*) If an external field **E** is applied, the electron cloud is distorted so that the center of negative charge, marked by the dot, and the center of positive charge no longer coincide. An electric dipole appears.

▶ **Example 7.** *An electric quadrupole.* An electric quadrupole, of which Fig. 27–21 is an example, consists of two electric dipoles so arranged that they almost, but not quite, cancel each other in their electric effects at distant points.* Calculate $V(r)$ for points on the axis of this quadrupole.

Applying Eq. 29–9 to Fig. 27–21 yields

$$V - \sum_n V_n = \frac{1}{4\pi\epsilon_0}\left(\frac{q}{r-a} - \frac{2q}{r} + \frac{q}{r+a}\right)$$

$$= \frac{q}{4\pi\epsilon_0}\frac{2a^2}{(r-a)(r)(r+a)}.$$

Assuming that $r \gg a$ allows us to put $a = 0$ in the denominator, yielding

$$V = \frac{1}{4\pi\epsilon_0}\frac{Q}{r^3},$$

where Q ($= 2qa^2$) is the *electric quadrupole moment* of the charge assembly of Fig. 27–21. Note that V varies (*a*) as $1/r$ for a point charge (see Eq. 29–8), (*b*) as $1/r^2$ for a dipole (see Eq. 29–11), and (*c*) as $1/r^3$ for a quadrupole.

Note too that (*a*) a dipole is two equal and opposite charges that do not coincide in space so that their electric effects at distant points do not quite cancel, and (*b*) a

---

* See Problem 18, Chapter 27.

quadrupole is two equal and opposite dipoles that do not coincide in space so that their electric effects at distant points again do not quite cancel. This pattern can be extended to define higher orders of charge distribution such as *octupoles*.

The potential at points at distances from an *arbitrary* charge distribution (continuous or discrete) that are large compared with the size of the distribution can always be written as the sum of separate potential distributions due to (*a*) a single charge—sometimes, in this context, called a *monopole*—(*b*) a dipole, (*c*) a quadrupole, etc. This process is called an *expansion in multipoles* and is a very useful technique in problem solving.   ◄

29–6   Electric Potential Energy *

If we raise a stone from the earth's surface, the work that we do against the earth's gravitational attraction is stored as *potential energy* in the system earth + stone. If we release the stone, the stored potential energy changes steadily into kinetic energy as the stone drops. After the stone comes to rest on the earth, this kinetic energy, equal in magnitude just before the time of contact to the originally stored potential energy, is transformed into heat energy in the system earth + stone.

A similar situation exists in electrostatics. Consider two charges q_1 and q_2 a distance r apart, as in Fig. 29–13. If we increase the separation between

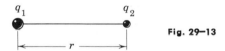

Fig. 29–13

them, an external agent must do work that will be positive if the charges are opposite in sign and negative otherwise. The energy represented by this work can be thought of as stored in the system $q_1 + q_2$ as *electric potential energy*. This energy, like all varieties of potential energy, can be transformed into other forms. If q_1 and q_2, for example, are charges of opposite sign and we release them, they will accelerate toward each other, transforming the stored potential energy into kinetic energy of the accelerating masses. The analogy to the earth + stone system is exact, save for the fact that electric forces may be either attractive or repulsive whereas gravitational forces are always attractive.

We define the electric potential energy of a system of point charges as the work required to assemble this system of charges by bringing them in from an infinite distance. We assume that the charges are all at rest when they are infinitely separated, that is, they have no initial kinetic energy.

In Fig. 29–13 let us imagine q_2 removed to infinity and at rest. The

---

* In mechanics the concept of *potential energy* (of compressed springs, falling masses, etc.) is more commonly used than the concept of *potential*. In electrostatics the reverse is true, electric potential being perhaps a more common concept than electric potential energy. In what follows the student must be careful not to confuse these quite different quantities, potential and potential energy.

electric potential at the original site of q_2, caused by q_1, is given by Eq. 29–8, or

$$V = \frac{1}{4\pi\epsilon_0} \frac{q_1}{r}.$$

If q_2 is moved in from infinity to the original distance r, the work required is, from the definition of electric potential, that is, from Eq. 29–2,

$$W = Vq_2. \tag{29–12}$$

Combining these two equations and recalling that this work W is precisely the *electric potential energy* U of the system $q_1 + q_2$ yields

$$U\ (= W) = \frac{1}{4\pi\epsilon_0} \frac{q_1 q_2}{r_{12}}. \tag{29–13}$$

The subscript of r emphasizes that the distance involved is that between the point charges q_1 and q_2.

For systems containing more than two charges the procedure is to compute the potential energy for every pair of charges separately and to add the results algebraically. This procedure rests on a physical picture in which (*a*) charge q_1 is brought into position, (*b*) q_2 is brought from infinity to its position near q_1, (*c*) q_3 is brought from infinity to its position near q_1 and q_2, etc.

The potential energy of continuous charge distributions (an ellipsoid of charge, for example) can be found by dividing the distribution into infinitesimal elements dq, treating each such element as a point charge, and using the procedures of the preceding paragraph, with the summation process replaced by an integration. We have not considered such problems in this text.

▶ **Example 8.** Two protons in a nucleus of U^{238} are 6.0×10^{-15} meter apart. What is their mutual electric potential energy?
From Eq. 29–13

$$U = \frac{1}{4\pi\epsilon_0} \frac{q_1 q_2}{r} = \frac{(9.0 \times 10^9 \text{ nt-m}^2/\text{coul}^2)(1.6 \times 10^{-19} \text{ coul})^2}{6.0 \times 10^{-15} \text{ meter}}$$

$$= 3.8 \times 10^{-14} \text{ joule} = 2.4 \times 10^5 \text{ ev}.$$

Example 9. Three charges are arranged as in Fig. 29–14. What is their mutual potential energy? Assume that $q = 1.0 \times 10^{-7}$ coul and $a = 10$ cm.

Fig. 29–14 Example 9. Three charges are fixed rigidly, as shown, by external forces.

The total energy of the configuration is the sum of the energies of each pair of particles. From Eq. 29–13,

$$U = U_{12} + U_{13} + U_{23}$$

$$= \frac{1}{4\pi\epsilon_0} \left[\frac{(+q)(-4q)}{a} + \frac{(+q)(+2q)}{a} + \frac{(-4q)(+2q)}{a} \right]$$

$$= -\frac{10}{4\pi\epsilon_0} \frac{q^2}{a}$$

$$= -\frac{(9.0 + 10^9 \text{ nt-m}^2/\text{coul}^2)(10)(1.0 \times 10^{-7} \text{ coul})^2}{0.10 \text{ meter}} = -9.0 \times 10^{-3} \text{ joule.}$$

The fact that the total energy is negative means that negative work would have to be done to assemble this structure, starting with the three charges separated and at rest at infinity. Expressed otherwise, 8.9×10^{-3} joule of work must be done to dismantle this structure, removing the charges to an infinite separation from one another.

When, as is common practice, infinity is taken as the zero of electric potential, a positive potential energy (as in Example 8) corresponds to repulsive electric forces and a negative potential energy (as in this example) to attractive electric forces. If the protons in Example 8 were not held in place by attractive (nonelectrical) nuclear forces, they would move away from each other. If the three particles in this example were released from their fixed positions, in which they are held by external forces, they would move toward each other. ◀

29–7 Calculation of E from V

We have stated that V and $\mathbf{E}$ are equivalent descriptions and have determined (Eq. 29–6) how to calculate V from $\mathbf{E}$. Let us now consider how to calculate $\mathbf{E}$ if V is known throughout a certain region.

This problem has already been solved graphically. If $\mathbf{E}$ is known at every point in space, the lines of force can be drawn; then a family of equipotentials can be sketched in by drawing surfaces at right angles. These equipotentials describe the behavior of V. Conversely, if V is given as a function of position, a set of equipotential surfaces can be drawn. The lines of force can then be found by drawing lines at right angles, thus describing the behavior of $\mathbf{E}$. It is the mathematical equivalent of this second graphical process that we seek here. Figure 29–15 shows some examples of lines of force and of the corresponding equipotential surfaces.

Figure 29–16 shows the intersection with the plane of the figure of a family of equipotential surfaces. The figure shows that $\mathbf{E}$ at a typical point P is at right angles to the equipotential surface through P, as it must be.

Let us move a test charge q_0 from P along the path marked $\Delta\mathbf{l}$ to the equipotential surface marked $V + \Delta V$. The work that must be done by the agent exerting the force $\mathbf{F}$ (see Eq. 29–1) is $q_0\Delta V$.

From another point of view we can calculate the work from *

$$\Delta W = \mathbf{F} \cdot \Delta\mathbf{l},$$

---

* We assume that the equipotentials are so close together that $\mathbf{F}$ is constant for all parts of the path $\Delta\mathbf{l}$. In the limit of a differential path ($d\mathbf{l}$) there will be no difficulty.

where $\mathbf{F}$ is the force that must be exerted on the charge to overcome exactly the electrical force $q_0\mathbf{E}$. Since $\mathbf{F}$ and $q_0\mathbf{E}$ have opposite signs and are equal in magnitude,

$$\Delta W = -q_0\mathbf{E}\cdot\Delta\mathbf{l} = -q_0E \cos (\pi - \theta)\, \Delta l = q_0E \cos \theta\; \Delta l.$$

These two expressions for the work must be equal, which gives

$$q_0\,\Delta V = q_0E \cos \theta\; \Delta l$$

or
$$E \cos \theta = \frac{\Delta V}{\Delta l}. \tag{29–14}$$

Now $E \cos \theta$ is the component of $\mathbf{E}$ in the direction $-\mathbf{l}$ in Fig. 29–16; the quantity $-E \cos \theta$, which we call E_l, would then be the component of $\mathbf{E}$ in the $+\mathbf{l}$ direction. In the differential limit Eq. 29–14 can then be written as

$$E_l = -\frac{dV}{dl}. \tag{29–15}$$

In words, this equation says: If we travel through an electric field along a straight line and measure V as we go, the rate of change of V with distance that we observe, when changed in sign, is the component of $\mathbf{E}$ in that direction. The minus sign implies that $\mathbf{E}$ points in the direction of decreasing V, as in Fig. 29–16. It is particularly clear from Eq. 29–15 that appropriate units for $\mathbf{E}$ are the volts/meter.

There will be one direction $\mathbf{l}$ for which the quantity dV/dl is a maximum. From Eq. 29–15, E_l will also be a maximum for this direction and will in fact be E itself. Thus

$$E = -\left(\frac{dV}{dl}\right)_{\text{max}}. \tag{29–16}$$

The maximum value of dV/dl at a given point is called the *potential gradient* at that point. The direction $\mathbf{l}$ for which dV/dl has its maximum value is always at right angles to the equipotential surface, corresponding to $\theta = 0$ in Fig. 29–16.

If we take the direction $\mathbf{l}$ to be, in turn, the directions of the x, y, and z axes, we can find the three components of $\mathbf{E}$ at any point, from Eq. 29–15.

$$E_x = -\frac{\partial V}{\partial x}; \qquad E_y = -\frac{\partial V}{\partial y}; \qquad E_z = -\frac{\partial V}{\partial z}. \tag{29–17}$$

Thus if V is known for all points of space, that is, if the function $V(x, y, z)$ is known, the components of $\mathbf{E}$, and thus $\mathbf{E}$ itself, can be found by taking derivatives.*

---

* The symbol $\partial V/\partial x$ is a *partial derivative*. It implies that in taking this derivative of the function $V(x, y, z)$ the quantity x is to be viewed as a variable and y and z are to be regarded as constants. Similar considerations hold for $\partial V/\partial y$ and $\partial V/\partial z$.

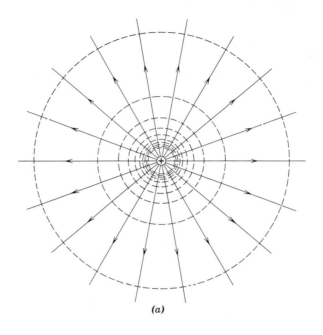

(a)

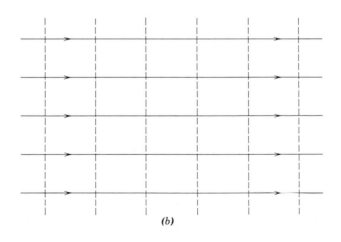

(b)

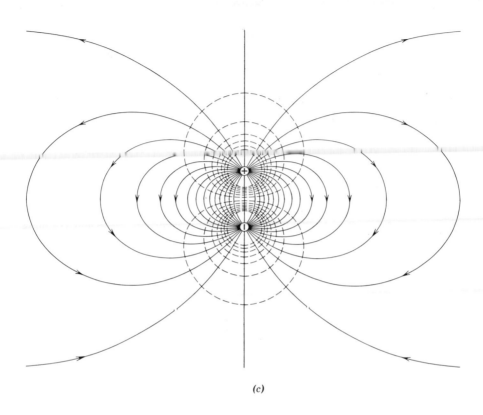

(c)

Fig. 29–15 Equipotential surfaces (dashed lines) and lines of force (solid lines) for (a) a point charge, (b) a uniform electric field, and (c) an electric dipole. In all figures there is a constant difference of potential ΔV between adjacent equipotential surfaces. Thus from Eq. 29–14, written for the case of $\theta = 180°$ as $\Delta l = -\Delta V/E$, the surfaces will be relatively close together where E is relatively large and relatively far apart where E is small. Similarly (see Section 27–3) the lines of force are relatively close together where E is large and far apart where E is small. See discussion and figures of Section 18–7 for other examples.

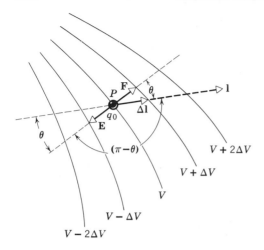

Fig. 29–16 A test charge q_0 is moved from one equipotential surface to another along an arbitrarily selected direction marked **l**.

▶ **Example 10.** Calculate $E(r)$ for a point charge q, using Eq. 29–16 and assuming that $V(r)$ is given as (see Eq. 29–8)

$$V = \frac{1}{4\pi\epsilon_0}\frac{q}{r}.$$

From symmetry, **E** must be directed radially outward for a (positive) point charge. Consider a point P in the field a distance r from the charge. It is clear that dV/dl at P has its greatest value if the direction l is identified with that of r. Thus, from Eq. 29–16,

$$E = -\frac{dV}{dr} = -\frac{d}{dr}\left(\frac{1}{4\pi\epsilon_0}\frac{q}{r}\right)$$

$$= -\frac{q}{4\pi\epsilon_0}\frac{d}{dr}\left(\frac{1}{r}\right) = \frac{1}{4\pi\epsilon_0}\frac{q}{r^2}.$$

This result agrees exactly with Eq. 27–4, as it must.

Example 11. **E** *for a dipole.* Figure 29–17 shows a (distant) point P in the field of a dipole located at the origin of an xy-axis system. V is given by Eq. 29–11, or

$$V = \frac{1}{4\pi\epsilon_0}\frac{p\cos\theta}{r^2}.$$

Calculate **E** as a function of position.

From symmetry, **E** lies entirely in the plane of Fig. 29–17. Thus it can be expressed in terms of its components E_x and E_y. Let us first express the potential function in rectangular coordinates rather than polar coordinates, making use of

$$r = (x^2 + y^2)^{1/2} \quad \text{and} \quad \cos\theta = \frac{y}{(x^2+y^2)^{1/2}}.$$

The result is

$$V = \frac{p}{4\pi\epsilon_0}\frac{y}{(x^2+y^2)^{3/2}}.$$

We find E_y from Eq. 29-17, recalling that x is to be treated as a constant in this calculation:

$$E_y = -\frac{\partial V}{\partial y} = -\frac{p}{4\pi\epsilon_0}\frac{(x^2 + y^2)^{3/2} - y\frac{3}{2}(x^2 + y^2)^{1/2}(2y)}{(x^2 + y^2)^3}$$

$$= -\frac{p}{4\pi\epsilon_0}\frac{x^2 - 2y^2}{(x^2 + y^2)^{5/2}}.$$

Note that putting $x = 0$ describes points along the dipole axis (that is, the y axis), and the expression for E_y reduces to

$$E_y = \frac{2p}{4\pi\epsilon_0}\frac{1}{y^3}.$$

This result agrees exactly with that found in Chapter 27 (see Problem 10), for, from symmetry, E_x equals zero on the dipole axis.

Putting $y = 0$ in the expression for E_y describes points in the median plane of the dipole and yields

$$E_y = -\frac{p}{4\pi\epsilon_0}\frac{1}{x^3},$$

which agrees exactly with the result found in Chapter 27 (see Example 3), for, again from symmetry, E_x equals zero in the median plane. The minus sign in this equation indicates that **E** points in the negative y direction (see Fig. 29–10).

The component E_x is also found from Eq. 29-17, recalling that y is to be taken as a constant during this calculation:

$$E_x = -\frac{\partial V}{\partial x} = -\frac{py}{4\pi\epsilon_0}(-\tfrac{3}{2})(x^2 + y^2)^{-5/2}(2x)$$

$$= \frac{3p}{4\pi\epsilon_0}\frac{xy}{(x^2 + y^2)^{5/2}}.$$

As expected, E_x vanishes both on the dipole axis ($x = 0$) and in the median plane ($y = 0$); see Fig. 29–10.   ◀

Fig. 29–17 Showing a point P in the field of an electric dipole **p**.

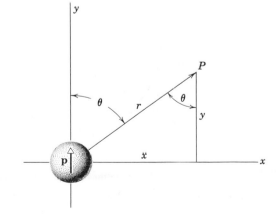

29–8   An Insulated Conductor

We proved in Section 28–4, using Gauss's law, that after a steady state is reached an excess charge q placed on an insulated conductor will move to its outer surface. We now assert that this charge q will distribute itself on this surface so that all points of the conductor, including *those on the surface and those inside*, have the same potential.

Consider any two points A and B in or on the conductor. If they were not at the same potential, the charge carriers in the conductor near the point of lower potential would tend to move toward the point of higher potential. We have assumed, however, that a steady-state situation, in which such currents do not exist, has been reached; thus all points, both on the surface and inside

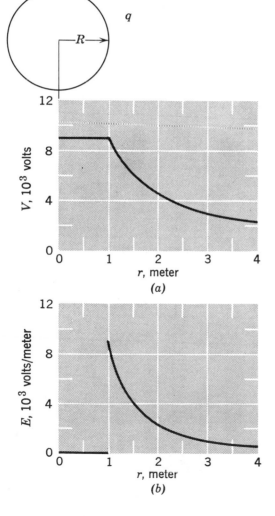

Fig. 29–18 (a) The potential and (b) the electric field strength, for points near a conducting spherical shell of 1.0 meter radius carrying a charge of $+1.0 \times 10^{-6}$ coul.

it, must have the same potential. Since the surface of the conductor is an equipotential surface, **E** for points on the surface must be at right angles to the surface.

We saw in Section 28–4 that a charge placed on an insulated conductor will spread over the surface until **E** equals zero for all points inside. We now have an alternative way of saying the same thing; the charge will move until all points of the conductor (surface points and interior points) are brought to the same potential, for if V is constant in the conductor then **E** is zero everywhere in the conductor ($E_l = -dV/dl$).

Figure 29–18a is a plot of potential against radial distance for an isolated spherical conducting shell of 1.0-meter radius carrying a positive charge of 1.0×10^{-6} coul. For points outside the shell $V(r)$ can be calculated from Eq. 29–8 because the charge q behaves, for such points, as if it were concentrated at the center of the sphere. Equation 29–8 is correct right up to the surface of the shell. Now let us push the test charge through the surface, assuming that there is a small hole, and into the interior. No extra work is needed because no electrical forces act on the test charge once it is inside the shell. Thus the potential everywhere inside is the same as that on the surface, as Fig. 29–18a shows.

Figure 29–18b shows the electric field strength for this same sphere. Note that E equals zero inside. The lower of these curves can be derived from the upper by differentiating, using Eq. 29–16; the upper can be derived from the lower by integration, using Eq. 29–6.

Figure 29–18 holds without change if the conductor is a solid sphere rather than a spherical shell as we have assumed. It is constructive to compare Fig. 29–18b (conducting shell or sphere) with Fig. 28–9, which holds for a *nonconducting* sphere. The student should try to understand the difference between these two figures, bearing in mind that in the first the charge lies on the surface whereas in the second it was assumed to have been spread uniformly throughout the volume of the sphere.

Finally we note that, as a general rule, the charge density tends to be high on isolated conducting surfaces whose radii of curvature are small, and conversely. For example, the charge density tends to be relatively high on sharp points and relatively low on plane regions on a conducting surface. The electric field strength E at points immediately above a charged surface is proportional to the charge density σ so that E may also reach very high values near sharp points. Glow discharges from sharp points during thunderstorms are a familiar example. The lightning rod acts in this way to neutralize charged clouds and thus prevent lightning strokes.

We can examine the qualitative relationship between σ and the curvature of the surface in a particular case by considering two spheres of different radii connected by a very long fine wire; see Fig. 29–19. Suppose that this entire assembly is raised

Fig. 29–19   Two spheres connected by a long fine wire.

to some arbitrary potential V. The (equal) potentials of the two spheres are, from Eq. 29–8,*

$$V = \frac{1}{4\pi\epsilon_0}\frac{q_1}{R_1} = \frac{1}{4\pi\epsilon_0}\frac{q_2}{R_2},$$

which yields

$$\frac{q_1}{q_2} = \frac{R_1}{R_2}, \tag{29–18}$$

where q_1 is the charge on the sphere of radius R_1 and q_2 is the charge on the sphere of radius R_2.

The *surface charge densities* for each sphere are given by

$$\sigma_1 = \frac{q_1}{4\pi R_1^2} \quad \text{and} \quad \sigma_2 = \frac{q_2}{4\pi R_2^2}.$$

Dividing gives

$$\frac{\sigma_1}{\sigma_2} = \frac{q_1}{q_2}\frac{R_2^2}{R_1^2}.$$

Combining with Eq. 29–18 yields

$$\frac{\sigma_1}{\sigma_2} = \frac{R_2}{R_1},$$

which is consistent with our qualitative statement above. Note that the larger sphere has the larger total charge but the smaller charge density.

The fact that σ, and thus **E**, can become very large near sharp points is important in the design of high-voltage equipment. *Corona discharge* can result from such points if the conducting object is raised to high potential and surrounded by air. Normally air is thought of as a nonconductor. However, it contains a small number of ions produced, for example, by the cosmic rays. A positively charged conductor will attract negative ions from the surrounding air and thus will slowly neutralize itself.

---

* Equation 29–8 holds only for an *isolated* point charge or spherically symmetric charge distribution. The spheres must be assumed to be so far apart that the charge on either one has a negligible effect on the distribution of charge on the other.

If the charged conductor has sharp points, the value of **E** in the air near the points can be very high. If the value is high enough, the ions, as they are drawn toward the conductor, will receive such large accelerations that, by collision with air molecules, they will produce vast additional numbers of ions. The air is thus made much more conducting, and the discharge of the conductor by this corona discharge may be very rapid indeed. The air surrounding sharp conducting points may even glow visibly because of light emitted from the air molecules during these collisions.

29–9   The Electrostatic Generator

The electrostatic generator was conceived by Lord Kelvin in 1890 and put into useful practice in essentially its modern form by R. J. Van de Graaff in 1931. It is a device for producing electric potential differences of the order of several millions of volts. Its chief application in physics is the use of this potential difference to accelerate charged particles to high energies. Beams of energetic particles made in this way can be used in many different "atom-smashing" experiments. The technique is to let a charged particle "fall" through a potential difference V, gaining kinetic energy as it does so.

Let a particle of (positive) charge q move in a vacuum under the influence of an electric field from one position A to another position B whose electric potential is lower by V. The electric potential energy of the system is reduced by qV because this is the work that an external agent would have to do to restore the system to its original condition. This decrease in potential energy appears as kinetic energy of the particle, or

$$K = qV. \tag{29–19}$$

K is in joules if q is in coulombs and V in volts. If the particle is an electron or a proton, q will be the quantum of charge e.

If we adopt the quantum of charge e as a unit in place of the coulomb, we arrive at another unit for energy, the *electron volt*, which is used extensively in atomic and nuclear physics. By substituting into Eq. 29–19,

$$1 \text{ electron volt} = (1 \text{ quantum of charge})(1 \text{ volt})$$

$$= (1.60 \times 10^{-19} \text{ coul})(1.00 \text{ volt})$$

$$= 1.60 \times 10^{-19} \text{ joule.}$$

The electron volt can be used interchangeably with any other energy unit. Thus a 10-gm object moving at 1000 cm/sec can be said to have a kinetic energy of 3.1×10^{18} ev. Most physicists would prefer to express this result as 0.50 joule, the electron volt being inconveniently small. In atomic and nuclear problems, however, the electron volt (ev) and its multiples the Mev ($= 10^6$ ev), the Bev ($= 10^9$ ev) and the Gev ($= 10^{12}$ ev) are the usual units of choice.

▶ **Example 12.**   *The electrostatic generator.*   Figure 29–20, which illustrates the basic operating principle of the electrostatic generator, shows a small sphere of radius r placed inside a large spherical shell of radius R. The two spheres carry charges q and Q, respectively.   Calculate their potential difference.

The potential of the large sphere is caused in part by its own charge and in part because it lies in the field set up by the charge q on the small sphere.   From Eq. 29–8,

$$V_R = \frac{1}{4\pi\epsilon_0} \left(\frac{Q}{R} + \frac{q}{R} \right).$$

The potential of the small sphere is caused in part by its own charge and in part because it is inside the large sphere; see Fig. 29–18a.   From Eq. 29–8,

$$V_r = \frac{1}{4\pi\epsilon_0} \left(\frac{q}{r} + \frac{Q}{R} \right).$$

The potential difference is

$$V_r - V_R = \frac{q}{4\pi\epsilon_0} \left(\frac{1}{r} - \frac{1}{R} \right).$$

Thus, assuming q is positive, the inner sphere will always be higher in potential than the outer sphere.   If the spheres are connected by a fine wire, the charge q will flow *entirely* to the outer sphere, regardless of the charge Q that may already be present.

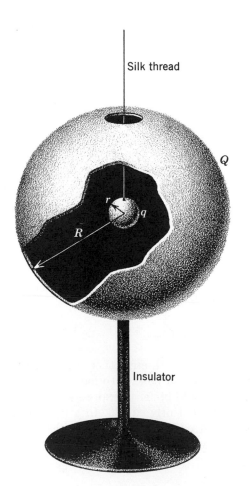

Fig. 29–20   Example 12.   A small charged sphere of radius r is suspended inside a charged spherical shell whose outer surface has radius R.

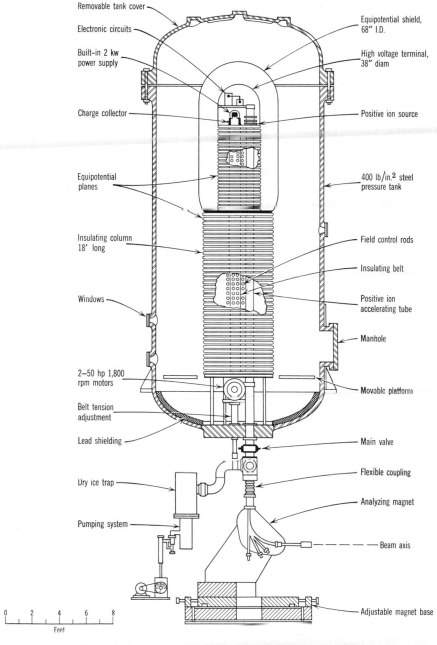

Fig. 29-21   An electrostatic generator at MIT capable of producing 9-Mev protons.   The proton beam is accelerated vertically downward, being deflected into a horizontal plane by the analyzing magnet shown at the bottom.   (Courtesy of J. G. Trump.)

From another point of view, we note that since the spheres when electrically connected form a single conductor at electrostatic equilibrium there can be only a single potential. This means that $V_r - V_R = 0$, which can occur only if $q = 0$.

In actual electrostatic generators charge is carried into the shell on rapidly moving belts made of insulating material. Charge is "sprayed" onto the belts outside the shell by corona discharge from a series of sharp metallic points connected to a source of moderately high potential difference. Charge is removed from the belts inside the shell by a similar series of points connected to the shell. Electrostatic generators can be built commercially to accelerate protons to energies up to 10 Mev, using a single acceleration. Figure 29–21 shows a schematic diagram of an electrostatic generator at MIT that can produce 9–Mev protons.

Generators can be built in which the accelerated particles are subject to successive accelerations. An electrostatic generator being constructed for the University of Pittsburgh will subject particles to three successive accelerations.

QUESTIONS

1. Are we free to call the potential of the earth $+100$ volts instead of zero? What effect would such an assumption have on measured values of (a) potentials and (b) potential differences?

2. What would happen to a person on an insulated stand if his potential was increased by 10,000 volts?

3. Do electrons tend to go to regions of high potential or of low potential?

4. Suppose that the earth has a net charge that is *not* zero. Is it still possible to adopt the earth as a standard reference point of potential and to assign the potential $V = 0$ to it?

5. Does the potential of a positively charged insulated conductor have to be positive? Give an example to prove your point.

6. Can two different equipotential surfaces intersect?

7. If **E** equals zero at a given point, must V equal zero for that point? Give some examples to prove your point.

8. If you know **E** at a given point, can you calculate V at that point? If not, what further information do you need?

9. If V equals a constant throughout a given region of space, what can you say about **E** in that region?

10. In Section 16–6 we saw that the gravitational field strength is zero inside a spherical shell of matter. The electrical field strength is zero not only inside an isolated charged spherical conductor but inside an isolated conductor of *any* shape. Is the gravitational field strength inside, say, a cubical shell of matter zero? If not, in what respect is the analogy not complete?

11. How can you insure that the electric potential in a given region of space will have a constant value?

12. An isolated conducting spherical shell carries a negative charge. What will happen if a positively charged metal object is placed in contact with the shell interior? Assume that the positive charge is (a) less than, (b) equal to, and (c) greater than the negative charge in magnitude.

13. An uncharged metal sphere suspended by a silk thread is placed in a uniform external electric field **E**. What is the magnitude of the electric field for points inside the sphere? Is your answer changed if the sphere carries a charge?

14. A charge is placed on an insulated conductor in the form of a perfect cube. What will be the relative charge density at various points on the cube (surfaces, edges, corners); what will happen to the charge if the cube is in air?

PROBLEMS

1. An infinite charged sheet has a surface charge density σ of 1.0×10^{-7} coul/meter^2. How far apart are the equipotential surfaces whose potentials differ by 5.0 volts?

2. A charge q is distributed uniformly throughout a nonconducting spherical volume of radius R. (a) Show that the potential a distance r from the center, where $r < R$, is given by

$$V = \frac{q(3R^2 - r^2)}{8\pi\epsilon_0 R^3}.$$

(b) Is it reasonable that, according to this expression, V is not zero at the center of the sphere?

3. A charge of 10^{-8} coul can be produced by simple rubbing. To what potential would such a charge raise an insulated conducting sphere of 10-cm radius?

4. Consider a point charge with $q = 1.5 \times 10^{-8}$ coul. (a) What is the radius of an equipotential surface having a potential of 30 volts? (b) Are surfaces whose potentials differ by a constant amount (say 1.0 volt) evenly spaced in radius?

5. In Fig. 29–22, locate the points (a) where $V = 0$ and (b) where $\mathbf{E} = 0$. Consider only points on the axis and choose $d = 1.0$ meter.

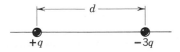

Fig. 29–22

6. In Fig. 29–22 (see Problem 5) sketch qualitatively (a) the lines of force and (b) the intersections of the equipotential surfaces with the plane of the figure. (Hint: Consider the behavior close to each point charge and at considerable distances from the pair of charges.)

7. In Fig. 29–23 derive an expression for $V_A - V_B$. Does your result reduce to the expected answer when $d = 0$? When $q = 0$?

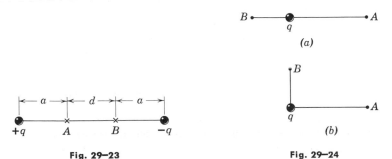

Fig. 29–23   **Fig. 29–24**

8. A point charge has $q = +1.0 \times 10^{-6}$ coul. Consider point A which is 2.0 meters distant and point B which is 1.0 meter distant in a direction diametrically opposite, as in Fig. 29–24a. (a) What is the potential difference $V_A - V_B$? (b) Repeat if points A and B are located as in Fig. 29–24b.

9. Calculate the dipole moment of a water molecule under the assumption that all ten electrons in the molecule circulate symmetrically about the oxygen atom, that the OH distance is 0.96×10^{-8} cm, and that the angle between the two OH bonds is 104°. Compare with the value quoted on p. 627; see Fig. 29–11.

10. For the charge configuration of Fig. 29–25, show that $V(r)$ for points on the vertical axis, assuming $r \gg a$, is given by

$$V = \frac{1}{4\pi\epsilon_0}\left(\frac{q}{r} + \frac{2qa}{r^2}\right).$$

Is this an expected result? (Hint: The charge configuration can be viewed as the sum of an isolated charge and a dipole.)

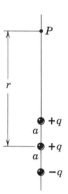

Fig. 29–25

11. In a typical lightning flash the potential difference between discharge points is about 10^9 volts and the quantity of charge transferred is about 30 coul. How much ice would it melt at 0°C if all the energy released could be used for this purpose?

12. Calculate (a) the electric potential established by the nucleus of a hydrogen atom at the mean distance of the circulating electron ($r = 5.3 \times 10^{-11}$ meter), (b) the electric potential energy of the atom when the electron is at this radius, and (c) the kinetic energy of the electron, assuming it to be moving in a circular orbit of this radius centered on the nucleus. (d) How much energy is required to ionize the hydrogen atom? Express all energies in electron volts.

13. What is the electric potential energy of the charge configuration of Fig. 29–7? Use the numerical values of Example 5.

14. (a) A spherical drop of water carrying a charge of 3×10^{-6} coul has a potential of 500 volts at its surface. What is the radius of the drop? (b) If two such drops, of the same charge and radius, combine to form a single spherical drop, what is the potential at the surface of the new drop so formed?

15. If the earth had a net charge equivalent to 1 electron/meter² of surface area, (a) what would the earth's potential be? (b) What would the electric field due to the earth be just outside its surface?

16. Figure 29–26 shows an idealized representation of a U^{238} nucleus ($Z = 92$) on the verge of fission. Calculate (a) the repulsive force acting on each fragment and (b) the mutual electric potential energy of the two fragments. Assume that the fragments are

Fig. 29–26

equal in size and charge, spherical, and just touching. The radius of the initially spherical U^{238} nucleus is 8.0×10^{-15} meter. Assume that the material out of which nuclei are made has a constant density.

17. In the Millikan oil drop experiment (see Fig. 27–24) an electric field of 1.92×10^5 nt/coul is maintained at balance across two plates separated by 1.50 cm. Find the potential difference between the plates.

18. (a) Show that the electric potential at a point on the axis of a ring of charge of radius a, computed directly from Eq. 29–10, is given by

$$V = \frac{1}{4\pi\epsilon_0} \frac{q}{\sqrt{x^2 + a^2}}.$$

(b) From this result derive an expression for E at axial points; compare with the direct calculation of E in Example 5, Chapter 27.

19. In Example 6 the potential at an axial point for a charged disk was shown to be

$$V = \frac{\sigma}{2\epsilon_0} \left(\sqrt{a^2 + r^2} - r \right).$$

From this result show that E for axial points is given by

$$E = \frac{\sigma}{2\epsilon_0} \left(1 - \frac{r}{\sqrt{a^2 + r^2}} \right).$$

Does this expression for E reduce to an expected result for (a) $r \gg a$ and (b) for $r = 0$?

20. (a) Starting from Eq. 29–11, find the magnitude E_r of the radial component of the electric field due to a dipole. (b) For what values of θ is E_r zero?

21. Can a conducting sphere 10 cm in radius hold a charge of 4×10^{-6} coul in air without breakdown? The dielectric strength (minimum field required to produce breakdown) of air at 1 atm is 3×10^6 volts/meter.

22. A Geiger counter has a metal cylinder 2.0 cm in diameter along whose axis is stretched a wire 0.005 in. in diameter. If 850 volts are applied between them, what is the electric field strength at the surface of (a) the wire and (b) the cylinder?

23. Two metal spheres are 3.0 cm in radius and carry charges of $+1.0 \times 10^{-8}$ coul and -3.0×10^{-8} coul, respectively, assumed to be uniformly distributed. If their centers are 2.0 meters apart, calculate (a) the potential of the point halfway between their centers and (b) the potential of each sphere.

24. In Fig. 29–19 let $R_1 = 1.0$ cm and $R_2 = 2.0$ cm. Before the spheres are connected by the fine wire, a charge of 2.0×10^{-7} coul is placed on the smaller sphere, the larger sphere being uncharged. Calculate (a) the charge, (b) the charge density, and (c) the potential for each sphere after they are connected.

25. The metal object in Fig. 29–27 is a figure of revolution about the horizontal axis. If it is charged negatively, sketch roughly a few equipotentials and lines of force. Use physical reasoning rather than mathematical analysis.

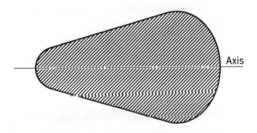

Axis

Fig. 29–27

26. Devise an arrangement of three point charges, separated by finite distances, that has zero electric potential energy.

27. Derive an expression for the work required to put the four charges together as indicated in Fig. 29–28.

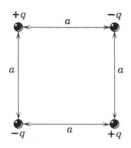

Fig. 29–28

28. A gold nucleus contains a positive charge equal to that of 79 protons. An α-particle ($Z = 2$) has a kinetic energy K at points far from this charge and is traveling directly toward the charge. The particle just touches the surface of the charge (assumed spherical) and is reversed in direction. Calculate K, assuming a nuclear radius of 5.0×10^{-15} meter. The actual α-particle energy used in the experiments of Rutherford and his collaborators was 5.0 Mev. What do you conclude?

29. What is the potential gradient, in volts/meter, at a distance of 10^{-12} meter from the center of the gold nucleus? What is the gradient at the nuclear surface?

30. For the spheres of Fig. 29–19, what is the ratio of electric field strengths at the surface?

31. (a) Through what potential difference must an electron fall, according to Newtonian mechanics, to acquire a speed v equal to the speed c of light? (b) Newtonian mechanics fails as $v \rightarrow c$. Therefore, using the correct relativistic expression for the kinetic energy

$$K = mc^2 \left[\frac{1}{\sqrt{1 - (v/c)^2}} - 1 \right]$$

in place of the Newtonian expression $K = \frac{1}{2}mv^2$, determine the actual electron speed acquired in falling through the potential difference computed in (a). Express this speed as an appropriate fraction of the speed of light.

32. Two insulated concentric conducting spheres of radii R_1 and R_2 carry charges q_1 and q_2, respectively. Derive expressions for $E(r)$ and $V(r)$, where r is the distance from the center of the spheres. Plot $E(r)$ and $V(r)$ from $r = 0$ to $r = 4.0$ meters for $R_1 = 0.50$ meter, $R_2 = 1.0$ meter, $q_1 = +2.0 \times 10^{-6}$ coul, and $q_2 = +1.0 \times 10^{-6}$ coul. Compare with Fig. 29–18.

33. Let the potential difference between the shell of an electrostatic generator and the point at which charges are sprayed onto the moving belt be 3.0×10^6 volts. If the belt transfers charge to the shell at the rate of 3.0×10^{-3} coul/sec, what power must be provided to drive the belt, considering only electrical forces?

34. (a) How much charge is required to raise an isolated metallic sphere of 1.0-meter radius to a potential of 1.0×10^6 volts? Repeat for a sphere of 1.0-cm radius. (b) Why use a large sphere in an electrostatic generator since the same potential can be achieved for a smaller charge with a small sphere?

35. An alpha particle is accelerated through a potential difference of one million volts in an electrostatic generator. (a) What kinetic energy does it acquire? (b) What kinetic energy would a proton acquire under these same circumstances? (c) Which particle would acquire the greater speed, starting from rest?

Capacitors and Dielectrics

CHAPTER 30

30–1 Capacitance

In Section 29–3 we showed that the potential of a charged conducting sphere, assumed to be completely isolated with no other bodies (conducting or nonconducting) nearby, is given by

$$V_+' = \frac{1}{4\pi\epsilon_0}\frac{q}{R},$$

(30-1)

in which q is the charge on the sphere and R is the sphere radius. The subscript on V indicates that we assume the charge to be positive. We represent this potential in Fig. 30-1 by the line marked V_+'. The line marked V_∞ in that figure represents the potential of an infinitely distant reference position; it has been assigned the value zero, following the usual convention.

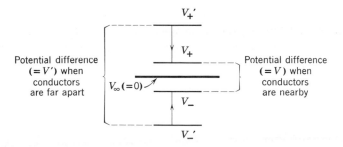

Fig. 30-1 The potential difference between two conductors that carry constant, equal, and opposite charges is reduced as the conductors are brought closer together.

Let us now imagine a second sphere of radius R, carrying a negative charge $-q$ and located a large distance ($\gg R$) from the first sphere so that each may still be considered to be electrically isolated. The potential of the second sphere is given by

$$V_-' = -\frac{1}{4\pi\epsilon_0}\frac{q}{R},$$
(30–2)

and this quantity also is represented in Fig. 30–1.

The potential difference V' between the two spheres is

$$V' = V_+' - V_-' = \frac{1}{4\pi\epsilon_0}\frac{2q}{R}.$$

This shows that V', the potential difference, and q, the magnitude of the charge on either sphere, are proportional to each other. We may rewrite the equation as

$$q = (2\pi\epsilon_0 R)V' = C'V',$$
(30–3)

in which the proportionality constant in parentheses is called the *capacitance* of the two spheres and assigned the symbol C'.

Let us move the two spheres close together. The presence of each will now spoil the spherical symmetry of the lines of force emanating from the other. Lines from a given sphere, which, for large sphere separations, radiated uniformly in all directions to infinity, now terminate, in part, on the other sphere. Under these conditions Eqs. 30–1 and 30–2 no longer apply, since they were derived (see Section 29–3) on the assumption that spherical symmetry existed, permitting the useful application of Gauss's law.

A positive charge brought near to an isolated object serves to raise the potential of that object and a negative charge serves to lower it, as the student can see by considering the work required to move a positive test charge from infinity to points near such charges. Thus the potential of the positively charged sphere will be lowered by the presence nearby of the negatively charged sphere, from V_+' to some lower value V_+. Similarly the potential of the negative sphere will be raised from V_-' to a higher value V_-. These new potentials are shown in Fig. 30–1, the potential changes for each sphere being suggested by the vertical arrows.

From Fig. 30–1, although the *charges* on the spheres have not changed, it is clear that the *potential difference* between the spheres has been considerably reduced. Put another way, the *capacitance* of the system of two spheres (see Eq. 30–3), defined from

$$C = \frac{q}{V},$$
(30–4)

has been made considerably larger than its initial value C' by bringing the spheres closer together.

It is also possible to use Eq. 30–4 to define the capacitance of a single isolated conductor such as a sphere. In such cases one may imagine that the second "plate," carrying an equal and opposite charge, is a conducting sphere of very large—essentially infinite—radius centered about the conductor. The potential of this infinitely distant sphere, according to the usual convention for potential measurements, is zero. The capacitance of an isolated sphere of radius R is given from Eqs. 30–4 and 30–1 as

$$C = \frac{q}{V} = 4\pi\epsilon_0 R.$$

The mks unit of capacitance that follows from Eq. 30–4 is the coul/volt. A special unit, the *farad*, is used to represent it. It is named in honor of Michael Faraday who, among other contributions, developed the concept of capacitance. Thus

$$1 \text{ farad} = 1 \text{ coul/volt.}$$

The submultiples of the farad, the *microfarad* (1 μf $= 10^{-6}$ farad) and the *micromicrofarad* (1 $\mu\mu$f $= 10^{-12}$ farad), are more convenient units in practice.

An analogy can be made between a capacitor carrying a charge q and a rigid container of volume υ containing $\mathfrak{n}$ moles of an ideal gas.

The gas pressure p is directly proportional to $\mathfrak{n}$, for a fixed temperature, according to the ideal gas law (Eq. 23–2)

$$\mathfrak{n} = \left(\frac{\upsilon}{RT}\right) p.$$

For the capacitor (Eq. 30–4)

$$q = (C)V.$$

Comparison shows that the capacitance of the capacitor, assuming a fixed temperature, is analogous to the volume υ of the container.

Note that any amount of charge can be put on the capacitor, and any mass of gas can be put in the container, up to certain limits. These correspond to electrical breakdown ("arcing over") for the capacitor and to rupture of the walls for the container.

Figure 30–2 shows a more general case of two nearby conductors, which are now permitted to be of any shape, carrying equal and opposite charges. Such an arrangement is called a *capacitor*, the conductors being called *plates*. The equal and opposite charges might be established by connecting the plates momentarily to opposite poles of a battery. The capacitance C of any capacitor is defined from Eq. 30–4 in which we remind the student that V is the *potential difference between the plates* and q is the magnitude of the *charge on either plate; q* must not be taken as the net charge of the capacitor, which is zero. The capacitance of a capacitor depends on the geometry of each plate, their spatial relationship to each other, and the medium in which the plates are immersed. For the present, we take this medium to be a vacuum.

Capacitors are very useful devices, of great interest to physicists and engineers. For example:

1. In this book we stress the importance of *fields* to the understanding of natural phenomena. A capacitor can be used to establish desired electric field configurations for various purposes. In Section 27–5 we described the deflection of an electron beam in a uniform field set up by a capacitor, al-

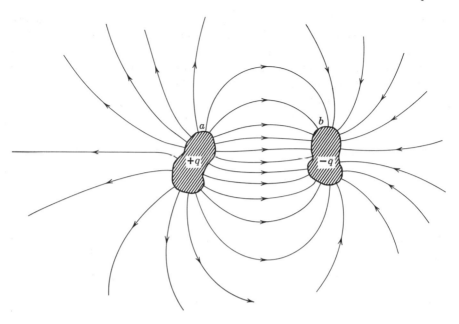

Fig. 30–2   Two insulated conductors carrying equal and opposite charges form a capacitor.

though we did not use this term in that section.   In later sections we discuss the behavior of dielectric materials when placed in an electric field (provided conveniently by a capacitor) and we shall see how the laws of electromagnetism can be generalized to take the presence of dielectric bodies more readily into account.

2. A second important concept stressed in this book is *energy*.   By analyzing a charged capacitor we show that electric energy may be considered to be stored in the electric field between the plates and indeed in any electric field, however generated.   Because capacitors can confine strong electric fields to small volumes, they can serve as useful devices for storing energy. In many electron synchrotrons, which are cyclotron-like devices for accelerating electrons, energy accumulated and stored in a large bank of capacitors over a relatively long period of time is made available intermittently to accelerate the electrons by discharging the capacitor in a much shorter time. Many researches and devices in plasma physics also make use of bursts of energy stored in this way.

3. The electronic age could not exist without capacitors.   They are used, in conjunction with other devices, to reduce voltage fluctuations in electronic power supplies, to transmit pulsed signals, to generate or detect electromagnetic oscillations at radio frequencies, and to provide time delays.   In most of these applications the potential difference between the plates will not be constant, as we assume in this chapter, but will vary with time, often in a sinusoidal or a pulsed fashion.   In later chapters we consider some aspects of the capacitor used as a circuit element.

30–2   Calculating Capacitance

Figure 30–3 shows a *parallel-plate* capacitor formed of two parallel conducting plates of area A separated by a distance d. If we connect each plate to the terminal of a battery, a charge $+q$ will appear on one plate and a charge $-q$ on the other. If d is small compared with the plate dimensions, the electric field strength **E** between the plates will be uniform, which means that the lines of force will be parallel and evenly spaced. The laws of electromagnetism (see Problem 20, Chapter 35) require that there be some "fringing" of the lines at the edges of the plates, but for small enough d it can be neglected for our present purpose.

We can calculate the capacitance of this device using Gauss's law. Figure 30–3 shows (dashed lines) a Gaussian surface of height h closed by plane caps of area A that are the shape and size of the capacitor plates. The flux of **E** is zero for the part of the Gaussian surface that lies inside the top capacitor plate because the electric field inside a conductor carrying a static charge is zero. The flux of **E** through the wall of the Gaussian surface is zero because, to the extent that the fringing of the lines of force can be neglected, **E** lies in the wall.

This leaves only the face of the Gaussian surface that lies between the plates. Here **E** is constant and the flux Φ_E is simply EA. Gauss's law gives

$$\epsilon_0 \Phi_E = \epsilon_0 EA = q. \qquad (30\text{–}5)$$

The work required to carry a test charge q_0 from one plate to the other can be expressed either as $q_0 V$ (see Eq. 29–1) or as the product of a force $q_0 E$ times a distance d or $q_0 Ed$. These expressions must be equal, or

$$V = Ed. \qquad (30\text{–}6)$$

More formally, Eq. 30–6 is a special case of the general relation (Eq. 29–5; see also Example 1, Chapter 29)

$$V = -\int \mathbf{E} \cdot d\mathbf{l},$$

where V is the difference in potential between the plates. The integral may

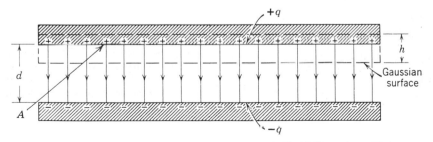

Fig. 30–3   A parallel-plate capacitor with plates of area A. The dashed line represents a Gaussian surface whose height is h and whose top and bottom caps are the same shape and size as the capacitor plates.

be taken over any path that starts on one plate and ends on the other because each plate is an equipotential and the electrostatic force is path independent. Although the simplest path between the plates is a perpendicular straight line, Eq. 30–6 follows no matter what path of integration we choose.

If we substitute Eqs. 30–5 and 30–6 into the relation $C = q/V$, we obtain

$$C = \frac{q}{V} = \frac{\epsilon_0 EA}{Ed} = \frac{\epsilon_0 A}{d}. \tag{30–7}$$

Equation 30–7 holds only for capacitors of the parallel-plate type; different formulas hold for capacitors of different geometry.

In Section 26–4 we stated that ϵ_0, which we first met in connection with Coulomb's law, was not measured in terms of that law because of experimental difficulties. Equation 30–7 suggests that ϵ_0 might be measured by building a capacitor of accurately known plate area and plate spacing and determining its capacitance experimentally by measuring q and V in the relation $C = q/V$. Thus Eq. 30–7 can be solved for ϵ_0 and a numerical value found in terms of the measured quantities A, d, and C; ϵ_0 has been measured accurately in this way.

▶ **Example 1.** The parallel plates of an air-filled capacitor are everywhere 1.0 mm apart. What must the plate area be if the capacitance is to be 1.0 farad?
From Eq. 30–7

$$A = \frac{dC}{\epsilon_0} = \frac{(1.0 \times 10^{-3}\ \text{meter})(1.0\ \text{farad})}{8.9 \times 10^{-12}\ \text{coul}^2/\text{nt-m}^2} = 1.1 \times 10^8\ \text{meter}^2.$$

This is the area of a square sheet more than 6 miles on edge; the farad is indeed a large unit.

Example 2. *A cylindrical capacitor.* A cylindrical capacitor consists of two coaxial cylinders (Fig. 30–4) of radius a and b and length l. What is the capacitance of this device? Assume that the capacitor is very long (that is, that $l \gg b$) so that fringing of the lines of force at the ends can be ignored for the purpose of calculating the capacitance.

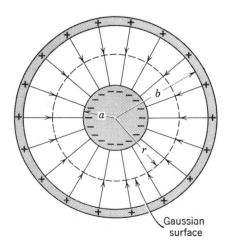

Fig. 30–4 Example 2. A cross section of a cylindrical capacitor. The dashed circle is a cross section of a cylindrical Gaussian surface of radius r and length l.

Gaussian
surface

As a Gaussian surface construct a coaxial cylinder of radius r and length l, closed by plane caps. Gauss's law

$$\epsilon_0 \oint \mathbf{E} \cdot d\mathbf{S} = q$$

gives

$$\epsilon_0 E(2\pi r)(l) = q,$$

the flux being entirely through the cylindrical surface and not through the end caps. Solving for E yields

$$E = \frac{q}{2\pi \epsilon_0 r l}.$$

The potential difference between the plates is given by Eq. 29–5 [note that $\mathbf{E}$ and $d\mathbf{l}$ (= $d\mathbf{r}$) point in opposite directions] or

$$V = -\int_a^b \mathbf{E} \cdot d\mathbf{l} = \int_a^b E \, dr = \int_a^b \frac{q}{2\pi \epsilon_0 l} \frac{dr}{r} = \frac{q}{2\pi \epsilon_0 l} \ln \frac{b}{a}.$$

Finally, the capacitance is given by

$$C = \frac{q}{V} = \frac{2\pi \epsilon_0 l}{\ln (b/a)},$$

Like the relation for the parallel-plate capacitor (Eq. 30–7), this relation also depends only on geometrical factors.

Example 3. *Capacitors in parallel.* Figure 30–5 shows three capacitors connected in parallel. What single capacitance C is equivalent to this combination? "Equivalent" means that if the parallel combination and the single capacitance were each in a box with wires a and b connected to terminals, it would not be possible to distinguish the two by electrical measurements external to the box.

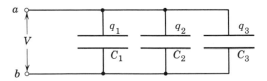

Fig. 30–5 Example 3. Three capacitors in parallel.

The potential difference across each capacitor in Fig. 30–5 will be the same. This follows because all of the upper plates are connected together and to terminal a, whereas all of the lower plates are connected together and to terminal b. Applying the relation $q = CV$ to each capacitor yields

$$q_1 = C_1 V; \qquad q_2 = C_2 V; \qquad \text{and} \qquad q_3 = C_3 V.$$

The total charge q on the combination is

$$q = q_1 + q_2 + q_3$$
$$= (C_1 + C_2 + C_3)V.$$

The equivalent capacitance C is

$$C = \frac{q}{V} = C_1 + C_2 + C_3.$$

This result can easily be extended to any number of parallel-connected capacitors.

Example 4. *Capacitors in series.* Figure 30–6 shows three capacitors connected in series. What single capacitance C is "equivalent" (see Example 3) to this combination?

For capacitors connected as shown, the magnitude q of the charge on each plate must be the same. This is true because the net charge on the part of the circuit enclosed by the dashed line in Fig. 30–6 must be zero; that is, the charge present on these plates initially is zero and connecting a battery between a and b will only produce a charge separation, the *net* charge on these plates still being zero. Assuming that neither C_1 nor C_2 "sparks over," there is no way for charge to enter or leave the region enclosed by the dashed line.

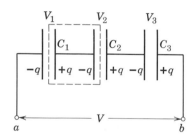

Fig. 30–6 Example 4. Three capacitors in series.

Applying the relation $q = CV$ to each capacitor yields

$$V_1 = q/C_1; \qquad V_2 = q/C_2; \qquad \text{and} \qquad V_3 = q/C_3.$$

The potential difference for the series combination is

$$V = V_1 + V_2 + V_3$$

$$= q\left(\frac{1}{C_1} + \frac{1}{C_2} + \frac{1}{C_3}\right).$$

The equivalent capacitance

$$C = \frac{q}{V} = \frac{1}{\dfrac{1}{C_1} + \dfrac{1}{C_2} + \dfrac{1}{C_3}},$$

or

$$\frac{1}{C} = \frac{1}{C_1} + \frac{1}{C_2} + \frac{1}{C_3}.$$

The equivalent series capacitance is always less than the smallest capacitance in the chain. ◀

30–3 Parallel-Plate Capacitor with Dielectric

Equation 30–7 holds only for a parallel-plate capacitor with its plates in a vacuum. Michael Faraday, in 1837, first investigated the effect of filling the space between the plates with a dielectric, say mica or oil. In Faraday's words:

> The question may be stated thus: suppose A an electrified plate of metal suspended in air, and B and C two exactly similar plates, placed parallel to and on each side of A at equal distances and insulated; A will then induce equally toward B and C [that is, equal charges will appear on these plates]. If in this position of the plates some other dielectric than air, as shell-lac, be introduced between A and

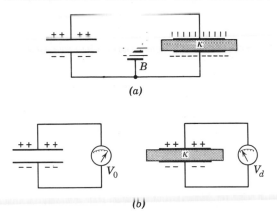

(a)

(b)

Fig. 30–7   (a) Battery B supplies the same potential difference to each capacitor; the one on the right has the higher charge.   (b) Both capacitors carry the same charge; the one on the right has the lower potential difference, as indicated by the meter readings.

C, will the induction between them remain the same?   Will the relation of C and B to A be unaltered, notwithstanding the difference of the dielectrics interposed between them?

Faraday answered this question by constructing two identical capacitors, in one of which he placed a dielectric, the other containing air at normal pressure.   When both capacitors were charged to the *same potential difference,* Faraday found by experiment that *the charge on the one containing the dielectric was greater than that on the other;* see Fig. 30–7a.

Faraday measured the relative charges on the plates of the two capacitors by touching a metal ball (fitted with an insulating handle) to the plates, thus sampling the charge quantitatively.   He then put this ball in a Coulomb torsion balance and measured the force of Coulomb repulsion on a second (standard) charged ball mounted on the balance arm.

Since q is larger, for the same V, if a dielectric is present, it follows from the relation $C = q/V$ that *the capacitance of a capacitor increases if a dielectric is placed between the plates.*   The ratio of the capacitance with the dielectric * to that without is called the *dielectric constant* κ of the material; see Table 30–1.

Instead of maintaining the two capacitors at the same potential difference, we can place the *same charge* on them, as in Fig. 30–7b.   Experiment then shows that the potential difference V_d between the plates of the right-hand capacitor is smaller than that for the left-hand capacitor by the factor $1/\kappa$, or

$$V_d = V_0/\kappa.$$

We are led once again to conclude, from the relation $C = q/V$, that the effect of the dielectric is to increase the capacitance by a factor κ.

---

* Assumed to fill completely the space between the plates.

Table 30–1

PROPERTIES OF SOME DIELECTRICS

Material	Dielectric Constant	Dielectric Strength * (kv/mm)
Vacuum	1.00000	∞
Air	1.00054	0.8
Water	78	—
Paper	3.5	14
Ruby mica	5.4	160
Amber	2.7	90
Porcelain	6.5	4
Fused quartz	3.8	8
Pyrex glass	4.5	13
Bakelite	4.8	12
Polyethylene	2.3	50
Polystyrene	2.6	25
Teflon	2.1	60
Neoprene	6.9	12
Pyranol oil	4.5	12
Titanium dioxide	100	6

* This is the maximum potential gradient that may exist in the dielectric without the occurrence of electrical breakdown. Dielectrics are often placed between conducting plates to permit a higher potential difference to be applied between them than would be possible with air as the dielectric.

For a parallel-plate capacitor we can write, as an experimental result,

$$C = \frac{\kappa \epsilon_0 A}{d}. \tag{30–8}$$

Equation 30–7 is a special case of this relation found by putting $\kappa = 1$, corresponding to a vacuum between the plates. Experiment shows that the capacitance of *all* types of capacitor is increased by the factor κ if the space between the plates is filled with a dielectric. Thus the capacitance of any capacitor can be written as

$$C = \kappa \epsilon_0 L,$$

where L depends on the geometry and has the dimensions of a length. For a parallel-plate capacitor (see Eq. 30–7) L is A/d; for a cylindrical capacitor (see Example 2) it is $2\pi l/\ln (b/a)$.

30–4 Dielectrics—An Atomic View

We now seek to understand, in atomic terms, what happens when a dielectric is placed in an electric field. There are two possibilities. The molecules of some dielectrics, like water, have permanent electric dipole moments.

In such materials (called *polar*) the electric dipole moments **p** tend to align themselves with an external electric field, as in Fig. 30–8; see also Section 27–6. Because the molecules are in constant thermal agitation, the degree of alignment will not be complete but will increase as the applied electric field is increased or as the temperature is decreased.

Whether or not the molecules have permanent electric dipole moments, they acquire them by *induction* when placed in an electric field. In Section 29–5 we saw that the external electric field tends to separate the negative and the positive charge in the atom or molecule. This *induced electric dipole moment* is present only when the electric field is present. It is proportional to the electric field (for normal field strengths) and is created already lined up with the electric field as Fig. 30–12 suggests.

Let us use a parallel-plate capacitor, carrying a fixed charge q and not connected to a battery (see Fig. 30–7b), to provide a uniform external electric field $\mathbf{E}_0$ into which we place a dielectric slab. The over-all effect of alignment and induction is to separate the center of positive charge of the entire slab slightly from the center of negative charge. The slab, as a whole, although remaining electrically neutral, becomes *polarized*, as Fig. 30–9b suggests. The net effect is a pile-up of positive charge on the right face of the slab and of negative charge on the left face; within the slab no excess charge appears in any given volume element. Since the slab as a whole remains neutral, the positive *induced surface charge* must be equal in magnitude to the negative induced surface charge. Note that in this process electrons in the dielectric

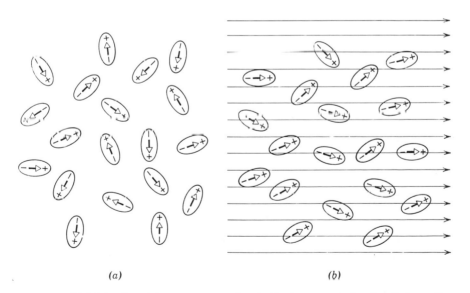

(a)   (b)

Fig. 30–8   (a) Molecules with a permanent electric dipole moment, showing their random orientation in the absence of an external electric field. (b) An electric field is applied, producing partial alignment of the dipoles. Thermal agitation prevents complete alignment.

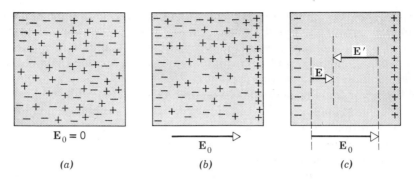

Fig. 30–9 (*a*) A dielectric slab, showing the random distribution of plus and minus charges. (*b*) An external field $\mathbf{E}_0$, established by putting the slab between the plates of a parallel-plate capacitor (not shown), separates the center of plus charge in the slab slightly from the center of minus charge, resulting in the appearance of surface charges. No *net* charge exists in any volume element located in the *interior* of the slab. (*c*) The surface charges set up a field $\mathbf{E}'$ which opposes the external field $\mathbf{E}_0$ associated with the charges on the capacitor plates. The resultant field $\mathbf{E}$ ($= \mathbf{E}_0 + \mathbf{E}'$) in the dielectric is thus less than $\mathbf{E}_0$.

are displaced from their equilibrium positions by distances that are considerably less than an atomic diameter. There is no transfer of charge over macroscopic distances such as occurs when a current is set up in a conductor.

Figure 30–9*c* shows that the induced surface charges will always appear in such a way that the electric field set up *by them* ($\mathbf{E}'$) opposes the external electric field $\mathbf{E}_0$. The *resultant* field in the dielectric $\mathbf{E}$ is the vector sum of $\mathbf{E}_0$ and $\mathbf{E}'$. It points in the same direction as $\mathbf{E}_0$ but is smaller. *If a dielectric is placed in an electric field, induced surface charges appear which tend to weaken the original field within the dielectric.*

This weakening of the electric field reveals itself in Fig. 30–7*b* as a reduction in potential difference between the plates of a charged isolated capacitor when a dielectric is introduced between the plates. The relation $V = Ed$ for a parallel-plate capacitor (see Eq. 30–6) holds whether or not dielectric is present and shows that the reduction in V described in Fig. 30–7*b* is directly connected to the reduction in E described in Fig. 30–9. More specifically, if a dielectric slab is introduced into a charged parallel-plate capacitor, then

$$\frac{E_0}{E} = \frac{V_0}{V_d} = \kappa \qquad (30\text{–}9)$$

where the symbols on the left refer to Fig. 30–9 and the symbols V_0 and V_d refer to Fig. 30–7*b*.*

Induced surface charge is the explanation of the most elementary fact of static electricity, namely, that a charged rod will attract uncharged bits of

---

* Equation 30–9 does not hold if the battery remains connected while the dielectric slab is introduced. In this case V (hence E) could not change. Instead, the charge q on the capacitor plates would increase by a factor κ, as Fig. 30–7*a* suggests.

Fig. 30–10 A charged rod attracts an uncharged piece of paper because unbalanced forces act on the induced surface charges.

paper, etc. Figure 30–10 shows a bit of paper in the field of a charged rod. Surface charges appear on the paper as shown. The negatively charged end of the paper will be pulled toward the rod and the positively charged end will be repelled. These two forces do not have the same magnitude because the negative end, being closer to the rod, is in a stronger field and experiences a stronger force. The net effect is an attraction. A dielectric body in a *uniform* electric field will not experience a net force.

30–5   Dielectrics and Gauss's Law

So far our use of Gauss's law has been confined to situations in which no dielectric was present. Now let us apply this law to a parallel-plate capacitor filled with a dielectric of dielectric constant κ.

Figure 30–11 shows the capacitor both with and without the dielectric. It is assumed that the charge q on the plates is the same in each case. Gaussian surfaces have been drawn after the fashion of Fig. 30–3.

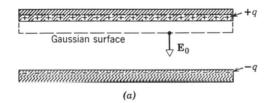

(a)

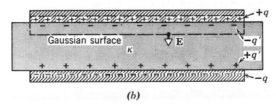

(b)

Fig. 30–11 A parallel-plate capacitor *(a)* without and *(b)* with a dielectric. The charge q on the plates is assumed to be the same in each case.

If no dielectric is present (Fig. 30–11a), Gauss's law (see Eq. 30–5) gives

$$\epsilon_0 \oint \mathbf{E} \cdot d\mathbf{S} = \epsilon_0 E_0 A = q$$

or

$$E_0 = \frac{q}{\epsilon_0 A}. \tag{30–10}$$

If the dielectric is present (Fig. 30–11b), Gauss's law gives

$$\epsilon_0 \oint \mathbf{E} \cdot d\mathbf{S} = \epsilon_0 E A = q - q'$$

or

$$E = \frac{q}{\epsilon_0 A} - \frac{q'}{\epsilon_0 A}, \tag{30–11}$$

in which $-q'$, the *induced surface charge*, must be distinguished from q, the so-called *free charge* on the plates. These two charges, both of which lie within the Gaussian surface, are opposite in sign; $q - q'$ is the *net* charge within the Gaussian surface.

Equation 30–9 shows that in Fig. 30–11

$$E = \frac{E_0}{\kappa}.$$

Combining this with Eq. 39–10, we have

$$E = \frac{E_0}{\kappa} = \frac{q}{\kappa \epsilon_0 A}. \tag{30–12}$$

Inserting this in Eq. 30–11 yields

$$\frac{q}{\kappa \epsilon_0 A} = \frac{q}{\epsilon_0 A} - \frac{q'}{\epsilon_0 A} \tag{30–13a}$$

or

$$q' = q\left(1 - \frac{1}{\kappa}\right). \tag{30–13b}$$

This shows correctly that the induced surface charge q' is always less in magnitude than the free charge q and is equal to zero if no dielectric is present, that is, if $\kappa = 1$.

Now we write Gauss's law for the case of Fig. 30–11b in the form

$$\epsilon_0 \oint \mathbf{E} \cdot d\mathbf{S} = q - q', \tag{30–14}$$

$q - q'$ again being the net charge within the Gaussian surface. Substituting from Eq. 30–13b for q' leads, after some rearrangement, to

$$\epsilon_0 \oint \kappa \mathbf{E} \cdot d\mathbf{S} = q. \tag{30–15}$$

This important relation, although derived for a parallel-plate capacitor, is true generally and is the form in which Gauss's law is usually written when dielectrics are present. Note the following:

1. The flux integral now contains a factor κ.
2. The charge q contained within the Gaussian surface is taken to be the *free charge only*. Induced surface charge is deliberately ignored on the right side of this equation, having been taken into account by the introduction of κ on the left side. Equations 30–14 and 30–15 are completely equivalent formulations.

▶ **Example 5.** Figure 30–12 shows a dielectric slab of thickness b and dielectric constant κ placed between the plates of a parallel-plate capacitor of plate area A and separation d. A potential difference V_0 is applied with no dielectric present. The battery is then disconnected and the dielectric slab inserted. Assume that $A = 100$ cm², $d = 1.0$ cm, $b = 0.50$ cm, $\kappa = 7.0$, and $V_0 = 100$ volts and (a) calculate the capacitance C_0 before the slab is inserted.

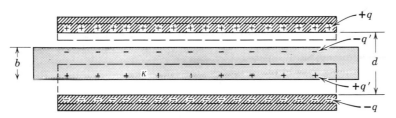

Fig. 30–12   Example 5. A parallel-plate capacitor containing a dielectric slab.

From Eq. 30–7, C_0 is found:

$$C_0 = \frac{\epsilon_0 A}{d} = \frac{(8.9 \times 10^{-12}\ \text{coul}^2/\text{nt-m}^2)(10^{-2}\ \text{meter}^2)}{10^{-2}\ \text{meter}} = 8.9\ \mu\mu\text{f}.$$

(b) Calculate the free charge q.
From Eq. 30–1,

$$q = C_0 V_0 = (8.9 \times 10^{-12}\ \text{farad})(100\ \text{volts}) = 8.9 \times 10^{-10}\ \text{coul}.$$

Because of the technique used to charge the capacitor, the free charge remains unchanged as the slab is introduced. If the charging battery had *not* been disconnected, this would not be the case.

(c) Calculate the electric field strength in the gap.
Applying Gauss's law in the form given in Eq. 30–15 to the Gaussian surface of Fig. 30–12 (upper plate) yields

$$\epsilon_0 \oint \kappa \mathbf{E} \cdot d\mathbf{S} = \epsilon_0 E_0 A = q,$$

or $E_0 = \dfrac{q}{\epsilon_0 A} = \dfrac{8.9 \times 10^{-10}\ \text{coul}}{(8.9 \times 10^{-12}\ \text{coul}^2/\text{nt-m}^2)(10^{-2}\ \text{meter}^2)} = 1.0 \times 10^4\ \text{volts/meter}.$

Note that we put $\kappa = 1$ here because the surface over which we evaluate flux integral does not pass through any dielectric. Note too that E_0 remains unchanged when the slab is introduced; this derivation takes no specific account of the presence of the dielectric.

(*d*) Calculate the electric field strength in the dielectric.

Applying Eq. 30–15 to the Gaussian surface of Fig. 30–12 (lower plate) yields

$$\epsilon_0 \oint \kappa \mathbf{E} \cdot d\mathbf{S} = \epsilon_0 \kappa E A = q.$$

Note that κ appears here because the surface cuts through the dielectric and that only the free charge q appears on the right. Thus we have

$$E = \frac{q}{\kappa \epsilon_0 A} = \frac{E_0}{\kappa} = \frac{1.0 \times 10^4 \text{ volts/meter}}{7.0} = 0.14 \times 10^4 \text{ volts/meter}.$$

(*e*) Calculate the potential difference between the plates.

Applying Eq. 29–5 to a straight perpendicular path from the lower plate (L) to the upper one (U) yields

$$V = -\int_L^U \mathbf{E} \cdot d\mathbf{l} = -\int_L^U E \cos 180° \, dl = \int_L^U E \, dl = E_0(d - b) + Eb.$$

Numerically

$$V = (1.0 \times 10^4 \text{ volts/meter})(5 \times 10^{-3} \text{ meter})$$

$$+ (0.14 \times 10^4 \text{ volts/meter})(5 \times 10^{-3} \text{ meter}) = 57 \text{ volts}.$$

This contrasts with the original applied potential difference of 100 volts; compare Fig. 30–7*b*.

(*f*) Calculate the capacitance with the slab in place.

From Eq. 30–4,

$$C = \frac{q}{V} = \frac{8.9 \times 10^{-10} \text{ coul}}{57 \text{ volts}} = 16 \ \mu\mu\text{f}.$$

When the dielectric slab is introduced, the potential difference drops from 100 to 57 volts and the capacitance rises from 8.9 to 16 $\mu\mu$f, a factor of 1.8. If the dielectric slab had filled the capacitor, the capacitance would have risen by a factor of κ ($= 7.0$) to 62 $\mu\mu$f.   ◀

30–6   Three Electric Vectors

For all situations that we encounter in this book our discussion of the behavior of dielectrics in an electric field is adequate. However, the problems that we treat are simple ones, such as that of a rectangular slab placed at right angles to a uniform external electric field. For more difficult problems, such as that of finding $\mathbf{E}$ at the center of a dielectric ellipsoid placed in a (possibly nonuniform) external electric field, it greatly simplifies the labor and leads to deeper insight if we introduce a new formalism. We do so largely so that students who take a second course in electromagnetism will have some familiarity with the concepts.

Let us rewrite Eq. 30–13*a*, which applies to a parallel-plate capacitor containing a dielectric, as

$$\frac{q}{A} = \epsilon_0 \left(\frac{q}{\kappa \epsilon_0 A} \right) + \frac{q'}{A}. \tag{30–16}$$

The quantity in parentheses (see Eq. 30–12) is simply the electric field strength E in the dielectric. The last term in Eq. 30–16 is the *induced surface charge per unit area*. We call it the *electric polarization P*, or

$$P = \frac{q'}{A}. \tag{30–17}$$

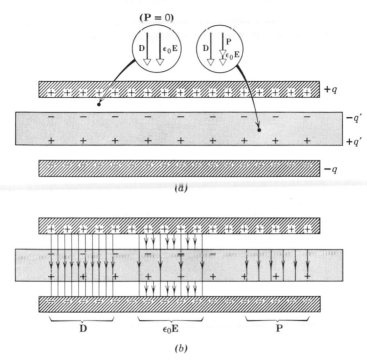

Fig. 30–13 (a) Showing **D**, $\epsilon_0\mathbf{E}$, and **P** in the dielectric (*upper right*) and in the gap (*upper left*) for a parallel-plate capacitor. (b) Showing samples of the lines associated with **D** (free charge), $\epsilon_0\mathbf{E}$ (all charges), and **P** (polarization charge).

The name is suitable because the induced surface charge q' appears when the dielectric is polarized.

The electric polarization P can be defined in an equivalent way by multiplying the numerator and denominator in Eq. 30–17 by d, the thickness of the dielectric slab in Fig. 30–11,

$$P = \frac{q'd}{Ad}. \tag{30–18}$$

The numerator is the product $q'd$ of the magnitude of the (equal and opposite) polarization charges by their separation. It is thus the induced electric dipole moment of the dielectric slab. Since the denominator Ad is the volume of the slab, we see that the electric polarization can also be defined as the induced electric dipole moment per unit volume in the dielectric. This definition suggests that since the electric dipole moment is a vector the electric polarization is also a vector, its magnitude being P. The direction of **P** is from the negative induced charge to the positive induced charge, as for any dipole. In Fig. 30–13, which shows a capacitor with a dielectric slab filling half the space between the plates, **P** points down.

We can now rewrite Eq. 30–16 as

$$\frac{q}{A} = \epsilon_0 E + P. \tag{30–19}$$

The quantity on the right occurs so often in electrostatic problems that we give it the special name *electric displacement D*, or

$$D = \epsilon_0 E + P \qquad (30\text{--}20a)$$

in which

$$D = \frac{q}{A}. \qquad (30\text{--}20b)$$

The name has historical significance only.

Since **E** and **P** are vectors, **D** must also be one, so that in the more general case we have

$$\mathbf{D} = \epsilon_0 \mathbf{E} + \mathbf{P}. \qquad (30\text{--}21)$$

In Fig. 30–13 all three vectors point down and each has a constant magnitude for every point in the dielectric (and also at every point in the air gap) so that the vector nature of Eq. 30–21 is not very important in this case. In more complicated problems, however, **E**, **P**, and **D** may vary in magnitude and direction from point to point. From their definitions we see the following:

1. **D** (see Eq. 30–20b) is connected with the *free charge* only. We can represent the vector field of **D** by *lines of* **D**, just as we represent the field of **E** by lines of force. Figure 30–13b shows that the lines of **D** begin and end on the free charges.

2. **P** (see Eq. 30–17) is connected with the *polarization charge* only. It is also possible to represent this vector field by lines. Figure 30–13b shows that the lines of **P** begin and end on the polarization charges.

3. **E** is connected with all charges that are actually present, whether free or polarization. The lines of **E** reflect the presence of both kinds of charge, as Fig. 30–13b shows. Note (Eqs. 30–17 and 30–20b) that the units for **P** and **D** (coul/meter^2) differ from those of **E** (nt/coul).

The electric field vector **E**, which is what determines the force that acts on a suitably placed test charge, remains of fundamental interest. **D** and **P** are auxiliary vectors useful as aids in the solution of problems more complex than that of Fig. 30–13.

The vectors **D** and **P** can both be expressed in terms of **E** alone. A convenient starting point is the identity

$$\frac{q}{A} = \kappa\epsilon_0 \left(\frac{q}{\kappa\epsilon_0 A} \right).$$

Comparison with Eqs. 30–12 and 30–20b shows that this, extended to vector form, can be written as

$$\mathbf{D} = \kappa\epsilon_0 \mathbf{E}. \qquad (30\text{--}22)$$

We can also write the polarization (see Eqs. 30–17 and 30–13b) as

$$P = \frac{q'}{A} = \frac{q}{A}\left(1 - \frac{1}{\kappa}\right).$$

Since $q/A = D$, we can rewrite this, using Eq. 30–22 and casting the result into vector form, as

$$\mathbf{P} = \epsilon_0(\kappa - 1)\mathbf{E}. \qquad (30\text{--}23)$$

This shows clearly that in a vacuum ($\kappa = 1$) the polarization vector **P** is zero.*

---

* Certain waxes, when polarized in their molten state, retain a permanent polarization after solidifying, even though the external polarizing field is removed. *Electrets*, manufactured in this way, are the electrostatic analog of permanent magnets in that they possess a gross permanent electric dipole moment. Materials from which electrets can be constructed are called *ferroelectric*. Electrets do not obey Eq. 30–23 because they have a nonvanishing value of **P** even though **E** = 0.

Equations 30–22 and 30–23 show that for isotropic materials, to which a single dielectric constant κ can be assigned, **D** and **P** both point in the direction of **E** at any given point.

The definition of **D** given by Eq. 30–22 allows us to write Eq. 30–15, that is, Gauss's law in the presence of a dielectric, simply as

$$\oint \mathbf{D} \cdot d\mathbf{S} = q, \tag{30–24}$$

where, as before, q represents the free charge only, the induced surface charges being excluded.

▶ **Example 6.** In Figure 30–13, using data from Example 5, calculate E, D, and P: (a) in the dielectric and (b) in the air gap.

(a) The electric field in the dielectric is calculated in Example 5 to be 1.43×10^9 volts/meter. From Eq. 30–22,

$$D = \kappa\epsilon_0 E$$

$$= (7.0)(8.9 \times 10^{-12}\ \text{coul}^2/\text{nt-m}^2)(1.43 \times 10^3\ \text{volts/meter})$$

$$= 8.9 \times 10^{-8}\ \text{coul/meter}^2$$

and, from Eq. 30–23,

$$P = \epsilon_0(\kappa - 1)E$$

$$= (8.9 \times 10^{-12}\ \text{coul}^2/\text{nt-m}^2)(7.0 - 1)(1.43 \times 10^3\ \text{volts/meter})$$

$$= 7.5 \times 10^{-8}\ \text{coul/meter}^2.$$

(b) The electric field E_0 in the air gap is calculated in Example 5 to be 1.00×10^4 volts/meter. From Eq. 30–22,

$$D_0 = \kappa\epsilon_0 E_0$$

$$= (1)(8.9 \times 10^{-12}\ \text{coul}^2/\text{nt-m}^2)(1.00 \times 10^4\ \text{volts/meter})$$

$$= 8.9 \times 10^{-8}\ \text{coul/meter}^2$$

and, from Eq. 30–23, recalling that $\kappa = 1$ in the air gap,

$$P_0 = \epsilon_0(\kappa - 1)E_0 = 0.$$

Note that **P** vanishes outside the dielectric, **D** has the same value in the dielectric and in the gap, and **E** has different values in the dielectric and in the gap. The student should verify that Eq. 30–21 ($\mathbf{D} = \epsilon_0\mathbf{E} + \mathbf{P}$) is correct both in the gap and in the dielectric.

It can be shown from Maxwell's equations that no matter how complex the problem the component of **D** *normal* to the surface of the dielectric has the same value on each side of the surface. In this problem **D** itself is normal to the surface, there being no component but the normal one. It can also be shown that the component of **E** *tangential* to the dielectric surface has the same value on each side of the surface. This *boundary condition*, like the one for **D**, is trivial in this problem, both tangential components being zero. In more complex problems these boundary conditions on **D** and **E** are very important. Table 30–2 summarizes the properties of the electric vectors **E**, **D**, and **P**. ◀

Table 30–2

THE ELECTRIC VECTORS

Name	Symbol	Associated with	Boundary Condition
Electric field strength	**E**	All charges	Tangential component continuous
Electric displacement	**D**	Free charges only	Normal component continuous
Polarization (electric dipole moment per unit volume)	**P**	Polarization charges only	Vanishes in a vacuum

Defining equation for **E**	$\mathbf{F} = q\mathbf{E}$	Eq. 27–2
General relation among the three vectors	$\mathbf{D} = \epsilon_0 \mathbf{E} + \mathbf{P}$	Eq. 30–21
Gauss's law when dielectric media are present	$\oint \mathbf{D} \cdot d\mathbf{S} = q$ (q = free charge only)	Eq. 30–24
Empirical relations for certain dielectric materials *	$\mathbf{D} = \kappa \epsilon_0 \mathbf{E}$ $\mathbf{P} = (\kappa - 1) \epsilon_0 \mathbf{E}$	Eq. 30–22 Eq. 30–23

* Generally true, with κ independent of **E**, except for certain materials called *ferroelectrics*; see footnote on page 666.

30–7   Energy Storage in an Electric Field

In Section 29–6 we saw that all charge configurations have a certain *electric potential energy* U, equal to the work W (which may be positive or negative) that must be done to assemble them from their individual components, originally assumed to be infinitely far apart and at rest. This potential energy reminds us of the potential energy stored in a compressed spring or the gravitational potential energy stored in, say, the earth-moon system.

For a simple example, work must be done to separate two equal and opposite charges. This energy is stored in the system and can be recovered if the charges are allowed to come together again. Similarly, a charged capacitor has stored in it an electrical potential energy U equal to the work W required to charge it. This energy can be recovered if the capacitor is allowed to discharge. We can visualize the work of charging by imagining that an external agent pulls electrons from the positive plate and pushes them onto the negative plate, thus bringing about the charge separation; normally the work of charging is done by a battery, at the expense of its store of chemical energy.

Suppose that at a time t a charge $q'(t)$ has been transferred from one plate to the other. The potential difference $V(t)$ between the plates at that moment will be $q'(t)/C$. If an extra increment of charge dq' is transferred, the small amount of additional work needed will be

$$dW = V \, dq = \left(\frac{q'}{C}\right) dq'.$$

If this process is continued until a total charge q has been transferred, the total work will be found from

$$W = \int dW = \int_0^q \frac{q'}{C} \, dq' = \frac{1}{2}\frac{q^2}{C}. \tag{30-25}$$

From the relation $q = CV$ we can also write this as

$$W \, (-U) = \tfrac{1}{2}CV^2. \tag{30-26}$$

It is reasonable to suppose that the energy stored in a capacitor resides in the electric field. As q or V in Eqs. 30-25 and 30-26 increase, for example, so does the electric field E; when q and V are zero, so is E.

In a parallel-plate capacitor, neglecting fringing, the electric field has the same value for all points between the plates. Thus the *energy density u*, which is the stored energy per unit volume, should also be uniform; u (see Eq. 30-26) is given by

$$u = \frac{U}{Ad} = \frac{\tfrac{1}{2}CV^2}{Ad},$$

where Ad is the volume between the plates. Substituting the relation $C = \kappa\epsilon_0 A/d$ (Eq. 30-8) leads to

$$u = \frac{\kappa\epsilon_0}{2}\left(\frac{V}{d}\right)^2.$$

However, V/d is the electric field strength E, so that

$$u = \tfrac{1}{2}\kappa\epsilon_0 E^2. \tag{30-27}$$

Although this equation was derived for the special case of a parallel-plate capacitor, it is true in general. *If an electric field* **E** *exists at any point in space, we can think of that point as the site of stored energy in amount, per unit volume, of* $\tfrac{1}{2}\kappa\epsilon_0 E^2$.

▶ **Example 7.** A capacitor C_1 is charged to a potential difference V_0. This charging battery is then removed and the capacitor is connected as in Fig. 30–14 to an uncharged capacitor C_2.

(a) What is the final potential difference V across the combination?

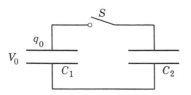

Fig. 30–14 Example 7. C_1 is charged and then connected to C_2 by closing switch S.

The original charge q_0 is now shared by the two capacitors. Thus

$$q_0 = q_1 + q_2.$$

Applying the relation $q = CV$ to each of these terms yields

$$C_1 V_0 = C_1 V + C_2 V$$

or

$$V = V_0 \frac{C_1}{C_1 + C_2}.$$

This suggests a way to measure an unknown capacitance (C_2, say) in terms of a known one.

(b) What is the stored energy before and after the switch in Fig. 30–14 is thrown?

The initial stored energy is

$$U_0 = \tfrac{1}{2} C_1 V_0{}^2.$$

The final stored energy is

$$U = \tfrac{1}{2} C_1 V^2 + \tfrac{1}{2} C_2 V^2 = \tfrac{1}{2}(C_1 + C_2) \left(\frac{V_0 C_1}{C_1 + C_2} \right)^2 = \left(\frac{C_1}{C_1 + C_2} \right) U_0.$$

Thus U is less than U_0! The "missing" energy appears as heat in the connecting wires as the charges move through them.

Example 8. A parallel-plate capacitor has plates with area A and separation d. A battery charges the plates to a potential difference V_0. The battery is then disconnected, and a dielectric slab of thickness d is introduced. Calculate the stored energy both before and after the slab is introduced and account for any difference.

The energy U_0 before introducing the slab is

$$U_0 = \tfrac{1}{2} C_0 V_0{}^2.$$

After the slab is in place, we have

$$C = \kappa C_0 \qquad \text{and} \qquad V = V_0/\kappa$$

and thus

$$U = \tfrac{1}{2} C V^2 = \tfrac{1}{2} \kappa C_0 \left(\frac{V_0}{\kappa} \right)^2 = \frac{1}{\kappa} U_0.$$

The energy after the slab is introduced is *less* by a factor $1/\kappa$. The "missing" energy would be apparent to the person who inserted the slab. He would feel a "tug" on the slab and would have to restrain it if he wished to insert the slab without acceleration. This means that he would have to do negative work on it, or, alternatively, that the condenser + slab system would do positive work on him. This positive work is

$$W = U_0 - U = \tfrac{1}{2} C_0 V_0{}^2 \left(1 - \frac{1}{\kappa} \right).$$

Figure 30–15 shows how the forces that do this work arise, in terms of attraction between the free charge on the plates and the induced surface charges that appear on the slab when it is introduced between the plates.

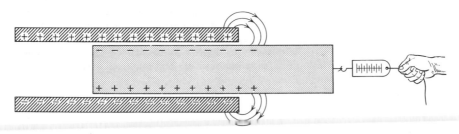

Fig. 30–15   When we introduce a dielectric slab into a charged capacitor, as shown, forces arise which tend to pull the slab into the capacitor.

Example 9.   A conducting sphere of radius R, in a vacuum, carries a charge q. (a) Compute the total electrostatic energy stored in the surrounding space. At any radius r from the center of the sphere (assuming $r > R$) E is given by

$$E = \frac{1}{4\pi\epsilon_0}\frac{q}{r^2}.$$

The energy density at any radius r is found from Eq. 30–27, assuming $\kappa = 1$, or

$$u = \tfrac{1}{2}\epsilon_0 E^2 = \frac{q^2}{32\pi^2\epsilon_0 r^4}.$$

The energy dU that lies in a spherical shell between the radii r and $r + dr$ is

$$dU = (4\pi r^2)(dr)u = \frac{q^2}{8\pi\epsilon_0}\frac{dr}{r^2},$$

where $(4\pi r^2)(dr)$ is the volume of the spherical shell. The total energy U is found by integration, or

$$U = \int dU = \frac{q^2}{8\pi\epsilon_0}\int_R^\infty \frac{dr}{r^2} = \frac{q^2}{8\pi\epsilon_0 R}.$$

Note that this relation follows at once from Eq. 30–25 ($U = q^2/2C$), where C (see p. 651) is the capacitance ($= 4\pi\epsilon_0 R$) of an isolated sphere of radius R.

(b) What is the radius R_0 of a spherical surface such that half the stored energy lies within it?

In the equation just given we put

$$\tfrac{1}{2}U = \frac{q^2}{8\pi\epsilon_0}\int_R^{R_0}\frac{dr}{r^2}$$

or

$$\frac{q^2}{16\pi\epsilon_0 R} = \frac{q^2}{8\pi\epsilon_0}\left(\frac{1}{R} - \frac{1}{R_0}\right),$$

which yields, after some rearrangement,

$$R_0 = 2R. \qquad \blacktriangleleft$$

QUESTIONS

1. A capacitor is connected across a battery. (*a*) Why does each plate receive a charge of exactly the same magnitude? (*b*) Is this true even if the plates are of different sizes?

2. Can there be a potential difference between two adjacent conductors that carry the same positive charge?

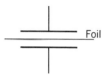

Fig. 30–16

3. The relation $\sigma \propto 1/R$ suggests that the charge placed on an isolated conductor concentrates on points and avoids flat surfaces, where $R = \infty$. How do we reconcile this with Fig. 30–3 in which the charge is definitely on the flat surface of either plate?

4. A sheet of aluminum foil of negligible thickness is placed between the plates of a capacitor as in Fig. 30–16. What effect has it on the capacitance if (*a*) the foil is electrically insulated and (*b*) the foil is connected to the upper plate.

5. Discuss similarities and differences when (*a*) a dielectric slab and (*b*) a conducting slab are inserted between the plates of a parallel-plate capacitor. Assume the slab thicknesses to be one-half the plate separation.

6. An oil-filled parallel-plate capacitor has been designed to have a capacitance C and to operate safely at or below a certain maximum potential difference V_m without arcing over. However, the designer did not do a good job and the capacitor occasionally arcs over. What can be done to redesign the capacitor, keeping C and V_m unchanged and using the same dielectric?

7. Would you expect the dielectric constant, for substances containing permanent molecular electric dipoles, to vary with temperature?

8. What is your estimate of the amount by which the center of positive charge and the center of negative charge are displaced in a situation like that of Fig. 30–9*b*? An intuitive guess is all that is called for.

9. For a given potential difference does a capacitor store more or less charge with a dielectric than it does without a dielectric (vacuum)? Explain in terms of the microscopic picture of the situation.

10. An isolated conducting sphere is given a positive charge. Does its mass increase, decrease, or remain the same?

11. A dielectric slab is inserted in one end of a charged parallel-plate capacitor (the plates being horizontal and the charging battery having been disconnected) and then released. Describe what happens. Neglect friction.

12. A capacitor is charged by using a battery, which is then disconnected. A dielectric slab is then slipped between the plates. Describe qualitatively what happens to the charge, the capacitance, the potential difference, the electric field strength, and the stored energy.

13. While a capacitor remains connected to a battery, a dielectric slab is slipped between the plates. Describe qualitatively what happens to the charge, the capacitance, the potential difference, the electric field strength, and the stored energy. Is work required to insert the slab?

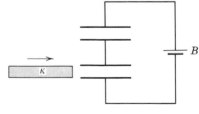

Fig. 30–17

14. Two identical capacitors are connected as shown in Fig. 30–17. A dielectric slab is slipped between the plates of one capacitor, the battery remaining connected. Describe qualitatively what happens to the charge, the capacitance, the potential difference, the electric field strength, and the stored energy for each capacitor.

15. Show that the dielectric constant of a conductor can be taken to be infinitely great.

PROBLEMS

1. A potential difference of 300 volts is applied to a 2.0-μf capacitor and an 8.0-μf capacitor connected in series. (a) What are the charge and the potential difference for each capacitor? (b) The charged capacitors are reconnected with their positive plates together and their negative plates together, no external voltage being applied. What are the charge and the potential difference for each? (c) The charged capacitors in (a) are reconnected with plates of *opposite* sign together. What are the charge and the potential difference for each?

2. Calculate the capacitance of the earth, viewed as a spherical conductor of radius 6400 km.

3. A 100-$\mu\mu$f capacitor is charged to a potential difference of 50 volts, the charging battery then being disconnected. The capacitor is then connected, as in Fig. 30–14, to a second capacitor. If the measured potential difference drops to 35 volts, what is the capacitance of this second capacitor?

4. If we solve Eq. 30–7 for ϵ_0, we see that its mks units are farads/meter. Show that these units are equivalent to those obtained earlier for ϵ_0, namely coul^2/nt-m^2.

5. Figure 30–18 shows two capacitors in series, the rigid center section of length b being movable vertically. Show that the equivalent capacitance of the series combination is independent of the position of the center section and is given by

$$C = \frac{\epsilon_0 A}{a - b}.$$

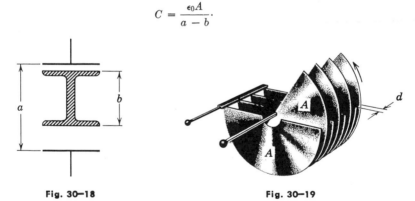

Fig. 30–18   Fig. 30–19

6. In Fig. 30–10 a variable air capacitor of the type used in tuning radios is shown. Alternate plates are connected together, one group being fixed in position, the other group being capable of rotation. Consider a pile of n plates of alternate polarity, each having an area A and separated from adjacent plates by a distance d. Show that this capacitor has a maximum capacitance of

$$C = \frac{(n - 1)\epsilon_0 A}{d}.$$

7. A spherical capacitor consists of two concentric spherical shells of radii a and b, with $b > a$. Show that its capacitance is

$$C = 4\pi\epsilon_0 \frac{ab}{b - a}.$$

8. A capacitor has square plates, each of side a, making an angle of θ with each other as shown in Fig. 30–20. Show that for small θ the capacitance is given by

$$C = \frac{\epsilon_0 a^2}{d}\left(1 - \frac{a\theta}{2d}\right)$$

(Hint: The capacitor may be divided into differential strips which are effectively in parallel.)

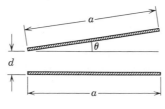

Fig. 30–20

9. Suppose that the two spherical shells of a spherical capacitor have their radii approximately equal. Under these conditions the device approximates a parallel plate capacitor with $b - a = d$. Show that the formula in Problem 7 does indeed reduce to Eq. 30–7 in this case.

10. A parallel-plate capacitor has circular plates of 8.0-cm radius and 1.0-mm separation. What charge will appear on the plates if a potential difference of 100 volts is applied?

11. In Fig. 30–21 find the equivalent capacitance of the combination. Assume that $C_1 = 10\ \mu f$, $C_2 = 5\ \mu f$, $C_3 = 4\ \mu f$, and $V = 100$ volts.

12. In Fig. 30–21 suppose that capacitor C_3 breaks down electrically, becoming equivalent to a conducting path. What *changes* in (a) the charge and (b) the potential difference occur for capacitor C_1?

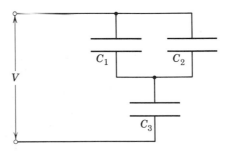

Fig. 30–21

13. Find the effective capacitance between points x and y in Fig. 30–22. Assume that $C_2 = 10\ \mu f$ and that the other capacitors are all 4.0 μf. (Hint: Apply a potential difference V between x and y and write down all the relationships that involve the charges and potential differences for the separate capacitors.)

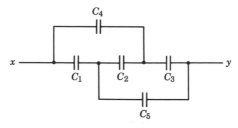

Fig. 30–22

14. If you have available several 2.0-μf capacitors, each capable of withstanding 200 volts without breakdown, how would you assemble a combination having an equivalent capacitance of (a) 0.40 μf or of (b) 1.2 μf, each capable of withstanding 1000 volts?

15. In Fig. 30–23 find the equivalent capacitance of the combination. Assume that $C_1 = 10$ μf, $C_2 = 5$ μf, $C_3 = 4$ μf, and $V = 100$ volts.

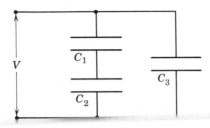

Fig. 30–23

16. In Fig. 30–24 the battery B supplies 12 volts. (a) Find the charge on each capacitor when switch S_1 is closed and (b) when switch S_2 is also closed. Take $C_1 = 1$ μf, $C_2 = 2$ μf, $C_3 = 3$ μf, and $C_4 = 4$ μf.

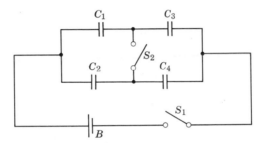

Fig. 30–24

17. A parallel-plate capacitor is filled with two dielectrics as in Fig. 30–25. Show that the capacitance is given by

$$C = \frac{\epsilon_0 A}{d}\left(\frac{\kappa_1 + \kappa_2}{2}\right).$$

Check this formula for all the limiting cases that you can think of. (Hint: Can you justify regarding this arrangement as two capacitors in parallel?)

Fig. 30–25   Fig. 30–26

18. A parallel-plate capacitor is filled with two dielectrics as in Fig. 30–26. Show that the capacitance is given by

$$C = \frac{2\epsilon_0 A}{d}\left(\frac{\kappa_1 \kappa_2}{\kappa_1 + \kappa_2}\right).$$

Check this formula for all the limiting cases that you can think of. (Hint: Can you justify regarding this arrangement as two capacitors in series?)

19. A dielectric slab of thickness b is inserted between the plates of a parallel-plate capacitor of plate separation d. Show that the capacitance is given by

$$C = \frac{\kappa \epsilon_0 A}{\kappa d - b(\kappa - 1)}.$$

(Hint: Derive the formula following the pattern of Example 5.) Does this formula predict the correct numerical result of Example 5? Does the formula seem reasonable for the special cases of $b = 0$, $\kappa = 1$, and $b = d$?

20. A slab of copper of thickness b is thrust into a parallel-plate capacitor as shown in Fig. 30–27; it is exactly halfway between the plates. What is the capacitance before and after the slab is introduced?

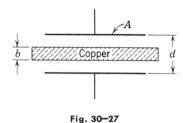

Fig. 30–27

21. For making a capacitor you have available two plates of copper, a sheet of mica (thickness $= 0.10$ mm, $\kappa = 6$), a sheet of glass (thickness $= 2.0$ mm, $\kappa = 7$), and a slab of paraffin (thickness $= 1.0$ cm, $\kappa = 2$). To obtain the largest capacitance, which sheet (or sheets) should you place between the copper plates?

22. In Example 5, suppose that the 100-volt battery remains connected during the time that the dielectric slab is being introduced. Calculate (a) the charge on the capacitor plates, (b) the electric field in the gap, (c) the electric field in the slab, and (d) the capacitance. For all of these quantities give the numerical values before and after the slab is introduced. Contrast your results with those of Example 5 by constructing a tabular listing.

23. A parallel-plate capacitor has a capacitance of 100 $\mu\mu$f, a plate area of 100 cm^2, and a mica dielectric. At 50 volts potential difference, calculate (a) E in the mica, (b) the free charge on the plates, and (c) the induced surface charge.

24. Two parallel plates of area 100 cm^2 are each given equal but opposite charges of 8.9×10^{-7} coul. Within the dielectric material filling the space between the plates the electric field strength is 1.4×10^6 volts/meter. (a) Find the dielectric constant of the material. (b) Determine the magitude of the charge induced on each dielectric surface.

25. Hard rubber has a dielectric constant of 2.8 and a dielectric strength of 18×10^6 volts/meter. If it is used as the dielectric material in a parallel-plate capacitor, what minimum area may the plates of the capacitor have in order that the capacitance be 7.0×10^{-2} μf and that the capacitor be able to withstand a potential difference of 4000 volts?

26. A cylindrical capacitor has radii a and b as in Fig. 30–4. Show that half the stored electric potential energy lies within a cylinder whose radius is

$$r = \sqrt{ab}.$$

27. An isolated metal sphere whose diameter is 10 cm has a potential of 8000 volts. What is the energy density at the surface of the sphere?

28. A parallel-plate capacitor has plates of area A and separation d and is charged to a potential difference V. The charging battery is then disconnected and the plates are pulled

apart until their separation is $2d$. Derive expressions in terms of A, d, and V for (a) the new potential difference, (b) the initial and the final stored energy, and (c) the work required to separate the plates.

29. Show that the plates of a parallel-plate capacitor attract each other with a force given by

$$F = \frac{q^2}{2\epsilon_0 A}.$$

Prove this by calculating the work necessary to increase the plate separation from x to $x + dx$.

30. In the capacitor of Example 5 the dielectric slab fills half the space between the plates. (a) What per cent of the energy is stored in the air gaps? (b) What per cent is stored in the slab?

31. A parallel-plate air capacitor has a capacitance of 100 μμf. (a) What is the stored energy if the applied potential difference is 50 volts? (b) Can you calculate the energy density for points between the plates?

32. For the capacitors of Problem 1, compute the energy stored for the three different connections of parts (a), (b), and (c). Compare your answers and explain any differences.

33. A charge q is placed on the surface of an originally uncharged soap bubble of radius R_0. Because of the mutual repulsion of the charged surface, the radius is increased to a somewhat larger value R. Show that

$$q = [\tfrac{3}{3}2\pi^2 \epsilon_0 p R_0 R(R^2 + R_0 R + R_0^2)]^{\frac{1}{2}}$$

in which p is the pressure of the atmosphere. Find q for $p = 1.00$ atm, $R_0 = 2.00$ cm, and $R = 2.10$ cm. (Hint: The work done by the bubble in pushing back the atmosphere must equal the decrease in the stored electric field energy that accompanies the expansion, from the conservation of energy principle.)

34. Two capacitors (2.0 μf and 4.0 μf) are connected in parallel across a 300-volt potential difference. Calculate the total stored energy in the system.

35. A parallel-connected bank of 2000 5.0-μf capacitors is used to store electric energy. What does it cost to charge this bank to 50,000 volts, assuming a rate of 2¢/kw-hr?

36. In Fig. 30–21 find (a) the charge, (b) the potential difference, and (c) the stored energy for each capacitor. Assume the numerical values of Problem 11.

37. In Fig. 30–23 find (a) the charge, (b) the potential difference, and (c) the stored energy for each capacitor. Assume the numerical values of Problem 15.

Current and Resistance

CHAPTER 31

31–1 Current and Current Density

The free electrons in an isolated metallic conductor, such as a length of copper wire, are in random motion like the molecules of a gas confined to a container. They have no net directed motion along the wire. If a hypothetical plane is passed through the wire, the rate at which electrons pass through it from right to left is the same as the rate at which they pass through from left to right; the *net* rate is zero.

If the ends of the wire are connected to a battery, an electric field will be set up at every point within the wire. If the potential difference maintained by the battery is 10 volts and if the wire (assumed uniform) is 5 meters long, the strength of this field at every point will be 2 volts/meter. This field **E** will act on the electrons and will give them a resultant motion in the direction of $-\mathbf{E}$. We say that an *electric current i* is established; if a net charge q passes through any cross section of the conductor in time t the current, assumed constant, is

$$i = q/t. \tag{31–1}$$

The appropriate mks units are amperes for i, coulombs for q, and seconds for t. The student will recall (Section 26–4) that Eq. 31–1 is the defining equation for the coulomb and that we have not yet given an operational definition of the ampere; we do so in Section 34–4.

If the rate of flow of charge with time is not constant, the current varies with time and is given by the differential limit of Eq. 31–1, or

$$i = dq/dt. \tag{31–2}$$

In the rest of this chapter we consider only constant currents.

The current i is the same for all cross sections of a conductor, even though the cross-sectional area may be different at different points. In the same way the rate at which water (assumed incompressible) flows past any cross section of a pipe is the same even if the cross section varies. The water flows faster where the pipe is smaller and slower where it is larger, so that the volume rate, measured perhaps in gal/min, remains unchanged. This constancy of the electric current follows because charge must be conserved; it does not pile up steadily or drain away steadily from any point in the conductor under the assumed steady-state conditions. In the language of Section 18-3 there are no "sources" or "sinks" of charge.

The existence of an electric field inside a conductor does not contradict Section 28-4, in which we asserted that $\mathbf{E}$ equals zero inside a conductor. In that section, which dealt with a state in which all net motion of charge had stopped (*electrostatics*), we assumed that the conductor was insulated and that no potential difference was deliberately maintained between any two points on it, as by a battery. In this chapter, which deals with charges in motion, we relax this restriction.

The electric field that acts on the electrons in a conductor does not produce a *net* acceleration because the electrons keep colliding with the atoms (strictly, ions) that make up the conductor. This array of ions, coupled together by strong spring-like forces of electric origin, is called the *lattice* (see Fig. 21-5). The over-all effect of these collisions is to transfer kinetic energy from the accelerating electrons into vibrational energy of the lattice. The electrons acquire a constant average *drift speed* v_d in the direction $-\mathbf{E}$. The analogy is to a marble rolling down a long flight of stairs and not to a marble falling freely from the same height. In the first case the acceleration caused by the (gravitational) field is effectively canceled by the decelerating effects of collisions with the stair treads so that, under proper conditions, the marble rolls down the stairs with zero average acceleration, that is, at constant average speed.

Although in metals the charge carriers are electrons, in electrolytes or in gaseous conductors they may also be positive or negative ions or both. A convention for labeling the directions of currents is needed because charges of opposite sign move in opposite directions in a given field. A positive charge moving in one direction is equivalent in nearly all external effects to a negative charge moving in the opposite direction. Hence, for simplicity and algebraic consistency, *we assume that all charge carriers are positive and we draw the current arrows in the direction that such charges would move.* If the charge carriers are negative, they simply move opposite to the direction of the current arrow (see Fig. 31-1). When we encounter a case (as in the *Hall effect;* see Section 33-5) in which the sign of the charge carriers makes a difference in the external effects, we will disregard the convention and take the actual situation into account.

Current i is a characteristic of a particular conductor. It is a macroscopic quantity, like the mass of an object, the volume of an object, or the length of a rod. A related microscopic quantity is the current density $\mathbf{j}$. It is a

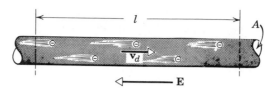

Fig. 31–1   Electrons drift in a direction opposite to the electric field in a conductor.

vector and is characteristic of a point inside a conductor rather than of the conductor as a whole. If the current is distributed uniformly across a conductor of cross-sectional area A, the magnitude of the current density for all points on that cross section is

$$j = i/A. \tag{31–3}$$

The vector $\mathbf{j}$ at any point is oriented in the direction that a positive charge carrier would move at that point. An electron at that point would move in the direction $-\mathbf{j}$.

The general relationship between $\mathbf{j}$ and i is that, for a particular surface in a conductor, i is the flux of the vector $\mathbf{j}$ over that surface, or

$$i = \int \mathbf{j} \cdot d\mathbf{S}, \tag{31–4}$$

where $d\mathbf{S}$ is an element of surface area and the integral is taken over the surface in question. Equation 31–3 (written as $i = jA$) is a special case of this relationship in which the surface of integration is a cross section of the conductor and in which $\mathbf{j}$ is constant over this surface and at right angles to it. However, Eq. 31–4 may be applied to any surface through which we wish to know the current. Equation 31–4 shows clearly that i is a scalar because the integrand $\mathbf{j} \cdot d\mathbf{S}$ is a scalar.

The arrow often associated with the current in a wire does not indicate that current is a vector but merely shows the *sense* of charge flow. Positive charge carriers either move in a certain direction along the wire or in the opposite direction, these two possibilities being represented by $+$ or $-$ in algebraic equations. Note that (a) the current in a wire remains unchanged if the wire is bent, tied into a knot, or otherwise distorted, and (b) the arrows representing the sense of currents do not in any way obey the laws of vector addition.

The drift speed v_d of charge carriers in a conductor can be computed from the current density j. Figure 31–1 shows the conduction electrons in a wire moving to the right at an assumed constant drift speed v_d. The number of conduction electrons in the wire is nAl where n is the number of conduction electrons per unit volume and Al is the volume of the wire. A charge of magnitude

$$q = (nAl)e$$

passes out of the wire, through its right end, in a time t given by

$$t = \frac{l}{v_d}.$$

The current i is given by

$$i = \frac{q}{t} = \frac{nAle}{l/v_d} = nAev_d.$$

Solving for v_d and recalling that $j = i/A$ (Eq. 31–3) yields

$$v_d = \frac{i}{nAe} = \frac{j}{ne}. \qquad (31\text{–}5)$$

▶ **Example 1.** An aluminum wire whose diameter is 0.10 in. is welded end to end to a copper wire with a diameter of 0.064 in. The composite wire carries a steady current of 10 amp. What is the current density in each wire?

The current is distributed uniformly over the cross section of each conductor, except near the junction, which means that the current density may be taken as constant for all points within each wire. The cross-sectional area of the aluminum wire is 0.0079 in.² Thus, from Eq. 31–3,

$$j_{Al} = \frac{i}{A} = \frac{10 \text{ amp}}{0.0079 \text{ in.}^2} = 1300 \text{ amp/in.}^2$$

The cross-sectional area of the copper wire is 0.0032 in.² Thus

$$j_{Cu} = \frac{i}{A} = \frac{10 \text{ amp}}{0.0032 \text{ in.}^2} = 3100 \text{ amp/in.}^2$$

The fact that the wires are of different materials does not enter into consideration here.

Example 2. What is v_d for the copper wire in Example 1?

We can write the current density for the copper wire as 480 amp/cm². To compute n we start from the fact that there is one free electron per atom in copper. The number of atoms per unit volume is dN_0/M where d is the density, N_0 is Avogadro's number, and M is the atomic weight. The number of free electrons per unit volume is then

$$n = \frac{dN_0}{M} = \frac{(9.0 \text{ gm/cm}^3)(6.0 \times 10^{23} \text{ atoms/mole})(1 \text{ electron/atom})}{64 \text{ gm/mole}}$$

$$= 8.4 \times 10^{22} \text{ electrons/cm}^3.$$

Finally, v_d is, from Eq. 31–5,

$$v_d = \frac{j}{ne} = \frac{480 \text{ amp/cm}^2}{(8.4 \times 10^{22} \text{ electrons/cm}^3)(1.6 \times 10^{-19} \text{ coul/electron})}$$

$$= 3.6 \times 10^{-2} \text{ cm/sec.}$$

It takes 28 sec for the electrons in this wire to drift 1.0 cm. Would you have guessed that v_d was so low? The drift speed of electrons must not be confused with the speed at which changes in the electric field configuration travel along wires, a speed which approaches that of light. When pressure is applied to one end of a long water-filled tube, a *pressure wave* travels rapidly along the tube. The speed at which *water* moves through the tube is much lower, however. ◀

31-2   Resistance, Resistivity, and Conductivity

If the same potential difference is applied between the ends of a rod of copper and of a rod of wood, very different currents result. The characteristic of the conductor that enters here is its *resistance*. We define the resistance of a conductor (often called a *resistor;* symbol ‑Ｍ‑) between two points by applying a potential difference V between those points, measuring the current i, and dividing:

$$R = V/i. \tag{31-6}$$

If V is in volts and i in amperes, the resistance R will be in *ohms*.

The flow of charge through a conductor is often compared with the flow of water through a pipe, which occurs because there is a difference in pressure between the ends of the pipe, established perhaps by a pump. This pressure difference can be compared with the potential difference established between the ends of a resistor by a battery. The flow of water (ft³/sec, say) is compared with the current (coul/sec or amp). The rate of flow of water for a given pressure difference is determined by the nature of the pipe. Is it long or short? Is it narrow or wide? Is it empty or filled, perhaps with gravel? These characteristics of the pipe are analogous to the resistance of a conductor.

Primary standards of resistance, kept at the National Bureau of Standards, are spools of wire whose resistances have been accurately measured. Because resistance varies with temperature, these standards, when used, are placed in an oil bath at a controlled temperature. They are made of a special alloy, called *manganin,* for which the change of resistance with temperature is very small. They are carefully annealed to eliminate strains, which also affect the resistance. These primary standard resistors are used chiefly to calibrate secondary standards for other laboratories.

Operationally, the primary resistance standards are not measured by using Eq. 31-6 but are measured in an indirect way which involves magnetic fields. Equation 31-6 is, in fact, used to measure V, by setting up an accurately known current i (using a *current balance;* see Section 34-4) in an accurately known resistance R. This operational procedure for potential difference is the one normally used in place of the conceptual definition introduced in Section 29-1, in which one measures the work per unit charge required to move a test charge between two points.

Related to resistance is the *resistivity* ρ, which is a characteristic of a material rather than of a particular specimen of a material; it is defined, for isotropic materials,* from

$$\rho = \frac{E}{j}. \tag{31-7}$$

The resistivity of copper is 1.7×10^{-8} ohm-m; that of fused quartz is about 10^{16} ohm-m. Few physical properties are measurable over such a range of values; Table 31-1 lists some values for common metals.

---

* These are materials whose properties (electrical in this case) do not vary with direction in the material.

Table 31–1

PROPERTIES OF METALS AS CONDUCTORS

	Resistivity (at 20°C), ohm-m	Temperature Coefficient of Resistivity,* α, per C°	Density, gm/cm³	Melting Point, °C
Aluminum	2.8×10^{-8}	3.9×10^{-3}	2.7	659
Copper	1.7×10^{-8}	0.9×10^{-3}	8.9	1080
Carbon (amorphous)	3.5×10^{-5}	-5×10^{-4}	1.9	3500
Iron	1.0×10^{-7}	5.0×10^{-3}	7.8	1530
Manganin	4.4×10^{-7}	1×10^{-5}	8.4	910
Nickel	7.8×10^{-8}	6×10^{-3}	8.9	1450
Silver	1.6×10^{-8}	3.8×10^{-3}	10.5	960
Steel	1.8×10^{-7}	3×10^{-3}	7.7	1510
Wolfram (tungsten)	5.6×10^{-8}	4.5×10^{-3}	19	3400

* This quantity, defined from

$$\alpha = \frac{1}{\rho} \frac{d\rho}{dT} \tag{31-8}$$

is the fractional change in resistivity $(d\rho/\rho)$ per unit change in temperature. It varies with temperature, the values here referring to 20°C. For copper ($\alpha = 3.9 \times 10^{-3}$/C°) the resistivity increases by 0.39 per cent for a temperature increase of 1 C° near 20°C. Note that α for carbon is negative, which means that the resistivity *decreases* with increasing temperature.

Consider a cylindrical conductor, of cross-sectional area A and length l, carrying a steady current i. Let us apply a potential difference V between its ends. If the cylinder cross sections at each end are equipotential surfaces, the electric field strength and the current density will be constant for all points in the cylinder and will have the values

$$E = \frac{V}{l} \quad \text{and} \quad j = \frac{i}{A}.$$

The resistivity ρ may then be written as

$$\rho = \frac{E}{j} = \frac{V/l}{i/A}.$$

But V/i is the resistance R which leads to

$$R = \rho \frac{l}{A}. \tag{31-9}$$

V, i, and R are *macroscopic* quantities, applying to a particular body or extended region. The corresponding *microscopic* quantities are $\mathbf{E}$, $\mathbf{j}$, and ρ; they have values at every point in a body. The macroscopic quantities are related to each other by Eq. 31–6 ($V = iR$) and the microscopic quantities by Eq. 31–7, which can be written in vector form as $\mathbf{E} = \mathbf{j}\rho$.

The macroscopic quantities can be found by integrating over the microscopic quantities, using relations already given, namely

$$i = \int \mathbf{j} \cdot d\mathbf{S} \tag{31–4}$$

and

$$V_{ab} = -\int_a^b \mathbf{E} \cdot d\mathbf{l}. \tag{29–5}$$

The integral in Eq. 31–4 is a surface integral, carried out over any cross section of the conductor. The integral in Eq. 29–5 is a line integral carried out along an arbitrary line drawn along the conductor, connecting any two equipotential surfaces, identified by a and b. For a long wire connected to a battery equipotential surface a might be chosen as a cross section of the wire near the positive battery terminal and b might be a cross section near the negative terminal.

The resistance of a conductor between a and b can be expressed in microscopic terms by dividing the two equations, or

$$R = \frac{V_{ab}}{i} = \frac{-\int_a^b \mathbf{E} \cdot d\mathbf{l}}{\int \mathbf{j} \cdot d\mathbf{S}}.$$

If the conductor is a long cylinder of cross section A and length l and if points a and b are its ends, the foregoing equation for R (see Eq. 31–7) reduces to

$$R = \frac{El}{jA} = \rho \frac{l}{A},$$

which is Eq. 31–9.

The macroscopic quantities V, i, and R are of primary interest when we are making electrical measurements on real conducting objects. They are the quantities that one reads on meters. The microscopic quantities $\mathbf{E}$, $\mathbf{j}$, and ρ are of primary importance when we are concerned with the fundamental behavior of matter (rather than of specimens of matter), as we usually are in the research area of *solid state physics*. Thus Section 31–4 deals appropriately with an atomic view of the *resistivity* of a metal and not of the *resistance* of a metallic specimen. The microscopic quantities are also important when we are interested in the interior behavior of irregularly shaped conducting objects.

▶ **Example 3.** A rectangular carbon block has dimensions 1.0 cm × 1.0 cm × 50 cm. (a) What is the resistance measured between the two square ends? (b) Between two opposing rectangular faces? The resistivity of carbon at 20°C is 3.5×10^{-5} ohm-m.

(a) The area of a square end is 1.0 cm² or 1.0×10^{-4} meter². Equation 31–9 gives for the resistance between the square ends:

$$R = \rho \frac{l}{A} = \frac{(3.5 \times 10^{-5} \text{ ohm-m})(0.50 \text{ meter})}{1.0 \times 10^{-4} \text{ meter}^2} = 0.18 \text{ ohm}.$$

(b) For the resistance between opposing rectangular faces (area = 5.0×10^{-3} meter²), we have

$$R = \rho \frac{l}{A} = \frac{(3.5 \times 10^{-5} \text{ ohm-m})(10^{-2} \text{ meter})}{5.0 \times 10^{-3} \text{ meter}^2} = 7.0 \times 10^{-5} \text{ ohm}.$$

Thus a given conductor can have a number of resistances, depending on how the potential difference is applied to it. The ratio of resistances for these two cases is 2000. We assume in each that the potential difference is applied to the block in such a way that the surfaces between which the resistance is desired are equipotential. Otherwise Eq. 31–9 would not be valid.   ◀

Figure 31–2 shows (solid curve) how the resistivity of copper varies with temperature. Sometimes, for practical use, such data are expressed in equation form. If we are interested in only a limited range of temperatures extending, say, from 0 to 500°C, we can fit a straight line to the curve of Fig. 31–2, making it pass through two arbitrarily selected points; see the dashed line. We choose the point labeled T_0, ρ_0 in the figure as a reference point, T_0 being 0°C in this case and ρ_0 being 1.56×10^{-8} ohm-m. The resistivity ρ at any temperature T can be found from the empirical equation of the dashed straight line in Fig. 31–2, which is

$$\rho = \rho_0[1 + \bar{\alpha}(T - T_0)]. \tag{31-10}$$

This relation shows correctly that $\rho \to \rho_0$ as $T \to T_0$.

If we solve Eq. 31–10 for $\bar{\alpha}$, we obtain

$$\bar{\alpha} = \frac{1}{\rho_0} \frac{\rho - \rho_0}{T - T_0},$$

Comparison with Eq. 31–8 shows that $\bar{\alpha}$ is a *mean temperature coefficient of resistivity* for a selected pair of temperatures rather than the temperature coefficient of resistivity at a particular temperature, which is the definition of α. For most practical purposes Eq. 31–10 gives results that are within the acceptable range of accuracy.

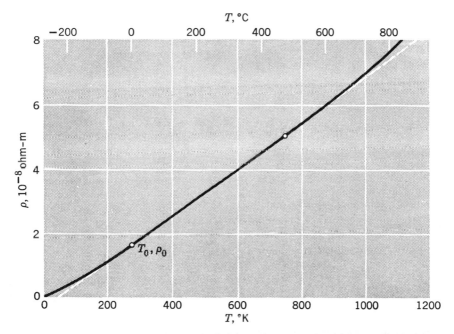

Fig. 31–2 The resistivity of copper as a function of temperature. The dashed line is an approximation chosen to fit the curve at the two circled points. The point marked T_0, ρ_0 is chosen as a reference point.

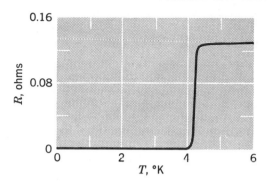

Fig. 31-3 The resistance of mercury disappears below about 4°K.

The curve of Fig. 31-2 does not go to zero at the absolute zero of temperature, even though it appears to do so, the residual resistivity at this temperature being 0.02×10^{-8} ohm-m. For many substances the resistance *does* become zero at some low temperature. Figure 31-3 shows the resistance of a specimen of mercury for temperatures below 6°K. In the space of about 0.05 K° the resistance drops abruptly to an immeasurably low value. This phenomenon, called *superconductivity*,[*] was discovered by Kamerlingh Onnes in the Netherlands in 1911. The resistance of materials in the superconducting state seems to be truly zero; currents, once established in closed superconducting circuits, persist for weeks without diminution, even though there is no battery in the circuit. If the temperature is raised slightly above the superconducting point, such currents drop rapidly to zero.

31-3   Ohm's Law

Let us apply a variable potential difference V between the ends of a 100-foot coil of #18 copper wire. For each applied potential difference, let us measure the current i and plot it against V as in Fig. 31-4. The straight line that results means that *the resistance of this conductor is the same no matter what applied voltage is used to measure it.* This important result, which holds for metallic conductors, is known as *Ohm's law*. We assume that the temperature of the conductor is essentially constant throughout the measurements.

Many conductors do not obey Ohm's law. Figure 31-5, for example, shows a V–i plot for a type 2A3 vacuum tube. The plot is not straight and the resistance depends on the voltage used to measure it. Also, the current for this device is almost vanishingly small if the polarity of the applied potential difference is reversed. For metallic conductors the current reverses direction when the potential difference is reversed, but its magnitude does not change.

Figure 31-6 shows a typical V–i plot for another nonohmic device, a *thermistor*. This is a semiconductor (see p. 558) with a large and negative temperature coefficient of resistivity α (see Table 31-1) that varies greatly with temperature. We note that two different currents through the thermistor can correspond to the same potential difference between its ends.

---

[*] See "Superconductivity" by B. T. Matthias, *Scientific American*, p. 92, November 1957.

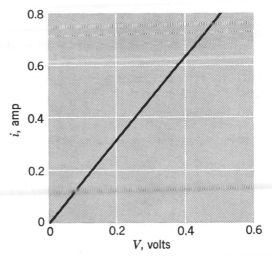

Fig. 31–4 The current in a particular copper conductor as a function of potential difference. This conductor obeys Ohm's law.

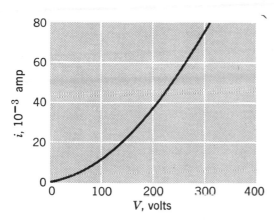

Fig. 31–5 The current in a type 2A3 vacuum tube as a function of potential difference. This conductor does not obey Ohm's law.

Fig. 31–6 A plot of current as a function of potential difference in a Western Electric 1–B thermistor. The curve shows how the voltage across the thermistor varies as the current through it is increased. The shape of the curve can be accounted for in terms of the large negative temperature coefficient of resistivity of the material of which the device is made.

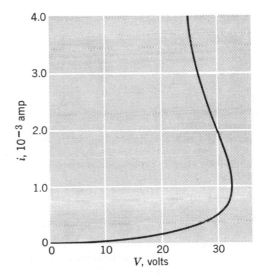

Thermistors are often used to measure the rate of energy flow in microwave beams by allowing the microwave beam to fall on the thermistor and heat it. The relatively small temperature rise so produced results in a relatively large change in resistance, which serves as a measure of the microwave power. Modern electronics, and therefore much of the character of our present technological civilization, depends in a fundamental way on the fact that many conductors, such as vacuum tubes, crystal rectifiers, thermistors, and transistors, do *not* obey Ohm's law.

We stress that the relationship $V = iR$ is *not* a statement of Ohm's law. A conductor obeys this law only if its $V - i$ curve is linear, that is, if R is independent of V and i. The relationship $R = V/i$ remains as the general definition of the resistance of a conductor whether or not the conductor obeys Ohm's law.

The microscopic equivalent of the relationship $V = iR$ is Eq. 31–7, or $\mathbf{E} = \mathbf{j}\rho$. A conducting *material* is said to obey Ohm's law if a plot of E versus j is linear, that is, if the resistivity ρ is independent of E and j. Ohm's law is a specific property of certain materials and is not a general law of electromagnetism, for example, like Gauss's law.

A close analogy exists between the flow of charge because of a potential difference and the flow of heat because of a temperature difference. Consider a thin electrically conducting slab of thickness Δx and area A. Let a potential difference ΔV be maintained between opposing faces. The current i is given by Eqs. 31–6 ($i = V/R$) and 31–9 ($R = \rho l/A$), or

$$i = \frac{\Delta V}{R} = \frac{\Delta V A}{\rho \Delta x}.$$

In the limiting case of a slab of thickness dx this becomes

$$i = \frac{1}{\rho} A \frac{dV}{dx}$$

or
$$\frac{dq}{dt} = -\sigma A \frac{dV}{dx}, \qquad (31\text{–}11)$$

where $\sigma\ (= 1/\rho)$ is the *conductivity* of the material. Since positive charge flows in the direction of decreasing V, we introduce a minus sign into Eq. 31–11, that is, dq/dt is positive when dV/dx is negative.

The analogous heat flow equation (see Section 22–3) is

$$\frac{dQ}{dt} = -kA \frac{dT}{dx}, \qquad (31\text{–}12)$$

which shows that k, the thermal conductivity, corresponds to σ and dT/dx, the temperature gradient, corresponds to dV/dx, the potential gradient. There is more than a formal mathematical analogy between Eqs. 31–11 and 31–12. Both heat energy and charge are carried by the free electrons in a metal; empirically, a good electrical conductor (silver, say) is also a good heat conductor and conversely.

31–4 Resistivity—an Atomic View

One can understand why metals obey Ohm's law on the basis of simple classical ideas. If these ideas are modified when necessary by the requirements of quantum physics, it is possible to go further and to calculate theoretical values of the resistivity ρ for various metals. These calculations are not simple, but when they have been carried out the agreement with the experimental value of ρ has usually been good.

In a metal the valence electrons are not attached to individual atoms but are free to move about within the lattice and are called *conduction electrons*. In copper there is one such electron per atom, the other 28 remaining bound to the copper nuclei to form ionic cores.

The speed distribution of conduction electrons can be described correctly only in terms of quantum physics. For our purposes, however, it suffices to consider only a suitably defined average speed $\bar{v}$; for copper $\bar{v} = 1.6 \times 10^8$ cm/sec. In the absence of an electron field, the directions in which the electrons move are completely random, like those of the molecules of a gas confined to a container.

The electrons collide constantly with the ionic cores of the conductor, that is, they interact with the lattice, often suffering sudden changes in speed and direction. These collisions remind us of the collisions of gas molecules confined to a container. As in the case of molecular collisions, we can describe electron-lattice collisions by a *mean free path* λ, where λ is the average distance that an electron travels between collisions.*

In an ideal metallic crystal at 0°K electron-lattice collisions would not occur, according to the predictions of quantum physics, that is, $\lambda \to \infty$ as $T \to 0°$K for ideal crystals. Collisions take place in actual crystals because (a) the ionic cores at any temperature T are vibrating about their equilibrium positions in a random way, (b) impurities, that is, foreign atoms, may be present, and (c) the crystal may contain lattice imperfections, such as rows of missing atoms and displaced atoms. On this view it is not surprising that the resistivity of a metal can be increased by (a) raising its temperature, (b) adding small amounts of impurities, and (c) straining it severely, as by drawing it through a die, to increase the number of lattice imperfections.

When an electric field is applied to a metal, the electrons modify their random motion in such a way that they drift slowly, in the opposite direction to that of the field, with an average drift speed v_d. This drift speed is much less than the effective average speed $\bar{v}$ mentioned above (see Example 2). Figure 31–7 suggests the relationship between these two speeds. The solid lines suggest a possible random path followed by an electron in the absence of an applied field; the electron proceeds from x to y, making six collisions on the way. The dashed curves show how this same event *might* have occurred if an electric field $\mathbf{E}$ had been applied. Note that the electron drifts steadily to the right, ending at y' rather than at y. In preparing Fig. 31–7, it has been assumed that the drift speed v_d is $0.02\bar{v}$; actually, it is more like $10^{-10}\bar{v}$, so that the "drift" exhibited in the figure is greatly exaggerated.

The drift speed v_d can be calculated in terms of the applied electric field E and of $\bar{v}$ and λ. When a field is applied to an electron initially at rest, it will experience a force eE which will impart to it an acceleration a given by Newton's second law,

$$a = \frac{eE}{m}.$$

---

* It can be shown that collisions between electrons occur only rarely and have little effect on the resistivity.

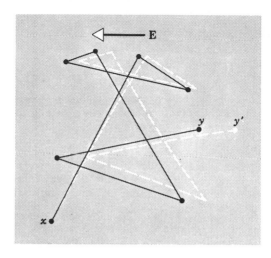

Fig. 31-7 The solid lines show an electron moving from x to y, making six collisions. The dashed curves show what the electron path *might* have been in the presence of an electric field **E**. Note the steady drift in the direction of $-$**E**.

This acceleration will act for a time $l/\bar{v}$, after which the electron will experience a collision.

The electron speed just before this collision is $a(\lambda/\bar{v})$; its *average* speed during the time τ is $\frac{1}{2}a(\lambda/\bar{v})$, since the initial speed was taken to be zero. We can identify this average speed with the drift speed v_d, or

$$v_d = \tfrac{1}{2}a\left(\frac{\lambda}{\bar{v}}\right) = \frac{eE\lambda}{2m\bar{v}}. \qquad (31\text{--}13)$$

The electron's motion through the conductor is analogous to the constant rate of fall of a stone in water. The gravitational force F_g on the stone is opposed by a viscous resisting force that is proportional to the velocity, or

$$F_g = mg = bv,$$

where b is a viscous coefficient (see Section 15–8). Thus the constant terminal speed of the stone is

$$v = \left(\frac{1}{b}\right)F_g.$$

We can rewrite Eq. 31–13 as

$$v_d = \left(\frac{\lambda}{2m\bar{v}}\right)F_E,$$

where $F_E \ (= eE)$ is the electrical force. Comparison of these equations shows that the equivalent "viscous coefficient" for the motion of an electron in a particular conductor is $\lambda/2m\bar{v}$. If λ is short, the conductor exhibits a greater "viscous effect" on the electron motion, and the drift speed v_d is proportionally lower.

We may express v_d in terms of the current density (Eq. 31–5) and combine with Eq. 31–13 to obtain

$$v_d = \frac{j}{ne} = \frac{eE\lambda}{2m\bar{v}}.$$

Combining this with Eq. 31–7 ($\rho = E/j$) leads finally to

$$\rho = \frac{2m\bar{v}}{ne^2\lambda}. \tag{31-14}$$

Equation 31–14 can be taken as a statement that metals obey Ohm's law *if* we can show that $\bar{v}$ and λ do not depend on the applied electric field E. In this case ρ will not depend on E, which (see Section 31–3) is the criterion that a material obey Ohm's law. The quantities $\bar{v}$ and λ depend on the speed distribution of the conduction electrons. We have seen that this distribution is affected only slightly by the application of even a relatively large electric field, since $\bar{v}$ is of the order of 10^8 cm/sec and v_d (see Example 1) only of the order of 10^{-2} cm/sec, a ratio of 10^{10}. We may be sure that whatever the values of $\bar{v}$ and λ are (for copper at 20°C, say) in the absence of a field they remain essentially unchanged when the field is applied. Thus the right side of Eq. 31–14 is independent of E and the material obeys Ohm's law. The numerical calculation of ρ from Eq. 31–14 is hampered by the difficulty of calculating λ, although the calculation has been carried out in a number of cases.

▶ **Example 4.** What are (a) the mean time τ between collisions and (b) the mean free path for free electrons in copper?

(a) From Eq. 31–14 (see also Example 2), we have

$$\tau = \frac{\lambda}{\bar{v}} = \frac{2m}{ne^2\rho} = \frac{(2)(9.1 \times 10^{-31} \text{ kg})}{(8.4 \times 10^{28}/\text{meter}^3)(1.6 \times 10^{-19} \text{ coul})^2(1.7 \times 10^{-8} \text{ ohm-m})}$$

$$= 5.0 \times 10^{-14} \text{ sec.}$$

(b) The mean free path is

$$\lambda = \tau\bar{v} = (5.0 \times 10^{-14} \text{ sec})(1.6 \times 10^8 \text{ cm/sec}) = 8.0 \times 10^{-6} \text{ cm.}$$

This is about 400 ionic diameters.   ◀

31–5   Energy Transfers in an Electric Circuit

Figure 31–8 shows a circuit consisting of a battery B connected to a "black box." A steady current i exists in the connecting wires and a steady potential difference V_{ab} exists between the terminals a and b. The box might contain a resistor, a motor, or a storage battery, among other things.

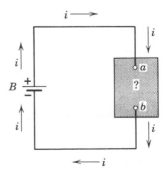

Fig. 31–8   A battery B sets up a current in a circuit containing a "black box."

Terminal a, connected to the positive battery terminal, is at a higher potential than terminal b.   If a charge dq moves through the box from a to b, this charge will decrease its electric potential energy by $dq\, V_{ab}$ (see Section 29–6).   The conservation-of-energy principle tells us that this energy is transferred in the box from electric potential energy to some other form. What that other form will be depends on what is in the box.   In a time dt the energy dU transferred inside the box is then

$$dU = dq\, V_{ab} = i\, dt\, V_{ab}.$$

We find the *rate* of energy transfer P by dividing by the time, or

$$P = \frac{dU}{dt} = iV_{ab}. \tag{31–15}$$

If the device in the box is a motor, the energy appears largely as mechanical work done by the motor; if the device is a storage battery that is being charged, the energy appears largely as stored chemical energy in this second battery.

If the device is a resistor, we assert that the energy appears as heat in the resistor.   To see this, consider a stone of mass m that falls through a height h. It decreases its gravitational potential energy by mgh.   If the stone falls in a vacuum or—for practical purposes—in air, this energy is transformed into kinetic energy of the stone.   If the stone falls in water, however, its speed eventually becomes constant, which means that the kinetic energy no longer increases.   The potential energy that is steadily being made available as the stone falls then appears as thermal energy in the stone and the surrounding water.   It is the viscous, friction-like drag of the water on the surface of the stone that stops the stone from accelerating, and it is at this surface that thermal energy appears.

The course of the electrons through the resistor is much like that of the stone through water.   The electrons travel with a constant drift speed v_d and thus do not gain kinetic energy.   The electric potential energy that they lose is transferred to the resistor as heat.   On a microscopic scale this can be understood in that collisions between the electrons and the lattice (see Fig. 21–5) increase the amplitude of the thermal vibrations of the lattice; on a macroscopic scale this corresponds to a temperature increase.   This effect, which is thermodynamically irreversible, is called *Joule heating*.

For a resistor we can combine Eqs. 31–15 and 31–6 ($R = V/i$) and obtain either

$$P = i^2R \tag{31–16}$$

or

$$P = \frac{V^2}{R}. \tag{31–17}$$

Note that Eq. 31–15 applies to electrical energy transfer of *all* kinds; Eqs. 31-16 and 31-17 apply only to the transfer of electrical energy to heat energy in a resistor. Equations 31–16 and 31–17 are known as *Joule's law*. This law is a particular way of writing the conservation-of-energy principle for the special case in which electrical energy is transferred into heat energy.

The unit of power that follows from Eq. 31–15 is the volt-amp. It can be written as

$$1 \text{ volt-amp} = 1 \text{ volt-amp} \left(\frac{1 \text{ joule}}{1 \text{ volt} \times 1 \text{ coul}} \right) \left(\frac{1 \text{ coul}}{1 \text{ amp} \times 1 \text{ sec}} \right)$$

$$= 1 \text{ joule/sec.}$$

The first conversion factor in parenthesis comes from the definition of the volt (Eq. 29–1); the second comes from the definition of the coulomb. The joule/sec is such a common unit that it is given a special name of its own, the *watt;* see Section 7–4. Power is not an exclusively electrical concept, of course, and we can express in watts the power ($= \mathbf{F} \cdot \mathbf{v}$) expended by an agent that exerts a force $\mathbf{F}$ while it moves with a velocity $\mathbf{v}$.

▶ **Example 5.** You are given a 20-ft length of heating wire made of the special alloy Nichrome; it has a resistance of 24 ohms. Can you obtain more heat by winding one coil or by cutting the wire in two and winding two separate coils? In each case the coils are to be connected individually across a 110-volt line.

The power P for the single coil is given by Eq. 31–17:

$$P = \frac{V^2}{R} = \frac{(110 \text{ volts})^2}{24 \text{ ohms}} = 500 \text{ watts.}$$

The power for a coil of half the length is given by

$$P' = \frac{(110 \text{ volts})^2}{12 \text{ ohms}} = 1000 \text{ watts.}$$

There are two "half-coils," so that the total power obtained by cutting the wire in half is 2000 watts, or four times that for the single coil. This would seem to suggest that we could buy a 500-watt heating coil, cut it in half, and rewind it to obtain 2000 watts. Why is this not a practical idea?   ◀

QUESTIONS

1. Name other physical quantities that, like current, are scalars having a sense represented by an arrow in a diagram.

2. What conclusions can you draw by applying Eq. 31–4 to a closed surface through which a number of wires pass in random directions, carrying steady currents of different sizes?

3. A potential difference V is applied to a circular cylinder of carbon by clamping it between circular copper electrodes, as in Fig. 31–9. Discuss the difficulty of calculating the resistance of the carbon cylinder, using the relation $R = \rho L/A$.

Copper

Carbon

Copper

Fig. 31–9

4. How would you measure the resistance of a pretzel-shaped conductor? Give specific details to clarify the concept.

5. Discuss the difficulties of testing whether the filament of a light bulb obeys Ohm's law.

6. Does the relation $V = iR$ apply to nonohmic resistors?

7. The temperature coefficient of resistance of a thermistor is negative and varies greatly with temperature. Account qualitatively for the shape of the curve of i versus V for the thermistor of Fig. 31–6.

8. A potential difference V is applied to a copper wire of diameter d and length l. What is the effect on the electron drift speed of (a) doubling V, (b) doubling l, and (c) doubling d?

9. If the drift speeds of the electrons in a conductor under ordinary circumstances are so slow (see Example 2), why do the lights in a room turn on so quickly after the switch is closed?

10. Can you think of a way to measure the drift speed for electrons by timing their travel along a conductor?

11. Why are the white lines in Fig. 31–7 curved slightly?

12. A current i enters the top of a copper sphere of radius R and leaves at a diametrically opposite point. Are all parts of the sphere equally effective in dissipating Joule heat?

13. What special characteristics must (a) heating wire and (b) fuse wire have?

14. Equation 31–16 ($P = i^2R$) seems to suggest that the rate of Joule heating in a resistor is reduced if the resistance is made less, Eq. 31–17 ($P = V^2/R$) seems to suggest just the opposite. How do you reconcile this apparent paradox?

15. Is the filament resistance lower or higher in a 500-watt light bulb than in a 100-watt bulb? Both bulbs are designed to operate on 110 volts.

16. Five wires of the same length and diameter are connected in turn between two points maintained at constant potential difference. Will heat be developed at the fastest rate in the wire of (a) the smallest or (b) the largest resistance?

PROBLEMS

1. A current of 5 amp exists in a 10-ohm resistance for 4 min. (a) How many coulombs and (b) how many electrons pass through any cross section of the resistor in this time?

2. A current is established in a gas discharge tube when a sufficiently high potential difference is applied across the two electrodes in the tube. The gas ionizes; electrons move toward the positive terminal and positive ions toward the negative terminal. What are the magnitude and sense of the current in a hydrogen discharge tube in which 3.1×10^{18} electrons and 1.1×10^{18} protons move past a cross-sectional area of the tube each second?

3. A copper wire and an iron wire of the same length have the same potential difference applied to them. (a) What must be the ratio of their radii if the current is to be the same? (b) Can the current density be made the same by suitable choices of the radii?

4. A current i enters one corner of a square sheet of copper and leaves at the opposite corner. Sketch arrows for various points within the square to represent the relative values of **j**. Intuitive guesses rather than detailed mathematical analysis are called for.

5. The belt of an electrostatic generator is 50 cm wide and travels at 30 meters/sec. The belt carries charge into the sphere at a rate corresponding to 10^{-4} amp. Compute the surface charge density on the belt.

6. A square aluminum rod is 1.0 meter long and 5.0 mm on edge. (a) What is the resistance between its ends? (b) What must be the diameter of a circular 1.0-meter copper rod if its resistance is to be the same?

7. A wire with a resistance of 6.0 ohms is drawn out so that its new length is three times its original length. Find the resistance of the longer wire, assuming that the resistivity and density of the material are not changed during the drawing process.

8. A copper wire and an iron wire of equal length l and diameter d are joined and a potential difference V is applied between the ends of the composite wire. Calculate (a) the electric field strength in each wire, (b) the current density in each wire, and (c) the potential difference across each wire. Assume that $l = 10$ meters, $d = 2.0$ mm, and $V = 100$ volts.

9. A rod of a certain metal is 1.00 meter long and 0.550 cm in diameter. The resistance between its ends (at 20°C) is 2.87×10^{-3} ohm. A round disk is formed of this same material, 2.00 cm in diameter and 1.00 mm thick. (a) What is the resistance between the opposing round faces? (b) What is the material?

10. Steel trolley-car rail has a cross-sectional area of 7.1 in.^{2} What is the resistance of 10 miles of single track? The resistivity of the steel is 6.0×10^{-7} ohm-m.

11. (a) At what temperature would the resistance of a copper conductor be double its resistance at 0°C? (b) Does this same temperature hold for all copper conductors, regardless of shape or size?

12. It is desired to make a long cylindrical conductor whose temperature coefficient of resistivity at 20°C will be close to zero. (a) If such a conductor is made by assembling alternate disks of iron and carbon, what is the ratio of the thickness of a carbon disk to that of an iron disk? Assume that the temperature remains essentially the same in each disk. (b) What is the ratio of the rate of Joule heating in a carbon disk to that in an iron disk?

13. When a metal rod is heated, not only its resistance but also its length and its cross-sectional area change. The relation $R = \rho l/A$ suggests that all three factors should be taken into account in measuring ρ at various temperatures. If the temperature changes by 1.0 C°, what per cent changes in R, l, and A occur for a copper conductor. What conclusion do you draw? The coefficient of linear expansion is $1.7 \times 10^{-5}/\text{C}°$.

14. The copper windings of a motor have a resistance of 50 ohms at 20 °C, when the motor is idle. After running for several hours the resistance rises to 58 ohms. What is the temperature of the windings?

15. (a) Using data from Fig. 31–5, plot the resistance of the vacuum tube as a function of applied potential difference. (b) Repeat for the thermistor of Fig. 31–6.

16. A small but measurable current of 10^{-10} amp exists in a copper wire whose diameter is 0.10 in. Calculate the electron drift speed.

17. Heat is developed in a resistor at a rate of 100 watts when the current is 3.0 amp. What is the resistance in ohms?

18. A potential difference of 1.0 volt is applied to a 100-ft length of #18 copper wire (diameter = 0.040 in.). Calculate (a) the current, (b) the current density, (c) the electric field strength, and (d) the rate of Joule heating.

19. The National Board of Fire Underwriters has fixed safe current-carrying capacities for various sizes and types of wire. For #10 rubber-coated copper wire (wire diameter = 0.10 in.) the maximum safe current is 25 amp. At this current, find (a) the current density, (b) the electric field strength, (c) the potential difference for 1000 ft of wire, and (d) the rate of Joule heating for 1000 ft of wire.

20. A 500-watt immersion heater is placed in a pot containing 2.0 liters of water at 20 °C. (a) How long will it take to bring the water to boiling temperature, assuming that 80% of the available energy is absorbed by the water? (b) How much longer will it take to boil half the water away?

21. A nichrome heater dissipates 500 watts when the applied potential difference is 110 volts and the wire temperature is 800 °C. How much power would it dissipate if the wire temperature were held to 200 °C by immersion in a bath of cooling oil? The applied potential difference remains the same; $\bar{\alpha}$ for nichrome is about $4 \times 10^{-4}/\text{C}°$.

22. A beam of 16-Mev deuterons from a cyclotron falls on a copper block. The beam is equivalent to a current of 15×10^{-6} amp. (a) At what rate do deuterons strike the block? (b) At what rate is heat produced in the block?

23. A "500-watt" heating unit is designed to operate from a 115-volt line. (a) By what percentage will its heat output drop if the line voltage drops to 110 volts? Assume no change in resistance. (b) Taking the variation of resistance with temperature into account, would the actual heat output drop be larger or smaller than that calculated in (a)?

24. Show that p, the power per unit volume transformed into Joule heat in a resistor, can be written as

$$p = j^2\rho \qquad \text{or} \qquad p = E^2/\rho.$$

Electromotive Force
and Circuits

CHAPTER 32

32–1   Electromotive Force

There exist in nature certain devices such as batteries and electric generators which are able to maintain a potential difference between two points to which they are attached. Such devices are called seats of *electromotive force* (abbr. emf). In this chapter we do not discuss their internal construction or detailed mode of action but confine ourselves to describing their gross electrical characteristics and to exploring their usefulness in electric circuits.

Figure 32–1a shows a seat of emf B, represented by a battery, connected to a resistor R. The seat of emf maintains its upper terminal positive and its lower terminal negative, as shown by the + and − signs. In the circuit external to B positive charge carriers would be driven in the direction shown by the arrows marked i. In other words, a clockwise current would be set up.

An emf is represented by an arrow which is placed next to the seat and points in the direction in which the seat, acting alone, would cause a positive charge carrier to move in the external circuit. A small circle is drawn on the tail of an emf arrow so that it will not be confused with a current arrow.

A seat of emf must be able to do work on charge carriers that enter it. In the circuit of Fig. 32–1a, for example, the seat acts to move positive charges from a point of low potential (the negative terminal) through the seat to a point of high potential (the positive terminal). This reminds us of a pump, which can cause water to move from a place of low gravitational potential to a place of high potential.

In Fig. 32–1a a charge dq passes through *any* cross section of the circuit in time dt. In particular, this charge enters the seat of emf ε at its low-potential

697

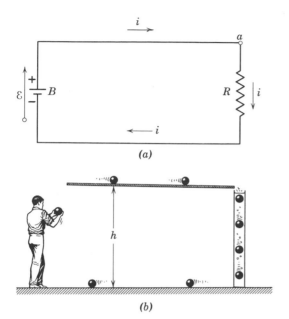

Fig. 32–1 (a) A simple electric circuit and (b) its gravitational analog.

end and leaves at its high-potential end. The seat must do an amount of work dW on the (positive) charge carriers to force them to go to the point of higher potential. The emf $\mathcal{E}$ of the seat is defined from

$$\mathcal{E} = dW/dq. \tag{32–1}$$

The unit of emf is the joule/coul (see Eq. 29–1) which is the *volt*. We might be inclined to say that a battery has an emf of 1 volt if it maintains a difference of potential of 1 volt between its terminals. This is true only under certain conditions, which we describe in Section 32–4.

If a seat of emf does work on a charge carrier, energy must be transferred within the seat. In a battery, for example, chemical energy is transferred into electrical energy. Thus we can describe a seat of emf as a device in which chemical, mechanical, or some other form of energy is changed (reversibly) into electrical energy. The chemical energy provided by the battery in Fig. 32–1a is stored in the electric and the magnetic * fields that surround the circuit. This stored energy does not increase because it is being drained away, by transfer to Joule heat in the resistor, at the same rate at which it is supplied. The electric and magnetic fields play an intermediary role in the energy transfer process, acting as a storage reservoir.

Figure 32–1b shows a gravitational analog of Fig. 32–1a. In the top figure the seat of emf B does work on the charge carriers. This energy, stored temporarily as electromagnetic field energy, appears eventually as Joule heat in resistor R. In the lower figure the man, in lifting the bowling balls from

---

* A current in a wire is surrounded by a magnetic field, and this field, like the electric field, can also be viewed as a site of stored energy (see Section 36–4).

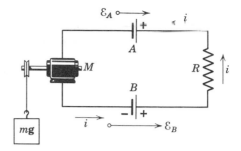

Fig. 32–2 Two batteries, a resistor, and a motor, connected in a single-loop circuit. It is given that $\mathcal{E}_B > \mathcal{E}_A$.

the floor to the shelf, does work on them. This energy is stored temporarily as gravitational field energy. The balls roll slowly and uniformly along the shelf, dropping from the right end into a cylinder full of viscous oil. They sink to the bottom at constant speed, are removed by a trapdoor mechanism not shown, and roll back along the floor to the left. The energy put into the system by the man appears eventually as heat in the viscous fluid. The energy supplied by the man comes from his own internal (chemical) energy. The circulation of charges in Fig. 32–1a will stop eventually if battery B is not charged; the circulation of bowling balls in Fig. 32–1b will stop eventually if the man does not replenish his store of internal energy by eating.

Figure 32–2 shows a circuit containing two (ideal) batteries, A and B, a resistor R, and an (ideal) electric motor employed in lifting a weight. The batteries are connected so that they tend to send charges around the circuit in opposite directions; the actual direction of the current is determined by B, which supplies the larger potential difference. The energy transfers in this circuit are

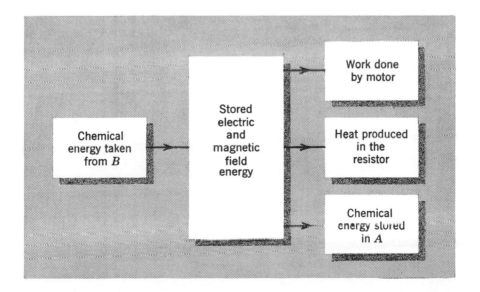

The chemical energy in B is being steadily depleted, the energy appearing in the three forms shown on the right. Battery A is being "charged" while battery B is being discharged. Again, the electric and magnetic fields that surround the circuit act as an intermediary.

It is part of the definition of an emf that the energy transfer process be *reversible*, at least in principle. The student will recall that a reversible process is one that passes through equilibrium states; its course can be reversed by making an infinitesimal change in the environment of the system; see Section 25–2. A battery, for example, can either be on charge or discharge; a generator can be driven mechanically, producing electric energy, or it can be operated backward as a motor. The (reversible) energy transfers here are

$$\text{electrical} \rightleftharpoons \text{chemical}$$

and $$\text{electrical} \rightleftharpoons \text{mechanical}.$$

Joule heating is an electric energy transfer that is *not* reversible. We can easily heat a conductor by supplying electric energy to it, but it is not possible to set up a current in a closed copper loop by heating the loop uniformly. Because of this lack of reversibility, we do not associate an emf with Joule heating.

32–2   Calculating the Current

In a time dt an amount of energy given by $i^2R\,dt$ will appear in the resistor of Fig. 32–1a as Joule heat. During this same time a charge $dq\ (= i\,dt)$ will have moved through the seat of emf, and the seat will have done work on this charge (see Eq. 32–1) given by

$$dW = \mathcal{E}dq = \mathcal{E}i\,dt.$$

From the conservation of energy principle, the work done by the seat must equal the Joule heat, or

$$\mathcal{E}i\,dt = i^2R\,dt.$$

Solving for i, we obtain

$$i = \mathcal{E}/R. \tag{32–2}$$

We can also derive Eq. 32–2 by considering that if electric potential is to have any meaning a given point can have only one value of potential at any given time. If we start at any point in the circuit of Fig. 32–1a and, in imagination, go around the circuit in either direction, adding up algebraically the changes in potential that we encounter, we must arrive at the same potential when we return to our starting point. In other words, *the algebraic sum of the changes in potential encountered in a complete traversal of the circuit must be zero.*

In Fig. 32–1a let us start at point a, whose potential is V_a,* and traverse the circuit clockwise. In going through the resistor, there is a change in potential of $-iR$. The minus sign shows that the top of the resistor is higher

---

* The actual value of V_a depends on assumptions made in the definition of potential (as described in Section 29–1). The numerical value of V_a is not important because, as in most electric circuit situations, we are concerned here with *differences* of potential. Point a in Fig. 32–1a (or any other single point in that figure) could be connected to ground (symbol ⊥) and assigned the potential $V_a = 0$, following a common practice.

in potential than the bottom, which must be true, because positive charge carriers move of their own accord from high to low potential. As we traverse the battery from bottom to top, there is an *increase* of potential $+\varepsilon$ because the battery does (positive) work on the charge carriers, that is, it moves them from a point of low potential to one of high potential. Adding the algebraic sum of the changes in potential to the initial potential V_a must yield the identical value V_a, or

$$V_a - iR + \varepsilon = V_a.$$

We write this as

$$-iR + \varepsilon = 0,$$

which is independent of the value of V_a and which asserts explicitly that the algebraic sum of the potential changes for a complete circuit traversal is zero. This relation leads directly to Eq. 32–2.

These two ways to find the current in single-loop circuits, based on the conservation of energy and on the concept of potential, are completely equivalent because potential differences are defined in terms of work and energy (Section 29–1). The statement that the sum of the changes in potential encountered in making a complete loop is zero is called *Kirchhoff's second rule;* for brevity we call it the *loop theorem.* It must always be borne in mind that this theorem is simply a particular way of stating the law of conservation of energy for electric circuits.

To prepare for the study of more complex circuits, let us examine the rules for finding potential differences; these rules follow from the previous discussion. They are not meant to be memorized but rather to be so thoroughly understood that it becomes trivial to re-derive them on each application.

1. If a resistor is traversed in the direction of the current, the change in potential is $-iR$; in the opposite direction it is $+iR$.

2. If a seat of emf is traversed in the direction of the emf, the change in potential is $+\varepsilon$; in the opposite direction it is $-\varepsilon$.

32–3   Other Single-Loop Circuits

Figure 32–3a shows a circuit which emphasizes that all seats of emf have an intrinsic internal resistance r. This resistance cannot be removed—although we would usually like to do so—because it is an inherent part of the device. The figure shows the internal resistance r and the emf separately, although, actually, they occupy the same region of space.

If we apply the loop theorem, starting at b and going around clockwise, we obtain

$$V_b + \varepsilon - ir - iR = V_b$$

or

$$+\varepsilon - ir - iR = 0.$$

The student should compare these equations with Fig. 32–2b, which shows the changes in potential graphically. In writing these equations, note that we traversed r and R in the direction of the current and ε in the direction of the

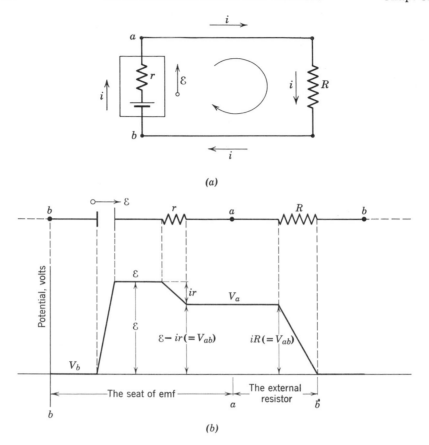

Fig. 32-3   A single-loop circuit.   The rectangular block is a seat of emf with internal resistance r.   (b) The same circuit is drawn for convenience as a straight line.   Directly below are shown the changes in potential that one encounters in traversing the circuit clockwise from point b.

emf.   The same equation follows if we start at any other point in the circuit or if we traverse the circuit in a counterclockwise direction.   Solving for i gives

$$i = \frac{\mathcal{E}}{R + r}.$$ (32–3)

▶ **Example 1.**   *Resistors in series.*   Resistors in series are connected so that there is only one conducting path through them, as in Fig. 32–4.   What is the equivalent resistance R of this series combination?   The equivalent resistance is the single resistance R which, substituted for the series combination between the terminals ab, will leave the current i unchanged.

Applying the loop theorem (going clockwise from a) yields

$$-iR_1 - iR_2 - iR_3 + \mathcal{E} = 0$$

or

$$i = \frac{\mathcal{E}}{R_1 + R_2 + R_3}.$$

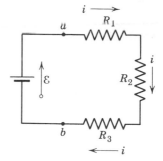

Fig. 32–4 Example 1. Three resistors are connected in series between terminals a and b.

For the equivalent resistance R

$$i = \frac{\mathcal{E}}{R}$$

or
$$R = R_1 + R_2 + R_3. \tag{32–4}$$

The extension to more than three resistors is clear. ◀

32–4 Potential Differences

We often want to compute the potential difference between two points in a circuit. In Fig. 32–3a for example, what is the relationship between the potential difference V_{ab} ($= V_a - V_h$) between points h and a and the fixed circuit parameters $\mathcal{E}$, r, and R? To find this relationship, let us start from point b and traverse the circuit to point a, passing through resistor R against the current. If V_b and V_a are the potentials at b and a, respectively, we have

$$V_b + iR = V_a$$

because we experience an increase in potential in traversing a resistor against the current arrow. We rewrite this relation as

$$V_{ab} = V_a - V_b = +iR,$$

which tells us that V_{ab}, the potential difference between points a and b, has the magnitude iR and that point a is more positive than point b. Combining this last equation with Eq. 32–3 yields

$$V_{ab} = \mathcal{E}\frac{R}{R + r}. \tag{32–5}$$

To sum up: To find the potential difference between any two points in a circuit start at one point and traverse the circuit to the other, following any path, and add up algebraically the potential changes encountered. This algebraic sum will be the potential difference. This procedure is similar to that for finding the current in a closed loop, except that here the potential differences are added up over part of a loop and not over the whole loop.

The potential difference between any two points can have only one value; thus we must obtain the same answer for all paths that connect these points.

If we consider two points on the side of a hill, the measured difference in gravitational potential (that is, in altitude) between them is the same no matter what path is followed in going from one to the other. In Fig. 32–3a let us calculate V_{ab}, using a path passing through the seat of emf. We have

$$V_b + \mathcal{E} - ir = V_a$$

or (see also Fig. 33–3b)

$$V_{ab} = V_a - V_b = +\mathcal{E} - ir.$$

Again, combining with Eq. 32–3 leads to Eq. 32–5.

The terminal potential difference of the battery V_{ab}, as Eq. 32–5 shows, is less than $\mathcal{E}$ unless the battery has no internal resistance ($r = 0$) or if it is on open circuit ($R = \infty$); then V_{ab} is equal to $\mathcal{E}$. Thus the emf of a device is equal to its terminal potential difference *when on open circuit*.

▶ **Example 2.** In Fig. 32–5a let $\mathcal{E}_1$ and $\mathcal{E}_2$ be 2.0 volts and 4.0 volts, respectively; let the resistances r_1, r_2, and R be 1.0 ohm, 2.0 ohms, and 5.0 ohms, respectively. What is the current?

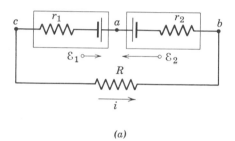

(a)

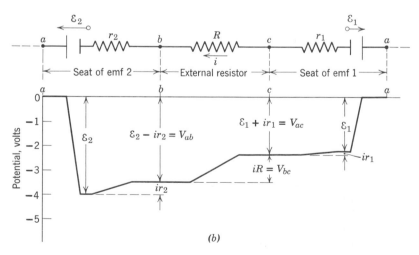

(b)

Fig. 32–5   (a) A single-loop circuit. (b) The same circuit is shown schematically as a straight line, the potential differences encountered in traversing the circuit clockwise from point a being displayed directly below. In the lower figure the potential of point a was assumed to be zero for convenience.

Emfs $\mathcal{E}_1$ and $\mathcal{E}_2$ oppose each other, but because $\mathcal{E}_2$ is larger it controls the direction of the current. Thus i will be counterclockwise. The loop theorem, going clockwise from a, yields

$$-\mathcal{E}_2 + ir_2 + iR + ir_1 + \mathcal{E}_1 = 0.$$

The student should check that the same result is obtained by going around counterclockwise. He should also compare this equation carefully with Fig. 32–5b, which shows the potential changes graphically.

Solving for i yields

$$i = \frac{\mathcal{E}_2 - \mathcal{E}_1}{R + r_1 + r_2} = \frac{4.0 \text{ volts} - 2.0 \text{ volts}}{5.0 \text{ ohms} + 1.0 \text{ ohm} + 2.0 \text{ ohms}}$$

$$= 0.25 \text{ amp.}$$

It is not necessary to know in advance what the actual direction of the current is. To show this, let us assume that the current in Fig. 32–5a is clockwise, an assumption that we know is incorrect. The loop theorem then yields (going clockwise from a)

$$-\mathcal{E}_2 - ir_2 - iR - ir_1 + \mathcal{E}_1 = 0$$

or

$$i = \frac{\mathcal{E}_1 - \mathcal{E}_2}{R + r_1 + r_2}.$$

Substituting numerical values (see above) yields -0.25 amp for the current. The minus sign tells us that the current is in the opposite direction from the one we have assumed.

In more complex circuit problems involving many loops and branches it is often impossible to know in advance the correct directions for the currents in all parts of the circuit. We can assume directions for the currents at random. Those currents for which positive numerical values are obtained will have the correct directions; those for which negative values are obtained will be exactly opposite to the assumed directions. In all cases the numerical values will be correct.

Example 3. What is the potential difference (a) between points b and a in Fig. 32–5a? (b) Between points a and c?

(a) For points a and b we start at b and traverse the circuit to a, obtaining

$$V_{ab} \, (= V_a - V_b) = -ir_2 + \mathcal{E}_2 = -(0.25 \text{ amp})(2.0 \text{ ohms}) + 4.0 \text{ volts}$$

$$= +3.5 \text{ volts.}$$

Thus a is more positive than b and the potential difference (3.5 volts) is *less than* the emf (4.0 volts); see Fig. 32–5b.

(b) For points c and a, we start at c and traverse the circuit to a, obtaining

$$V_{ac} \, (= V_a - V_c) = +\mathcal{E}_1 + ir_1 = +2.0 \text{ volts} + (0.25 \text{ amp})(1.0 \text{ ohm})$$

$$= +2.25 \text{ volts.}$$

This tells us that a is at a higher potential than c. The terminal potential difference of $\mathcal{E}_1$ (2.25 volts) is *larger than* the emf (2.0 volts); see Fig. 32–5b. Charge is being forced through $\mathcal{E}_1$ in a direction opposite to the one in which it would send charge if it were acting by itself; if $\mathcal{E}_1$ is a storage battery, it is being charged at the expense of $\mathcal{E}_2$.

Let us test the first result by proceeding from b to a along a different path, namely, through R, r_1, and $\mathcal{E}_1$. We have

$$V_{ab} = iR + ir_1 + \mathcal{E}_1 = (0.25 \text{ amp})(5.0 \text{ ohms})$$

$$+ (0.25 \text{ amp})(1.0 \text{ ohm}) + 2.0 \text{ volts} = +3.5 \text{ volts,}$$

which is the same as the earlier result.   ◀

32–5 Multiloop Circuits

Figure 32–6 shows a circuit containing two loops. For simplicity, we have neglected the internal resistances of the batteries. There are two *junctions*, b and d, and three *branches* connecting these junctions. The branches are the left branch bad, the right branch bcd, and the central branch bd. If the emfs and the resistances are given, what are the currents in the various branches?

We label the currents in the branches as i_1, i_2, and i_3, as shown. Current i_1 has the same value for any cross section of the left branch from b to d. Similarly, i_2 has the same value everywhere in the right branch and i_3 in the central branch. The directions of the currents have been chosen arbitrarily. The careful reader will note that i_3 must point in a direction opposite to the one we have shown. We have deliberately drawn it in wrong to show how the formal mathematical procedures will always indicate this to us.

The three currents i_1, i_2, and i_3 carry charge either toward junction d or away from it. Charge does not accumulate at junction d, nor does it drain away from this junction because the circuit is in a steady-state condition. Thus charge must be removed from the junction by the currents at the same rate that it is brought into it. If we arbitrarily call a current approaching the junction positive and the one leaving the junction negative, then

$$i_1 + i_3 - i_2 = 0.$$

This equation suggests a general principle for the solution of multiloop circuits: *At any junction the algebraic sum of the currents must be zero.* This *junction theorem* is also known as *Kirchhoff's first rule*. Note that it is simply a statement of the conservation of charge. Thus our basic tools for solving circuits are (*a*) the conservation of energy (see p. 701) and (*b*) the conservation of charge.

For the circuit of Fig. 32–6, the junction theorem yields only one relationship among the three unknowns. Applying the theorem at junction b leads to exactly the same equation, as the student should verify. To solve for the three unknowns, we need two more independent equations; they can be found from the loop theorem.

In single-loop circuits there is only one conducting loop around which to apply the loop theorem, and the current is the same in all parts of this loop.

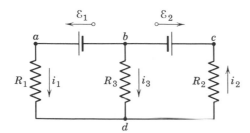

Fig. 32–6 A multiloop circuit.

In multiloop circuits there is more than one loop, and the current in general will not be the same in all parts of any given loop.

If we traverse the left loop of Fig. 32-6 in a counterclockwise direction, the loop theorem gives

$$\mathcal{E}_1 - i_1 R_1 + i_3 R_3 = 0. \tag{32-6}$$

The right loop gives

$$-i_3 R_3 - i_2 R_2 - \mathcal{E}_2 = 0. \tag{32-7}$$

These two equations, together with the relation derived earlier with the junction theorem, are the three simultaneous equations needed to solve for the unknowns i_1, i_2, and i_3. Doing so yields

$$i_1 = \frac{\mathcal{E}_1(R_2 + R_3) - \mathcal{E}_2 R_3}{R_1 R_2 + R_2 R_3 + R_1 R_3}, \tag{32-8a}$$

$$i_2 = \frac{\mathcal{E}_1 R_3 - \mathcal{E}_2(R_1 + R_3)}{R_1 R_2 + R_2 R_3 + R_1 R_3}, \tag{32-8b}$$

and

$$i_3 = \frac{-\mathcal{E}_1 R_2 - \mathcal{E}_2 R_1}{R_1 R_2 + R_2 R_3 + R_1 R_3}. \tag{32-8c}$$

The student should supply the missing steps. Equation 32-8c shows that no matter what numerical values are given to the emfs and to the resistances the current i_3 will always have a negative value. This means that it will always point up in Fig. 32-6 rather than down, as we deliberately assumed. The currents i_1 and i_2 may be in either direction, depending on the particular numerical values given.

The student should verify that Eqs. 32-8 reduce to sensible conclusions in special cases. For $R_3 = \infty$, for example, we find

$$i_1 = i_2 = \frac{\mathcal{E}_1 - \mathcal{E}_2}{R_1 + R_2} \quad \text{and} \quad i_3 = 0.$$

What do these equations reduce to for $R_2 = \infty$?

The loop theorem can be applied to a large loop consisting of the entire circuit *abcda* of Fig. 32-6. This fact might suggest that there are more equations than we need, for there are only three unknowns and we already have three equations written in terms of them. However, the loop theorem yields for this loop

$$-i_1 R_1 - i_2 R_2 - \mathcal{E}_2 + \mathcal{E}_1 = 0,$$

which is nothing more than the sum of Eqs. 32-6 and 32-7. Thus this large loop does not yield another *independent* equation. It will never be found in solving multiloop circuits that there are more independent equations than variables.

▶ **Example 4.** *Resistors in parallel.* Figure 32–7 shows three resistors connected across the same seat of emf. Resistances across which the identical potential difference is applied are said to be in parallel. What is the equivalent resistance R of this parallel combination? The equivalent resistance is that single resistance which, substituted for the parallel combination between terminals ab, would leave the current i unchanged.

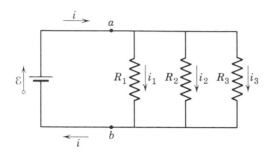

Fig. 32–7 Example 4. Three resistors are connected in parallel betweeen terminals a and b.

The currents in the three branches are

$$i_1 = \frac{V}{R_1}, \qquad i_2 = \frac{V}{R_2}, \qquad \text{and} \qquad i_3 = \frac{V}{R_3},$$

where V is the potential difference that appears between points a and b. The total current i is found by applying the junction theorem to junction a, or

$$i = i_1 + i_2 + i_3 = V\left(\frac{1}{R_1} + \frac{1}{R_2} + \frac{1}{R_3}\right).$$

If the equivalent resistance is used instead of the parallel combination, we have

$$i = \frac{V}{R}.$$

Combining these two equations gives

$$\frac{1}{R} = \frac{1}{R_1} + \frac{1}{R_2} + \frac{1}{R_3}. \tag{32–9}$$

This formula can easily be extended to more than three resistances. Note that the equivalent resistance of a parallel combination is less than any of the resistances that make it up.   ◀

32–6   Measuring Currents and Potential Differences

A meter to measure currents is called an *ammeter* (or a *milliammeter* or *micro-ammeter*, depending on the size of the current to be measured). To determine the current in a wire, it is necessary to break or cut the wire and to insert the ammeter, so that the current to be measured passes through the meter (see Fig. 32–8).*

It is essential that the resistance R_A of the ammeter be *small* compared to other resistances in the circuit. Otherwise the act of inserting the meter will in itself change

---

* The meter must be connected so that the direction of current through it (assuming positive charge carriers) is *into* the meter terminal marked +. Otherwise the meter will deflect in a direction opposite to that intended.

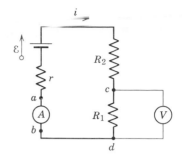

Fig. 32-8 An ammeter (A) is connected to read the current in a circuit, and a voltmeter (V) is connected to read the potential difference across resistor R_1.

the current to be measured. An ideal ammeter would have zero resistance. In the circuit of Fig. 32-8 the required condition, assuming that the voltmeter is not connected, is

$$R_A \ll r + R_1 + R_2.$$

A meter to measure potential differences is called a *voltmeter* (or a *millivoltmeter* or *microvoltmeter*). To find the potential difference between two points in a circuit, it is necessary to connect one of the voltmeter terminals to each of the circuit points, without breaking the circuit (see **Fig. 32-8**).*

It is essential that the resistance of the voltmeter R_V be *large* compared to any circuit resistance across which the voltmeter is connected. Otherwise the meter will itself constitute an important circuit element and will alter the circuit current and the potential difference to be measured. An ideal voltmeter would have an infinite resistance. In Fig. 32-8 the required condition is

$$R_V \gg R_1$$

In measuring potential difference in electronic circuits, where the effective circuit resistance may be of the order of 10^6 ohms or higher, it becomes necessary to use a *vacuum-tube voltmeter*, which is an electron-tube device designed specifically to have an extremely high effective resistance between its input terminals.

32-7   The Potentiometer

Figure 32-9 shows the rudiments of a *potentiometer*, which is a device for measuring an unknown emf $\mathcal{E}_x$. The currents and emfs are marked as shown. Applying the loop theorem to loop *abcd* yields

$$-\mathcal{E}_x - ir + (i_0 - i)R = 0,$$

where $i_0 - i$, by application of the junction theorem at a, is the current in resistor R. Solving for i yields

$$i = \frac{i_0 R - \mathcal{E}_x,}{R + r}$$

in which R is a variable resistor. This relation shows that if R is adjusted to have the value R_x where

$$i_0 R_x = \mathcal{E}_x, \tag{32-10}$$

the current i in the branch *abcd* becomes zero. To *balance* the potentiometer in this way, R must be adjusted manually until the sensitive meter G reads zero.

---

* The voltmeter terminal marked + must be connected to the point of higher potential. Otherwise the meter will deflect in a direction opposite to that intended.

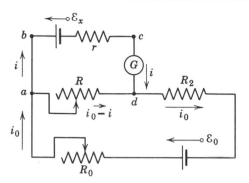

Fig. 32-9 Elements of a potentiometer

The emf can be obtained from Eq. 32–10 if the current i_0 is known. However, it is standard practice to replace $\mathcal{E}_x$ by a known standard emf $\mathcal{E}_s$, and once again to adjust R to the zero-current condition. This yields, assuming the current i_0 remains unchanged

$$i_0 R_s = \mathcal{E}_g.$$

Combining the last two equations yields

$$\mathcal{E}_x = \mathcal{E}_s \frac{R_x}{R_s}, \tag{32–11}$$

which allows us to compare emfs with precision. Note that the internal resistance r of the emf plays no role. In practice, potentiometers are conveniently packaged units, containing a *standard cell* which, after calibration at the National Bureau of Standards or elsewhere, serves as a convenient known standard seat of emf $\mathcal{E}_s$. Switching arrangements for replacing the unknown emf by the standard and arrangements for ascertaining that the current i_0 remains constant are also incorporated.

32–8   RC Circuits

The preceding sections dealt with circuits in which the circuit elements were resistors and in which the currents did not vary with time. Here we introduce the capacitor as a circuit element, which will lead us to the concept of time-varying currents. In Fig. 32–10 let switch S be thrown to position a. What current is set up in the single-loop circuit so formed? Let us apply conservation of energy principles.

In time dt a charge dq ($= i\, dt$) moves through any cross section of the circuit. The work done by the seat of emf ($= \mathcal{E}\, dq$; see Eq. 32–1) must equal the energy that appears as Joule heat in the resistor during time

Fig. 32-10   An *RC* circuit.

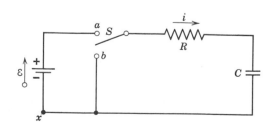

$dt \; (= i^2R \, dt)$ plus the increase in the amount of energy U that is stored in the capacitor $[= dU = d(q^2/2C)$, see Eq. 30–25]. In equation form

$$\varepsilon \, dq = i^2R \, dt + d\left(\frac{q^2}{2C}\right)$$

or

$$\varepsilon \, dq = i^2R \, dt + \frac{q}{C} \, dq.$$

Dividing by dt yields

$$\varepsilon \frac{dq}{dt} = i^2R + \frac{q}{C}\frac{dq}{dt}.$$

But dq/dt is simply i, so that this equation becomes

$$\varepsilon = iR + \frac{q}{C}. \tag{32–12}$$

This equation also follows from the loop theorem, as it must, since the loop theorem was derived from the conservation of energy principle. Starting from point x and traversing the circuit clockwise, we experience an increase in potential in going through the seat of emf and decreases in potential in traversing the resistor and the capacitor, or

$$\varepsilon - iR - \frac{q}{C} = 0,$$

which is identical with Eq. 32–12.

We cannot immediately solve Eq. 32–12 because it contains two variables, q and i, which, however, are related by

$$i = \frac{dq}{dt}, \tag{32–13}$$

Substituting for i into Eq. 32–12 gives

$$\varepsilon = R \frac{dq}{dt} + \frac{q}{C}. \tag{32–14}$$

Our task now is to find the function $q(t)$ that satisfies this *differential equation*. Although this particular equation is not difficult to solve, we choose to avoid mathematical complexity by simply presenting the solution, which is

$$q = C\varepsilon(1 - e^{-t/RC}). \tag{32–15}$$

We can easily test whether this function $q(t)$ is really a solution of Eq. 32–14 by substituting it into that equation and seeing whether an identity results. Differentiating Eq. 32–15 with respect to time yields

$$\frac{dq}{dt}(= i) = \frac{\varepsilon}{R}e^{-t/RC}. \tag{32–16}$$

Substituting q (Eq. 32–15) and dq/dt (Eq. 32–16) into Eq. 32–14 yields an identity, as the student should verify. Thus Eq. 32–15 is a solution of Eq. 32–14.

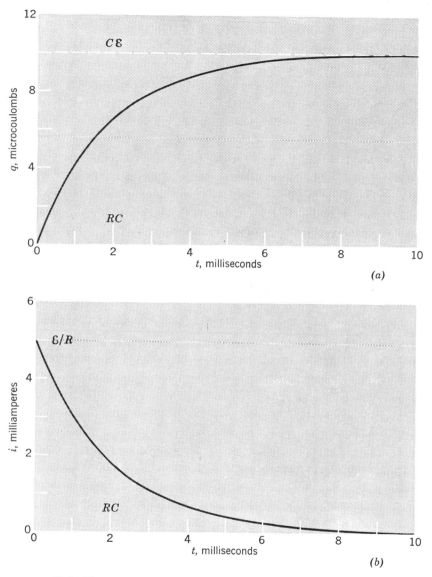

Fig. 32–11 If, in Fig. 32–10, we assume that $R = 2000$ ohms, $C = 1.0$ μf, and $\varepsilon = 10$ volts, then (a) shows the variation of q with t during the charging process and (b) the variations of i with t. The time constant is $RC = 2.0 \times 10^{-3}$ sec.

Figure 32–11 shows some plots of Eqs. 32–15 and 32–16 for a particular case. Study of these plots and of the corresponding equations shows that (a) at $t = 0$, $q = 0$ and $i = \varepsilon/R$, and (b) as $t \to \infty$, $q \to C\varepsilon$ and $i \to 0$: that is, the current is initially ε/R and finally zero; the charge on the capacitor plates is initially zero and finally $C\varepsilon$.

The quantity RC in Eqs. 32–15 and 32–16 has the dimensions of time (since the exponent must be dimensionless) and is called the *capacitative time constant* of the circuit. It is the time at which the charge on the capacitor has increased to within a factor of $(1 - e^{-1})$ $(= 63\%)$ of its equilibrium value. To show this, we put $t = RC$ in Eq. 32–15 to obtain

$$q = C\varepsilon(1 - e^{-1}) = 0.63C\varepsilon.$$

Since $C\varepsilon$ is the equilibrium charge on the capacitor, corresponding to $t \to \infty$, the foregoing statement follows.

▶ **Example 5.** After how many time constants will the energy stored in the capacitor in Fig. 32–10 reach one-half its equilibrium value?

The energy is given by Eq. 30–25, or

$$U = \frac{1}{2C} q^2,$$

the equilibrium energy U_∞ being $(1/2C)(C\varepsilon)^2$. From Eq. 32–15, we can write the energy as

$$U = \frac{1}{2C} (C\varepsilon)^2(1 - e^{-t/RC})^2$$

or $$U = U_\infty(1 - e^{-t/RC})^2.$$

Putting $U = \frac{1}{2}U_\infty$ yields

$$\tfrac{1}{2} = (1 - e^{-t/RC})^2$$

and solving this relation for t yields finally

$$t = 1.22 \ RC = 1.22 \text{ time constants.} \qquad ◀$$

Figure 32–11 shows that if a resistance is included in the circuit the rate of increase of the charge of a capacitor toward its final equilibrium value is *delayed* in a way measured by the time constant RC. With no resistor present ($RC = 0$), the charge would rise immediately to its equilibrium value. Although we have shown that this time delay follows from an application of the loop theorem to RC circuits, it is important that the student develop a physical understanding of the causes of the delay.

When switch S in Fig. 32–10 is closed on a, the resistor experiences instantaneously an applied potential difference of ε, and an initial current of ε/R is set up. Initially, the capacitor experiences no potential difference because its initial charge is zero, the potential difference always being given by q/C. The flow of charge through the resistor starts to charge the capacitor, which has several effects. First, the existence of a capacitor charge means that there must now be a potential difference ($= q/C$) across the capacitor; this, in turn, means that the potential difference across the resistor must decrease by this amount, since the sum of the two potential differences must always equal ε. This decrease in the potential difference across R means that the charging current is reduced. Thus the charge of the capacitor builds up and the charging current decreases until the capacitor is fully charged. At this point the full emf ε is applied to the capacitor, there being no potential drop ($i = 0$) across the resistor. This is precisely the reverse of the initial situation. The student should review the derivations of Eqs. 32–15 and 32–16 and should study Fig. 32–11 with the qualitative arguments of this paragraph in mind.

Assume now that the switch S in Fig. 32–10 has been in position a for a time t such that $t \gg RC$. The capacitor is then fully charged for all practical purposes. The switch S is then thrown to position b. How do the charge of the capacitor and the current vary with time?

With the switch S closed on b, there is no emf in the circuit and the loop theorem gives simply

$$iR + \frac{q}{C} = 0. \tag{32-17}$$

Putting $i = dq/dt$ allows us to write, as the differential equation of the circuit (compare Eq. 32-14),

$$R\frac{dq}{dt} + \frac{q}{C} = 0. \tag{32-18a}$$

The solution is

$$q = q_0 e^{-t/RC}, \tag{32-18b}$$

as the student may readily verify by substitution, q_0 being the initial charge on the capacitor. The capacitative time constant RC appears in this expression for capacitor discharge as well as in that for the charging process (Eq. 32-15). We see that at a time such that $t = RC$ the capacitor charge is reduced to $q_0 e^{-1}$, which is 37% of the initial charge q_0.

The current during discharge follows from differentiating Eq. 32-18b, or

$$i = \frac{dq}{dt} = -\frac{q_0}{RC} e^{-t/RC}. \tag{32-19}$$

The negative sign shows that the current is in the direction opposite to that shown in Fig. 32-10. This is as it should be, since the capacitor is discharging rather than charging. Since $q_0 = C\mathcal{E}$, we can write Eq. 32-19 as

$$i = -\frac{\mathcal{E}}{R} e^{-t/RC},$$

in which $\mathcal{E}/R$ appears as the initial current, corresponding to $t = 0$. This is reasonable because the initial potential difference for the fully charged capacitor is $\mathcal{E}$.

The behavior of the RC circuit of Fig. 32-10 during charge and discharge can be studied with a cathode-ray oscilloscope. This familiar laboratory device can display on its fluorescent screen plots of the variation of potential with time. Figure 32-12 shows the circuit of Fig. 32-10 with connections made to display (a) the potential difference V_C across the capacitor and (b) the potential difference V_R across the resistor as functions of time. V_C and V_R are given by

$$V_C = \left(\frac{1}{C}\right) q$$

and

$$V_R = (R)i,$$

the former being proportional to the charge and the latter to the current.

Figure 32-13 shows oscillograph plots of V_C and V_R that result when, in effect, switch S in Fig. 32-10 is thrown regularly back and forth between positions a and b, being left in each position for a time equal to several time constants. Intervals during which the charge is building up are labeled ch and those during which it is decaying are labeled dis.

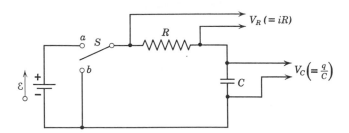

Fig. 32–12 The circuit of Fig. 32–10 with connections made to display the potential variations across the resistor and the capacitor on a cathode ray oscilloscope.

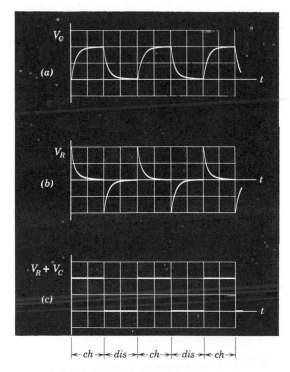

Fig. 32–13 In Fig. 32–10 switch *S* is thrown periodically, by electronic means, between positions *a* and *b*. The variations with time of the potential differences across (*a*) the capacitor, and (*b*) the resistor are shown, as displayed on a cathode ray oscilloscope. (*c*) The appearance of the screen when the oscilloscope is connected to display the sum of V_R and V_C. (Courtesy E. K. Hege, Rensselaer Polytechnic Institute.)

The "charge" intervals in plot a (see Eq. 32–15) are represented by

$$V = \left(\frac{1}{C}\right) q = \mathcal{E}(1 - e^{-t/RC})$$

and the "discharge" intervals (see Eq. 32–18b) by

$$V = \left(\frac{1}{C}\right) q = \mathcal{E}e^{-t/RC}.$$

Note that the current, as indicated by plot b, is in opposite directions during the charge and discharge intervals, in agreement with Eqs. 32–16 and 32–19.

In plot c in Fig. 32–13 the oscillograph has been connected to show the algebraic sum of plots a and b. According to the loop theorem this sum should equal $\mathcal{E}$ during the charge intervals and should be zero during the discharge intervals, when the battery is no longer in the circuit, that is,

$$V_R + V_C = \mathcal{E} \text{ during charge (see Eq. 32–12)}$$

$$V_R + V_C = 0 \text{ during discharge (see Eq. 32–17).}$$

Plot c is in exact agreement with this expectation.

QUESTIONS

1. Does the direction of the emf provided by a battery depend on the direction of current flow through the battery?

2. Figure 32–1b shows a gravitational analog of a single-loop electric circuit. Is the source of "gravitational emf" in this figure reversible as far as energy exchanges are concerned?

3. Discuss in detail the statement that the energy method and the loop theorem method for solving circuits are perfectly equivalent.

4. It is possible to generate a 10,000-volt potential difference by rubbing a pocket comb with wool. Why is this large voltage not dangerous when the much lower voltage provided by an ordinary electric outlet is very dangerous?

5. Devise a method for measuring the emf and the internal resistance of a battery.

6. A 25-watt, 110-volt bulb glows at normal brightness when connected across a bank of batteries. A 500-watt, 110-volt bulb glows only dimly when connected across the same bank. Explain.

7. Under what circumstances can the terminal potential difference of a battery exceed its emf?

8. What is the difference between an emf and a potential difference?

9. In the flow of incompressible fluids, what are the analogies to (a) the loop theorem and (b) the junction theorem?

10. Compare and contrast the formulas for the effective values of (a) capacitors and (b) resistors, in series and in parallel.

11. Does the time required for the charge on a capacitor in an RC circuit to build up to a given fraction of its equilibrium value depend on the value of the applied emf?

12. Devise a method whereby an RC circuit can be used to measure very high resistances.

PROBLEMS

1. A 5.0-amp current is set up in an external circuit by a 6.0-volt storage battery for 6.0 min. By how much is the chemical energy of the battery reduced?

2. The current in a simple series circuit is 5 amp. When an additional resistance of 2 ohms is inserted, the current drops to 4 amp. What was the resistance of the original circuit?

3. In Example 2 an ammeter whose resistance is 0.05 ohm is inserted in the circuit. What per cent change in the current results because of the presence of the meter?

4. In Fig. 32–3a put $\varepsilon = 2.0$ volts and $r = 100$ ohms. Plot (a) the current, and (b) the potential difference across R, as functions of R over the range 0 to 500 ohms. Make both plots on the same graph. (c) Make a third plot by multiplying together, for each value of R, the two curves plotted. What is the physical significance of this plot?

5. (a) In the circuit of Fig. 32–3a show that the power delivered to R as Joule heat is a maximum when R is equal to the internal resistance r of the battery. (b) Show that this maximum power is $P = \varepsilon^2/4r$.

6. Heat is to be generated in a 0.10-ohm resistor at the rate of 10 watts by connecting it to a battery whose emf is 1.5 volts. (a) What is the internal resistance of the battery? (b) What potential difference exists across the resistor?

7. (a) In Fig. 32–14 what value must R have if the current in the circuit is to be 0.001 amp? Take $\varepsilon_1 = 2.0$ volts, $\varepsilon_2 = 3.0$ volts, and $r_1 = r_2 = 3.0$ ohms. (b) What is the rate of Joule heating in R?

8. A wire of resistance 5.0 ohms is connected to a battery whose emf ε is 2.0 volts and whose internal resistance is 1.0 ohm. In 2.0 min (a) how much energy is transferred from chemical to electric form? (b) How much energy appears in the wire as Joule heat? (c) Account for the difference between (a) and (b).

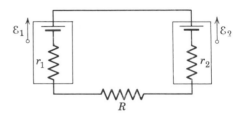

Fig. 32–14

9. In Fig. 32–6 calculate the potential difference between points c and d by as many paths as possible. Assume that $\varepsilon_1 = 4.0$ volts, $\varepsilon_2 = 1.0$ volt, $R_1 = R_2 = 10$ ohms, and $R_3 = 5$ ohms.

10. In Fig. 32–5 calculate the potential difference between a and c by considering a path that contains R and ε_2.

11. (a) In Fig. 32–15 what is the equivalent resistance of the network shown? (b) What are the currents in each resistor? Put $R_1 = 100$ ohms, $R_2 = R_3 = 50$ ohms, $R_4 = 75$ ohms, and $\varepsilon = 6.0$ volts.

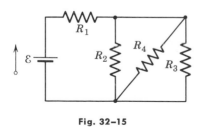

Fig. 32–15

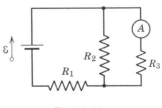

Fig 32–16

12. In Fig. 32–16 imagine an ammeter inserted in the branch containing R_3. (a) What will it read, assuming $\varepsilon = 5.0$ volts, $R_1 = 2.0$ ohms, $R_2 = 4.0$ ohms, and $R_3 = 6.0$ ohms? (b) The ammeter and the source of emf are now physically interchanged. Show that the

ammeter reading remains unchanged. This reciprocity relationship holds for any circuit that contains only one source of emf.

13. Two batteries of emf ε and internal resistance r are connected in parallel across a resistor R as in Fig. 32–20b. (a) For what value of R is the power delivered to the resistor a maximum? (b) What is the maximum power?

14. By using only two resistance coils—singly, in series, or in parallel—a student is able to obtain resistances of 3, 4, 12, and 16 ohms. What are the separate resistances of the coils?

15. *The Wheatstone bridge.* In Fig. 32–17 R_s is to be adjusted in value until points a and b are brought to exactly the same potential. (One tests for this condition by momentarily connecting a sensitive meter between a and b; if these points are at the same potential, the meter will not deflect.) Show that when this adjustment is made the following relation holds:

$$R_x = R_s \frac{R_2}{R_1}.$$

Unknown resistors (R_x) can be measured in terms of standards (R_s) using this device, which is called a Wheatstone bridge.

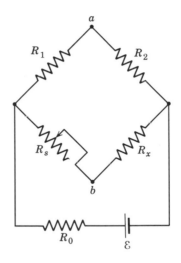

Fig. 32–17

16. If points a and b in Fig. 32–17 are connected by a wire of resistance r, show that the current in the wire is

$$i = \frac{\varepsilon(R_s - R_x)}{(R + 2r)(R_s + R_x) + 2R_sR_x},$$

where ε is the emf of the battery. Assume that R_1 and R_2 are equal ($R_1 = R_2 = R$) and that R_0 equals zero. Is this formula consistent with the result of Problem 15?

17. Two resistors, R_1 and R_2, may be connected either in series or parallel across a (resistanceless) battery with emf ε. We desire the Joule heating for the parallel combination to be five times that for the series combination. If R_1 equals 100 ohms, what is R_2?

18. Four 100-watt heating coils are to be connected in all possible series-parallel combinations and plugged into a 100-volt line. What different rates of heat dissipation are possible?

19. What is the equivalent resistance between the terminal points x and y of the circuits shown in (a) Fig. 32–18a, (b) Fig. 32–18b, and (c) Fig. 32–18c? Assume that the resistance of each resistor is 10 ohms.

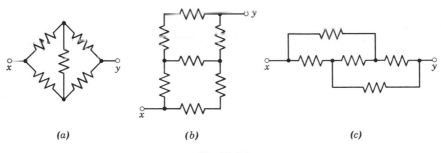

(a)   *(b)*   *(c)*

Fig. 32–18

20. In Fig. 32–19 find the current in each resistor and the potential difference between a and b. Put $\varepsilon_1 = 6.0$ volts, $\varepsilon_2 = 5.0$ volts, $\varepsilon_3 = 4.0$ volts, $R_1 = 100$ ohms, and $R_2 = 50$ ohms.

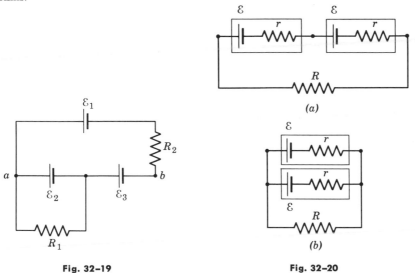

Fig. 32–19   **Fig. 32–20**

21. You are given two batteries of emf ε and internal resistance r. They may be connected either in series or in parallel and are used to establish a current in a resistor R, as in Fig. 32–20. Derive expressions for the current in R for both methods of connection. Which connection yields the larger current if (*a*) $R > r$ and if (*b*) $R < r$?

22. (*a*) In Fig. 32–21 what power appears as Joule heat in R_1? In R_2? In R_3? (*b*) What power is supplied by ε_1? By ε_2? (*c*) Discuss the energy balance in this circuit. Assume that $\varepsilon_1 = 3.0$ volts, $\varepsilon_2 = 1.0$ volt, $R_1 = 5.0$ ohms, $R_2 = 2.0$ ohms, and $R_3 = 4.0$ ohms.

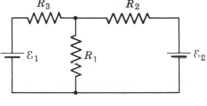

Fig. 32–21

23. For manual control of the current in a circuit, a student uses a parallel combination of variable resistors of the sliding contact type, as in Fig. 32–22, with $R_1 = 20R_2$. (*a*) What procedure is used to adjust the current to the desired value? (*b*) Why is the parallel combination better than a single-variable resistor?

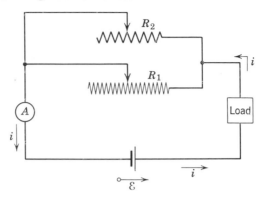

Fig. 32–22

24. *Resistance measurement.* A voltmeter (resistance R_V) and an ammeter (resistance R_A) are connected to measure a resistance R, as in Fig. 32–23a. The resistance is given by $R = V/i$, where V is the voltmeter reading and i is the current *in the resistor R*. Some of the current registered by the ammeter (i') goes through the voltmeter so that the ratio of the meter readings ($= V/i'$) gives only an *apparent* resistance reading R'. Show that R and R' are related by

$$\frac{1}{R} = \frac{1}{R'} - \frac{1}{R_V}.$$

Note that if $R_V \gg R$, then $R \cong R'$.

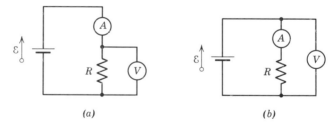

(a)   (b)

Fig. 32–23

25. *Resistance measurement.* If meters are used to measure resistance, they may also be connected as they are in Fig. 32–23b. Again the ratio of the meter readings gives only an apparent resistance resistance R'. Show that R' is related to R by

$$R = R' - R_A,$$

in which R_A is the ammeter resistance. Note that if $R_A \ll R$, then $R \cong R'$.

26. In Fig. 32–8 assume that $\varepsilon = 5.0$ volts, $r = 2.0$ ohms, $R_1 = 5.0$ ohms, and $R_2 = 4.0$ ohms. If $R_A = 0.10$ ohm, what per cent error is made in reading the current? Assume that the voltmeter is not present.

27. In Fig. 32–8 assume that $\varepsilon = 5.0$ volts, $r = 20$ ohms, $R_1 = 50$ ohms, and $R_2 = 40$ ohms. If $R_v = 1000$ ohms, what per cent error is made in reading the potential differences across R_1? Ignore the presence of the ammeter.

28. (a) Find the three currents in Fig. 32–24. (b) Find V_{ab}. Assume that $R_1 = 1.0$ ohm, $R_2 = 2.0$ ohms, $\mathcal{E}_1 = 2.0$ volts, and $\mathcal{E}_2 = \mathcal{E}_3 = 4.0$ volts.

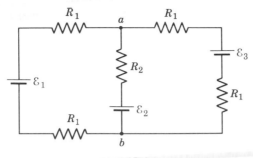

Fig. 32–24

29. How many time constants must elapse before a capacitor in an RC circuit is charged to within 1.0 per cent of its equilibrium charge?

30. In the circuit of Fig. 32–25 let i_1, i_2, and i_3 be the currents through resistors R_1, R_2, and R_3, respectively, and let V_1, V_2, V_3, and V_C be the corresponding potential differences across the resistors and across the capacitor C. (a) Plot qualitatively as a function of time after switch S is closed the currents and voltages listed above. (b) After being closed for a large number of time constants, the switch S is now opened. Plot qualitatively as a function of time after the switch is opened the currents and voltages listed above.

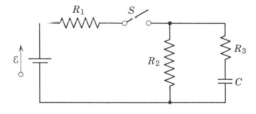

Fig. 32–25

31. Show that the units of RC are indeed time units, that is, that 1 ohm $\times$ 1 farad $= 1$ sec.

32. Prove that when switch S in Fig. 32–10 is thrown from a to b all the energy stored in the capacitor is transformed into Joule heat in the resistor. Assume that the capacitor is fully charged before the switch is thrown.

33. A 3.0×10^6-ohm resistor and a 1.0-μf capacitor are connected in a single-loop circuit with a seat of emf with $\mathcal{E} = 4.0$ volts. At 1.0 sec after the connection is made, what are the rates at which (a) the charge of the capacitor is increasing, (b) energy is being stored in the capacitor, (c) Joule heat is appearing in the resistor, and (d) energy is being delivered by the seat of emf?

The Magnetic Field

33–1 The Magnetic Field

The science of magnetism grew from the observation that certain "stones" (magnetite) would attract bits of iron. The word *magnetism* comes from the district of Magnesia in Asia Minor, which is one of the places at which the stones were found. Figure 33–1 shows a modern permanent magnet, the lineal descendant of these natural magnets. Another "natural magnet" is the earth itself, whose orienting action on a magnetic compass needle has been known since ancient times.

In 1820 Oersted first discovered that a current in a wire can also produce magnetic effects, namely, that it can change the orientation of a compass needle. We pointed out in Section 26–1 how this important discovery linked the then separate sciences of magnetism and electricity. The magnetic ef-

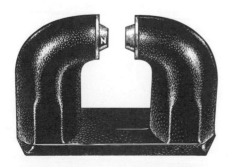

Fig. 33–1 A permanent magnet. Lines of magnetic induction leave the north pole face, marked N, and enter the south pole face on the other side of the air gap.

Fig. 33–2 A research-type electromagnet showing iron frame F, pole faces P, and coils C. The pole faces are 12 in. in diameter. (Courtesy Varian Associates.)

fect of a current in a wire can be intensified by forming the wire into a coil of many turns and by providing an iron core. Figure 33–2 shows how this is done in a large electromagnet of a type commonly used for research involving magnetism.

We define the space around a magnet or a current-carrying conductor as the site of a *magnetic field*, just as we defined the space near a charged rod as the site of an electric field. The basic magnetic field vector **B**, which we define in the following section, is called the *magnetic induction:* * it can be represented by *lines of induction*, just as the electric field was represented by lines of force. As for the electric field (see Section 27–3), the magnetic field vector is related to its lines of induction in this way:

1. The tangent to a line of induction at any point gives the *direction* of **B** at that point.

2. The lines of induction are drawn so that the number of lines per unit cross-sectional area is proportional to the *magnitude* of the magnetic field vector **B**. Where the lines are close together B is large and where they are far apart B is small.

As for the electric field, the field vector **B** is of fundamental importance, the lines of induction simply giving a graphic representation of the way **B** varies throughout a certain region of space.

The *flux* Φ_B for a magnetic field can be defined in exact analogy with the flux Φ_E for the electric field, namely

$$\Phi_B = \int \mathbf{B} \cdot d\mathbf{S}, \qquad (33\text{--}1)$$

in which the integral is taken over the surface (closed or open) for which Φ_B is defined

---

* *Magnetic field strength* would be a more suitable name for **B**, but it has been usurped for historical reasons by another vector connected with the magnetic field (see Section 37–7).

33–2 The Definition of B

This chapter is not concerned with the *causes* of the magnetic field; we seek to determine (*a*) whether a magnetic field exists at a given point and (*b*) the action of this field on charges moving through it. As for the electric field, a particle of charge q_0 serves as a test body. We assume that there is no electric field present, which means that, neglecting gravity, no force will act on the test body if it is placed *at rest* at the point in question.

Let us fire a positive test charge with arbitrary velocity **v** through a point *P*. *If a sideways deflecting force* **F** *acts on it, we assert that a magnetic field is present at P* and we define the magnetic induction **B** of this field in terms of **F** and other measured quantities.

If we vary the direction of **v** through point *P*, keeping the magnitude of **v** unchanged, we find, in general, that although **F** will always remain at right angles to **v** its magnitude *F* will change. For a particular orientation of **v** (and also for the opposite orientation −**v**) the force **F** becomes zero. We define this direction as the direction of **B**, the specification of the sense of **B** (that is, the way it points along this line) being left to the more complete definition of **B** that we give below.

Having found the *direction* of **B**, we are now able to orient **v** so that the test charge moves at right angles to **B**. We will find that the force **F** is now a maximum, and we define the *magnitude* of **B** from the measured magnitude of this maximum force $F_\perp$, or

$$B = \frac{F_\perp}{q_0 v}. \tag{33–2}$$

Let us regard this definition of **B** (in which we have specified its magnitude and direction, but not its sense) as preliminary to the complete vector definition that we now give: *If a positive test charge q_0 is fired with velocity* **v** *through a point P and if a (sideways) force* **F** *acts on the moving charge, a magnetic induction* **B** *is present at point P, where* **B** *is the vector that satisfies the relation*

$$\mathbf{F} = q_0 \mathbf{v} \times \mathbf{B}, \tag{33–3a}$$

v, q_0, and **F** being measured quantities. The magnitude of the magnetic deflecting force **F**, according to the rules for vector products, is given by *

$$F = q_0 v B \sin\theta, \tag{33–3b}$$

in which θ is the angle between **v** and **B**.

Figure 33–3 shows the relations among the vectors. We see that **F**, being at right angles to the plane formed by **v** and **B**, will always be at right angles to **v** (and also to **B**) and thus will always be a sideways force. Equation 33–3a is consistent with the observed facts that (*a*) the magnetic force vanishes as $v \to 0$, (*b*) the magnetic force vanishes if **v** is either parallel or antiparallel to the direction of **B** (in these cases $\theta = 0$ or 180° and $\mathbf{v} \times \mathbf{B} = 0$), and (*c*) if **v** is at right angles to **B** ($\theta = 90°$), the deflecting force has its maximum value, given by Eq. 33–2, that is, $F_\perp = q_0 v B$.

---

* The student may wish to review Section 2–4, which deals with vector products.

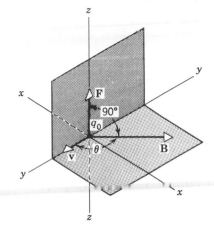

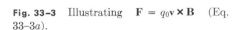

Fig. 33–3   Illustrating $\mathbf{F} = q_0\mathbf{v} \times \mathbf{B}$ (Eq. 33–3*a*).

This definition of **B** is similar in spirit, although more complex, than the definition of the electric field strength **E**, which we can cast into this form: *If a positive test charge q_0 is placed at point P and if an (electric) force **F** acts on the stationary charge, an electric field **E** is present at P, where **E** is the vector satisfying the relation*

$$\mathbf{F} = q_0\mathbf{E},$$

q_0 and **F** being measured quantities. In defining **E**, the only characteristic direction to appear is that of the electric force $\mathbf{F}_E$ which acts on the positive test body; the direction of **E** is taken to be that of $\mathbf{F}_E$. In defining **B**, *two* characteristic directions appear, those of **v** and of the magnetic force $\mathbf{F}_B$; they prove always to be at right angles.

In Fig. 33–4 a positive and a negative electron are created at point P in a bubble chamber. A magnetic field is perpendicular to the chamber, pointing out of the plane of the figure (symbol $\odot$).* The relation $\mathbf{F} = q_0\mathbf{v} \times \mathbf{B}$ (Eq. 33–3*a*) shows that the deflecting forces acting on the two particles are as indicated in the figure. These deflecting forces would make the tracks deflect as shown.

The unit of **B** that follows from Eq 33–3 is the (nt/coul)/(meter/sec). This is given the special name of the weber/meter², or, recalling that a coul/sec is an ampere,

$$1 \text{ weber/meter}^2 = \frac{1 \text{ nt}}{\text{coul (meter/sec)}} = \frac{1 \text{ nt}}{\text{amp-m}}.$$

An earlier unit for **B**, still in common use, is the *gauss;* the relationship is

$$1 \text{ weber/meter}^2 = 10^4 \text{ gauss}.$$

The *weber* is used to measure Φ_B, the flux of **B**; see Eq. 33–1.

The fact that the magnetic force is always at right angles to the direction of motion means that (for steady magnetic fields) the work done by this

---

* The symbol $\otimes$ indicates a vector into the page, the $\times$ being thought of as the tail of an arrow; the symbol $\odot$ indicates a vector out of the page, the dot being thought of as the tip of an arrow.

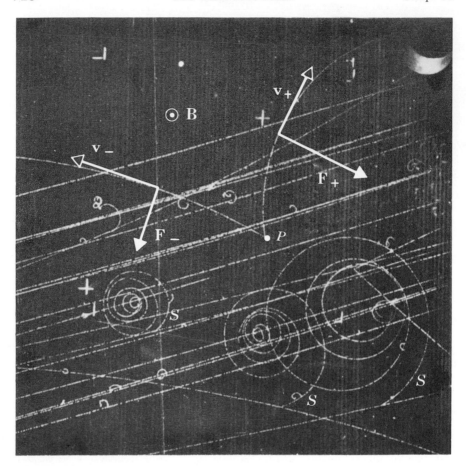

Fig. 33–4 A *bubble chamber* is a device for rendering visible, by means of small bubbles, the tracks of charged particles that pass through the chamber. The figure is a photograph taken with such a chamber immersed in a field of magnetic induction B and exposed to radiations from a large cyclotron-like accelerator. The curved V at point P is formed by a positive and a negative electron, which deflect in opposite directions in the magnetic field. The spirals S are the tracks of three low-energy electrons. (Courtesy E. O. Lawrence Radiation Laboratory, University of California.)

force on the particle is zero. For an element of the path of the particle of length $d\mathbf{l}$, this work dW is $\mathbf{F}_B \cdot d\mathbf{l}$; dW is zero because $\mathbf{F}_B$ and $d\mathbf{l}$ are always at right angles. Thus a static magnetic field cannot change the kinetic energy of a moving charge; it can only deflect it sideways.

If a charged particle moves through a region in which both an electric field and a magnetic field are present, the resultant force is found by combining Eqs. 27–2 and 33–3a, or

$$\mathbf{F} = q_0 \mathbf{E} + q_0 \mathbf{v} \times \mathbf{B}. \qquad (33\text{–}4)$$

This is sometimes called the *Lorentz relation* in tribute to H. A. Lorentz who did so much to develop and clarify the concepts of the electric and magnetic fields.

▶ **Example 1.** A uniform field of magnetic induction **B** points horizontally from south to north; its magnitude is 1.5 webers/meter². If a 5.0-Mev proton moves vertically downward through this field, what force will act on it?

The kinetic energy of the proton is

$$K = (5.0 \times 10^6 \text{ ev})(1.6 \times 10^{-19} \text{ joule/ev}) = 8.0 \times 10^{-13} \text{ joule.}$$

Its speed can be found from the relation $K = \frac{1}{2}mv^2$, or

$$v = \sqrt{\frac{2K}{m}} = \sqrt{\frac{(2)(8.0 \times 10^{-13} \text{ joule})}{1.7 \times 10^{-27} \text{ kg}}} = 3.1 \times 10^7 \text{ meters/sec.}$$

Equation 33-3b gives

$$F = qvB \sin \theta = (1.6 \times 10^{-19} \text{ coul})(3.1 \times 10^7 \text{ meters/sec})(1.5 \text{ webers/meter}^2)(\sin 90°)$$

$$= 7.4 \times 10^{-12} \text{ nt.}$$

The student can show that this force is about 4×10^{14} times greater than the weight of the proton.

The relation $\mathbf{F} = q\mathbf{v} \times \mathbf{B}$ shows that the *direction* of the deflecting force is to the east. If the particle had been negatively charged, the deflection would have been to the west. This is predicted automatically by Eq. 33-3a if we substitute $-e$ for q_0. ◀

33-3 Magnetic Force on a Current

A current is an assembly of moving charges. Because a magnetic field exerts a sideways force on a moving charge, we expect that it will also exert a sideways force on a wire carrying a current. Figure 33-5 shows a length l of wire carrying a current i and placed in a field of magnetic induction **B**. For simplicity we have oriented the wire so that the current density vector **j** is at right angles to **B**.

The current i in a metal wire is carried by the free (or conduction) electrons, n being the number of such electrons per unit volume of the wire. The magnitude of the average force on one such electron is given by Eq. 33-3b, or, since $\theta = 90°$,

$$F' = q_0vB \sin \theta = ev_dB$$

where v_d is the drift speed. From the relation $v_d = j/ne$ (Eq. 31-5),

$$F' = e\left(\frac{j}{ne}\right)B = \frac{jB}{n}.$$

Fig. 33-5 A wire carrying a current i is placed at right angles to a field of magnetic induction **B**.

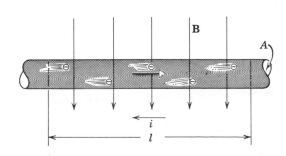

The length l of the wire contains nAl free electrons, Al being the volume of the section of wire of cross section A that we are considering. The total force on the free electrons in the wire, and thus on the wire itself, is

$$F = (nAl)F' = nAl\frac{jB}{n}.$$

Since jA is the current i in the wire, we have

$$F = ilB. \tag{33--5}$$

The negative charges, which move to the right in the wire of Fig. 33–5, are equivalent to positive charges moving to the left, that is, in the direction of the current arrow. For such a positive charge the velocity $\mathbf{v}$ would point to the left and the force on the wire, given by Eq. 33–3a ($\mathbf{F} = q_0\mathbf{v} \times \mathbf{B}$) points up, out of the page. This same conclusion follows if we consider the actual negative charge carriers for which $\mathbf{v}$ points to the right but q_0 has a negative sign. Thus by measuring the sideways magnetic force on a wire carrying a current and placed in a magnetic field we cannot tell whether the current carriers are negative charges moving in a given direction or positive charges moving in the opposite direction.

Equation 33–5 holds only if the wire is at right angles to $\mathbf{B}$. We can express the more general situation in vector form as

$$\mathbf{F} = i\mathbf{l} \times \mathbf{B}, \tag{33--6a}$$

where $\mathbf{l}$ is a (displacement) vector that points along the (straight) wire in the direction of the current. Equation 33–6a is equivalent to the relation $\mathbf{F} = q_0\mathbf{v} \times \mathbf{B}$ (Eq. 33–3a); either can be taken as a defining equation for $\mathbf{B}$. The student should note that the vector $\mathbf{l}$ in Fig. 33–5 points to the left and that the magnetic force $\mathbf{F}$ ($= i\mathbf{l} \times \mathbf{B}$) points up, out of the page. This agrees with the conclusion obtained by analyzing the forces that act on the individual charge carriers.

If we consider a differential element of a conductor of length $d\mathbf{l}$, the force $d\mathbf{F}$ acting on it can be found, by analogy with Eq. 33–6a, from

$$d\mathbf{F} = i\,d\mathbf{l} \times \mathbf{B}. \tag{33--6b}$$

By integrating this formula in an appropriate way we can find the force $\mathbf{F}$ on a nonlinear conductor.

▶ **Example 2.** A wire bent as shown in Fig. 33–6 carries a current i and is placed in a uniform field of magnetic induction $\mathbf{B}$ that emerges from the plane of the figure. Calculate the force acting on the wire. The magnetic field is represented by lines of induction, shown emerging from the page. The dots show that the sense of $\mathbf{B}$ is up, out of the page.

The force on each straight section, from Eq. 33–6a, has the magnitude

$$F_1 = F_3 = ilB$$

and points down as shown by the arrows in the figure.

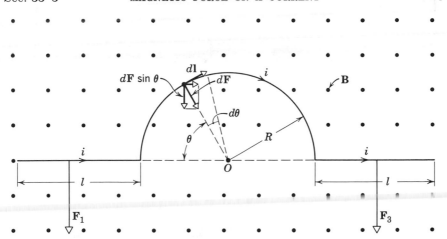

Fig. 33-6 Example 2.

A segment of wire of length dl on the arc has a force $d\mathbf{F}$ on it whose magnitude is

$$dF = iB \, dl = iB(R \, d\theta)$$

and whose direction is radially toward O, the center of the arc. Only the downward component of this force is effective, the horizontal component being canceled by an oppositely directed component associated with the corresponding arc segment on the other side of O. Thus the total force on the semicircle of wire about O points down and is

$$F_2 = \int_0^\pi dF \sin \theta = \int_0^\pi (iBR \, d\theta) \sin \theta = iBR \int_0^\pi \sin \theta \, d\theta = 2iBR.$$

The resultant force on the whole wire is

$$F = F_1 + F_2 + F_3 = 2ilB + 2iBR = 2iB(l + R).$$

Notice that this force is the same as that acting on a straight wire of length $2l + 2R$.

◄

Figure 33-7 shows the arrangement used by Thomas, Driscoll, and Hipple at the National Bureau of Standards to measure the magnetic induction provided by a laboratory magnet such as that of Fig. 33-2. The rectangle is a coil of nine turns whose width a and length b are about 10 cm and 70 cm, respectively. The lower end of the coil is placed in the field of magnetic induction $\mathbf{B}$ and the upper end is hung from the arm of a balance; $\mathbf{B}$ enters the plane of the figure at right angles.

An accurately known current i of about 0.10 amp is set up in the coil in the direction shown, and weights are placed in the right-hand balance pan until the system is balanced. The magnetic force $\mathbf{F}$ ($= i\mathbf{l} \times \mathbf{B}$; see Eq. 33-6a) on the bottom leg of the coil points upward, as shown in the figure. Equation 33-5 also shows that the force *on each wire* at the bottom of the coil is iaB. Since there are nine wires, the total force on the bottom leg of the coil is $9iaB$. The forces on the vertical sides of the coil ($= i\mathbf{l} \times \mathbf{B}$) are sideways; because they are equal and opposite, they cancel and produce no effect.

After balancing the system, the experimenters reversed the direction of the current, which changed the sign of all the magnetic forces acting on the coil. In particular, $\mathbf{F}$ then pointed downward, which caused the rest point of the balance to move. A mass

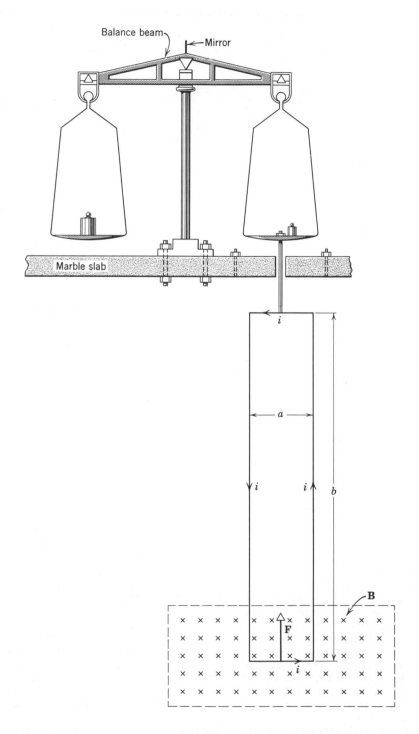

Fig. 33-7 Apparatus used to measure **B**. The zero point of the balance is observed by means of a light beam reflected from the mirror attached to the balance beam.

m of about 8.78 gm had to be added to the left balance pan to restore the original rest point. The *change* in force when the current is reversed is $2F$, and this must equal the weight added to the left balance pan, or

$$mg = 2(9iaB) = 18iaB.$$

This gives

$$B = \frac{mg}{18ai} = \frac{(8.78 \times 10^{-3}\ \text{kg})(9.80\ \text{meters/sec}^2)}{(18)(0.10\ \text{meter})(0.10\ \text{amp})} = 0.48\ \text{weber/meter}^2 = 4800\ \text{gauss.}$$

The Bureau of Standards' workers made this measurement with much more care than these approximate numbers suggest. In one series of measurements, for example, they found a magnetic induction of 4697.55 gauss.

33–4 Torque on a Current Loop

Figure 33–8 shows a rectangular loop of wire of length a and width b placed in a uniform field of induction **B**, with sides 1 and 3 normal to the field direction. The normal nn' to the plane of the loop makes an angle θ with the direction of **B**.

Assume the current to be as shown in the figure. Wires must be provided to lead the current into the loop and out of it. If these wires are twisted tightly together, there will be no net magnetic force on the twisted pair because the currents in the two wires are in opposite directions. Thus the lead wires may be ignored. Also, some way of supporting the loop must be provided. Let us imagine it to be suspended from a long string attached to the loop at its center of mass. In this way the loop will be free to turn, through a small angle at least, about any axis through the center of mass.

The net force on the loop is the resultant of the forces on the four sides of the loop. On side 2 the vector **l** points in the direction of the current and has the magnitude b. The angle between **l** and **B** for side 2 (see Fig. 33–8b) is

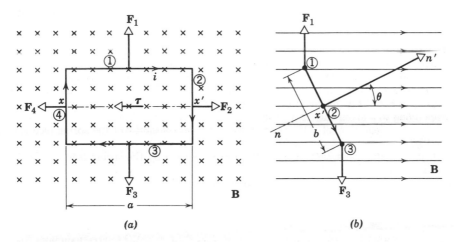

(a)   *(b)*

Fig. 33–8 A rectangular coil carrying a current i is placed in a uniform external magnetic field.

$90° - \theta$. Thus the magnitude of the force on this side is

$$F_2 = ibB \sin (90° - \theta) = ibB \cos \theta.$$

From the relation $\mathbf{F} = i\mathbf{l} \times \mathbf{B}$ (Eq. 33–6a), we find the direction of $\mathbf{F}_2$ to be out of the plane of Fig. 33–8b. The student can show that the force $\mathbf{F}_4$ on side 4 has the same magnitude as $\mathbf{F}_2$ but points in the opposite direction. Thus $\mathbf{F}_2$ and $\mathbf{F}_4$, taken together, have no effect on the motion of the loop. The net force they provide is zero, and, since they have the same line of action, the net torque due to these forces is also zero.

The common magnitude of $\mathbf{F}_1$ and $\mathbf{F}_3$ is iaB. These forces, too, are oppositely directed so that they do not tend to move the coil bodily. As Fig. 33–8b shows, however, they do *not* have the same line of action if the coil is in the position shown; there is a net torque, which tends to rotate the coil clockwise about the line xx'. The coil can be supported on a rigid axis that lies along xx', with no loss of its freedom of motion. This torque can be represented in Fig. 33–8b by a vector pointing into the figure at point x' or in Fig. 33–8a by a vector pointing along the xx' axis from right to left.

The magnitude of the torque τ' is found by calculating the torque caused by $\mathbf{F}_1$ about axis xx' and doubling it, for $\mathbf{F}_3$ exerts the same torque about this axis that $\mathbf{F}_1$ does. Thus

$$\tau' = 2(iaB)\left(\frac{b}{2}\right)(\sin \theta) = iabB \sin \theta.$$

This torque acts on every turn of the coil. If there are N turns, the torque on the entire coil is

$$\tau = N\tau' = NiabB \sin \theta = NiAB \sin \theta, \tag{33–7}$$

in which A, the area of the coil, is substituted for ab.

This equation can be shown to hold for *all plane loops of area A, whether they are rectangular or not.* A torque on a current loop is the basic operating principle of the electric motor and of most electric meters used for measuring current or potential difference.

▶ **Example 3.** *A galvanometer.* Figure 33–9 shows the rudiments of a galvanometer, which is a device used to measure currents. The coil is 2.0 cm high and 1.0 cm wide; it has 250 turns and is mounted so that it can rotate about a vertical axis in a uniform *radial* magnetic field with $B = 2000$ gauss. A spring Sp provides a countertorque that cancels out the magnetic torque, resulting in a steady angular deflection ϕ corresponding to a given current i in the coil. If a current of 1.0×10^{-4} amp produces an angular deflection of $30°$, what is the *torsional constant κ* of the spring (see Eq. 15–18)?

Equating the magnetic torque to the torque caused by the spring (see Eq. 33–7) yields

$$\tau = NiAB \sin \theta = \kappa\phi$$

or

$$\kappa = \frac{NiAB \sin \theta}{\phi}$$

$$= \frac{(250)(1.0 \times 10^{-4} \text{ amp})(2.0 \times 10^{-4} \text{ meter}^2)(0.20 \text{ weber/meter}^2)(\sin 90°)}{30°}$$

$$= 3.3 \times 10^{-8} \text{ nt-m/deg.}$$

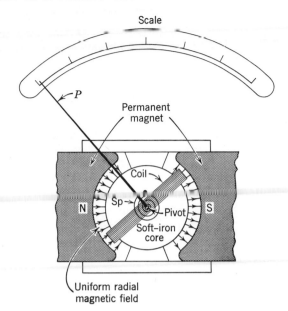

Fig. 33-9 Example 3. The elements of a galvanometer, showing the coil, the helical spring Sp, and pointer P.

Note that the normal to the plane of the coil (that is, the pointer P) is always at right angles to the (radial) magnetic field so that $\theta = 90°$.   ◄

A current loop orienting itself in an external magnetic field reminds us of the action of a compass needle in such a field. One face of the loop behaves like the north pole of the needle; * the other face behaves like the south pole. Compass needles, bar magnets, and current loops can all be regarded as *magnetic dipoles*. We show this here for the current loop, reasoning entirely by analogy with *electric* dipoles.

A structure is called an electric dipole if (a) when placed in an *external* electric field it experiences a torque given by Eq. 27-11,

$$\boldsymbol{\tau} = \mathbf{p} \times \mathbf{E}, \tag{33-8}$$

where $\mathbf{p}$ is the electric dipole moment, and (b) it sets up a field of its own at distant points, described qualitatively by the lines of force of Fig. 29-10 and quantitatively by Eq. 29-11. These two requirements are not independent; if one is fulfilled, the other follows automatically.

The magnitude of the torque described by Eq. 33-8 is

$$\tau = pE \sin\theta, \tag{33-9}$$

where θ is the angle between $\mathbf{p}$ and $\mathbf{E}$. Let us compare this with Eq. 33-7, the expression for the torque on a current loop:

$$\tau = (NiA)B \sin\theta. \tag{33-7}$$

---

* The north pole of a compass needle is the end that points toward the geographic north.

In each case the appropriate field (E or B) appears, as does a term $\sin \theta$. Comparison suggests that NiA in Eq. 33–7 can be taken as the *magnetic dipole moment* μ, corresponding to p in Eq. 33–9, or

$$\mu = NiA. \tag{33–10}$$

Equation 33–7 suggests that we write the torque on a current loop in vector form, in analogy with Eq. 33–8, or

$$\boldsymbol{\tau} = \boldsymbol{\mu} \times \mathbf{B}. \tag{33–11}$$

The magnetic dipole moment of the loop $\boldsymbol{\mu}$ must be taken to lie along the axis of the loop; its direction is given by the following rule: Let the fingers of the right hand curl around the loop in the direction of the current; the extended right thumb will then point in the direction of $\boldsymbol{\mu}$. The student should check carefully that, if $\boldsymbol{\mu}$ is defined by this rule and Eq. 33–10, Eq. 33–11 correctly describes in every detail the torque acting on a current loop in an external field (see Fig. 33–8).

Since a torque acts on a current loop, or other magnetic dipole, when it is placed in an external magnetic field, it follows that work (positive or negative) must be done by an external agent to change the orientation of such a dipole. Thus a magnetic dipole has *potential energy* associated with its orientation in an external magnetic field. This energy may be taken to be zero for any arbitrary position of the dipole. By analogy with the assumption made for electric dipoles in Section 27–6, we assume that the magnetic energy U is zero when $\boldsymbol{\mu}$ and $\mathbf{B}$ are at right angles, that is, when $\theta = 90°$. This choice of a zero-energy configuration for U is arbitrary because we are interested only in the *changes* in energy that occur when the dipole is rotated.

The magnetic potential energy in any position θ is defined as the work that an external agent must do to turn the dipole from its zero-energy position ($\theta = 90°$) to the given position θ. Thus

$$U = \int_{90°}^{\theta} \tau \, d\theta = \int_{90°}^{\theta} NiAB \sin \theta \, d\theta = \mu B \int_{90°}^{\theta} \sin \theta \, d\theta = -\mu B \cos \theta,$$

in which Eq. 33–7 is used to substitute for τ. In vector symbolism this relation can be written as

$$U = -\boldsymbol{\mu} \cdot \mathbf{B}, \tag{33–12}$$

which is in perfect correspondence with Eq. 27–13, the expression for the energy of an *electric* dipole in an external *electric* field,

$$U = -\mathbf{p} \cdot \mathbf{E}.$$

▶ **Example 4.** A circular coil of N turns has an effective radius a and carries a current i. How much work is required to turn it in an external magnetic field $\mathbf{B}$ from a position in which θ equals zero to one in which θ equals 180°? Assume that $N = 100$, $a = 5.0$ cm, $i = 0.10$ amp, and $B = 1.5$ webers/meter².

The work required is the difference in energy between the two positions, or, from Eq. 33–12,

$$W = U_{\theta = 180°} - U_{\theta = 0} = (-\mu B \cos 180°) - (-\mu B \cos 0) = 2\mu B.$$

But $\mu - NiA$, so that

$$W = 2NiAB = 2Ni(\pi a^2)B$$

$$= (2)(100)(0.10 \text{ amp})(\pi)(5 \times 10^{-2} \text{ meter})^2(1.5 \text{ webers/meter}^2) = 0.24 \text{ joule.} \quad \blacktriangleleft$$

33–5   The Hall Effect

In 1879 E. H. Hall devised an experiment that gives the sign of the charge carriers in a conductor; see p. 679.   Figure 33–10 shows a flat strip of copper, carrying a current i in the direction shown.   As usual, the direction of the current arrow, labeled i, is the direction in which the charge carriers would move *if* they were positive.   The current arrow can represent either positive charges moving down (as in Fig. 33–10a) or negative charges moving up (as in Fig. 33–10b).   The Hall effect can be used to decide between these two possibilities.

A field of magnetic induction **B** is set up at right angles to the strip by placing the strip between the polefaces of an electromagnet.   This field exerts a deflecting force **F** on the strip (given by $i\mathbf{l} \times \mathbf{B}$), which points to the right in the figure.   Since the sideways force on the strip is due to the sideways forces on the charge carriers (given by $q\mathbf{v} \times \mathbf{B}$), it follows that these carriers, whether they are positive or negative, will tend to drift toward the right in Fig. 33–10 as they drift along the strip, producing a *transverse Hall potential difference* V_{xy} between points such as x and y.   The sign of the charge carriers is determined by the sign of this Hall potential difference. If the carriers are positive, y will be at a higher potential than x; if they are negative, y will be at a lower potential than x.   Experiment shows that in metals the charge carriers are negative.

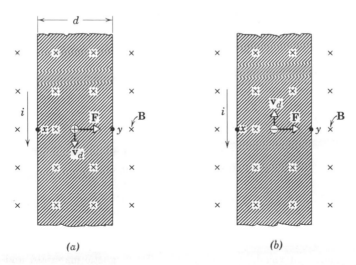

(a)   (b)

Fig. 33–10   A current i is set up in a copper strip placed in a field of magnetic induction **B**, assuming (a) positive carriers and (b) negative carriers.

To analyze the Hall effect quantitatively, let us use the *free-electron* model of a metal, the same model used in Section 31–4 to explain resistivity. The charge carriers can be assumed to move along the conductor with a certain constant drift speed v_d. The magnetic deflecting force that causes the moving charge carriers to drift toward the right edge of the strip is given by $q\mathbf{v}_d \times \mathbf{B}$ (see Eq. 33–3a).

The charge carriers do not build up without limit on the right edge of the strip because the displacement of charge gives rise to a transverse *Hall electric field* $\mathbf{E}_H$, which acts, inside the conductor, to oppose the sideways drift of the carriers. This Hall electric field is another manifestation of the Hall potential difference and is related to it by

$$E_H = V_{xy}/d.$$

Eventually an equilibrium is reached in which the sideways magnetic deflecting force on the charge carriers is just canceled by the oppositely directed electric force $q\mathbf{E}_H$ caused by the Hall electric field, or

$$q\mathbf{E}_H + q\mathbf{v}_d \times \mathbf{B} = 0,$$

which can be written

$$\mathbf{E}_H = -\mathbf{v}_d \times \mathbf{B}. \tag{33–13}$$

This equation shows explicitly that if $\mathbf{E}_H$ and $\mathbf{B}$ are measured $\mathbf{v}_d$ can be determined both in magnitude and direction; given the direction of $\mathbf{v}_d$, the sign of the charge carriers follows at once, as Fig. 33–10 shows.

The number of charge carriers per unit volume (n) can also be found from Hall effect measurements. If we write Eq. 33–13 in terms of magnitudes, for the case in which $\mathbf{v}_d$ and $\mathbf{B}$ are at right angles, we obtain $E_H = v_d B$. Combining this with Eq. 31–5 ($v_d = j/ne$) leads to

$$E_H = \frac{j}{ne} B \quad \text{or} \quad n = \frac{jB}{eE_H}. \tag{33–14}$$

The agreement between experiment and Eq. 33–14 is rather good for monovalent metals, as Table 33–1 shows.

Table 33–1

NUMBER OF CONDUCTION ELECTRONS PER UNIT VOLUME

Metal	Based on Hall Effect Data, $10^{22}/cm^3$	Calculated, Assuming One Electron/Atom, $10^{22}/cm^3$
Li	3.7	4.8
Na	2.5	2.6
K	1.5	1.3
Cs	0.80	0.85
Cu	11	8.4
Ag	7.4	6.0
Au	8.7	5.9

For nonmonovalent metals, for iron and similar magnetic materials, and for so-called semiconductors such as germanium, the simple interpretation of the Hall effect in terms of the free-electron model is not valid. A theoretical interpretation of the

Hall effect based on modern quantum physics gives a reasonable agreement with experiment in all cases.

▶ **Example 5.** A copper strip 2.0 cm wide and 1.0 mm thick is placed in a magnetic field with $B = 1.5$ webers/meter^2, as in Fig. 33–10. If a current of 200 amp is set up in the strip, what Hall potential difference appears across the strip?

From Eq. 33–14,

$$E_H = \frac{jB}{ne},$$

but $$E_H = \frac{V_{xy}}{d} \quad \text{and} \quad j = \frac{i}{A} = \frac{i}{dh},$$

where h is the thickness of the strip. Combining these equations gives

$$V_{xy} = \frac{iB}{neh} = \frac{(200 \text{ amp})(1.5 \text{ webers/meter}^2)}{(8.4 \times 10^{28}/\text{meter}^3)(1.6 \times 10^{-19} \text{ coul})(1.0 \times 10^{-3} \text{ meter})}$$

$$= 2.2 \times 10^{-5} \text{ volt} = 22\mu v.$$

These potential differences are not large. See p. 681 for the calculation of n. ◀

33–6 Circulating Charges

Figure 33–11 shows a negatively charged particle introduced with velocity **v** into a uniform field of magnetic induction **B**. We assume that **v** is at right angles to **B** and thus lies entirely in the plane of the figure. The relation **F** = q**v** × **B** (Eq. 33–3a) shows that the particle will experience a sideways deflecting force of magnitude qvB. This force will lie in the plane of the figure, which means that the particle cannot leave this plane.

This reminds us of a stone held by a rope and whirled in a horizontal circle on a smooth surface. Here, too, a force of constant magnitude, the tension in the rope, acts in a plane and at right angles to the velocity. The charged particle, like the stone, also moves with constant speed in a circular

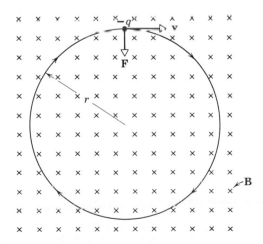

Fig. 33–11 A charge $-q$ circulates at right angles to a uniform magnetic field.

path. From Newton's second law we have

$$qvB = \frac{mv^2}{r} \quad \text{or} \quad r = \frac{mv}{qB}, \quad (33\text{--}15)$$

which gives the radius of the path. The three spirals in Fig. 33–4 show relatively low-energy electrons in a bubble chamber. The paths are not circles because the electrons lose energy by collisions in the chamber as they move.

The angular velocity ω is given by v/r or, from Eq. 33–15,

$$\omega = \frac{v}{r} = \frac{qB}{m}.$$

The frequency f measured, say, in rev/sec, is given by

$$f = \frac{\omega}{2\pi} = \frac{qB}{2\pi m}. \quad (33\text{--}16)$$

Note that f *does not depend on the speed of the particle.* Fast particles move in large circles (Eq. 33–15) and slow ones in small circles, but all require the same time T (the *period*) to complete one revolution in the field.

The frequency f is a characteristic frequency for the charged particle in the field and may be compared to the characteristic frequency of a swinging pendulum in the earth's gravitational field or to the characteristic frequency of an oscillating mass-spring system. It is sometimes called the *cyclotron frequency* of the particle in the field because particles circulate at this frequency in the cyclotron.

▶ **Example 6.** A 10-ev electron is circulating in a plane at right angles to a uniform field of magnetic induction of 1.0×10^{-4} weber/meter^2 ($= 1.0$ gauss).

(a) What is its orbit radius?

The velocity of an electron whose kinetic energy is K can be found from

$$v = \sqrt{\frac{2K}{m}}.$$

The student should verify that this yields 1.9×10^6 meters/sec for v. Then, from Eq. 33–15,

$$r = \frac{mv}{qB} = \frac{(9.1 \times 10^{-31}\,\text{kg})(1.9 \times 10^6\,\text{meters/sec})}{(1.6 \times 10^{-19}\,\text{coul})(1.0 \times 10^{-4}\,\text{weber/meter}^2)} = 0.11\,\text{meter} = 11\,\text{cm}.$$

(b) What is the cyclotron frequency? From Eq. 33–16,

$$f = \frac{qB}{2\pi m} = \frac{(1.6 \times 10^{-19}\,\text{coul})(1.0 \times 10^{-4}\,\text{weber/meter}^2)}{(2\pi)(9.1 \times 10^{21-}\,\text{kg})} = 2.8 \times 10^6\,\text{rev/sec}.$$

(c) What is the period of revolution T?

$$T = \frac{1}{f} = \frac{1}{2.8 \times 10^6\,\text{rev/sec}} = 3.6 \times 10^{-7}\,\text{sec}.$$

Thus an electron requires 0.36 μsec to make 1 revolution in a 1.0-gauss field.

(d) What is the direction of circulation as viewed by an observer sighting along the field?

In Fig. 33–11 the magnetic force $q\mathbf{v} \times \mathbf{B}$ must point radially inward, since it provides the centripetal force. Since $\mathbf{B}$ points into the plane of the paper, $\mathbf{v}$ would have to point to the left at the position shown in the figure if the charge q were positive. However, the charge is an electron, with $q = -e$, which means that $\mathbf{v}$ must point to the right. Thus the charge circulates clockwise as viewed by an observer sighting in the direction of $\mathbf{B}$. ◄

33–7 The Cyclotron

The cyclotron, first put into operation by Ernest Lawrence (1902–1958) in 1932, accelerates charged particles, such as protons or deuterons,* to high energies so that they can be used in atom-smashing experiments. Figure 33–12 shows the University of Pittsburgh cyclotron.

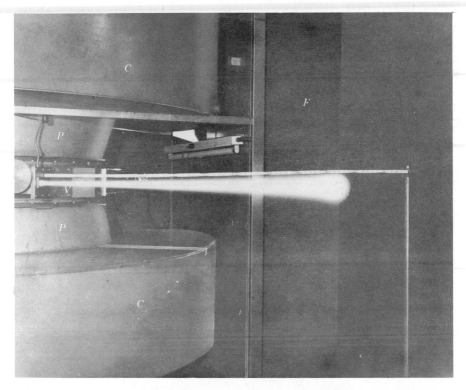

Fig. 33–12 The University of Pittsburgh cyclotron. Note vacuum chamber V, magnet frame F, magnetic pole faces P, magnet coils C, and the deuteron beam emerging into the air of the laboratory. The rule is 6 ft long. (Courtesy A. J. Allen.)

In an *ion source* at the center of the cyclotron molecules of deuterium are bombarded with electrons whose energy is high enough (say 100 ev) so that many positive ions are formed during the collisions. Many of these ions are free deuterons, which enter the cyclotron proper through a small hole in the wall of the ion source and are available to be accelerated.

---

* Deuterons are the nuclei of heavy hydrogen.

The cyclotron uses a modest potential difference for accelerating (say 10^5 volts), but it requires the ion to pass through this potential difference a number of times. To reach 10 Mev with 10^5 volts accelerating potential requires 100 passages. A magnetic field is used to bend the ions around so that they may pass again and again through the same accelerating potential.

Figure 33–13 is a top view of the part of the cyclotron that is inside the vacuum tank marked V in Fig. 33–12. The two D-shaped objects, called *dees*, are made of copper sheet and form part of an electric oscillator which establishes an accelerating potential difference across the gap between the dees. The direction of this potential difference is made to change sign some millions of times per second.

The dees are immersed in a magnetic field ($B \cong 1.6$ webers/meter^2) whose direction is out of the plane of Fig. 33–13. The field is set up by a large electromagnet, marked F in Fig. 33–12. Finally, the space in which the ions move is evacuated to a pressure of about 10^{-6} mm Hg. If this were not done, the ions would continually collide with air molecules.

Suppose that a deuteron, emerging from the ion source, finds the dee that it is facing to be negative; it will accelerate toward this dee and will enter it. Once inside, it is screened from electrical forces by the metal walls of the dees. The magnetic field is not screened by the dees so that the ion bends in a circular path whose radius, which depends on the velocity, is given by Eq. 33–15, or

$$r = \frac{mv}{qB}.$$

After a time t_0 the ion emerges from the dee on the other side of the ion source. Let us assume that the accelerating potential has now changed sign. Thus the ion *again* faces a negative dee, is further accelerated, and again describes a semicircle, of somewhat larger radius (see Eq. 33–15), in the dee.

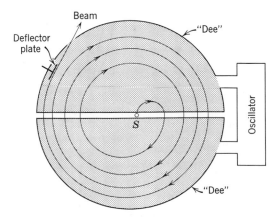

Fig. 33–13 The elements of a cyclotron showing the ion source S and the dees. The deflector plate, held at a suitable negative potential, deflects the particles out of the dee system.

The time of passage through this dee, however, is still t_0. This follows because the period of revolution T of an ion circulating in a magnetic field does not depend on the speed of the ion; see Eq. 33–16. This process goes on until the ion reaches the outer edge of one dee where it is pulled out of the system by a negatively charged deflector plate.

The key to the operation of the cyclotron is that the characteristic frequency f at which the ion circulates in the field must be equal to the fixed frequency f_0 of the electric oscillator, or

$$f = f_0.$$

This *resonance condition* says that if the energy of the circulating ion is to increase energy must be fed to it at a frequency f_0 that is equal to the natural frequency f at which the ion circulates in the field. In the same way we feed energy to a swing by pushing it at a frequency equal to the natural frequency of oscillation of the swing.

From Eq. 33–16 ($f = qB/2\pi m$), we can rewrite the resonance equation as

$$\frac{qB}{2\pi m} = f_0. \tag{33–17}$$

Once we have selected an ion to be accelerated, q/m is fixed; usually the oscillator is designed to work at a single frequency f_0. We then "tune" the cyclotron by varying B until Eq. 33–17 is satisfied and an accelerated beam appears.

The *energy* of the particles produced in the cyclotron depends on the radius R of the dees. From Eq. 33–15 ($r = mv/qB$), the velocity of a particle circulating at this radius is given by

$$v = \frac{qBR}{m}.$$

The kinetic energy is then

$$K = \tfrac{1}{2}mv^2 = \frac{q^2 B^2 R^2}{2m}. \tag{33–18}$$

▶ **Example 7.** The University of Pittsburgh cyclotron has an oscillator frequency of 12×10^6 cycles/sec and a dee radius of 21 in. (*a*) What value of magnetic induction B is needed to accelerate deuterons?

From Eq. 33–17, $f_0 = qB/2\pi m$, so that

$$B = \frac{2\pi f_0 m}{q} = \frac{(2\pi)(12 \times 10^6/\text{sec})(3.3 \times 10^{-27}\ \text{kg})}{1.6 \times 10^{-19}\ \text{coul}} = 1.6\ \text{webers/meter}^2.$$

Note that the deuteron has the same charge as the proton but (very closely) twice the mass.

(*b*) What deuteron energy results?

From Eq. 33–18,

$$K = \frac{q^2 B^2 R^2}{2m} = \frac{(1.6 \times 10^{-19}\ \text{coul})^2 (1.6\ \text{webers/meter}^2)^2 (21 \times 0.0254\ \text{meter})^2}{(2)(3.3 \times 10^{-27}\ \text{kg})}$$

$$= (2.8 \times 10^{-12}\ \text{joule}) \left(\frac{1\ \text{ev}}{1.6 \times 10^{-19}\ \text{joule}}\right) = 17\ \text{Mev}. \qquad ◀$$

The cyclotron fails to operate at high energies because one of its assumptions, that the frequency of rotation of an ion circulating in a magnetic field is independent of its speed, is true only for speeds much less than that of light. As the particle speed increases, we must use the *relativistic mass m* in Eq. 33–16. The relativistic mass increases with velocity (Eq. 8–13) so that at high enough speeds f decreases with velocity. Thus the ions get out of step with the electric oscillator, and eventually the energy of the circulating ion stops increasing.

Another difficulty associated with the acceleration of particles to high energies is that the size of the magnet that would be required to guide such particles in a circular path is very large. For a 30-Bev proton, for example, in a field of 15,000 gauss the radius of curvature is 65 meters. A magnet of the cyclotron type of this size (about 430 ft in diameter) would be prohibitively expensive. Incidentally, a 30-Bev proton has a speed equal to 0.99998 that of light.

Both the relativistic and the economic limitations have been removed by techniques that can be understood in terms of Eq. 33–17 in which m is now taken to be the relativistic mass, given by Eq. 8–13, or

$$m = \frac{m_0}{\sqrt{1 - (v/c)^2}},$$

v being the speed of the particle and c being that of light.

As the particle speed increases, the relativistic mass m also increases. To maintain the equality in Eq. 33–17, and thus insure resonance, one may decrease the oscillator frequency f_0 as the particle (assumed to be a proton) accelerates in such a way that the product $f_0 m$ remains constant. Accelerators that use this technique are called *synchrocyclotrons*.

To remove the magnet cost limitation one can vary *both* B and f_0 in a cyclic fashion in such a way that not only is Eq. 33–17 satisfied at all times but the particle orbit radius remains constant during the acceleration process. This permits the use of an annular (or ring-shaped) magnet, rather than the conventional cyclotron type, at great saving in cost. With the *two* variables B and f_0 at our disposal, it is possible to preserve *two* equalities during the acceleration process, one being Eq. 33–17 and the other being the relation

$$v = \omega_0 R_0 = (2\pi f_0)R_0$$

in which R_0 is the desired (fixed) orbit radius. Accelerators that use this technique are called *synchrotrons*. Table 33–2 shows some characteristics of the accel-

Table 33–2

THE CERN PROTON SYNCHROTRON

Orbit diameter	560 ft
Vacuum chamber cross section	5.5 in. $\times$ 2.7 in.
Maximum magnetic field	1.4 webers/meter^2
Frequency range per cycle	7 mc/sec
Pulse rate	20/min
Maximum proton energy	28 Bev
Energy gain per cycle	54 kev
Distance traveled by a proton	5×10^4 miles
Protons per pulse	10^{11}
Cost	$\$28 \times 10^6$

erator built at Geneva, Switzerland, by the European Council for Nuclear Research (CERN), and embodying these principles.

33–8   Thomson's Experiment

In 1897 J. J. Thomson, working at the Cavendish Laboratory in Cambridge, measured the ratio of the charge e of the electron to its mass m by observing its deflection in combined electric and magnetic fields. The discovery of the electron is usually said to date from this historic experiment, although H. A. Lorentz and P. Zeeman (1865–1943), during the previous year, had measured this same quantity for electrons bound in atoms, using a method entirely different from Thomson's.

In Fig. 33–14, which is a modernized version of Thomson's apparatus, electrons are emitted from hot filament F and accelerated by an applied potential difference V. They then enter a region in which they move at right angles to an electric field $\mathbf{E}$ and a field of magnetic induction $\mathbf{B}$; $\mathbf{E}$ and $\mathbf{B}$ are themselves at right angles to each other. The beam is made visible as a spot of light when it strikes fluorescent screen S. The entire region in which the electrons move is highly evacuated so that collisions with air molecules will not occur.

The resultant force on a charged particle moving through an electric and a magnetic field is given by Eq. 33–4, or

$$\mathbf{F} = q_0\mathbf{E} + q_0\mathbf{v} \times \mathbf{B}.$$

Study of Fig. 33–14 shows that the electric field deflects the particle upward and the magnetic field deflects it downward. If these deflecting forces are to

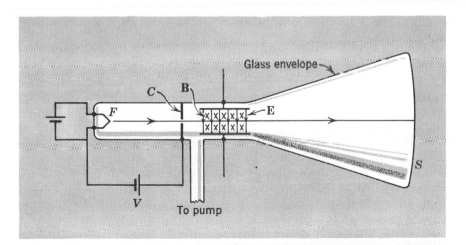

Fig. 33–14   Electrons from the heated filament F are accelerated by a potential difference V and pass through a hole in the screen C. After passing through a region in which perpendicular electric and magnetic fields are present, they strike the fluorescent screen S.

cancel (that is, if $\mathbf{F} = 0$), this equation, for this problem, reduces to

$$eE = evB$$

or $$E = vB. \tag{33–19}$$

Thus for a given electron speed v the condition for zero deflection can be satisfied by adjusting E or B.

Thomson's procedure was (a) note the position of the undeflected beam spot, with $\mathbf{E}$ and $\mathbf{B}$ both equal to zero; (b) apply a fixed electric field $\mathbf{E}$, measuring on the fluorescent screen the deflection so caused; and (c) apply a magnetic field and adjust its value until the beam deflection is restored to zero.

In Section 27–5 we saw that the deflection y of an electron in a purely electric field (step b), measured at the far edge of the deflecting plates, is given by Eq. 27–9, or, with small changes in notation,

$$y = \frac{eEl^2}{2mv^2},$$

where v is the electron speed and l is the length of the deflecting plates; y is not measurable directly, but it may be calculated from the measured displacement of the spot on the screen if the geometry of the apparatus is known. Thus y, E, and l are known; the ratio e/m and the velocity v are unknown. We cannot calculate e/m until we have found the velocity, which is the purpose of step c above.

If (step c) the electric force is set equal and opposite to the magnetic force, the net force is zero and we can write (Eq. 33–19)

$$v = \frac{E}{B}.$$

Substituting this equation into the equation for y and solving for the ratio e/m leads to

$$\frac{e}{m} = \frac{2yE}{B^2l^2}, \tag{33–20}$$

in which all the quantities on the right can be measured. Thomson's value for e/m was 1.7×10^{11} coul/kg, in excellent agreement with the modern value of 1.75890×10^{11} coul/kg.

QUESTIONS

1. Of the three vectors in the equation $\mathbf{F} = q\mathbf{v} \times \mathbf{B}$, which pairs are always at right angles? Which may have any angle between them?

2. Why do we not simply define the magnetic induction $\mathbf{B}$ to point in the direction of the magnetic force that acts on the moving charge?

3. Imagine that you are sitting in a room with your back to one wall and that an electron beam, traveling horizontally from the back wall toward the front wall, is deflected to your right. What is the direction of the field of magnetic induction that exists in the room?

4. If an electron is not deflected in passing through a certain region of space, can we be sure that there is no magnetic field in that region?

5. If a moving electron is deflected sideways in passing through a certain region of space, can we be sure that a magnetic field exists in that region?

6. A beam of protons is deflected sideways. Could this deflection be caused (a) by an electric field? (b) By a magnetic field? (c) If either could be responsible, how would you be able to tell which was present?

7. A conductor, even though it is carrying a current, has zero net charge. Why, then, does a magnetic field exert a force on it?

8. Equation 33–11 ($\tau = \mu \times B$) shows that there is no torque on a current loop in an external magnetic field if the angle between the axis of the loop and the field is (a) 0° or (b) 180°. Discuss the nature of the equilibrium (that is, is it stable, neutral, or unstable?) for these two positions.

9. In Example 4 we showed that the work required to turn a current loop end for end in an external magnetic field is $2\mu B$. Does this hold no matter what the original orientation of the loop was?

10. Imagine that the room in which you are seated is filled with a uniform magnetic field with **B** pointing vertically upward. A circular loop of wire has its plane horizontal. For what direction of current in the loop, as viewed from above, will the loop be in stable equilibrium with respect to forces and torques of magnetic origin?

11. A rectangular current loop is in an arbitrary orientation in an external magnetic field. Is any work required to rotate the loop about an axis perpendicular to its plane?

12. (a) In measuring Hall potential differences, why must we be careful that points x and y in Fig. 33–10 are exactly opposite to each other? (b) f one of the contacts is movable, what procedure might we follow in adjusting it to make sure that the two points are properly located?

13. A uniform magnetic field fills a certain cubical region of space. Can an electron be fired into this cube from the outside in such a way that it will travel in a closed circular path inside the cube?

14. Imagine the room in which you are seated to be filled with a uniform magnetic field with **B** pointing vertically downward. At the center of the room two electrons are suddenly projected horizontally with the same speed but in opposite directions. (a) Discuss their motions. (b) Discuss their motions if one particle is an electron and one a positron.

15. In Fig. 33–4, why are the low-energy electron tracks spirals? That is, why does the radius of curvature change in the constant magnetic field in which the chamber is immersed?

16. What are the primary functions of (a) the electric field and (b) the magnetic field in the cyclotron?

17. For Thomson's e/m experiment to work properly (Section 33–8), is it essential that the electrons have a fairly constant speed?

PROBLEMS

1. The electrons in the beam of a television tube have an energy of 12 kev. The tube is oriented so that the electrons move horizontally from south to north. The vertical component of the earth's magnetic field points down and has $B = 5.5 \times 10^{-5}$ weber/meter^2. (a) In what direction will the beam deflect? (b) What is the acceleration of a given electron? (c) How far will the beam deflect in moving 20 cm through the television tube?

2. In a nuclear experiment a 1.0-Mev proton moves in a uniform magnetic field in a circular path. What energy must (a) an alpha particle and (b) a deuteron have if they are to circulate in the same orbit?

3. A wire 1.0 meter long carries a current of 10 amp and makes an angle of 30° with a uniform magnetic field with $B = 1.5$ webers/meter^2. Calculate the magnitude and direction of the force on the wire.

4. A wire of 60 cm length and mass 10 gm is suspended by a pair of flexible leads in a magnetic field of induction 0.40 weber/meter². What are the magnitude and direction of the current required to remove the tension in the supporting leads? See Fig. 33–15.

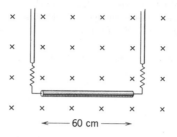

Fig. 33–15

5. Express magnetic induction B and magnetic flux Φ in terms of the fundamental dimensions M, L, T, and Q (mass, length, time, and charge).

6. A metal wire of mass m slides without friction on two rails spaced a distance d apart, as in Fig. 33–16. The track lies in a verti-

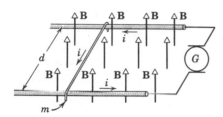

Fig. 33–16

cal uniform field of magnetic induction **B**. A *constant current* i flows from generator G along one rail, across the wire, and back down the other rail. Find the velocity (speed and direction) of the wire as a function of time, assuming it to be at rest at $t = 0$.

7. A U-shaped wire of mass m and length l is immersed with its two ends in mercury (Fig. 33–17). The wire is in a homogeneous field of magnetic induction **B**. If a charge, that is, a current pulse $q = \int i\, dt$, is sent through the wire, the wire will jump up. Calculate, from the height h that the wire reaches, the size of the charge or current pulse, assuming that the time of the current pulse is very small in comparison with the time of flight. Make use of the fact that impulse of force equals $\int F\, dt$, which equals mv. (Hint: Try to relate $\int i\, dt$ to $\int F\, dt$.) Evaluate q for $B = 0.1$ weber/meter², $m = 10$ gm, $l = 20$ cm, and $h = 3$ meters.

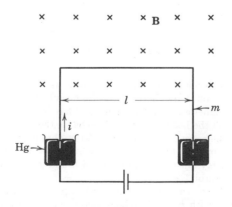

Fig. 33–17

8. Figure 33–18 shows a wire ring of radius a at right angles to the general direction of a radially symmetric diverging magnetic field. The magnetic induction at the ring is everywhere of the same magnitude B, and its direction at the ring is everywhere at an angle θ with a normal to the plane of the ring. The twisted lead wires have no effect on the problem. Find the magnitude and direction of the force the field exerts on the ring if the ring carries a current i as shown in the figure.

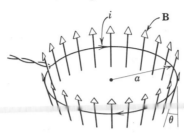

Fig. 33–18

9. A copper rod weighing 0.30 lb rests on two rails 1.0 ft apart and carries a current of 50 amp from one rail to the other. The coefficient of starting friction is 0.60. What is the smallest magnetic field that would cause the bar to slide and what is its direction?

10. Figure 33–19 shows a wire of arbitrary shape carrying a current i between points a and b. The wire lies in a plane at right angles to a uniform field of magnetic induction **B**. Prove that the force on the wire is the same as that on a straight wire carrying a current i directly from a to b. (Hint: Replace the wire by a series of "steps" parallel and perpendicular to the straight line joining a and b.)

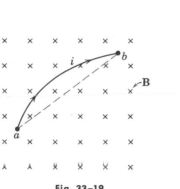

Fig. 33–19

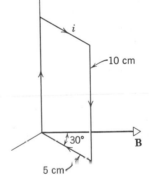

Fig. 33–20

11. Figure 33–20 shows a rectangular twenty-turn loop of wire, 10 cm by 5.0 cm. It carries a current of 0.10 amp and is hinged at one side. What torque (direction and magnitude) acts on the loop if it is mounted with its plane at an angle of 30° to the direction of a uniform field of magnetic induction 0.50 weber/meter²?

12. Prove that the relation $\tau = NAiB \sin \theta$ holds for closed loops of arbitrary shape. (Hint: Replace the loop of arbitrary shape by an assembly of adjacent long, thin—approximately rectangular—loops which are equivalent to it as far as the distribution of current is concerned.)

13. A length L of wire carries a current i. Show that if the wire is formed into a circular coil the maximum torque in a given magnetic field is developed when the coil has *one* turn only and the maximum torque has the value

$$\tau = \frac{1}{4\pi} L^2 iB.$$

14. Figure 33–21 shows a wooden cylinder with a mass m of 0.25 kg, a radius R, and a length l of 0.1 meter with N equal to ten turns of wire wrapped around it longitudinally, so that the plane of the wire loop contains the axis of the cylinder. What is the least current through the loop that will prevent the cylinder from rolling down an inclined plane whose surface is inclined at an angle θ to the horizontal, in the presence of a vertical field of magnetic induction 0.5 weber/meter², if the plane of the windings is parallel to the inclined plane?

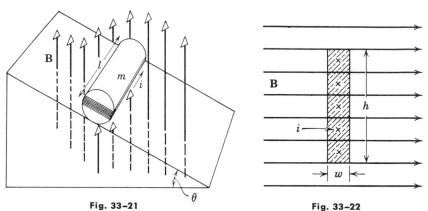

Fig. 33–21   Fig. 33–22

15. A current i, indicated by the crosses in Fig. 33–22, is established in a strip of copper of height h and width w. A uniform field of magnetic induction **B** is applied at right angles to the strip. (*a*) Calculate the drift speed v_d for the electrons. (*b*) What are the magnitude and direction of the magnetic force **F** acting on the electrons? (*c*) What would the magnitude and direction of a homogeneous electric field **E** have to be in order to counterbalance the effect of the magnetic field? (*d*) What is the voltage V necessary between two sides of the conductor in order to create this field **E**? Between which sides of the conductor would this voltage have to be applied? (*e*) If no electric field is applied *from the outside*, the electrons will be pushed somewhat to one side and therefore will give rise to a uniform electric field $\mathbf{E}_H$ across the conductor until the forces of this electrostatic field $\mathbf{E}_H$ balance the magnetic forces encountered in part (*b*). What will be the magnitude and direction of the field $\mathbf{E}_H$? Assume that n, the number of conduction electrons per unit volume, is 1.1×10^{29}/meter³ and that $h = 0.02$ meter, $w = 0.1$ cm, $i = 50$ amp, and $B = 2$ webers/meter².

16. (*a*) Show that the ratio of the Hall electric field E_H to the electric field E responsible for the current is

$$\frac{E_H}{E} = \frac{B}{ne\rho}.$$

(*b*) What is the angle between $\mathbf{E}_H$ and $\mathbf{E}$? (*c*) Evaluate this ratio for the conditions of Example 5.

17. A proton, a deuteron, and an α-particle, accelerated through the same potential difference, enter a region of uniform magnetic field, moving at right angles to **B**. (*a*) Compare their kinetic energies. (*b*) If the radius of the proton's circular path is 10 cm, what are the radii of the deuteron and the α-particle paths?

18. A proton, a deuteron, and an α-particle with the same kinetic energies enter a region of uniform magnetic field, moving at right angles to **B**. Compare the radii of their circular paths.

19. An α-particle travels in a circular path of radius 0.45 meter in a magnetic field with $B = 1.2$ webers/meter². Calculate (*a*) its speed, (*b*) its period of revolution, (*c*) its kinetic energy, and (*d*) the potential difference through which it would have to be accelerated to achieve this energy.

20. An electron is accelerated through 15,000 volts and is then allowed to circulate at right angles to a uniform magnetic field with B = 250 gauss. What is its path radius?

21. Electrons are observed to be ejected in various directions with negligible speed from the negative plate of a parallel-plate capacitor when the plate is illuminated by light of a certain wavelength (photoelectric effect). The plates are separated by a distance d and a potential difference V is maintained between them. Show that none of these electrons will reach the positive plate if a magnetic field is applied at right angles to the electric field and the magnetic induction has a value

$$B > \left(\frac{2Vm}{ed^2}\right)^{\frac{1}{2}},$$

in which m and e are the electron mass and charge, respectively.

22. Show that the radius of curvature of a charged particle moving at right angles to a magnetic field is proportional to its momentum.

23. What is the smallest magnetic field (magnitude and direction) that can be set up at the equator to permit a proton of speed 1.0×10^7 meters/sec to circulate around the earth?

24. A deuteron in a large cyclotron is moving in a magnetic field with B = 1.5 webers/meter^2 and an orbit radius of 2.0 meters. Because of a grazing collision with a target, the deuteron breaks up, with a negligible loss of kinetic energy, into a proton and a neutron. Discuss the subsequent motions of each. Assume that the deuteron energy is shared equally by the proton and neutron at breakup.

25. A 2-kev positron is projected into a uniform field of induction B of 0.10 weber/meter^2 with its velocity vector making an angle of 89° with **B**. Convince yourself that the path will be a helix, its axis being the direction of **B**. Find the period, the pitch p, and the radius r of the helix; see Fig. 33–23.

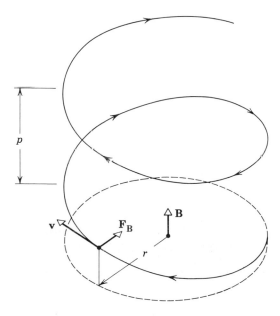

Fig. 33-23

26. (a) In a magnetic field with B = 0.50 weber/meter^2, for what path radius will an electron circulate at 0.1 the speed of light? (b) What will its kinetic energy be?

27. *Time-of-flight spectrometer.* S. A. Goudsmit has devised a method for measuring accurately the masses of heavy ions by timing their period of circulation in a known magnetic field. A singly charged ion of iodine makes 7 rev in a field of 4.5×10^{-2} weber/meter^2 in about 1.29×10^{-3} sec. What (approximately) is its mass in kilograms? Actually, the mass measurements are carried out to much greater accuracy than these approximate data suggest.

28. *Mass spectrometer.* Figure 33–24 shows an arrangement used by Dempster to measure the masses of ions. An ion of mass M and charge $+q$ is produced essentially at rest in source S, a chamber in which a gas discharge is taking place. The ion is accelerated by potential difference V and allowed to enter a field of magnetic induction $\mathbf{B}$. In the field it moves in a semicircle, striking a photographic plate at distance x from the entry slit and being recorded. Show that the mass M is given by

$$M = \frac{B^2 q}{8V} x^2.$$

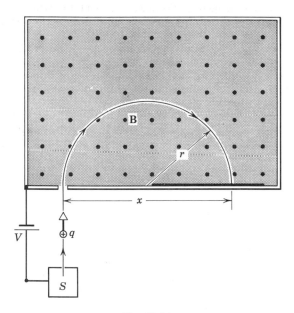

Fig. 33–24

29. *Zeeman effect.* In Bohr's theory of the hydrogen atom the electron can be thought of as moving in a circular orbit of radius r about the proton. Suppose that such an atom is placed in a magnetic field, with the plane of the orbit at right angles to $\mathbf{B}$. (a) If the electron is circulating clockwise, as viewed by an observer sighting along $\mathbf{B}$, will the angular frequency increase or decrease? (b) What if the electron is circulating counterclockwise? Assume that the orbit radius does not change. [Hint: The centripetal force is now partially electric ($\mathbf{F}_E$) and partially magnetic ($\mathbf{F}_B$) in origin.]

30. In Problem 29 show that the change in frequency of rotation caused by the magnetic field is given approximately by

$$\Delta f = \pm \frac{Be}{4\pi m}.$$

Such frequency shifts were actually observed by Zeeman in 1896. (Hint: Calculate the frequency of rotation without the magnetic field and also with it. Subtract, bearing in mind that because the effect of the magnetic field is very small some—but not all—terms containing B can be set equal to zero with little error.)

31. The University of Pittsburgh cyclotron is normally adjusted to accelerate deuterons. (a) What energy of protons could it produce, using the same oscillator frequency as that used for deuterons? (b) What magnetic induction would be required? (c) What energy of protons could be produced if the magnetic induction was left at the value used for deuterons? (d) What oscillator frequency would then be required? (e) Answer the same questions for α-particles.

32. Estimate the total path length traversed by a deuteron in the University of Pittsburgh cyclotron during the acceleration process. Assume an accelerating potential between the dees of 80,000 volts.

33. In a synchrocyclotron producing 400-Mev protons, what must the ratio be of the oscillator frequency at the beginning of an accelerating cycle to that at the end? Such a proton has a speed of 0.70c, where c is the speed of light.

34. A 10-kev electron moving horizontally enters a region of space in which there is a downward-directed electric field of magnitude 100 volts/cm. (a) What are the magnitude and direction of the (smallest) field of magnetic induction that will allow the electron to continue to move horizontally? Ignore gravitational forces, which are rather small. (b) Is it possible for a proton to pass through this combination of fields undeflected? If so, under what circumstances?

35. An electric field of 1500 volts/meter and a magnetic field of 0.40 weber/meter² act on a moving electron to produce no force. (a) Calculate the minimum electron speed v. (b) Draw the vectors **E**, **B**, and **v**.

Ampère's Law

34–1 Ampère's Law

One class of problems involving magnetic fields, dealt with in Chapter 33, concerns the forces exerted by a magnetic field on a moving charge or on a current-carrying conductor and the torque exerted on a magnetic dipole. A second class concerns the *production* of a magnetic field by a current-carrying conductor or by moving charges. This chapter deals with problems of this second class.

The discovery that currents produce magnetic effects was made by Oersted in 1820. Figure 34–1, which shows a wire surrounded by a number of small magnets, illustrates a modification of his experiment. If there is no current in the wire, all the magnets are aligned with the earth's magnetic field. When a strong current is present, the magnets point so as to suggest that the magnetic lines of induction form closed circles around the wire. This view is strengthened by the experiment of Fig. 34–2, which shows iron filings on a horizontal glass plate, through the center of which a current-carrying conductor passes.

Today we write the quantitative relationship between current i and the magnetic field $\mathbf{B}$ as

$$\oint \mathbf{B} \cdot d\mathbf{l} = \mu_0 i, \qquad (34\text{–}1)$$

which is known as *Ampère's law*. Ampère, being an advocate of the action-at-a-distance point of view, did not formulate his results in terms of fields; this was first done by Maxwell. Ampère's law, including an important ex-

Fig. 34–1 An array of compass needles near a wire carrying a strong current. The black ends of the compass needles are their north poles. The dot shows the current emerging from the page. As usual, the direction of a current is taken as the direction of flow of positive charge.

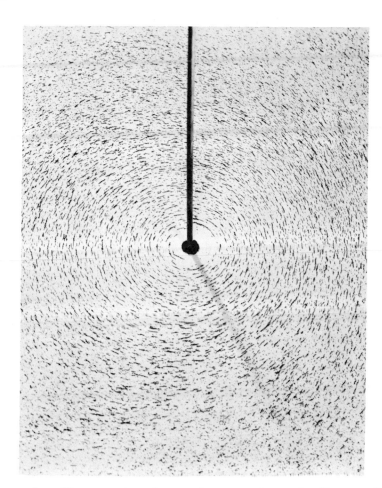

Fig. 34–2 Iron filings around a wire carrying a strong current. (Courtesy Physical Science Study Committee.)

tension of it made later by Maxwell, is one of the basic equations of electromagnetism (see Table 38–3).

We can gain an appreciation of the way Ampère's law developed historically by considering a hypothetical experiment which has, in fact, much in common with experiments that were actually carried out. The experiment consists of measuring **B** at various distances r from a long straight wire of circular cross section and carrying a current i. This can be done by making quantitative the qualitative observation of Fig. 34–1.

Let us put a small compass needle a distance r from the wire. Such a needle, a small magnetic dipole, tends to line up with an external magnetic field, with its north pole pointing in the direction of **B**. Figure 34–1 makes it clear that **B** at the site of the dipole is tangent to a circle of radius r centered on the wire.

If the current in the wire of Fig. 34–1 is reversed in direction, all the compass needles would reverse end-for-end. This experimental result leads to the "right-hand rule" for finding the direction of **B** near a wire carrying a current i: *Grasp the wire with the right hand, the thumb pointing in the direction of the current. The fingers will curl around the wire in the direction of* **B**.

Let us now turn the dipole through an angle θ from its equilibrium position. To do this, we must exert an external torque just large enough to overcome the restoring torque $\boldsymbol{\tau}$ that will act on the dipole. $\boldsymbol{\tau}$, θ, and **B** are related by Eq. 33–11 ($\boldsymbol{\tau} = \boldsymbol{\mu} \times \mathbf{B}$), which can be written in terms of magnitudes as

$$\tau = \mu B \sin \theta \tag{34–2}$$

and in which μ is the magnitude of the magnetic moment of the dipole, θ being the angle between the vectors $\boldsymbol{\mu}$ and **B**. Even though we may not know the value of μ for the compass needle, we may take it to be a constant, independent of the position or orientation of the needle. Thus by measuring τ and θ in Eq. 34–2 we can obtain a *relative* measure of B for various distances r and for various currents i in the wire. The experimental results can be described by the proportionality

$$B \propto \frac{i}{r}. \tag{34–3}$$

We can convert this proportionality into an equality by inserting a proportionality constant. As for Coulomb's law, and for similar reasons (see Section 26–4), we do not write this constant simply as k but in a more complex form, namely $\mu_0/2\pi$, in which μ_0 is called the *permeability constant*.* Equation 34–3 then becomes

$$B = \frac{\mu_0 i}{2\pi r}, \tag{34–4}$$

which we choose to write in the form

$$(B)(2\pi r) = \mu_0 i. \tag{34–5}$$

---

* μ_0 has no connection with the dipole moment μ that appears in Eq. 34–2.

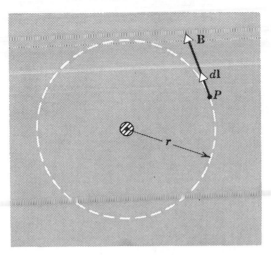

Fig. 34-3 A circular path of integration surrounding a wire. The central dot suggests a current i in the wire emerging from the page. Note that the angle between **B** and $d\mathbf{l}$ is zero so that $\mathbf{B} \cdot d\mathbf{l} = B \, dl$.

The left side of Eq. 34-5 can easily be shown to be $\oint \mathbf{B} \cdot d\mathbf{l}$ for a path consisting of a circle of radius r centered on the wire. For all points on this circle **B** has the same (constant) magnitude B and $d\mathbf{l}$, which is always tangent to the path of integration and points in the same direction as **B**, as Fig. 34-3 shows. Thus

$$\oint \mathbf{B} \cdot d\mathbf{l} = \oint B \, dl = B \oint dl = (B)(2\pi r),$$

$\oint dl$ being simply the circumference of the circle. *In this special case*, therefore, we can write the experimentally observed connection between the field and the current as

$$\oint \mathbf{B} \cdot d\mathbf{l} = \mu_0 i, \tag{34-1}$$

which is Ampère's law. A host of other experiments suggests that Eq. 34-1 is true in general * for *any* magnetic field configuration, for *any* assembly of currents, and for *any* path of integration.

In applying Ampère's law in the general case, we construct a *closed linear path* in the magnetic field as shown in Fig. 34-4. This path is divided into elements of length $d\mathbf{l}$, and for each element the quantity $\mathbf{B} \cdot d\mathbf{l}$ is evaluated. Recall that $\mathbf{B} \cdot d\mathbf{l}$ has the magnitude $B \, dl \cos \theta$ and can be interpreted as the product of dl and the component of **B** ($= B \cos \theta$) parallel to $d\mathbf{l}$. The inte-

---

* If a *time-varying electric flux* exists within the path of integration, Eq. 34-1 must be extended in a way first done by Maxwell (see Section 38-7). In this chapter we assume that such situations do not arise.

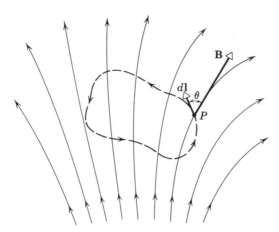

Fig. 34–4 A path of integration in a magnetic field.

gral is the sum of the quantities **B**·d**l** for all path elements in the complete loop. The term i on the right of Eq. 34 1 is the *net* current that passes through the area bounded by the closed path.

The permeability constant in Ampère's law has an assigned value of

$$\mu_0 = 4\pi \times 10^{-7} \text{ weber/amp-m.}$$

Both this and the permittivity constant (ϵ_0) occur in electromagnetic formulas when the mks system of units is used.

The student may wonder why ϵ_0 in Coulomb's law is a measured quantity, whereas μ_0 in Ampère's law is an assigned quantity. The answer is that the ampere, which is the mks unit for the current i in Ampère's law, is defined by a laboratory technique (the *current balance*) that involves forces exerted by magnetic fields and in which this same constant μ_0 appears. In effect, as we show in detail in Section 34–4, the size of the current that we agree to define as one ampere is adjusted so that μ_0 may have exactly the value assigned to it above. In Coulomb's law, on the other hand, the quantities **F**, q, and r are measured in ways in which the constant ϵ_0 plays no role. This constant must then take on the particular value that makes the left side of Coulomb's law equal to the right side; no arbitrary assignment is possible.

34–2 B Near a Long Wire

We have seen that the lines of magnetic induction for a long straight wire carrying a current i are concentric circles centered on the wire and that B at a distance r from the wire is given by Eq. 34–4:

$$B = \frac{\mu_0 i}{2\pi r}. \tag{34–4}$$

We may regard this as an experimental result consistent with, and readily derivable from, Ampère's law.

It is interesting to compare Eq. 34–4 with the expression for the electric field near a long line of charge, or

$$E = \frac{1}{2\pi\epsilon_0}\frac{\lambda}{r}. \tag{28–7}$$

In each case there are multiplying constants, namely $\mu_0/2\pi$ and $1/2\pi\epsilon_0$, and factors describing the device responsible for the field, namely i and λ. Finally, each field varies as $1/r$.

Equation 28–7 may be derived from Gauss's law by relating the electric field at a Gaussian surface to the net charge within this surface. The (surface) integral in Gauss's law is evaluated for a closed cylindrical surface to which the lines of **E** are everywhere perpendicular.

Equation 34–4 may be derived from Ampère's law by relating the magnetic field at a path of integration to the net current that pierces this path. The (line) integral in Ampère's law is evaluated for a closed circular path to which the lines of **B** are everywhere tangent.

▶ **Example 1** Derive an expression for **B** at a distance r from the center of a long cylindrical wire of radius R, where $r < R$. The wire carries a current i_0, distributed uniformly over the cross section of the wire.

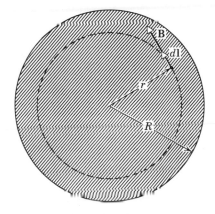

Fig. 34–5 Example 1. A circular path of integration inside a wire. A current i_0, distributed uniformly over the cross section of the wire, emerges from the page.

Figure 34–5 shows a circular path of integration inside the wire. Symmetry suggests that **B** is tangent to the path as shown. Ampère's law,

$$\oint \mathbf{B}\cdot d\mathbf{l} = \mu_0 i,$$

gives

$$(B)(2\pi r) = \mu_0 i_0 \frac{\pi r^2}{\pi R^2},$$

since only the fraction of the current that passes through the path of integration is included in the factor i on the right. Solving for B and dropping the subscript on the current yields

$$B = \frac{\mu_0 i r}{2\pi R^2}.$$

At the surface of the wire ($r = R$) this equation reduces to the same expression as that found by putting $r = R$ in Eq. 34–4 ($B = \mu_0 i/2\pi R$).

Example 2. Figure 34–6 shows a flat strip of copper of width a and negligible thickness carrying a current i. Find the magnetic field at a distance R from the center of the strip, at right angles to the strip.

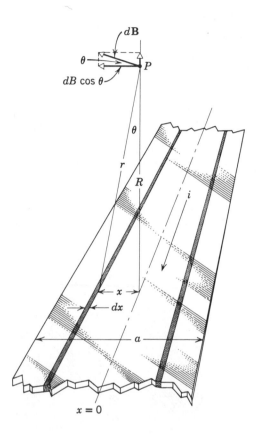

Fig. 34–6 Example 2. A flat strip of width a carries a current i.

Let us subdivide the strip into long infinitesimal filaments of width dx, each of which may be treated as a wire carrying a current di given by $i(dx/a)$. The field contribution dB at point P in Fig. 34–6 is given, for the element shown, by the differential form of Eq. 34–4, or

$$dB = \frac{\mu_0}{2\pi} \frac{di}{r} = \frac{\mu_0}{2\pi} \frac{i(dx/a)}{R \sec \theta}.$$

Note that the vector $d\mathbf{B}$ is at right angles to the line marked r.

Only the horizontal component of $d\mathbf{B}$, namely $dB \cos \theta$, is effective, the vertical component being canceled by the contribution associated with a symmetrically located filament on the other side of the origin. Thus B at point P is given by the (scalar) integral

$$B = \int dB \cos \theta = \int \frac{\mu_0 i(dx/a)}{2\pi R \sec \theta} \cos \theta$$

$$= \frac{\mu_0 i}{2\pi a R} \int \frac{dx}{\sec^2 \theta}.$$

The variables x and θ are not independent, being related by

$$x = R \tan \theta$$

or
$$dx = R \sec^2 \theta \, d\theta.$$

Bearing in mind that the limits on θ are $\pm \tan^{-1}(a/2R)$ and eliminating dx from this expression for B, we find

$$B = \frac{\mu_0 i}{2\pi a R} \int \frac{R \sec^2 \theta \, d\theta}{\sec^2 \theta}$$

$$= \frac{\mu_0 i}{2\pi a} \int_{-\tan^{-1}a/2R}^{+\tan^{-1}a/2R} d\theta = \frac{\mu_0 i}{\pi a} \tan^{-1} \frac{a}{2R}.$$

At points far from the strip, $a/2R$ is a small angle, for which $\tan^{-1}\alpha \cong \alpha$. Thus we have, as an approximate result,

$$B \cong \frac{\mu_0 i}{\pi a}\left(\frac{a}{2R}\right) = \frac{\mu_0}{2\pi}\frac{i}{R}.$$

This result is expected because at distant points the strip cannot be distinguished from a cylindrical wire (see Eq. 34–4). ◀

34–3 Magnetic Lines of Induction

Figure 34–7 shows the lines of magnetic induction representing the field of **B** near a long straight wire. Note the increase in the spacing of the lines with increasing distance from the wire. This represents the $1/r$ decrease in B predicted by Eq. 34–4.

Figure 34–8 shows the resultant lines of magnetic induction associated with a current in a wire that is oriented at right angles to a uniform *external* field $\mathbf{B}_e$. At any point the resultant magnetic induction **B** will be the vector sum of $\mathbf{B}_e$ and $\mathbf{B}_i$, where $\mathbf{B}_i$ is the magnetic induction set up by the current in the wire. The fields $\mathbf{B}_e$ and $\mathbf{B}_i$ tend to cancel above the wire and to re-enforce each other below the wire. At point P in Fig. 34–8 $\mathbf{B}_e$ and $\mathbf{B}_i$ cancel exactly. Very near the wire the field is represented by circular lines and is essentially $\mathbf{B}_i$.

Michael Faraday, who originated the concept of lines of induction, endowed them with more reality than they are currently given. He imagined

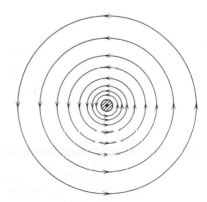

Fig. 34–7 Lines of **B** near a long cylindrical wire. A current i, suggested by the central dot, emerges from the page.

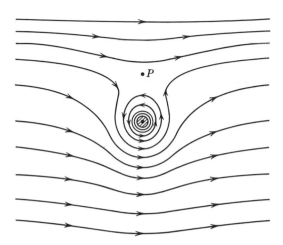

Fig. 34–8 Lines of **B** near a long current-carrying wire immersed in a uniform external field **B**$_e$ that points to the right. The current i is emerging from the page.

that, like stretched rubber bands, they represent the site of mechanical forces. On this picture can we not visualize that the wire in Fig. 34–8 will be pushed up? Today we use lines of induction largely for purposes of visualization. For quantitative calculations we use the field vectors, describing the force on the wire in Fig. 34–8, for example, from the relation $\mathbf{F} = i\mathbf{l} \times \mathbf{B}$.

In applying this relation to Fig. 34–8, we recall that **B** is always the *external field* in which the wire is immersed; that is, it is **B**$_e$ and thus points to the right. Since **l** points out of the page, the magnetic force on the wire ($= i\mathbf{l} \times \mathbf{B}_e$) does indeed point up. It is necessary to use only the external field in such calculations because the field set up by the current in the wire cannot exert a force on the wire, just as the gravitational field of the earth cannot exert a force on the earth itself but only on another body. In Fig. 34–7, for example, there is no magnetic force on the wire because no external magnetic field is present.

Faraday's idea of lines of induction was instrumental in overthrowing the older action-at-a-distance theory of magnetic (and electric) attraction. Like many new ideas, it was not immediately accepted. In 1851, for example, Faraday wrote:

> I cannot refrain from again expressing my conviction of the truthfulness of the representation, which the idea of lines of force affords in regard to magnetic action. All the points that are experimentally established in regard to that action—i.e., all that is not hypothetical—appear to be well and truly represented by it.

On the other hand, four years later another well-known British scientist, Sir George Airy, wrote:

> I declare that I can hardly imagine anyone who practically and numerically knows this agreement [with the action-at-a-distance theory] to hesitate an instant in the choice between this simple and precise action, on the one hand, and anything so vague as lines of force, on the other hand.

34–4   Two Parallel Conductors

Figure 34–9 shows two long parallel wires separated by a distance d and carrying currents i_a and i_b. It is an experimental fact, noted by Ampère only one week after word of Oersted's experiments reached Paris, that two such conductors attract each other.

Some of Ampère's colleagues thought that in view of Oersted's experiment this attraction between two conductors was an obvious result and did not need to be proved. They reasoned that if wire a and wire b each exert forces on a compass needle they should exert forces on each other. This conclusion is wrong. When he heard it, Arago, a contemporary of Ampère, drew two iron keys from his pocket and replied, "Each of these keys attracts a magnet. Do you believe that they therefore also attract each other?"

Wire a in Fig. 34–9 will produce a field of induction $\mathbf{B}_a$ at all nearby points. The magnitude of $\mathbf{B}_a$, due to the current i_a, at the site of the second wire is, from Eq. 34–4,

$$B_a = \frac{\mu_0 i_a}{2\pi d}.$$

The right-hand rule shows that the direction of $\mathbf{B}_a$ at wire b is down, as shown in the figure.

Wire b, which carries a current i_b, finds itself immersed in an *external* field of magnetic induction $\mathbf{B}_a$. A length l of this wire will experience a sideways magnetic force ($= i\mathbf{l} \times \mathbf{B}$) whose magnitude is

$$F_b = i_b l B_a = \frac{\mu_0 l i_b i_a}{2\pi d}. \tag{34–6}$$

The vector rule of signs tells us that $\mathbf{F}_b$ lies in the plane of the wires and points to the left in Fig. 34–9.

We could have started with wire b, computed the field of induction which it produces at the site of wire a, and then computed the force on wire a. The

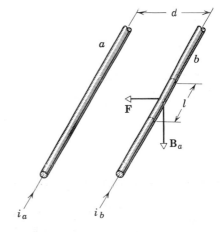

Fig. 34–9   Two parallel wires that carry parallel currents attract each other.

force on wire a would, for parallel currents, point to the right. The forces that the two wires exert on each other are equal and opposite, as they must be according to Newton's law of action and reaction. For antiparallel currents the two wires repel each other.

This discussion reminds us of our discussion of the electric field between two point charges in Section 27–1. There we saw that the charges act on each other through the intermediary of the electric field. The conductors in Fig. 34–9 act on each other through the intermediary of the *magnetic* field. We think in terms of

$$\text{current} \rightleftharpoons \text{field}$$

and not, as in the action-at-a-distance point of view, in terms of

$$\text{current} \rightleftharpoons \text{current.}$$

The attraction between long parallel wires is used to define the ampere. Suppose that the wires are 1 meter apart ($d = 1.0$ meter) and that the two currents are equal ($i_a = i_b = i$). If this common current is adjusted until, by measurement, the force of attraction per unit length between the wires is 2×10^{-7} nt/meter, the current is defined to be 1 *ampere*. From Eq. 34–6,

$$\frac{F}{l} = \frac{\mu_0 i^2}{2\pi d} = \frac{(4\pi \times 10^{-7} \text{ weber/amp-m})(1 \text{ amp})^2}{(2\pi)(1 \text{ meter})}$$

$$= 2 \times 10^{-7} \text{ nt/meter}$$

as expected.*

At the National Bureau of Standards primary measurements of current are made with a *current balance*. This consists of a carefully wound coil placed between two other coils, as in Fig. 34–10. The outer pair of coils is fastened to the table, and the inner one is hung from the arm of a balance. The coils are so connected that the current to be measured exists, as a common current, in all three of them.

The coils exert forces on one another—just as the parallel wires of Fig. 34–9 do—which can be measured by loading weights on the balance pan. The current is defined in terms of this measured force and the dimensions of the coils. The current balance is perfectly equivalent to the long parallel wires of Fig. 34–9 but is a much more practical arrangement. Current balance measurements are used primarily to standardize other, more convenient, secondary methods of measuring currents.

▶ **Example 3.** A long horizontal rigidly supported wire carries a current i_a of 100 amp. Directly above it and parallel to it is a fine wire that carries a current i_b of 20 amp and weighs 0.0050 lb/ft (= 0.073 nt/meter). How far above the lower wire should this second wire be strung if we hope to support it by magnetic repulsion?

To provide a repulsion, the two currents must point in opposite directions. For equilibrium, the magnetic force per unit length must equal the weight per unit length and must be oppositely directed.

---

* Note that μ_0 appears in this relation used to define the ampere. As stated on page 756, μ_0 is assigned the (arbitrary) value of $4\pi \times 10^{-7}$ weber/amp-m, and the size of the current that we define as 1 ampere is adjusted to give the required force of attraction per unit length.

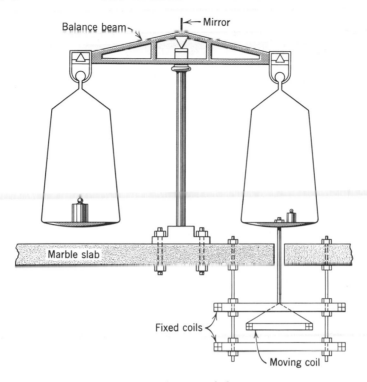

Fig. 34–10 A current balance.

Solving Eq. 34–6 for d yields

$$d = \frac{\mu_0 i_a i_b}{2\pi(F/l)} = \frac{(4\pi \times 10^{-7} \text{ weber/amp-m})(100 \text{ amp})(20 \text{ amp})}{(2\pi)(0.073 \text{ nt/meter})}$$

$$= 5.5 \times 10^{-3} \text{ meter} = 5.5 \text{ mm}.$$

We assume that the wire diameters are much smaller than their separation. This assumption is necessary because in deriving Eq. 34–6 we tacitly assumed that the magnetic induction produced by one wire is uniform for all points within the second wire.

Is the equilibrium of the suspended wire stable or unstable against vertical displacements? This can be tested by displacing the wire vertically and examining how the forces on the wire change.

Suppose that the fine wire is suspended *below* the rigidly supported wire. How may it be made to "float"? Is the equilibrium against vertical displacements stable or unstable?

Example 4. Two parallel wires a distance d apart carry equal currents i in opposite directions. Find the magnetic induction for points between the wires and at a distance x from one wire.

Study of Fig. 34–11 shows that $\mathbf{B}_a$ due to the current i_a and $\mathbf{B}_b$ due to the current i_b point in the same direction at P. Each is given by Eq. 34–4 $(B - \mu_0 i/2\pi r)$ so that

$$B = B_a + B_b = \frac{\mu_0 i}{2\pi}\left(\frac{1}{x} + \frac{1}{d - x}\right).$$

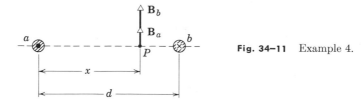

Fig. 34–11   Example 4.

This relationship does not hold for points inside the wires because Eq. 34–4 is not valid there.   ◀

34–5   B for a Solenoid

A *solenoid* is a long wire wound in a close-packed helix and carrying a current i. We assume that the helix is very long compared with its diameter. What is the nature of the field of **B** that is set up?

For points close to a single turn of the solenoid, the observer is not aware that the wire is bent in an arc. The wire behaves magnetically almost like a long straight wire, and the lines of **B** due to this single turn are almost concentric circles.

The solenoid field is the vector sum of the fields set up by all the turns that make up the solenoid. Figure 34–12, which shows a "solenoid" with widely spaced turns, suggests that the fields tend to cancel between the wires. It suggests also that, at points inside the solenoid and reasonably far from the wires, **B** is parallel to the solenoid axis. In the limiting case of adjacent square tightly packed wires, the solenoid becomes essentially a cylindrical current sheet and the requirements of symmetry then make the statement just given necessarily true. We assume that it is true in what follows.

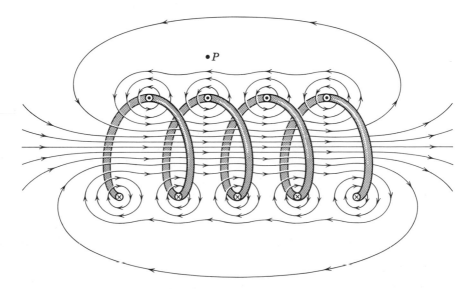

Fig. 34–12   A loosely wound solenoid.

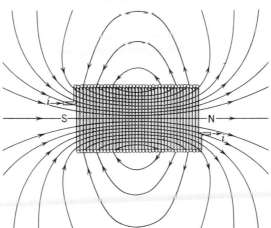

Fig. 34–13 A solenoid of finite length. The right end, from which lines of **B** emerge, behaves like the north pole of a compass needle. The left end behaves like the south pole.

For points such as P in Fig. 34–12 the field set up by the upper part of the solenoid turns (marked $\odot$) points to the left and tends to cancel the field set up by the lower part of the solenoid turns (marked $\otimes$), which points to the right. As the solenoid becomes more and more ideal, that is, as it approaches the configuration of an infinitely long cylindrical current sheet, the field of induction at outside points approaches zero. Taking the external field to be zero is not a bad assumption for a practical solenoid if its length is much greater than its diameter and if we consider only external points near the central region of the solenoid, that is, away from the ends. Figure 34–13 shows the lines of induction for a real solenoid, which is far from ideal in that the length is not much greater than the diameter. Even here the spacing of the lines of induction in the central plane shows that the external field is much weaker than the internal field.

Let us apply Ampère's law,

$$\oint \mathbf{B} \cdot d\mathbf{l} = \mu_0 i,$$

to the rectangular path $abcd$ in the ideal solenoid of Fig. 34–14. We write the integral $\oint \mathbf{B} \cdot d\mathbf{l}$ as the sum of four integrals, one for each path segment:

$$\oint \mathbf{B} \cdot d\mathbf{l} = \int_a^b \mathbf{B} \cdot d\mathbf{l} + \int_b^c \mathbf{B} \cdot d\mathbf{l} + \int_c^d \mathbf{B} \cdot d\mathbf{l} + \int_d^a \mathbf{B} \cdot d\mathbf{l}.$$

Fig. 34–14 A section of an ideal solenoid, made of adjacent square turns, equivalent to an infinitely long cylindrical current sheet.

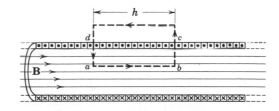

The first integral on the right is Bh, where B is the magnitude of the magnetic induction inside the solenoid and h is the arbitrary length of the path from a to b. Note that path ab, though parallel to the solenoid axis, need not coincide with it.

The second and fourth integrals are zero because for every element of these paths $\mathbf{B}$ is at right angles to the path. This makes $\mathbf{B} \cdot d\mathbf{l}$ zero and thus the integrals are zero. The third integral, which includes the part of the rectangle that lies outside the solenoid, is zero because we have taken $\mathbf{B}$ as zero for all external points for an ideal solenoid.

Thus $\oint \mathbf{B} \cdot d\mathbf{l}$ for the entire rectangular path has the value Bh. The net current i that passes through the area bounded by the path of integration is not the same as the current i_0 in the solenoid because the path of integration encloses more than one turn. Let n be the *number of turns per unit length;* then

$$i = i_0(nh).$$

Ampère's law then becomes

$$Bh = \mu_0 i_0 nh$$

or $$B = \mu_0 i_0 n. \tag{34-7}$$

Although Eq. 34-7 was derived for an infinitely long ideal solenoid, it holds quite well for actual solenoids for internal points near the center of the solenoid. It shows that B does not depend on the diameter or the length of the solenoid and that B is constant over the solenoid cross section. A solenoid is a practical way to set up a known uniform magnetic field for experimentation, just as a parallel-plate capacitor is a practical way to set up a known uniform electric field.

▶ **Example 5.** A solenoid is 1.0 meter long and 3.0 cm in mean diameter. It has five layers of windings of 850 turns each and carries a current of 5.0 amp.

(a) What is B at its center? From Eq. 34-7,

$$B = \mu_0 i_0 n = (4\pi \times 10^{-7} \text{ weber/amp-m})(5.0 \text{ amp})(5 \times 850 \text{ turns/meter})$$

$$= 2.7 \times 10^{-2} \text{ weber/meter}^2.$$

We can use Eq. 34-7 even if the solenoid has more than one layer of windings because the diameter of the windings does not enter.

(b) What is the magnetic flux Φ_B for a cross section of the solenoid at its center? To the extent that $\mathbf{B}$ is constant, we can calculate the flux from

$$\Phi_B = \int \mathbf{B} \cdot d\mathbf{S} = BA,$$

where A is the effective cross-sectional area. Let us assume that A represents the area of a circular disk whose diameter is the mean diameter of the windings (3.0 cm). The effective area can then be shown to be 7.1×10^{-4} meter^2, and

$$\Phi_B = BA = (2.7 \times 10^{-2} \text{ weber/meter}^2)(7.1 \times 10^{-4} \text{ meter}^2)$$

$$= 1.9 \times 10^{-5} \text{ weber.}$$

Example 6. *A toroid.* Figure 34–15 shows a toroid, which may be described as a solenoid of finite length bent into the shape of a doughnut. Calculate **B** at interior points.

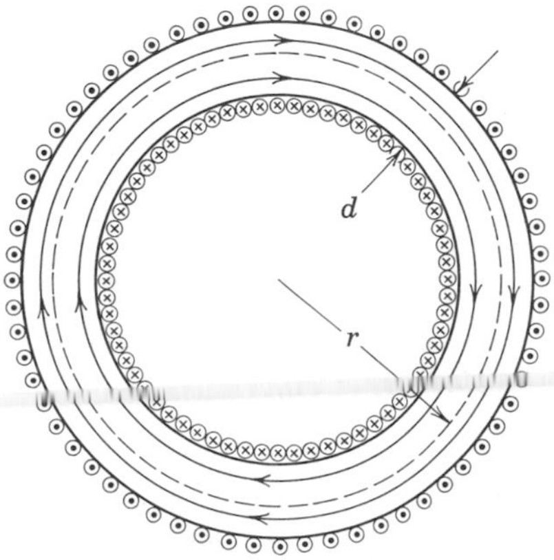

Fig. 34–15 Example 6. A toroid.

From symmetry the lines of **B** form concentric circles inside the toroid, as shown in the figure. Let us apply Ampère's law to the circular path of integration of radius r:

$$\oint \mathbf{B} \cdot d\mathbf{l} = \mu_0 i$$

or

$$(B)(2\pi r) = \mu_0 i_0 N,$$

where i_0 is the current in the toroid windings and N is the total number of turns. This gives

$$B = \frac{\mu_0}{2\pi} \frac{i_0 N}{r}.$$

In contrast to the solenoid, B is not constant over the cross section of a toroid. Show from Ampère's law that B equals zero for points outside an ideal toroid. ◄

34–6 The Biot-Savart Law

Ampère's law can be used to calculate magnetic fields only if the symmetry of the current distribution is high enough to permit the easy evaluation of the line integral $\oint \mathbf{B} \cdot d\mathbf{l}$. This requirement limits the usefulness of the law in practical problems. The law does not fail; it simply becomes difficult to apply in a useful way.

Similarly, in electrostatics, Gauss's law can be used to calculate electric fields only if the symmetry of the charge distribution is high enough to permit the easy evaluation of the surface integral $\oint \mathbf{E} \cdot d\mathbf{S}$. We can, for example, use Gauss's law to find the electric field due to a long uniformly charged rod but we cannot apply it usefully to an electric dipole, for the symmetry is not high enough in this case.

To compute E at a given point for an *arbitrary* charge distribution, we divided the distribution into *charge elements dq* and (see Section 27–4) we used Coulomb's law to calculate the field contribution $d\mathbf{E}$ due to each ele-

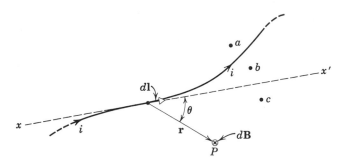

Fig. 34–16 The current element dl establishes a magnetic field contribution $d\mathbf{B}$ at point P.

ment at the point in question. We found the field $\mathbf{E}$ at that point by adding, that is, by integrating, the field contributions $d\mathbf{E}$ for the entire distribution.

We now describe a similar procedure for computing $\mathbf{B}$ at any point due to an arbitrary current distribution. We divide the current distribution into *current elements* and, using the law of Biot and Savart (which we describe below), we calculate the field contribution $d\mathbf{B}$ due to each current element at the point in question. We find the field $\mathbf{B}$ at that point by integrating the field contributions for the entire distribution.

Figure 34–16 shows an arbitrary current distribution consisting of a current i in a curved wire. The figure also shows a typical current element; it is a length dl of the conductor carrying a current i. Its direction is that of the tangent to the conductor (dashed line). A current element cannot exist as an isolated entity because a way must be provided to lead the current into the element at one end and out of it at the other. Nevertheless, we can think of an actual circuit as made up of a large number of current elements placed end to end.

Let P be the point at which we want to know the magnetic induction $d\mathbf{B}$ associated with the current element. According to the Biot-Savart law, $d\mathbf{B}$ is given in magnitude by

$$dB = \frac{\mu_0 i}{4\pi} \frac{dl \sin \theta}{r^2}, \qquad (34\text{–}8)$$

where $\mathbf{r}$ is a displacement vector from the element to P and θ is the angle between this vector and $d\mathbf{l}$. The direction of $d\mathbf{B}$ is that of the vector $d\mathbf{l} \times \mathbf{r}$. In Fig. 34–16, for example, $d\mathbf{B}$ at point P for the current element shown is directed into the page at right angles to the plane of the figure. Note that Eq. 34–8, being an inverse square law that describes the magnetic induction due to a current element, may be viewed as the magnetic equivalent of Coulomb's law, which is an inverse square law that describes the electric field due to a charge element.

The law of Biot and Savart may be written in vector form as

$$d\mathbf{B} = \frac{\mu_0 i}{4\pi} \frac{d\mathbf{l} \times \mathbf{r}}{r^3}. \qquad (34\text{–}9)$$

This formulation reduces to that of Eq. 34–8 when expressed in terms of magnitudes; it also gives complete information about the direction of $d\mathbf{B}$, namely that it is the same as the direction of the vector $d\mathbf{l} \times \mathbf{r}$.

The resultant field at P is found by integrating Eq. 34–9, or

$$\mathbf{B} = \int d\mathbf{B}, \tag{34–10}$$

where the integral is a vector integral.

▶ **Example 7.** *A long straight wire.* We illustrate the law of Biot and Savart by applying it to find $\mathbf{B}$ due to a current i in a long straight wire. We discussed this problem at length in connection with Ampère's law in Section 34–1.

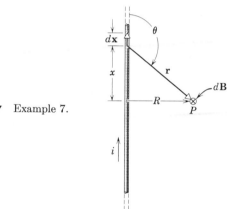

Fig. 34–17 Example 7.

Figure 34–17, a side view of the wire, shows a typical current element dx. The magnitude of the contribution $d\mathbf{B}$ of this element to the magnetic field at P is found from Eq. 34–8, or

$$dB = \frac{\mu_0 i}{4\pi} \frac{dx \sin \theta}{r^2}.$$

The directions of the contributions $d\mathbf{B}$ at point P for all elements are the same, namely, into the plane of the figure at right angles to the page. Thus the vector integral of Eq. 34–10 reduces to a scalar integral, or

$$B = \int dB = \frac{\mu_0 i}{4\pi} \int_{x=-\infty}^{x=+\infty} \frac{\sin \theta \, dx}{r^2}.$$

Now, x, θ, and r are not independent, being related (see Fig. 34–17) by

$$r = \sqrt{x^2 + R^2}$$

and

$$\sin \theta \, [= \sin (\pi - \theta)] = \frac{R}{\sqrt{x^2 + R^2}},$$

so that the expression for B becomes

$$B = \frac{\mu_0 i}{4\pi} \int_{-\infty}^{+\infty} \frac{R\, dx}{(x^2 + R^2)^{3/2}}$$

$$= \frac{\mu_0 i}{4\pi R} \left| \frac{x}{(x^2 + R^2)^{1/2}} \right|_{x=-\infty}^{x=+\infty}$$

$$= \frac{\mu_0}{2\pi} \frac{i}{R}.$$

This is the result that we arrived at earlier for this problem (see Eq. 34–4). The law of Biot and Savart will always yield results that are consistent with Ampère's law and with experiment.

This problem reminds us of its electrostatic equivalent. We derived an expression for $\mathbf{E}$ due to a long charged rod, using Gauss's law (Section 28–6); we also solved this problem by integration methods, using Coulomb's law (Section 27–4).

Example 8. *A circular current loop.* Figure 34–18 shows a circular loop of radius R carrying a current i. Calculate $\mathbf{B}$ for points on the axis.

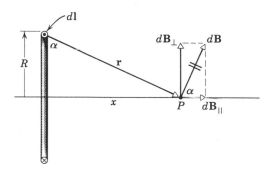

Fig. 34–18   Example 8.   A ring of radius R carrying a current i.

The vector $d\mathbf{l}$ for a current element at the top of the loop points perpendicularly out of the page. The angle θ between $d\mathbf{l}$ and $\mathbf{r}$ is 90°, and the plane formed by $d\mathbf{l}$ and $\mathbf{r}$ is normal to the page. The vector $d\mathbf{B}$ for this element is at right angles to this plane and thus lies in the plane of the figure and at right angles to $\mathbf{r}$, as the figure shows.

Let us resolve $d\mathbf{B}$ into two components, one, $d\mathbf{B}_\parallel$, along the axis of the loop and another, $d\mathbf{B}_\perp$, at right angles to the axis. Only $d\mathbf{B}_\parallel$ contributes to the total induction $\mathbf{B}$ at point P. This follows because the components $d\mathbf{B}_\parallel$ for all current elements lie on the axis and add directly; however, the components $d\mathbf{B}_\perp$ point in different directions perpendicular to the axis, and their resultant for the complete loop is zero, from symmetry. Thus

$$B = \int dB_\parallel,$$

where the integral is a simple scalar integration over the current elements.

For the current element shown in Fig. 34–18 we have, from the Biot-Savart law (Eq. 34–8),

$$dB = \frac{\mu_0 i}{4\pi} \frac{dl \sin 90°}{r^2}.$$

We also have
$$dB_\parallel = dB \cos \alpha.$$

Combining gives
$$dB_\parallel = \frac{\mu_0 i \cos \alpha \, dl}{4\pi r^2}.$$

Figure 34–18 shows that r and α are not independent of each other. Let us express each in terms of a new variable x, the distance from the center of the loop to the point P. The relationships are

$$r = \sqrt{R^2 + x^2}$$

and
$$\cos \alpha = \frac{R}{r} = \frac{R}{\sqrt{R^2 + x^2}}.$$

Substituting these values into the expression for $dB_\parallel$ gives

$$dB_\parallel = \frac{\mu_0 i R}{4\pi (R^2 + x^2)^{3/2}} \, dl.$$

Note that i, R, and x have the same values for all current elements. Integrating this equation, noting that $\int dl$ is simply the circumference of the loop ($= 2\pi R$), yields

$$B = \int dB_\parallel = \frac{\mu_0 i R}{4\pi (R^2 + x^2)^{3/2}} \int dl$$

$$= \frac{\mu_0 i R^2}{2(R^2 + x^2)^{3/2}}. \tag{34–11}$$

◀

If we put $x \gg R$ in Example 8 so that points close to the loop are not considered, Eq. 34–11 reduces to

$$B = \frac{\mu_0 i R^2}{2x^3}.$$

Recalling that πR^2 is the area A of the loop and considering loops with N turns, we can write this equation as

$$B = \frac{\mu_0}{2\pi} \frac{(NiA)}{x^3} = \frac{\mu_0}{2\pi} \frac{\mu}{x^3},$$

where μ is the *magnetic dipole moment* of the current loop. This reminds us of the result derived in Problem 10, Chapter 27 [$E = (1/2\pi\epsilon_0)(p/x^3)$], which is the formula for the *electric* field strength on the axis of an *electric* dipole.

Thus we have shown in two ways that a current loop can be regarded as a magnetic dipole: It experiences a torque given by $\tau = \mu \times B$ when placed in an *external* magnetic field (Eq. 33–11); it generates its own magnetic field given, for points on the axis, by the equation just developed.

Table 34–1 is a summary of the properties of electric and magnetic dipoles.

Table 34–1

SOME DIPOLE EQUATIONS

Property	Dipole Type	Equation
Torque in an external field	electric	$\boldsymbol{\tau} = \mathbf{p} \times \mathbf{E}$
	magnetic	$\boldsymbol{\tau} = \boldsymbol{\mu} \times \mathbf{B}$
Energy in an external field	electric	$U = -\mathbf{p} \cdot \mathbf{E}$
	magnetic	$U = -\boldsymbol{\mu} \cdot \mathbf{B}$
Field at distant points along axis	electric	$E = \dfrac{1}{2\pi\epsilon_0} \dfrac{p}{x^3}$
	magnetic	$B = \dfrac{\mu_0}{2\pi} \dfrac{\mu}{x^3}$
Field at distant points along perpendicular bisector	electric	$E = \dfrac{1}{4\pi\epsilon_0} \dfrac{p}{x^3}$
	magnetic	$B = \dfrac{\mu_0}{4\pi} \dfrac{\mu}{x^3}$

▶ **Example 9.** In the Bohr model of the hydrogen atom the electron circulates around the nucleus in a path of radius 5.1×10^{-11} meter at a frequency f of 6.8×10^{15} rev/sec. (*a*) What value of B is set up at the center of the orbit?

The current is the rate at which charge passes any point on the orbit and is given by

$$i = ef = (1.6 \times 10^{-19} \text{ coul})(6.8 \times 10^{15}/\text{sec}) = 1.1 \times 10^{-3} \text{ amp.}$$

B at the center of the orbit is given by Eq. 34–11 with $x = 0$, or

$$B = \frac{\mu_0 i R^2}{2(R^2 + x^2)^{3/2}} = \frac{\mu_0 i}{2R}$$

$$= \frac{(4\pi \times 10^{-7} \text{ weber/amp-m})(1.1 \times 10^{-3} \text{ amp})}{(2)(5.1 \times 10^{-11} \text{ meter})}$$

$$= 14 \text{ webers/meter}^2.$$

(*b*) What is the equivalent magnetic dipole moment? From Eq. 33–10,

$$\mu = NiA = (1)(1.1 \times 10^{-3} \text{ amp})(\pi)(5.1 \times 10^{-11} \text{ meter})^2$$

$$= 9.0 \times 10^{-24} \text{ amp-m}^2. \qquad ◀$$

QUESTIONS

1. Can the path of integration around which we apply Ampère's law pass *through* a conductor?

2. Suppose we set up a path of integration around a cable that contains twelve wires with different currents (some in opposite directions) in each wire. How do we calculate i in Ampère's law in such a case?

3. Apply Ampère's law qualitatively to the three paths shown in Fig. 34–19.

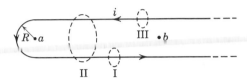

Fig. 34–19

4. Is **B** constant in magnitude for points that lie on a given line of induction?

5. Discuss and compare Gauss's law and Ampère's law.

6. A current is set up in a long copper pipe. Is there a magnetic field (*a*) inside and (*b*) outside the pipe?

7. Equation 34–4 ($B = \mu_0 i/2\pi r$) suggests that a strong magnetic field is set up at points near a long wire carrying a current. Since there is a current i and a magnetic field **B**, why is there not a force on the wire in accord with the equation $\mathbf{F} = i\mathbf{l} \times \mathbf{B}$?

8. In electronics, wires that carry equal but opposite currents are often twisted together to reduce their magnetic effect at distant points. Why is this effective?

9. A beam of 20-Mev protons emerges from a cyclotron. Is a magnetic field associated with these particles?

10. Test the "floating" wire of Example 3 for equilibrium under *horizontal* displacements. Consider that the wire floats above the rigidly supported wire and also below it. Summarize the equilibrium situation for both wire positions and for both vertical and horizontal displacements.

11. Explain qualitatively the forces of interaction between parallel wires carrying parallel or antiparallel currents in terms of Faraday's lines of induction representation.

12. Comment on this statement: "The magnetic induction outside a long solenoid cannot be zero, if only for the reason that the helical nature of the windings produces a field for external points like that of a straight wire along the solenoid axis."

13. A current is sent through a vertical spring from whose lower end a weight is hanging; what will happen?

14. Does Eq. 34–7 ($B = \mu_0 in$) hold for a solenoid of square cross section?

15. What is the direction of the magnetic fields at points *a*, *b*, and *c* in Fig. 34–16 set up by the particular current element shown?

16. In a circular loop of wire carrying a current i, is **B** uniform for all points within the loop?

17. Discuss analogies and differences between Coulomb's law and the Biot-Savart law.

18. Equation 34–9 gives the law of Biot and Savart in vector form. Write its electrostatic equivalent [that is, Eq. 27–6, or $dE = dq/(4\pi\epsilon_0 r^2)$] in vector form.

19. How might you measure the magnetic dipole moment of a compass needle?

20. What is the basis for saying that a current-loop is a magnetic dipole?

PROBLEMS

1. A #10 bare copper wire (0.10 in. in diameter) can carry a current of 50 amp without overheating. For this current, what is B at the surface of the wire?

2. A surveyor is using a compass 20 ft below a power line in which there is a steady current of 100 amp. Will this interfere seriously with the compass reading? The horizontal component of the earth's magnetic field is about 0.2 gauss.

3. A long straight wire carries a current of 50 amp. An electron, traveling at 10^7 meters/sec, is 5.0 cm from the wire. What force acts on the electron if the electron velocity is directed (a) toward the wire, (b) parallel to the wire, and (c) at right angles to the directions defined by (a) and (b)?

4. A conductor consists of an infinite number of adjacent wires, each infinitely long and carrying a current i. Show that the lines of **B** will be as represented in Fig. 34–20 and that B for all points in front of the infinite current sheet will be given by

$$B = \tfrac{1}{2}\mu_0 ni,$$

where n is the number of conductors per unit length. Derive both by direct application of Ampère's law and by considering the problem as a limiting case of Example 2.

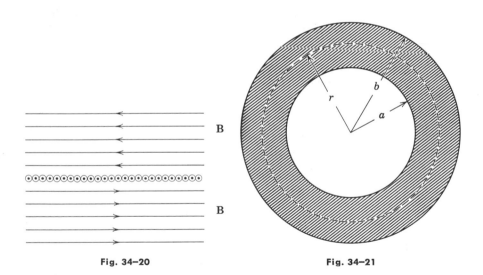

Fig. 34–20   Fig. 34–21

5. Figure 34–21 shows a hollow cylindrical conductor of radii a and b which carries a current i uniformly spread over its cross section. (a) Show that the magnetic field B for points inside the body of the conductor (that is, $a < r < b$) is given by

$$B = \frac{\mu_0 i}{2\pi(b^2 - a^2)} \frac{r^2 - a^2}{r}.$$

Check this formula for the limiting case of $a = 0$. (b) Make a rough plot of the general behavior of $B(r)$ from $r = 0$ to $r \to \infty$.

6. A long coaxial cable consists of two concentric conductors with the dimensions shown in Fig. 34–22. There are equal and opposite currents i in the conductors. (*a*) Find the magnetic induction B at r within the inner conductor ($r < a$). (*b*) Find B between the two conductors ($a < r < b$). (*c*) Find B within the outer conductor ($b < r < c$). (*d*) Find B outside the cable ($r > c$).

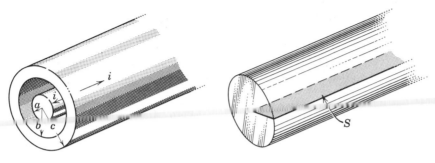

Fig. 34–22   Fig. 34–23

7. A long copper wire carries a current of 10 amp. Calculate the magnetic flux per meter of wire for a plane surface S inside the wire, as in Fig. 34–23.

8. Two long, parallel #10 copper wires (diameter = 0.10 in.) carry currents of 10 amp in opposite directions. (*a*) If their centers are 2.0 cm apart, calculate the flux per meter that exists in the space between the axes of the wires. (*b*) What fraction of the flux in (*a*) lies inside the wires? (*c*) Repeat the calculation of (*a*) for parallel currents.

9. A long wire carrying a current of 100 amp is placed in a uniform external magnetic field of 50 gauss. The wire is at right angles to this external field. Locate the points at which the *resultant* magnetic field is zero.

10. Two long wires a distance d apart carry equal antiparallel currents i, as in Fig. 34–24. Show that B at point P, which is equidistant from the wires, is given by

$$B = \frac{2\mu_0 i d}{\pi(4R^2 + d^2)}.$$

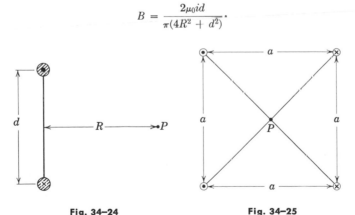

Fig. 34–24   Fig. 34–25

11. Four long #10 copper wires are parallel to each other, their cross section forming a square 20 cm on edge. A 20-amp current is set up in each wire in the direction shown in Fig. 34–25. What are the magnitude and direction of $\mathbf{B}$ at the center of the square?

12. In Problem 11 what is the force per meter acting on the lower left wire, in magnitude and direction?

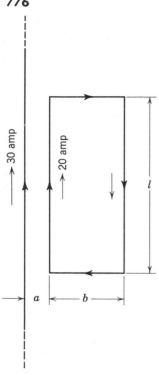

Fig. 34–26

13. Figure 34–26 shows a long wire carrying a current of 30 amp. The rectangular loop carries a current of 20 amp. Calculate the resultant force acting on the loop. Assume that $a = 1.0$ cm, $b = 8.0$ cm, and $l = 30$ cm.

14. Derive the solenoid equation (Eq. 34–7) starting from the expression for the field on the axis of a circular loop (Example 8). (Hint: Subdivide the solenoid into a series of current loops of infinitesimal thickness and integrate.)

15. A square loop of wire of edge a carries a current i. Show that the value of B at the center is given by

$$B = \frac{2\sqrt{2}\,\mu_0 i}{\pi a}.$$

16. A square loop of wire of edge a carries a current i. (a) Show that B for a point on the axis of the loop and a distance x from its center is given by

$$B = \frac{4\mu_0 i a^2}{\pi(4x^2 + a^2)(4x^2 + 2a^2)^{\frac{1}{2}}}.$$

(b) Does this reduce to the result of Problem 15 for $x = 0$? (c) Does the square loop behave like a dipole for points such that $x \gg a$? If so, what is its dipole moment?

17. A straight wire segment of length l carries a current i. (a) Show that the field of induction **B** to be associated with this segment, at a distance R from the segment along a perpendicular bisector (see Fig. 34–27), is given in magnitude by

$$B = \frac{\mu_0 i}{2\pi R}\frac{l}{(l^2 + 4R^2)^{\frac{1}{2}}}.$$

(b) Does this expression reduce to an expected result as $l \rightarrow \infty$?

18. The wire shown in Fig. 34–28 carries a current i. What is the magnetic induction at the center C of the semicircle arising from (a) each straight segment of length l, (b) the semicircular segment of radius R, and (c) the entire wire?

19. (a) A wire in the form of a regular polygon of n sides is just enclosed by a circle of radius a. If the current in this

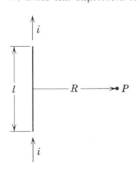

Fig. 34–27

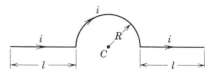

Fig. 34–28

wire is i, show that the magnetic induction at the center of the circle is given by

$$B = \frac{\mu_0 n i}{2\pi a}\tan(\pi/n).$$

(b) Show that as $n \rightarrow \infty$ this result approaches that of a circular loop.

20. (a) Show that B at the center of a rectangle of length l and width d, carrying a current i, is given by

$$B = \frac{2\mu_0 i}{\pi} \frac{(l^2 + d^2)^{\frac{1}{2}}}{ld}.$$

(b) What does B reduce to for $l \gg d$? Is this a result that you expect?

21. *Helmholtz coils.* Two 300-turn coils are arranged a distance apart equal to their radius, as in Fig. 34–29. For $R = 5.0$ cm and $i = 50$ amp, plot B as a function of distance x along the common axis over the range $x = -5$ cm to $x = +5$ cm, taking $x = 0$ at point P. (Such coils provide an especially uniform field of B near point P.)

22. In Problem 21 let the separation of the coils be a variable z. Show that if z equals R, then not only the first derivative (dB/dx) but also the second (d^2B/dx^2) of B is zero at point P. This accounts for the uniformity of B near point P for this particular coil separation.

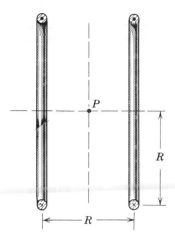

Fig. 34–29

23. A long "hairpin" is formed by bending a piece of wire as shown in Fig. 34–19. If a 10-amp current is set up, what are the direction and magnitude of B at point a? At point b? Take $R = 0.50$ cm.

24. Calculate B at point P in Fig. 34–30. Assume that $i = 10$ amp and $a = 8.0$ cm.

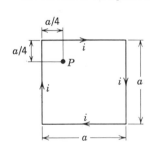

Fig. 34–30

25. A plastic disk of radius R has a charge q uniformly distributed over its surface. If the disk is rotated at an angular frequency ω about its axis, show that (a) the induction at the center of the disk is

$$B = \frac{\mu_0 \omega q}{2\pi R}$$

and (b) the magnetic dipole moment of the disk is

$$\mu = \frac{\omega q R^2}{4}.$$

(Hint: The rotating disk is equivalent to an array of current loops; see Example 8.)

26. You are given a length l of wire in which a current i may be established. The wire may be formed into a circle or a square. Which yields the larger value for B at the central point? See Problem 15.

27. A circular copper loop of radius 10 cm carries a current of 15 amp. At its center is placed a second loop of radius 1.0 cm, having 50 turns and a current of 1.0 amp. (a) What magnetic induction B does the large loop set up at its center? (b) What torque acts on the small loop? Assume that the planes of the two loops are at right angles and that the induction B provided by the large loop is essentially uniform throughout the volume occupied by the small loop.

28. Show that it is impossible for a uniform magnetic field B to drop abruptly to zero as one moves at right angles to it, as suggested by the horizontal arrow in Fig. 34–31 (see point a). In actual magnets fringing of the lines of force always occurs, which means that B approaches zero in a continuous and gradual way. (Hint: Apply Ampère's law to the rectangular path shown by the dashed lines.)

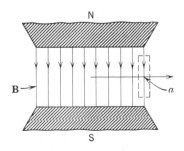

Fig. 34–31

Faraday's Law

CHAPTER 35

35–1 Faraday's Experiments

For some physical laws it is hard to find experiments that lead in a direct and convincing way to the formulation of the law. Gauss's law, for example, emerged only slowly as the common factor with whose aid all electrostatic experiments could be interpreted and correlated. In Chapter 28 we found it best to state Gauss's law first and then to show that the underlying experiments were consistent with it.

Faraday's *law of electromagnetic induction*, which is one of the basic equations of electromagnetism (see Table 38–3), is different in that there are a number of simple experiments from which the law can be—and was—deduced directly. Such experiments were carried out by Michael Faraday in England in 1831 and by Joseph Henry in the United States at about the same time.

Figure 35–1 shows the terminals of a coil connected to a galvanometer. Normally we would not expect this instrument to deflect because there seems to be no electromotive force in this circuit; but if we push a bar magnet toward the coil, with its north pole facing the coil, a remarkable thing happens. *While the magnet is moving*, the galvanometer deflects, showing that a current has been set up in the coil. If the magnet is held stationary with respect to the coil, the galvanometer does not deflect. If the magnet is moved away from the coil, the galvanometer again deflects, but in the opposite direction, which means that the current in the coil is in the opposite direction. If we use the south pole end of a magnet instead of the north pole end, the experiment works as described but the deflections are reversed. Further experimentation shows that *what matters is the relative motion of the*

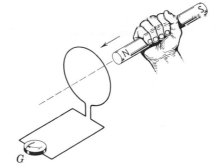

Fig. 35–1 Galvanometer G deflects while the
magnet is moving with respect to the coil.

magnet and the coil. It makes no difference whether the magnet is moved
toward the coil or the coil toward the magnet.

The current that appears in this experiment is called an *induced current*
and is said to be set up by an *induced electromotive force.* Faraday was able
to deduce from experiments like this the law that gives their magnitude and
direction. Such emfs are very important in practice. The chances are good
that the lights in the room in which you are reading this book are operated
from an induced emf produced in a commercial electric generator.

In another experiment the apparatus of Fig. 35–2 is used. The coils are
placed close together but at rest with respect to each other. When the
switch S is closed, thus setting up a steady current in the right-hand coil, the
galvanometer deflects momentarily; when the switch is opened, thus interrupting this current, the galvanometer again deflects momentarily, but in
the opposite direction. No gross objects are moving in this experiment.
In Faraday's words:

> When the contact was made, there was a sudden and very slight effect at the
> galvanometer, and there was also a similar slight effect when the contact with the
> battery was broken. But whilst the voltaic current was continuing to pass through
> the one helix, no galvanometrical appearances nor any effect like induction upon
> the other helix could be perceived, although the active power of the battery was
> proved to be very great. . . .

Experiment shows that there will be an induced emf in the left coil of
Fig. 35–2 whenever the current in the right coil is *changing.* It is the *rate
at which the current is changing* and *not the size of the current* that is significant.

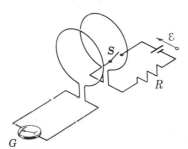

Fig. 35–2 Galvanometer G deflects momentarily when switch S is closed or opened.

35-2 Faraday's Law of Induction

Faraday had the insight to perceive that the change in the flux Φ_B of magnetic induction for the left coil in the preceding experiments is the important common factor. This flux may be set up by a bar magnet or a current loop. Faraday's law of induction says that the induced emf $\mathcal{E}$ in a circuit is equal to the negative rate at which the flux through the circuit is changing. If the rate of change of flux is in webers/sec, the emf $\mathcal{E}$ will be in volts. In equation form

$$\mathcal{E} = -\frac{d\Phi_B}{dt}. \tag{35-1}$$

This equation is called *Faraday's law of induction*. The minus sign is an indication of the *direction* of the induced emf, a matter we discuss further in Section 35-3.

If Eq. 35-1 is applied to a coil of N turns, an emf appears in every turn and these emfs are to be added. If the coil is so tightly wound that each turn can be said to occupy the same region of space, the flux through each turn will then be the same. The flux through each turn is also the same for (ideal) toroids and solenoids (see Section 34-5). The induced emf in all such devices is given by

$$\mathcal{E} = -N\frac{d\Phi_B}{dt} = -\frac{d(N\Phi_B)}{dt}, \tag{35-2}$$

where $N\Phi_B$ measures the so-called *flux linkages* in the device.

Figures 35-1 and 35-2 suggest that there are at least two ways in which we can make the flux through a circuit change and thus induce an emf in that circuit. The coil that is connected to the galvanometer cannot tell in which of these experiments it is participating; it is aware only that the flux passing through its cross-sectional area is changing. The flux through a circuit can also be changed by changing its shape, that is, by squeezing or stretching it.

▶ **Example 1.** A long solenoid has 200 turns/cm and carries a current of 1.5 amp; its diameter is 3.0 cm. At its center we place a 100-turn, close-packed coil of diameter 2.0 cm. This coil is arranged so that **B** at the center of the solenoid is parallel to its axis. The current in the solenoid is reduced to zero and then raised to 1.5 amp in the other direction at a steady rate over a period of 0.050 sec. What induced emf appears in the coil while the current is being changed?

The induction B at the center of the solenoid is given by Eq. 34-7, or

$$B = \mu_0 ni = (4\pi \times 10^{-7} \text{ weber/amp-m})(200 \times 10^2 \text{ turns/meter})(1.5 \text{ amp})$$

$$= 3.8 \times 10^{-2} \text{ weber/meter}^2.$$

The area of the coil (not of the solenoid) is 3.1×10^{-4} meter^2. The initial flux Φ_B through each turn of the coil is given by

$$\Phi_B = BA = (3.8 \times 10^{-2} \text{ weber/meter}^2)(3.1 \times 10^{-4} \text{ meter}^2) = 1.2 \times 10^{-5} \text{ weber}.$$

The flux goes from an initial value of 1.2×10^{-5} weber to a final value of -1.2×10^{-5} weber. The *change* in flux $\Delta\Phi_B$ for each turn of the coil during the 0.050-sec period is thus twice the initial value. The induced emf is given by

$$\mathcal{E} = -\frac{N\Delta\Phi_R}{\Delta t} = -\frac{(100)(2 \times 1.2 \times 10^{-5} \text{ weber})}{0.050 \text{ sec}} = -4.8 \times 10^{-2} \text{ volt} = -48 \text{ mv}.$$

The minus sign deals with the *direction* of the emf, as we explain below.   ◀

35–3   Lenz's Law

So far we have not specified the directions of the induced emfs. Although these directions can be found from a formal analysis of Faraday's law, we prefer to find them from the conservation-of-energy principle which, in this context, takes the form of Lenz's law: *The induced current will appear in such a direction that it opposes the change that produced it.** The minus sign in Faraday's law suggests this opposition. In mechanics the energy principle

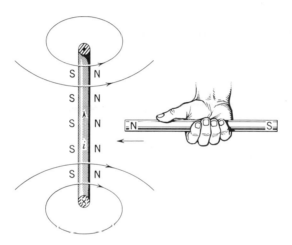

Fig. 35–3 If the magnet is moved toward the loop, the induced current points as shown, setting up a magnetic field that opposes the motion of the magnet.

often allows us to draw conclusions about mechanical systems without analyzing them in detail. We use the same approach here.

Lenz's law refers to induced *currents*, which means that it applies only to closed circuits. If the circuit is open, we can usually think in terms of what would happen if it were closed and in this way find the direction of the induced emf.

Consider the first of Faraday's experiments described in Section 35–1. Figure 35–3 shows the north pole of a magnet and a cross section of a nearby conducting loop. As we push the magnet toward the loop, an induced current is set up in the loop. What is its direction?

---

* Heinrich Friedrich Lenz (1804–1865) deduced this law in 1834. Faraday also discovered how to determine the directions of induced emfs, but he did not express his results as succinctly as Lenz.

A current loop sets up a magnetic field at distant points like that of a magnetic dipole, one face of the loop being a north pole, the opposite face being a south pole. The north pole, as for bar magnets, is that face *from* which the lines of **B** emerge. If, as Lenz's law predicts, the loop in Fig. 35–3 is to oppose the motion of the magnet toward it, the face of the loop toward the magnet must become a north pole. The two north poles—one of the current loop and one of the magnet—will repel each other. The right-hand rule shows that for the magnetic field set up by the loop to emerge from the right face of the loop the induced current must be as shown. The current will be counterclockwise as we sight along the magnet toward the loop.

When we push the magnet toward the loop (or the loop toward the magnet), an induced current appears. In terms of Lenz's law this pushing is the "change" that produces the induced current, and, according to this law, the induced current will oppose the "push." If we pull the magnet away from the coil, the induced current will oppose the "pull" by creating a *south* pole on the right-hand face of the loop of Fig. 35–3. To make the right-hand face a south pole, the current must be opposite to that shown in Fig. 35–3. Whether we pull or push the magnet, its motion will always be automatically opposed.

The agent that causes the magnet to move, either toward the coil or away from it, will always experience a resisting force and will thus be required to do work. From the conservation-of-energy principle this work done on the system must be exactly equal to the Joule heat produced in the coil, since these are the only two energy transfers that occur in the system. If we move the magnet more rapidly, we will have to do work at a faster rate and the rate of the Joule heating will increase correspondingly. If we cut the loop and then perform the experiment, there will be no induced current, no Joule heating, no force on the magnet, and no work required to move it. There will still be an emf in the loop, but, like a battery connected to an open circuit, it will not set up a current.

If the current in Fig. 35–3 were in the *opposite* direction to that shown, the face of the loop toward the magnet would be a south pole, which would pull the bar magnet toward the loop. We would only need to push the magnet slightly to start the process and then the action would be self-perpetuating. The magnet would accelerate toward the loop, increasing its kinetic energy all the time. At the same time Joule heat would appear in the loop at a rate that would increase with time. This would indeed be a something-for-nothing situation! Needless to say, it does not occur.

Let us apply Lenz's law to Fig. 35–3 in a different way. Figure 35–4 shows the lines of **B** for the bar magnet.* On this point of view the "change" is the increase in Φ_B through the loop caused by bringing the magnet nearer. The induced current opposes this change by setting up a field that tends to oppose the increase in flux caused by the moving magnet. Thus the field

---

* There are two fields of **B** in this problem —one connected with the current loop and one with the bar magnet. The student must always be certain which one is meant.

Fig. 35-4 In moving the magnet toward the loop, we increase Φ_B through
the loop.

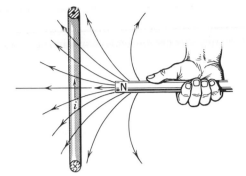

due to the induced current must point from left to right through the plane
of the coil, in agreement with our earlier conclusion.

It is not significant here that the induced field opposes the magnet *field*
but rather that it opposes the *change*, which in this case is the *increase* in
Φ_B through the loop. If we withdraw the magnet, we reduce Φ_B through the
loop. The induced field will now oppose this decrease in Φ_B (that is, the
change) by *re-enforcing* the magnet field. In each case the induced field
opposes the change that gives rise to it.

35-4 Induction—A Quantitative Study

The example of Fig. 35-4, although easy to understand qualitatively, does
not lend itself to quantitative calculations. Consider then Fig. 35-5, which
shows a rectangular loop of wire of width l, one end of which is in a uniform
field **B** pointing at right angles to the plane of the loop. This field of **B** may
be produced in the gap of a large electromagnet like that of Fig. 33-2. The
dashed lines show the assumed limits of the magnetic field. The experiment
consists in pulling the loop to the right at a constant speed v.

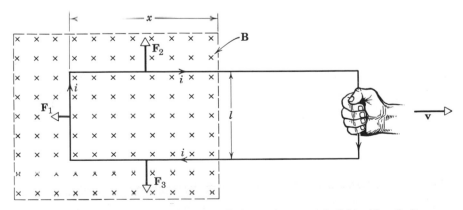

Fig. 35-5 A rectangular loop is pulled out of a magnetic field with velocity v.

Note that the situation described by Fig. 35–5 does not differ in any essential particular from that of Fig. 35–4. In each case a conducting loop and a magnet are in relative motion; in each case the flux of the field of the magnet through the loop is being caused to change with time.

The flux Φ_B enclosed by the loop in Fig. 35–5 is

$$\Phi_B = Blx,$$

where lx is the area of that part of the loop in which B is not zero. The emf $\mathcal{E}$ is found from Faraday's law, or

$$\mathcal{E} = -\frac{d\Phi_B}{dt} = -\frac{d}{dt}(Blx) = -Bl\frac{dx}{dt} = Blv, \tag{35–3}$$

where we have set $-dx/dt$ equal to the speed v at which the loop is pulled out of the magnetic field. Note that the only dimension of the loop that enters into Eq. 35–3 is the length l of the left end conductor. As we shall see later, the induced emf in Fig. 35–5 may be regarded as localized here. An induced emf such as this, produced by pulling a conductor through a magnetic field, is sometimes called a *motional emf*.

The emf Blv sets up a current in the loop given by

$$i = \frac{\mathcal{E}}{R} = \frac{Blv}{R}, \tag{35–4}$$

where R is the loop resistance. From Lenz's law, this current (and thus $\mathcal{E}$) must be clockwise in Fig. 35–5; it opposes the "change" (the decrease in Φ_B) by setting up a field that is parallel to the external field within the loop.

The current in the loop will cause forces $\mathbf{F}_1$, $\mathbf{F}_2$, and $\mathbf{F}_3$ to act on the three conductors, in accord with Eq. 33–6a, or

$$\mathbf{F} = i\mathbf{l} \times \mathbf{B}. \tag{35–5}$$

Because $\mathbf{F}_2$ and $\mathbf{F}_3$ are equal and opposite, they cancel each other; $\mathbf{F}_1$, which is the force that opposes our effort to move the loop, is given in magnitude from Eqs. 35–5 and 35–4 as

$$F_1 = ilB \sin 90° = \frac{B^2l^2v}{R}.$$

The agent that pulls the loop must do work at the steady rate of

$$P = F_1v = \frac{B^2l^2v^2}{R}. \tag{35–6}$$

From the principle of the conservation of energy, Joule heat must appear in the resistor at this same rate. We introduced the conservation-of-energy principle into our derivation when we wrote down the expression for the current (Eq. 35–4); the student will recall that the relation $i = \mathcal{E}/R$ for single-loop circuits is a direct consequence of this principle. Thus we should be able to write down the expression for the rate of Joule heating in the loop with the expectation that we will obtain a result identical with Eq. 35–6. Recalling Eq. 35–4, we put

$$P_J = i^2 R = \left(\frac{Blv}{R}\right)^2 R = \frac{B^2 l^2 v^2}{R},$$

which is indeed the expected result. This example provides a quantitative illustration of the conversion of mechanical energy (the work done by an external agent) into electrical energy (the induced emf) and finally into thermal energy (the Joule heating).

Figure 35–6 shows a side view of the coil in the field. In Fig. 35–6a the coil is stationary; in Fig. 35–6b we are moving it to the right; in Fig. 35–6c we are moving it to the left. The lines of induction in these figures represent the *resultant field* produced by the vector addition of the field $\mathbf{B}_0$ due to the magnet and the field $\mathbf{B}_i$ due to the induced current, if any, in the coil.

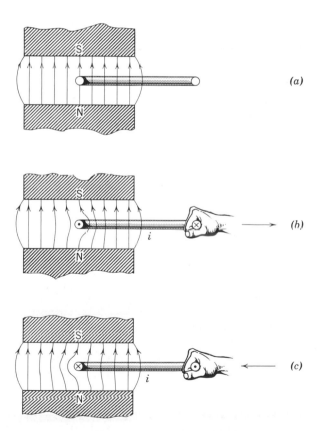

(a)

(b)

(c)

Fig. 35–6   Side view of a rectangular loop in a magnetic field showing the loop (a) at rest, (b) being pulled out, and (c) being pushed in.

These lines suggest convincingly that the agent moving the coil always experiences an opposing force.

▶ **Example 2.** Figure 35–7 shows a rectangular loop of resistance R, width l, and length a being pulled at constant speed v through a region of thickness d in which a uniform field of induction **B** is set up by a magnet.

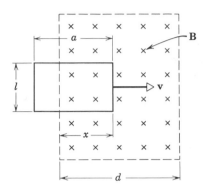

Fig. 35–7 Example 2. A rectangular loop is caused to move with a velocity **v** through a magnetic field. The position of the loop is measured by x, the distance between the effective left edge of the field **B** and the right end of the loop.

(a) Plot the flux Φ_B through the loop as a function of the coil position x. Assume that $l = 4$ cm, $a = 10$ cm, $d = 15$ cm, $R = 16$ ohms, $B = 2.0$ webers/meter^2, and $v = 1.0$ meter/sec.

The flux Φ_B is zero when the loop is not in the field; it is Bla when the loop is entirely in the field; it is Blx when the loop is entering the field and $Bl[a - (x - d)]$ when the loop is leaving the field. These conclusions, which the student should verify, are shown graphically in Fig. 35–8a.

(b) Plot the induced emf $\mathcal{E}$.

The induced emf $\mathcal{E}$ is given by $\mathcal{E} = -d\Phi_B/dt$, which can be written as

$$\mathcal{E} = -\frac{d\Phi_B}{dt} = -\frac{d\Phi_B}{dx}\frac{dx}{dt} = -\frac{d\Phi_B}{dx}v,$$

where $d\Phi_B/dx$ is the slope of the curve of Fig. 35–8a. $\mathcal{E}(x)$ is plotted in Fig. 35–8b. Lenz's law, from the same type of reasoning as that used for Fig. 35–5, shows that when the coil is entering the field the emf $\mathcal{E}$ acts counterclockwise as seen from above. Note that there is no emf when the coil is entirely in the magnetic field because the flux Φ_B through the coil is not changing with time, as Fig. 35–8a shows.

(c) Plot the rate P of Joule heating in the loop.

This is given by $P = \mathcal{E}^2/R$. It may be calculated by squaring the ordinate of the curve of Fig. 35–8b and dividing by R. The result is plotted in Fig. 35–8c.

If the fringing of the magnetic field, which cannot be avoided in practice (see Problem 34–28), is taken into account, the sharp bends and corners in Fig. 35–8 will be replaced by smooth curves. What changes would occur in the curves of Fig. 35–8 if the coil were open circuited?

Example 3. A copper rod of length L rotates at angular frequency ω in a uniform field of magnetic induction **B** as shown in Fig. 35–9. Find the emf $\mathcal{E}$ developed between the two ends of the rod.

If a wire of length $d\mathbf{l}$ is moved at velocity **v** at right angles to a field **B**, a motional emf $d\mathcal{E}$ will be developed (see Eq. 35–3) given by

$$d\mathcal{E} = Bv\, dl.$$

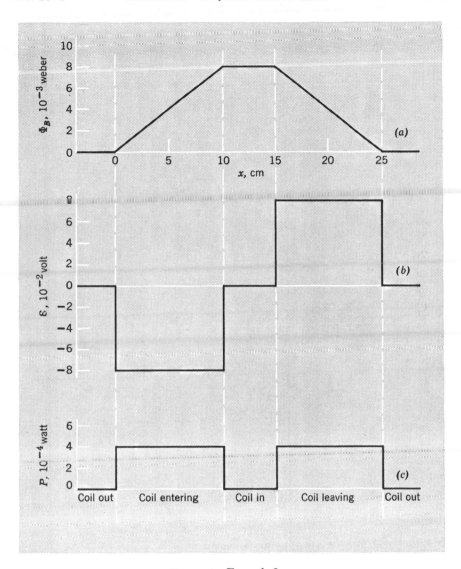

Fig. 35–8   Example 2.

The rod of Fig. 35–9 may be divided into elements of length dl, the linear speed v of each element being ωl. Each element is perpendicular to **B** and is also moving in a direction at right angles to **B** so that

$$\mathcal{E} = \int d\mathcal{E} = \int_0^L Bv\, dl = \int_0^L B(\omega l)\, dl = \tfrac{1}{2}B\omega L^2.$$

For a second approach, consider that at any instant the flux enclosed by the sector aOb in Fig. 35–9 is given by

$$\Phi_B = BA = B(\tfrac{1}{2}L^2\theta),$$

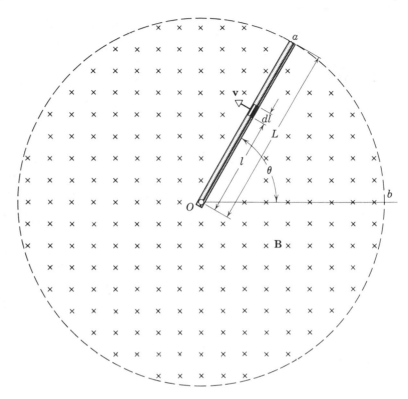

Fig. 35–9 Example 3.

where $\frac{1}{2}L^2\theta$ can be shown to be the area of the sector. Differentiating gives

$$\frac{d\Phi_B}{dt} = \tfrac{1}{2}BL^2\frac{d\theta}{dt} = \tfrac{1}{2}B\omega L^2.$$

From Faraday's law, this is precisely the magnitude of $\mathcal{E}$, which agrees with the result just derived. ◀

35–5 Time-Varying Magnetic Fields

So far we have considered emfs induced by the relative motion of magnets and coils. In this section we assume that there is no physical motion of gross objects but that the magnetic field may vary with time. If a conducting loop is placed in such a time-varying field, the flux through the loop will change and an induced emf will appear in the loop. This emf will set the charge carriers in motion, that is, it will induce a current.

From a microscopic point of view we can say, equally well, that the changing flux of **B** sets up an induced electric field **E** at various points around the loop. These induced electric fields are just as real as electric fields set up by static charges and will exert a force **F** on a test charge q_0 given by $\mathbf{F} = q_0\mathbf{E}$. Thus we can restate Faraday's law of induction in a loose but informative way as: *A changing magnetic field produces an electric field.*

To fix these ideas, consider Fig. 35-10, which shows a uniform field of induction **B** at right angles to the plane of the page. We assume that **B** is increasing in magnitude at the same constant rate dB/dt at every point. This could be done by causing the current in the windings of the electromagnet that establishes the field to increase with time in the proper way.

The circle of arbitrary radius r shown in Fig. 35-10 encloses, at any instant, a flux Φ_B. Because this flux is changing with time, an induced emf given by $\mathcal{E} = -d\Phi_B/dt$ will appear around the loop. The electric fields **E** induced at various points of the loop must, from symmetry, be tangent to the loop. Thus the electric lines of force that are set up by the changing magnetic field are in this case concentric circles.

If we consider a test charge q_0 moving around the circle of Fig. 35-10, the work W done on it per revolution is, in terms of the definition of an emf, simply $\mathcal{E}q_0$. From another point of view, it is $(q_0E)(2\pi r)$, where q_0E is the force that acts on the charge and $2\pi r$ is the distance over which the force acts. Setting the two expressions for W equal and canceling q_0 yields

$$\mathcal{E} = E2\pi r. \tag{35-7}$$

In a more general case than that of Fig. 35-10 we must write

$$\mathcal{E} = \oint \mathbf{E}\cdot d\mathbf{l}. \tag{35-8}$$

If this integral is evaluated for the conditions of Fig. 35-10, we obtain Eq. 35-7 at once. If Eq. 35-8 is combined with Eq. 35-1 ($\mathcal{E} = -d\Phi_B/dt$), Faraday's law of induction can be written as

$$\oint \mathbf{E}\cdot d\mathbf{l} = -\frac{d\Phi_B}{dt}, \tag{35-9}$$

which is the form in which this law is expressed in Table 38-3.

Fig. 35-10 The induced electric fields at four points produced by an increasing magnetic field. We assume that B has symmetry about an axis perpendicular to the page through the center of the circle of radius r. This can be arranged by assuming that the magnetic induction decreases slightly along a radius starting from the center of the figure, the value of B being constant for a particular value of r. (The magnetic field cannot end abruptly at radius R—unless a special arrangement of currents is provided—but must approach zero gradually. This "fringing" does not change any of the arguments of this section.

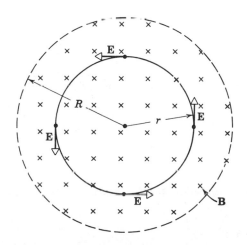

▶ **Example 4.** Let B in Fig. 35–10 be increasing at the rate dB/dt. Let R be the radius of the cylindrical region in which the magnetic field is assumed to exist. What is the magnitude of the electric field $\mathbf{E}$ at any radius r? Assume that $dB/dt = 0.10$ weber/m²-sec and $R = 10$ cm.

(a) For $r < R$, the flux Φ_B through the loop is

$$\Phi_B = B(\pi r^2).$$

Substituting into Faraday's law (Eq. 35–9),

$$\oint \mathbf{E} \cdot d\mathbf{l} = -\frac{d\Phi_B}{dt}$$

yields

$$(E)(2\pi r) = -\frac{d\Phi_B}{dt} = -(\pi r^2)\frac{dB}{dt}.$$

Solving for E yields

$$E = -\tfrac{1}{2}r\frac{dB}{dt}.$$

The minus sign is retained to suggest that the induced electric field $\mathbf{E}$ acts to *oppose* the change of the magnetic field. Note that $E(r)$ depends on dB/dt and not on B. Substituting numerical values, assuming $r = 5$ cm, yields, for the magnitude of E,

$$E = \tfrac{1}{2}r\frac{dB}{dt} = (\tfrac{1}{2})(5 \times 10^{-2}\text{ meter})\left(\frac{0.10\text{ weber}}{\text{m}^2\text{-sec}}\right) = 2.5 \times 10^{-3}\text{ volt/meter}.$$

(b) For $r > R$ the flux through the loop is

$$\Phi_B = \int \mathbf{B} \cdot d\mathbf{S} = B(\pi R^2).$$

This equation is true because $\mathbf{B} \cdot d\mathbf{S}$ is zero for those points of the loop that lie outside the effective boundary of the magnetic field.

From Faraday's law (Eq. 35–9),

$$(E)(2\pi r) = -\frac{d\Phi_B}{dt} = -(\pi R^2)\frac{dB}{dt}.$$

Solving for E yields

$$E = -\frac{1}{2}\frac{R^2}{r}\frac{dB}{dt}.$$

These two expressions for $E(r)$ yield the same result, as they must, for $r = R$. Figure 35–11 is a plot of the magnitude of $E(r)$ for the numerical values given.   ◀

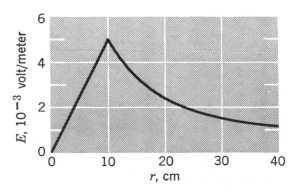

Fig. 35–11 Example 4. If the fringing of the field in Fig. 35–10 were to be taken into account, the result would be a rounding of the sharp cusp at $r = R$ (= 10 cm).

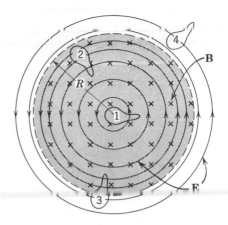

Fig. 35-12 Showing the circular lines of E from an increasing magnetic field. The four loops are imaginary paths around which an emf can be calculated.

In applying Lenz's law to Fig. 35–10, imagine that a circular conducting loop is placed concentrically in the field. Since Φ_B through this loop is increasing, the induced current in the loop will tend to oppose this "change" by setting up a magnetic field of its own that points up within the loop. Thus the induced current i must be counterclockwise, which means that the lines of the induced electric field E, which is responsible for the current, must also be counterclockwise. If the magnetic field in Fig. 35–10 were *decreasing* with time, the induced current and the lines of force of the induced electric field E would be clockwise, again opposing the *change* in Φ_B.

Figure 35–12 shows four of many possible loops to which Faraday's law may be applied. For loops 1 and 2, the induced emf $\mathcal{E}$ is the same because these loops lie entirely within the changing magnetic field and thus have the same value of $d\Phi_B/dt$. Note that even though the emf $\mathcal{E}$ $(= \oint \mathbf{E} \cdot d\mathbf{l})$ is the same for these two loops, the distribution of electric fields E around the perimeter of each loop, as indicated by the electric lines of force, is different. For loop 3 the emf is less because Φ_B and $d\Phi_B/dt$ for this loop are less, and for loop 4 the induced emf is zero.

The induced electric fields that are set up by the induction process are not associated with charges but with a changing magnetic flux. Although both kinds of electric fields exert forces on charges, there is a difference between them. The simplest manifestation of this difference is that lines of E associated with a changing magnetic flux can form closed loops (see Fig. 35–12); lines of E associated with charges cannot but can always be drawn to start on a positive charge and end on a negative charge.

Equation 29–5, which defined the potential difference between two points a and b, is

$$V_b - V_a = \frac{W_{ab}}{q_0} = -\int_a^b \mathbf{E} \cdot d\mathbf{l}.$$

We have insisted that if potential is to have any useful meaning this integral (and W_{ab}) must have the same value for every path connecting a with b. This proved to be true for every case examined in earlier chapters.

An interesting special case comes up if a and b are the same point. The path connecting them is now a closed loop; V_a must be identical with V_b and this equation reduces to

$$\oint \mathbf{E} \cdot d\mathbf{l} = 0. \tag{35-10}$$

However, when changing magnetic flux is present, $\oint \mathbf{E} \cdot d\mathbf{l}$ is precisely *not* zero but is, according to Faraday's law (see Eq. 35–9), $-d\Phi_B/dt$. Electric fields associated with stationary charges are *conservative*, but those associated with changing magnetic fields are *nonconservative;* see Section 8–2. Electric potential, which can be defined only for a conservative force, *has no meaning for electric fields produced by induction*.

35–6 The Betatron

The betatron is a device used to accelerate electrons to high speeds by allowing them to be acted upon by induced electric fields that are set up by a changing magnetic flux. It provides an excellent illustration of the "reality" of such induced fields. The energetic electrons can be used for fundamental research in physics or to produce penetrating X-rays which are useful in cancer therapy and in industry.

Figure 35–13 shows the 100-Mev betatron at the General Electric Company. At this energy the electron speed is $0.999986c$, where c is the speed of light, so that relativistic mechanics must certainly be used in the analysis of its operation. Figure 35–14 shows a vertical cross section through the central part of the betatron to which the man in Fig. 35–13 is pointing.

The magnetic field in the betatron has several functions: (*a*) it guides the electrons in a circular path; (*b*) it accelerates the electrons in this path;

Fig. 35–13 A 100-Mev betatron. M shows the magnet, C the magnetizing coils, and D the region in which the "doughnut" is located. (Courtesy General Electric Company.)

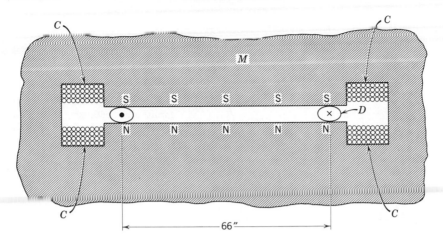

Fig. 35–14 Cross section of a betatron, showing magnet M, coils C, and "doughnut" D. Electrons emerge from the page at the left and enter it at the right.

(c) it keeps the radius of the orbit in which the electrons are moving a constant; (d) it introduces the electrons into the orbit initially and removes them from the orbit after they have reached full energy; and finally (e) it provides a restoring force that resists any tendency for the electrons to leave their orbit, either vertically or radially. It is remarkable that it is possible to do all these things by proper shaping and control of the magnetic field.

The object marked D in Fig. 35–14 is an evacuated glass "doughnut" inside which the electrons travel. Their orbit is a circle at right angles to the plane of the figure. The electrons emerge from the plane at the left ($\cdot$) and enter it at the right ($\times$). In the General Electric machine the radius of the electron path is 33 in. The coils C and the 130-ton steel magnet shown in Fig. 35–13 provide the magnetic flux that passes through the plane of this orbit.

The current in coils C is made to alter periodically, 60 times/sec, to produce a changing flux through the orbit, shown in Fig. 35–15. Here Φ_B is taken as positive when **B** is pointing up, as in Fig. 35–14. If the electrons are to circulate in the direction shown, they must do so during the positive half-cycle, marked ac in Fig. 35–15. The student should verify this (see Section 33–6). The electrons are accelerated by electric fields set up by the changing flux. The direction of these induced fields depends on the sign of $d\Phi_B/dt$ and must be chosen to accelerate, and not to decelerate, the electrons. Thus only half the positive half-cycle in Fig. 35–15 can be used for acceleration; it will prove to be ab.

The average value of $d\Phi_B/dt$ during the quarter cycle ab is the slope of the dashed line, or

$$\overline{\frac{d\Phi_B}{dt}} = \frac{1.8 \text{ weber}}{4.2 \times 10^{-3} \text{ sec}} = 430 \text{ volts.}$$

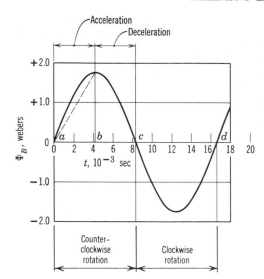

Fig. 35–15 The flux through the orbit of a betatron, during one cycle. Rotation of the electrons in the desired direction (counter-clockwise as viewed from above in Fig. 35–14) is possible only during half-cycle *ac*.

From Faraday's law (Eq. 35–1), this is also the emf in volts. The electron will thus increase its energy by 430 ev every time it makes a trip around the orbit in the changing flux. If the electron gains only 430 ev of energy per revolution, it must make about 230,000 rev to gain its full 100 Mcv. For an orbit radius of 33 in., this corresponds to a length of path of some 750 miles.

The betatron provides a good example of the fact that electric potential has no meaning for electric fields produced by induction. If a potential exists, it must be true that, as Eq. 35–10 shows, $\oint \mathbf{E} \cdot d\mathbf{l} = 0$ for any closed path. In the betatron, however, this integral, evaluated around the orbit, is precisely *not* zero but is, in our example, 430 volts. It must not be thought, of course, that the betatron violates the conservation of energy principle. The gain in kinetic energy of the circulating electron (430 ev/rev) must be supplied by an identifiable energy source. It comes, in fact, from the generator that energizes the magnet coils, thus providing the changing magnetic field. The energy is transmitted to the electron through the intermediary of this changing field.

▶ **Example 5.** In the betatron of Fig. 35–13, which is the "accelerating" quarter-cycle?

Let us assume that it is *ab* in Fig. 35–15, during which Φ_B through the orbit is *increasing*. If a conducting loop were placed to coincide with the orbit, an induced current would appear in the loop to oppose the tendency of Φ_B to increase. This means that a magnetic field would be set up that would oppose the field of the large magnet. Thus **E** would point outward at the right side of "doughnut" *D* in Fig. 35–14 and inward on the left side. The force ($-e\mathbf{E}$) acting on the electron is in the opposite direction to **E** because of the negative charge of the electron. Thus the tangential force acting on the electron is in the same direction as that at which it circulates in its orbit; this means that the speed of the electron will increase, as desired. The student should go through this same analysis carefully, assuming (incorrectly, as it will turn out) that the accelerating half-cycle is *bc* in Fig. 35–15 rather than *ab*.

Example 6. In the betatron, what condition must be met if the orbit radius is not to change as the electrons are accelerated?

The magnetic field in the betatron changes not only with time (Fig. 35–15) but also with distance r from the central axis and thus may be expressed as a function $B(r,t)$. Let us assume that, at a given instant, electrons are circulating at an assumed orbit radius R and that the magnetic field *at the orbit* has the value B_R. From Newton's second law, applied to the *centripetal* acceleration (see Section 33–6), we can write

$$F_{\text{cent}} = B_R ev = m \frac{v^2}{R}$$

or

$$p = mv = B_R Re. \tag{35–11}$$

This equation shows that if we can so arrange matters that the linear momentum p increases with time in proportion to B_R, the orbit radius R must remain constant; otherwise Eq. 35–11 could not be satisfied at all times.

To see how this can be done, let us now apply Newton's second law to the *tangential* acceleration produced by the induced electric field $\mathbf{E}$. We have

$$F_{\text{tan}} = eE = \frac{dp}{dt}. \tag{35–12}$$

We can also write Faraday's law (Eq. 35–9) as

$$E(2\pi R) = \frac{d\Phi_B}{dt} \quad \text{or} \quad E = \frac{1}{2\pi R}\frac{d\Phi_B}{dt}.$$

We have omitted the minus sign here because it deals only with the *sign* of E and we are concerned with magnitudes. The question of sign is fully discussed in Example 5.

Differentiating Eq. 35–11 gives

$$\frac{dp}{dt} = \frac{dB_R}{dt} Re.$$

Substituting these last two expressions into Eq. 35–12 leads to

$$\frac{e}{2\pi R}\frac{d\Phi_B}{dt} = \frac{dB_R}{dt} Re$$

or

$$d\Phi_B = 2\pi R^2 \, dB_R.$$

Integrating, under the assumption that B_R and Φ_B equal zero at the start of the acceleration process ($t = 0$), leads to

$$\Phi_B = 2\pi R^2 B_R.$$

We must now distinguish between B_R, which is the value of B *at the orbit position*, and $\bar{B}$, which is the *average value* of B over the orbit area; $\bar{B}$ is defined from

$$\bar{B} = \frac{\Phi_B}{\pi R^2},$$

which, combined with the equation just given, leads to

$$\bar{B} = 2B_R.$$

Thus, to keep the orbit radius constant, it is necessary to shape the field so that $\bar{B}$, the *average magnetic induction* over the space enclosed by the orbit, is exactly twice the value of B at the orbit. This condition must be satisfied at all times during the acceleration cycle, even though both $\bar{B}$ and B_R vary with time. To satisfy this relation, a strong central flux must be provided. ◀

35–7   Induction and Relative Motion

Faraday's law, in the form $\varepsilon = -d\Phi_B/dt$, gives correctly the induced emf no matter whether the change in Φ_B is produced by moving a coil, moving a magnet, changing the strength of a magnetic field, changing the shape of a conducting loop, or in other ways. However, observers who are in relative motion with respect to each other, even though they would all agree on the numerical value of the emf, would give different microscopic descriptions of the induction process. In electromagnetic systems, as well as in mechanical systems, it is important that the state of motion of the observer be made perfectly clear.

Figure 35–16 shows a closed loop which is caused to move at velocity **v** with respect to a magnet that provides a uniform field **B** in the region shown. We consider first an observer, identified as S, who is *at rest with respect to the magnet* used to establish the field **B**; see Fig. 35–16a. The induced emf in this case is called a *motional emf* because the conducting loop is moving with respect to the observer.

Consider a positive charge carrier at the center of the left end of the conducting loop. To observer S, this charge, constrained to move to the right along with the loop, is a charge q moving with velocity **v** in a magnetic field **B** and as such it experiences a sideways magnetic deflecting force $\mathbf{F}_m$ given by Eq. 33–3a, or

$$\mathbf{F}_m = q\mathbf{v} \times B. \tag{35–13}$$

The right-hand rule for vector products shows that $\mathbf{F}_m$ is directed to cause positive charge carriers to circulate clockwise in Fig. 35–16a.

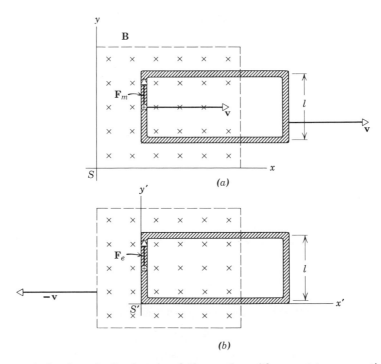

Fig. 35–16   A closed conducting loop in relative motion with respect to a magnetic field. (a) An observer S, fixed with respect to the magnet that produces the field **B**, sees the loop moving to the right. (b) An observer S', fixed with respect to the loop, sees the field moving to the left.

As the charge moves a distance $d\mathbf{l}$ along the loop, the force $\mathbf{F}_m$ does work on it given by

$$dW = \mathbf{F}_m \cdot d\mathbf{l}.$$

For the complete loop of Fig. 35–16a, the total work done by this force is

$$W = \oint dW = \oint \mathbf{F}_m \cdot d\mathbf{l} = F_m l, \tag{35–14}$$

where l is the length of the left end of the loop. Note that $\mathbf{F}_m \cdot d\mathbf{l}$ is zero for the top and bottom conductors, $\mathbf{F}_m$ and $d\mathbf{l}$ being at right angles here; $\mathbf{F}_m \cdot d\mathbf{l}$ is also zero for the right end of the loop because this conductor is outside the magnetic field and no magnetic force acts on the charge carriers here (that is, $\mathbf{F}_m = 0$). Thus work is done on the charge carriers only in the left end of the loop.

An agent that does work on charge carriers, thus establishing a current in a circuit, can be viewed as an emf. We can write, making use of Eq. 35–13,

$$\mathcal{E} = \frac{W}{q} = \frac{F_m l}{q} = \frac{(qvB)l}{q} = Blv,$$

in agreement with Eq. 35–3. Thus a motional emf is intimately connected with the sideways deflection of a charged particle moving through a magnetic field.

We now consider how the situation of Fig. 35–16 would appear to an observer S' who is *at rest with respect to the loop*. To this observer, the magnet and its associated field are moving to the left in Fig. 35–16b with velocity $-\mathbf{v}$, and the charge q is at rest as far as its left-to-right motion is concerned. However S' observes that the charge drifts clockwise around the loop. He accounts for this by postulating that an electric field $\mathbf{E}$ is induced in the left end of the loop by the moving magnetic field. This induced field $\mathbf{E}$, which is of the same character as the induced fields that we discussed in Section 35–5, exerts an electric force on the charge given by

$$\mathbf{F}_e = q\mathbf{E}.$$

$\mathbf{F}_e$ must be identical with the force $\mathbf{F}_m$ observed by S, since they both produce the same motion of the charge carrier, that is, both observers agree on the value of the induced emf $\mathcal{E}$ in the loop. Thus (see Eq. 35–13)

$$q\mathbf{E} = q\mathbf{v} \times \mathbf{B},$$

which reduces to $$\mathbf{E} = \mathbf{v} \times \mathbf{B}. \tag{35–15}$$

Observer S' associates the emf $\mathcal{E}$ with the electric force $\mathbf{F}_e$. The work done by this force acting around the loop (compare with Eq. 35–14) is

$$W = \oint dW = \oint \mathbf{F}_e \cdot d\mathbf{l} = F_e l$$

and the associated emf is

$$\mathcal{E} = \frac{W}{q} = \frac{F_e l}{q} = \frac{(qE)l}{q} = El. \tag{35–16}$$

We see at once that this is a special case of Eq. 35–8 ($\mathcal{E} = \oint \mathbf{E} \cdot d\mathbf{l}$). In view of Eq. 35–15, written for the present case as $E = vB$, Eq. 35–16 is identical with Eq. 35–3 ($\mathcal{E} = Blv$). This is as it should be because both observers agree on the numerical value of the emf, even though they account for its presence by different microscopic formalisms.

We summarize the situation of Fig. 35–16:

1. S observes only a magnetic field B at the site of the charge carrier. He accounts for the motion of the charge, and thus for the induced (motional) emf, by saying that the charge experiences a sideways deflecting force of magnetic origin, given by $\mathbf{F}_m = q\mathbf{v} \times \mathbf{B}$.

2. S' observes not only the magnetic field B but also an induced electric field E, given by Eq. 35–15, at the site of the charge carrier. He postulates that this field arises because of the motion of the magnet with respect to him. He accounts for the motion of the charge, and thus for the induced emf, by saying that this induced field E acts on the charge. S' does not describe the emf as *motional* because the loop is not in motion with respect to him.

An experiment carried out in 1926 by the German physicist Wilhelm Wien (1864–1928) gives concrete support to our microscopic descriptions of the effect of the motion of an observer on the nature of the electric and magnetic fields that he observes. The radiations emitted from atoms vary slightly in wavelength if the atom is immersed in either a magnetic or an electric field. The atom can thus be used as a probe to examine the nature of such fields. Wien fired a beam of atoms with velocity $\mathbf{v}$ through a magnetic field B. The radiations emitted were identical in the distribution of their wavelengths with those that would have been emitted by a *resting* atom immersed in (a) the magnetic field B *and* (b) an induced electric field E given by Eq. 35–15.

▶ **Example 7.** In Fig. 35–16 assume that $B = 2.0$ webers/meter^2, $l = 10$ cm, and $v = 1.0$ meter/sec. Calculate (a) the induced electric field observed by S', (b) the force acting on a charge carrier with charge $+e$ ($= 1.6 \times 10^{-19}$ coul), and (c) the emf induced in the loop.

(a) The electric field, which is apparent only to observer S', is associated with the moving magnetic field and is given in magnitude (see Eq. 35–15) by

$$E = vB$$

$$= (1.0 \text{ meter/sec})(2.0 \text{ webers/meter}^2)$$

$$= 2.0 \text{ volt/meter.}$$

(b) Observer S would calculate the force on the charge carrier from

$$F = qvB$$

$$= (1.6 \times 10^{-19} \text{ coul})(1.0 \text{ meter/sec})(2.0 \text{ webers/meter}^2)$$

$$= 3.2 \times 10^{-19} \text{ nt.}$$

Observer S' would use the relationship

$$F = qE$$

$$= (1.6 \times 10^{-19} \text{ coul})(2.0 \text{ volt/meter})$$

$$= 3.2 \times 10^{-19} \text{ nt.}$$

As expected, both observers obtain the same numerical result for the force, even though they account for its presence in different ways.

(c) Observer S would calculate the induced (motional) emf from

$$\mathcal{E} = Blv$$

$$- (2.0 \text{ webers/meter}^2)(1.0 \times 10^{-1} \text{ meter})(1.0 \text{ meter/sec})$$

$$= 0.20 \text{ volt.}$$

Observer S' would not regard the emf as motional and would use the relationship

$$\mathcal{E} = El$$

$$= (2.0 \text{ volt/meter})(1.0 \times 10^{-1} \text{ meter})$$

$$= 0.20 \text{ volt.}$$

Again, as expected, both observers agree as to the numerical value of the emf.   ◀

QUESTIONS

1. The north pole of a magnet is moved away from a metallic ring, as in Fig. 35–17. In the part of the ring farthest from the reader, which way does the current point?

Fig. 35–17

2. *Eddy currents.* A sheet of copper is placed in a magnetic field as shown in Fig. 35–18. If we attempt to pull it out of the field or push it further in, an automatic resisting force appears. Explain its origin. (Hint: Currents, called eddy currents, are induced in the sheet in such a way as to oppose the motion.)

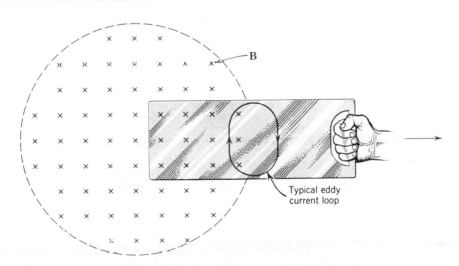

Typical eddy current loop

Fig. 35–18

3. *Electromagnetic shielding.* Consider a conducting sheet lying in a plane perpendicular to a magnetic field **B**, as shown in Fig. 35–19. (*a*) If **B** suddenly changes, the full *change* in **B** is not immediately detected in region *P*. Explain. (*b*) If the resistivity of the sheet is zero, the *change* is not ever detected at *P*. Explain. (*c*) If **B** changes periodically at high frequency and the conductor is made of a material of low resistivity, the region near *P* is almost completely shielded from the *changes* in flux. Explain. (*d*) Is such a conductor useful as a shield from *static* magnetic fields? Explain.

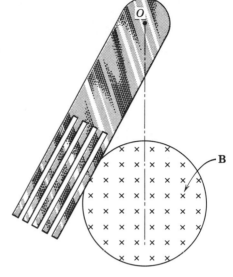

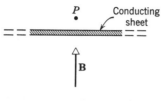

Fig. 35–19   **Fig. 35–20**

4. *Magnetic damping.* A strip of copper is mounted as a pendulum about *O* in Fig. 35–20. It is free to swing through a magnetic field normal to the page. If the strip has slots cut in it as shown, it can swing freely through the field. If a strip without slots is substituted, the vibratory motion is strongly damped. Explain. (Hint: Use Lenz's law; consider the paths that the charge carriers in the strip must follow if they are to oppose the motion.)

5. Two conducting loops face each other a distance *d* apart (Fig. 35–21). An observer sights along their common axis. If a clockwise current *i* is suddenly established in the larger loop, (*a*) what is the direction of the induced current in the smaller loop? (*b*) What is the direction of the force (if any) that acts on the smaller loop?

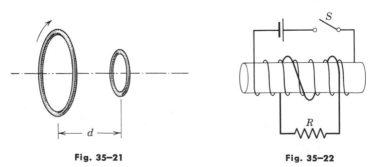

Fig. 35–21   **Fig. 35–22**

6. What is the direction, if any, of the conventional current through resistor *R* in Fig. 35–22 (*a*) immediately after switch *S* is closed, (*b*) some time after switch *S* was closed, and (*c*) immediately after switch *S* is opened. (*d*) When switch *S* is held closed, which end of the coil acts as a north pole?

7. A current-carrying solenoid is moved toward a conducting loop as in Fig. 35-23. What is the direction of circulation of current in the loop as we sight toward it as shown?

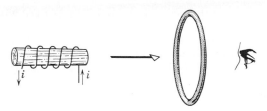

Fig. 35-23

8. If the resistance R in the left-hand circuit of Fig. 35-24 is increased, what is the direction of the induced current in the right-hand circuit?

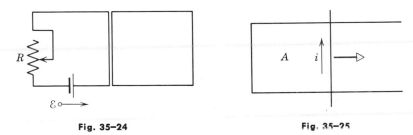

Fig. 35-24   **Fig. 35-25**

9. In Fig. 35-25 the movable wire is moved to the right, causing an induced current as shown. What is the direction of **B** in region A?

10. A loop, shown in Fig. 35-26, is removed from the magnet by pulling it vertically upward. (a) What is the direction of the induced current? (b) Is a force required to remove the loop? (c) Does the total amount of Joule heat produced in removing the loop depend on the time taken to remove it?

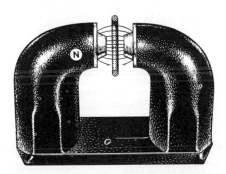

Fig. 35-26

11. A magnet is dropped down a long vertical copper tube. Show that, even neglecting air resistance, the magnet will reach a constant terminal velocity.

12. A magnet is dropped from the ceiling along the axis of a copper loop lying flat on the floor. If the falling magnet is photographed with a time sequence camera, what differences, if any, will be noted if (a) the loop is at room temperature and (b) the loop is packed in dry ice?

13. A copper ring and a wooden ring of the same dimensions are placed so that there is the same changing magnetic flux through each. How do the induced electric fields in each ring compare?

14. In Fig. 35–12 how can the induced emfs around paths 1 and 2 be identical? The induced electric fields are much weaker near path 1 than near path 2, as the spacing of the lines of force shows. See also Fig. 35–11.

15. In a certain betatron the electrons rotate counterclockwise as seen from above. In what direction must the magnetic field point and how must it change with time while the electron is being accelerated?

16. Why can a betatron be used for acceleration only during one-quarter of a cycle?

17. To make the electrons in a betatron orbit spiral outward, would it be necessary to increase or to decrease the central flux? Assume that **B** at the orbit remains essentially unchanged.

18. A cyclotron is a so-called *resonance device*. Does a betatron depend on resonance?

PROBLEMS

1. A hundred turns of insulated copper wire are wrapped around an iron cylinder of cross-sectional area 0.001 meter^2 and are connected to a resistor. The total resistance in the circuit is 10 ohms. If the longitudinal magnetic induction in the iron changes from 1 weber/meter^2 in one direction to 1 weber/meter^2 in the opposite direction, how much charge flows through the circuit?

2. In Fig. 35–27 a closed copper coil with 100 turns and a total resistance of 5.0 ohms is placed *outside* a solenoid like that of Example 1. If the current in the solenoid is changed as in that example, what current appears in the coil?

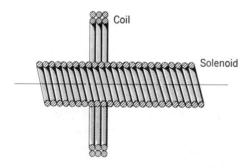

Coil

Solenoid

Fig. 35–27

3. A circular loop of wire 10 cm in diameter is placed with its normal making an angle of 30° with the direction of a uniform 5000-gauss magnetic field. The loop is "wobbled" so that its normal rotates about the field direction at the constant rate of 100 rev/min; the angle between the normal and the field direction (= 30°) remains unchanged during this process. What emf appears in the loop?

4. A uniform field of induction **B** is normal to the plane of a circular ring 10-cm in diameter made of #10 copper wire (diameter = 0.10 in.). At what rate must B change with time if an induced current of 10 amp is to appear in the ring?

5. A uniform field of induction **B** is changing in magnitude at a constant rate dB/dt. You are given a mass m of copper which is to be drawn into a wire of radius r and formed into a circular loop of radius R. Show that the induced current in the loop does not depend

on the size of the wire or of the loop and, assuming **B** perpendicular to the loop, is given by

$$i = \frac{m}{4\pi\rho\delta}\frac{dB}{dt},$$

where ρ is the resistivity and δ the density of copper.

6. You are given 50 cm of #18 copper wire (diameter = 0.040 in.). It is formed into a circular loop and placed at right angles to a uniform magnetic field that is increasing with time at the constant rate of 100 gauss/sec. At what rate is Joule heat generated in the loop?

7. A small bar magnet is pulled rapidly through a conducting loop, along its axis. Sketch qualitatively (a) the induced current and (b) the rate of Joule heating as a function of the position of the center of the magnet. Assume that the north pole of the magnet enters the loop first and that the magnet moves at constant speed. Plot the induced current as positive if it is clockwise as viewed along the path of the magnet.

8. *Alternating current generator.* A rectangular loop of N turns and of length a and width b is rotated at a frequency f in a uniform field of induction **B**, as in Fig. 35–28. (a) Show that an induced emf given by

$$\mathcal{E} = 2\pi fNbaB \sin 2\pi ft = \mathcal{E}_0 \sin 2\pi ft$$

appears in the loop. This is the principle of the commercial alternating-current generator. (b) Design a loop that will produce an emf with $\mathcal{E}_0 = 150$ volts when rotated at 60 rev/sec in a field of magnetic induction of 5000-gauss.

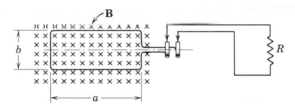

Fig. 35–28

9. A stiff wire bent into a semicircle of radius R is rotated with a frequency f in a uniform field of induction **B**, as shown in Fig. 35–29. What are the amplitude and frequency of the induced voltage and of the induced current when the internal resistance of the meter M is R_M and the remainder of the circuit has negligible resistance?

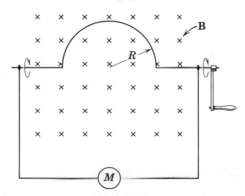

Fig. 35–29

10. A circular copper disk 10 cm in diameter rotates at 1800 rev/min about an axis through its center and at right angles to the disk. A uniform field of induction **B** of 10,000 gauss is perpendicular to the disk. What potential difference develops between the axis of the disk and its rim?

11. Figure 35–30 shows a copper rod moving with velocity **v** parallel to a long straight wire carrying a current i. Calculate the induced emf in the rod, assuming that $v = 5.0$ meters/sec, $i = 100$ amp, $a = 1.0$ cm, and $b = 20$ cm.

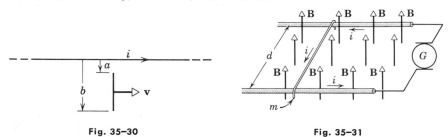

Fig. 35–30   Fig. 35–31

12. A metal wire of mass m slides without friction on two rails spaced a distance d apart, as in Fig. 35–31. The track lies in a vertical uniform field of induction **B**. (a) A *constant current i* flows from generator G along one rail, across the wire, and back down the other rail. Find the velocity (speed and direction) of the wire as a function of time, assuming it to be at rest at $t = 0$. (b) The generator is replaced by a battery with *constant emf* ε. The velocity of the wire now approaches a constant final value. What is this terminal speed? (c) What is the current in part (b) when the terminal speed has been reached?

13. In Fig. 35–32 the magnetic flux through the loop perpendicular to the plane of the coil and directed into the paper is varying according to the relation

$$\Phi_B = 6t^2 + 7t + 1,$$

where Φ_B is in milliwebers (1 milliweber $= 10^{-3}$ weber) and t is in seconds. (a) What is the magnitude of the emf induced in the loop when $t = 2$ sec? (b) What is the direction of the current through R?

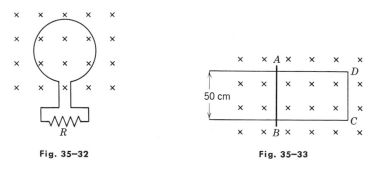

Fig. 35–32   Fig. 35–33

14. In Fig. 35–33 a conducting rod AB makes contact with the metal rails AD and BC which are 50 cm apart in a uniform magnetic field of induction 1.0 weber/meter^2 perpendicular to the plane of the paper as shown. The total resistance of the circuit $ABCD$ is 0.4 ohm (assumed constant). (a) What is the magnitude and direction of the emf induced in the rod when it is moved to the left with a velocity of 8 meters/sec? (b) What force is required to keep the rod in motion? (c) Compare the rate at which mechanical work is done by the force **F** with the rate of development of heat in the circuit.

15. A square wire of length l, mass m, and resistance R slides without friction down parallel conducting rails of negligible resistance, as in Fig. 35–34. The rails are connected

to each other at the bottom by a resistanceless rail parallel to the wire, so that the wire and rails form a closed rectangular conducting loop. The plane of the rails makes an angle θ with the horizontal, and a uniform vertical field of magnetic induction **B** exists throughout the region. (a) Show that the wire acquires a steady-state velocity of magnitude

$$v = \frac{mgR \sin \theta}{B^2 l^2 \cos^2 \theta}.$$

(b) Prove that this result is consistent with the conservation-of-energy principle. (c) What change, if any, would there be if **B** were directed down instead of up?

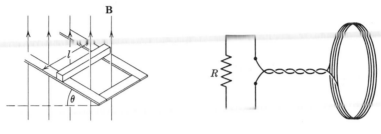

Fig. 35–34   Fig. 35–35

16. Prove that if the flux of magnetic induction through the coil of N turns of Fig. 35–35 changes in any way from Φ_1 to Φ_2, then the charge q that flows through the circuit of total resistance R is given by

$$q = \frac{N(\Phi_2 - \Phi_1)}{R}.$$

17. Figure 35–36 shows a uniform field of induction **B** confined to a cylindrical volume of radius R. **B** is decreasing in magnitude at a constant rate of 100 gauss/sec. What is the instantaneous acceleration (direction and magnitude) experienced by an electron placed at a, at b, and at c? Assume $r = 5.0$ cm. (The necessary fringing of the field beyond R will not change your answer as long as there is axial symmetry about a perpendicular axis through b.)

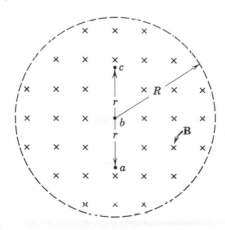

Fig. 35–36

18. A uniform magnetic field of induction **B** fills a cylindrical volume of radius R. A metal rod of length l is placed as shown in Fig. 35–37. If B is changing at the rate dB/dt,

show that the emf that is produced by the changing magnetic field and that acts between the ends of the rod is given by

$$\mathcal{E} = \frac{dB}{dt}\frac{l}{2}\sqrt{R^2 - \left(\frac{l}{2}\right)^2}.$$

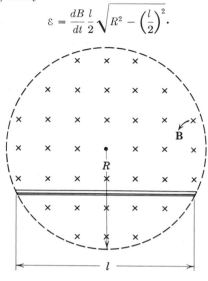

Fig. 35–37

19. Some measurements of the maximum magnetic induction as a function of radius for the General Electric Company betatron are as follows:

r, cm	B, gauss	r, cm	B, gauss
0	4000	81.2	4090
10.2	9500	83.7	4000
68.2	9500	88.9	3810
73.2	5280	91.4	3720
75.2	4510	93.5	3600
77.3	4280	95.5	3400

Show by graphical analysis that the relation $\bar{B} = 2B_R$ is satisfied at the orbit radius, $R = 84$ cm. (Hint: Note that $\bar{B}(R) = \dfrac{1}{\pi R^2}\displaystyle\int_0^R B(r)(2\pi r)\,dr$ and evaluate the integral graphically.)

20. Prove that the electric field **E** in a charged parallel-plate capacitor cannot drop abruptly to zero as one moves at right angles to it, as suggested by the arrow in Fig. 35–38 (see point a). In actual capacitors fringing of the lines of force always occurs, which means that **E** approaches zero in a continuous and gradual way. See Problem 34–28. (Hint: Apply Faraday's law to the rectangular path shown by the dashed lines.)

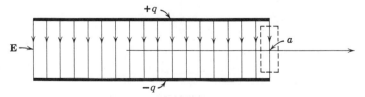

Fig. 35–38

Inductance

CHAPTER 36

36-1 Inductance

If two coils are near each other, a current i in one coil will set up a flux Φ_B through the second coil. If this flux is changed by changing the current, an induced emf will appear in the second coil according to Faraday's law. However, two coils are not needed to show an inductive effect. An induced emf appears in a coil if the current *in that same coil* is changed. This is called *self-induction* and the electromotive force produced is called a *self induced emf*. It obeys Faraday's law of induction just as other induced emfs do.

Consider first a "close-packed" coil, a toroid, or the central section of a long solenoid. In all three cases the flux Φ_B set up in each turn by a current i is essentially the same for every turn. Faraday's law for such coils (Eq. 35–2)

$$\mathcal{E} = -\frac{d(N\Phi_B)}{dt} \tag{36-1}$$

shows that the number of *flux linkages* $N\Phi_B$ (N being the number of turns) is the important characteristic quantity for induction. For a given coil, provided no magnetic materials such as iron are nearby, this quantity is proportional to the current i, or

$$N\Phi_B = Li, \tag{36-2}$$

in which L, the proportionality constant, is called the *inductance* of the device.

From Faraday's law (see Eq. 36–1) the induced emf can be written as

$$\mathcal{E} = -\frac{d(N\Phi_B)}{dt} = -L\frac{di}{dt}. \tag{36-3a}$$

Written in the form $$L = - \frac{\varepsilon}{di/dt},$$ (36–3b)

this relation may be taken as the defining equation for inductance for coils of all shapes and sizes, whether or not they are close-packed and whether or not iron or other magnetic material is nearby. It is analogous to the defining relation for capacitance, namely

$$C = \frac{q}{V}.$$

If no iron or similar materials are nearby, L depends only on the geometry of the device. In an *inductor* (symbol ⟋⟍⟋⟍⟍) the presence of a *magnetic field* is the significant feature, corresponding to the presence of an *electric field* in a *capacitor*.

The unit of inductance, from Eq. 36–3b, is the volt-sec/amp. A special name, the *henry*, has been given to this combination of units, or

1 henry = 1 volt-sec/amp.

The unit of inductance is named after Joseph Henry (1797–1878), an American physicist and a contemporary of Faraday. Henry independently discovered the law of induction at about the same time Faraday did. The units *millihenry* (1 mh = 10^{3} henry) and *microhenry* (1 μh = 10^{-6} henry) are also commonly used.

The direction of a self-induced emf can be found from Lenz's law. Suppose that a steady current i, produced by a battery, exists in a coil. Let us suddenly reduce the (battery) emf in the circuit to zero. The current i will start to decrease at once; this *decrease* in current, in the language of Lenz's law, is the "change" which the self-induction must oppose. To oppose the falling current, the induced emf must point in the same direction as the current, as in Fig. 36–1a. When the current in a coil is increased, Lenz's law shows that the self-induced emf points in the *opposite* direction to that of the current, as in Fig. 36–1b. In each case the self-induced emf acts to op-

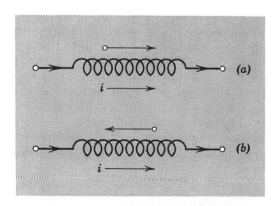

Fig. 36–1 In (a) the current i is *decreasing* and in (b) it is *increasing*. The self-induced emf ε_L opposes the *change* in each case.

pose the *change* in the current. The minus sign in Eq. 36–3 shows that ε and di/dt are opposite in sign, since L is always a positive quantity.

36–2   Calculation of Inductance

It has proved possible to make a direct calculation of capacitance in terms of geometrical factors for a few special cases, such as the parallel-plate capacitor. In the same way, it is possible to calculate the self-inductance L for a few special cases.

For a close-packed coil with no iron nearby, we have, from Eq. 36–2,

$$L = \frac{N\Phi_B}{i}. \tag{36–4}$$

Let us apply this equation to calculate L for a section of length l near the center of a long solenoid. The number of flux linkages in the length l of the solenoid is

$$N\Phi_B = (nl)(BA),$$

where n is the number of turns per unit length, B is the magnetic induction inside the solenoid, and A is the cross-sectional area. From Eq. 34–7, B is given by

$$B = \mu_0 ni.$$

Combining these equations gives

$$N\Phi_B = \mu_0 n^2 liA.$$

Finally, the inductance, from Eq. 36–4, is

$$L = \frac{N\Phi_B}{i} = \mu_0 n^2 lA. \tag{36–5}$$

The inductance of a length l of a solenoid is proportional to its volume (lA) and to the square of the number of turns per unit length. Note that it depends on geometrical factors only. The proportionality to n^2 is expected. If the number of turns per unit length is doubled, not only is the *total* number of turns N doubled but also the flux *through each turn* Φ_B is also doubled, an over-all factor of four for the flux linkages $N\Phi_B$, hence also a factor of four for the inductance (Eq. 36–4).

▶ **Example 1.** Derive an expression for the inductance of a toroid of rectangular cross section as shown in Fig. 36–2. Evaluate for $N = 10^3$, $a = 5.0$ cm, $b = 10$ cm, and $h = 1.0$ cm.

The lines of **B** for the toroid are concentric circles. Applying Ampère's law,

$$\oint \mathbf{B} \cdot d\mathbf{l} = \mu_0 i,$$

to a circular path of radius r yields

$$(B)(2\pi r) = \mu_0 i_0 N,$$

where N is the number of turns and i_0 is the current in the toroid windings; recall that

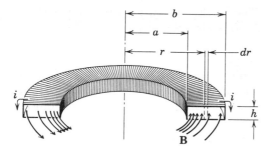

Fig. 36–2 Example 1. A cross section of a toroid, showing the current in the windings and the magnetic field.

i in Ampère's law is the *total* current that passes through the path of integration. Solving for B yields

$$B = \frac{\mu_0 i_0 N}{2\pi r}.$$

The flux Φ_B for the cross section of the toroid is

$$\Phi_B = \int \mathbf{B} \cdot d\mathbf{S} = \int_a^b (B)(h\,dr) = \int_a^b \frac{\mu_0 i_0 N}{2\pi r} h\,dr$$

$$= \frac{\mu_0 i_0 N h}{2\pi} \int_a^b \frac{dr}{r} = \frac{\mu_0 i_0 N h}{2\pi} \ln \frac{b}{a},$$

where $h\,dr$ is the area of the elementary strip shown in the figure.

The inductance follows from Eq. 36–4, or

$$L = \frac{N \Phi_B}{i_0} = \frac{\mu_0 N^2 h}{2\pi} \ln \frac{b}{a}.$$

Substituting numerical values yields

$$L = \frac{(4\pi \times 10^{-7}\text{ weber/amp-m})(10^3)^2(1.0 \times 10^{-2}\text{ meter})}{2\pi} \ln \frac{10 \times 10^{-2}\text{ meter}}{5 \times 10^{-2}\text{ meter}}$$

$$= 1.4 \times 10^{-3}\text{ weber/amp} = 1.4\text{ mh.} \qquad \blacktriangleleft$$

36–3 An *LR* Circuit

In Section 32–8 we saw that if an emf ε is suddenly introduced, perhaps by using a battery, into a single loop circuit containing a resistor R and a capacitor C the charge does not build up immediately to its final equilibrium value $(= C\varepsilon)$ but approaches it in an exponential fashion described by Eq. 32–15, or

$$q = C\varepsilon\,(1 - e^{-t/\tau_c}). \tag{36–6}$$

The delay in the rise of the charge is described by the *capacitative time constant* τ_c, defined from

$$\tau_c = RC. \tag{36–7}$$

If in this same circuit the battery emf ε is suddenly removed, the charge does not immediately fall to zero but approaches zero in an exponential fashion, described by Eq. 32–18b, or

$$q = C\varepsilon\,e^{-t/\tau_c}. \tag{36–8}$$

The same time constant τ_c describes the fall of the charge as well as its rise.

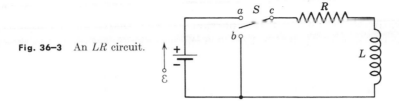

Fig. 36–3 An LR circuit.

An analogous delay in the rise or fall of the current occurs if an emf ε is suddenly introduced into, or removed from, a single loop circuit containing a resistor R and an inductor L. When the switch S in Fig. 36–3 is closed on a, for example, the current in the resistor starts to rise. If the inductor were not present, the current would rise rapidly to a steady value ε/R. Because of the inductor, however, a self-induced emf ε_L appears in the circuit and, from Lenz's law, this emf opposes the *rise* of current, which means that it opposes the battery emf ε in polarity. Thus the resistor responds to the difference between two emfs, a constant one ε due to the battery and a variable one ε_L ($= -L\, di/dt$) due to self-induction. As long as this second emf is present, the current in the resistor will be less than ε/R.

As time goes on, the rate at which the current increases becomes less rapid and the self-induced emf ε_L, which is proportional to di/dt, becomes smaller. Thus a time delay is introduced, and the current in the circuit approaches the value ε/R asymptotically.

When the switch S in Fig. 36–3 is thrown to a, the circuit reduces to that of Fig. 36–4. Let us apply the loop theorem, starting at x in this figure and going clockwise around the loop. For the direction of current shown, x will be higher in potential than y, which means that we encounter a drop in potential of $-iR$ as we traverse the resistor. Point y is higher in potential than point z because, for an increasing current, the induced emf will oppose the *rise* of the current by pointing as shown. Thus as we traverse the inductor from y to z we encounter a drop in potential of $-L(di/dt)$. We encounter a rise in potential of $+\varepsilon$ in traversing the battery from z to x. The loop theorem thus gives

$$-iR - L\frac{di}{dt} + \varepsilon = 0$$

or

$$L\frac{di}{dt} + iR = \varepsilon. \tag{36–9}$$

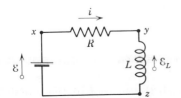

Fig. 36–4 The circuit of Fig. 36–3 just after switch S is closed on a.

Equation 36–9 is a *differential equation* involving the variable i and its first derivative di/dt. We seek the function $i(t)$ such that when it and its first derivative are substituted in Eq. 36–9 the equation is satisfied.

Although there are formal rules for solving various classes of differential equations (and Eq. 36–9 can, in fact, be easily solved by direct integration, after rearrangement) we often find it simpler to guess at the solution, guided by physical reasoning and by previous experience. Any proposed solution can be tested by substituting it in the differential equation and seeing whether this equation reduces to an identity.

The solution to Eq. 36–9 is, we assert,

$$i = \frac{\mathcal{E}}{R} (1 - e^{-Rt/L}). \tag{36–10}$$

To test this solution by substitution, we find the derivative di/dt, which is

$$\frac{di}{dt} = \frac{\mathcal{E}}{L} e^{-Rt/L}. \tag{36–11}$$

Substituting i and di/dt into Eq. 36–9 leads to an identity, as the student can easily verify. Thus Eq. 36–10 is a solution of Eq. 36–9. Figure 36–5 shows how the potential difference V_R across the resistor ($= iR$; see Eq. 36–10) and V_L across the inductor ($= L\,di/dt$; see Eq. 36–11) vary with time for particular values of $\mathcal{E}$, L, and R. The student should compare this figure carefully with the corresponding figure for an RC circuit (Fig. 32–11).

We can rewrite Eq. 36–10 as

$$i = \frac{\mathcal{E}}{R} (1 - e^{-t/\tau_L}), \tag{36–12}$$

in which τ_L, the *inductive time constant*, is given by

$$\tau_L = L/R. \tag{36–13}$$

The student should note the correspondence between Eqs. 36–12 and 36–6.

To show that the quantity τ_L ($= L/R$) has the dimensions of time, we put

$$\frac{1 \text{ henry}}{\text{ohm}} = \frac{1 \text{ henry}}{\text{ohm}} \left(\frac{1 \text{ volt-sec}}{1 \text{ henry-amp}} \right) \left(\frac{1 \text{ ohm-amp}}{1 \text{ volt}} \right) = 1 \text{ sec.}$$

The first quantity in parenthesis is a conversion factor based on the defining equation for inductance $[L = -\mathcal{E}/(di/dt)$; Eq. 36–3b]. The second conversion factor is based on the relation $V = iR$.

The physical significance of the time constant follows from Eq. 36–12. If we put $t = \tau_L = L/R$ in this equation, it reduces to

$$i = \frac{\mathcal{E}}{R} (1 - e^{-1}) = (1 - 0.37) \frac{\mathcal{E}}{R} = 0.63 \frac{\mathcal{E}}{R}.$$

Thus the time constant τ_L is that time at which the current in the circuit

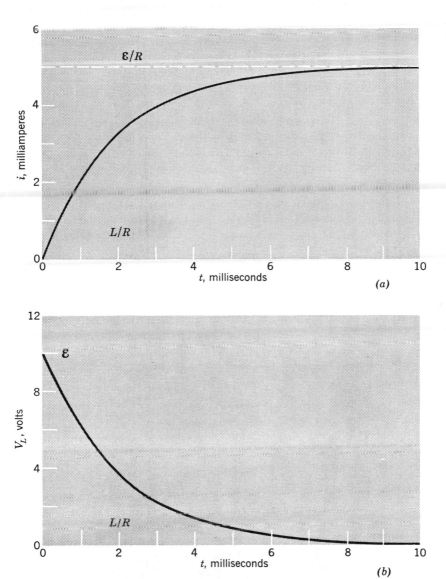

Fig. 36–5 If in Fig. 36–3 we assume that $R = 2000$ ohms, $L = 4$ henrys and $\varepsilon = 10$ volts, then (a) shows the variation of i with t during the current buildup after switch S is closed on a, and (b) the variations of V_L with t. The time constant is $L/R = 2.0 \times 10^{-3}$ sec.

will reach a value within $1/e$ (about 37%) of its final equilibrium value (see Fig. 36–5).

If the switch S in Fig. 36–3, having been left in position a long enough for the equilibrium current ε/R to be established, is thrown to b, the effect is to remove the battery from the circuit. The differential equation that governs the subsequent decay of the current in the circuit can be found by putting $\mathcal{E} = 0$ in Eq. 36–9, or

$$L\frac{di}{dt} + iR = 0. \qquad (36\text{–}14)$$

The student can show by the test of substitution that the solution of this differential equation is

$$i = \frac{\mathcal{E}}{R} e^{-t/\tau_L}. \qquad (36\text{–}15)$$

Just as for the RC circuit, the behavior of the circuit of Fig. 36–3 can be investigated experimentally, using a cathode-ray oscilloscope. If switch S in this figure is thrown periodically between a and b, the applied emf alternates between the values $\mathcal{E}$ and zero. If the terminals of an oscilloscope are connected across b and c in Fig. 36–3, the oscilloscope will display the waveform of this applied emf on its screen, as in Fig. 36–6c.

If the terminals of the oscilloscope are connected across the resistor, the waveform displayed (Fig. 36–6a) will be that of the current in the circuit, since the potential drop across R, which determines the oscilloscope deflection, is given by $V_R = iR$. During the intervals marked *inc* in Fig. 36–6, the current is increasing and the waveform (see Eq. 36–12) is given by

$$V_R (= iR) = \mathcal{E}(1 - e^{-t/\tau_L}).$$

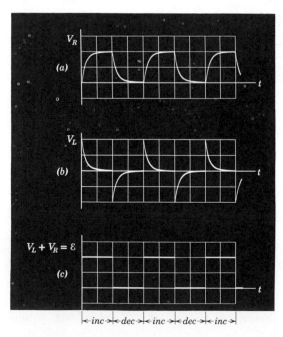

Fig. 36–6 Oscilloscope photograph showing the variation with time of (*a*) the potential drop V_R across the resistor, (*b*) the potential drop V_L across the inductor, and (*c*) the applied emf $\mathcal{E}$. During the intervals marked *inc* the current is increasing; during those marked *dec* it is decreasing. Compare with Fig. 32–13. (Courtesy E. K. Hege.)

During the intervals marked *dec*, the current is decreasing and V_R (see Eq. 36-15) is given by

$$V_R (= iR) = \mathcal{E}e^{-t/\tau_L}.$$

Note that both the growth and the decay of the current are delayed.

If the oscilloscope terminals are connected across the inductor, the screen will show a plot of the potential difference across it as a function of time (Fig. 36-6b). While the current is increasing, the equation of the trace (see Eq. 36-11) should be

$$V_L \left(= L\frac{di}{dt} \right) = \mathcal{E}e^{-t/\tau_L}.$$

When the current is decreasing, V_L is given in terms of the time derivative of Eq. 36-15 and is

$$V_L \left(= L\frac{di}{dt} \right) = -\mathcal{E}e^{-t/\tau_L}.$$

Note that V_L is opposite in sign when the current is increasing (di/dt positive) and when it is decreasing (di/dt negative), as is true also for the induced emf $\mathcal{E}_L[= -L(di/dt) = -V_L]$.

Examination of Fig. 36-6 shows that at any instant the sum of curves *a* and *b* always yields curve *c*. This is an expected consequence of the loop theorem, as Eq. 36-9 shows.

▶ **Example 2.** A solenoid has an inductance of 50 henrys and a resistance of 30 ohms. If it is connected to a 100-volt battery, how long will it take for the current to reach one-half its final equilibrium value?

The equilibrium value of the current is reached as $t \to \infty$; from Eq. 36-12 it is $\mathcal{E}/R$. If the current has half this value at a particular time t_0, this equation becomes

$$\frac{1}{2}\frac{\mathcal{E}}{R} = \frac{\mathcal{E}}{R}(1 - e^{-t_0/\tau_L}).$$

Solving for t_0 yields

$$t_0 = \tau_L \ln 2 = 0.69\frac{L}{R}.$$

Putting $\tau_L = L/R$ and using the values given, this reduces to

$$t_0 = 0.69\tau_L = 0.69 \left(\frac{50 \text{ henrys}}{30 \text{ ohms}} \right) = 1.2 \text{ sec.} \qquad ◀$$

36-4 Energy and the Magnetic Field

In Section 30-7 we saw that the electric field could be viewed as the site of stored energy, the energy per unit volume being given, in a vacuum, by

$$u_E = \tfrac{1}{2}\epsilon_0 E^2,$$

where E is the electric field strength at the point in question. Although this formula was derived for a parallel-plate capacitor, it holds for all kinds of electric field configurations.

Energy can also be stored in a magnetic field. For example, two parallel wires carrying currents in the same direction attract each other, and to pull them further apart work must be done. It is useful to think that this expended energy is stored in the magnetic field between and around the wires. The energy can be recovered from the field if the wires are allowed to move back to their original separation. In the electrostatic case the same argument was applied to the pulling apart of two unlike charges and in the gravitational case to the pulling apart of two masses.

To derive a quantitative expression for the storage of energy in the magnetic field, consider Fig. 36–4, which shows a source of emf $\mathcal{E}$ connected to a resistor R and an inductor L.

$$\mathcal{E} = iR + L\frac{di}{dt}, \tag{36–9}$$

is the differential equation that describes the growth of current in this circuit. We stress that this equation follows immediately from the loop theorem and that the loop theorem in turn *is an expression of the principle of conservation of energy for single-loop circuits*. If we multiply each side of Eq. 36–9 by i, we obtain

$$\mathcal{E}i = i^2R + Li\frac{di}{dt}, \tag{36–16}$$

which has the following physical interpretation in terms of work and energy:

1. If a charge dq passes through the seat of emf $\mathcal{E}$ in Fig. 36–4 in time dt, the seat does work on it in amount $\mathcal{E}\,dq$. The *rate* of doing work is $(\mathcal{E}\,dq)/dt$, or $\mathcal{E}i$. Thus the left term in Eq. 36–16 is the *rate at which the seat of emf delivers energy to the circuit*.

2. The second term in Eq. 36–16 is the *rate at which energy appears as Joule heat in the resistor*.

3. Energy that does not appear as Joule heat must, by our hypothesis, be stored in the magnetic field. Since Eq. 36–16 represents a statement of the conservation of energy for LR circuits, the last term must represent the *rate dU_B/dt at which energy is stored in the magnetic field*, or

$$\frac{dU_B}{dt} = Li\frac{di}{dt}. \tag{36–17}$$

We can write this as $dU_B = Li\,di$.
Integrating yields

$$U_B = \int_0^{U_B} dU_B = \int_0^i Li\,di = \tfrac{1}{2}Li^2, \tag{36–18}$$

which represents the total stored magnetic energy in an inductance L carrying a current i.

This relation can be compared with the expression for the energy associated with a capacitor C carrying a charge q, namely

$$U_E = \frac{1}{2}\frac{q^2}{C}.$$

Here the energy is stored in an electric field. In each case the expression for the stored energy was derived by setting it equal to the work that must be done to set up the field.

▶ **Example 3.**   A coil has an inductance of 5.0 henrys and a resistance of 20 ohms. If a 100-volt emf is applied, what energy is stored in the magnetic field after the current has built up to its maximum value $\mathcal{E}/R$?

The maximum current is given by

$$i = \frac{\mathcal{E}}{R} = \frac{100 \text{ volts}}{20 \text{ ohms}} = 5.0 \text{ amp.}$$

The stored energy is given by Eq. 36–18:

$$U_B = \tfrac{1}{2}Li^2 = \tfrac{1}{2}(5.0 \text{ henrys})(5.0 \text{ amp})^2 = 63 \text{ joules.}$$

Note that the time constant for this coil ($= L/R$) is 0.25 sec. After how many time constants will *half* of this equilibrium energy be stored in the field?

Example 4.   A 3.0-henry inductor is placed in series with a 10-ohm resistor, an emf of 3.0 volts being suddenly applied to the combination. At 0.30 sec (which is one inductive time constant) after the contact is made, (a) what is the rate at which energy is being delivered by the battery?

The current is given by Eq. 36–12, or

$$i = \frac{\mathcal{E}}{R}(1 - e^{-t/\tau_L}),$$

which at $t = 0.30$ sec ($= \tau_L$) has the value

$$i = \left(\frac{3.0 \text{ volts}}{10 \text{ ohms}}\right)(1 - e^{-1}) = 0.189 \text{ amp.}$$

The rate $P_\mathcal{E}$ at which energy is delivered by the battery is

$$P_\mathcal{E} = \mathcal{E}i$$

$$= (3.0 \text{ volts})(0.189 \text{ amp})$$

$$= 0.567 \text{ watt.}$$

(b) At what rate does energy appear as Joule heat in the resistor? This is given by

$$P_J = i^2 R$$

$$= (0.189 \text{ amp})^2(10 \text{ ohms})$$

$$= 0.357 \text{ watt.}$$

(c) At what rate P_B is energy being stored in the magnetic field? This is given by the last term in Eq. 36–16, which requires that we know di/dt. Differentiating Eq. 36–12 yields

$$\frac{di}{dt} = \left(\frac{\mathcal{E}}{R}\right)\left(\frac{R}{L}\right)e^{-t/\tau_L}$$

$$-\frac{\mathcal{E}}{L}e^{-t/\tau_L}.$$

At $t = \tau_L$ we have

$$\frac{di}{dt} = \left(\frac{3.0 \text{ volts}}{3.0 \text{ henrys}}\right)e^{-1} = 0.37 \text{ amp/sec.}$$

From Eq. 36–17, the desired rate is

$$P_B = \frac{dU_B}{dt} = Li\frac{di}{dt}$$

$$= (3.0 \text{ henrys})(0.189 \text{ amp})(0.37 \text{ amp/sec})$$

$$= 0.210 \text{ watt.}$$

Note that as required by the principle of conservation of energy (see Eq. 36–16)

$$P_\varepsilon = P_J + P_B,$$

or $0.567 \text{ watt} = 0.357 \text{ watt} + 0.210 \text{ watt}$

$$= 0.567 \text{ watt.} \qquad \blacktriangleleft$$

36–5   Energy Density and the Magnetic Field

We now derive an expression for the *density* of energy u in a magnetic field. Consider a length l near the center of a very long solenoid; Al is the volume associated with this length. The stored energy must lie entirely within this volume because the magnetic field outside such a solenoid is essentially zero. Moreover, the stored energy must be uniformly distributed throughout the volume of the solenoid because the magnetic field is uniform everywhere inside.

Thus we can write $u_B = \dfrac{U_B}{Al}$

or, since $U_B = \frac{1}{2}Li^2,$

$$u_B = \frac{\frac{1}{2}Li^2}{Al}.$$

To express this in terms of the magnetic field, we can substitute for L in this equation, using the relation $L = \mu_0 n^2 lA$ (Eq. 36–5). Also we can solve Eq. 34–7 ($B = \mu_0 in$) for i and substitute in this equation. Doing so yields finally

$$u_B = \frac{1}{2}\frac{B^2}{\mu_0}. \qquad (36\text{–}19)$$

This equation gives the energy density stored at any point (in a vacuum or in a nonmagnetic substance) where the magnetic induction is **B**. The equation is true for all magnetic field configurations, even though it was derived by considering a special case, the solenoid. Equation 36–19 is to be compared with Eq. 30–27,

$$u_E = \frac{1}{2}\epsilon_0 E^2, \qquad (\kappa = 1) \qquad (36\text{–}20)$$

which gives the energy density (in a vacuum) at any point in an electric field. Note that both u_B and u_E are proportional to the square of the appropriate field quantity, B or E.

The solenoid plays a role with relationship to magnetic fields similar to the role the parallel-plate capacitor plays with respect to electric fields. In each case we have a simple device that can be used for setting up a uniform field throughout a well-defined region of space and for deducing, in a simple way, some properties of these fields.

▶ **Example 5.**   A long *coaxial cable* (Fig. 36–7) consists of two concentric cylinders with radii a and b. Its central conductor carries a steady current i, the outer conductor providing the return path.   (a) Calculate the energy stored in the magnetic field for a length l of such a cable.

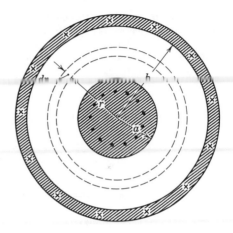

Fig. 36–7   Example 5.   Cross section of a coaxial cable, showing steady currents in the central and outer conductors.

In the space between the two conductors Ampère's law

$$\oint \mathbf{B} \cdot d\mathbf{l} = \mu_0 i$$

leads to

$$(B)(2\pi r) = \mu_0 i$$

or

$$B = \frac{\mu_0 i}{2\pi r}.$$

Ampère's law shows further that the magnetic field is zero for points outside the outer conductor (why?).   Magnetic fields exist *inside* each of the conductors; although their values can readily be found from Ampère's law, we choose to ignore them, on the assumption that the cable dimensions are chosen so that most of the stored magnetic energy is in the space between the conductors.

The energy density for points between the conductors, from Eq. 36–19, is

$$u = \frac{1}{2\mu_0} B^2 = \frac{1}{2\mu_0} \left(\frac{\mu_0 i}{2\pi r} \right)^2 = \frac{\mu_0 i^2}{8\pi^2 r^2}.$$

Consider a volume element dV consisting of a cylindrical shell whose radii are r and $r + dr$ and whose length is l.   The energy dU contained in it is

$$dU = u \, dV = \frac{\mu_0 i^2}{8\pi^2 r^2} (2\pi r l)(dr) = \frac{\mu_0 i^2 l}{4\pi} \frac{dr}{r}.$$

The total stored magnetic energy is found by integration, or

$$U = \int dU = \frac{\mu_0 i^2 l}{4\pi} \int_a^b \frac{dr}{r} = \frac{\mu_0 i^2 l}{4\pi} \ln \frac{b}{a},$$

which is the desired expression.

(b) What is the inductance of a length l of coaxial cable?

The inductance L can be found from Eq. 36–18 ($U = \frac{1}{2}Li^2$), which leads to

$$L = \frac{2U}{i^2} = \frac{\mu_0 l}{2\pi} \ln \frac{b}{a}.$$

The student should also derive this expression directly from the definition of inductance, using the procedures of Example 1.

Example 6. Compare the energy required to set up, in a cube 10 cm on edge, (a) a uniform electric field of 10^5 volts/meter and (b) a uniform magnetic field of 1 weber/meter^2 ($= 10^4$ gauss). Both these fields would be judged reasonably large but they are readily available in the laboratory.

(a) In the electric case we have, where V_0 is the volume of the cube,

$$U_E = u_E V_0 = \frac{1}{2}\epsilon_0 E^2 V_0$$

$$= (0.5)(8.9 \times 10^{-12} \text{ coul}^2/\text{nt-m}^2)(10^5 \text{ volts/meter})^2(0.1 \text{ meter})^3$$

$$= 4.5 \times 10^{-5} \text{ joule.}$$

(b) In the magnetic case, from Eq. 36–19, we have

$$U_B = u_B V_0 = \frac{B^2}{2\mu_0} V_0 = \frac{(1 \text{ weber/meter}^2)^2(0.1 \text{ meter})^3}{(2)(4\pi \times 10^{-7} \text{ weber/amp-m})}$$

$$= 400 \text{ joules.}$$

In terms of fields normally available in the laboratory, much larger amounts of energy can be stored in a magnetic field than in an electric one, the ratio being about 10^7 in this example. Conversely, much more energy is required to set up a magnetic field of reasonable laboratory magnitude than is required to set up an electric field of similarly reasonable magnitude.   ◀

QUESTIONS

1. Two coils are connected in series. Does their equivalent inductance depend on their geometrical relationship to each other?

2. Is the inductance per unit length for a solenoid near its center (a) the same as, (b) less than, or (c) greater than the inductance per unit length near its ends?

3. Two solenoids, A and B, have the same diameter and length and contain only one layer of windings, with adjacent turns touching, insulation thickness being negligible. Solenoid A contains many turns of fine wire and solenoid B contains fewer turns of heavier wire. (a) Which solenoid has the larger inductance? (b) Which solenoid has the larger inductive time constant?

4. If the flux passing through each turn of a coil is the same, the inductance of the coil may be computed from $L = N\Phi_B/i$ (Eq. 36–4). How might one compute L for a coil for which this assumption is not valid?

5. If a current in a source of emf is in the direction of the emf, the energy of the source decreases; if a current is in a direction opposite to the emf (as in charging a battery), the energy of the source increases. Do these statements apply to the inductor in Fig. 36–1a and 36–1b?

6. Show that the dimensions of the two expressions for L, $N\Phi_B/i$ (Eq. 36–4) and $\mathcal{E}/(di/dt)$ (Eq. 36–3b), are the same.

7. You are given N turns of wire connected in series. How should the turns be arranged to obtain the maximum self-inductance?

8. Does the time required for the current in a particular LR circuit to build up to any given fraction of its equilibrium value depend on the value of the applied emf?

9. A steady current is set up in a coil with a very large inductive time constant. When the current is interrupted with a switch, a heavy arc tends to appear at the switch blades. Explain. (Note: Interrupting currents in highly inductive circuits can be dangerous.)

10. In an LR circuit like that of Fig. 36–4 can the self-induced emf ever be larger than the battery emf?

11. In an LR circuit like that of Fig. 36–4 is the current in the resistance *always* the same as the current in the inductance?

12. In the circuit of Fig. 36–4 the self-induced emf is a maximum at the instant the switch is closed on a. How can this be since there is no current in the inductance at this instant?

13. Give some arguments to show that energy can be stored in a magnetic field.

14. The switch in Fig. 36–3 is thrown from a to b. What happens to the energy stored in the inductor?

15. In a toroid is the energy density larger near the inner radius or near the outer radius?

PROBLEMS

1. A 10-henry inductor carries a steady current of 2.0 amp. How can a 100-volt self-induced emf be made to appear in the inductor?

2. Two inductances L_1 and L_2 are connected in series and are separated by a large distance. (a) Show that the equivalent inductance L is $L_1 + L_2$. (b) Why must their separation be large?

3. Show that if two inductors with equal inductance L are connected in parallel the equivalent inductance of the combination is $\frac{1}{2}L$. The inductors are separated by a large distance.

4. Two parallel wires whose centers are a distance d apart carry equal currents in opposite directions. Show that, neglecting the flux within the wires themselves, the inductance of a length l of such a pair of wires is given by

$$L = \frac{\mu_0 l}{\pi} \ln \frac{d - a}{a},$$

where a is the wire radius. See Example 4, Chapter 34.

5. A long thin solenoid can be bent into a ring to form a toroid. Show that if the solenoid is long and thin enough the equation for the inductance of a toroid (see Example 1) reduces to that for a solenoid (Eq. 36–5).

6. A solenoid is wound with a single layer of #10 copper wire (diameter, 0.10 in.). It is 4.0 cm in diameter and 2.0 meters long. What is the inductance per unit length for the solenoid near its center? Assume that adjacent wires touch and that insulation thickness is negligible.

7. The inductance of a close-packed coil of 400 turns is 8 mh. What is the magnetic flux through the coil when the current is 5×10^{-3} amp?

8. A wooden toroidal core with a square cross section has an inner radius of 10 cm and an outer radius of 12 cm. It is wound with one layer of #18 wire (diameter, 0.040 in.; resistance, 160 ft/ohm). What are (a) the inductance and (b) the inductive time constant? Ignore the thickness of the insulation.

9. The current in an LR circuit builds up to one-third of its steady-state value in 5.0 sec. What is the inductive time constant?

10. How many "time constants" must we wait for the current in an LR circuit to build up to within 0.1 per cent of its equilibrium value?

11. The switch S in Fig. 36–3 is thrown from b to a. After one inductive time constant show that (a) the total energy transformed to Joule heat in the resistor is $0.168\varepsilon^2\tau_L/R$

and that (b) the energy stored in the magnetic field is $0.200\varepsilon^2\tau_L/R$. (c) Show that the equilibrium energy stored in the magnetic field is $0.500\varepsilon^2\tau_L/R$.

12. Show that the inductive time constant τ_L can also be defined as the time that would be required for the current in an LR circuit to reach its equilibrium value *if it continued to increase at its initial rate*.

13. A 50-volt potential difference is suddenly applied to a coil with $L = 50$ mh and $R = 180$ ohms. At what rate is the current increasing after 0.001 sec?

14. A coil with an inductance of 2.0 henrys and a resistance of 10 ohms is suddenly connected to a resistanceless battery with $\varepsilon = 100$ volts. At 0.1 sec after the connection is made, what are the rates at which (a) energy is being stored in the magnetic field, (b) Joule heat is appearing, and (c) energy is being delivered by the battery?

15. A coil with an inductance of 2.0 henrys and a resistance of 10 ohms is suddenly connected to a resistanceless battery with $\varepsilon = 100$ volts. (a) What is the equilibrium current? (b) How much energy is stored in the magnetic field when this current exists in the coil?

16. Prove that when switch S in Fig. 36-3 is thrown from a to b all the energy stored in the inductor appears as Joule heat in the resistor.

17. A circular loop of wire 5.0 cm in radius carries a current of 100 amp. What is the energy density at the center of the loop?

18. What is the magnetic energy density at the center of a circulating electron in the hydrogen atom (see Example 9, Chapter 34)?

19. A long wire carries a current of uniform density. Let i be the total current carried by the wire and show that the magnetic energy per unit length stored *within* the wire equals $\mu_0 i^2/16\pi$. Note that it does not depend on the wire diameter.

20. Show that the self-inductance for a length l of a long wire associated with the flux *inside* the wire only is $\mu_0 l/8\pi$, independent of the wire diameter.

21. The coaxial cable of Example 5 has $a = 1.0$ mm, $b = 4.0$ mm, and $c = 5.0$ mm (c is the radius of the outer surface of the outer conductor). It carries a current of 10 amp in the inner conductor and an equal but oppositely directed return current in the outer conductor. Calculate and compare the stored magnetic energy per meter of cable length (a) within the central conductor, (b) in the space between the conductors, and (c) within the outer conductor.

22. A length of #10 copper wire carries a current of 10 amp. Calculate (a) the magnetic energy density and (b) the electric energy density at the surface of the wire. The wire diameter is 0.10 in. and its resistance per unit length is 1.0 ohm/1000 ft.

23. What must be the strength of a uniform electric field if it is to have the same energy density as that possessed by a 5000-gauss magnetic field?

Magnetic Properties
of Matter

CHAPTER 37

37-1 Poles and Dipoles

In electricity the *isolated charge q* is the simplest structure that can exist. If two such charges of opposite sign are placed near each other, they form an *electric dipole*, characterized by an electric dipole moment **p**. In magnetism isolated magnetic "poles," which would correspond to isolated electric charges, apparently do not exist. The simplest magnetic structure is the *magnetic dipole*, characterized by a magnetic dipole moment **μ**. Table 34–1 summarizes some characteristics of electric and magnetic dipoles.

A current loop, a bar magnet, and a solenoid of finite length are examples of magnetic dipoles. Their magnetic dipole moments can be measured by placing the dipole in an external magnetic field **B**, measuring the torque **τ** that acts on it, and computing **μ** from Eq. 33–11, or

$$\boldsymbol{\tau} = \boldsymbol{\mu} \times \mathbf{B}. \tag{37-1}$$

Alternatively, we can measure **B** due to the dipole at a point along its axis a distance r from its center and compute μ from the expression in Table 34–1, or

$$B = \frac{\mu_0}{2\pi} \frac{\mu}{r^3}. \tag{37-2}$$

Figure 37–1, which shows iron filings sprinkled on a sheet of paper under which there is a bar magnet, suggests that this dipole might be viewed as two "poles" separated by a distance d. However, all attempts to isolate these poles fail. If the magnet is broken, as in Fig. 37–2, the fragments prove to be dipoles and not isolated poles. If we break up a magnet into the electrons

Fig. 37–1 A bar magnet is a magnetic dipole. The iron filings suggest the pattern of lines of force in Fig. 37–4a. (Courtesy Physical Science Study Committee.)

and nuclei that make up its atoms, it will be found that even these elementary particles are magnetic dipoles. Figure 37–3 contrasts the electric and the magnetic characters of the free electron.

All electrons have a characteristic *"spin" angular momentum* about a certain axis, which has the value of

$$L_s = 0.52723 \times 10^{-34} \text{ joule-sec.}$$

This is suggested by the vector $\mathbf{L}_s$ in Fig. 37–3b. Such a spinning charge can be viewed classically as being made up of infinitesimal current loops. Each such loop is a tiny magnetic dipole, its moment being given by (Eq. 33–10)

$$\mu = NiA, \qquad (37\text{–}3)$$

Fig. 37–2 If a bar magnet is broken, each fragment becomes a small dipole.

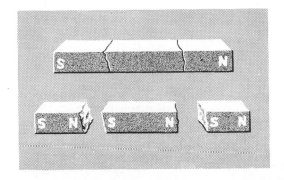

where i is the equivalent current in each infinitesimal loop and A is the loop area. The number of turns, N, is unity for each loop. The magnetic dipole moment of the spinning charge can be found by integrating over the moments of the infinitesimal current loops that make it up; see Problem 2.

Although this model of the spinning electron is too mechanistic and is not in accord with modern quantum physics, it remains true that the magnetic dipole moments of elementary particles are closely connected with their intrinsic angular momenta, or spins. Those particles and nuclei whose spin angular momentum is zero (the α-particle, the pion, the O^{16} nucleus, etc.) have no magnetic dipole moment. The "intrinsic" or "spin" magnetic mo-

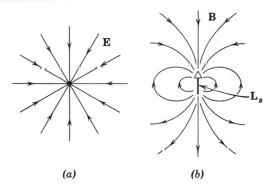

(a)   (b)

Fig. 37–3   (a) The lines of **E** and (b) the lines of **B** for an electron. The magnetic dipole moment of the electron, μ_l, is directed opposite to the spin angular momentum vector, $\mathbf{L}_s$.

ment of the electron must be distinguished from any additional magnetic moment it may have because of its *orbital* motion in an atom; see Example 2.

▶ **Example 1.**   Devise a method for measuring μ for a bar magnet.

(a) Place the magnet in a uniform external magnetic field **B**, with **μ** making an angle θ with **B**. The magnitude of the torque acting on the magnet (see Eq. 37–1) is given by

$$\tau = \mu B \sin \theta.$$

Clearly μ can be learned if τ, B, and θ are measured.

(b) A second technique is to suspend the magnet from its center of mass and to allow it to oscillate about its stable equilibrium position in the external field **B**. For *small* oscillations, $\sin \theta$ can be replaced by θ and the equation just given becomes

$$\tau = -(\mu B)\theta = -\kappa\theta,$$

where κ is a constant. The minus sign has been inserted to show that τ is a *restoring torque*. Since τ is proportional to θ, the condition for simple angular harmonic motion is met. The frequency f is given by the reciprocal of Eq. 15–21, or

$$f = \frac{1}{2\pi}\sqrt{\frac{\kappa}{I}} = \frac{1}{2\pi}\sqrt{\frac{\mu B}{I}}.$$

With this equation μ can be found from the measured quantities f, B, and I.

Example 2. An electron in an atom circulating in an assumed circular orbit of radius r behaves like a tiny current loop and has an *orbital magnetic dipole moment* * usually represented by μ_l. Derive a connection between μ_l and the *orbital angular momentum L_l*.

Newton's second law ($F = ma$) yields, if we substitute Coulomb's law for F,

$$\frac{1}{4\pi\epsilon_0}\frac{e^2}{r^2} = ma = \frac{mv^2}{r}$$

or

$$v = \sqrt{\frac{e^2}{4\pi\epsilon_0 mr}}. \qquad (37\text{-}4)$$

The angular velocity ω is given by

$$\omega = \frac{v}{r} = \sqrt{\frac{e^2}{4\pi\epsilon_0 mr^3}}.$$

The current for the orbit is the rate at which charge passes any given point, or

$$i = ef = e\left(\frac{\omega}{2\pi}\right) = \sqrt{\frac{e^4}{16\pi^3\epsilon_0 mr^3}}.$$

The orbital dipole moment μ_l is given from Eq. 37–3 if we put $N = 1$ and $A = \pi r^2$, or

$$\mu_l = NiA = (1)\sqrt{\frac{e^4}{16\pi^3\epsilon_0 mr^3}}(\pi r^2) = \frac{e^2}{4}\sqrt{\frac{r}{\pi\epsilon_0 m}}. \qquad (37\text{-}5)$$

The orbital angular momentum L_l is

$$L_l = (mv)r.$$

Combining with Eq. 37–4 leads to

$$L_l = \sqrt{\frac{e^2 mr}{4\pi\epsilon_0}}.$$

Finally, eliminating r between this equation and Eq. 37–5 yields

$$\mu_l = L_l\left(\frac{e}{2m}\right),$$

which shows that the orbital magnetic moment of an electron is proportional to its orbital angular momentum.

For $r = 5.1 \times 10^{-11}$ meter, which corresponds to hydrogen in its normal state, we have from Eq. 37–5

$$\mu_l = \frac{e^2}{4}\sqrt{\frac{r}{\pi\epsilon_0 m}}$$

$$= \frac{(1.6 \times 10^{-19}\ \text{coul})^2}{4}\sqrt{\frac{5.1 \times 10^{-11}\ \text{meter}}{(\pi)(8.9 \times 10^{-12}\ \text{coul}^2/\text{nt-m}^2)(9.1 \times 10^{-31}\ \text{kg})}}$$

$$= 9.1 \times 10^{-24}\ \text{amp-m}^2. \qquad \blacktriangleleft$$

---

* This must not be confused with the magnetic dipole moment μ_s of the electron spin, which is also present.

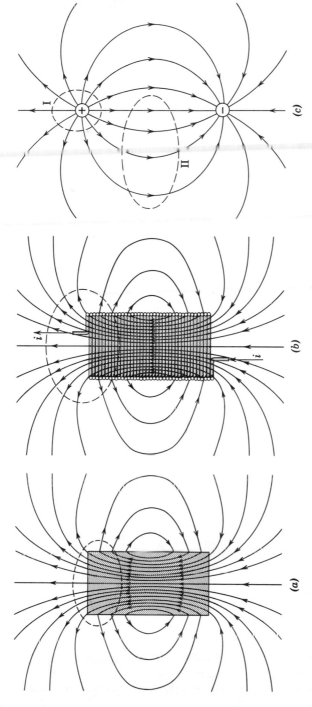

Fig. 37–4 Lines of **B** (*a*) for a bar magnet and (*b*) for a short solenoid. (*c*) Lines of **E** for an electric dipole. At large enough distances all three fields vary like those for a dipole. The four dashed curves are intersections with the plane of the figure of closed Gaussian surfaces. Note that Φ_B equals zero for (*a*) or (*b*). Φ_E equals zero for surfaces like II in (*c*), which do not contain any charge, but Φ_E is not zero for surfaces like I.

37-2   Gauss's Law for Magnetism

Gauss's law for magnetism, which is one of the basic equations of electro-magnetism (see Table 38–3), is a formal way of stating a conclusion that seems to be forced on one by the facts of magnetism, namely, that *isolated magnetic poles do not exist*. This equation asserts that the flux Φ_B through any *closed* Gaussian surface must be zero, or

$$\Phi_B = \oint \mathbf{B} \cdot d\mathbf{S} = 0, \tag{37-6}$$

where the integral is to be taken over the entire closed surface. We contrast this with Gauss's law for electricity, which is

$$\epsilon_0 \oint \mathbf{E} \cdot d\mathbf{S} = q. \tag{37-7}$$

The fact that a zero appears at the right of Eq. 37–6, but not at the right of Eq. 37–7, means that in magnetism there is no counterpart to the free charge q in electricity.

Figure 37–4a shows a Gaussian surface that encloses one end of a bar magnet. Note that the lines of $\mathbf{B}$ enter the surface for the most part inside the magnet and leave it for the most part outside the magnet. There is thus an inward (or negative) flux inside the magnet and an outward (or positive) flux outside it. The total flux for the whole surface is zero. In Section 37–7 the interested student will find a fuller discussion of why the lines of $\mathbf{B}$ for a bar magnet are drawn in the way shown.

Figure 37–4b shows a similar surface for a solenoid of finite length which, like a bar magnet, is also a magnetic dipole. Here, too, Φ_B equals zero. Figures 37–4a and b show clearly that there are no "sources" of $\mathbf{B}$; that is, there are no points from which lines of $\mathbf{B}$ emanate. Also, there are no "sinks" of $\mathbf{B}$; that is, there are no points toward which $\mathbf{B}$ converges. In other words, *there are no free magnetic poles*.

Figure 37–4c shows a Gaussian surface (I) surrounding the positive end of an electric dipole. Here there *is* a net flux of the lines of $\mathbf{E}$. There is a "source" of $\mathbf{E}$; it is the charge q. If q is negative, we have a "sink" of $\mathbf{E}$ because the lines of $\mathbf{E}$ end on negative charges. For surfaces like surface II in Fig. 37–4c for which the charge inside is zero, the flux of $\mathbf{E}$ over the surface is also zero.

37-3   Paramagnetism

Magnetism as we know it in our daily experience is an important but special branch of the subject called *ferromagnetism;* we discuss this in Section 37–5. Here we discuss a weaker form of magnetism called *paramagnetism.*

For most atoms and ions, the magnetic effects of the electrons, including both their spins and orbital motions, exactly cancel so that the atom or ion

is not magnetic. This is true for the rare gases such as neon and for ions *
such as Cu^+, which makes up ordinary copper. These materials do not exhibit paramagnetism. For other atoms or ions the magnetic effects of the
electrons do not cancel, so that the atom as a whole has a magnetic dipole
moment **μ**. Examples are found among the so-called transition elements,
such as Mn^{++}, the rare earths, such as Gd^{+++}, and the actinide elements,
such as U^{++++}.

If a sample of N atoms, each of which has a magnetic dipole moment **μ**,
is placed in a magnetic field, the elementary atomic dipoles tend to line up
with the field. For perfect alignment, the sample as a whole would have a
magnetic dipole moment of N**μ**. However, the aligning process is seriously
interfered with by the collisions that take place between the atoms if the
sample is a gas and by temperature vibrations if the sample is a solid. The
importance of this thermal agitation effect may be measured by comparing
two energies: one $(= \frac{3}{2}kT)$ is the mean kinetic energy of translation of a
gas atom at temperature T; the other $(= 2\mu B)$ is the difference in energy
between an atom lined up with the magnetic field and one pointing in the
opposite direction. As Example 3 shows, the effect of the collisions at
ordinary temperatures and fields is very great. The sample acquires a magnetic moment when placed in an external magnetic field, but this moment
is usually much smaller than the maximum possible moment $N\mu$.

▶ **Example 3.** A paramagnetic gas, whose atoms (see Example 2) have a magnetic
dipole moment of about 10^{-23} amp-m^2, is placed in an external magnetic field of
magnitude 1 weber/meter^2. At room temperature ($T = 300°K$) calculate and compare U_T, the mean kinetic energy of translation ($= \frac{3}{2}kT$), and U_B, the magnetic
energy ($= 2\mu B$):

$$U_T = \tfrac{3}{2}kT = (\tfrac{3}{2})(1.38 \times 10^{-23} \text{ joule/°K})(300°K) = 6 \times 10^{-21} \text{ joule},$$

$$U_B = 2\mu B = (2)(10^{-23} \text{ amp-m}^2)(1 \text{ weber/meter}^2) = 2 \times 10^{-23} \text{ joule}.$$

Because U_T equals 300 U_B, we see that energy exchanges in collisions can interfere
seriously with the alignment of the dipoles with the external field. ◀

If a specimen of a paramagnetic substance is placed in a nonuniform magnetic
field, such as that near the pole of a strong magnet, it will be attracted toward the
region of higher field, that is, toward the pole. We can understand this by drawing
an analogy with the corresponding electric case of Fig. 37–5, which shows a dielectric
specimen (a sphere) in a nonuniform electric field. The net electric force points to
the right in the figure and is

$$F_e = q(E + \Delta E) - q(E - \Delta E) = q(2\Delta E),$$

which can be written as

$$F_e = \frac{(q\,\Delta x)}{\Delta x} 2\Delta E = p\left(\frac{2\Delta E}{\Delta x}\right) \cong p\left(\frac{dE}{dx}\right)_{\text{max}}.$$

Here p ($= q\,\Delta x$) is the induced electric dipole moment of the sphere. In the differential limit of a very small sphere ($2\Delta E/\Delta x$) approaches $(dE/dx)_{\text{max}}$, the gradient of
the electric field at the center of the sphere.

---

* Cu^+ indicates a copper atom from which one electron has been removed; Al^{+++} indicates an aluminum atom from which three electrons have been removed, etc.

In the corresponding magnetic case we have, by analogy,

$$F_m = p \left(\frac{dB}{dx}\right)_{max}. \tag{37-8}$$

Thus, by measuring the magnetic force F_m that acts on a small paramagnetic specimen when it is placed in a nonuniform magnetic field whose field gradient $(dB/dx)_{max}$ is known, we can learn its magnetic dipole moment p. The *magnetization* $\mathbf{M}$ is defined as the magnetic moment per unit volume, or

$$\mathbf{M} = \frac{\mathbf{p}}{V},$$

where V is the volume of the specimen. It is a vector because $\mathbf{p}$, the dipole moment of the specimen, is a vector.

In 1895 Pierre Curie (1859–1906) discovered experimentally that the magnetization M of a paramagnetic specimen is directly proportional to B, the effective value of magnetic induction in which the specimen is placed, and inversely proportional to the temperature, or

$$M = C \frac{B}{T}, \tag{37-9}$$

in which C is a constant. This equation is known as *Curie's law*. The law is physically reasonable in that increasing B tends to align the elementary dipoles in the specimen, that is, to increase M, whereas increasing T tends to interfere with this alignment, that is, to decrease M. Curie's law is well verified experimentally, provided that the ratio B/T does not become too large.

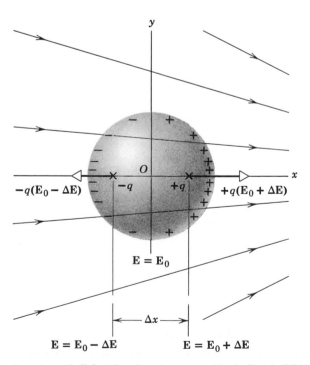

Fig. 37-5 A dielectric sphere in a nonuniform electric field.

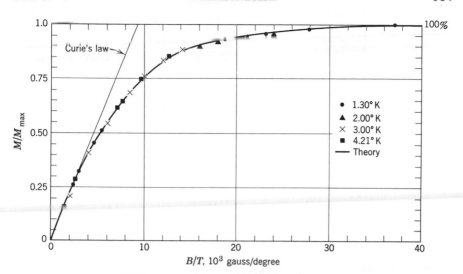

Fig. 37–6 The ratio M/M_{max} for a paramagnetic salt (chromium potassium alum) in various magnetic fields and at various temperatures. The curve through the experimental points is a theoretical curve calculated from modern quantum physics. (From measurements by W. E. Henry.)

M cannot increase without limit, as Curie's law implies, but must approach a value M_{max} ($= \mu N/V$) corresponding to the complete alignment of the N dipoles contained in the volume V of the specimen. Figure 37–6 shows this saturation effect for a sample of $CrK(SO_4)_2 \cdot 12H_2O$. The chromium ions are responsible for all the paramagnetism of this salt, all the other elements being paramagnetically inert. To achieve 99.5% saturation, it is necessary to use applied magnetic fields as high as 50,000 gauss and temperatures as low as 1.3°K. Note that for more readily achievable conditions, such as $B = 10,000$ gauss and $T = 10°K$, the abscissa in Fig. 37–6 is only 1.0 so that Curie's law would appear to be well obeyed for this and for all lower values of B/T. The curve that passes through the experimental points in this figure is calculated from a theory based on modern quantum physics; it is in excellent agreement with experiment.

37–4 Diamagnetism

In 1846 Michael Faraday discovered that a specimen of bismuth brought near to the pole of a strong magnet is *repelled*. He called such substances *diamagnetic*. Diamagnetism, present in all substances, is such a feeble effect that its presence is masked in substances made of atoms that have a net magnetic dipole moment, that is, in paramagnetic or ferromagnetic substances.

Figures 37–7a and b show an electron circulating in a diamagnetic atom at angular frequency ω_0 in an assumed circular orbit of radius r. Each electron is moving under the action of a centripetal force $\mathbf{F}_E$ of electrostatic origin where, from Newton's second law,

$$F_E = ma = m\omega_0^2 r \qquad (37\text{--}10)$$

Each rotating electron has an orbital magnetic moment, but for the atom as a whole the orbits are randomly oriented so that there is no *net* magnetic effect. In Fig. 37–7a, for example, the magnetic dipole moment $\mathbf{\mu}_l$ points into the page; in Fig.

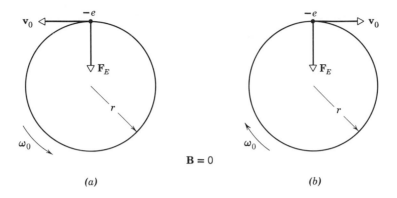

B = 0

(a)   (b)

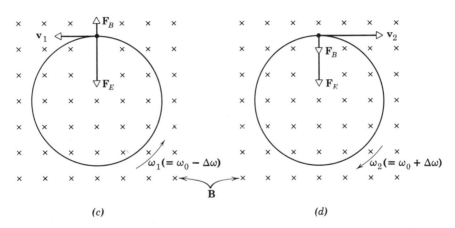

(c)   (d)

Fig. 37-7   (a) An electron circulating in an atom.   (b) An electron circulating in the opposite direction.   (c) A magnetic field is introduced, *decreasing* the linear speed of the electron in (a), that is, $v_1 < v_0$.   (d) The magnetic field *increases* the linear speed of the electron in (b), that is, $v_2 > v_0$.

37-7b it points out and the net effect for the two orbits shown is cancellation.   This cancellation is also shown at the left in Fig. 37-8.

If an external field **B** is applied as in Fig. 37-7c and d, an *additional* force, given by $-e(\mathbf{v} \times \mathbf{B})$, acts on the electron.   This magnetic force acts always at right angles to the direction of motion; its magnitude is

$$F_B = evB = e(\omega r)B. \qquad (37\text{--}11)$$

The student should show that in Fig. 37-7c $\mathbf{F}_B$ and $\mathbf{F}_E$ point in opposite directions and that in Fig. 37-7d they point in the same direction.   Note that since the centripetal force changes when the magnetic field is applied (the radius can be shown to remain constant), the angular velocity must also change; thus ω in Eq. 37-11 differs from ω_0 in Eq. 37-10.

Applying Newton's second law to Figs. 37-7c and d, and allowing for both directions of circulation, yields for the *resultant* forces on the electrons

$$F_E \pm F_B = ma = m\omega^2 r.$$

Substituting Eqs. 37–10 and 37–11 into this equation yields

$$m\omega_0^2 r \pm e\omega r B - m\omega^2 r$$

or
$$\omega^2 \mp \left(\frac{eB}{m}\right)\omega - \omega_0^2 = 0. \qquad (37\text{–}12)$$

This quadratic equation can be solved for ω, the new angular velocity. Rather than doing this, we take advantage of the fact (presented without proof; see Problem 7) that ω differs only slightly from ω_0, even in the strongest external magnetic fields. Thus

$$\omega = \omega_0 + \Delta\omega \qquad (37\text{–}13)$$

where $\Delta\omega \ll \omega_0$. Substituting this equation into Eq. 37–12 yields

$$[\omega_0^2 + 2\omega_0\,\Delta\omega + (\Delta\omega)^2] \pm [\beta\omega_0 + \beta\Delta\omega] - \omega_0^2 = 0,$$

where β is a convenient abbreviation for eB/m. The two terms ω_0^2 cancel each other; the terms $(\Delta\omega)^2$ and $\beta\Delta\omega$ are small compared to the remaining terms and may be set equal to zero with only small error. This leads, as an excellent approximation, to

$$\Delta\omega \cong \mp \tfrac{1}{2}\beta = \mp \frac{eB}{2m} \qquad (37\text{–}14)$$

or, from Eq. 37–13,
$$\omega = \omega_0 \mp \frac{eB}{2m}.$$

Thus the effect of applying a magnetic field is to increase or decrease (depending on the direction of circulation) the angular velocity. This, in turn, increases or decreases the orbital magnetic moment of the circulating electron (see Example 2).

In Fig. 37–7c the angular velocity is reduced (because the centripetal force is reduced) so that the magnitude of the magnetic moment is reduced. In Fig. 37–7d, however, the angular velocity is increased so that the magnitude of μ_l is increased. These effects are shown on the right in Fig. 37–8, where it will be noted that the two magnetic moments *no longer cancel*.

We see that if a magnetic field **B** is applied to a diamagnetic substance (zero net magnetic moment in absence of applied field), a magnetic moment will be *induced* whose direction (out of the plane of Fig. 37–7) is *opposite* to **B**; see also Fig. 37–8. This is precisely the reverse of paramagnetism, in which the (*permanent*) magnetic dipoles tend to point in the *same* direction as the applied field.

We can now understand why a diamagnetic specimen is repelled when brought near to the pole of a strong magnet. If the pole is a north pole, there exists a non-uniform magnetic field of induction with **B** pointing away from the pole. If a sphere

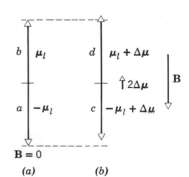

Fig. 37–8 The magnetic moments of the two oppositely circulating electrons in an atom cancel when there is no external magnetic field, as in (*a*), but do *not* cancel when a field is applied, as in (*b*). Note that the resultant moment in (*b*) points in the *opposite* direction to **B**. Compare carefully with Fig. 37–7.

made of a diamagnetic material (bismuth, say) is brought near to this pole, the magnetization **M** that is induced in it points toward the pole, that is, *opposite to* **B**. Thus the side of the sphere closest to the magnet behaves like a north pole and is *repelled* by the nearby north pole of the magnet. For a paramagnetic sphere, the vector **M** points *along the direction of* **B** and the side of the sphere nearest to the magnet is a south pole, which is *attracted* to the north pole of the magnet.

▶ **Example 4.** Calculate the *change* in magnetic moment for a circulating electron, as described in Example 2, if a magnetic field of induction **B** of 2.0 webers/meter² acts at right angles to the plane of the orbit.

We obtain μ from Eq. 37–3, or

$$\mu = NiA = (1)(ef)(\pi r^2) = (1)\left(\frac{e\omega}{2\pi}\right)(\pi r^2) = \tfrac{1}{2}er^2\omega.$$

The *change* in μ is
$$\Delta\mu = \tfrac{1}{2}er^2\,\Delta\omega$$

or, from Eq. 37–14,
$$\Delta\mu = \pm\,\tfrac{1}{2}er^2\left(\frac{eB}{2m}\right) = \pm\,\frac{e^2Br^2}{4m}.$$

Substituting numbers yields

$$\Delta\mu = \pm\,\frac{(1.6\times10^{-19}\ \text{coul})^2(2.0\ \text{webers/meter}^2)(5.1\times10^{-11}\ \text{meter})^2}{(4)(9.1\times10^{-31}\ \text{kg})}$$

$$= \pm3.7\times10^{-29}\ \text{amp-m}^2.$$

In Example 2 the moment μ_l was 9.1×10^{-24} amp-m², so that the change induced by even a strong external magnetic field is rather small, the ratio $\Delta\mu/\mu_l$ being about 4×10^{-6}. ◀

37–5 Ferromagnetism

For five elements (Fe, Co, Ni, Gd, and Dy) and for a variety of alloys of these and other elements a special effect occurs which permits a specimen to achieve a high degree of magnetic alignment in spite of the randomizing tendency of the thermal motions of the atoms. In such materials, described as *ferromagnetic*, a special form of interaction called *exchange coupling* occurs between adjacent atoms, coupling their magnetic moments together in rigid parallelism.* Modern quantum physics successfully predicts that this will occur only for the five elements listed. If the temperature is raised above a certain critical value, called the *Curie temperature*, the exchange coupling suddenly disappears and the materials become simply paramagnetic. For iron the Curie temperature is 1043°K. Ferromagnetism is evidently a property not only of the individual atom or ion but also of the interaction of each atom or ion with its neighbors in the crystal lattice (see Fig. 21–5) of the solid.

Figure 37–9 shows a *magnetization curve* for a specimen of iron. To obtain such a curve, we form the specimen, assumed initially unmagnetized, into a ring and wind a toroidal coil around it as in Fig. 37–10, to form a so-called *Rowland ring*. When a current i is set up in the coil, *if the iron core is not present*, a field of induction is set up within the toroid given by (Eq. 34–4)

$$B_0 = \mu_0 ni, \tag{37–15}$$

---

* Exchange coupling, a purely quantum effect, cannot be "explained" in terms of classical physics.

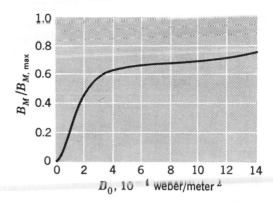

Fig. 37–9 A magnetization curve for iron.

where n is the number of turns per unit length for the toroid. Although this formula was derived for a long solenoid, it can be applied to a toroid if $d \ll r$ in Fig. 37–10. Because of the iron core, the actual value of **B** in the toroidal space will exceed $\mathbf{B}_0$, by a large factor in many cases, since the elementary atomic dipoles in the core line up with the applied field $\mathbf{B}_0$, thereby setting up their own field of induction. Thus we can write

$$B = B_0 + B_M \tag{37–16}$$

where B_M is the magnetic induction due to the specimen; it is proportional to the magnetization M of the specimen. Often $B_M \gg B_0$.

The field B_0 is proportional to the current in the toroid and can be calculated readily, using Eq. 37–15; B can be measured in a way that is described below. An experimental value for B_M can be derived from Eq.

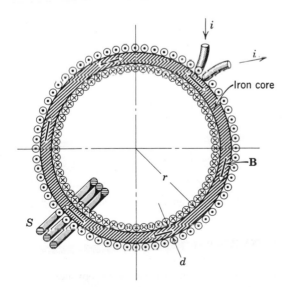

Fig. 37–10 A Rowland ring, showing a secondary coil S.

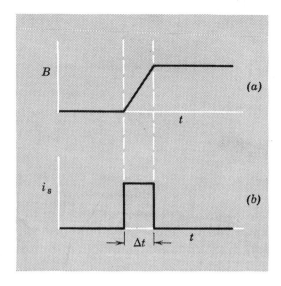

(a)

(b)

Fig. 37–11 (a) B for a Rowland ring as the current in the windings is increased from zero during an interval Δt. (b) The corresponding induced current in the secondary coil. Both curves are idealized; in practice, the sharp corners would be rounded off.

37–16. It has a maximum value $B_{M,\max}$ corresponding to complete alignment of the atomic dipoles in the iron. Thus we can plot, as in Fig. 37–9, the fractional degree of alignment ($= B_M/B_{M,\max}$) as a function of B_0. For this specimen a value of 96.5% saturation is achieved at $B_0 = 0.13$ weber/meter² ($= 1300$ gauss; this point is about 16 ft to the right of the origin in the figure); increasing B_0 to 1.0 weber/meter² ($= 10,000$ gauss; about 120 ft to the right in Fig. 37–9) increases the fractional saturation only to 97.7%.

To measure B in the system of Fig. 37–10, let the current in the toroid windings be increased from zero to i. The flux through the secondary coil S will change by BA, where A is the area of the toroid. While the flux is changing, an induced emf will appear in coil S, according to Faraday's law. For simplicity, we assume that the current in the toroid is so adjusted that B increases linearly with time for an interval Δt, as shown in Fig. 37–11a. The emf in coil S during this interval, from Faraday's law,[*] will then be

$$\mathcal{E} = N\frac{\Delta\Phi_B}{\Delta t} = \frac{NBA}{\Delta t},$$

where N is the number of turns in coil S. This emf will set up a current i_s in coil S given by

$$i_s = \frac{\mathcal{E}}{R} = \frac{NBA}{R\,\Delta t}$$

or

$$B = \frac{(i_s\,\Delta t)R}{NA} = \frac{qR}{NA},$$

in which R is the resistance of coil S and $i_s\,\Delta t$ is the charge q that passes through this coil during time Δt. If a so-called *ballistic galvanometer* is connected to S, its deflection will be a measure of the charge q. Thus it is possible to find B for any value of the current i in the toroid windings. In practice, it is not necessary that the curve $B(t)$ in Fig. 37–11a be linear during the interval Δt.

---

[*] We ignore the minus sign because we are concerned only with the magnitude of $\mathcal{E}$.

Fig. 37–12　A magnetization curve (*ab*) for a specimen of iron and an associated hysteresis loop (*ebcde*).

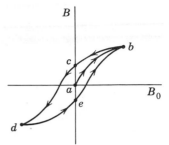

Magnetization curves for ferromagnetic materials *do not retrace themselves* as we increase and then decrease the toroid current. Figure 37–12 shows the following operations with a Rowland ring: (1) starting with the iron unmagnetized (point *a*), increase the toroid current until $B_0 (= \mu_0 ni)$ has the value corresponding to point *b*; (2) reduce the current in the toroid winding back to zero (point *c*); (3) reverse the toroid current and increase it in magnitude until point *d* is reached; (4) reduce the current to zero again (point *e*); (5) reverse the current once more until point *b* is reached again. The lack of retraceability shown in Fig. 37–12 is called *hysteresis*. Note that at points *c* and *e* the iron core is magnetized, even though there is no current in the toroid windings; this is the familiar phenomenon of *permanent magnetism*.

The magnetization curve for paramagnetism (Fig. 37–6) is explained in terms of the mutually opposing tendencies of alignment with the external field and of randomization because of the temperature motions. In ferromagnetism, however, we have assumed that adjacent atomic dipoles are locked in rigid parallelism. Why, then, does the magnetic moment of the specimen not reach its saturation value for very low—even zero—values of B_0? The modern interpretation is to assume the existence within the specimen of *domains*, that is, of local regions within which there is essentially perfect alignment. The domains themselves, however, as Fig. 37–13 suggests, are not parallel at moderately low values of $\mathbf{B}_0$.

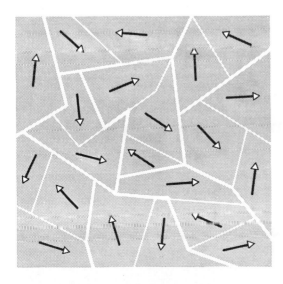

Fig. 37–13　The separate magnetic domains in an unmagnetized polycrystalline ferromagnetic sample are oriented to produce little external effect. Each domain, however, is made up of completely aligned atomic dipoles, as suggested by the arrows. The heavy boundaries define the crystals that make up the solid; the light boundaries define the domains within the crystals.

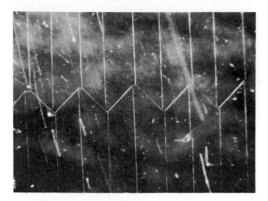

Fig. 37-14 Domain patterns for a single crystal of iron containing 3.8% silicon. The white lines show the boundaries between the domains. These boundaries are regular rather than irregular, as in Fig. 37-13, because the specimen is a single crystal. In Fig. 37-13 the specimen is made up of many crystallites or grains. (Courtesy H. J. Williams, Bell Telephone Laboratories.)

Figure 37-14 shows some domain photographs, taken by sprinkling a colloidal suspension of finely powdered iron oxide on a properly etched single crystal of iron. The domain boundaries, which are thin regions in which the alignment of the elementary dipoles changes from a certain direction in one domain to an entirely different direction in the other, are the sites of intense but highly localized and nonuniform magnetic fields. The suspended colloidal particles are attracted to these regions. Although the atomic dipoles in the individual domains are completely aligned, the specimen as a whole may have a very small resultant magnetic moment. This is the state of affairs in an unmagnetized iron nail.

As we magnetize a piece of iron by placing it in an external magnetic field, two effects take place. One is a growth in size of the domains that are favorably oriented at the expense of those that are not, as in Fig. 37-15. Second, the direction of orientation of the dipoles within a domain may swing around as a unit, becoming closer to the field direction. Hysteresis comes about because the domain boundaries do not move completely back to their original positions when the external field $\mathbf{B}_0$ is removed.

Two other types of magnetism, closely related to ferromagnetism, are *antiferromagnetism* and *ferrimagnetism* (note spelling). In antiferromagnetic substances, of

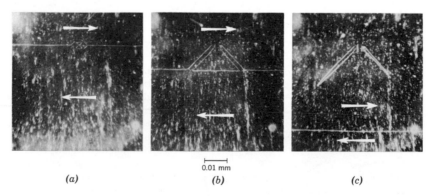

$\overset{\longmapsto}{0.01 \text{ mm}}$

     (a)   *(b)*   *(c)*

Fig. 37-15 *(a)* A boundary between two domains, with the magnetization in each domain as shown by the white arrows. *(b)* If an external magnetic field pointing from left to right is imposed on the specimen, the upper domain will grow at the expense of the lower. The domain boundary will move down as the elementary dipoles reverse themselves. *(c)* The process continues. The boundary has moved across a region in which there is a crystal imperfection. (Courtesy H. J. Williams, Bell Telephone Laboratories.)

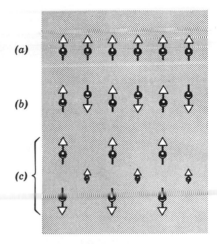

Fig. 37–16 Showing how elementary magnetic dipoles are oriented by the interatomic exchange coupling in (a) ferromagnetism, (b) antiferromagnetism, and (c) ferrimagnetism.

which MnO_2 is an example, the exchange coupling to which we referred on page 834 serves to lock adjacent ions into rigid *antiparallelism* (see Fig. 37–16b). Such materials exhibit very little gross external magnetism. However, if they are heated above a certain temperature, called the *Néel temperature*, the exchange coupling ceases to act and the material becomes paramagnetic. In ferrimagnetic substances, of which iron ferrite is an example, two different kinds of magnetic ions are present. In iron ferrite the two ions are Fe^{++} and Fe^{+++}. The exchange coupling locks the ions into a pattern like that of Fig. 37–16c, in which the external effects are intermediate between ferromagnetism and antiferromagnetism. Here, too, the exchange coupling disappears if the material is heated above a certain characteristic temperature.

37–6 Nuclear Magnetism

Many nuclei have magnetic dipoles, and the possibility arises that a specimen of matter may exhibit gross external magnetic effects associated with its nuclei. However, nuclear magnetic moments are several orders of magnitude smaller than those associated with the electronic motions in an atom or ion. The magnetic moment of an electron associated with its spin, for example, exceeds that of the proton (the nucleus of hydrogen) by a factor of 660.

Gross external effects for nuclear magnetism are smaller than the corresponding (electronic) paramagnetic effects by the *square* of ratios of this order of magnitude, because (a), *all else being equal*, the external magnetism is reduced by such a ratio, but (b) the very fact that the magnetic dipole moment of the nucleus is smaller means that (see Example 3) the thermal vibrations are proportionally (to a good approximation) more effective in reducing the degree of alignment of the elementary dipoles in an external magnetic field; thus all else is *not* equal and the ratio enters twice.

Techniques such as the Rowland ring (Fig. 37–10) are far too insensitive to detect nuclear magnetism. We describe here a *nuclear resonance technique* by means of which nuclear magnetism can readily reveal itself. This method is also vastly useful for studying paramagnetism, ferromagnetism, antiferromagnetism, and ferrimagnetism, in all of which cases the magnetic effects are associated not with the nuclei but with the atomic electrons. The nuclear-resonance technique was developed in 1946 by E. M. Purcell and his co-workers at Harvard. Simultaneously and independently, F. Bloch and his co-workers at Stanford discovered a very similar method. For these achievements the two physicists received a Nobel prize.

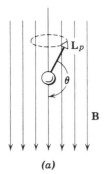
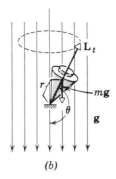

Fig. 37-17 (a) A spinning proton precessing in an external magnetic field and (b) a spinning top precessing in an external gravitational field. $\mathbf{L}_p$ and $\mathbf{L}_t$ are the two angular momentum vectors.

(a)   (b)

We focus our attention on the problem of measuring the magnitude μ of the magnetic moment of the proton. In principle, this can be done by placing a specimen containing protons in an external field of magnetic induction $\mathbf{B}$ and by measuring the energy $(= 2\mu B)$ required to turn the protons end for end. A rigorously correct description of the procedures cannot be given without using quantum physics. The description given, although based entirely on classical physics, nevertheless leads to the correct conclusions.

Figure 37-17a shows a spinning proton with its axis making an angle θ with a uniform external magnetic field $\mathbf{B}$. Figure 37-17b shows a spinning top with its axis making an angle θ with a uniform external gravitational field $\mathbf{g}$. In each case there is a torque that tends to align the axis of the spinning object with the field. For the proton (Eq. 33-11) it is given by

$$\tau_p = \mu B \sin \theta. \qquad (37\text{-}17a)$$

For the top it is given by $$\tau_t = mgr \sin \theta, \qquad (37\text{-}17b)$$

where r locates the center of mass of the top and m is its mass.

In Example 5, Chapter 13, we saw that the spinning top processes about a vertical axis with an angular frequency given by

$$\omega_t = \frac{mgr}{L_t}, \qquad (37\text{-}18a)$$

in which L_t is the spin angular momentum of the top.

The proton, which has a quantized spin angular momentum L_p, will also precess about the direction of the (magnetic) field because of the action of the (magnetic) torque. The student should derive the expression for the frequency of precession, being guided by the derivation of Example 5, Chapter 13, but using the magnetic torque (Eq. 37-17a) instead of the gravitational torque (Eq. 37-17b). The relation is

$$\omega_p = \frac{\mu B}{L_p}. \qquad (37\text{-}18b)$$

▶ **Example 5.** What is the precession frequency of a proton in a magnetic field of 0.5 weber/meter²?

The quantities μ and L_p in Eq. 37-18b are 1.4×10^{-26} amp-m² and 0.53×10^{-34} joule-sec. This equation then yields

$$f_p = \frac{\omega_p}{2\pi} = \frac{\mu B}{2\pi L_p} = \frac{(1.4 \times 10^{-26} \text{ amp-m}^2)(0.50 \text{ weber/meter}^2)}{(2\pi)(0.53 \times 10^{-34} \text{ joule-sec})} = 2.1 \times 10^7 \text{ cps.}$$

This frequency $(= 21 \text{ mc/sec})$ is in the radio-frequency range.   ◀

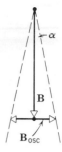

Fig. 37–18   In the nuclear magnetic resonance method a small oscillating magnetic field $\mathbf{B}_{osc}$ is placed at right angles to a steady field $\mathbf{B}$.

It is possible to change the energy of any system in periodic motion if we allow an external influence to act on it at the same frequency as that of its motion. This is the familiar *resonance* condition. As an "external influence" for the precessing proton, we use a small alternating magnetic field $\mathbf{B}_{osc}$ arranged to be at right angles to the steady field $\mathbf{B}$. This oscillating field combines vectorially with the steady field so that the *resultant* field rocks back and forth between the limits shown by the dashed lines in Fig. 37–18. Typical values for B and for the amplitude of $\mathbf{B}_{osc}$ are 5000 gauss and 1 gauss, respectively, so that the rocking angle α in the figure is quite small. If the angular frequency ω_0 of the oscillating field is chosen equal to the angular precession frequency ω_p of the proton, it turns out that the precessing proton can absorb energy. An increase in energy means an increase in θ in Fig. 37–17a.

The resonance condition

$$\omega_0 = \frac{\mu B}{L_p} \qquad (37\text{–}19)$$

can be used to measure μ. We place the spinning proton in a known field $\mathbf{B}$, apply a "perturbing field" at right angles to it, and vary the angular frequency ω_0 of this perturbing field until resonance occurs. It is possible to tell when Eq. 37–19 is satisfied because, at resonance, many spinning protons will tend to turn end for end in the field, absorbing energy which can be detected by appropriate electronic techniques.

Figure 37–19 is a schematic diagram of an experimental arrangement. The protons, present as hydrogen nuclei in a small vial V of water, are immersed in a strong steady magnetic field caused by the electromagnet whose pole faces N and S are shown. A rapidly alternating current in the small coil C provides the (horizontal) weak, perturbing magnetic field $\mathbf{B}_{osc}$. This current is provided by a radio-frequency oscillator

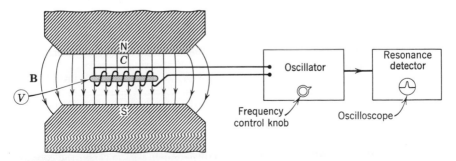

Fig. 37–19   An arrangement to observe nuclear resonance. The oscillating field is horizontal within the coil.

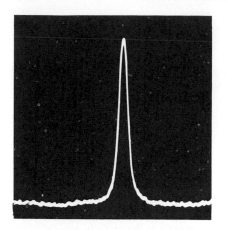

Fig. 37-20 An oscilloscope photograph of a proton resonance peak showing energy absorbed from the oscillator versus oscillator frequency. (From Bloembergen et al., *Phys. Rev.*, **73**, 679.)

whose angular frequency ω_0 can be varied; an electronic "resonance detector," also connected to the oscillator, serves to indicate when energy is being drained from the oscillator and used to "flip the protons." In principle, the oscillator angular frequency ω_0 is varied until the resonance detector shows that Eq. 37–19 is satisfied (see Fig. 37–20). The magnetic moment μ can then be determined by measuring B and ω_0. Surprisingly enough, magnetic moments can be measured in this and similar ways to a much greater accuracy than we can measure μ for a bar magnet. For the proton we have

$$\mu_p = 1.41044 \times 10^{-26} \text{ amp-m}^2.$$

37–7 Three Magnetic Vectors

In Chapter 30 we saw that if a dielectric is placed in an electric field polarization charges will appear on its surface. These surface charges, which find their origin in the elementary electric dipoles (permanent or induced) that make up the dielectric, set up a field of their own that modifies the original field. For the simple case discussed in Chapter 30—a dielectric slab in a parallel-plate capacitor—this complication can readily be handled in terms of the electric field strength vector **E** and some knowledge of the electric properties of the slab material, such as the dielectric constant. For more complex problems we asserted that it was useful to introduce two other (subsidiary) electric vectors, the *electric polarization* **P** and the *electric displacement* **D**. Table 30–2 shows some of the characteristics of these three vectors.

In magnetism we find a similar situation. If magnetic materials are placed in a field of induction, the elementary magnetic dipoles (permanent or induced) will act to set up a field of induction of their own that will modify the original field. For the simple case discussed in this chapter—a Rowland ring with a ferromagnetic core—this complication can readily be handled in terms of the magnetic induction vector **B** and some knowledge of the magnetic properties of the ring material, such as that provided by Fig. 37–9. For more complex problems we find it useful to introduce two other (subsidiary) magnetic vectors, the *magnetization* **M** and the *magnetic field strength* **H**. We do so largely so that the student who takes a second course in electromagnetism will have some familiarity with them.

Consider a Rowland ring carrying a current i_0 in its windings and designed so that its core, assumed to be iron, can be removed. The magnetic induction B, measured by the methods of Section 37–5, will be much greater when the core is in place than when it is not, assuming that the current in the windings remains unchanged.

Physically we can understand the large value of B in the iron core in terms of the alignment of the elementary dipoles in the iron. A hypothetical slice out of the iron core, as in Fig. 37–21b, has a magnetic moment $d\mu$ equal to the vector sum of all of the elementary dipoles contained in it. We define our first subsidiary vector, the *magnetization* **M**, as the magnetic moment per unit volume of the core material. For the slice of Fig. 37–21b we have

$$d\mu = \mathbf{M}(A \, dl),$$

where $(A \, dl)$ is the volume of the slice, A being the cross section of the core.

When we discussed Ampère's law in Chapter 34, we assumed that no magnetic materials were present. If we apply this law, namely

$$\oint \mathbf{B} \cdot d\mathbf{l} = \mu_0 i, \qquad (37\text{--}20)$$

to the circular path of integration shown in Fig. 37–21a, we obtain

$$(B)(2\pi r_0) = \mu_0(N_0 i_0), \qquad (37\text{--}21)$$

in which r_0 is the mean radius of the core, N_0 is the number of turns, and i_0 is the current in each turn. We see at once that Ampère's law, in the form of Eq. 37–20,

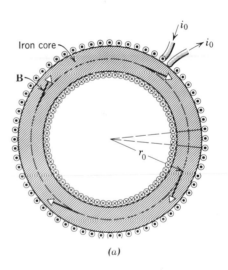

(a)

Fig. 37–21 (a) A Rowland ring with an iron core. (b) A slice of the core, showing its magnetic moment $d\mu$ caused by the alignment of the elementary magnetic dipoles in the iron.

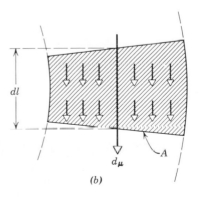

(b)

is not valid when magnetic materials are present. Equation 37–21 predicts that, since the right side is the same whether or not the core is in place, the induction B should also be the same, a prediction not in accord with experiment.

We can increase B in the absence of the iron core to the value that it has when the core is in place if we increase the current in the windings by an amount $i_{M,0}$. The magnetization of the iron core is thus *equivalent in its effect on* **B** to such a hypothetical current increase. We choose to modify Ampère's law by arbitrarily inserting a *magnetizing current* term i_M on the right, obtaining

$$\oint \mathbf{B} \cdot d\mathbf{l} = \mu_0(i + i_M). \tag{37–22}$$

If we give i_M a suitable value when the iron core is in place, it is clear that Ampère's law, in this new form, can remain valid. It remains to relate this (largely hypothetical) magnetizing current to something more physical, the magnetization **M**.*

Applying Eq. 37–22 to the iron ring of Fig. 37–21a yields

$$(B)(2\pi r_0) = \mu_0(N_0 i_0) + \mu_0(N_0 i_{M,0}). \tag{37–23}$$

We can relate $i_{M,0}$ to the magnetization **M** if we recall (Eq. 33–10) that the magnetic moment of a magnetic dipole in the form of a current loop is given by

$$\mu = NiA,$$

where N is the number of turns in the loop, i is the loop current, and A is the loop area. Let us use this equation to find what increase $i_{M,0}$ in current in the windings around the slice of Fig. 37–21b would produce a magnetic moment equivalent to that actually produced by the alignment of elementary dipoles in the slice. We have

$$M(A \, dl) = \left(N_0 \frac{dl}{2\pi r_0} \right) (i_{M,0})(A),$$

the quantity in the first parentheses on the right being the number of turns associated with the slice of thickness dl. This reduces to

$$N_0 i_{M,0} = M(2\pi r_0). \tag{37–24}$$

Substituting this into Eq. 37–23 yields

$$(B)(2\pi r_0) = \mu_0(N_0 i_0) + \mu_0(M)(2\pi r_0). \tag{37–25}$$

We now choose to generalize from the special case of the Rowland ring by writing Eq. 37–25 as

$$\oint \mathbf{B} \cdot d\mathbf{l} = \mu_0 i + \mu_0 \oint \mathbf{M} \cdot d\mathbf{l}$$

or

$$\oint \left(\frac{\mathbf{B} - \mu_0 \mathbf{M}}{\mu_0} \right) \cdot d\mathbf{l} = i.$$

---

* It is possible to give reality to the magnetizing current by viewing it as a real current that flows around the magnet at its surface, being the resultant macroscopic effect of all the microscopic current loops that constitute the atomic electron orbits. This *Amperian current* viewpoint however does not take the magnetization due to electron spin readily into account. Since we do not attempt to measure magnetizing currents experimentally, other than through their (postulated) magnetic effects, we prefer to view the magnetizing current as a convenient formalism.

The quantity $(\mathbf{B} - \mu_0\mathbf{M})/\mu_0$ occurs so often in magnetic situations that we give it a special name, the *magnetic field strength* $\mathbf{H}$, or

$$\mathbf{H} = \frac{\mathbf{B} - \mu_0\mathbf{M}}{\mu_0}$$

which we write as $\qquad\qquad \mathbf{B} = \mu_0\mathbf{H} + \mu_0\mathbf{M}. \qquad\qquad\qquad (37\text{–}26)$

Ampère's law can now be written in the simple form

$$\oint \mathbf{H}\cdot d\mathbf{l} = i, \qquad\qquad\qquad (37\text{–}27)$$

which holds in the presence of magnetic materials and in which i is the *true current only*, that is, it does not include the magnetizing current. This reminds us that the electric displacement vector $\mathbf{D}$ permitted us to write Gauss's law for the case in which dielectric materials are present, in a form involving free charges only, that is, not polarization charges; see Table 30–2.

We state without proof (see Problems 12 and 13) that at a boundary between two media (1) the component of $\mathbf{H}$ tangential to the surface has the same value on each side of the surface * and (2) the component of $\mathbf{B}$ perpendicular to the surface has the same value on each side of the surface. These *boundary conditions* are of great value in solving complex problems.

To find H in our Rowland ring, let us apply Ampère's law in the generalized form of Eq. 37–27. We have

$$(H)(2\pi r_0) = N_0 i_0,$$

where i_0 is the (true) current in the windings. This gives

$$H = \left(\frac{N_0}{2\pi r_0}\right) i_0 = n i_0, \qquad\qquad\qquad (37\text{–}28)$$

in which n is the number of turns per unit length. Since we have not introduced any information describing the core into Eq. 37–27, the value of H computed from Eq. 37–28 is independent of the core material.

B can be measured experimentally by the method of Section 37–5 and M can then be calculated from Eq. 37–26. The student should note in passing (see Eq. 37–15) that the abscissa B_0 in Fig. 37–9 is proportional to H ($= \mu_0 H$), the ordinate being proportional to B. Curves such as this and that of Fig. 37–12 are called *B-H curves*.

Let us assume that we have made measurements of $\mathbf{H}$, $\mathbf{B}$, and $\mathbf{M}$ for a wide variety of magnetic materials, using either the technique described or an equivalent one. For *paramagnetic* and *diamagnetic* materials we would find, as an experimental result, that $\mathbf{B}$ is directly proportional to $\mathbf{H}$, or

$$\mathbf{B} = \kappa_m\mu_0\mathbf{H}, \qquad\qquad\qquad (37\text{–}29)$$

in which κ_m, the *permeability* of the magnetic medium, is a constant for a given temperature and density of the material. Eliminating $\mathbf{B}$ between Eqs. 37–29 and 37–26 allows us to write

$$\mathbf{M} = (\kappa_m - 1)\mathbf{H}, \qquad\qquad\qquad (37\text{–}30)$$

which is another expression of the linear or proportional character of paramagnetic and diamagnetic materials.

---

* Assuming that there are no true currents at the surface, as there are in the Rowland ring of Fig. 37–21a, for example.

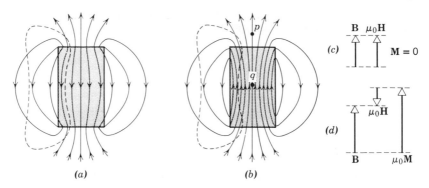

Fig. 37–22 (*a*) The lines of **H** and (*b*) the lines of **B** for a permanent magnet. The closed dashed curves are paths of integration around which Ampère's law may be applied. The relation $\mathbf{B} = \mu_0\mathbf{H} + \mu_0\mathbf{M}$ is shown to be satisfied for (*c*) a particular outside point p and (*d*) a particular inside point q.

For a vacuum, in which there are no magnetic dipoles present to be aligned, the magnetization **M** must be zero. Putting $\mathbf{M} = 0$ in Eq. 37–26 leads to

$$\mathbf{B} = \mu_0\mathbf{H} \qquad \text{(a vacuum)}. \tag{37–31}$$

Comparison with Eq. 37–29 shows that a vacuum must be described by $\kappa_m = 1$. Equation 37–30 verifies that the magnetization vanishes if we put κ_m equal to unity. For paramagnetic materials κ_m is slightly greater than unity. For diamagnetic materials it is slightly less than unity; Eq. 37–30 shows that this requires **M** and **H** to be oppositely directed, a fact discussed at length in Section 37–4.

In ferromagnetic materials the relationship between **B** and **H** is far from linear, as Figs. 37–9 and 37–12 show. Experimentally, κ_m proves to be a function not only of the value of H but also, because of hysteresis, of the magnetic and thermal history of the specimen.*

An interesting special case of ferromagnetism is the permanent magnet, for which **H**, **M**, and **B** all have nonvanishing values inside the magnet even though there is no true current. Figure 37–22 shows typical lines of **B** and **H** associated with such a magnet. The lines of **B** may be drawn as continuous loops, the boundary condition (2), mentioned above, being satisfied where the lines enter and leave the magnet. Equation 37–22 shows that the vector **B** is associated with the *total* current, both true and magnetizing. In Fig. 37–22*a* $\oint \mathbf{B} \cdot d\mathbf{l}$ around any loop such as that shown by the dashed curve is not zero and must be associated with a hypothetical magnetizing current i_M imagined to circulate around the magnet at its surface; actual or true currents (i) do not exist in this problem. Figure 37–22*b* shows that **H** reverses direction at the boundary. Since **H** (see Eq. 37–27) is associated with true currents only, we must have $\oint \mathbf{H} \cdot d\mathbf{l}$ around any loop such as that shown by the dashed lines.

---

* In the dielectric case there are waxy materials, called *ferroelectrics*, for which the relationship between **D** and **E** is nonlinear, which exhibit hysteresis, and from which quasi-permanent electric dipoles (*electrets*) can be constructed. However, most commonly useful dielectric materials are linear whereas most commonly useful magnetic materials are nonlinear.

The reversal of **H** at the boundary makes this possible. Note that **M** and **H** point in opposite directions within the magnet. Table 37–1 summarizes the properties of the three vectors **B**, **H**, and **M**.

Table 37–1

THE MAGNETIC VECTORS

Name	Symbol	Associated with	Boundary Condition
Magnetic induction	B	All currents	Normal component continuous
Magnetic field strength	H	True currents only	Tangential component continuous †
Magnetization (magnetic dipole moment per unit volume)	M	Magnetization currents only	Vanishes in a vacuum

Defining equations for **B**	$\mathbf{F} = q\mathbf{v} \times \mathbf{B}$ or $= i\mathbf{l} \times \mathbf{B}$	Eq. 33–3a Eq. 33–6a
General relation among the three vectors	$\mathbf{B} = \mu_0\mathbf{H} + \mu_0\mathbf{M}$	Eq. 37–26
Ampère's law when magnetic materials are present	$\oint \mathbf{H}\cdot d\mathbf{l} = i$ (i = true current only)	Eq. 37–27
Empirical relations for certain magnetic materials *	$\mathbf{B} = \kappa_m \mu_0 \mathbf{H}$ $\mathbf{M} = (\kappa_m - 1)\mathbf{H}$	Eq. 37–29 Eq. 37–30

* For paramagnetic and diamagnetic materials only, if κ_m is to be independent of **H**.
† Assuming no true currents exist at the boundary.

▶ **Example 6.** In the Rowland ring the (true) current i_0 in the windings is 2.0 amp and the number of turns per unit length (n) in the toroid is 10 turns/cm. B, measured by the technique of Section 37–5, is 1.0 weber/meter². Calculate (a) H, (b) M, and (c) the magnetizing current $i_{M,0}$ both when the core is in place and when it is removed. (d) For these particular operating conditions, what is κ_m?

(a) H is independent of the core material and may be found from Eq. 37–28:

$$H = ni$$

$$= (10 \text{ turns/cm})(2.0 \text{ amp})$$

$$= 2.0 \times 10^3 \text{ amp/meter}.$$

(b) M is zero when the core is removed. With the core in place, we may solve Eq. 37-26 for M, obtaining for the magnitude of M,

$$M = \frac{B - \mu_0 H}{\mu_0}$$

$$= \frac{(1.0 \text{ weber/meter}^2) - (4\pi \times 10^{-7} \text{ weber/amp-m})(2.0 \times 10^3 \text{ amp/meter})}{(4\pi \times 10^{-7} \text{ weber/amp-m})}$$

$$= 7.9 \times 10^5 \text{ amp/meter.}$$

(c) The effective magnetizing current follows from Eq. 37-24:

$$i_{M,0} = M\left(\frac{2\pi r_0}{N_0}\right) = \frac{M}{n}$$

$$= \frac{7.9 \times 10^5 \text{ amp/meter}}{2.0 \times 10^3 \text{ turns/meter}}$$

$$= 390 \text{ amp.}$$

An *additional* current of this amount in the windings would produce the same value of B in the absence of a core as that obtained, by alignment of the elementary dipoles, with the core in place.

(d) The permeability can be found from Eq. 37-29, or

$$\kappa_m = \frac{B}{\mu_0 H}$$

$$= \frac{1.0 \text{ weber/meter}^2}{(4\pi \times 10^{-7} \text{ weber/amp-m})(2.0 \times 10^3 \text{ amp/meter})}$$

$$= 397.$$

We emphasize that this value of κ_m holds only for the special conditions of this experiment. ◀

QUESTIONS

1. Two iron bars are identical in appearance. One is a magnet and one is not. How can you tell them apart? You are not permitted to suspend either bar as a compass needle or to use any other apparatus.

2. How could you reverse the magnetism of a compass needle?

3. Two iron bars always attract, no matter the combination in which their ends are brought near each other. Can you conclude that one of the bars must be unmagnetized?

4. If we sprinkle iron filings on a particular bar magnet, they cling both to the ends *and to the middle*. Sketch roughly the lines of **B**, both outside and inside the magnet.

5. The earth is a huge magnetic dipole. (a) Is the magnetic pole in the Northern Hemisphere a north or a south magnetic pole? (b) In the Northern Hemisphere do the magnetic lines of force associated with the earth's magnetic field point toward the earth's surface or away from it?

6. Cosmic rays are charged particles that strike our atmosphere from some external source. We find that more low-energy cosmic rays reach the earth at the north and south magnetic poles than at the (magnetic) equator. Why is this so?

7. How might the magnetic dipole moment of the earth be measured?

8. Give three reasons for believing that the flux Φ_B of the earth's magnetic field is greater through the boundaries of Alaska than through those of Texas.

9. The neutron, which has no charge, has a magnetic dipole moment. Is this possible on the basis of classical electromagnetism, or does this evidence alone indicate that classical electromagnetism has broken down?

10. Is the magnetization at saturation for a paramagnetic substance very much different from that for a saturated ferromagnetic substance of about the same size?

11. Explain why a magnet attracts an unmagnetized iron object such as a nail.

12. Does any net force or torque act on (a) an unmagnetized iron bar or (b) a permanent bar magnet when placed in a uniform magnetic field?

13. A nail is placed at rest on a smooth table top near a strong magnet. It is released and attracted to the magnet. What is the source of the kinetic energy it has just before it strikes the magnet?

14. The magnetization induced in a given diamagnetic sphere by a given external magnetic field does not vary with temperature, in sharp contrast to the situation in paramagnetism. Is this understandable in terms of the description that we have given of the origin of diamagnetism?

15. Compare the magnetization curves for a paramagnetic substance (Fig. 37–6) and for a ferromagnetic substance (Fig. 37–9). What would a similar curve for a diamagnetic substance look like? Do you think that it would show saturation effects in strong applied fields (say 10 weber/meter^2)?

16. Distinguish between the precession frequency and the cyclotron frequency of a proton in a magnetic field.

17. In our discussion of nuclear magnetism we said that energy absorption occurs because the dipoles are turned end for end. However, a given dipole might initially be lined up either with the field or against it. In the first case there would be an *absorption* of energy, but in the second case there would be a *release* of energy, each amount being $2\mu B$. Why do we observe a *net* absorption? These two events would seem to cancel.

18. Discuss similarities and differences in Tables 30–2 and 37–1.

PROBLEMS

1. The earth has a magnetic dipole moment of 6.4×10^{21} amp-m^2. (a) What current would have to be set up in a single turn of wire going around the earth at its magnetic equator if we wished to set up such a dipole? (b) Could such an arrangement be used to cancel out the earth's magnetism at points in space well above the earth's surface? (c) On the earth's surface?

2. Assume that the electron is a small sphere of radius R, its charge and mass being spread uniformly throughout its volume. Such an electron has a "spin" angular momentum L of 0.53×10^{-34} joule-sec and a magnetic moment μ of 9.3×10^{-24} amp-m^2. Show that $e/m = 2\mu/L$. Is this prediction in agreement with experiment? (Hint: The spherical electron must be divided into infinitesimal current loops and an expression for the magnetic moment found by integration. This model of the electron is too mechanistic to be in the spirit of the modern quantum view of this particle.)

3. Calculate (a) the electric field strength and (b) the magnetic induction at a point 1.0 A (one angstrom unit) away from a proton, measured along its axis of spin. The magnetic moment of the proton is 1.4×10^{-26} amp-m^2.

4. A Rowland ring is formed of ferromagnetic material. It is circular in cross section, with an inner radius of 5.0 cm and an outer radius of 6.0 cm and is wound with 400 turns of wire. (a) What current must be set up in the windings to attain $B_0 = 2 \times 10^{-4}$ weber/meter^2 in Fig. 37–9? (b) A secondary coil wound around the toroid has 50 turns and has a resistance of 8.0 ohms. If, for this value of B_0, we have $D_M = 800B_0$, how much charge moves through the secondary coil when the current in the toroid windings is turned on?

5. The dipole moment associated with an atom of iron in an iron bar is 1.8×10^{-23} amp-m^2. Assume that all the atoms in the bar, which is 5 cm long and has a cross-sec-

tional area of 1 cm², have their dipole moments aligned. (*a*) What is the dipole moment of the bar? (*b*) What torque must be exerted to hold this magnet at right angles to an external field of 15,000 gauss?

6. Can you give an explanation of diamagnetism based on Faraday's law of induction? In Figs. 37–7*a* and *b*, for example, what inductive effects can be expected as the magnetic field is built up from zero to the final value **B**?

7. Prove that $\Delta\omega \ll \omega_0$ in Eq. 37–13.

8. Show that, classically, a spinning positive charge will have a spin magnetic moment that points in the same direction as its spin angular momentum.

9. Assume that the nuclei (protons) in 1 gm of water *could all be aligned*. What magnetic induction B would be produced 5.0 cm from the sample, along its alignment axis?

10. It is possible to measure e/m for the electron by measuring (*a*) the cyclotron frequency f_c of electrons in a given magnetic field and (*b*) the precession frequency f_p of protons in the same field. Show that the relation is

$$\frac{e}{m} = \frac{f_c}{f_p}\frac{\mu_s}{L_s}.$$

Since μ_s and L_s for the proton are accurately known, this experiment gives us our most precise value of e/m today.

11. *Dipole-dipole interaction.* The exchange coupling mentioned in Section 37–5 as being responsible for ferromagnetism is *not* the mutual magnetic interaction energy between two elementary magnetic dipoles. To show this (*a*) compute B a distance a ($= 1.0$ A) away from a dipole of moment μ ($= 1.8 \times 10^{-23}$ amp-m²); (*b*) compute the energy ($= 2\mu B$) required to turn a second similar dipole end for end in this field. What do you conclude about the strength of this dipole-dipole interaction? Compare with the results of Example 3. (Note: for the same distance, the field in the median plane of a dipole is only half as large as on the axis; see Eq. 37–2.)

12. *Boundary condition for* **B**. Prove that at the boundary between two media the normal component of **B** has the same value on each side of the surface. (Hint: Construct a closed Gaussian surface shaped like a flat pillbox with one face in each medium and apply Gauss's law for magnetism.)

13. *Boundary condition for* **H**. Prove that at the boundary between two media the tangential component of **H** has the same value on each side of the surface, assuming that there is no current at the surface. (Hint: Construct a closed rectangular loop, the two opposite longer sides being parallel to the surface, with one side in each medium. Use Ampère's law in the form that applies when magnetic materials are present.)

14. The magnetic energy density can be shown to be given in its most general form as

$$\mu_B = \tfrac{1}{2}\mathbf{B}\cdot\mathbf{H}.$$

Does this reduce to a familiar result for a vacuum?

Electromagnetic Oscillations

CHAPTER 38

38–1 LC Oscillations

The LC system of Fig. 38–1 resembles a mass-spring system (see Fig. 8–3) in that, among other things, each system has a characteristic frequency of oscillation. To see this, we assume that initially the capacitor C in Fig. 38–1a carries a charge q_m and the current i in the inductor is zero. At this instant the energy stored in the capacitor is given by Eq. 30–25, or

$$U_E = \frac{1}{2}\frac{q_m{}^2}{C}. \tag{38–1}$$

The energy stored in the inductor, given by

$$U_B = \tfrac{1}{2}Li^2, \tag{38–2}$$

is zero because the current is zero. The capacitor now starts to discharge through the inductor, positive charge carriers moving counterclockwise, as shown in Fig. 38–1b. This means that a current i, given by dq/dt and pointing down in the inductor, is established.

As q decreases, the energy stored in the electric field in the capacitor also decreases. This energy is transferred to the magnetic field that appears around the inductor because of the current i that is building up there. Thus the electric field decreases, the magnetic field builds up, and energy is transferred from the former to the latter.

At a time corresponding to Fig. 38–1c, all the charge on the capacitor will have disappeared. The electric field in the capacitor will be zero, the energy stored there having been transferred entirely to the magnetic field of the

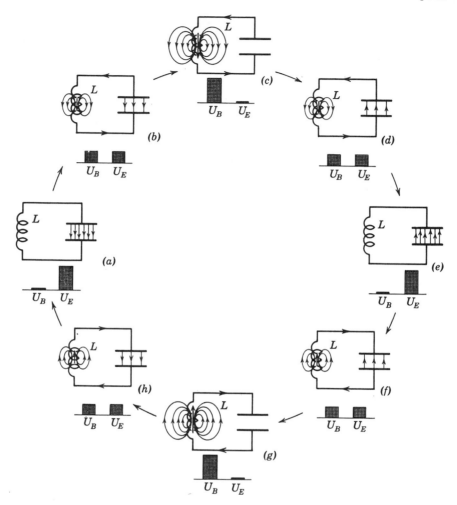

Fig. 38–1 Showing eight stages in a cycle of oscillation of an LC circuit. The bar graphs below each figure show the stored magnetic and electric potential energy. The vertical arrows on the inductor axis show the current. The student should compare this figure in detail with Fig. 8–3, to which it exactly corresponds.

inductor. According to Eq. 38–2, there must then be a current—and indeed one of maximum value—in the inductor. Note that even though q equals zero the current (which is dq/dt) is *not* zero at this time.

The large current in the inductor in Fig. 38–1c continues to transport positive charge from the top plate of the capacitor to the bottom plate, as shown in Fig. 38–1d; energy now flows from the inductor back to the capacitor as the electric field builds up again. Eventually, the energy will have been transferred completely back to the capacitor, as in Fig. 38–1e. The situation of Fig. 38–1e is like the initial situation, except that the capacitor is charged in the opposite direction.

The capacitor will start to discharge again, the current now being clockwise, as in Fig. 38–1*f*. Reasoning as before, we see that the circuit eventually returns to its initial situation and that the process continues at a definite frequency *f* (measured, say, in cycles/sec) to which corresponds a definite *angular* frequency ω ($= 2\pi f$ and measured, say, in radians/sec). Once started, such *LC* oscillations (in the ideal case described, in which the circuit contains no resistance) continue indefinitely, energy being shuttled back and forth between the electric field in the capacitor and the magnetic field in the inductor. Any configuration in Fig. 38–1 can be set up as an initial condition. The oscillations will then continue from that point, proceeding clockwise around the figure. The student should compare these oscillations carefully with those of the mass-spring system described in Fig. 8–3.

To measure the charge *q* as a function of time, we can measure the variable potential difference $V_C(t)$ that exists across capacitor *C*. The relation

$$V_C = \left(\frac{1}{C}\right) q$$

shows that V_C is proportional to *q*. To measure the current we can insert a small resistance *R* in the circuit and measure the potential difference across it. This is proportional to *i* through the relation

$$V_R = (R)i.$$

We assume here that *R* is so small that its effect on the behavior of the circuit is negligible. Both *q* and *i*, or more correctly V_C and V_R, which are proportional to them, can be displayed on a cathode-ray oscilloscope. This instrument can plot automatically on its screen graphs proportional to $q(t)$ and $i(t)$, as in Fig. 38–2.

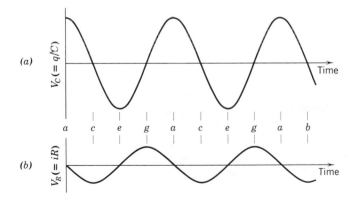

Fig. 38-2 A drawing of an oscilloscope screen showing potential differences proportional to (*a*) the charge and (*b*) the current, in the circuit of Fig. 38–1, as a function of time. The letters indicate corresponding phases of oscillation in that figure. Note that because $i = dq/dt$ the lower curve is proportional to the derivative of the upper.

▶ **Example 1.** A 1.0-μf capacitor is charged to 50 volts. The charging battery is then disconnected and a 10-mh coil is connected across the capacitor, so that LC oscillations occur. What is the maximum current in the coil? Assume that the circuit contains no resistance.

The maximum stored energy in the capacitor must equal the maximum stored energy in the inductor, from the conservation-of-energy principle. This leads, from Eqs. 38–1 and 38–2, to

$$\frac{1}{2}\frac{q_m^2}{C} = \frac{1}{2}Li_m^2,$$

where i_m is the *maximum* current and q_m is the *maximum* charge. Note that the maximum current and the maximum charge do not occur at the same time but one-fourth of a cycle apart; see Figs. 38–1 and 38–2. Solving for i_m and substituting CV_0 for q_m gives

$$i_m = V_0\sqrt{\frac{C}{L}} = (50 \text{ volts})\sqrt{\frac{1.0 \times 10^{-6} \text{ farad}}{10 \times 10^{-3} \text{ henry}}} = 0.50 \text{ amp.}\qquad ◀$$

In an actual LC circuit the oscillations will not continue indefinitely because there is always some resistance present that will drain away energy by Joule heating. The oscillations, once started, will die away, as in Fig. 38–3. This figure should be compared to Fig. 15–17, which shows the decay of the mechanical oscillations of a mass-spring system caused by frictional damping.

It is possible to have sustained electromagnetic oscillations if arrangements are made to supply, automatically and periodically (once a cycle, say), enough energy from an outside source to compensate for that lost to Joule heat. We are reminded of a clock escapement, which is a device for feeding energy from a spring or a falling weight into an oscillating pendulum, thus compensating for frictional losses that would otherwise cause the oscillations to die away. Oscillators whose frequency f may be varied between certain limits are commercially available as packaged units over a wide range of frequencies, extending from low audio-frequencies (lower than 10 cycles/sec) to microwave frequencies (higher than 10^{10} cycles/sec).

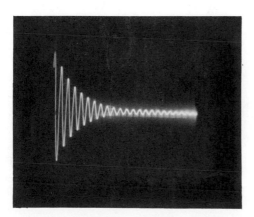

Fig. 38–3 A photograph of an oscilloscope trace showing how the oscillations in an LRC circuit die away because energy is lost to Joule heat in the resistor. The figure is a plot of the potential difference across the resistor as a function of time.

38–2   Analogy to Simple Harmonic Motion

Figure 8–3 shows that in a mass-spring system performing simple harmonic motion, as in an oscillating LC circuit, two kinds of energy occur. One is potential energy of the compressed or extended spring; the other is kinetic energy of the moving mass. These are given by the familiar formulas in the first column of Table 38–1. The table suggests that a capacitor is in

Table 38–1

Some Energy Formulas

Mechanical		Electromagnetic	
spring	$U_P = \frac{1}{2}kx^2$	capacitor	$U_E = \frac{1}{2}\frac{q^2}{C}$
mass	$U_K = \frac{1}{2}mv^2$	inductor	$U_B = \frac{1}{2}Li^2$
	$v = dx/dt$		$i = dq/dt$

some formal way like a spring and an inductor is like a mass and that certain electromagnetic quantities "correspond" to certain mechanical ones, namely,

$$q \text{ corresponds to } x,$$
$$i \text{ corresponds to } v,$$
$$C \text{ corresponds to } 1/k,$$
$$L \text{ corresponds to } m.$$

Comparison of Fig. 38–1, which shows the oscillations of the LC circuit, with Fig. 8–3, which shows the oscillations in a mass-spring system, indicates how close the correspondence is. Note how v and i correspond in the two figures; also x and q. Note, too, how in each case the energy alternates between two forms, magnetic and electric for the LC system, and kinetic and potential for the mass-spring system.

In Section 15–3 we saw that the natural angular frequency of oscillation of an undamped mass-spring system is

$$\omega = 2\pi f = \sqrt{\frac{k}{m}}.$$

The method of correspondences suggests that to find the natural frequency for the LC circuit k should be replaced by $1/C$ and m by L, obtaining

$$\omega = 2\pi f = \sqrt{\frac{1}{LC}}. \tag{38–3}$$

This formula is indeed correct, as we show in the next section.

38–3   Electromagnetic Oscillations—Quantitative

We now derive an expression for the frequency of oscillation of an LC circuit, our derivation being based on the conservation-of-energy principle. The total energy U present at any instant in an oscillating LC circuit is given by

$$U = U_B + U_E = \tfrac{1}{2}Li^2 + \frac{1}{2}\frac{q^2}{C},$$

which expresses the fact that at any arbitrary time the energy is stored partly in the magnetic field in the inductor and partly in the electric field in the capacitor. If we assume the circuit resistance to be zero, there is no energy transfer to Joule heat and U remains constant with time, even though i and q vary. In more formal language, dU/dt must be zero. This leads to

$$\frac{dU}{dt} = \frac{d}{dt}\left(\tfrac{1}{2}Li^2 + \frac{1}{2C}q^2\right) = Li\frac{di}{dt} + \frac{q}{C}\frac{dq}{dt} = 0. \tag{38–4}$$

Now, q and i are not independent variables, being related by

$$i = \frac{dq}{dt}.$$

Differentiating yields

$$\frac{di}{dt} = \frac{d^2q}{dt^2}.$$

Substituting these two expressions into Eq. 38–4 leads to

$$L\frac{d^2q}{dt^2} + \frac{1}{C}q = 0. \tag{38–5}$$

This is the differential equation that describes the oscillations of a (resistanceless) LC circuit. To solve it, the student should note that Eq. 38–5 is mathematically of exactly the same form as Eq. 15–3,

$$m\frac{d^2x}{dt^2} + kx = 0, \tag{15–3}$$

which is the differential equation for the mass-spring oscillations. Fundamentally, it is by comparing these two equations that the correspondences on p. 855 arise.

The solution of Eq. 15–3 proved to be

$$x = A\cos(\omega t + \delta), \tag{15–5}$$

where A ($= x_m$) is the amplitude of the motion and δ is an arbitrary *phase angle*. Since q corresponds to x, we can write the solution of Eq. 38–5 as

$$q = q_m\cos(\omega t + \delta), \tag{38–6}$$

where ω is the still unknown angular frequency of the electromagnetic oscillations.

We can test whether Eq. 38-6 is indeed a solution of Eq. 38-5 by substituting it and its second derivative in that equation. To find the second derivative, we write

$$\frac{dq}{dt} = i = -\omega q_m \sin (\omega t + \delta) \tag{38-7}$$

and

$$\frac{d^2q}{dt^2} = -\omega^2 q_m \cos (\omega t + \delta).$$

Substituting q and d^2q/dt^2 into Eq. 38-5 yields

$$-L\omega^2 q_m \cos (\omega t + \delta) + \frac{1}{C} q_m \cos (\omega t + \delta) = 0.$$

Canceling $q_m \cos (\omega t + \delta)$ and rearranging leads to

$$\omega = \sqrt{\frac{1}{LC}}.$$

Thus, if ω is given the constant value $1/\sqrt{LC}$, Eq. 38-6 is indeed a solution of Eq. 38-5. This expression for ω agrees with Eq. 38-3, which was arrived at by the method of correspondences.

The phase angle δ in Eq. 38-6 is determined by the conditions that prevail at $t = 0$. If the initial condition is as represented by Fig. 38-1a, then we put $\delta = 0$ in order that Eq. 38-6 may predict $q = q_m$ at $t = 0$. What initial condition in Fig. 38-1 is implied if we select $\delta = 90°$?

▶ **Example 2.** (a) In an oscillating LC circuit, what value of charge, expressed in terms of the maximum charge, is present on the capacitor when the energy is shared equally between the electric and the magnetic field? (b) How much time is required for this condition to arise, assuming the capacitor to be fully charged initially? Assume that $L = 10$ mh and $C = 1.0$ μf.

(a) The stored energy and the *maximum* stored energy in the capacitor are, respectively,

$$U_E = \frac{q^2}{2C} \quad \text{and} \quad U_{E,m} = \frac{q_m^2}{2C}.$$

Substituting $U_E = \frac{1}{2}U_{E,m}$ yields

$$\frac{q^2}{2C} = \frac{1}{2}\frac{q_m^2}{2C} \quad \text{or} \quad q = \frac{1}{\sqrt{2}} q_m.$$

(b) To find the time, we write, assuming $\delta = 0$ in Eq. 38-6,

$$q = q_m \cos \omega t = \frac{1}{\sqrt{2}} q_m,$$

which leads to

$$\omega t = \cos^{-1}\frac{1}{\sqrt{2}} = \frac{\pi}{4} \quad \text{or} \quad t = \frac{\pi}{4\omega}.$$

The angular frequency ω is found from Eq. 38-3, or

$$\omega = \sqrt{\frac{1}{LC}} = \sqrt{\frac{1}{(10 \times 10^{-3} \text{ henry})(1.0 \times 10^{-6} \text{ farad})}} = 1.0 \times 10^4 \text{ radians/sec.}$$

The time t is then

$$t = \frac{\pi}{4\omega} = \frac{\pi}{(4)(1.0 \times 10^4 \text{ radians/sec})} = 7.9 \times 10^{-5} \text{ sec.}$$

What is the frequency f in cycles/sec? ◄

The stored electric energy in the LC circuit, using Eq. 38–6, is

$$U_E = \frac{1}{2}\frac{q^2}{C} = \frac{q_m{}^2}{2C} \cos^2{(\omega t + \delta)}, \qquad (38\text{–}8)$$

and the magnetic energy, using Eq. 38–7, is

$$U_B = \tfrac{1}{2}Li^2 = \tfrac{1}{2}L\omega^2 q_m{}^2 \sin^2{(\omega t + \delta)}.$$

Substituting the expression for ω (Eq. 38–3) into this last equation yields

$$U_B = \frac{q_m{}^2}{2C} \sin^2{(\omega t + \delta)}. \qquad (38\text{–}9)$$

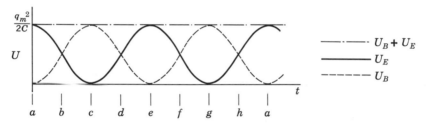

Fig. 38–4 The stored magnetic and electric energy in the circuit of Fig. 38–1. Note that their sum is a constant. The letters indicate corresponding phases of oscillation in Fig. 38–1.

Figure 38–4 shows plots of $U_E(t)$ and $U_B(t)$ for the case of $\delta = 0$. Note that (a) the maximum values of U_E and U_B are the same ($= q_m{}^2/2C$); (b) at any instant the sum of U_E and U_B is a constant ($= q_m{}^2/2C$); and (c) when U_E has its maximum value, U_B is zero and conversely. This analysis supports the qualitative analysis of Section 38–1. The student should compare this discussion with that given in Section 15–4 for the energy transfers in a mass-spring system.

► **Example 3.** *The LCR circuit.* (a) Derive an expression for the quantity $q(t)$ for a single-loop circuit containing a resistance R as well as an inductance L and a capacitance C. (b) After how long a time will the charge oscillations decay to half-amplitude if $L = 10$ mh, $C = 1.0$ μf, and $R = 0.1$ ohm?

(a) If U is the total stored field energy, we have, as before,

$$U = \tfrac{1}{2}Li^2 + \frac{1}{2}\frac{q^2}{C}.$$

U is no longer constant but rather

$$\frac{dU}{dt} = -i^2 R,$$

the minus sign signifying that the stored energy U *decreases* with time, being converted to Joule heat at the rate i^2R. Combining these two equations leads to

$$Li\frac{di}{dt} + \frac{q}{C}\frac{dq}{dt} = -i^2R.$$

Substituting dq/dt for i and d^2q/dt^2 for di/dt leads finally to

$$L\frac{d^2q}{dt^2} + R\frac{dq}{dt} + \frac{1}{C}q = 0,$$

which is the differential equation that describes the damped LC oscillations. If we put $R = 0$, this equation reduces, as expected, to Eq. 38–5.

The student should compare this differential equation for damped LC oscillations with Eq. 15–28, or

$$m\frac{d^2x}{dt^2} + b\frac{dx}{dt} + kx = 0, \tag{15–28}$$

which describes damped mass-spring oscillations. Once again the equations are mathematically identical, the resistance R corresponding to the mechanical damping constant b.

The solution of the LCR circuit follows at once, by correspondence, from the solution of Eq. 15–28. It is (see Eqs. 15–29 and 15–30) for R reasonably small, and for an initial condition in which the capacitor has a maximum charge

$$q = q_m e^{-Rt/2L}\cos\omega't, \tag{38–10}$$

where

$$\omega' = \sqrt{\frac{1}{LC} - \left(\frac{R}{2L}\right)^2}. \tag{38–11}$$

Note that Eq. 38–10, which can be described as a cosine function with an exponentially decreasing amplitude, is the equation of the decay curve of Fig. 38–3. Note, too (Eq. 38–11), that the presence of resistance reduces the oscillation frequency. These two equations reduce to familiar results as $R \to 0$.

(b) The oscillation amplitude will have decreased to half when the amplitude factor $e^{-Rt/2L}$ in Eq. 38–10 has the value one-half, or

$$\tfrac{1}{2} = e^{-Rt/2L},$$

which leads readily to

$$t = \frac{2L}{R}\ln 2 = \frac{(2)(10 \times 10^{-3}\text{ henry})(0.69)}{0.10\text{ ohm}} = 0.14\text{ sec.}$$

The angular frequency, from Eq. 38–11, is

$$\omega' = \sqrt{\frac{1}{(10 \times 10^{-3}\text{ henry})(1.0 \times 10^{-6}\text{ farad})} - \left(\frac{0.10\text{ ohm}}{2 \times 10 \times 10^{-3}\text{ henry}}\right)^2}$$

$$= \sqrt{10^8\text{ radians/sec}^2 - 25\text{ radians/sec}^2} = 1.0 \times 10^4\text{ radians/sec.}$$

Note that the second term is rather small, so that in this case, as in many practical cases, the resistance has a negligible effect on the frequency. The student should show that 0.14 sec, the time at which the oscillations decrease to half-amplitude, corresponds to about 220 cycles of oscillation. The damping is much less severe than that illustrated in Fig. 38–3. ◀

38–4   Forced Oscillations and Resonance

Figure 38–5 shows an LCR circuit containing a sinusoidally varying emf $\mathcal{E}(t)$ given by

$$\mathcal{E} = \mathcal{E}_m \cos \omega'' t,$$

in which ω'' can be varied at will. The emf $\mathcal{E}(t)$ might be provided by a variable-frequency oscillator. What amplitudes of electromagnetic oscillations are set up in this circuit for various angular frequencies ω'' of the "driving force"?

The problem corresponds to that of forced oscillations in the damped mass-spring system of Section 15–9. The differential equation describing that motion is

$$m \frac{d^2x}{dt^2} + b \frac{dx}{dt} + kx = F_m \cos \omega'' t, \tag{15–31}$$

where ω'' is the angular frequency of the external periodic driving force applied to the system and F_m is its amplitude.

For the circuit of Fig. 38–5, the differential equation that follows from the correspondences of p. 855, and the additional reasonable correspondence of $\mathcal{E}$ to F, is

$$L \frac{d^2q}{dt^2} + R \frac{dq}{dt} + \frac{1}{C} q = \mathcal{E}_m \cos \omega'' t. \tag{38–12}$$

This equation can also be derived by applying the energy conservation principle to the circuit of Fig. 38–5.

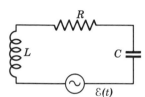

Fig. 38–5   An LCR circuit containing a sinusoidal emf of angular frequency ω''.

We can use the correspondences of p. 855 to write down the solution to Eq. 38–12. Starting from Eq. 15–32 and making the appropriate substitutions, we obtain

$$q = \frac{\mathcal{E}_m}{G} \sin (\omega'' t - \alpha), \tag{38–13}$$

where

$$G = \sqrt{\left(\omega''^2 L - \frac{1}{C}\right)^2 + R^2 \omega''^2},$$

and α, the *phase angle* between the "driving force" and the "response," is given by

$$\alpha = \cos^{-1} \frac{R\omega''}{G}.$$

As often as not, we are interested in the current $i(t)$ in the circuit, rather than the charge; the current corresponds to the velocity $v(t)$ of the moving mass in Section 15–9. We can find $i(t)$ by differentiating Eq. 38–13, or

$$i = \frac{dq}{dt} = \frac{\omega'' \mathcal{E}_m}{G} \cos (\omega'' t - \alpha) = i_m \cos (\omega'' t - \alpha).$$

The amplitude i_m of the current oscillations is given, from these equations, by

$$i_m = \frac{\omega'' \mathcal{E}_m}{G} = \frac{\mathcal{E}_m}{\sqrt{\left(\omega'' L - \frac{1}{\omega'' C}\right)^2 + R^2}}. \tag{38-14}$$

Inspection of Eq. 38-14 shows that the current (not the charge; see Question 5) will have its maximum amplitude when

$$\omega'' L = \frac{1}{\omega'' C},$$

which can be written as

$$\omega'' = \sqrt{\frac{1}{LC}}. \tag{38-15}$$

Comparison with Eq. 38-3 shows that the maximum amplitude of the current oscillations occurs when the frequency ω'' of the applied emf is exactly equal to the natural (undamped) frequency ω of the system.

At *resonance* ($\omega'' = \omega$) the amplitude of the current oscillations is determined entirely by the resistance; this follows by combining Eqs. 38-14 and 38-15, or

$$i_m = \frac{\mathcal{E}_m}{R} \qquad \text{(at resonance)}.$$

Figure 38-6 shows i_m as a function of ω'' for an oscillating LCR circuit containing three different values of resistance. Note that the smaller the resistance, the sharper the resonance curve. The sharpness of such a curve is measured by its *half-width*, which is the difference between two frequencies, each of which corresponds to a current amplitude of one-half the maximum current amplitude. The half-width of the curve for $R = 10$ ohms in Fig. 38-6 is shown in that figure by the arrow marked $\Delta\omega$.

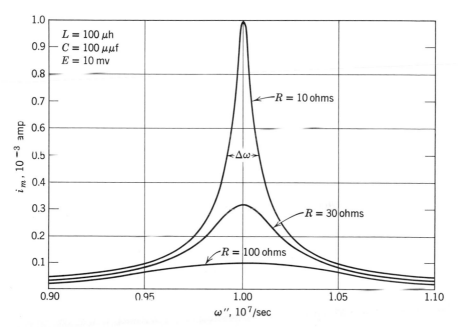

Fig. 38-6 The current amplitude as a function of frequency in the circuit of Fig. 38-5. The arrow marked $\Delta\omega$ on the curve for $R = 10$ ohms is the *half-width* of that curve.

38–5 Lumped and Distributed Elements

In the oscillating mass-spring system the two kinds of energy involved appear in separate parts of the system, the potential energy being stored in the spring and the kinetic energy in the moving mass. An *acoustic cavity resonator*, such as an organ pipe, is a mechanical oscillating system in which the two forms of energy are *not* separated in space. Kinetic energy, associated with moving air in the cavity, and potential energy, associated with compressions or rarefactions of the air, can both be present throughout the volume of the cavity. Such a cavity is an example of an oscillating system with *distributed* rather than *lumped* (as in the mass-spring system) elements.

A similar distinction exists in electromagnetic systems. The *LC* circuit of Fig. 38–1 is an example of lumped elements, in that the two kinds of energy are stored in rather different places; the circuit is described by giving the (lumped) system parameters *L* and *C*. Actually, in modern engineering practice and in physics research electromagnetic systems with *distributed elements* play a fundamental role.

Figure 38–7, a series of "snapshots" taken one-eighth of a cycle apart, shows the pressure and velocity variations in the fundamental mode of a particular acoustic resonator. There is a pressure node at the center and a pressure antinode at each end. There is a velocity * node at each end and a velocity antinode at the center. When the pressure variation is the greatest, the velocity is zero (Figs. 38–7a and e). When the pressure is uniform, the velocities have their maximum values (Figs. 38–7c, and g).

The energy in the acoustic resonator alternates between kinetic energy associated with the moving gas and potential energy associated with the compression and rarefaction of the gas. In Figs. 38–7c and g the energy is all kinetic and in Figs. 38–7a and e it is all potential. In intermediate phases it is part of each.

The kinetic energy of a small mass Δm of the gas, which is moving parallel to the cylinder axis with a speed v_g, is $\frac{1}{2}\Delta m v_g^2$. The *kinetic energy density*, that is, the kinetic energy per unit volume, is

$$u_K = \frac{1}{2}\frac{\Delta m}{\Delta V}v_g^2 = \tfrac{1}{2}\rho_0 v_g^2,$$

in which ΔV is the volume of the gas element and ρ_0 is the mean density of the gas.

The potential energy per unit volume in the gas, that is, the *potential energy density*, associated with the compressions and rarefactions of the gas may be given by

$$u_P = \tfrac{1}{2}B\left(\frac{\Delta\rho}{\rho_0}\right)^2.$$

Here B is the bulk modulus of elasticity of the gas and $\Delta\rho/\rho_0$, which is positive for a compression and negative for a rarefaction, is the fractional change in gas density.

---

* The velocity of interest here is the directed velocity v_g of small volume elements of the gas which are, however, large enough to contain a great number of molecules. The thermal velocities of the molecules have no directional preference and are ignored.

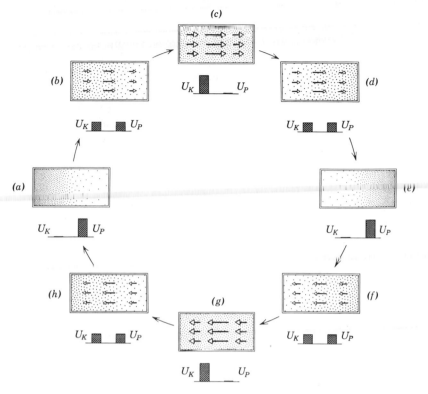

Fig. 38–7 Showing eight stages in a cycle of oscillation of a cylindrical acoustic resonant cavity. The bar graphs below each figure show the kinetic and potential energy. The arrows represent the directed velocities of small volume elements of the gas. Compare with Fig. 38–1.

The angular frequency of oscillation for the cavity of Fig. 38–7, in the fundamental (or lowest frequency) mode shown in that figure, is found from

$$\omega_1 = 2\pi f = \frac{2\pi v}{\lambda} = \frac{\pi v}{l},$$

where v is the speed of sound in the gas and l is the length of the cavity. From Eq. 20–1 we may write v as $\sqrt{B_0/\rho_0}$. Note that in the above we have put $\lambda = 2l$, corresponding to the fundamental mode. What are the frequencies ω_2, ω_3, etc., of the higher frequency modes?

38–6 Electromagnetic Cavity Oscillator

Consider now a second closed cylinder, of radius a and length l, whose walls are made of copper or some other good conductor. A system of oscillating electric and magnetic fields can be set up in such a cavity even if, as in the common case that we consider, the cavity contains no material medium. Such an *electromagnetic cavity resonator* is a distributed electromagnetic oscillator, in contrast to an *LC* circuit, which is a lumped system. As for the acoustic resonator, many modes of oscillation with discrete frequencies are possible; we describe only the fundamental mode, which has the lowest frequency. The cavity oscillations can be set up by suitably connecting the cavity, through a small hole in its side wall, to a source of electromagnetic radiation such as a magnetron. If the cavity dimensions are of the order of a few centimeters, the resonant frequencies will be of the order of 10^{10} cycles/sec. This is far higher than the acoustic frequencies in cavities of the same size, reflecting the fact that the speed of electromagnetic disturbances in free space ($= 3 \times 10^8$ meters/sec) is much greater than the speed of sound in air (about 350 meters/sec).

Figure 38–8, which is a series of "snapshots" taken one-eighth of a cycle apart, shows, by the horizontal lines, how the electric field **E** varies with time in the cavity. The electric lines of force originate on positive charges at one end of the cylinder and terminate on negative charges at the other end. As **E** changes with time, eventually reversing itself, currents flow from one end of the cylinder to the other on the inner cylinder wall. At any point

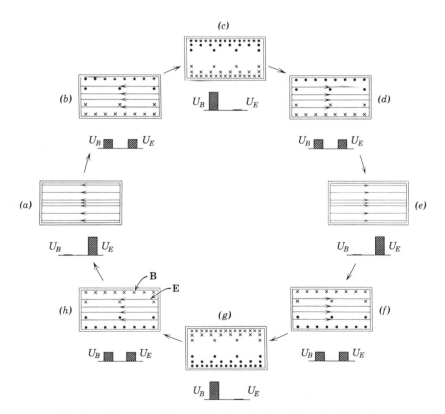

Fig. 38–8 Showing eight stages in a cycle of oscillation of a cylindrical electromagnetic resonant cavity. The bar graphs below each figure show the stored electric and magnetic energy. The dots and crosses represent circular lines of **B**; the horizontal lines represent **E**. Compare with Fig. 38–7.

in the cavity, energy is stored in the electric field in an amount per unit volume given by Eq. 30-27, or

$$u_E = \tfrac{1}{2}\epsilon_0 E^2. \tag{38-16}$$

Figure 38-8 also shows, by the dots and crosses, how the magnetic field **B** varies with time. The magnetic lines form circles about the cylinder axis. Note that the magnetic field has a maximum value when the electric field is zero, and conversely. At any point in the cavity energy is stored in the magnetic field in an amount per unit volume given by Eq. 36-19, or

$$u_B = \frac{1}{2\mu_0} B^2. \tag{38-17}$$

Thus, as in the LC circuit, energy is shuttled back and forth between the electric and the magnetic fields. However, these fields no longer occupy completely separate regions of space.

We state without proof that the angular frequency of oscillation for the electromagnetic cavity of Fig. 38-8 is, in the fundamental mode shown in that figure,

$$\omega_1 = \frac{1.19c}{a},$$

in which a is the cavity radius and c is the speed of electromagnetic radiations in free space. We will see in Section 39-5 that c may be written in terms of electromagnetic quantities as $1/\sqrt{\mu_0\epsilon_0}$. As the field patterns of Fig. 38-8 suggest, the resonant frequency of oscillation of the cavity, for the mode of oscillation shown, depends only on the radius of the cavity and not on its length.

Table 38-2 summarizes some characteristics of the four oscillating systems that we have discussed so far. For lumped systems it gives expressions for the two kinds

Table 38-2

FOUR OSCILLATING SYSTEMS

	Mechanical Systems	Electromagnetic Systems
Lumped systems	Mass + spring $U_K = \tfrac{1}{2}mv^2$ $U_P = \tfrac{1}{2}kx^2$ $\omega = \sqrt{\dfrac{k}{m}}$	LC circuit $U_B = \tfrac{1}{2}Li^2$ $U_E = \tfrac{1}{2}(1/C)q^2$ $\omega = \sqrt{\dfrac{(1/C)}{L}}$
Distributed systems	Acoustic cavity $u_K = \tfrac{1}{2}\rho_0 v_g{}^2$ $u_P = \tfrac{1}{2}B(\Delta\rho/\rho_0)^2$ $\omega_1 = \dfrac{3.14v}{l}; \qquad v = \sqrt{\dfrac{B}{\rho_0}}$	Electromagnetic cavity $u_B = \tfrac{1}{2}(1/\mu_0)B^2$ $u_E = \tfrac{1}{2}\epsilon_0 E^2$ $\omega_1 = \dfrac{1.19c}{a}; \qquad c = \sqrt{\dfrac{1}{\epsilon_0\mu_0}}$

of energy involved and for the (single) oscillation frequency. For the distributed systems it gives expressions for the two kinds of energy density involved and for the oscillation frequency in the fundamental mode. The student should study carefully all the correspondences, similarities, and differences that occur in the table.

The expression given above for the fundamental resonant angular frequency ω_1 of the cavity is derived by applying the basic equations of electromagnetism (Table 38–3) to the space inside the cavity and by invoking this boundary condition: **E** *must be zero inside the cavity wall and can have no tangential component anywhere on the cavity wall.* If this were not true, an infinite current would be set up in the assumed resistanceless wall by the tangential component of **E**. This boundary condition is similar in spirit to the requirement that a clamped string must have zero amplitude of oscillation at the points at which it is clamped or that a velocity node must exist at the end walls of an acoustic cavity resonator. Granted this boundary condition, on **E**, it can be shown that, assuming a perfectly conducting wall, (*a*) no time-varying magnetic field can exist inside the cavity wall and (*b*) no time-varying currents can exist inside the wall. A tangential magnetic field can exist *on the surface,* however; surface charges can exist, and surface currents can flow.

▶ **Example 4.** In the cavity of Fig. 38–8, what is the relationship between the "average" value of **E** throughout the cavity, measured at the instant corresponding to Fig. 38–8*a*, to the "average" value of **B**, measured at the instant corresponding to Fig. 38–8*c*?

At the first instant the energy is all electric and at the second it is all magnetic. The total energy U, found by integrating the energy density over the volume of the cavity, must be the same at these two instants, or

$$U = \int u_{E,m}\, dV = \int u_{B,m}\, dV,$$

where dV is a volume element in the cavity and $u_{E,m}$ and $u_{B,m}$ are the *maximum* values of u_E and of u_B at the site of this volume element; these maximum values occur one-fourth of a cycle apart, as Fig. 38–8 shows. Substituting Eqs. 38–16 and 38–17 leads to

$$\int \frac{\epsilon_0 E_m{}^2}{2}\, dV = \int \frac{B_m{}^2}{2\mu_0}\, dV$$

or

$$\mu_0 \epsilon_0 \int E_m{}^2\, dV = \int B_m{}^2\, dV.$$

The quantity $\int E_m{}^2\, dV$ can be written as $\overline{E_m{}^2}V$, where V is the cavity volume and $\overline{E_m{}^2}$ is the average value of $E_m{}^2$ throughout the cavity. Treating B_m in the same way leads to

$$\mu_0 \epsilon_0 \overline{E_m{}^2} = \overline{B_m{}^2}$$

or, taking square roots, $\sqrt{\overline{B_m{}^2}} = \sqrt{\mu_0\epsilon_0}\,\sqrt{\overline{E_m{}^2}}.$

We can represent $\sqrt{\overline{B_m{}^2}}$ by B_{rms}, a so-called "root-mean-square" value of B_m. In computing B_{rms}, note that the averaging is done throughout the volume of the cavity, at the instant corresponding to Fig. 38–8*c*. It is not a time average for a particular point in the cavity. Doing the same for **E** yields

$$B_{\mathrm{rms}} = \sqrt{\mu_0 \epsilon_0}\, E_{\mathrm{rms}} = \sqrt{(4\pi \times 10^{-7}\ \text{weber/amp-m})(8.9 \times 10^{-12}\ \text{coul}^2/\text{nt-m}^2)}\ E_{\mathrm{rms}}$$

$$= (3.3 \times 10^{-9}\ \text{sec/meter}) E_{\mathrm{rms}}.$$

If E_{rms} equals 10^4 volts/meter, a reasonable value, then

$$B_{rms} = (3.3 \times 10^{-9} \text{ sec/meter})(10^4 \text{ volts/meter})$$

$$= 3.3 \times 10^{-5} \text{ weber/meter}^2 = 0.33 \text{ gauss.}$$

What is the total stored energy in the cavity under these conditions, assuming the cavity to be 10 cm long and 3.0 cm in diameter?

The student will recall that in Example 6, Chapter 36, we showed the energy density for a magnetic field of "ordinary" laboratory magnitude (say, 1 weber/meter^2) to be enormously greater than that for an electric field of "ordinary" magnitude (say, 10^5 volts/meter). This fact is consistent with the present example. ◀

38-7   Induced Magnetic Fields

To understand the electromagnetic cavity oscillations in terms of electromagnetic theory, we must complete our description of the basic equations of electromagnetism by introducing a new concept, namely, that *a changing electric field produces a magnetic field*. This concept, which is the symmetrical counterpart of Faraday's law of induction, is of fundamental significance. We will develop this concept by a symmetry argument and will let the agreement with experiment of our final conclusions speak for itself. This comparison with experiment, which is worked out largely in Chapters 39 and 40, forms one of the chief experimental bases of electromagnetic theory. A central achievement was the demonstration that the experimentally measured speed c of visible light in free space could be related to purely electromagnetic quantities by

$$c = \frac{1}{\sqrt{\mu_0 \epsilon_0}}. \tag{38-18}$$

This demonstration not only revealed optics as a branch of electromagnetism but led directly to the concept of the electromagnetic spectrum, which in turn resulted in the discovery of radio waves.

Figure 38-9a shows a uniform electric field **E** filling a cylindrical region of space. It might be produced by a circular parallel-plate capacitor, as suggested in Fig. 38-9b. We assume that E is increasing at a steady rate dE/dt, which means that charge must be supplied to the capacitor plates at a steady rate; to supply this charge requires a steady current i into the positive plate and an equal steady current i out of the negative plate.

If a sufficiently delicate experiment could be performed, it would be found that *a magnetic field is set up by this changing electric field*. Figure 38-9a shows **B** for four arbitrary points. Figure 38-9 suggests a beautiful example of the symmetry of nature. A changing *magnetic* field induces an *electric* field (Faraday's law); now we see that a changing *electric* field induces a *magnetic* field.

To describe this new effect quantitatively, we are guided by analogy with Faraday's law of induction,

$$\oint \mathbf{E} \cdot d\mathbf{l} = -\frac{d\Phi_B}{dt}, \tag{38-19}$$

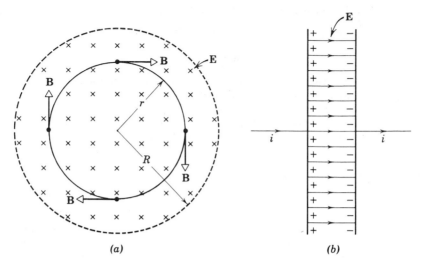

Fig. 38–9 (a) Showing the induced magnetic fields **B** at four points, produced by a changing electric field **E**. The electric field is increasing in magnitude. Compare Fig. 35–10. (b) Such a changing electric field may be produced by charging a parallel-plate capacitor as shown.

which asserts that an electric field (left term) is produced by a changing magnetic field (right term). For the symmetrical counterpart we might write *

$$\oint \mathbf{B} \cdot d\mathbf{l} = \mu_0 \epsilon_0 \frac{d\Phi_E}{dt}. \tag{38–20}$$

Equation 38–20 asserts that a magnetic field (left term) can be produced by a changing electric field (right term). The student should compare carefully Fig. 35–10, which illustrates the production of an electric field by a changing magnetic field, with Fig. 38–9a. In each case the appropriate flux Φ_B or Φ_E is *increasing*. However, experiment shows that the lines of **E** in Fig. 35–10 are *counterclockwise*, whereas those of **B** in Fig. 38–9a are *clockwise*. This difference requires that the minus sign of Eq. 38–19 be omitted from Eq. 38–20.

In Section 34–1 we saw that a magnetic field can also be set up by a current in a wire. We described this quantitatively by Ampère's law:

$$\oint \mathbf{B} \cdot d\mathbf{l} = \mu_0 i,$$

in which i is the conduction current passing through the loop around which the line integral is taken. Thus there are at least two ways of setting up

---

* Our system of units requires that we insert the constants ϵ_0 and μ_0 in Eq. 38–20. In some unit systems they would not appear.

a magnetic field: (a) by a changing electric field and (b) by a current.   In general, both possibilities must be allowed for, or *

$$\oint \mathbf{B} \cdot d\mathbf{l} = \mu_0 \epsilon_0 \frac{d\Phi_E}{dt} + \mu_0 i. \qquad (38\text{–}21)$$

Maxwell is responsible for this important generalization of Ampère's law.

In Chapter 34 we assumed that no changing electric fields were present so that the term $d\Phi_E/dt$ in Eq. 38–21 is zero.   In the discussion just given we assumed that there were no conduction currents in the space containing the electric field.   Thus the term i in Eq. 38–21 is zero.   We see now that each of these situations is a special case.

▶ **Example 5.** A parallel-plate capacitor with circular plates is being charged as in Fig. 38–9. (a) Derive an expression for the induced magnetic field at various radii r.   Consider both $r < R$ and $r > R$.

From Eq. 38–20,

$$\oint \mathbf{B} \cdot d\mathbf{l} = \mu_0 \epsilon_0 \frac{d\Phi_E}{dt},$$

we can write, for $r \lessgtr R$,

$$(B)(2\pi r) = \mu_0 \epsilon_0 \frac{d}{dt}[(E)(\pi r^2)] = \mu_0 \epsilon_0 \pi r^2 \frac{dE}{dt}.$$

Solving for B yields $B = \frac{1}{2}\mu_0 \epsilon_0 r \dfrac{dE}{dt} \qquad (r \lessgtr R).$

For $r \gtrless R$, Eq. 38–20 yields

$$(B)(2\pi r) = \mu_0 \epsilon_0 \frac{d}{dt}[(E)(\pi R^2)] = \mu_0 \epsilon_0 \pi R^2 \left(\frac{dE}{dt}\right),$$

or $B = \dfrac{\mu_0 \epsilon_0 R^2}{2r} \dfrac{dE}{dt} \qquad (r \gtrless R).$

(b) Find B at $r = R$ for $dE/dt = 10^{12}$ volts/m-sec and for $R = 5.0$ cm.   At $r = R$ the two equations for B reduce to the same expression, or

$$B = \tfrac{1}{2}\mu_0 \epsilon_0 R \frac{dE}{dt}$$

$$= (\tfrac{1}{2})(4\pi \times 10^{-7} \text{ weber/amp-m})(8.9 \times 10^{-12} \text{ coul}^2/\text{nt-m}^2)$$

$$(5.0 \times 10^{-2} \text{ meter})(10^{12} \text{ volts/m-sec})$$

$$= 2.8 \times 10^{-7} \text{ weber/meter}^2 = 0.0028 \text{ gauss}.$$

This shows that the induced magnetic fields in this example are so small that they can scarcely be measured with simple apparatus, in sharp contrast to induced *electric* fields (Faraday's law), which can be demonstrated easily.   This experimental dif-

---

* Actually, there is a third way of setting up a magnetic field, by the use of magnetized bodies.   In Section 37–7 we saw that this could be accounted for by inserting a *magnetizing current* term i_M on the right side of Ampère's law.   This law would then read, in its full generality,

$$\oint \mathbf{B} \cdot d\mathbf{l} = \mu_0 \epsilon_0 \frac{d\Phi_E}{dt} + \mu_0 i + \mu_0 i_M.$$

In all that follows we assume that no magnetic materials are present so that $i_M = 0$.

ference is in part due to the fact that induced emfs can easily be multiplied by using a coil of many turns. No technique of comparable efficiency exists for magnetic fields. In experiments involving oscillations at very high frequencies dE/dt above can be very large, resulting in significantly larger values of the induced magnetic field.   ◀

38–8   Displacement Current

Equation 38–21 shows that the term $\epsilon_0 \, d\Phi_E/dt$ has the dimensions of a current. Even though no motion of charge is involved, there are advantages in giving this term the name *displacement* * *current*. Thus we can say that a magnetic field can be set up either by a conduction current i or by a displacement current i_d ($= \epsilon_0 \, d\Phi_E/dt$), and Eq. 38–21 can be rewritten as †

$$\oint \mathbf{B} \cdot d\mathbf{l} = \mu_0(i_d + i). \tag{38–22}$$

The concept of displacement current permits us to retain the notion that *current is continuous*, a principle established for steady conduction currents in Section 31–1. In Fig. 38–9b, for example, a current i enters the positive plate and leaves the negative plate. The *conduction* current is *not* continuous across the capacitor gap because no charge is transported across this gap. However, the displacement current i_d in the gap will prove to be exactly i, thus retaining the concept of the continuity of current.

To calculate the displacement current, recall (see Eq. 30–5) that E in the gap is given by

$$E = \frac{q}{\epsilon_0 A}.$$

Differentiating gives $\dfrac{dE}{dt} = \dfrac{1}{\epsilon_0 A} \dfrac{dq}{dt} = \dfrac{1}{\epsilon_0 A} i.$

The displacement current i_d is by definition

$$i_d = \epsilon_0 \frac{d\Phi_E}{dt} = \epsilon_0 \frac{d(EA)}{dt} = \epsilon_0 A \frac{dE}{dt}.$$

Combining these two equations leads to

$$i_d = (\epsilon_0 A) \left(\frac{1}{\epsilon_0 A} i \right) = i,$$

which shows that the displacement current in the gap is identical with the conduction current in the lead wires.

---

* The word "displacement" was introduced for historical reasons that need not concern us here.

† We may write this more generally, taking the presence of magnetic materials into account, as

$$\oint \mathbf{B} \cdot d\mathbf{l} = \mu_0(i_d + i + i_M).$$

See the footnote on p. 869.

▶ **Example 6.** What is the displacement current for the capacitor of Example 5? From the definition of displacement current,

$$i_d = \epsilon_0 \frac{d\Phi_E}{dt} = \epsilon_0 \frac{d}{dt}[(E)(\pi R^2)] = \epsilon_0 \pi R^2 \frac{dE}{dt}$$

$$= (8.9 \times 10^{-12}\ \text{coul}^2/\text{nt-m}^2)(\pi)(5.0 \times 10^{-2}\ \text{meter})^2(10^{12}\ \text{volts/m-sec})$$

$$= 0.070\ \text{amp.}$$

Even though this displacement current is reasonably large, it produces only a small magnetic field (see Example 5) because it is spread out over a large area.   ◀

38–9   Maxwell's Equations

Equation 38–21 completes our presentation of the basic equations of electromagnetism, called *Maxwell's equations*. They are summarized in Table 38–3. All equations of physics that serve, as these do, to correlate experiments in a vast area and to predict new results have a certain beauty about them and can be appreciated, by those who understand them, on an aesthetic level. This is true for Newton's laws of motion, for the laws of thermodynamics, for the theory of relativity, and for the theories of quantum physics. As for Maxwell's equations, the German physicist Ludwig Boltzmann (quoting a line from Goethe) wrote "Was it a god who wrote these lines. . . ." In more recent times J. R. Pierce,* in a book chapter entitled "Maxwell's Wonderful Equations" says: "To anyone who is motivated by anything beyond the most narrowly practical, it is worth while to understand Maxwell's equations simply for the good of his soul." The scope of these equations is remarkable, including as it does the fundamental operating principles of all large-scale electromagnetic devices such as motors, cyclotrons, electronic computers, television, and microwave radar.

38–10   Maxwell's Equations and Cavity Oscillations

In this section we show how the oscillations of an electromagnetic cavity can be understood in terms of Maxwell's equations. A completely formal treatment, which is beyond our scope here, would start from these equations and would end with mathematical expressions for the variation of **B** and **E** with time and with position in the cavity for all modes of oscillation of the cavity. We confine ourselves to the fundamental mode only, illustrated in Fig. 38–8, for which we *postulated* the variations of **B** and **E** given in that figure; we will show that these postulated fields are completely consistent with Maxwell's equations.

Figure 38–10 presents two views of the cavity of Fig. 38–8*d*, in which both electric and magnetic fields are present. Study of Fig. 38–8 reveals that **B** is *decreasing* in magnitude and **E** is *increasing* at this phase of the cycle of oscillation. Let us apply Faraday's law,

$$\oint \mathbf{E} \cdot d\mathbf{l} = -\frac{d\Phi_B}{dt},$$

---

* *Electrons, Waves and Messages*, Hanover House, 1956. This book is recommended as collateral reading in electromagnetism.

Table 38-3

THE BASIC EQUATIONS OF ELECTROMAGNETISM (MAXWELL'S EQUATIONS) *

Name	Equation	Describes	Crucial Experiment	Text Reference
Gauss's law for electricity	$\epsilon_0 \oint \mathbf{E} \cdot d\mathbf{S} = q$	Charge and the electric field	1. Like charges repel and unlike charges attract, as the inverse square of their separation. 1'. A charge on an insulated conductor moves to its outer surface.	Chapter 28
Gauss's law for magnetism	$\oint \mathbf{B} \cdot d\mathbf{S} = 0$	The magnetic field	2. It is impossible to create an isolated magnetic pole.	Section 37–2
Ampère's law (as extended by Maxwell)	$\oint \mathbf{B} \cdot d\mathbf{l}$ $= \mu_0 \epsilon_0 \dfrac{d\Phi_E}{dt} + \mu_0 i$	The magnetic effect of a changing electric field or of a current	3. The speed of light can be calculated from purely electromagnetic measurements. 3'. A current in a wire sets up a magnetic field near the wire.	Section 39–5 Chapter 34
Faraday's law of induction	$\oint \mathbf{E} \cdot d\mathbf{l} = -\dfrac{d\Phi_B}{dt}$	The electrical effect of a changing magnetic field	4. A bar magnet, thrust through a closed loop of wire, will set up a current in the loop.	Chapter 35

* Written on the assumption that no dielectric or magnetic material is present.

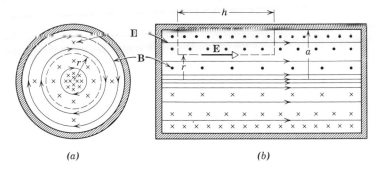

Fig. 38–10   Two cross sections of an electromagnetic resonant cavity at a phase of oscillation corresponding to Fig. 38-8*d*.   (*a*) The dashed circle is a path suitable for applying Ampère's law.   (*b*) The dashed rectangle is a path suitable for applying Faraday's law.

to the rectangle of dimensions h and $a - r$.   There is a definite flux Φ_B through the rectangular path in question, and this flux is decreasing with time because **B** is decreasing.   The line integral above is

$$\oint \mathbf{E} \cdot d\mathbf{l} = hE(r),$$

in which $E(r)$ is the value of E at a radius r from the center of the cavity.

Note that **E** equals zero for the upper leg of the integration path (which lies in the cavity wall) and that **E** and $d\mathbf{l}$ are at right angles on the two side legs.   Combining these equations yields

$$E(r) = -\frac{1}{h}\frac{d\Phi_B}{dt}. \qquad (38\text{–}23)$$

Equation 38–23 shows that $E(r)$ depends on the rate at which Φ_B through the path shown is changing with time and that it has its maximum value when $d\Phi_B/dt$ is a maximum.   This occurs when **B** is zero, that is, when **B** is changing its direction; the student will recall that a sine or cosine is changing most rapidly, that is, it has the steepest tangent, at the instant it crosses the axis between positive and negative values.   Thus the electric field pattern in the cavity will have its *maximum* value when the magnetic field is *zero* everywhere, consistent with Figs. 38–8*a* and *e* and with the concept of the interchange of energy between electric and magnetic forms.   The student should demonstrate, by applying Lenz's law, that the electric field in Fig. 38–10*b* points to the right as shown, if the magnetic field is decreasing.

Figure 38–10*a* shows an end view of the cavity; the electric lines of force are entering the page at right angles to the page and the magnetic lines form clockwise circles.   Let us apply Ampère's law in the form

$$\oint \mathbf{B} \cdot d\mathbf{l} = \mu_0 \epsilon_0 \frac{d\Phi_E}{dt} + \mu_0 i, \qquad (38\text{–}21)$$

to the circular path of radius r shown in the figure. No charge is transported through the ring so that the conduction current i in Eq. 38–21 is zero. The line integral on the left is $(B)(2\pi r)$ so that the equation reduces to

$$B(r) = \frac{\mu_0 \epsilon_0}{2\pi r} \frac{d\Phi_E}{dt}. \tag{38–24}$$

Equation 38–24 shows that the magnetic field $B(r)$ is proportional to the rate at which the electric flux Φ_E through the ring is changing with time. The field $B(r)$ has its maximum value when $d\Phi_E/dt$ is at its maximum; this occurs when $\mathbf{E} = 0$, that is, when $\mathbf{E}$ is reversing its direction. Thus we see that $\mathbf{B}$ has its *maximum* value when $\mathbf{E}$ is *zero* for all points in the cavity. This is consistent with Figs. 38–8c and g and with the concept of the interchange of energy between electric and magnetic forms. A comparison with Fig. 38–9a, which, like Fig. 38–10a, corresponds to an increasing electric field, shows that the lines of $\mathbf{B}$ are indeed clockwise, as viewed along the direction of the electric field.

Comparison of Eqs. 38–23 and 38–24 suggests the complete interdependence of $\mathbf{B}$ and $\mathbf{E}$ in the cavity. As the magnetic field changes with time, it induces the electric field in a way described by Faraday's law. The electric field, which also changes with time, induces the magnetic field in a way described by Maxwell's extension of Ampère's law. The oscillations, once established, sustain each other and would continue indefinitely were it not for losses due to Joule heating in the cavity walls or leakage of energy from openings that might be present in the walls. In Chapter 39 we show that this interplay of $\mathbf{B}$ and $\mathbf{E}$ occurs not only in standing electromagnetic waves in cavities but also in traveling electromagnetic waves, such as radio waves or visible light.

Let us now analyze the currents—both conduction and displacement—that occur in the cavity and examine their connections to the electric and the magnetic fields. Figure 38–11 shows two views of the cavity, taken at an instant corresponding to that of Fig. 38–10. For simplicity the fields $\mathbf{E}$ and $\mathbf{B}$ are not shown; the arrows represent currents.

Since $\mathbf{E}$ is increasing at this instant, the positive charge on the left end cap must be increasing. Thus there must be conduction currents in the walls pointing from right to left in Fig. 38–11b. These currents are also shown by the dots (representing the tips of arrows) near the cavity walls in Fig. 38–11a.

Bearing in mind that $\epsilon_0 \, d\Phi_E/dt$ is a displacement current, we can write Eq. 38–24 as

$$B(r) = \frac{\mu_0}{2\pi r} \epsilon_0 \frac{d\Phi_E}{dt} = \frac{\mu_0}{2\pi r} i_d.$$

This equation stresses that $\mathbf{B}$ in the cavity is associated with a displacement current; compare Eq. 34–4. Applying the right-hand rule in Fig. 38–10a shows that the displacement current i_d must be directed into the plane of the figure if it is to be associated with the clockwise lines of $\mathbf{B}$ that are present.

The displacement current is represented in Fig. 38–11b by the arrows that point to the right and in Fig. 38–11a by the crosses that represent arrows entering the page. Study of Fig. 38–11 shows that the current is continuous, being directed up the

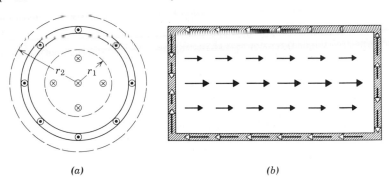

(a)   *(b)*

Fig. 38-11   The cavity of Fig. 38-10 showing (a) the conduction current coming up the walls and displacement current going down the cavity volume and (b) the displacement current (black arrowheads) in the volume of the cavity and the conduction currents (white arrowheads) in the walls. The arrows in each case represent *current densities*. Note the continuity of current (conduction + displacement). (For a *truly* resistanceless cavity the conduction current would lie *entirely* on the surface, requiring a modification of our definition of current density; we leave this small complication for the student to consider.)

walls as a conduction current and then back down through the volume of the cavity as a displacement current. If we apply Ampère's law as extended by Maxwell,

$$\oint \mathbf{B} \cdot d\mathbf{l} = \mu_0 (i_d + i),\qquad (38\text{--}25)$$

to the circular path of radius r_1 in Fig. 38-11a, we see that **B** at that path is due entirely to the displacement current, the conduction current i *within the path* being zero.

For the path of radius r_2, the *net* current enclosed is zero because the conduction current in the walls is exactly equal and opposite to the displacement current in the cavity volume. Since i equals i_d in magnitude, but is oppositely directed, it follows from Eq. 38-25 that B must be zero for all points outside the cavity, in agreement with observation.

QUESTIONS

1. Why doesn't the LC circuit of Fig. 38-1 simply stop oscillating when the capacitor has been completely discharged?

2. How might you start an LC circuit into oscillation with its initial condition being represented by Fig. 38-1c? Devise a switching scheme to bring this about.

3. In an oscillating LC circuit, assumed resistanceless, what determines (a) the frequency and (b) the amplitude of the oscillations?

4. Tabulate as many mechanical or electric systems as you can think of that possess a natural frequency, along with the formula for that frequency if given in the text.

5. Resonance in LC circuits, judged by Eq. 38-14 and Fig. 38-6, occurs when the frequency ω'' of the "driving force" is exactly equal to the (undamped) natural frequency of the LC circuit. In Section 15-9 we saw that resonance for mass-spring systems, judged by Eq. 15-32 and Fig. 15-18, occurs when ω'' is close to, *but not exactly equal to*, the (undamped) natural frequency of the mass-spring system. Is there a failure of the principle of correspondence here?

6. Suppose that, in a low frequency oscillating LCR circuit, one could display on the screen of a cathode-ray oscilloscope a potential difference proportional to the temperature of the (specially designed) resistor as it changed with time in response to the heating effect of the oscillating current. What would the connection be between the frequency of this temperature-time waveform and that of the oscillations of current, as measured by the potential difference across the resistor?

7. Discuss the periodic flow of energy, if any, from point to point in an acoustic resonant cavity.

8. Can a given circuit element (a capacitor, say) behave like a "lumped" element under some circumstances and like a "distributed" element under others?

9. List as many (a) lumped and (b) distributed mechanical oscillating systems as you can.

10. An air-filled acoustic resonant cavity and an electromagnetic resonant cavity of the same size have resonant frequencies that are in the ratio of 10^6 or so. Which has the higher frequency and why?

11. What constructional difficulties would you encounter if you tried to build an LC circuit of the type shown in Fig. 38–1 to oscillate (a) at 0.01 cps, or (b) at 10^{10} cycles/sec?

12. Could an electromagnetic cavity of the type shown in Fig. 38–8 be designed to operate at 60 cycles/sec? If so, give some details of its construction.

13. The "sharpness of tuning" of a copper electromagnetic cavity can be considerably increased by immersing it in liquid air. Explain. Be guided by Fig. 38–6, which shows "tuning curves" for an LC circuit.

14. Electromagnetic cavities are often silver plated on the inside. Explain.

15. Why is Faraday's law of induction more familiar than its symmetrical counterpart, Eq. 38–20?

16. Why is the quantity $\epsilon_0 \, d\Phi_E/dt$ referred to as a (displacement) *current?*

17. In Fig. 38–1c a displacement current is needed to maintain continuity of current in the capacitor. How can one exist, since there is no charge on the capacitor?

18. Discuss the symmetries that appear between (a) the first two and (b) the second two of Maxwell's equations.

19. At what parts of the cycle will (a) the conduction current and (b) the displacement current in the cavity of Fig. 38–8 be zero?

20. Discuss the time variation during one complete cycle of the charges that appear at various points on the inner walls of the oscillating electromagnetic cavity of Fig. 38–8.

PROBLEMS

1. You are given a 10-mh inductor and two capacitors, of 5.0- and 2.0-μf capacitance. What resonant frequencies can be obtained by connecting these elements in various ways?

2. Given a 1.0-mh inductor, how would you make it oscillate at 1.0×10^6 cycles/sec?

3. An inductor is connected across a capacitor whose capacitance can be varied by turning a knob. We wish to make the frequency of the LC oscillations vary linearly with the angle of rotation of the knob, going from 2×10^5 cycles/sec to 4×10^5 cycles/sec as the knob turns through 180°. If $L = 1.0$ mh, plot C as a function of angle for the 180° rotation.

4. A 10-henry coil has a resistance of 180 ohms. What size of capacitor must be put in series with it if the combination is to "resonate" when connected to a 60-cycle/sec outlet?

5. Derive the differential equation for an LC circuit (Eq. 38–5) using the loop theorem.

6. Derive Eq. 38–12, the differential equation for forced oscillations in an LCR circuit, from the principle of conservation of energy.

7. Show that a damped LC circuit (see Example 3) loses half its energy to Joule heat in a time given approximately by $0.69\tau_L$, in which τ_L is the inductive time constant.

8. A circuit has $L = 10$ mh and $C = 1.0$ μf. How much resistance must be inserted in the circuit to reduce the (undamped) resonant frequency by 0.01%?

9. Suppose that in an oscillating LCR circuit the amplitude of the charge oscillations drops to one-half its initial value after n cycles. Show that the fractional reduction in the frequency of resonance, caused by the presence of the resistor, is given to a close approximation by

$$\frac{\omega - \omega'}{\omega} = \frac{0.0061}{n^2},$$

which is independent of L, C, or R. Apply to the decay curve of Fig. 38–3.

10. Show that the current in a damped LC circuit is given by

$$i = -q_m \omega' e^{-Rt/2L} \sin(\omega't + \delta),$$

in which

$$\delta = \tan^{-1} \frac{R}{2L\omega'}.$$

Start from Eq. 38–10.

11. *"Q" for a circuit.* In the damped LC circuit of Example 3 show that the fraction of the energy lost per cycle of oscillation, $\Delta U/U$, is given to a close approximation by $2\pi R/\omega L$. The quantity $\omega L/R$ is often called the *"Q"* of the circuit (for "quality"). A "high-Q" circuit has low resistance, low fractional energy loss per cycle ($= 2\pi/Q$) and (see Fig. 38–6) a sharp resonance or "tuning" curve.

12. Show that the amplitude of the charge oscillations in an oscillating LCR circuit is given by

$$q_m = \frac{\mathcal{E}_m}{\sqrt{\left(\omega''^2 L - \dfrac{1}{C}\right)^2 + (\omega'' R)^2}}.$$

For what value of ω'' will q_m be a maximum?

13. An LCR circuit has $L = 1.0$ henry, $C = 20$ μf, and $R = 20$ ohms. For what frequency ω'' of an applied emf will it resonate with maximum response? At what frequencies will the response be one-half its maximum value?

14. Show that the fractional half-width of the resonance curves of Fig. 38–6 is given, to a close approximation, by

$$\frac{\Delta\omega}{\omega} = \frac{\sqrt{3}R}{\omega L},$$

in which ω is the resonant frequency and $\Delta\omega$ is the width of the resonance peak at $i = \frac{1}{2}i_m$. Note (see Problem 11) that this expression may be written as $\sqrt{3}/Q$ which shows clearly that a "high-Q" circuit has a sharp resonance peak, that is, a small $\Delta\omega/\omega$.

15. A resistor-inductor-capacitor combination R_1, L_1, C_1 (connected in series) exhibits resonance at the same frequency as a second combination R_2, L_2, C_2. If the two combinations are now connected in series, at what frequency would the whole circuit resonate?

16. In Example 5 show that the *displacement current density* j_d is given, for $r < R$, by

$$j_d = \epsilon_0 \frac{dE}{dt}.$$

17. Prove that the displacement current in a parallel-plate capacitor can be written as

$$i_d = C \frac{dV}{dt}.$$

18. You are given a 1.0-μf capacitor. How would you establish an (instantaneous) displacement current of 1.0 amp in the space between its plates?

19. In Example 5 how does the displacement current through a concentric circular loop of radius r vary with r? Consider both $r < R$ and $r > R$.

20. In microscopic terms the principle of continuity of current may be expressed as

$$\oint (\mathbf{j} + \mathbf{j}_d) \cdot d\mathbf{S} = 0,$$

in which $\mathbf{j}$ is the conduction current density and $\mathbf{j}_d$ is the displacement current density. The integral is to be taken over any closed surface; the equation essentially says that whatever current flows into the enclosed volume must also flow out. (a) Apply this equation to the surface shown by the dashed lines in Fig. 38–12 shortly after switch S is closed. (b) Apply it to various surfaces that may be drawn in the cavity of Fig. 38–11, including some that cut the cavity walls.

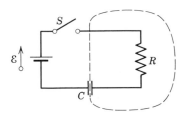

Fig. 38–12

21. A cylindrical electromagnetic cavity 5.0 cm in diameter and 7.0 cm long is oscillating in the mode shown in Fig. 38–8. (a) Assume that, for points on the axis of the cavity, $E_m = 10^4$ volts/meter. For such axial points what is the maximum rate $(dE/dt)_m$ at which E changes? (b) Assume that the average value of $(dE/dt)_m$, for all points over a cross section of a cavity, is about one-half the value found above for axial points. On this assumption, what is the maximum value of B at the cylindrical surface of the cavity?

22. Collect and tabulate expressions for the following four quantities, considering both $r < R$ and $r > R$. Copy down the derivations side by side and study them as interesting applications of Maxwell's equations to problems having cylindrical symmetry.

(a) $B(r)$ for a current i in a long wire of radius R (see Section 34–2).

(b) $E(r)$ for a long uniform cylinder of charge of radius R (see Section 28–6; also Problem 14, Chapter 28).

(c) $B(r)$ for a parallel-plate capacitor, with circular plates of radius R, in which E is changing at a constant rate (see Section 38–7).

(d) $E(r)$ for a cylindrical region of radius R in which a uniform magnetic field B is changing at a constant rate (see Section 35–5).

Electromagnetic Waves

CHAPTER 39

39–1 Transmission Line

In Chapter 38 we studied electromagnetic energy confined, as a standing wave, to a restricted region of space, the interior of an electromagnetic resonant cavity. Such energy can also be transferred from place to place as a traveling wave. An arrangement of conductors for facilitating such transfers is called a *transmission line*. Figure 39–1 shows one type of line, a *coaxial cable*, its input end being connected to a switch S. For the time being we assume that the cable is infinitely long and that the cable elements have zero resistance.

When S is closed on b, the central and the outer conductors are at the same potential. If the switch is then thrown to a, a potential difference V suddenly appears between these elements. This potential difference does not appear instantaneously all along the line but is propagated with a finite

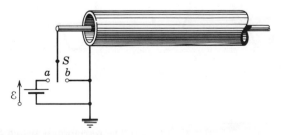

Fig. 39–1 An electromagnetic pulse can be sent along the coaxial cable by throwing switch S from b to a.

speed c that will turn out to be exactly that of light, assuming a resistanceless line. Figure 39–2a shows that the potential difference between the conductors at a distance l along the line suddenly rises, at a time given by $t = l/c$, from zero to a value determined by the battery emf. We can also consider the variation of V with position x along the line at a given time t_1 after closing the switch. Figure 39–2b shows such an instantaneous "snapshot." It, too, suggests a traveling "wavefront" moving along the line at speed c. At $t = t_1$ the signal has not yet reached points where $x > ct_1$.

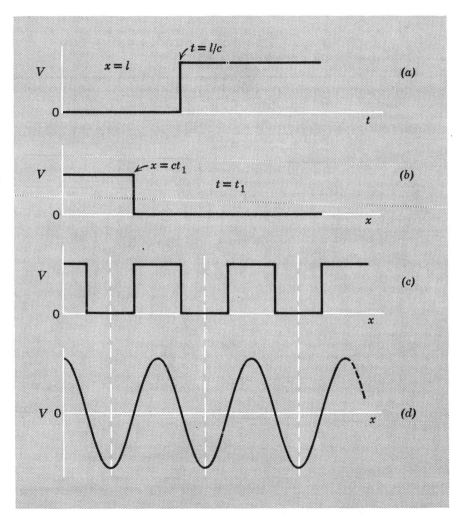

Fig. 39–2   (a) The variation with time of the potential difference between the conductors of a coaxial cable at a distance l from the input end. (b) An instantaneous "snapshot" of the pulse in the cable at a certain time t_1. (c) The waveform if switch S in Fig. 39–1 is periodically thrown between a and b. (d) The waveform if switch S is replaced by an electromagnetic oscillator with a sinusoidal output.

If switch S is periodically thrown from b to a and back again, a wave disturbance like that of Fig. 39 2c is propagated. This suggests that if the battery and switch arrangement is replaced by an electromagnetic oscillator with a sinusoidal output of frequency f a wave like that of Fig. 39–2d will be propagated.

A traveling wave in a resistanceless transmission line will exhibit a wavelength λ given by

$$\lambda = \frac{c}{f}.$$

If the oscillator frequency is 60 cycles/sec, the common commercial power frequency, the wavelength is 5×10^6 meters, which is about 3000 miles. At this low frequency traveling waves are not apparent in any line of normal length. By the time the polarity of the oscillator has changed appreciably, the energy fed into the line at the oscillator end has been delivered to the load.

Frequencies in the radio or the microwave range are much higher and the wavelengths correspondingly smaller. Commercial television frequencies as established by the Federal Communications Commission range from 54×10^6 to 980×10^6 cycles/sec. In terms of wavelength this is a range of 5.6 to 0.31 meter. At these wavelengths the patterns of potential difference in the transmission lines used to send television signals across the country can be described aptly as traveling waves. Microwaves, used in radar systems and for communication purposes, have even smaller wavelengths, in the range of about 20 cm to about 0.5 mm.

These considerations suggest another way of viewing the difference between lumped and distributed circuit elements. A system is "distributed" if the wavelength is about the same size as, or less than, the dimensions of the system. If the wavelength is much larger than the dimensions of the system, we are dealing with lumped components. A transmission line 50 meters long would be a lumped system for electromagnetic radiation at 60 cycles/sec ($\lambda = 5 \times 10^6$ meters) but a distributed system at 10^8 cycles/sec ($\lambda = 3$ meters). In a lumped system the circuit analysis is normally carried out in terms of lumped system parameters such as L, C, and R; in a distributed system the analysis is often carried out in terms of the fields that are set up and the charges and currents that are related to them.

▶ **Example 1.** A potential difference given by

$$V_0 = V_m \sin \omega t$$

is applied between the terminals of a long resistanceless transmission line; the frequency f ($= \omega/2\pi$) is 3×10^9 cycles/sec. Write an equation for $V(t)$ at a point Γ which is 1.5 wavelengths down the line from the oscillator.

The general equation for a wave traveling in the x direction (see Eq. 19–10) is

$$V = V_m \sin(\omega t - kx),$$

where $k \; (= 2\pi/\lambda)$ is the wave number. At $x = 0$ this gives correctly the time variation of the input terminal potential difference. At $x = 1.5\lambda$ we have

$$V_P = V_m \sin \left[\omega t - \left(\frac{2\pi}{\lambda}\right)(1.5\lambda) \right] = V_m \sin (\omega t - 3\pi)$$

$$= -V_m \sin \omega t.$$

Thus V_P is always equal in magnitude to V_0 but is opposite in sign. What is the wavelength in this example? ◄

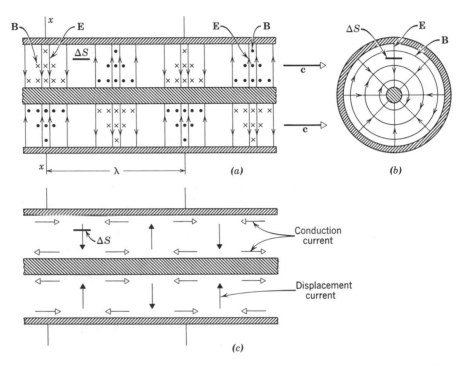

Fig. 39–3 (a) The electric and magnetic fields in a coaxial cable, showing a wave traveling to the right at speed c. (b) A cross-sectional view at a plane through xx in (a); the wave is emerging from the page. (c) Conduction current (open arrows) and displacement currents (filled arrows) associated with the wave in (a); the arrows in each case represent current density vectors.

39–2　Coaxial Cable—Fields and Currents

Figures 39–3a and b are "snapshots" of the electric and magnetic field configurations in a coaxial cable. The electric field is radial and the magnetic field forms concentric lines about the central conductor. The entire pattern moves along the line, assumed resistanceless, at speed c.

The field patterns in this figure obey the *boundary condition* required for a line that is assumed to be resistanceless, namely, that **E** for all points on either conducting surface has no tangential component (see p. 866). The field patterns can be deduced mathematically from Maxwell's equations by imposing this requirement. The configuration shown is the simplest of many different wave patterns that can travel along the line. The coaxial cable, unlike the electromagnetic cavity of Fig. 38–8, is not a resonant device. The angular frequency ω of waves that travel along it can be varied continuously, as is the case for all traveling waves, such as transverse waves in a long stretched cord.

Figure 39–3c shows the currents in the cable at the instant corresponding to Figs. 39–3a and b. The arrows parallel to the cable axis represent conduction currents in the central and the outer conductors. The vertical arrows with filled heads represent displacement currents that exist in the space between the conductors. Note that the conduction current and the displacement current arrows form closed loops, preserving the concept of the continuity of current.

▶ **Example 2.** Verify that the displacement current represented in Fig. 39–3c is consistent with the pattern of **B** and **E** shown in Fig. 39–3a.

Consider a small surface element ΔS shown edge-on in Fig. 39–3; it is shown as viewed from above in Fig. 39–4. This hypothetical element is stationary with respect to the cable while the field configuration moves through it at speed c. Figure 39–4a shows the electric lines of force in the vicinity of this element. It is clear from symmetry that, at the instant shown, the net flux Φ_E through this area is zero. However, even though Φ_E is zero in magnitude, it is, at this instant, *changing at its most rapid*

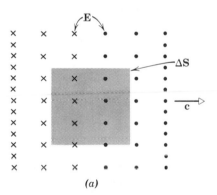

(a)

Fig. 39–4 The area element S in Fig. 39–3 enlarged and viewed from above, showing the adjacent (a) electric and (b) magnetic fields.

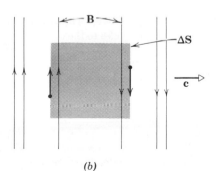

(b)

rate, since **E** at the element ΔS is at the very moment of reversing its direction as the wave moves through. Thus the displacement current, which is given by

$$i_d = \epsilon_0 \frac{d\Phi_E}{dt},$$

also has its maximum value.

Figure 39–4*b* shows the magnetic field in the vicinity of the element of area. Let us apply the generalized form of Ampère's law,

$$\oint \mathbf{B} \cdot d\mathbf{l} = \mu_0(i + i_d),$$

to the element. The conduction current i is zero since no charge is transported through ΔS. The displacement current i_d is not zero, having, in fact, its maximum value. Thus, since the right side of this equation ($= \mu_0 i_d$) does not vanish, the left side must not vanish. Study of Fig. 39–4*b* shows that $\oint \mathbf{B} \cdot d\mathbf{l}$ around the boundary of this square has, indeed, a nonzero value. Thus the field and displacement current configurations of Figs. 39–3*a–c* are consistent. We have not discussed the direction of i_d; that is, does it point into the plane of Fig. 39–4, as Fig. 39–3*c* asserts, or out of it? We leave this as a question for the student. He may be guided by considering the direction of the displacement current in Figs. 38–9*a* and *b*.

Example 3. Show that the conduction currents in Fig. 39–3*c* are appropriately related to the magnetic field pattern.

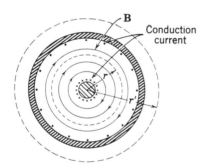

Fig. 39–5 Example 3. The coaxial cable of Fig. 39–3*b*, showing the conduction currents in the central and outer conductors. The wave is emerging from the page.

Figure 39–5 shows a cross section of the cable at a plane through xx in Fig. 39–3*a*. Let us apply Ampère's law,

$$\oint \mathbf{B} \cdot d\mathbf{l} = \mu_0(i + i_d),$$

to the ring of radius r. The displacement current through this ring is zero, the current being at right angles to the central conductor. The conduction current i in the central conductor, shown by the $\times$'s in the figure, does pass through this ring so that the equation becomes

$$(B)(2\pi r) = \mu_0 i,$$

or

$$B = \frac{\mu_0 i}{2\pi r}.$$

Note that **B** is related to the current in the central conductor by the usual right-hand rule and that the expression for B is that found earlier (Eq. 34–4) for a long straight wire carrying a steady current.

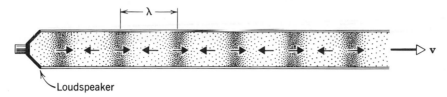

Fig. 39–6 An acoustic transmission line, showing a sound wave traveling to the right. The small arrows with filled heads show the directed drift velocities for small volume elements of the gas. Compare Fig. 39–3a.

If we apply Ampère's law to the large ring of radius r', we must put the net conduction current equal to zero because the current in the outer conductor, shown by the dots, is equal and opposite to that in the inner conductor. This means that **B** must be zero for points outside the cable, in agreement with experiment. ◄

It is interesting to compare the electromagnetic oscillations in a typical *traveling* wave, such as that of Fig. 39–3, to those in a cavity resonator, such as that of Fig. 38–8. The latter oscillations are an electromagnetic *standing* wave. In a traveling wave **E** and **B** are in phase, which means that at a given position along the transmission line they reach their maxima at the same time. However, Fig. 38–8 shows that at a given position in a cavity resonator **E** and **B** reach their maxima one-fourth of a cycle apart; they are 90° out of phase.

A complete analogy exists in mechanical systems. In the acoustic resonator of Fig. 38–7 the time variations of pressure and velocity for the standing acoustic wave are also 90° out of phase, in exact correspondence to the electromagnetic cavity oscillations of Fig. 38–8. The acoustic analogy to a transmission line (Fig. 39–6) would be an infinitely long gas-filled tube, one end being connected to an acoustic oscillator such as a loud-speaker. The entire configuration of Fig. 39–6 moves to the right with speed v. The pressure variations, suggested by the dots, and the instantaneous velocities, suggested by the arrows, are *in phase*, just as are **E** and **B** in the coaxial cable of Fig. 39–3.

39–3   Waveguide

It is possible to send electromagnetic waves through a hollow metal pipe. We assume that the inner walls of such a pipe, or *waveguide* as it is called, are resistanceless and that the cross section is rectangular.

Figure 39–7 shows a typical electric and magnetic field pattern. We imagine that a microwave oscillator is connected to the left end and sends electromagnetic energy down the guide. Figure 39–7a shows a side view of the guide and Fig. 39–7b, a top view; Fig. 39–7c shows the cross section. As for the coaxial cable, the field patterns are such that **E** has no tangential component for any point on the inner surface of the guide. The fields **E** and **B** are in phase, again like the coaxial cable.

As for all traveling waves, the angular frequency ω of electromagnetic waves traveling down a guide can be varied continuously. In a waveguide of given dimensions, however, there exists, for every mode of transmission, that is, for every pattern of **E** and **B**, a so-called *cutoff frequency* ω_0. A given guide will not transmit waves in a given mode if their frequency is below the cutoff value for that mode in that guide. The field patterns of Fig. 39–7 show the *dominant mode* for a rectangular guide; this is the mode with the lowest cutoff frequency. Given the frequency ω of electromagnetic waves to be transmitted, it is common practice to select a guide whose dimensions are such that ω is larger than the cutoff frequency ω_0 for the dominant mode

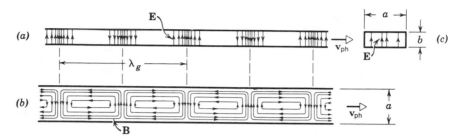

Fig. 39–7   A waveguide, showing (*a*) a side view of the lines of **E**, (*b*) a top view of the lines of **B**, and (*c*) a cross-sectional view of the lines of **E**.   In (*c*) the wave is emerging from the page.   For simplicity the lines of **B** are not shown in (*a*) and (*c*), nor are the lines of **E** shown in (*b*).

but smaller than the cutoff frequencies of all other modes.   Under these conditions the dominant mode of propagation is the only one possible.

In a (resistanceless) coaxial cable the wave patterns travel at speed *c*.   In the acoustic transmission line of Fig. 39–6 (assumed "resistanceless") the waves also travel at a speed *v*, which is the same as the propagation speed in an infinite medium. In a waveguide, however, the speed is *not c*.   In waveguides we must distinguish between (*a*) the *phase speed* v_{ph}, which is the speed at which the wave patterns of Fig. 39–7 travel, and (*b*) the *group speed* v_{gr}, which is the speed at which electromagnetic energy or information-carrying "signals" travel along the guide.   These speeds, which are identical for electromagnetic waves in a coaxial cable and for acoustic waves in a tube, are different for waves in a waveguide.

The phase speed is not directly measurable.   The wave pattern is a repetitive structure, and there is no way to distinguish one wave maximum from another.   The waves can be observed to enter one end of the guide and to leave at the other, but there is no way to identify a particular wave maximum so that its passage down the guide can be timed.   We can put a "signal" on the wave by increasing the power level of the oscillator for a short time.   This power pulse could be timed as it passes through the guide, but there is no guarantee that it travels at the same speed as the wave pattern and, indeed, it does not.   The speed of such signals or markers is the speed at which *energy* is propagated, that is, the group speed.

From Maxwell's equations it can be shown that the phase speed and the group speed for the mode of Fig. 39–7 are

$$v_{\mathrm{ph}} = \frac{c}{\sqrt{1 - \left(\dfrac{\lambda}{2a}\right)^2}} \tag{39-1}$$

and

$$v_{\mathrm{gr}} = c\sqrt{1 - \left(\frac{\lambda}{2a}\right)^2}, \tag{39-2}$$

in which *a* is the width of the guide and λ the free-space wavelength.   Note that as $a \to \infty$, which corresponds to free-space conditions, $v_{\mathrm{ph}} = v_{\mathrm{gr}} = c$.

The phase speed v_{ph} is *greater* than the velocity of light, the group speed v_{gr} being correspondingly less.   In relativity theory we learn that no speed at which signals or energy travel can be faster than that of light.   However, signals or energy cannot be transmitted down a guide at speeds exceeding *c*; they travel with speed v_{gr} which is always less than *c* so there is no conflict with the theory of relativity.

The wavelength λ in Eqs. 39–1 and 39–2 is the wavelength that would be measured for the oscillations in free space, that is,

$$\lambda = \frac{c}{f}, \qquad (39\text{-}3)$$

where c is the speed in free space and f is the frequency. For waves of a given frequency, the wavelength exhibited in a guide (λ_g) must differ from the free-space wavelength λ because the speed v_{ph} has changed. The so-called *guide wavelength* λ_g is given by

$$\lambda_g = \frac{v_{ph}}{f} = \frac{v_{ph}}{c/\lambda} = \lambda \frac{v_{ph}}{c}.$$

From Eq. 39–1 this yields

$$\lambda_g = \frac{\lambda}{\sqrt{1 - \left(\frac{\lambda}{2a}\right)^2}}. \qquad (39\text{-}4)$$

Thus the guide wavelength, which is the wavelength exhibited by the field patterns in Fig. 39–7, is larger than the free-space wavelength.

▶ **Example 4.** What must be the width a of a rectangular guide such that the energy of electromagnetic radiation whose free-space wavelength is 3.0 cm travels down the guide (a) at 95% of the speed of light? (b) At 50% of the speed of light?
From Eq. 39–2 we have

$$v_{gr} = 0.95c = c\sqrt{1 - \left(\frac{\lambda}{2a}\right)^2}.$$

Solving for a yields $a = 4.8$ cm; repeating for $v_{gr} = 0.50c$ yields $a = 1.7$ cm.

This formula illustrates the cutoff phenomenon described above. If $\lambda = 2a$, then $v_{gr} = 0$ and energy cannot travel down the guide. For the radiation considered in this example λ = 3.0 cm, so that the guide must have a width a of *at least* $\frac{1}{2}$ x 3.0 cm = 1.5 cm if it is to transmit this wave. The guide whose width we calculated in (a) above can transmit radiations whose free-space wavelength is 2 x 4.8 cm = 9.6 cm *or less.* ◀

39–4 Radiation

The acoustic transmission line of Fig. 39–6 cannot be infinitely long. Its far end may be sealed by a solid cap or left open, or it may have a flange, a horn, or some similar device mounted on it. If the far end is not sealed, energy will escape into the medium beyond. This is called *acoustic radiation*. In general, some energy will also be reflected back down the transmission line. If acoustic radiation is desirable, the designer's task is to fashion a termination (that is, an "acoustic antenna") for the transmission line such that the smallest possible fraction of the incident energy will be reflected back down the line. Such a termination might take the form of a flared horn. Acoustic radiation, of course, requires a medium such as air in order to be propagated.

An electromagnetic transmission line such as a coaxial cable or a waveguide can also be terminated in many ways, and energy can escape from the end of the line into the space beyond. In contrast to sound waves, a physical

Fig. 39–8 An electric dipole antenna on the end of a coaxial cable.

medium is not required. Thus electromagnetic energy can be radiated from the end of the transmission line, to form a traveling electromagnetic wave in free space.

Figure 39–8 shows an effective termination for a coaxial cable; it consists of two wires arranged as shown and is called an *electric dipole antenna*. The potential difference between the two conductors alternates sinusoidally as the wave reaches them, the effect being that of an electric dipole whose dipole moment **p** varies with time.

Figure 39–9 shows such a dipole, represented by two equal and opposite charges. Its dipole moment, represented by the arrows marked **p** in the

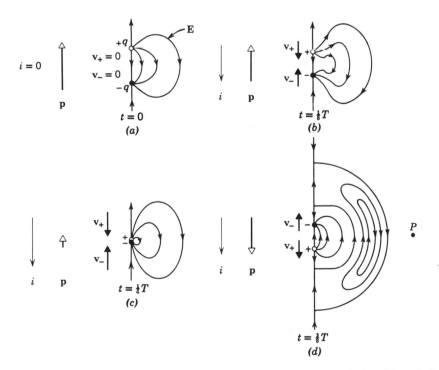

Fig. 39–9 Showing how radiation escapes from an oscillating electric dipole. The velocities of the charges, the electric dipole moment, the equivalent current, and the lines of **E** are shown at four stages of oscillation, one-eighth of a period apart. The lines of **B** are not shown. (Adapted from Attwood, *Electric and Magnetic Fields*, John Wiley and Sons, third edition, 1949.)

figure, oscillates sinusoidally as the charges oscillate; in Fig. 39–9c it is on the verge of reversing its direction. The four views, one-eighth of a cycle apart, show how the electric lines of force break away from the dipole and form closed loops that travel through free space with speed c. The oscillating charges constitute a current, which is represented by the arrows marked i in Fig. 39–9. These oscillating currents generate a field of **B** which, for simplicity, is not represented in the figure. The lines of **B** as well as those of **E** also form closed loops that move away from the dipole with speed c. These traveling electric and magnetic fields, which, as we shall see, are strongly interdependent, constitute *electromagnetic radiation*.

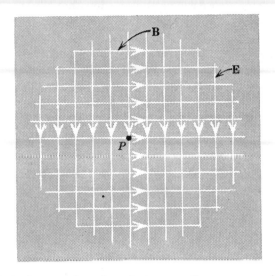

Fig. 39–10 An instantaneous view of an electromagnetic wave as seen by an observer at P in Fig. 39–9d.

Figure 39–10 shows a part of the wavefront as it would appear to an observer at point P in Fig. 39–9d. The wave is moving directly out of the page. One-half a period later the observer at P will see a field pattern like that of Fig. 39–10, except that the directions of both the electric and the magnetic fields will be reversed. The speed c of the wave in free space is given by $c = f\lambda$, which can be written as

$$c = \frac{\omega}{k},\qquad(39\text{–}5)$$

where ω, the angular frequency, and k, the wave number, are related to the frequency f and the wavelength λ by

$$\omega = 2\pi f \qquad \text{and} \qquad k = 2\pi/\lambda.$$

39-5 Traveling Waves and Maxwell's Equations

In earlier sections we have postulated the existence of certain magnetic and electric field distributions, in resonant cavities, coaxial cables, and waveguides, and we have shown that these postulated distributions are consistent with Maxwell's equations, as are the distributions of conduction and displacement currents associated with the fields. The student who pursues his studies of electromagnetism will learn how to derive mathematical expressions for **E** and **B** by subjecting Maxwell's equations to the boundary conditions appropriate to the problem at hand. In this section we continue our program by showing that the postulated patterns of **E** and **B** for a traveling electromagnetic wave are completely consistent with Maxwell's equations. In doing so, we will be able to show that the speed of such waves in free space is that of visible light and thus that visible light is itself an electromagnetic wave.

If the observer at P in Fig. 39–9d is a considerable distance from the source, the *wavefronts* described by the electric and magnetic fields that reach him (see Fig. 39–10) will be planes and the wave that moves past him will be a *plane wave* (see Section 19–2). Figure 39–11 shows a "snapshot" of a plane wave traveling in the x direction. The lines of **E** are parallel to the z axis and those of **B** are parallel to the y axis. The values of **B** and **E** for this wave depend only on x and t (not on y or z). We postulate that they are given in magnitude by

$$B = B_m \sin (kx - \omega t) \tag{39-6}$$

and $$E = E_m \sin (kx - \omega t). \tag{39-7}$$

Figure 39–12 shows two sections through the three-dimensional diagram of Fig. 39–11. In Fig. 39–12a the plane of the page is the xz plane and in

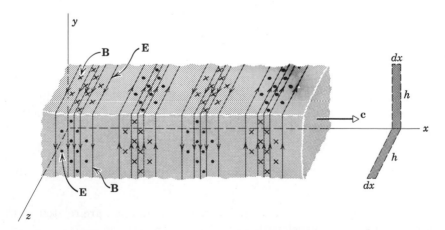

Fig. 39–11 A plane electromagnetic wave traveling to the right at speed c. Lines of **B** are parallel to the y axis; those of **E** are parallel to the z axis. The shaded rectangles on the right refer to Fig. 39–12.

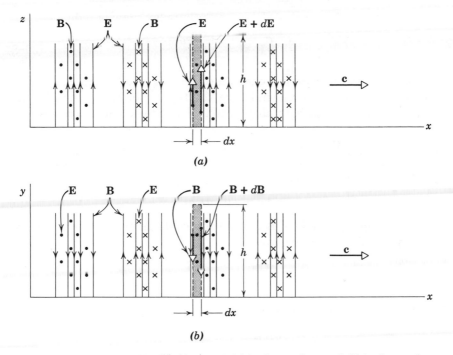

Fig. 39–12   The wave of Fig. 39–11 viewed (a) in the xz plane and (b) in the xy plane.

Fig. 39–12b it is the xy plane.   Note that, as for the traveling waves in a coaxial cable (Fig. 39–3a) and in a waveguide (Fig. 39–7), **E** and **B** are in phase, that is, at any point through which the wave is moving they reach their maximum values at the same time.

The shaded rectangle of dimensions dx and h in Fig. 39–12a is fixed in space.   As the wave passes over it, the magnetic flux Φ_B through the rectangle will change, which will give rise to induced electric fields around the rectangle, according to Faraday's law of induction.   These induced electric fields are, in fact, simply the electric component of the traveling wave.

Let us apply Lenz's law to this induction process.   The flux Φ_B for the shaded rectangle of Fig. 39–12a is *decreasing* with time because the wave is moving through the rectangle to the right and a region of weaker magnetic fields is moving into the rectangle.   The induced field will act to oppose this change, which means that if we imagine that the boundary of the rectangle is a conducting loop a *counterclockwise* induced current would appear in it. This current would produce a field of **B** that, within the rectangle, would point out of the page, thus opposing the decrease in Φ_B.   There is, of course, no conducting loop, but the net induced electric field **E** does indeed act counterclockwise around the rectangle because $E + dE$, the magnitude of **E** at the right edge of the rectangle, is greater than E, the magnitude of **E** at the left edge.   Thus the electric field configuration is entirely consistent with the concept that it is induced by the changing magnetic field.

For a more detailed analysis let us apply Faraday's law of induction, or

$$\oint \mathbf{E} \cdot d\mathbf{l} = -\frac{d\Phi_B}{dt}, \tag{39–8}$$

going counterclockwise around the shaded rectangle of Fig. 39–12a. There is no contribution to the integral from the top or bottom of the rectangle because $\mathbf{E}$ and $d\mathbf{l}$ are at right angles here. The integral then becomes

$$\oint \mathbf{E} \cdot d\mathbf{l} = [(E + dE)(h)] - [(E)(h)] = dE\,h.$$

The flux Φ_B for the rectangle is

$$\Phi_B = (B)(dx\,h),$$

where B is the magnitude of $\mathbf{B}$ at the rectangular strip and $dx\,h$ is the area of the strip. Differentiating gives

$$\frac{d\Phi_B}{dt} = h\,dx\,\frac{dB}{dt}.$$

From Eq. 39–8 we have then

$$dE\,h = -h\,dx\,\frac{dB}{dt},$$

or
$$\frac{dE}{dx} = -\frac{dB}{dt}. \tag{39–9}$$

Actually, both B and E are functions of x and t; see Eqs. 39–6 and 39–7. In evaluating dE/dx, it is assumed that t is constant because Fig. 39–12a is an "instantaneous snapshot." Also, in evaluating dB/dt it is assumed that x is constant since what is required is the time rate of change of B at a particular place, the strip in Fig. 39–12a. The derivatives under these circumstances are called *partial derivatives*, and a somewhat different notation is used for them; see the footnote on p. 633. In this notation Eq. 39–9 becomes

$$\frac{\partial E}{\partial x} = -\frac{\partial B}{\partial t}. \tag{39–10}$$

The minus sign in this equation is appropriate and necessary, for, although E is increasing with x at the site of the shaded rectangle in Fig. 39–12a, B is decreasing with t. Since $E(x,t)$ and $B(x,t)$ are known (see Eqs. 39–6 and 39–7), Eq. 39–10 reduces to

$$kE_m \cos(kx - \omega t) = \omega B_m \cos(kx - \omega t),$$

or (see Eq. 39–5)
$$\frac{\omega}{k} = \frac{E_m}{B_m} = c. \tag{39–11a}$$

Thus the speed of the wave c is the ratio of the amplitudes of the electric and the magnetic components of the wave. From Eqs. 39–6 and 39–7 we see that the ratio of amplitudes is the same as the ratio of instantaneous values, or

$$E = cB. \tag{39–11b}$$

This important result will be useful in later sections.

We now turn our attention to Fig. 39–12b, in which the flux Φ_E for the shaded rectangle is decreasing with time as the wave moves through it. According to Maxwell's third equation (with $i = 0$, because there are no conduction currents in a traveling electromagnetic wave),

$$\oint \mathbf{B} \cdot d\mathbf{l} = \mu_0 \epsilon_0 \frac{d\Phi_E}{dt}, \tag{39–12}$$

this changing flux will induce a magnetic field at points around the periphery of the rectangle. This induced magnetic field is simply the magnetic component of the electromagnetic wave. Thus, as in the cavity resonator of Section 38–10, the electric and the magnetic components of the wave are intimately connected with each other, each depending on the time rate of change of the other.

Comparison of the shaded rectangles in Fig. 39–12 shows that for each the appropriate flux, Φ_B or Φ_E, is *decreasing* with time. However, if we proceed counterclockwise around the upper and lower shaded rectangles, we see that $\oint \mathbf{E} \cdot d\mathbf{l}$ is *positive*, whereas $\oint \mathbf{B} \cdot d\mathbf{l}$ is *negative*. This is as it should be. If the student will compare Figs. 35–10 and 38–9a, he will be reminded that although the fluxes Φ_B and Φ_E in those figures are changing with time in the same way (both are increasing) the lines of the induced fields, $\mathbf{E}$ and $\mathbf{B}$, respectively, circulate in opposite directions.

The integral in Eq. 39–12, evaluated by proceeding counterclockwise around the shaded rectangle of Fig. 39–12b, is

$$\oint \mathbf{B} \cdot d\mathbf{l} = [-(B + dB)(h)] + [(B)(h)] = -h \, dB,$$

where B is the magnitude of $\mathbf{B}$ at the left edge of the strip and $B + dB$ is its magnitude at the right edge.

The flux Φ_E through the rectangle of Fig. 39–12b is

$$\Phi_E = (E)(h \, dx).$$

Differentiating gives

$$\frac{d\Phi_E}{dt} = h \, dx \frac{dE}{dt}.$$

Equation 39–12 can thus be written

$$-h \, dB = \mu_0 \epsilon_0 \left(h \, dx \frac{dE}{dt} \right)$$

or, substituting partial derivatives,

$$-\frac{\partial B}{\partial x} = \mu_0 \epsilon_0 \frac{\partial E}{\partial t}. \tag{39–13}$$

Again, the minus sign in this equation is appropriate and necessary, for, although B is increasing with x at the site of the shaded rectangle in Fig. 39–12b, E is decreasing with t.

Combining this equation with Eqs. 39–6 and 39–7 yields

$$-kB_m \cos (kx - \omega t) = -\mu_0 \epsilon_0 \omega E_m \cos (kx - \omega t),$$

or (see Eq. 39–5)
$$\frac{E_m}{B_m} = \frac{k}{\mu_0 \epsilon_0 \omega} = \frac{1}{\mu_0 \epsilon_0 c}. \qquad (39\text{–}14)$$

Eliminating E_m/B_m between Eqs. 39–11a and 39–14 yields

$$c = \frac{1}{\sqrt{\mu_0 \epsilon_0}}. \qquad (39\text{–}15)$$

Substituting numerical values yields

$$c = \frac{1}{\sqrt{(4\pi \times 10^{-7} \text{ weber/amp-m})(8.9 \times 10^{-12} \text{ coul}^2/\text{nt-m}^2)}}$$

$$= 3.0 \times 10^8 \text{ meters/sec}, \qquad (39\text{–}16)$$

which is the speed of light in free space! This emergence of the speed of light from purely electromagnetic considerations is the crowning achievement of Maxwell's electromagnetic theory. Maxwell made this prediction before radio waves were known and before it was realized that light was electromagnetic in nature. His prediction led to the concept of the electromagnetic spectrum, which we discuss in Chapter 40, and to the discovery of radio waves by Heinrich Hertz in 1890. It made it possible to discuss optics as a branch of electromagnetism and to derive its fundamental laws from Maxwell's equations.

A conclusion as fundamental as Eq. 39–15 must be subject to rigorous experimental verification. Of the three quantities in that equation, one, μ_0, has an assigned value, namely, $4\pi \times 10^{-7}$ weber/amp-m. The speed of light c is one of the most precisely measured physical constants, having the presently accepted value of 2.997924×10^8 meters/sec. The remaining quantity, ϵ_0, can be measured by making measurements on an accurately constructed parallel-plate capacitor, as described in Section 30–2. The best measured value, by Rosa and Dorsey of the National Bureau of Standards (U.S.A.) in 1906, is 8.84025×10^{-12} coul^2/nt-m^2. To this accuracy Eq. 39–15 is completely verified. Our confidence in electromagnetic theory, bolstered by numerous successful predictions and agreements with experiment, is now such that we reverse the foregoing procedure and calculate our presently accepted value of ϵ_0 (see Appendix A) from the measured speed of light, using Eq. 39–15.

39–6   The Poynting Vector

One of the important characteristics of an electromagnetic wave is that it can transport energy from point to point. As we show below, the rate of energy flow per unit area in a plane electromagnetic wave can be described by a vector **S**, called the *Poynting vector* after John Henry Poynting (1852–1914), who first pointed out its properties. We define **S** from

$$S = \frac{1}{\mu_0} \, E \times B. \tag{39–17}$$

In the mks system **S** is expressed in watts/meter^2; the direction of **S** gives the direction in which the energy moves. The vectors **E** and **B** refer to their instantaneous values at the point in question. If Eq. 39–17 is applied to the traveling plane electromagnetic wave of Fig. 39–11, it is clear that **E × B**, hence **S**, point in the direction of propagation. Note, too, that **S** points parallel to the axis for all points in the coaxial cable of Fig. 39–3.

We get meaningful results if we extend the Poynting vector concept to other electromagnetic situations involving either traveling or standing electromagnetic waves, as we will see in Examples 5 and 6. If we extend it to circuit situations involving steady or almost steady currents and lumped circuit elements, we are led to some interesting conclusions, which we explore in Problems 11, 17, and 18.

▶ **Example 5.**   Analyze energy flow in the cavity of Fig. 38–8, using the Poynting vector.

Study of Fig. 39–13 shows that when the energy is all electric (Figs. 39–13a and e) it is concentrated along the axis, because this is the region in which **E** has its maximum

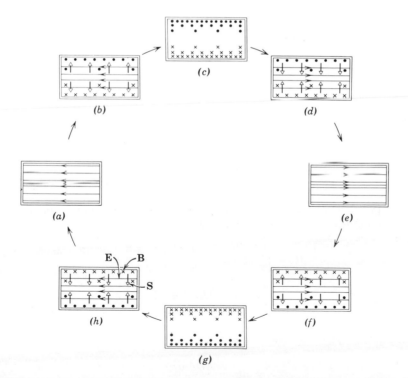

Fig. 39–13   Example 5. Energy surges back and forth periodically between the central region of the cavity and the region near the walls, as indicated by the Poynting vector **S**.

value. When the energy is all magnetic (Figs. 39–13c and g), it is concentrated near the walls. Thus the energy surges back and forth periodically between the central region and the region near the walls. The figure shows, by the open arrows, the direction of **S** at various points in the cavity and at various times in the cycle. Note that **S** equals zero for Figs. 39–13a, c, e, and g, which is appropriate because at these instants of time the field configurations are momentarily stationary and energy is not flowing. A pendulum bob at the end of its swing and at the bottom of its trajectory forms a mechanical analogy. The student should verify from Eq. 39–17 that these arrows point in the correct directions. ◀

Figure 39–14 can be used to derive the Poynting relation for the special case of a traveling plane electromagnetic wave. It shows a cross section of a traveling plane wave, along with a thin "box" of thickness dx and area A. The box, a mathematical construction, is fixed with respect to the axes while the wave moves through it.

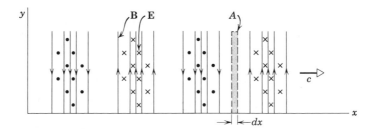

Fig. 39–14 A plane wave is traveling to the right at speed c; compare Fig. 39–12b. The dashed rectangle in this figure represents a three-dimensional box, of area A and thickness dx, that extends at right angles to the plane of the figure.

At any instant the energy stored in the box, from Eqs. 30–27 and 36–19, is

$$dU = dU_E + dU_B = (u_E + u_B)(A\,dx)$$

$$= \left(\tfrac{1}{2}\epsilon_0 E^2 + \frac{1}{2\mu_0} B^2 \right) A\,dx, \tag{39–18}$$

where $A\,dx$ is the volume of the box and E and B are the instantaneous values of the field vectors in the box.

Using Eq. 39–11b ($E = cB$) to eliminate *one* of the E's in the first term in Eq. 39–18 and *one* of the B's in the second term leads to

$$dU = \left[\tfrac{1}{2}\epsilon_0 E(cB) + \frac{1}{2\mu_0} B \left(\frac{E}{c}\right) \right] A\,dx$$

$$= \frac{(\mu_0\epsilon_0 c^2 + 1)(EBA\,dx)}{2\mu_0 c}.$$

From Eq. 39–15, however, $\mu_0\epsilon_0 c^2 = 1$, so that

$$dU = \frac{EBA\,dx}{\mu_0 c}.$$

This energy dU will pass through the right face of the box in a time dt equal to dx/c. Thus the energy per unit area per unit time, which is S, is given by

$$S = \frac{dU}{dt\,A} = \frac{EBA\,dx}{\mu_0 c\,(dx/c)\,A} = \frac{1}{\mu_0} EB.$$

This is exactly the prediction of the more general relation Eq. 39–17 for a traveling plane wave.

This relation refers to values of S, E, and B at any instant of time. We are usually more interested in the *average* value of S, taken over one or more cycles of the wave. An observer making intensity measurements on a wave moving past him would measure this average value $\bar{S}$. We can easily show (see Example 6) that $\bar{S}$ is related to the *maximum* values of E and B by

$$\bar{S} = \frac{1}{2\mu_0} E_m B_m.$$

▶ **Example 6.** An observer is at a great distance r from a point light source whose power output is P_0. Calculate the magnitudes of the electric and the magnetic fields. Assume that the source is monochromatic, that it radiates uniformly in all directions, and that at distant points it behaves like the traveling plane wave of Fig. 39–11.

The power that passes through a sphere of radius r is $(\bar{S})(4\pi r^2)$, where $\bar{S}$ is the *average* value of the Poynting vector at the surface of the sphere. This power must equal P_0, or

$$P_0 = \bar{S}4\pi r^2.$$

From the definition of S (Eq. 39–17), we have

$$\bar{S} = \overline{\left(\frac{1}{\mu_0} EB \right)}.$$

Using the relation $E = cB$ (Eq. 39–11b) to eliminate B leads to

$$\bar{S} = \frac{1}{\mu_0 c} \overline{E^2}.$$

The average value of E^2 over one cycle is $\frac{1}{2}E_m{}^2$, since E varies sinusoidally (see Eq. 39–7). This leads to

$$P_0 = \left(\frac{E_m{}^2}{2\mu_0 c} \right)(4\pi r^2),$$

or

$$E_m = \frac{1}{r}\sqrt{\frac{P_0\mu_0 c}{2\pi}}.$$

For $P_0 = 10^3$ watts and $r = 1.0$ meter this yields

$$E_m = \frac{1}{(1.0m)}\sqrt{\frac{(10^3 \text{ watts})(4\pi \times 10^{-7} \text{ weber/amp-m})(3 \times 10^8 \text{ meters/sec})}{2\pi}}$$

$$= 240 \text{ volts/meter.}$$

The relationship $E_m = cB_m$ (Eq. 39–11a) leads to

$$B_m = \frac{E_m}{c} = \frac{240 \text{ volts/meter}}{3 \times 10^8 \text{ meters/sec}} = 8 \times 10^{-7} \text{ weber/meter}^2.$$

Note that E_m is appreciable as judged by ordinary laboratory standards but that B_m (= 0.008 gauss) is quite small.   ◀

QUESTIONS

1. In the coaxial cable of Fig. 39–1, what are the directions of the conduction current (a) in the central conductor and (b) in the outer conductor, shortly after the switch is thrown to position a? Consider points that have been reached by the wavefront of Fig. 39–2a and b and those that have not.

2. Compare a coaxial cable and a waveguide, used as a transmission line. Point out both similarities and differences.

3. What is the relation between the wavelength in the cable and that in free space for a coaxial cable?

4. Can traveling waves with a continuous range of wavelengths be sent down (a) a coaxial cable and (b) a waveguide? Can standing waves with a continuous range of wavelengths be set up in a resonant cavity? Develop mechanical or acoustical analogies to support your answers.

5. If a certain wavelength is larger than the cutoff wavelength for a guide in its dominant mode, can energy be sent down it in any other mode?

6. Explain why the term $\epsilon_0 \, d\Phi_E/dt$ is needed in Ampère's equation to understand the propagation of electromagnetic waves.

7. In the equation $c = 1/\sqrt{\mu_0 \epsilon_0}$ (Eq. 39–15), how can c always have the same value if μ_0 is arbitrarily assigned and ϵ_0 is measured?

8. Is it conceivable that electromagnetic theory might some day be able to predict the value of c (3×10^8 meters/sec), not in terms of μ_0 and ϵ_0, but directly and numerically without recourse to any measurements?

9. What is the direction of the displacement current in Fig. 39–4? Give an argument to support your answer.

10. In a coaxial cable is the energy transported in the conductors, through the agency of the currents, or in the space between them, through the agency of the fields?

PROBLEMS

1. Using Gauss's law, sketch the instantaneous charges that appear on the conductors of the coaxial cable of Fig. 39–3 and show that this pattern of charges is appropriately related to the conduction currents shown in Fig. 39–3c.

2. For a rectangular guide of width 3.0 cm, plot the phase speed, the group speed, and the guide wavelength as a function of the free-space wavelength. Assume the dominant mode.

3. For a rectangular guide of width 3.0 cm, what must the free-space wavelength of radiation be if it is to require 1.0 μsec (= 10^{-6} sec) for energy to traverse a 100-meter length of guide? What is the phase speed under these circumstances?

4. Under what conditions will the guide wavelength in the guide of Fig. 39–7 be double the free-space wavelength?

5. How does the displacement current vary with space and time in a traveling plane electromagnetic wave?

6. Prove that for any point in an electromagnetic wave such as that of Fig. 39–11 the density of energy stored in the electric field equals that stored in the magnetic field.

7. A resonant cavity is constructed by closing each end of the coaxial cable of Fig. 39–3 with a metal cap. The cavity contains three half-waves. Describe the patterns of **E** and **B**

that occur, assuming the same mode of oscillation as that shown in Fig. 39–3. (Hint: Remember that **E** can have no tangential component at a conducting surface and that **B** and **E** must be 90° out of phase.)

8. If a coaxial cable has resistance, energy must flow from the fields into the conducting surfaces to provide the Joule heating. How must the electric lines of force of Fig. 39–3a be modified in this case? (Hint: The Poynting vector near the surface must have a component pointing toward the surface.)

9. What guide wavelength does 10-cm radiation (free-space wavelength) exhibit in a rectangular guide whose width is 6.0 cm? Assume the dominant mode. What is the cutoff wavelength for this guide?

10. Sketch five more figures to complete the sequence of Fig. 39–9, showing radiation from an oscillating dipole. Include an indication of the lines of **B** in your drawings.

11. Figure 39–15 shows a long resistanceless transmission line, delivering power from a battery to a resistive load. A steady current i exists as shown. (a) Sketch qualitatively the electric and magnetic fields around the line, and (b) show that, according to the Poynting vector point of view, energy travels from the battery to the resistor through the space around the line and not through the line itself. (Hint: Each conductor in the line is an equipotential surface, since the line has been assumed to have no resistance.)

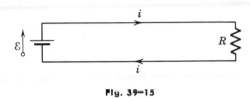

Fig. 39–15

12. Analyze the flow of energy in the waveguide of Fig. 39–7, using the Poynting vector.

13. A cube of edge a has its edges parallel to the x-, y-, and z-axes of a rectangular coordinate system. A uniform electric field **E** is parallel to the y-axis and a uniform magnetic field **B** is parallel to the x-axis. Calculate (a) the rate at which, according to the Poynting vector point of view, energy may be said to pass through each face of the cube and (b) the net rate at which the energy stored in the cube may be said to change.

14. A #10 copper wire (diameter, 0.10 in.; resistance per 1000 ft, 1.00 ohm) carries a current of 25 amp. Calculate **E**, **B**, and **S** for a point on the surface of the wire.

15. Sunlight strikes the earth, outside its atmosphere, with an intensity of 2.0 cal/cm²-min. Calculate E_m and B_m for sunlight, assuming it to be a wave like that of Fig. 39–10.

16. A plane radio wave has $E_m \cong 10^{-4}$ volt/meter. Calculate (a) B_m and (b) the intensity of the wave, as measured by $\overline{\textbf{S}}$.

17. Figure 39–16 shows a cylindrical resistor of length l, radius a, and resistivity ρ, carrying a current i. (a) Show that the Poynting vector **S** at the surface of the resistor is everywhere directed normal to the surface, as shown. (b) Show that the rate P at which energy flows into the resistor through its cylindrical surface, calculated by integrating the Poynting vector over this surface, is equal to the rate at which Joule heat is produced; that is,

$$\int \textbf{S} \cdot d\textbf{A} = i^2 R,$$

where $d\textbf{A}$ is an element of area of the cylindrical surface. This shows that, according to the Poynting vector point of view, the energy that appears in a resistor as Joule heat does not enter it through the connecting wires but through the space around the wires and the resistor. (Hint: **E** is parallel to the axis of the cylinder, in the direction of the current; **B** forms concentric circles around the cylinder, in a direction given by the right-hand rule.)

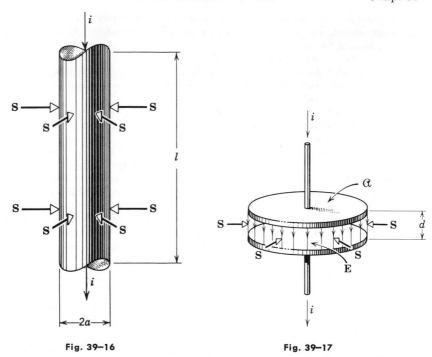

Fig. 39–16   Fig. 39–17

18. Figure 39–17 shows a parallel-plate capacitor being charged. (a) Show that the Poynting vector $\mathbf{S}$ points everywhere radially into the cylindrical volume. (b) Show that the rate P at which energy flows into this volume, calculated by integrating the Poynting vector over the cylindrical boundary of this volume, is equal to the rate at which the stored electrostatic energy increases; that is, that

$$\int \mathbf{S} \cdot d\mathbf{A} = a d \frac{d}{dt} (\tfrac{1}{2} \epsilon_0 E^2),$$

where ad is the volume of the capacitor and $\tfrac{1}{2} \epsilon_0 E^2$ is the energy density for all points within that volume. This analysis shows that, according to the Poynting vector point of view, the energy stored in a capacitor does not enter it through the wires but through the space around the wires and the plates. (Hint: To find $\mathbf{S}$ we must first find $\mathbf{B}$, which is the magnetic field set up by the displacement current during the charging process; see Fig. 38–9. Ignore fringing of the lines of $\mathbf{E}$.)

Nature and Propagation of Light

CHAPTER 40

40–1 Light and the Electromagnetic Spectrum

Light was shown by Maxwell to be a component of the *electromagnetic spectrum* of Fig. 40–1. All these waves are electromagnetic in nature and have the same speed c in free space. They differ in wavelength (and thus in frequency) only, which means that the sources that give rise to them and the instruments used to make measurements with them are rather different.* The electromagnetic spectrum has no definite upper or lower limit. The labeled regions in Fig. 40–1 represent frequency intervals within which a common body of experimental technique, such as common sources and common detectors, exists. All such regions overlap. For example, we can produce radiation of wavelength 10^{-3} meter either by microwave techniques (microwave oscillators) or by infrared techniques (incandescent sources).

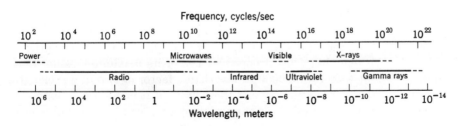

Fig. 40–1 The electromagnetic spectrum. Note that the wavelength and frequency scales are logarithmic.

* For a report of electromagnetic waves with wavelengths as long as 1.9×10^{7} miles the student should consult an article by James Heirtzler in the *Scientific American* for March 1962.

901

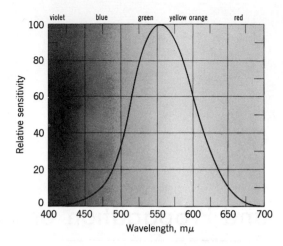

Fig. 40–2   The relative eye sensitivity of an assumed *standard observer* at different wavelengths for normal levels of illumination. The shaded areas represent the (continuously graded) color sensations for normal vision.

"Light" is defined here as radiation that can affect the eye. Figure 40–2, which shows the relative eye sensitivity of an assumed *standard observer* to radiations of various wavelengths, shows that the center of the visible region is about 5.55×10^{-7} meter. Light of this wavelength produces the sensation of yellow-green.*

In optics we often use the micron (abbr. μ) the millimicron (abbr. mμ), and the Angstrom (abbr. A) as units of wavelength. They are defined from

$$1 \ \mu = 10^{-6} \text{ meter}$$

$$1 \ m\mu = 10^{-9} \text{ meter}$$

$$1 \ A = 10^{-10} \text{ meter.}$$

Thus the center of the visible region can be expressed as $0.555 \ \mu$, 555 mμ, or 5550 A.

The limits of the visible spectrum are not well defined because the eye sensitivity curve approaches the axis asymptotically at both long and short wavelengths. If the limits are taken, arbitrarily, as the wavelengths at which the eye sensitivity has dropped to 1% of its maximum value, these limits are about 4300 A and 6900 A, less than a factor of two in wavelength. The eye can detect radiation beyond these limits if it is intense enough. In many experiments in physics one can use photographic plates or light-sensitive electronic detectors in place of the human eye.

---

* See "Experiments in Color Vision" by Edwin H. Land, *Scientific American*, p. 84, May 1959, and especially "Color and Perception: the Work of Edwin Land in the Light of Current Concepts" by M. H. Wilson and R. W. Brocklebank, *Contemporary Physics*, p. 91, December 1961, for a fascinating discussion of the problems of perception and the distinction between color as a characteristic óf light and color as a perceived property of objects.

40–2   Energy and Momentum

Energy is carried by electromagnetic waves from the sun to the earth or from an open fire to a hand placed nearby. The transport of energy by such a wave in free space was described in Section 39–6 by the Poynting vector $\mathbf{S}$, or

$$\mathbf{S} = \frac{1}{\mu_0}\, \mathbf{E} \times \mathbf{B}, \tag{40–1}$$

where $\mathbf{E}$ and $\mathbf{B}$ are the instantaneous values of the electric and magnetic field vectors.

Less familiar is the fact that electromagnetic waves may also transport linear momentum. In other words, it is possible to exert a pressure (a *radiation pressure* *) on an object by shining a light on it. Such forces must be small in relation to forces of our daily experience because we do not ordinarily notice them. The first measurement of radiation pressure was made in 1901–1903 by Nichols and Hull in this country and by Lebedev in Russia, about thirty years after the existence of such effects had been predicted theoretically by Maxwell.

Let a parallel beam of light fall on an object for a time t, the incident light being *entirely absorbed* by the object. If energy U is absorbed during this time, the momentum p delivered to the object is given, according to Maxwell's prediction, by

$$p = \frac{U}{c} \qquad \text{(total absorption)}, \tag{40–2a}$$

where c is the speed of light. The direction of $\mathbf{p}$ is the direction of the incident beam. If the light energy U is *entirely reflected*, the momentum delivered will be twice that given above, or

$$p = \frac{2U}{c} \qquad \text{(total reflection)}. \tag{40–2b}$$

In the same way, twice as much momentum is delivered to an object when a perfectly elastic tennis ball is bounced from it as when it is struck by a perfectly inelastic ball of the same mass and speed. If the light energy U is partly reflected and partly absorbed, the delivered momentum will lie between U/c and $2U/c$.

▶ **Example 1.** A parallel beam of light with an energy flux S of 10 watts/cm² falls for 1 hr on a perfectly reflecting plane mirror of 1.0-cm² area. (*a*) What momentum is delivered to the mirror in this time and (*b*) what force acts on the mirror?

(*a*) The energy that is reflected from the mirror is

$$U = (10 \text{ watts/cm}^2)(1.0 \text{ cm}^2)(3600 \text{ sec}) = 3.6 \times 10^4 \text{ joules}.$$

The momentum delivered after 1 hr's illumination is

$$p = \frac{2U}{c} = \frac{(2)(3.6 \times 10^4 \text{ joules})}{3 \times 10^8 \text{ meters/sec}} = 2.4 \times 10^{-4} \text{ kg-m/sec}.$$

---

* See "Radiation Pressure," G. E. Henry, *Scientific American*, p. 99, June 1957.

(b) From Newton's second law, the average force on the mirror is equal to the average rate at which momentum is delivered to the mirror, or

$$F = \frac{p}{t} = \frac{2.4 \times 10^{-4}\,\text{kg-m/sec}}{3600\,\text{sec}} = 6.7 \times 10^{-8}\,\text{nt}.$$

This is a small force.   ◄

Nichols and Hull, in 1903, measured radiation pressures and verified Eq. 40–2, using a torsion balance technique. They allowed light to fall on mirror M in Fig. 40–3; the radiation pressure caused the balance arm to turn through a measured angle θ, twisting the torsion fiber F. Assuming a suitable calibration for their torsion fiber, the experimenters could arrive at a numerical value for this pressure. Nichols and Hull measured the intensity of their light beam by allowing it to fall on a blackened metal disk of known absorptivity and by measuring the temperature rise of this disk. In a particular run these experimenters measured a radiation pressure of 7.01×10^{-6} nt/meter^2; for their light beam, the value predicted, using Eq. 40–2, was 7.05×10^{-6} nt/meter^2, in excellent agreement. Assuming a mirror area of 1 cm^2, this represents a force on the mirror of only 7×10^{-10} nt, about 100 times smaller than the force calculated in Example 1.

The success of the experiment of Nichols and Hull was the result in large part of the care they took to eliminate spurious deflecting effects caused by changes in the speed distribution of the molecules in the gas surrounding the mirror. These changes were brought about by the small rise in the temperature of the mirror as it absorbed light energy from the incident beam. This "radiometer effect" is responsible for the spinning action of the familiar toy radiometers when placed in a beam of sunlight. In a perfect vacuum such effects would not occur, but in the best vacuums available in 1903 radiometer effects were present and had to be taken specifically into account in the design of the experiment.

To demonstrate the transport of momentum from Maxwell's equations in a particular case, let a plane electromagnetic wave traveling in the z direction fall on a

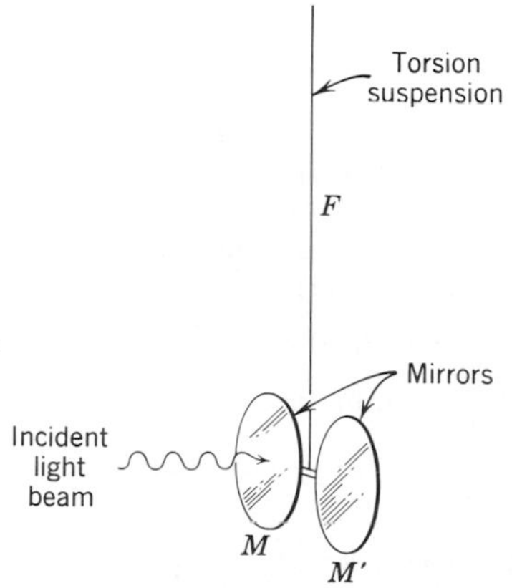

Fig. 40–3

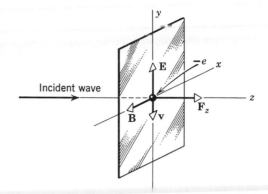

Fig. 40–4 An incident plane light wave falls on an electron in a thin resistive sheet. Instantaneous values of **E**, **B**, the electron velocity **v**, and the radiation force $\mathbf{F}_z$ are shown.

large thin sheet of a material of high resistivity as in Fig. 40–4. A small part of the incident energy will be absorbed within the sheet, but most of it will be transmitted if the sheet is thin enough.*

The incident wave **E** and **B** vary with time at the sheet as

$$\mathbf{E} = \mathbf{E}_m \sin \omega t \tag{40–3}$$

and

$$\mathbf{B} = \mathbf{B}_m \sin \omega t \tag{40–4}$$

where **E** is parallel to the $\pm y$ axis and **B** is parallel to the $\pm x$ axis.

In Section 31–4 we saw that the effect of a (constant) electric force $(- -eE)$ on a conduction electron in a metal was to make it move with a (constant) drift speed v_d. The electron behaves as if it is immersed in a viscous fluid, the electric force acting on it being counterbalanced by a "viscous" force, which may be taken as proportional to the electron speed. Thus for a constant field E, after equilibrium is established,

$$eE = bv_d, \tag{40–5}$$

where b is a resistive damping coefficient. The electron equilibrium speed, dropping the subscript d, is thus

$$v = \frac{eE}{b}. \tag{40–6}$$

If the applied electric field varies with time and if the variation is slow enough, the electron speed can continually readjust itself to the changing value of E so that its speed continues to be given essentially by its equilibrium value (Eq. 40–6) at all times. These readjustments are more rapidly made the more viscous the medium, just as a stone falling in air reaches a constant equilibrium rate of descent only relatively slowly but one falling in a viscous oil does so quite rapidly. We assume that the sheet in Fig. 40–4 is so viscous, that is, that its resistivity is so high, that Eq. 40–6 remains valid even for the rapid oscillations of E in the incident light beam.

As the electron vibrates parallel to the y axis, it experiences a *second* force due to the *magnetic* component of the wave. This force $\mathbf{F}_z$ $(= -e\mathbf{v} \times \mathbf{B})$ points in the z direction, being at right angles to the plane formed by **v** and **B**, that is, the xy plane. The instantaneous magnitude of $\mathbf{F}_z$ is given by

$$F_z \quad evB = \frac{e^2EB}{b}. \tag{40–7}$$

---

* Some of the incident energy will also be reflected, but the reflected wave is of such low intensity that it can be ignored in the derivation that follows; see *Optics* by B. Rossi, Addison-Wesley Publishing Company, p. 411, 1957, from which this derivation is adapted.

F_z always points in the positive z direction because **v** and **B** reverse their directions simultaneously; this force is, in fact, the mechanism by which the radiation pressure acts on the sheet of Fig. 40–4.

From Newton's second law, F_z is the rate dp_e/dt at which the incident wave delivers momentum to each electron in the sheet, or

$$\frac{dp_e}{dt} = \frac{e^2 EB}{b}. \tag{40–8}$$

Momentum is delivered at this rate to every electron in the sheet and thus to the sheet itself. It remains to relate the momentum transfer to the sheet to the absorption of energy within the sheet.

The electric field component of the incident wave does work on each oscillating electron at an instantaneous rate (see Eq. 40–6) given by

$$\frac{dU_e}{dt} = F_E v = (eE) \left(\frac{eE}{b}\right) = \frac{e^2 E^2}{b}.$$

Note that the magnetic force F_z, always being at right angles to the velocity **v**, does no work on the oscillating electron. Equation 39–11b shows that for a plane wave in free space B and E are related by

$$E = Bc.$$

Substituting above for *one* of the E's leads to

$$\frac{dU_e}{dt} = \frac{e^2 EBc}{b}. \tag{40–9}$$

This equation represents the rate, per electron, at which energy is absorbed from the incident wave.

Comparing Eqs. 40–8 and 40–9 shows that

$$\frac{dp_e}{dt} = \frac{1}{c}\frac{dU_e}{dt}.$$

Integrating yields

$$\int_0^t \frac{dp_e}{dt}\,dt = \frac{1}{c}\int_0^t \frac{dU_e}{dt}\,dt,$$

or

$$p_e = \frac{U_e}{c}, \tag{40–10}$$

where p_e is the momentum delivered to a single electron in any given time t and U_e is the energy absorbed by that electron in the same time interval. Multiplying each side by the number of free electrons in the sheet leads to Eq. 40–2a.

Although we derived this relation (Eq. 40–10) for a particular kind of absorber, no characteristics of the absorber—for example, the resistive damping coefficient b—remain in the final expression. This is as it should be because Eq. 40–10 is a general property of radiation absorbed by *any* material.

40–3   The Speed of Light *

Light travels so fast that there is nothing in our daily experience to suggest that its speed is not infinite. It calls for considerable insight even to ask "How fast does light travel?" Galileo asked himself this question and tried to answer it experimentally. His chief work, *Two New Sciences*, published

---

* See "The Speed of Light," J. H. Rush, *Scientific American*, p. 67, August 1955.

in the Netherlands in 1638, is written in the form of a conversation among three fictitious persons called Salvlatl, Sagredo, and Simplicio. Here is part of what they say about the speed of light.

Simplicio: Everyday experience shows that the propagation of light is instantaneous; for when we see a piece of artillery fired, at a great distance, the flash reaches our eyes without lapse of time; but the sound reaches the ear only after a noticeable interval.

Sagredo: Well, Simplicio, the only thing I am able to infer from this familiar bit of experience is that sound, in reaching our ear, travels more slowly than light; it does not inform me whether the coming of the light is instantaneous or whether, although extremely rapid, it still occupies time. . . .

Sagredo, who evidently is Galileo himself, then describes a possible method for measuring the speed of light. He and an assistant stand facing each other some distance apart, at night. Each carries a lantern which can be covered or uncovered at will. Galileo started the experiment by uncovering his lantern. When the light reached the assistant he uncovered his own lantern, whose light was then seen by Galileo. Galileo tried to measure the time between the instant at which he uncovered his own lantern and the instant at which the light from his assistant's lantern reached him. For a 1-mile separation we now know that the round trip travel time would be only 11 × 10^{-6} sec. This is much less than human reaction times, so the method fails.

To measure a large velocity directly, we must either measure a small time interval or use a long base line. This situation suggests that astronomy, which deals with great distances, might be able to provide an experimental value for the speed of light; this proved to be true. Although it would be desirable to time the light from the sun as it travels to the earth, there is no way of knowing when the light that reaches us at any instant left the sun; we must use subtler astronomical methods.

Note, however, that microwave pulses are quite regularly reflected from the moon; this gives a 7.68 × 10^8-meter base line (there and back) for timing purposes. The speed of light (and of microwaves) is so well known now from other experiments that these measurements are used to measure the lunar distance accurately. Microwave signals have also been reflected from Venus.

In 1675 Ole Roemer, a Danish astronomer working in Paris, made some observations of the moons of Jupiter (see Problem 9) from which a speed of light of 2 × 10^8 meters/sec may be deduced. About fifty years later James Bradley, an English astronomer, made some astronomical observations of an entirely different kind from which a value of 3.0 × 10^8 meters/sec may be deduced.

In 1849 Hippolyte Louis Fizeau (1819-1896), a French physicist, first measured the speed of light by a nonastronomical method, obtaining a value of 3.13 × 10^8 meters/sec. Figure 40-5 shows Fizeau's apparatus. Let us first ignore the toothed wheel. Light from source S is made to converge by lens L_1, is reflected from mirror M_1, and forms in space at F an image of the source. Mirror M_1 is a so-called "half-silvered mirror"; its reflecting coating is so thin that only half the light that falls on it is reflected, the other half being transmitted.

Light from the image at F enters lens L_2 and emerges as a parallel beam; after passing through lens L_3 it is reflected back along its original direction by mirror M_2. In Fizeau's experiment the distance l between M_2 and F was

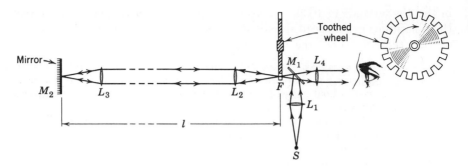

Fig. 40-5 Fizeau's apparatus for measuring the speed of light.

8630 meters or 5.36 miles. When the light strikes mirror M_1 again, some will be transmitted, entering the eye of the observer through lens L_4.

The observer will see an image of the source formed by light that has traveled a distance $2l$ between the wheel and mirror M_2 and back again. To time the light beam a marker of some sort must be put on it. This is done by "chopping" it with a rapidly rotating toothed wheel. Suppose that during the round-trip travel time of $2l/c$ the wheel has turned just enough so that, when the light from a given "burst" returns to the wheel, point F is covered by a tooth. The light will hit the face of the tooth that is toward M_2 and will not reach the observer's eye.

If the speed of the wheel is exactly right, the observer will not see any of the bursts because each will be screened by a tooth. The observer measures c by increasing the angular speed ω of the wheel from zero until the image of source S disappears. Let θ be the angular distance from the center of a gap to the center of a tooth. The time needed for the wheel to rotate a distance θ is the round-trip travel time $2l/c$. In equation form,

$$\frac{\theta}{\omega} = \frac{2l}{c} \quad \text{or} \quad c = \frac{2\omega l}{\theta}. \tag{40–11}$$

This "chopped beam" technique, suitably modified, is used today to measure the speeds of neutrons and other particles.

▶ **Example 2.** The wheel used by Fizeau had 720 teeth. What is the smallest angular speed at which the image of the source will vanish?

The angle θ is $1/1440$ rev; solving Eq. 40–11 for ω gives

$$\omega = \frac{c\theta}{2l} = \frac{(3.00 \times 10^8 \text{ meters/sec})(1/1440 \text{ rev})}{(2)(8630 \text{ meters})} = 12.1 \text{ rev/sec.} \quad ◀$$

The French physicist Foucault (1819–1868) greatly improved Fizeau's method by substituting a rotating mirror for the toothed wheel. The American physicist Albert A. Michelson (1852–1931) conducted an extensive series of measurements of c, extending over a fifty-year period, using this technique.

Table 40-1

THE SPEED OF ELECTROMAGNETIC RADIATION IN FREE SPACE
(Some selected measurements)

Date	Experimenter	Country	Method	Speed, km/sec	Uncertainty, km/sec
1600(?)	Galileo	Italy	Lanterns and shutters	"If not instantaneous, it is extraordinarily rapid"	
1675	Roemer	France	Astronomical	200,000	
1729	Bradley	England	Astronomical	304,000	
1849	Fizeau	France	Toothed wheel	313,300	
1862	Foucault	France	Rotating mirror	298,000	500
1876	Cornu	France	Toothed wheel	299,990	200
1880	Michelson	U.S.A.	Rotating mirror	299,910	50
1883	Newcomb	England	Rotating mirror	299,860	30
1883	Michelson	U.S.A.	Rotating mirror	299,853	60
1906	Rosa and Dorsey	U.S.A.	Electromagnetic theory	299,781	10
1923	Mercier	France	Standing waves on wires	299,782	15
1926	Michelson	U.S.A.	Rotating mirror	299,796	4
1928	Karolus and Mittelstaedt	Germany	Kerr cell	299,778	10
1932	Michelson, Pease, and Pearson	U.S.A.	Rotating mirror	299,774	11
1940	Huettel	Germany	Kerr cell	299,768	10
1941	Anderson	U.S.A.	Kerr cell	299,776	14
1950	Bergstrand	Sweden	Geodimeter	299,792.7	0.25
1950	Essen	England	Microwave cavity	299,792.5	3
1950	Houston	Scotland	Vibrating crystal	299,775	9
1950	Bol and Hansen	U.S.A.	Microwave cavity	299,789.3	0.4
1951	Aslakson	U.S.A.	Shoran radar	299,794.2	1.9
1952	Rank, Ruth, and Ven der Sluis	U.S.A.	Molecular spectra	299,776	7
1952	Froome	England	Microwave interferometer	299,792.6	0.7
1954	Florman	U.S.A.	Radio interferometer	299,795.1	3.1
1954	Rank, Shearer, and Wiggins	U.S.A.	Molecular spectra	299,780.8	3.0
1956	Edge	Sweden	Geodimeter	299,792.9	0.2

We must view the speed of light within the larger framework of the speed of electromagnetic radiation in general. It is a significant experimental confirmation of Maxwell's theory of electromagnetism that the speed in free space of waves in all parts of the electromagnetic spectrum has the same value c. Table 40–1 shows some selected measurements that have been made of the speed of electromagnetic radiation since Galileo's day. It stands as a monument to man's persistence and ingenuity. Note in the last column how the uncertainty in the measurement has improved through the years. Note also the international character of the effort and the variety of methods.

The task of arriving at a single "best" value of c from the many listed in the table is difficult, for it involves a careful study of each reported measurement and a selection from among them, based on the reported uncertainty and the selector's judgment of the probable presence or absence of hidden error. In the final averaging measurements with small uncertainties will be given more weight than those with large ones. By careful analysis of such measurements R. T. Birge arrived at a "best" value, as of 1957, of

$$c = 2.997924 \times 10^8 \text{ meters/sec.}$$

The uncertainty of measurement is less than 0.000010×10^8 meters/sec or 0.0003%.

Since about 1940, nearly all precise measurements of c have been made in the microwave or the short radio wave region of the electromagnetic spectrum. We describe here the "microwave cavity method" used by Essen in England and by Bol and Hansen in the U.S.A. It employs standing electromagnetic waves confined to a cavity rather than traveling waves in free space.

It is possible to convert a section of waveguide such as that of Fig. 39–7 into a resonant cavity by closing it with two metal caps; see Fig. 40–6. The pattern of oscillations in the cavity is closely related to that in the guide and exhibits the same "guide wavelength" λ_g. The guide wavelength is related to the cavity length l by

$$\lambda_g = \frac{2l}{n} \qquad n = 1, 2, 3, \cdots, \tag{40–12}$$

which is the same relationship used for acoustic waves in closed pipes; n ($= 3$ for Fig. 40–6) gives the number of half-waves contained in the cavity.

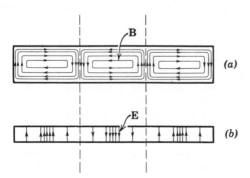

(a)

(b)

Fig. 40–6 A resonant cavity constructed from a section of waveguide; compare Fig. 39–7. For simplicity the lines of **E** are not shown in (a) and those of **B** are not shown in (b).

The procedure is to measure λ_g for such a cavity, which has been tuned to resonance, and then, using Eq. 39–4,

$$\lambda_g = \frac{\lambda}{\sqrt{1 - \left(\frac{\lambda}{2a}\right)^2}}, \tag{40-13}$$

calculate the free-space wavelength λ. From the measured resonant frequency, the speed c can be found from $c = \lambda f$.

▶ **Example 3.** Essen of the National Physical Laboratory in England made a resonant cavity measurement of the speed of electromagnetic waves. His cavity was made of a circular waveguide rather than a rectangular one; it can be shown that, for the oscillation pattern used by him, the geometrical factor $2a$ in Eq. 40–13 must be replaced by $1.64062R$, where R is the guide radius. The cavity radius was 3.25876 cm; the cavity length was 15.64574 cm and it proved to resonate at 9.498300×10^9 cycles/sec. At resonance it was determined that there were eight half-waves in the cavity. What value of c results?

From Eq. 40–12, computing only an approximate result,

$$\lambda_g = \frac{2l}{n} = \frac{(2)(15.6 \text{ cm})}{8} = 3.90 \text{ cm}.$$

Substituting into Eq. 40–13, suitably modified for a circular waveguide, yields

$$3.90 \text{ cm} = \frac{\lambda}{\sqrt{1 - \left(\frac{\lambda}{(1.64)(3.26 \text{ cm})}\right)^2}}.$$

Solving this equation for λ yields $\lambda = 3.15$ cm. Finally, we have

$$c = \lambda f = (3.15 \text{ cm})(9.50 \times 10^9 \text{ cycles/sec}) = 2.99 \times 10^8 \text{ meters/sec}.$$

For practical reasons Essen analyzed his data in a more roundabout way than that given. His final result, based on many measurements under different conditions and carried to much greater accuracy than that illustrated in the above example, was 2.997925×10^8 meters/sec with an uncertainty of 0.000030×10^8 meters/sec. ◀

40–4 Moving Sources and Observers

When we say that the speed of sound in dry air at $0°C$ is 331.7 meters/sec, we imply a reference frame fixed with respect to the air mass. When we say that the speed of light in free space is 2.997924×10^8 meters/sec, what reference frame is implied? It cannot be the medium through which the light wave travels because, in contrast to sound, no medium is required.

The concept of a wave requiring no medium was abhorrent to the physicists of the nineteenth century, influenced as they then were by a false analogy between light waves and sound waves or other purely mechanical disturbances. These physicists postulated the existence of an *ether*, which was a tenuous substance that filled all space and served as a medium of transmission for light. The ether was required to have a vanishingly small density to account for the fact that it could not be observed by any known means in an evacuated space.

The ether concept, although it proved useful for many years, did not survive the test of experiment. In particular, careful attempts to measure

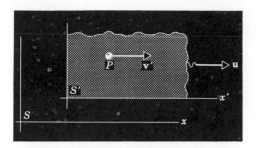

Fig. 40–7 Observers S and S', who are in relative motion, each observe a light pulse P. The pulse is emitted from a source, not shown, that is at rest in the S' frame of reference.

the speed of the earth through the ether always gave the result of zero.* Physicists were not willing to believe that the earth was permanently at rest in the ether and that all other bodies in the universe were in motion through it. Other hypotheses about the nature of the propagation of light also proved unsatisfactory for one reason or another.

Einstein in 1905 resolved the difficulty of understanding the propagation of light by making a bold postulate: If a number of observers are moving (at uniform velocity) with respect to each other and to a source of light and if each observer measures the speed of the light emerging from the source, *they will all obtain the same value.* This is the fundamental assumption of Einstein's theory of relativity. It does away with the need for an ether by asserting that the speed of light is the same in *all* reference frames; none is singled out as fundamental. The theory of relativity, derived from this postulate, has been subject to many experimental tests, from which agreement with the predictions of theory has always emerged. These agreements, extending over half a century, lend strong support to Einstein's basic postulate about light propagation.

Figure 40–7 focuses specifically on the fundamental problem of light propagation. A source of light, at rest in reference frame S', emits a light pulse P whose speed v' is measured by an observer at rest in this same frame. From the point of view of an observer in reference frame S, frame S' and its associated observer are moving in the positive x direction at speed u. Question: What speed v would observer S measure for the light pulse P? Einstein's hypothesis asserts that *each* observer would measure the same speed c, or that

$$v = v' = c.$$

This hypothesis contradicts the classical law of addition of velocities (see Section 4–6), which asserts that

$$v = v' + u. \tag{40–14}$$

This law, which is so familiar that it seems (incorrectly) to be intuitively true, is in fact based on observations of gross moving objects in the world about us. Even the fastest of these—an earth satellite, say—is moving at

---

* See Section 43–7, which describes the crucial experiment of Michelson and Morley.

a speed that is quite small compared to that of light. The body of experimental evidence that underlies Eq. 40–14 thus represents a severely restricted area of experience, namely, experiences in which $v' \ll c$ and $u \ll c$. If we assume that Eq. 40–14 holds for all particles regardless of speed, we are making a gross extrapolation. Einstein's theory of relativity predicts that this extrapolation is indeed not valid and that Eq. 40–14 is a limiting case of a more general relationship that holds for light pulses and for material particles, whatever their speed, or

$$ v = \frac{v' + u}{1 + v'u/c^2}. \tag{40-15} $$

Equation 40–15 is quite indistinguishable from Eq. 40–14 at low speeds, that is, when $v' \ll c$ and $u \ll c$; see Example 4.

If we apply Eq. 40–15 to the case in which the moving object is a light pulse, and if we put $v' = c$, we obtain

$$ v = \frac{c + u}{1 + cu/c^2} = c. $$

This is consistent, as it must be, with the fundamental assumption on which the derivation of Eq. 40–15 is based; it shows that *both* observers measure the same speed c for light. Equation 40–14 predicts (incorrectly) that the speed measured by S will be $c + u$. Figure 40–8 shows that the (correct) Eq. 40–15 and the (approximate) Eq. 40–14 cannot be distinguished from each other at speeds that are small compared to the speed of light.

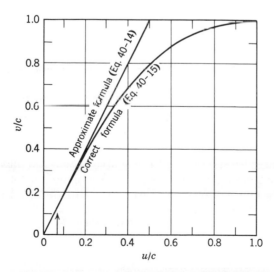

Fig. 40–8 The speed of a particle P, as seen by observer S in Fig. 40–7, for the special case of $v' = u$. All speeds are expressed as a ratio to c, the speed of light. The vertical arrow corresponds to 5×10^7 miles/hr.

▶ **Example 4.** Suppose that $v' = u = 25{,}000$ miles/hr. What per cent error is made in using Eq. 40–14 rather than Eq. 40–15 to calculate v? The speed of light is 6.7×10^8 miles/hr.

Equation 40–14 gives

$$v = v' + u = 25{,}000 \text{ miles/hr} + 25{,}000 \text{ miles/hr} = 50{,}000 \text{ miles/hr}.$$

Equation 40–15 gives

$$v = \frac{v' + u}{1 + v'u/c^2}$$

$$= \frac{25{,}000 \text{ miles/hr} + 25{,}000 \text{ miles/hr}}{1 + \dfrac{(25{,}000 \text{ miles/hr})^2}{(6.7 \times 10^8 \text{ miles/hr})^2}}$$

$$= \frac{50{,}000 \text{ miles/hr}}{1.0000000014}.$$

Even at 25,000 miles/hr the error in Eq. 40–14 is immeasurably small.

Example 5. Two electrons are ejected in opposite directions from radioactive atoms in a sample of radioactive material. Let each electron have a speed, as measured by a laboratory observer, of $0.6c$ (this corresponds to a kinetic energy of 130 kev). What is the speed of one electron as seen from the other?

Equation 40–14 gives

$$v = v' + u = 0.6c + 0.6c = 1.2c.$$

Equation 40–15 gives

$$v = \frac{v' + u}{1 + v'u/c^2} = \frac{0.6c + 0.6c}{1 + (0.6c)^2/c^2} = 0.88c.$$

This example shows that for speeds that are comparable to c, Eqs. 40–14 and 40–15 yield rather different results. A wealth of indirect experimental evidence points to the latter result as being correct.   ◀

40–5 Doppler Effect

We have seen that the same speed is measured for light no matter what the relative speeds of the light source and the observer are. The measured frequency and wavelength will change, but always in such a way that their product, which is the velocity of light, remains constant. Such frequency shifts are called *Doppler shifts*, after Johann Doppler (1803–1853), who first predicted them.

In Section 20–7 we showed that if a source of *sound* is moving away from an observer at a speed u, the frequency heard by the observer (see Eq. 20–10, which has been rearranged with u substituted for v_s) is

$$f' = f \frac{1}{1 + u/v} \cdot \qquad \begin{cases} \text{1. sound wave} \\ \text{2. observer fixed in medium} \\ \text{3. source receding from observer} \end{cases} \qquad (40\text{–}16)$$

In this equation f is the frequency heard when the source is at rest and v is the speed of sound.

If the source is at rest in the transmitting medium but the observer is moving away from the source at speed u, the observed frequency (see Eq. 20-9, in which u has been substituted for v_0) is

$$f' = f\left(1 - \frac{u}{v}\right).$$

$$\begin{cases} \text{1. sound wave} \\ \text{2. source fixed in medium} \\ \text{3. observer receding from source} \end{cases} \tag{40-17}$$

Even if the relative separation speeds u of the source and the observer are the same, the frequencies predicted by Eqs. 40-16 and 40-17 are different. This is not surprising, because a sound source moving through a medium in which the observer is at rest is physically different from an observer moving through that medium with the source at rest, as comparison of Figs. 20-11 and 20-12 shows.

We might be tempted to apply Eqs. 40-16 and 40-17 to light, substituting c, the speed of light, for v, the speed of sound. For light, as contrasted with sound, however, it has proved impossible to identify a medium of transmission relative to which the source and the observer are moving. This means that "source receding from observer" and "observer receding from source" are physically identical situations and must exhibit *exactly the same* Doppler frequency. As applied to light, either Eq. 40-16 or Eq. 40-17 or both must be incorrect. The Doppler frequency predicted by the theory of relativity is, in fact,

$$f' = f\frac{1 - u/c}{\sqrt{1 - (u/c)^2}}.$$

$$\begin{cases} \text{1. light wave} \\ \text{2. source and observer} \\ \quad\text{separating} \end{cases} \tag{40-18}$$

In all three of the foregoing equations we obtain the appropriate relations for the source and the observer *approaching* each other if we replace u by $-u$.

Equations 40-16, 40-17, and 40-18 are not so different as they seem if the ratio u/c is small enough. This was made clear in Example 3, Chapter 20, for the first two of these equations. Let us expand Eqs. 40-16, 40-17 and 40-18 by the binomial theorem, as in the example referred to. The equations then become, substituting c for v,

$$f' = f\left[1 - \frac{u}{c} + \left(\frac{u}{c}\right)^2 + \cdots\right], \tag{40-16a}$$

$$f' = f\left(1 - \frac{u}{c}\right), \tag{40-17a}$$

and
$$f' = f\left[1 - \frac{u}{c} + \frac{1}{2}\left(\frac{u}{c}\right)^2 + \cdots\right]. \tag{40-18a}$$

The ratio u/c for all available monochromatic light sources, even those of atomic dimensions, is small. This means that successive terms in these equations become small rapidly and, depending on the accuracy required, only a limited number of terms need be retained.

Under nearly all circumstances the differences among these three equations are not important. Nevertheless, it is of extreme interest to carry out at least one experiment precisely enough to serve as a test of Eq. 40–18a and thus, in part, of the theory of relativity.

H. E. Ives and G. R. Stilwell carried out such a precision experiment in 1938. They sent a beam of hydrogen atoms, generated in a gas discharge, down a tube at speed u, as in Fig. 40–9a. They could observe light emitted by these atoms in a direction opposite to **u** (atom 1, for example) using a mirror, and also in a direction parallel to **u** (atom 2, for example). With a precision spectrograph, they could photograph a particular characteristic spectrum line in this light, obtaining, on a frequency scale, the lines marked f_1' and f_2' in Fig. 40–9b. It is also possible to photograph, on the same photographic plate, a line corresponding to light emitted from *resting* atoms; such a line appears as f in Fig. 40–9b. A fundamental measured quantity in this experiment is $\Delta f/f$, defined from

$$\frac{\Delta f}{f} = \frac{\Delta f_2 - \Delta f_1}{f}, \tag{40–19}$$

(see Fig. 40–9b). It measures the extent to which the frequency of the light from resting atoms fails to lie halfway between the frequencies f_1' and f_2'. Table 40–2 shows that the measured results agree with the formula predicted by the theory of relativity (Eq. 40–18a) and not with the classical formula borrowed from the theory of sound propagation in a material medium (Eq. 40–16a).

Ives and Stilwell did not present their experimental results as evidence for the support of Einstein's theory of relativity but rather gave them an alternative theoretical explanation. Modern observers, looking not only at their excellent experiment but at the whole range of experimental evidence, now give the Ives-Stilwell experiment the interpretation we have described for it above.

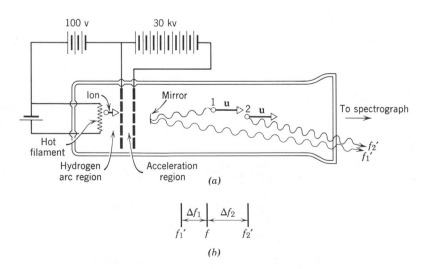

Fig. 40–9 The Ives-Stilwell experiment.

Table 40–2

THE IVES-STILWELL EXPERIMENT *

$\frac{\Delta f}{f}$, 10^{-5}	Speed of moving atoms ($= u$), 10^6 meters/sec			
	0.865	1.01	1.15	1.33
Theoretical value according to classical theory (Eq. 40–16a)	1.67	2.26	2.90	3.94
Theoretical value according to the theory of relativity (Eq. 40–18a)	0.835	1.13	1.45	1.97
Experimental value	0.762	1.1	1.42	1.9

* See Eq. 40–19; the table shows only part of the data taken by Ives and Stilwell.

The Doppler effect for light finds many applications in astronomy, where it is used to determine the speeds at which luminous heavenly bodies are moving toward us or receding from us. Such Doppler shifts measure only the radial or line-of-sight components of the relative velocity. All galaxies * for which such measurements have been made (Fig. 40–10) appear to be receding from us, the recession velocity being greater for the more distant galaxies; these observations are the basis of the expanding-universe concept.

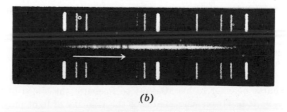

(a)   (b)

Fig. 40–10 (a) The central spot is a nebula in the constellation Corona Borealis; it is 130,000,000 light years distant. (b) The central streak shows the distribution in wavelength of the light emitted from this nebula. The two vertical dark bands show the presence of calcium. The horizontal arrow shows that these calcium lines occur at longer wavelengths than those for terrestrial light sources containing calcium, the length of the arrow representing the wavelength shift. Measurement of this shift shows that the galaxy is receding from us at 13,400 miles/sec. The lines above and below the central streak represent light from a terrestrial source, used to establish a wavelength scale. (Courtesy Mount Wilson and Mount Palomar Observatories.)

* See "The Red-Shift," Allen R. Sandage, *Scientific American*, p. 171, September 1956.

▶ **Example 6.** Certain characteristic wavelengths in the light from a galaxy in the constellation Virgo are observed to be increased in wavelength, as compared with terrestrial sources, by about 0.4%. What is the radial speed of this galaxy with respect to the earth? Is it approaching or receding?

If λ is the wavelength for a terrestrial source, then

$$\lambda' = 1.004\lambda.$$

Since we must have $\lambda'f' = \lambda f = c$, we can write this as

$$f' = 0.996f.$$

This frequency shift is so small that, in calculating the source velocity, it makes no practical difference whether we use Eq. 40–16, 40–17, or 40–18. Using Eq. 40–17 we obtain

$$f' = 0.996f = f\left(1 - \frac{u}{c}\right).$$

Solving yields $u/c = 0.004$, or $u = (0.004)(3 \times 10^8 \text{ meters/sec}) = 1.2 \times 10^6 \text{ meters/sec}$ or 2.7×10^6 miles/hr. The galaxy is *receding;* had u turned out to be negative, the galaxy would have been moving toward us. ◀

QUESTIONS

1. How might an eye-sensitivity curve like that of Fig. 40–2 be measured?

2. Why are danger signals in red, when the eye is most sensitive to yellow-green?

3. Comment on this definition of the limits of the spectrum of visible light given by a physiologist: "The limits of the visible spectrum occur when the eye is no better adapted than any other organ of the body to serve as a detector."

4. How can an object absorb light energy without absorbing momentum?

5. A searchlight sends out a parallel beam of light. Does the searchlight experience any force associated with the emission of light?

6. Name two historic experiments, in addition to the radiation pressure measurements of Nichols and Hull, in which a torsion balance was used. Both are described in this book, one in Part 1 and one in Part 2.

7. Show that for complete absorption of a parallel beam of light the radiation pressure on the absorbing object is given by $p = S/c$, where S is the magnitude of the Poynting vector and c is the speed of light in free space.

8. How could Galileo test experimentally that reaction times were an overwhelming source of error in his attempt to measure the speed of light, described on p. 907?

9. It has been suggested that the velocity of light may change slightly in value as time goes on. Can you find any evidence for this in Table 40–1?

10. A friend asserts that Einstein's postulate (that the speed of light is not affected by the uniform motion of the source or the observer) must be discarded because it violates "common sense." How would you answer him?

11. In a vacuum, does the speed of light depend on (a) the wavelength, (b) the frequency, (c) the intensity, (d) the speed of the source, or (e) the speed of the observer?

12. Can a galaxy be so distant that its recession speed equals c? If so, how can we see the galaxy? That is, will its light ever reach us?

PROBLEMS

1. (a) At what wavelengths does the eye sensitivity have half its maximum value? (b) What are the frequency and the period of the light for which the eye is most sensitive?

2. It has been proposed that a spaceship might propel itself in the solar system by radiation pressure, using a large sail made of aluminum foil. How large must the sail be if the radiation force is to be equal in magnitude to the sun's gravitational attraction? Assume that the mass of the *ship + sail* is 100 slugs, that the sail is perfectly reflecting, and that the sail is oriented at right angles to the sun's rays. The sun's mass is 1.97×10^{30} kg.

3. Radiation from the sun striking the earth has an intensity of 1400 watts/meter². Assuming that the earth behaves like a flat disk at right angles to the sun's rays and that all the incident energy is absorbed, calculate the force on the earth due to radiation pressure. Compare it with the force due to the sun's gravitational attraction.

4. Prove, for a plane wave at normal incidence on a plane surface, that the radiation pressure on the surface is equal to the energy density in the beam outside the surface. This relation holds no matter what fraction of the incident energy is reflected.

5. Prove, for a stream of bullets striking a plane surface at right angles, that the "pressure" is *twice* the (kinetic) energy density in the stream above the surface; assume that the bullets are completely "absorbed" by the surface. Contrast this with the behavior of light (Problem 4).

6. A small spaceship whose mass, with occupant, is 100 slugs is drifting in outer space, where no gravitational field exists. If it shines a searchlight, which radiates 10^4 watts, into space, what speed would the ship attain in one day because of the reaction force associated with the momentum carried away by the light beam?

7. What is the radiation pressure 1.0 meter away from a 500-watt light bulb? Assume that the surface on which the pressure is exerted faces the bulb and is perfectly absorbing and that the bulb radiates uniformly in all directions.

8. The uncertainty of the distance to the moon, as measured by the reflection of radar waves from it, is about 0.5 mile. Assuming that this uncertainty is associated only with the measurement of the elapsed time, what uncertainty in this time is implied?

9. Roemer's method for measuring the speed of light consisted in observing the apparent times of re-

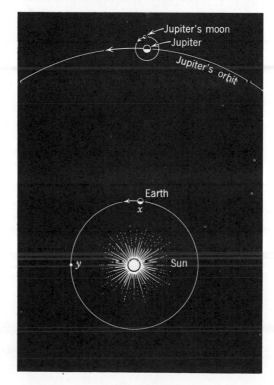

Fig. 40–11

volution of one of the moons of Jupiter. The true period of revolution is 42.5 hr. (a) Taking into account the finite speed of light, how would you expect the apparent time of revolution to alter as the earth moves in its orbit from point x to point y in Fig. 40–11? (b) What observations would be needed to compute the speed of light? Neglect the motion of Jupiter in its orbit. Figure 40–11 is not drawn to scale.

10. Suppose that light is timed over a 1-mile base line and its speed is measured to the accuracy quoted on p. 910. How large an error in the length of the base line could be tolerated, assuming other sources of error to be negligible?

11. For what value of u/c does Eq. 40–14 differ from Eq. 40–15 by 1%?

12. The "red shift" of radiation from a distant nebula consists of the light (H_γ), known to have a wavelength of 4340×10^{-8} cm when observed in the laboratory, appearing to have a wavelength of 6562×10^{-8} cm. What is the speed of the nebula in the line of sight relative to the earth? (*b*) Is it approaching or receding?

13. The difference in wavelength between an incident microwave beam and one reflected from an approaching or receding car is used to determine automobile speeds on the highway. (*a*) Show that if v is the speed of the car and f the frequency of the incident beam, the change of frequency is approximately $2vf/c$, where c is the speed of the electromagnetic radiation. (*b*) For microwaves of frequency 2450 megacycles/sec, what is the change of frequency per mile/hr of speed?

14. Show that, for slow speeds, the Doppler shift can be written in the approximate form

$$\frac{\Delta\lambda}{\lambda} = \frac{u}{c},$$

where $\Delta\lambda$ is the change in wavelength.

15. The period of rotation of the sun at its equator is 24.7 days; its radius is 7.0×10^8 meters. What Doppler wavelength shifts are expected for characteristic wavelengths in the vicinity of 5500 A emitted from the edge of the sun's disk?

16. An earth satellite, transmitting on a frequency of 40×10^6 cycles/sec (exactly), passes directly over a radio receiving station at an altitude of 250 miles and at a speed of 18,000 miles/hr. Plot the change in frequency, attributable to the Doppler effect, as a function of time, counting $t = 0$ as the instant the satellite is over the station. (Hint: The speed u in the Doppler formula is not the actual velocity of the satellite but its component in the direction of the station. Use the nonrelativistic formula (Eq. 40–17a) and neglect the curvature of the earth and of the satellite orbit.)

17. A rocketship is receding from the earth at a speed of 0.2c. A light in the rocketship appears blue to passengers on the ship. What color would it appear to be to an observer on the earth? See Fig. 40–2.

18. In the experiment of Ives and Stilwell the speed u of the hydrogen atoms in a particular run was 8.61×10^5 meters/sec. Calculate Δf_1, Δf_2, and $\Delta f/f$, on the assumptions that (*a*) Eq. 40–18a is correct and (*b*) that Eq. 40–16a is correct; compare your results with those given in Table 40–2 for this speed. Retain the first three terms only in Eqs. 40–18a and 40–16a.

Reflection and Refraction—
Plane Waves
and Plane Surfaces

CHAPTER 41

41–1 Reflection and Refraction

In Fig. 41–1a a light beam falling on a water surface is both reflected from the surface and bent (that is, *refracted*) as it enters the water. The incident beam is represented in Fig. 41–1b by a single line, the *incident ray*, parallel to the direction of propagation. The incident beam is assumed in Fig. 41–1b to be a *plane wave*, the wavefronts being normal to the incident ray. The reflected and refracted beams are also represented by rays. The angles of *incidence* (θ_1), of *reflection* (θ_1'), and of *refraction* (θ_2) are measured between the normal to the surface and the appropriate ray, as shown in the figure.

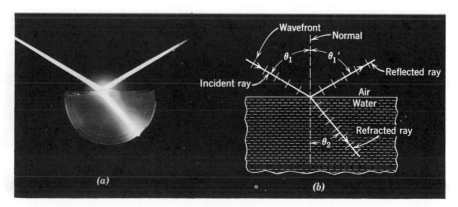

Fig. 41–1 (*a*) A photograph showing reflection and refraction at an air-water interface. (*b*) A representation using rays.

The laws governing reflection and refraction can easily be found from experiment:

1. The reflected and the refracted rays lie in the plane formed by the incident ray and the normal to the surface at the point of incidence, that is, the plane of Fig. 41–1b.

2. For reflection:

$$\theta_1' = \theta_1. \tag{41-1}$$

3. For refraction:

$$\frac{\sin \theta_1}{\sin \theta_2} = n_{21}, \tag{41-2}$$

where n_{21} is a constant called the *index of refraction* of medium 2 with respect to medium 1. Table 41–1 shows the indices of refraction for some common

Table 41–1

SOME INDICES OF REFRACTION *
(For $\lambda = 5890$ A)

Medium	Index of Refraction
Water	1.33
Ethyl alcohol	1.36
Carbon bisulfide	1.63
Air (1 atm and 20°C)	1.0003
Methylene iodide	1.74
Fused quartz	1.46
Glass, crown	1.52
Glass, dense flint	1.66
Sodium chloride	1.53
Polyethylene	1.50–1.54
Fluorite	1.43

* Measured with respect to a vacuum. The index with respect to air (except, of course, the index of air itself—see item 4) will be negligibly different in most cases.

substances with respect to a vacuum for a wavelength of 5890 A (sodium light).

The index of refraction of one medium with respect to another generally varies with wavelength, as Fig. 41–2 shows. Because of this fact refraction, unlike reflection, can be used to analyze a beam of light into its component wavelengths. Figure 41–3, taken from Newton's *Opticks*, shows how Newton, using glass prism ABC, formed a spectrum of sunlight entering his window through a small hole at F.

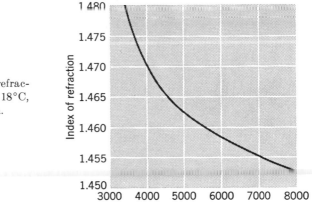

Fig. 41–2 The index of refraction of fused quartz at 18°C, with respect to a vacuum.

The law of reflection was known to Euclid. That of refraction was discovered experimentally by Willebrod Snell (1591–1626) and deduced from the early corpuscular theory of light by René Descartes (1596–1650). The law of refraction is known as Snell's law or (in France) as Descartes' law.

The laws of reflection and refraction can be derived from Maxwell's equations, which means that these laws should hold for all regions of the electromagnetic spectrum. Figure 41 4a shows an experimental setup for investigating the reflection of microwaves from a large metal sheet. Figure 41–4b shows the reading of the detector as a function of the angular position of the mirror. The existence of a reflected beam at the proper angle confirms the law of reflection for microwaves. There is ample experimental evidence that Eqs. 41–1 and 41–2 correctly describe the behavior of reflected and refracted beams in all parts of the electromagnetic spectrum.

It is common knowledge that a polished steel surface will form a well-defined reflected beam if an incident beam falls on it, but a sheet of paper will reflect light more or less in all directions (*diffuse reflection*). It is largely by diffuse reflection that we see nonluminous objects around us. The difference between diffuse and *specular* (that is, mirror-like) reflection is a matter of surface roughness; a reflected beam will

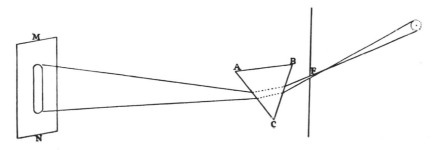

Fig. 41–3 Sunlight from a hole F in a screen is refracted by prism ABC, forming a spectrum on screen MN; from Newton's *Opticks* (1704).

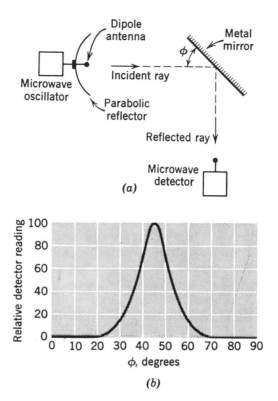

Fig. 41–4   (a) An apparatus to test the law of reflection for microwaves.   (b) A reflected beam (for $\lambda \cong 10$ cm) appears for the expected orientation of the mirror.

be formed only if the average depth of the surface irregularities of the reflector is substantially less than the wavelength of the incident light.   This criterion of surface roughness has different implications in different regions of the electromagnetic spectrum.   The bottom of a cast-iron skillet for example is a good reflector for microwaves of wavelength 0.5 cm but it is not a good reflector for visible light (that is, one cannot shave by it).

A second requirement for the existence of a reflected beam is that the transverse dimensions of the reflector must be substantially larger than the wavelength of the incident beam.   If a beam of visible light falls on a polished metal disk the size of a dime, a reflected beam will be formed.   However, if the same disk is placed in a beam of short radio waves with, say, $\lambda = 1.0$ meter, radiation will be scattered in all directions from it, and no well-defined unidirectional beam will appear. We investigate this phenomenon of *diffraction* in Chapter 44.   The requirements that surfaces be "smooth" and "large" also apply to the formation of refracted beams.   If these two requirements are not met the description of reflection and refraction in terms of rays, whose behavior is governed by Eqs. 41–1 and 41–2, is not valid.

▶ **Example 1.**   Figure 41–5 shows an incident ray i striking a plane mirror MM' at angle of incidence θ.   Trace this ray.

The reflected ray makes an angle θ with the normal at b and falls as an incident ray on mirror $M'M''$.   Its angle of incidence θ' on this mirror is $\pi/2 - \theta$.   A second reflected ray r' makes an angle θ' with the normal erected at b'. Rays i and r' are antiparallel for any value of θ. To see this, note that

$$\phi = \pi - 2\theta' = \pi - 2\left(\frac{\pi}{2} - \theta\right) = 2\theta.$$

Two lines are parallel if their opposite interior angles for an intersecting line (ϕ and 2θ) are equal.

Repeat the problem if the angle between the mirrors is 120° rather than 90°.

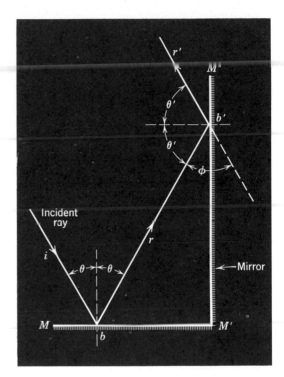

Fig. 41–5 Example 1.

Example 2. An incident ray in air falls on the plane surface of a block of quartz and makes an angle of 30° with the normal. This beam contains two wavelengths, 4000 and 5000 A. The indices of refraction for quartz with respect to air (n_{qa}) at these wavelengths are 1.4702 and 1.4624, respectively. What is the angle between the two refracted beams?

From Eq. 41–2 we have, for the 4000-A beam,

$$\sin \theta_1 = n_{qa} \sin \theta_2,$$

or

$$\sin 30° = (1.4702) \sin \theta_2,$$

which leads to

$$\theta_2 = 19.88°.$$

For the 5000-A beam we have

$$\sin 30° = (1.4624) \sin \theta_2',$$

or

$$\theta_2' = 19.99°.$$

The angle $\Delta\theta$ between the beams is 0.11°, the shorter wavelength component being bent through the larger angle, that is, having the smaller angle of refraction.

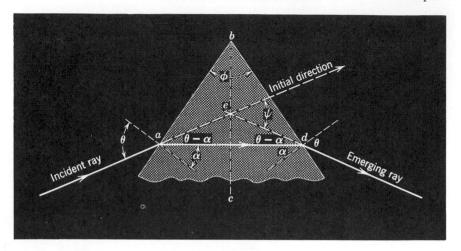

Fig. 41–6 Example 3.

Example 3. An incident ray falls on one face of a glass prism in air as in Fig. 41–6. The angle θ is so chosen that the emerging ray also makes an angle θ with the normal to the other face. Derive an expression for the index of refraction of the prism material with respect to air.

Note that $\angle\ abc = \alpha$, the two angles having their sides mutually perpendicular. Therefore

$$\alpha = \tfrac{1}{2}\phi. \tag{41-3}$$

The *deviation angle* ψ is the sum of the two opposite interior angles in triangle *aed*, or

$$\psi = 2(\theta - \alpha).$$

Substituting $\tfrac{1}{2}\phi$ for α and solving for θ yields

$$\theta = \tfrac{1}{2}(\psi + \phi). \tag{41-4}$$

At point a, θ is the angle of incidence and α the angle of refraction. The law of refraction (see Eq. 41–2) is

$$\sin \theta = n_{ga} \sin \alpha,$$

in which n_{ga} is the index of refraction of the glass with respect to air.

From Eqs. 41–3 and 41–4 this yields

$$\sin \frac{\psi + \phi}{2} = n_{ga} \sin \frac{\phi}{2}$$

or

$$n_{ga} = \frac{\sin \tfrac{1}{2}(\psi + \phi)}{\sin (\phi/2)},$$

which is the desired relation. This equation holds only for θ so chosen that the light ray passes symmetrically through the prism. For this condition the deviation angle ψ is a minimum; if θ is either increased or decreased, a larger deviation will be produced. ◄

41–2 Huygens' Principle

A theory of light would not be accepted if it were not able to predict the well-established laws of reflection and refraction. These laws can be derived from Maxwell's equations, but mathematical complexity prevents us from doing so. Fortunately, these and several other laws of optics can be derived on the basis of a simpler but less comprehensive theory of light, put forward by the Dutch physicist Christian Huygens in 1678. This theory simply assumes that light is a wave rather than, say, a stream of particles. It says nothing about the nature of the wave and, in particular—since Maxwell's theory of electromagnetism appeared only after the lapse of a century— gives no hint of the electromagnetic character of light. Huygens did not know whether light was a transverse wave or a longitudinal one; he did not know the wavelengths of visible light; he had little knowledge of the speed of light. Nevertheless, his theory was a useful guide to experiment for many years and remains useful today for pedagogic and certain other practical purposes. We must not expect it to yield the same wealth of detailed information that Maxwell's more complete electromagnetic theory does.

Huygens' theory is based on a geometrical construction, called *Huygens' principle*, that allows us to tell where a given wavefront will be at any time in the future if we know its present position; it is: *All points on a wavefront can be considered as point sources for the production of spherical secondary wavelets. After a time t the new position of the wavefront will be the surface of tangency to these secondary wavelets.*

We illustrate this by a trivial example: Given a wavefront (*ab* in Fig. 41-7) in a plane wave in free space, where will the wavefront be a time *t* later? Following Huygens' principle, we let several points on this plane (see dots) serve as centers for secondary spherical wavelets. In a time *t* the radius of these spherical waves is *ct*, where *c* is the speed of light in free space. The plane of tangency to these spheres at time *t* is represented by *de*. As we

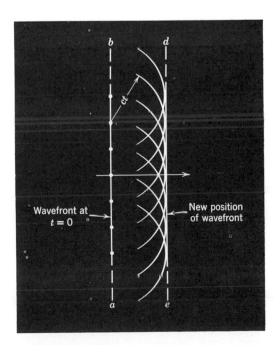

Fig. 41-7 The propagation of a plane wave in free space is described by the Huygens construction. Note that the ray (horizontal arrow) representing the wave is perpendicular to the wavefronts.

expect, it is parallel to plane ab and a perpendicular distance ct from it. Thus plane wavefronts are propagated as planes and with speed c. Note that the Huygens method involves a three-dimensional construction and that Fig. 41–7 is the intersection of this construction with the plane of the page.

We might expect that, contrary to observation, a wave should be radiated backward as well as forward from the dots in Fig. 41–7. This result is avoided by assuming that the *intensity* of the spherical wavelets is not uniform in all directions but varies continuously from a maximum in the forward direction to a minimum of zero in the back direction. This is suggested by the shading of the circular arcs in Fig. 41–7. Huygens' method can be applied quantitatively to *all* wave phenomena; see Problem 1. The method was put on a firm mathematical footing by Augustin Fresnel (1788–1827).

41–3 Huygens' Principle and the Law of Reflection

Figure 41–8a shows three wavefronts in a plane wave falling on mirror MM'. For convenience they are chosen to be one wavelength apart. Note that θ_1, the angle between the wavefronts and the mirror, is the same as the angle between the incident ray and the normal to the mirror. In other

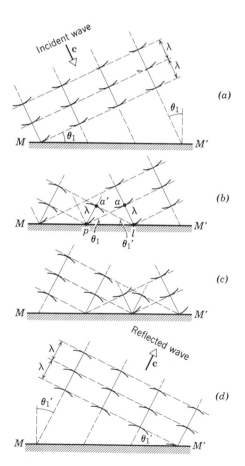

Fig. 41–8 The reflection of a plane wave as described by the Huygens construction.

words, θ_1 is the *angle of incidence*. The three wavefronts are related to each other by the Huygens construction, as in Fig. 41–7.

In Fig. 41–8*b* a Huygens wavelet centered on point *a* will expand to include point *l* after a time λ/c. Light from point *p* in this same wavefront cannot move beyond the mirror but must expand upward as a spherical Huygens wavelet. Setting a compass to radius λ and swinging an arc about *p* provides a semicircle to which the reflected wavefront must be tangent. Since point *l* must lie on the new wavefront, this tangent must pass through *l*. Note that the angle θ_1' between the wavefront and the mirror is the same as the angle between the reflected ray and the normal to the mirror. In other words, θ_1' is the *angle of reflection*.

Consider right triangles *alp* and *a'lp*. They have side *lp* in common and side *al* ($= \lambda$) is equal to side *a'p*. The two right triangles are thus congruent and we may conclude that

$$\theta_1 = \theta_1',$$

as required by the law of reflection. If the student recalls that the Huygens construction is three-dimensional and that the arcs shown represent segments of spherical surfaces, he will be able to convince himself that the reflected ray lies in the plane formed by the incident ray and the normal to the mirror, that is, the plane of Fig. 41–8. This is also a requirement of the law of reflection; see p. 922

41–4   Huygens' Principle and the Law of Refraction

Figure 41–9 shows four stages in the refraction of three successive wavefronts in a plane wave falling on an interface between air (medium 1) and glass (medium 2). For convenience, we assume that the incident wavefronts are separated by λ_1, the wavelength as measured in medium 1. Let the speed of light in air be v_1 and that in glass be v_2. We assume that

$$v_2 < v_1. \tag{41–5}$$

This assumption about the speeds is vital to the derivation that follows. It was not possible to test it experimentally because of technical difficulties until 1850, when the assumption was shown by Foucault to be correct.

The wavefronts in Fig. 41–9*a* are related to each other by the Huygens construction of Fig. 41–7. As in Fig. 41–8, θ_1 is the angle of incidence. In Fig. 41–9*b* consider the time ($= \lambda_1/v_1$) during which a Huygens wavelet from point *e* moves to include point *c*. Light from point *h*, traveling through glass at a reduced speed (recall the assumption of Eq. 41–5) will move a shorter distance

$$\lambda_2 = \lambda_1 \frac{v_2}{v_1} \tag{41–6}$$

during this time. The refracted wavefront must be tangent to an arc of this radius centered on *h*. Since *c* lies on the new wavefront, the tangent must pass through this point, as shown. Note that θ_2, the angle between the refracted wavefront and the air-glass interface, is the same as the angle

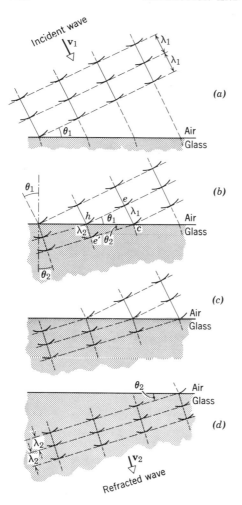

(a)

(b)

(c)

(d)

Fig. 41–9 The refraction of a plane wave as described by the Huygens construction; the reflected wave is omitted for simplicity. Note the change in wavelength on refraction.

between the refracted ray and the normal to this interface. In other words, θ_2 is the *angle of refraction*. Note, too, that the wavelength in glass (λ_2) is less than the wavelength in air (λ_1).

For the right triangles *hce* and *hce′* we may write

$$\sin \theta_1 = \frac{\lambda_1}{hc} \quad \text{(for } hce\text{)}$$

and

$$\sin \theta_2 = \frac{\lambda_2}{hc} \quad \text{(for } hce'\text{)}.$$

Dividing and using Eq. 41–6 yields

$$\frac{\sin \theta_1}{\sin \theta_2} = \frac{\lambda_1}{\lambda_2} = \frac{v_1}{v_2} = \text{a constant.} \tag{41–7}$$

The law of refraction, as stated in Eq. 41–2, is

$$\frac{\sin \theta_1}{\sin \theta_2} = n_{21}, \tag{41–2}$$

so that n_{21} is now revealed as the ratio of the speeds of light in the two media, or

$$n_{21} = \frac{v_1}{v_2}. \tag{41–8}$$

We may rewrite Eq. 41–7 as

$$\left(\frac{c}{v_1}\right) \sin \theta_1 = \left(\frac{c}{v_2}\right) \sin \theta_2, \tag{41–9}$$

in which c is the speed of light in free space. The quantities (c/v_1) and (c/v_2) (see Eq. 41–8) are the indices of refraction of medium 1 and of medium 2, respectively, with respect to a vacuum. Introducing the symbols n_1 and n_2 for these quantities allows us to write the law of refraction as

$$n_1 \sin \theta_1 = n_2 \sin \theta_2. \tag{41–10}$$

If we assume that the medium above the glass in Fig. 41–9 is a vacuum rather than air, the speed v_1 becomes c and the wavelength, called λ_1 in Fig. 41–9, assumes a value λ that is characteristic of the wave in free space. Equation 41–6 may thus be written

$$\lambda_2 = \lambda \frac{v_2}{c} = \frac{\lambda}{n_2}. \tag{41–11}$$

This shows specifically that the wavelength of light in a material medium is less than the wavelength of the same wave in a vacuum. Figure 41–9 shows clearly the difference in wavelength in the two media.

The application of Huygens' principle to refraction requires that if a light ray is bent toward the normal in passing from air to an optically dense medium then the speed of light in that optically dense medium (glass, say) must be *less* than that in air; see Eq. 41–5. This requirement holds for all wave theories of light. For the early particle theory of light put forward by Newton, refraction can be explained only if the speed of light in the medium in which light is bent toward the normal (the optically dense medium) is *greater* than that in air. The dense medium was thought to exert attractive forces on the light "corpuscles" as they neared the surface, speeding them up and changing their direction to cause them to make a smaller angle with the normal. Figure 41–10 shows a figure from a 1637 work of René Descartes, in which he makes an analogy between the refraction of light and the motion of a tennis ball on entering a medium in which it moves more slowly.

An experimental comparison of the speed of light in water and in air is decisive, therefore, between the wave and corpuscular theories of light. Such a measurement was first carried out by Foucault in 1850; he showed conclusively that *light travels more slowly in water than in air*, thus ruling out the corpuscular theory of Newton.

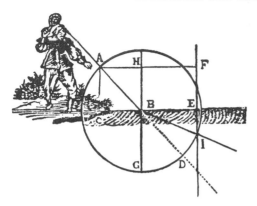

Fig. 41–10 According to the early (incorrect) corpuscular theory of light, ABI is the path of a ray on entering a medium in which its speed is *less*. The (correct) wave theory predicts that for the ray shown the speed in the lower medium (below BE) must be *greater;* from Descartes' *La Dioptrique* (1637).

41–5   Total Internal Reflection

Let light rays in an optically dense medium (glass, say) fall on a surface on the other side of which is a less optically dense medium (air, say); see Fig. 41–11. As the angle of incidence θ is increased, a situation is reached (see ray e) at which the refracted ray points along the surface, the angle of refraction being 90°. For angles of incidence larger than this *critical angle* θ_c no refracted ray exists, giving rise to a phenomenon called *total internal reflection*.

The critical angle is found by putting $\theta_2 = 90°$ in the law of refraction (see Eq. 41–10):

$$n_1 \sin \theta_c = n_2 \sin 90°,$$

or
$$\sin \theta_c = \frac{n_2}{n_1}. \tag{41–12}$$

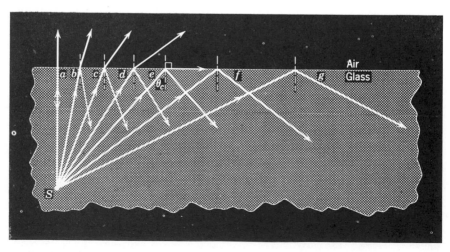

Fig. 41–11   Showing the total internal reflection of light from a source S; the *critical angle* is θ_c.

For glass and air $\sin \theta_c = (1.00/1.50) = 0.667$, which yields $\theta_c = 41.8°$. Total internal reflection does not occur when light originates in the medium of lower index of refraction.

Light can be "piped" from one point to another with little loss by allowing it to enter one end of a rod of transparent plastic. The light will undergo total internal

Fig. 41–12 A bundle of tapered fibers (*below*) is placed over the letter S. Above, with the aid of a mirror, we see that the image, reduced in size, is transmitted to the top of the bundle by total internal reflection in the individual fibers. (Courtesy Dr. N. S. Kapany, Optics Technology, Inc.)

reflection at the boundary of the rod and will follow its contour, emerging at its far end. Images may be transferred from one location to another, using a bundle of fine glass fibers, each fiber transmitting a small fraction of the image * Such bundles can be made in which a (flexible) seven-foot length delivers half the energy entering it at the far end. In a fiber in such a bundle a typical ray may undergo 48,000 reflections. Most of the energy loss is due to absorption within the glass, reflection being almost

---

* See "Fiber Optics," by N. S. Kapany, *Scientific American*, November 1960.

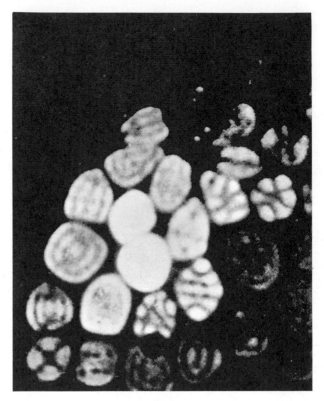

Fig. 41–13 A photomicrograph of light emerging from the end of a bundle of fibers. The fiber diameters approach the wavelength of light so that each fiber acts like an "optical waveguide." We have here convincing visual evidence that light is an electromagnetic wave. (Courtesy of Dr. N. S. Kapany, Optics Technology, Inc.)

truly total. Measurable amounts of light can be transmitted through single fibers 150 feet long.

Fiber optics techniques make possible many useful optical devices for transmitting and transforming luminous images. Figure 41–12 shows a short fiber bundle constructed so that the fibers taper in diameter along its length. The wide end is shown placed over the letter S in the printed word "OPTICS." We see, with the aid of a mirror placed above the bundle, that a letter S, reduced in size, has been transmitted by total internal reflection through the bundle to its narrow end.

Figure 41–13 is an enlarged view of a cross section of such a fiber bundle in which the diameters of the individual fibers are made so small that they are of the order of magnitude of the wavelength of light. This condition violates the spirit of our assumption of p. 924, namely that the transverse dimensions of reflecting and refracting surfaces would be large compared to the wavelength of light. Consequently, a description of the reflection and refraction of light in terms of rays, as in Figs. 41–1b and 41–11, is not possible. Figure 41–13 is readily interpreted, however, on the basis of the electromagnetic wave theory of light and provides convincing pictorial supporting evidence for that theory. The fibers behave like waveguides *

---

* A dielectric rod can serve as a waveguide in the same way that a hollow metal pipe can, and it has similar properties.

(see Section 39–3), and the patterns of darkness and light represent the distribution of the **E** and **B** vectors for various modes of oscillation of the electromagnetic waves traveling down the "guides."

▶ **Example 4.** Figure 41–14a shows a triangular prism of glass, a ray incident normal to one face being totally reflected. If θ_1 is 45°, what can you conclude about the index of refraction n of the glass?

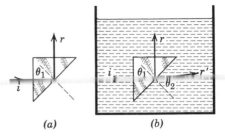

Fig. 41–14   Example 4.

(a)   *(b)*

The angle θ_1 must be equal to or greater than the critical angle θ_c where θ_c is given by Eq. 41–12:

$$\sin \theta_c = \frac{n_2}{n_1} = \frac{1}{n},$$

in which, for all practical purposes, the index of refraction of air ($-n_2$) is set equal to unity. Suppose that the index of refraction of the glass is such that total internal reflection just occurs, that is, that $\theta_c = 45°$. This would mean

$$n = \frac{1}{\sin 45°} = 1.41.$$

Thus the index of refraction of the glass must be *equal to or larger than* 1.41. If it were less, total internal reflection would not occur.

Example 5. What happens if the prism in Example 4 (assume that $n = 1.50$) is immersed in water ($n = 1.33$)? See Fig. 41–14b.

The new critical angle, given by Eq. 41–12, is

$$\sin \theta_c = \frac{n_2}{n_1} = \frac{1.33}{1.50} = 0.887,$$

which corresponds to $\theta_c = 62.5°$. The actual angle of incidence ($= 45°$) is less than this so that we do *not* have total internal reflection.

There is a reflected ray, with an angle of reflection of 45°, as Fig. 41–14b shows. There is also a refracted ray, with an angle of refraction given by

$$n_1 \sin \theta_1 = n_2 \sin \theta_2$$

$$(1.50)(\sin 45°) = (1.33) \sin \theta_2,$$

which yields $\theta_2 = 52.9°$.   ◀

Maxwell's equations permit us to calculate how the incident energy is divided between the reflected and the refracted beams. Figure 41–15 shows the theoretical

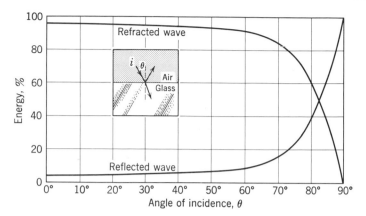

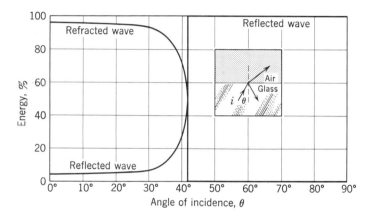

Fig. 41–15 (a) The per cent of the energy reflected and refracted when an incident wave in air falls on glass ($n = 1.50$). (b) The same for the incident wave in glass, showing total internal reflection.

prediction for (a) a light beam in air falling on a glass-air interface and (b) a light beam in glass falling on such an interface. Figure 41–15a shows that for angles of incidence up to about 50°, less than 10% of the light energy is reflected. At grazing incidence, however (that is, angles of incidence near 90°), the surface becomes an excellent reflector. We are all familiar with the high reflecting power of a wet road for light from automobile headlights that strikes near grazing incidence.

Figure 41–15b shows clearly that at a certain critical angle (41.8° in this case; see Eq. 41–12) *all* the light is reflected. For angles of incidence appreciably below this value, about 4% of the energy is reflected.

41–6 Fermat's Principle

In 1650 Pierre Fermat discovered a remarkable principle which we often express today in these terms: *A light ray traveling from one point to another will follow a path such that, compared with nearby paths, the time required is either a minimum or a maximum or will remain unchanged (that is, it will be stationary).*

The laws of reflection and refraction can readily be derived from this principle.

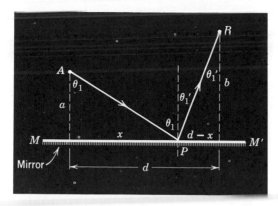

Fig. 41–16   A ray from A passes through B after reflection at P.

Figure 41–16 shows two fixed points A and B and a ray APB connecting them.* The total length l of this ray is

$$l = \sqrt{a^2 + x^2} + \sqrt{b^2 + (d - x)^2},$$

where x locates the point P at which the ray touches the mirror.

According to Fermat's principle, P will have a position such that the time of travel of the light must be a minimum (or a maximum or must remain unchanged). Expressed in another way, the total length l of the ray must be a minimum (or a maximum or must remain unchanged). In either case, the methods of the calculus require that dl/dx be zero. Taking this derivative yields

$$\frac{dl}{dx} = (\tfrac{1}{2})(a^2 + x^2)^{-1/2}(2x) + \tfrac{1}{2}[b^2 + (d - x)^2]^{-1/2}(2)(d - x)(-1) = 0,$$

which can be rewritten as

$$\frac{x}{\sqrt{a^2 + x^2}} = \frac{d - x}{\sqrt{b^2 + (d - x)^2}}.$$

Comparison with Fig. 41–16 shows that this can be written as

$$\sin \theta_1 = \sin \theta_1',$$

or

$$\theta_1 = \theta_1',$$

which is the law of reflection.

To prove the law of refraction from Fermat's principle, consider Fig. 41–17, which shows two points A and B in two different media and a ray APB connecting them. The time t is given by

$$t = \frac{l_1}{v_1} + \frac{l_2}{v_2}.$$

Using the relation $n = c/v$ this can be written as

$$t = \frac{n_1 l_1 + n_2 l_2}{c} = \frac{l}{c}.$$

The quantity l ($= n_1 l_1 + n_2 l_2$) is called the *optical path length* of the ray. Equation 41–11 (written as $\lambda = n\lambda_n$) shows that the optical path length is equal to the length

---

* We assume that ray APB lies in the plane of the figure; see Problem 20.

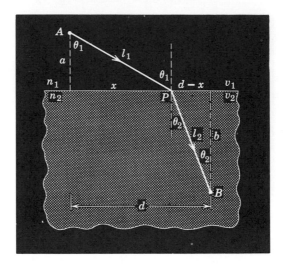

Fig. 41–17   A ray from A passes through B after refraction at P.

that this same number of waves would have if the medium were a vacuum.   The optical path length must not be confused with the geometrical path length, which is $l_1 + l_2$.

Fermat's principle requires that l be a minimum (or a maximum or must remain unchanged) which, in turn, requires that x be so chosen that $dl/dx = 0$.   The optical path length is

$$l = n_1 l_1 + n_2 l_2 = n_1 \sqrt{a^2 + x^2} + n_2 \sqrt{b^2 + (d - x)^2}.$$

Differentiating yields

$$\frac{dl}{dx} = n_1(\tfrac{1}{2})(a^2 + x^2)^{-1/2}(2x) + n_2(\tfrac{1}{2})[b^2 + (d - x)^2]^{-1/2}(2)(d - x)(-1) = 0,$$

which can be rewritten as

$$n_1 \frac{x}{\sqrt{a^2 + x^2}} = n_2 \frac{d - x}{\sqrt{b^2 + (d - x)^2}}.$$

Comparison with Fig. 41–17 shows that this, in turn, can be written as

$$n_1 \sin \theta_1 = n_2 \sin \theta_2,$$

which is the law of refraction.

In each of the examples of this section the time required, or, what is equivalent, the optical path length, proves to be a *minimum*.   Problem 22 describes a case in which it may be a maximum, a minimum, or stationary.

QUESTIONS

1. Discuss the propagation of spherical and of cylindrical waves, using Huygens' principle.

2. Does Huygens' principle apply to sound waves in air?

3. If Huygens' principle predicts the laws of reflection and refraction, why is it necessary or desirable to view light as an electromagnetic wave, with all its attendant complexity?

4. Would you expect sound waves to obey the laws of reflection and of refraction obeyed by light waves?

5. A street light, viewed by reflection across a body of water in which there are ripples, appears very elongated. Explain.

6. The light beam in Fig. 41–1a is broadened on entering the water. Explain.

7. By what per cent does the speed of blue light in fused quartz differ from that of red light?

8. Can (a) reflection phenomena or (b) refraction phenomena be used to determine the wavelength of light?

9. How did Foucault's measurement of the speed of light in water decide between the wave and the particle theories of light?

10. Why does a diamond "sparkle" more than a glass imitation cut to the same shape?

11. Is it plausible that the wavelength of light should change in passing from air into glass but that its frequency should not? Explain.

12. How can one determine the indices of refraction of the media in Table 41–1 relative to water, given the data in that table?

13. You are given a cube of glass. How can you find the speed of light (from a sodium light source) in this cube?

14. Describe and explain what a fish sees as he looks in various directions above his "horizon."

15. Design a periscope, taking advantage of total internal reflection. What are the advantages compared with silvered mirrors?

16. What characteristics must a material have in order to serve as an efficient "light pipe"?

17. Can the optical path length between two points ever be less than the geometrical path length between those points?

PROBLEMS

1. One end of a stick is dragged through water at a speed v which is greater than the speed u of water waves. Applying Huygens' construction to the water waves, show that a conical wavefront is set up and that its half-angle α is given by

$$\sin \alpha = u/v.$$

This is familiar as the bow wave of a ship or the shock wave caused by an object moving through air with a speed exceeding that of sound, as in Fig. 20–13.

2. Prove that if a mirror is rotated through an angle α, the reflected beam is rotated through an angle 2α. Is this result reasonable for $\alpha = 45°$?

3. What is the speed in fused quartz of light of wavelength 5500 A; see Fig. 41–2?

4. The wavelength of yellow sodium light in air is 5890 A. (a) What is its frequency? (b) What is its wavelength in glass whose index of refraction is 1.52? (c) From the results of (a) and (b) find its speed in this glass.

5. The speed of yellow sodium light in a certain liquid is measured to be 1.92×10^8 meters/sec. What is the index of refraction of this liquid, with respect to air, for sodium light?

6. Suppose that the speed of light in air has been measured with an uncertainty of, say, 1 km/sec. In calculating the speed in vacuum, suppose that it is not certain whether n for air is 1.00029 or 1.00030. (a) How much extra uncertainty is introduced into the calculated value for c? (b) Estimate how accurately n should be known for this purpose.

7. In Fig. 41–6 show by graphical ray tracing, using a protractor, that if θ for the incident ray is *either* increased *or* decreased, the deviation angle ψ is increased. The symmetrical situation shown in this figure is called the *position of minimum deviation*.

8. A ray of light is incident normally on the face ab of a glass prism ($n = 1.52$), as shown in Fig. 41–18. (a) Assuming that the prism is immersed in air, find the largest value

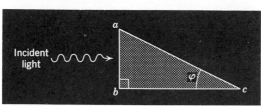

for the angle ϕ so that the ray is totally reflected at face ac. (b) Find ϕ if the prism is immersed in water.

9. Show that for a thin prism (ϕ small) and light not far from normal incidence (θ_1 small) the deviation angle is independent of the angle of incidence and is equal to $(n - 1) \phi$ (see Fig. 41–6).

Fig. 41–18

10. A glass prism with an apex angle of 60° has $n = 1.60$. (a) What is the smallest angle of incidence for which a ray can enter one face of the prism and emerge from the other? (b) What angle of incidence would be required for the ray to pass through the prism symmetrically, as in Fig. 41–6?

11. A 60° prism is made of fused quartz. A ray of light falls on one face, making an angle of 45° with the normal. Trace the ray through the prism graphically with some care, showing the paths traversed by rays representing (a) blue light, (b) yellow-green light, and (c) red light. See Figs. 40–2 and 41–2.

12. Ptolemy, who lived at Alexandria toward the end of the first century A.D., gave the following measured values for the angle of incidence θ_1 and the angle of refraction θ_2 for a light beam passing from air to water:

θ_1	θ_2	θ_1	θ_2
10°	7°45′	50°	35°0′
20°	15°30′	60°	40°30′
30°	22°30′	70°	45°30′
40°	29°0′	80°	50°0′

Are these data consistent with Snell's law; if so, what index of refraction results? These data are interesting as the oldest recorded physical measurements.

13. Prove that a ray of light incident on the surface of a sheet of plate glass of thickness t emerges from the opposite face parallel to its initial direction but displaced sideways, as in Fig. 41–19. Show that, for small angles of incidence θ, this displacement is given by

$$x = t\theta \frac{n - 1}{n}$$

where n is the index of refraction and θ is measured in radians.

14. A plane wave of white light traveling in fused quartz strikes a plane surface of the quartz, making an angle of incidence θ. Is it possible for the internally reflected beam to appear (a) bluish or (b)

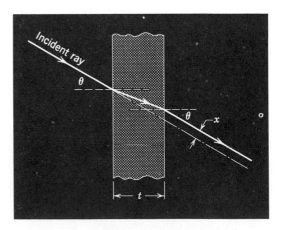

Fig. 41–19

reddish? Roughly what value of θ must be used? (Hint: White light will appear bluish if wavelengths corresponding to red are removed from the spectrum.)

15. A point source of light is placed a distance h below the surface of a large deep lake. (a) Show that the fraction f of the light energy that escapes directly from the water surface

ıs independent of h and ıs gıven by

$$f = \frac{1}{2} - \frac{1}{2n} \sqrt{n^2 - 1}$$

where n is the index of refraction of water. (Note: Absorption within the water and reflection at the surface—except where it is total—have been neglected.) (b) Evaluate this fraction for $n = 1.33$.

16. Figure 41–20 shows a *constant-deviation prism*. Although made of one piece of glass, it is equivalent to two $30°$–$60°$–$90°$ prisms and one $45°$–$45°$–$90°$ prism. White light is incident in the direction i. θ_1 is changed by rotating the prism so that, in turn, light of any desired wavelength may be made to follow the path shown, emerging at r. Show that, if $\sin \theta_1 = \frac{1}{2}n$, then $\theta_2 = \theta_1$ and beams i and r are at right angles.

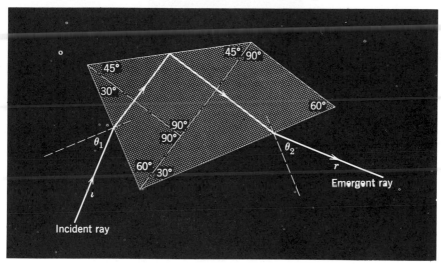

Fig. 41–20

17. A drop of liquid may be placed on a semicircular slab of glass as in Fig. 41–21. Show how to determine the index of refraction of the liquid by observing total internal reflection. The index of refraction of the glass is unknown and must also be determined. Is the range of indices of refraction that can be measured in this way restricted in any sense?

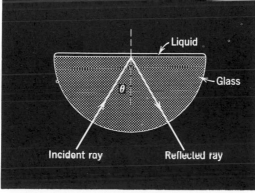

Fig. 41–21

18. A light ray falls on a square glass slab as in Fig. 41–22. What must the index of refraction of the glass be if total internal reflection occurs at the vertical face?

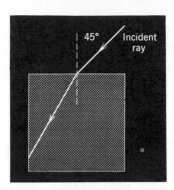

Fig. 41–22

19. A glass cube has a small spot at its center. What parts of the cube face must be covered to prevent the spot from being seen, no matter what the direction of viewing? What fraction of the cube surface must be so covered? Assume a cube edge of 1.0 cm and an index of refraction of 1.50. (Neglect the subsequent behavior of an internally reflected ray.)

20. Using Fermat's principle, prove that the reflected ray, the incident ray, and the normal lie in one plane.

21. Prove that the optical path lengths for reflection and refraction in Figs. 41–16 and 41–17 are minima when compared with other nearby paths connecting the same two points.

22. Figure 41–23 shows two points A and B connected by a light ray AvB. Show that, by comparison with nearby rays, such as AcB, the ray AvB represents a minimum, a stationary, or a maximum optical path, depending on whether the distance a is respectively less than, equal to, or greater than, the quantity

$$R \frac{n+1}{n-1}.$$

R is the radius of curvature of the spherical surface and n is the index of refraction of the medium to the right of this surface. (Hint: Express the optical path length l of the arbitrary path AcB in terms of the angle ϕ in Fig. 41–23. Use approximations that are appropriate when ϕ is small, since AcB must be a *nearby* path. Take the first and second derivatives of l with respect to ϕ.)

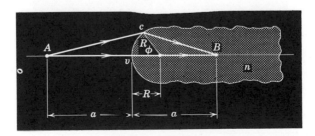

Fig. 41–23

Reflection and Refraction—
Spherical Waves
and Spherical Surfaces

CHAPTER 42

42-1 Geometrical Optics and Wave Optics

In Chapter 41 we described the reflection and refraction of plane waves at plane surfaces. In this chapter we consider the more general case of spherical waves falling on spherical reflecting and refracting surfaces. All of the results of Chapter 41 will emerge as special cases of the results of this chapter, since a plane can be viewed as a spherical surface with an infinite radius of curvature.

Both in Chapter 41 and in this chapter we make extensive use of *rays*. Although a ray is a convenient construction, it proves impossible to isolate one physically. Figure 42–1a shows schematically a plane wave of wavelength λ falling on a slit of width $a = 5\lambda$. We find that the light flares out into the geometrical shadow of the slit, a phenomenon called *diffraction*. Figures 42–1b ($a = 3\lambda$) and 42–1c ($a = \lambda$) show that diffraction becomes more pronounced as $a/\lambda \to 0$ and that attempts to isolate a single ray from the incident plane wave are futile.

Figure 42–2 shows water waves in a shallow *ripple tank*, produced by tapping the water surface periodically and automatically with the edge of a flat stick. We see that the plane wave so generated flares out by diffraction when it encounters a gap in a barrier placed across it. Diffraction is characteristic of waves of all types. We can hear around corners, for example, because of the diffraction of sound waves.

The diffraction of waves at a slit (or at an obstacle such as a wire) is expected from Huygens' principle. Consider the portion of the wavefront that arrives at the position of the slit in Fig. 42–1. Every point on it can be

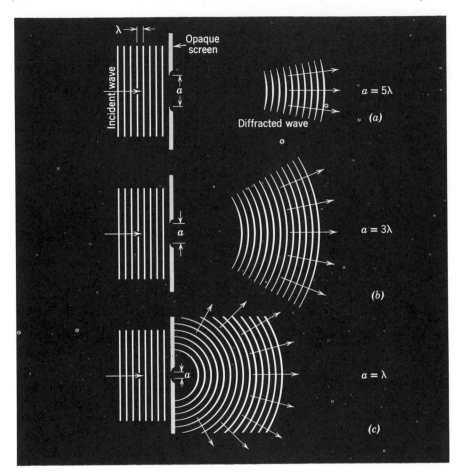

Fig. 42–1 An attempt to isolate a ray by reducing the slit width a fails because of diffraction, which becomes more pronounced as a/λ approaches zero.

viewed as the site of an expanding spherical Huygens' wavelet. The "bending" of light into the region of the geometrical shadow is associated with the blocking off of Huygens' wavelets from those parts of the incident wavefront that lie behind the slit edges.

Figure 42–3 was made by allowing parallel light to fall on a slit placed 50 cm in front of a photographic plate. In Fig. 42–3a the slit width was about 6×10^{-3} mm. The central band of light is much wider than this, showing that light has "flared out" into the geometric shadow of the slit. In addition, many secondary maxima, omitted from Fig. 42–1 for simplicity, appear. Figure 42–3b shows what happens when the slit width is *reduced* by a factor of two. The central maximum becomes *wider*, in agreement with Fig. 42–1. Figure 42–3c shows the effect of reducing the slit width by an additional factor of 7, to 4×10^{-4} mm. The central maximum is now much wider and the secondary maxima, whose intensities relative to the central

Fig. 42–2 Diffraction of water waves at a slit in a ripple tank. Note that the slit width is about the same size as the wavelength. (Courtesy of Educational Services Incorporated.)

maximum have been deliberately overemphasized by long exposure, are very evident.

Diffraction can be ignored if the ratio a/λ is large enough, a being a measure of the smallest sideways dimension of the slit or obstacle. If $a \gg \lambda$, light appears to travel in straight lines which can be represented by rays that obey the laws of reflection (Eq. 41–1) and refraction (Eq. 41–2). In Chapter 41 this condition, called *geometrical optics*, prevailed, the lateral dimensions of all mirrors, prisms, etc., being much greater than the wavelength. We assume in this chapter also that the conditions for geometrical optics are satisfied.

Fig. 42–3 (a) The intensity of light diffracted from a slit of width $a \cong 6 \times 10^{-3}$ mm and falling on a screen 50 cm beyond. (b) The slit width is reduced by a factor of two. (c) The slit width is further reduced by an additional factor of seven. Note that secondary maxima, made prominent in this case by deliberate overexposure, appear on either side of the central maximum. These secondary maxima have been omitted from Fig. 42–1 for simplicity.

If the requirement for geometrical optics is not met, we cannot describe the behavior of light by rays but must take its wave nature specifically into account. This subject is called *wave optics;* it includes geometrical optics as an important limiting case. We will treat wave optics in succeeding chapters.

42–2   Spherical Waves—Plane Mirror

Figure 42–4 shows a point source of light O, the *object*, placed a distance o in front of a plane mirror. The light falls on the mirror as a spherical wave represented in the figure by rays emanating from O.* At the point at which each ray strikes the mirror we construct a reflected ray. If the reflected rays are extended backward, they intersect in a point I which is the same distance

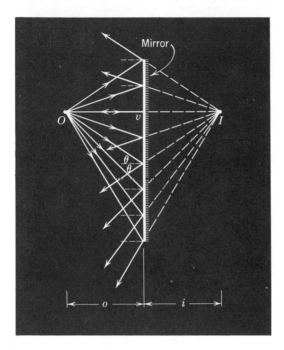

Fig. 42–4 A point object O forms a virtual image I in a plane mirror. The rays appear to emanate from I, but actually light energy does not pass through this point.

behind the mirror that the object O is in front of it; I is called the *image* of O.

Images may be *real* or *virtual*. In a real image light energy actually passes through the image point; in a virtual image the light behaves as though it diverges from the image point, although, in fact, it does not pass through this point; see Fig. 42–4. Images in plane mirrors are always virtual. We know from daily experience how "real" such a virtual image appears to be and how definite is its location in the space behind the mirror, even though this space may, in fact, be occupied by a brick wall.

Figure 42–5 shows two rays from Fig. 42–4. One strikes the mirror at v, along a perpendicular line. The other strikes it at an arbitrary point a, making an angle of incidence θ with the normal at that point. Elementary

---

* In our discussion of reflection from mirrors in Chapter 41 (see Fig. 41–8) we assumed an incident *plane* wave; the incident rays are parallel to each other in that case.

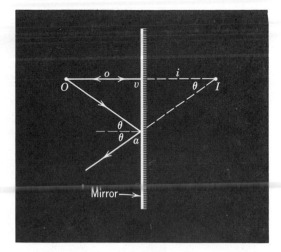

Fig. 42–5 Two rays from Fig. 42–4; ray Oa makes an arbitrary angle θ with the normal.

geometry shows that the angles aOv and aIv are also equal to θ. Thus the right triangles $aOva$ and $aIva$ are congruent and

$$o = -i, \tag{42–1}$$

in which the minus sign is arbitrarily introduced to show that I and O are on opposite sides of the mirror. Equation 42–1 does not involve θ, which means that *all* rays striking the mirror pass through I when extended backward, as we have seen above. Beyond assuming that the mirror is truly plane and that the conditions for geometrical optics hold, we have made no approximations in deriving Eq. 42–1. A point object produces a point image in a plane mirror, with $o = -i$, no matter how large the angle θ in Fig. 42–5.

Because of the finite diameter of the pupil of the eye, only rays that lie fairly close together can enter the eye after reflection at a mirror. For the eye position shown in Fig. 42–6 only a small patch of the mirror near point a is effective in forming the image; the rest of the mirror may be covered up or removed. If the eye is moved to another location, a different patch of the mirror will be effective; the location of the virtual image I will remain unchanged, however, as long as the object remains fixed.

If the object is an extended source such as the head of a person, a virtual image is also formed. From Eq. 42–1, every point of the source has an image point that lies an equal distance directly behind the plane of the mirror. Thus the image reproduces the object point by point.

Images in plane mirrors differ from objects in that left and right are interchanged. The image of a printed page is different from the page itself. Similarly, if a top is made to spin clockwise, the image, viewed in a vertical mirror, will seem to spin counterclockwise. Figure 42–7 shows an image of a left hand, constructed by using point by point application of Eq. 42–1; the image has the symmetry of a right hand.*

---

* See "The Overthrow of Parity" by Philip Morrison, *Scientific American*, April, 1957, for a discussion of the distinction in nature between right and left.

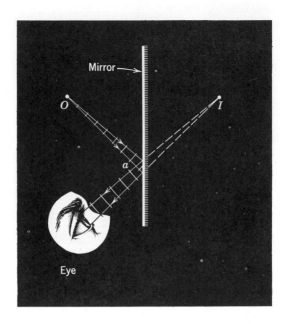

Fig. 42–6   A pencil of rays from O enters the eye after reflection at the mirror.   Only a small portion of the mirror near a is effective.   The small arcs represent portions of spherical wavefronts.

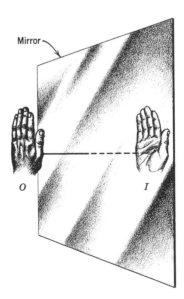

Fig. 42–7   A plane mirror reverses right and left.

▶ **Example 1.** How tall must a vertical mirror be if a person 6 ft high is to be able to see his entire length? Assume that his eyes are 4 in. below the top of his head.

Figure 42–8 shows the paths followed by light rays leaving the top of the man's head and the tips of his toes. These rays, chosen so that they will enter the eye e after reflection, strike the vertical mirror at points a and b, respectively. The mirror need occupy only the region between these two points. Calculation shows that b is 2 ft, 10 in. and a is 5 ft, 10 in. above the floor. The length of the mirror is thus 3 ft, or half the height of the person. Note that this height is independent of the distance between the person and the mirror. Mirrors that extend below point b show reflections of the floor between the person and the mirror.

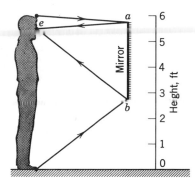

Fig. 42–8 Example 1. A person can view his full-length image in a mirror that is only half his height.

Example 2. Two plane mirrors are placed at right angles, and a point object O is located on the perpendicular bisector, as shown in Fig. 42–9a. Locate the images. Images I_1 and I_2 are formed in mirrors ab and cd, respectively. There is also a third image; it may be considered to be the image of I_1 in mirror cd or the image of I_2 in mirror ab. The three images and the object O lie on a circle whose center is on the line of intersection of the mirrors and whose plane is at right angles to that line.

In viewing I_3 the light entering the observer's eye is reflected *twice* after leaving the source. Figure 42–9b shows a typical bundle of rays. In viewing I_1 or I_2, the light is reflected only once, as in Fig. 42–6. ◀

42–3 Spherical Waves—Spherical Mirror

In Fig. 42–10 a spherical light wave from a point object O falls on a concave spherical mirror whose radius of curvature is r.* A line through O and the center of curvature C makes a convenient reference axis.

A ray from O that makes an arbitrary angle α with this axis intersects the axis at I after reflection from the mirror at a. A ray that leaves O along the axis will be reflected back along itself at v and will also pass through I. Thus, for these two rays at least, I is the image of O; it is a *real* image because light energy actually passes through I. Let us find the location of I.

A useful theorem is that the exterior angle of a triangle is equal to the sum of the two opposite interior angles. Applying this to triangles OaC and

---

* A spherical shell, viewed from inside, is everywhere *concave;* viewed from outside it is everywhere *convex*. In this chapter concave and convex will always be judged from the point of view of an observer sighting along the direction of the incident light.

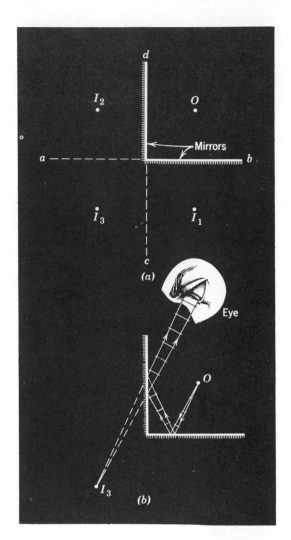

Fig. 42–9 Example 2. (*a*) Object *O* has three virtual images. (*b*) A typical bundle of rays used to view I_3.

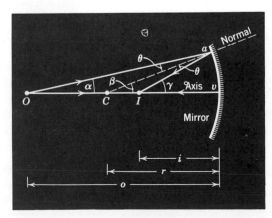

Fig. 42–10 Two rays from *O* converge after reflection in a spherical concave mirror, forming a real image at *I*.

$OaIO$ in Fig. 42–10 yields

$$\beta = \alpha + \theta$$

and

$$\gamma = \alpha + 2\theta.$$

Eliminating θ between these equations leads to

$$\alpha + \gamma = 2\beta. \tag{42-2}$$

In radian measure we can write angles α, β, and γ as

$$\alpha \cong \frac{av}{vO} = \frac{av}{o}$$

$$\beta = \frac{av}{vC} = \frac{av}{r} \tag{42-3}$$

$$\gamma \cong \frac{av}{vI} = \frac{av}{i}$$

Note that only the equation for β is exact, for the reason that the center of curvature of arc av is at C and not at O or I. However, the equations for α and for γ are approximately correct if these angles are sufficiently small. *In all that follows we assume that the rays diverging from the object make only a small angle α with the axis of the mirror.* Such rays, which lie close to the mirror axis, are called *paraxial rays*. We did not find it necessary to make such an assumption for plane mirrors. Substituting these equations into Eq. 42–2 and canceling av yields

$$\frac{1}{o} + \frac{1}{i} = \frac{2}{r}, \tag{42-4}$$

in which o is the *object distance* and i is the *image distance*. Both these distances are measured from the *vertex* of the mirror, which is the point v at which the axis intercepts the mirror.

Significantly, Eq. 42–4 does not contain α (or β, γ, or θ), so that it holds for all rays that strike the mirror provided that they are sufficiently paraxial. In an actual case the rays can be made as paraxial as one likes by putting a circular diaphragm in front of the mirror, centered about the vertex v; this will impose a certain maximum value of α.

As α in Fig. 42–10 is permitted to become larger, it will become less true that a point object will form a point image; the image will become extended and fuzzy. No sharp criterion for deciding whether a given ray is paraxial can be laid down. If the maximum permitted value of α is reduced, the rays will become more paraxial and the image will become sharper. Unfortunately, the image will also become fainter because less total light energy will be reflected from the mirror. A compromise must often be made between image brightness and image quality.

As for plane mirrors, the image (real or virtual) in a spherical mirror can be seen only if the eye is located so that light rays from the object can enter

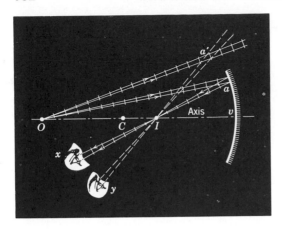

Fig. 42–11 The eye must be properly located to see image I.

it after reflection. In Fig. 42–11 a bundle of light rays is shown entering the eye in position x; only the small patch of mirror near a is effective for this eye position. If the observer moves his eye to position y, the image will vanish for him because the mirror does not exist near point a'.

Although Eq. 42–4 was derived for the special case in which the object is located beyond the center of curvature, it is generally true, no matter where the object is located. It is also true for convex mirrors, as in Fig. 42–12.

In applying Eq. 42–4, we must be careful to follow a consistent convention of signs for o, i, and r. As the basis for the sign conventions to be used in this book, we start from this statement:

> In Fig. 42–10, in which light *diverges* from a *real* object, falls on a *concave* mirror, and *converges* after reflection to form a *real* image, the quantities o, i, and r in Eq. 42–4 are given positive numerical values.

Figure 42–10 was used to derive Eq. 42–4 and the student should associate them in his mind as an aid in getting the signs correct.

Let us fix our minds on the side of the mirror from which incident light comes. Because mirrors are opaque, the light, after reflection, must remain on this side, and if an image is formed here it will be a *real* image. There-

Fig. 42–12 Two rays from O diverge after reflection in a spherical convex mirror, forming a virtual image at I, the point from which they appear to originate. Compare Fig. 42–10.

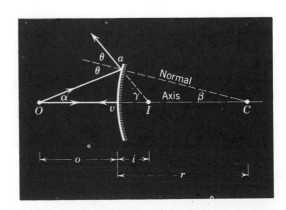

fore, we call the side of the mirror from which the light comes the *R-side* (for *real image*). We call the back of the mirror the *V-side* (for *virtual image*), because images formed on this side of the mirror must be virtual, no light energy being present on this side.*

In the indented statement above we associated real images with positive image distances. This suggests our first sign convention:

1. The image distance i is positive if the image (real) lies on the R-side of the mirror, as in Fig. 42–10; i is negative if the image (virtual) lies on the V-side, as in Fig. 42–12.

If the mirror in Fig. 42–10, which is concave as viewed from the direction of the incident light, is made convex, the rays will *diverge after reflection* and will form a *virtual* image, as Fig. 42–12 shows. Thus the indented statement above suggests our second sign convention:

2. The radius of curvature r is positive if the center of curvature of the mirror lies on the R-side, as in Fig. 42–10; r is negative if the center of curvature lies on the V-side, as in Fig. 42–12.

The student should not commit these sign conventions to memory but should deduce them in each case from the basic statement on p. 952, using Fig. 42–10 as a mnemonic aid.

For all cases in this book the object distance o is to be taken as positive. In systems of two or more mirrors (or combinations of mirrors and refracting surfaces) it is possible to arrange that *converging* light falls on the mirror. In such cases the object is called *virtual* and the object distance o is negative; we limit our discussion here to real objects.

▶ **Example 3.**   A convex mirror has a radius of curvature of 20 cm. If a point source is placed 14 cm away from the mirror, as in Fig. 42–12, where is the image?

A rough graphical construction, applying the law of reflection at a in the figure, shows that the image will be on the V-side of the mirror and thus will be virtual. We may verify this quantitatively and analytically from Eq. 42–4, noting that r is negative here because the center of curvature of the mirror is on its V-side. We have

$$\frac{1}{o} + \frac{1}{i} = \frac{2}{r}$$

or

$$\frac{1}{+14 \text{ cm}} + \frac{1}{i} = \frac{2}{-20 \text{ cm}},$$

which yields $i = -5.8$ cm, in agreement with the graphical prediction. The negative sign for i reminds us that the image is on the V-side of the mirror and thus is virtual.   ◀

When *parallel* light falls on a mirror (Fig. 42–13), the image point (real or virtual) is called the *focal point F* of the mirror. The focal length f is the distance between F and the vertex. If we put $o \rightarrow \infty$ in Eq. 42–4, thus insuring parallel incident light, we have

$$i = \tfrac{1}{2}r = f.$$

---

* This nomenclature may seem unnecessarily cumbersome at this point. We adopt it because of the later extension of these ideas to refracting surfaces and lenses.

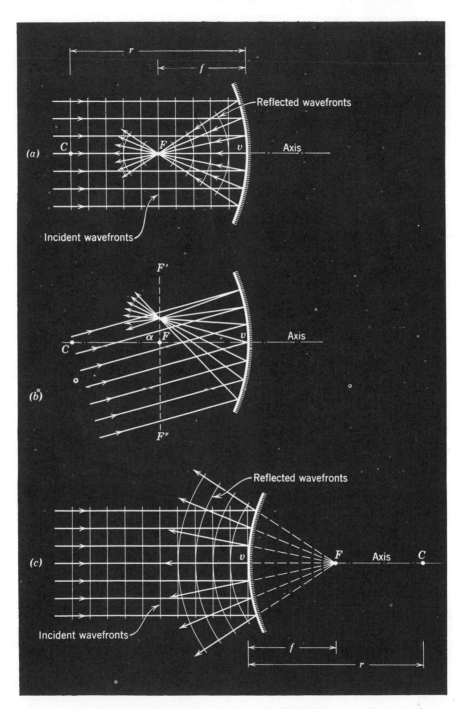

Fig. 42–13 (*a*) The focal point for a concave spherical mirror, showing both the rays and the wavefronts. *F* and *C* lie on the R-side, the focal point is real, and the focal length *f* of the mirror is positive (as is *r*). (*b*) The same, except that the incident light makes an angle α with the mirror axis; the rays are focused at a point in the *focal plane* *F'F''*. (*c*) Same as (*a*) except that the mirror is convex; *F* and *C* lie on the V-side of the mirror. The focal point is virtual and the focal length *f* is negative (as is *r*).

Equation 42–4 can then be rewritten

$$\frac{1}{o} + \frac{1}{i} = \frac{1}{f},$$ (42–5)

where f, like r, is taken as positive for mirrors whose centers of curvature are on the R-side (that is, for *concave*, or *converging* mirrors; see Fig. 42–13a) and negative for those whose centers of curvature are on the V-side (that is, for *convex*, or *diverging* mirrors; see Fig. 42–13c). Figure 42–13b shows an incident plane wave that makes a small angle α with the mirror axis. The rays are focused at a point in the *focal plane* of the mirror. This is a plane at right angles to the mirror axis at the focal point.

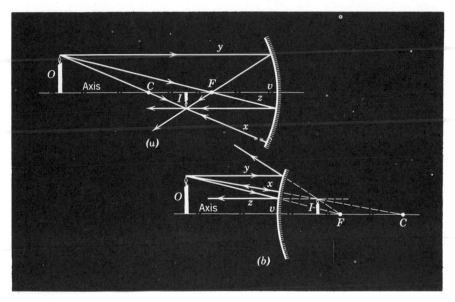

Fig. 42–14   The image of an extended object in (a) a concave mirror and (b) a convex mirror is located graphically. Any two of the three special rays shown are sufficient.

We now consider objects that are not points. Figure 42–14 shows a candle in front of (a) a concave mirror and (b) a convex mirror. We choose to draw the mirror axis through the foot of the candle and, of course, through the center of curvature. The image of any off-axis point, such as the tip of the candle, can be found graphically, using the following facts:

1. A ray that strikes the mirror after passing (either directly or upon being extended) through the center of curvature C returns along itself (ray x in Fig. 42–13). Such rays strike the mirror at right angles.

2. A ray that strikes the mirror parallel to its axis passes (or will pass when extended) through the focal point (ray y).

3. A ray that strikes the mirror after passing (either directly or upon being extended) through the focal point emerges parallel to the axis (ray z).

Figure 42–15 shows a ray (dve) that originates on the tip of the object candle of Fig. 42–14a, is reflected from the mirror at point v, and passes through the tip of the image candle. The law of reflection demands that this ray make equal angles θ with the mirror axis as shown. For the two similar right triangles in the figure we can write

$$\frac{ce}{bd} = \frac{vc}{vb}.$$

The quantity on the left (apart from a question of sign) is the *lateral magnification m* of the mirror. Since we want to represent an *inverted* image by a *negative* magnification, we arbitrarily define m for this case as $-(ce/bd)$. Since $vc = i$ and $vb = o$, we have at once

$$m = -\frac{i}{o}. \tag{42–6}$$

This equation gives the magnification for spherical and plane mirrors under all circumstances. For a plane mirror, $o = -i$ and the predicted magnification is $+1$ which, in agreement with experience, indicates an *erect* image the same size as the object.

Images in spherical mirrors suffer from several "defects" that arise because the assumption of paraxial rays is never completely justified. In general, a point source will not produce a point image; see Problem 5. Apart from this, distortion arises because the magnification varies somewhat with distance from the mirror axis, Eq. 42–6 being strictly correct only for paraxial rays. Superimposed on these defects are *diffraction effects* which come about because the basic assumption of geometrical optics, that light travels in straight lines, must always be considered an approximation.

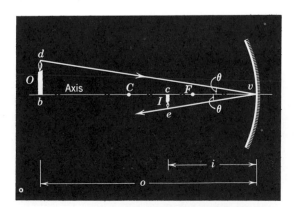

Fig. 42–15 A particular ray for the arrangement of Fig. 42–14, used to show that the *lateral magnification m* is given by $-i/o$.

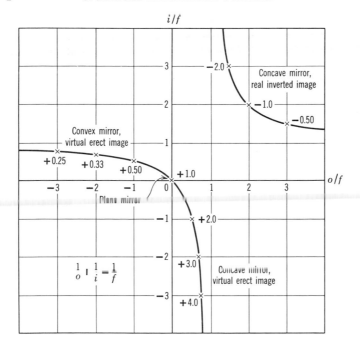

Fig. 42–16 A graphical representation of the mirror formula (Eq. 42–5). The numbers on the curves give the lateral magnifications (Eq. 42–6).

Figure 42–16 summarizes the predictions of the mirror equation (Eq. 42–5) and of the lateral magnification equation (Eq. 42–6). For convex mirrors the image is always virtual. For concave mirrors the image is virtual if the object is inside the focal point ($o/f < 1$) and real otherwise ($o/f > 1$). As $o \to \infty$ for both types of mirror, the image approaches the focal point ($i/f \to 1$). A plane mirror ($m = +1$) is represented in the figure by a point at the origin. It is appropriate that this point form the central point of the lower-left branch of Fig. 42–16 because both convex and concave mirrors approach plane mirrors as r is increased in magnitude, that is, as $f \to \infty$ (or as $o/f \to 0$ in Fig. 42–16, assuming a fixed object distance).

42–4 Spherical Refracting Surface

Figure 42–17 shows a point source O near a convex spherical *refracting* surface of radius of curvature r. The surface separates two media whose indices of refraction differ, *that of the medium in which the incident light falls on the surface being* n_1 and that on the other side of the surface being n_2.

From O we draw a line through the center of curvature C of the refracting surface, thus establishing a convenient axis which intercepts the surface at vertex v. From O we draw a ray that makes a small but arbitrary angle α with the axis and strikes the refracting surface at a, being refracted according to

$$n_1 \sin \theta_1 = n_2 \sin \theta_2.$$

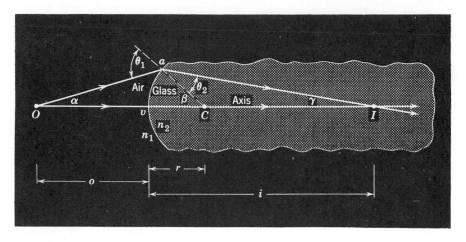

Fig. 42–17 Two rays from O converge after refraction at a spherical surface, forming a real image at I.

The refracted ray intersects the axis at I. A ray from O that travels along the axis will not be bent on entering the surface and will also pass through I. Thus, for these two rays at least, I is the image of O.

As in the derivation of the mirror equation, we use the theorem that the exterior angle of a triangle is equal to the sum of the two opposite interior angles. Applying this to triangles $COaC$ and $ICaI$ yields

$$\theta_1 = \alpha + \beta \tag{42–7}$$

and

$$\beta = \theta_2 + \gamma. \tag{42–8}$$

As α is made small, angles β, γ, θ_1, and θ_2 in Fig. 42–17 also become small. *We at once assume that α, hence all these angles, are arbitrarily small,* this paraxial ray assumption was also made for spherical mirrors. Replacing the sines of the angles by the angles themselves—since the angles are required to be small—permits us to write the law of refraction as

$$n_1\theta_1 \cong n_2\theta_2. \tag{42–9}$$

Combining Eqs. 42–8 and 42–9 leads to

$$\beta = \frac{n_1}{n_2}\theta_1 + \gamma.$$

Eliminating θ_1 between this equation and Eq. 42–7 leads, after rearrangement, to

$$n_1\alpha + n_2\gamma = (n_2 - n_1)\beta. \tag{42–10}$$

In radian measure the angles α, β, and γ in Fig. 42–17 are

$$\alpha \cong \frac{uv}{o}$$

$$\beta = \frac{av}{r} \tag{42–11}$$

$$\gamma \cong \frac{av}{i}.$$

Only the second of these equations is exact. The other two are approximate because I and O are *not* the centers of circles of which av is an arc. However, for paraxial rays (u small enough) the inaccuracies in Eq. 42–11 can be made as small as desired.

Substituting Eqs. 42–11 into Eq. 42–10 leads readily to

$$\frac{n_1}{o} + \frac{n_2}{i} = \frac{n_2 - n_1}{r}. \tag{42–12}$$

This equation holds whenever light is refracted from point objects at spherical surfaces, assuming only that the rays are paraxial. As with the mirror formula, care must be taken to use Eq. 42–12 with consistent signs for o, i, and r. Once again we establish our sign conventions by physical reasoning from a particular case, that of Fig. 42–17:

> In Fig. 42–17, in which light *diverges* from a *real* object, falls on a *convex* refracting surface, and *converges* after refraction to form a *real* image, the quantities o, i, and r in Eq. 42–12 have positive numerical values.

Figure 42–17 was used to derive Eq. 42–12, and the student should associate them in his mind as an aid in getting the signs correct. This basic statement is quite similar to that which we made for mirrors on p. 952.

We fix our attention on the side of the refracting surface from which the incident light falls on the surface. In contrast to mirrors, the light energy *passes through* a refracting surface to the other side, and if a real image is formed it must appear on the far side, which we call the R-side. The side from which the incident light comes is called the V-side because virtual images must appear here. Figure 42–18 suggests this important distinction between reflection and refraction.

In the indented statement above we associated real images with positive-image distances. Thus we are led to the sign convention:

1. The image distance i is positive if the image (real) is on the R-side of the refracting surface, as in Fig. 42–17; i is negative if the image (virtual) lies on the V-side, as in Fig. 42–19.

The refracting surface in Fig. 42–17 is convex. If it is made concave (still assuming that $n_2 > n_1$), the rays will *diverge* after refraction and form

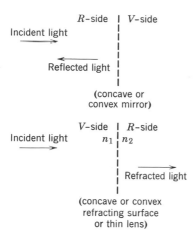

Fig. 42-18 Real images are formed on the same side as the incident light for mirrors but on the opposite side for refracting surfaces and thin lenses. This is so because the incident light is reflected back by mirrors but is transmitted through by refracting surfaces.

a *virtual* image, as Fig. 42–19 shows. Thus we are led to our second sign convention:

2. The radius of curvature r is positive if the center of curvature of the refracting surface lies on the R-side, as in Fig. 42–17; r is negative if the center of curvature is on the V-side, as in Fig. 42–19.

The sign conventions for refracting surfaces are the same as for mirrors (p. 953), the fundamental difference between the two situations being absorbed in the definitions of R-side and V-side in Fig. 42–18. This difference is easily remembered on physical grounds.

For all cases in this book the object distance o is to be taken as positive. In systems of two or more refracting surfaces (or combinations of refracting surfaces and mirrors) it is possible to arrange that *converging* light falls on the refracting surface. In such cases the object is called *virtual* and the object distance o is negative; we limit our discussions here to real objects.

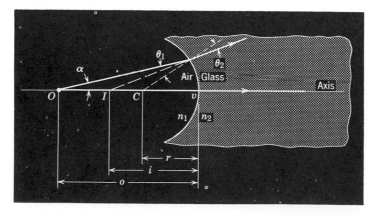

Fig. 42-19 Two rays from O diverge after refraction at a spherical surface, forming a virtual image at I.

▶ **Example 4.** Locate the image for the geometry shown in Fig. 42–17, assuming the radius of curvature to be 10 cm, n_2 to be 2.0, and n_1 to be 1.0. Let the object be 20 cm to the left of v.

From Eq. 42–12,

$$\frac{n_1}{o} + \frac{n_2}{i} = \frac{n_2 - n_1}{r},$$

we have

$$\frac{1.0}{+20 \text{ cm}} + \frac{2.0}{i} = \frac{2.0 - 1.0}{+10 \text{ cm}}.$$

Note that r is positive because the center of curvature of the surface lies on the R-side. This relation yields $i = +40$ cm in agreement with the graphical construction. The light energy actually passes through I so that the image is real, as indicated by the positive sign for i.

Example 5. An object is immersed in a medium with $n_1 = 2.0$, being 15 cm from the spherical surface whose radius of curvature is -10 cm, as in Fig. 42–20; r is negative because C lies on the V-side. Locate the image.

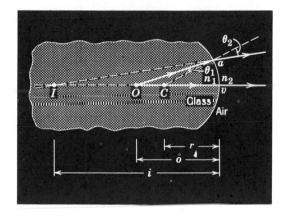

Fig. 42–20 Two rays from O appear to originate from I (virtual image) after refraction at a spherical surface.

Figure 42–20 shows a ray traced through the surface by applying the law of refraction at point a. A second ray from O along the axis emerges undeflected at v. The image I is found by extending these two rays backward; it is virtual.

From Eq. 42–12,

$$\frac{n_1}{o} + \frac{n_2}{i} = \frac{n_2 - n_1}{r},$$

we have

$$\frac{2.0}{+15 \text{ cm}} + \frac{1.0}{i} = \frac{1.0 - 2.0}{-10 \text{ cm}},$$

which yields $i = -30$ cm, in agreement with Fig. 42–20 and with the sign conventions. Note that n_1 always refers to the medium on the side of the surface from which the light comes.

Example 6. What is the relationship between i and o if the refracting surface is plane?

A plane surface has an infinite radius of curvature. Putting $r \to \infty$ in Eq. 42–12 leads to

$$i = -o\frac{n_2}{n_1}.$$

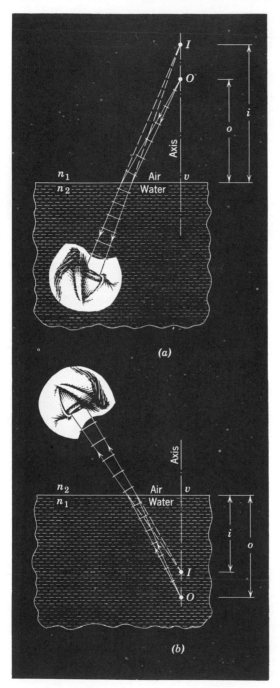

(a)

(b)

Fig. 42–21 Refraction at a plane surface at near-normal incidence, showing a pencil of rays and the corresponding wavefronts entering the pupil. (a) Source in air and (b) source in water.

Figure 42–21 illustrates the situation graphically (*a*) for an object in air as seen from below water and (*b*) for an object in water with air above. This shows that a diver, looking upward at, say, an overhanging tree branch, will think it higher than it is by the factor 1.33/1.00. Similarly, an observer in air will think that objects on the bottom of a water tank are closer to the surface than they actually are, in the ratio 1.00/1.33. These considerations, being based on Eq. 42–12, hold only for paraxial rays, which means that the incident rays can make only a small angle with the normal; this angle has been exaggerated in the figure for clarity. Note again that n_1 is always identified with the medium that lies on the side of the surface containing the incident light.   ◀

42–5   Thin Lenses

In most refraction situations there is more than one refracting surface. This is true even for a spectacle lens, the light passing from air into glass and then from glass into air. In microscopes, telescopes, cameras, etc., there are often many more than two surfaces.

Figure 42–22*a* shows a thick glass "lens" of length *l* whose surfaces are ground to radii r' and r''. A point object O' is placed near the left surface as shown. A ray leaving O' along the axis is not deflected on entering or leaving the lens because it falls on each surface along a normal.

A second ray leaving O', at an arbitrary angle α with the axis, strikes the surface at point a', is refracted, and strikes the second surface at point a''. The ray is again refracted and crosses the axis at I'', which, being the intersection of two rays from O'', is the image of point O', formed after refraction at two surfaces.

Figure 42–22*b* shows the first surface, which forms a virtual image of O' at I'. To locate I', we use Eq. 42–12,

$$\frac{n_1}{o} + \frac{n_2}{i} = \frac{n_2 - n_1}{r}.$$

Putting $n_1 = 1.0$ and $n_2 = n$ and bearing in mind that the image distance is negative (that is, $i = -i'$ in Fig. 42–22*b*), we obtain

$$\frac{1}{o'} - \frac{n}{i'} = \frac{n - 1}{r'}. \tag{42–13}$$

In this equation i' will be a positive number because we have arbitrarily introduced the minus sign appropriate to a virtual image.

Figure 42–22*c* shows the second surface. Unless an observer at point a'' were aware of the existence of the first surface, he would think that the light striking that point originated at point I' in Fig. 42–22*b* and that the region to the left of the surface was filled with glass. Thus the (virtual) image I' formed by the first surface serves as a real object O'' for the second surface. The distance of this object from the second surface is

$$o'' = i' + l. \tag{42–14}$$

In applying Eq. 42–12 to the second surface, we insert $n_1 = n$ and $n_2 = 1.0$ because the object behaves as if it were imbedded in glass. If we use

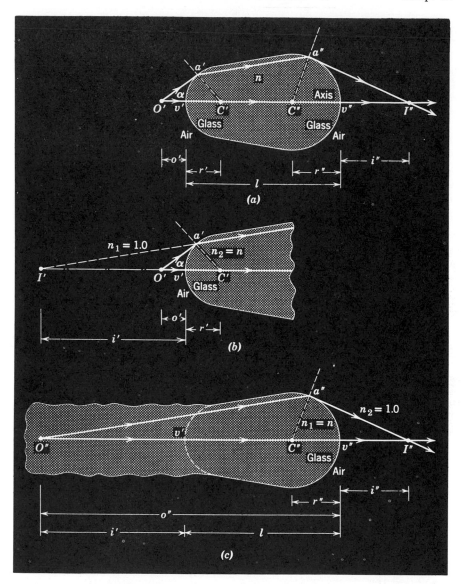

Fig. 42–22   (a) Two rays from O' intersect at I'' (real image) after refraction at two spherical surfaces.   (b) The first surface and (c) the second surface shown separately.   The quantities α and n have been exaggerated for clarity.

Eq. 42–14, Eq. 42–12 becomes

$$\frac{n}{i' + l} + \frac{1}{i''} = \frac{1 - n}{r''}. \tag{42–15}$$

Let us now assume that the thickness l of the "lens" in Fig. 42–22 is so small that it can be neglected in comparison with other linear quantities in this figure (such as o', i', o'', i'', r', and r''). In all that follows we make this *thin-lens approximation*. Putting $l = 0$ in Eq. 42–15 leads to

$$\frac{n}{i'} + \frac{1}{i''} = -\frac{n-1}{r''}.$$ (42–16)

Adding Eqs. 42–13 and 42–16 leads to

$$\frac{1}{o'} + \frac{1}{i''} = (n-1)\left(\frac{1}{r'} - \frac{1}{r''}\right).$$

Finally, calling the original object distance simply o and the final image distance simply i leads to

$$\frac{1}{o} + \frac{1}{i} = (n-1)\left(\frac{1}{r'} - \frac{1}{r''}\right).$$ (42–17)

This equation holds only for paraxial rays and only if the lens is so thin that it essentially makes no difference from which surface of the lens the quantities o and i are measured. In Eq. 42–17 r' refers to the first surface struck by the light as it traverses the lens and r'' to the second surface.

The sign conventions for Eq. 42–17 are the same as those for mirrors and for single refracting surfaces. Because the lens is assumed to be thin, we refer to the R-side and the V-side of the lens itself (see Fig. 42–18) rather than those of its separate surfaces. The sign conventions then are the following:

1. The image distance i is positive if the image (real) lies on the R-side of the lens, as in Fig. 42–23a; i is negative if the image (virtual) lies on the V-side of the lens, as in Fig. 42–23b.

2. The radii of curvature r' and r'' are positive if their respective centers

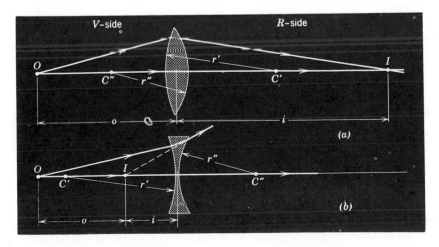

Fig. 42–23   Illustrations used to establish sign conventions for thin lenses.

of curvature lie on the R-side of the lens. They are negative if their centers lie on the V-side. In Fig. 42–23a, r' is positive and r'' is negative; in Fig. 42–23b, r' is negative and r'' is positive.

Figure 42–24a and c shows parallel light from a distant object falling on a thin lens. The image location is called the *second focal point* F_2 of the lens. The distance from F_2 to the lens is called the *focal length f*. The *first focal point* for a thin lens (F_1 in figure) is the object position for which the image

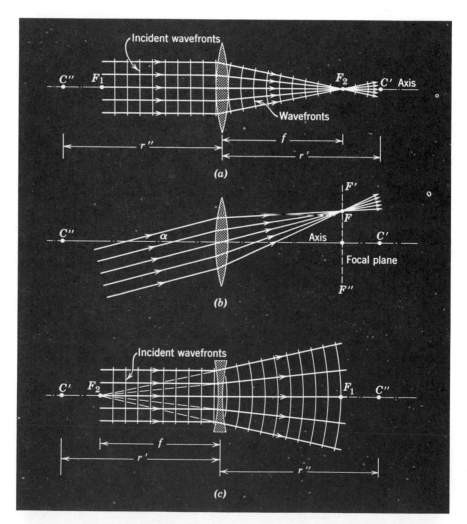

Fig. 42–24 (a) Parallel light passes through the second focal point F_2 of a converging lens. (b) The incident light makes an angle α with the lens axis, the rays being focused in the focal plane $F'F''$. (c) Parallel light, passing through a diverging lens, seems to originate at the second focal point F_2. C' and C'' are centers of curvature for the lens surfaces; F_1 is the first focal point.

is at infinity. For thin lenses the first and second focal points are on opposite sides of the lens and are equidistant from it.

The focal length can be computed from Eq. 42–17 by inserting $o \to \infty$ and $i = f$. This yields

$$\frac{1}{f} = (n - 1)\left(\frac{1}{r'} - \frac{1}{r''}\right). \tag{42–18}$$

This relation is called the *lens maker's equation* because it allows us to compute the focal length of a lens in terms of the radii of curvature and the index of refraction of the material. Combining Eqs. 42–17 and 42–18 allows us to write the thin-lens equation as

$$\frac{1}{o} + \frac{1}{i} = \frac{1}{f}. \tag{42–19}$$

Figure 42–24b shows parallel incident rays that make a small angle α with the lens axis; they are brought to a focus in the *focal plane* $F'F''$, as shown. This is a plane normal to the lens axis at the focal point.

In Fig. 42–24a we note that all rays in the figure contain the same number of wavelengths; in other words, they have the same *optical path lengths;* see Section 41–6. The optical path lengths are the same because the wavefronts are surfaces over which the wave disturbance has the same constant value and because all the rays shown pass through the same number of wavefronts.

▶ **Example 7.** The lenses of Fig. 42–24 have radii of curvature of magnitude 40 cm and are made of glass with $n = 1.65$. Compute their focal lengths.

Since C' lies on the R-side of the lens in Fig. 42–24a, r' is positive ($= +40$ cm). Since C'' lies on the V-side, r'' is negative ($= -40$ cm). Substituting in Eq. 42–18 yields

$$\frac{1}{f} = (n - 1)\left(\frac{1}{r'} - \frac{1}{r''}\right) = (1.65 - 1)\left(\frac{1}{+40 \text{ cm}} - \frac{1}{-40 \text{ cm}}\right),$$

or

$$f = +31 \text{ cm}.$$

A positive focal length indicates that in agreement with Fig. 42–24a the focal point F_2 is on the R-side of the lens and parallel incident light converges after refraction to form a real image.

In Fig. 42–24c C' lies on the V-side of the lens so that r' is negative ($= -40$ cm). Since r'' is positive ($= +40$ cm), Eq. 42–17 yields

$$f = -31 \text{ cm}.$$

A negative focal length indicates that in agreement with Fig. 42–24c the focal point F_2 is on the V-side of the lens and incident light diverges after refraction to form a virtual image. ◀

The location of the image of an extended object such as a candle (Fig. 42–25) can be found graphically by using the following three facts:

1. A ray parallel to the axis and falling on the lens passes, either directly or when extended, through the second focal point (ray x in Fig. 42–25).

2. A ray falling on a lens after passing, either directly or when extended,

through the first focal point will emerge from the lens parallel to the axis (ray y).

3. A ray falling on the lens at its center will pass through undeflected. There is no deflection because the lens, near its center, behaves like a thin piece of glass with parallel sides. The direction of the light rays is not changed and the sideways displacement can be neglected because the lens thickness has been assumed to be negligible (ray z; see also Problem 13, Chapter 41).

Figure 42–26, which represents part of Fig. 42–25a, shows a ray passing from the tip of the object through the center of curvature to the tip of the image. For the similar triangles abc and dec we may write

$$\frac{de}{ab} = \frac{dc}{ac}.$$

The right side of this equation is i/o and the left side is $-m$, where m is the

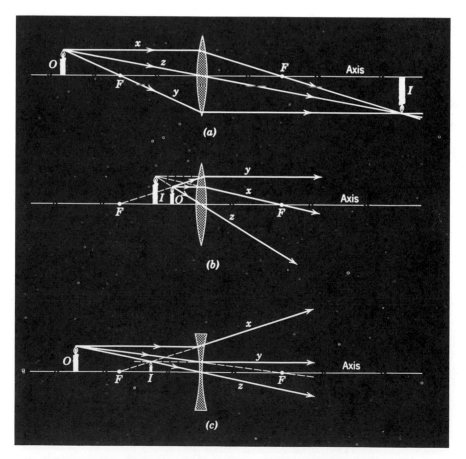

Fig. 42–25   Showing the graphical location of images for three thin lenses.

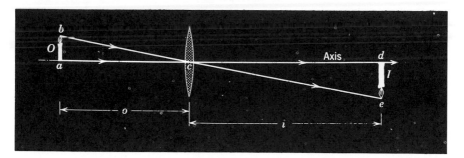

Fig. 42–26 Two rays for the situation of Fig. 42–25a.

lateral magnification. The minus sign is required because we wish m to be negative for an inverted image. This yields

$$m = -\frac{i}{o},$$ (42–20)

which holds for all types of thin lenses and for all object distances.

▶ **Example 8.** A converging thin lens has a focal length of $+24$ cm. An object is placed 9.0 cm from the lens as in Fig. 42–25b; describe the image.
From Eq. 42–19,

$$\frac{1}{o} + \frac{1}{i} = \frac{1}{f},$$

we have

$$\frac{1}{+9.0 \text{ cm}} + \frac{1}{i} = \frac{1}{+24 \text{ cm}},$$

which yields $i = -14.4$ cm, in agreement with the figure. The minus sign means that the image is on the V-side of the lens and is thus virtual.
The lateral magnification is given by

$$m = -\frac{i}{o} = -\frac{-14.4 \text{ cm}}{+9.0 \text{ cm}} = +1.6,$$

again in agreement with the figure. The plus signifies an erect image.   ◀

Images formed by lenses suffer from defects similar to those discussed for mirrors on p. 956. There are effects connected with the failure of a point object to form a point image, with the variation of magnification with distance from the lens axis, and with diffraction. For lenses, but not for mirrors, there are also *chromatic aberrations* associated with the fact that the refracting properties of the lens vary with wavelength because the index of refraction of the lens material does. If a point object on the lens axis emits white light, the image, neglecting other lens defects, will be a series of colored points spread out along the axis. We have all seen the colored images produced by inexpensive lenses. A great deal of ingenious optical engineering goes into the design of lenses (more commonly lens systems) in which the various lens defects are minimized. The lens surfaces are normally not spherical.

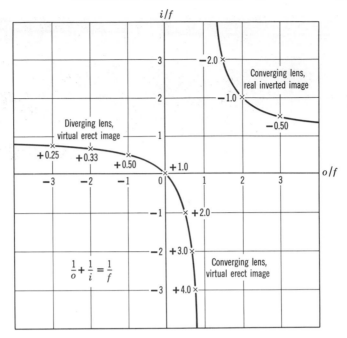

Fig. 42–27 A graphical representation of the thin-lens formula (Eq. 42–19). The numbers on the curves give the lateral magnifications (Eq. 42–20). Compare Fig. 42–16.

Figure 42–27 is a graphical representation of the object-image relationships for thin lenses; see Eqs. 42–19 and 42–20. The fact that it is identical in form with Fig. 42–16, which holds for mirrors, is not surprising because the basic equations for mirrors and thin lenses (Eqs. 42–19 and 42–5; Eqs. 42–20 and 42–6) are identical. A converging lens of a given focal length is quantitatively similar to a concave mirror of the same focal length, the difference being that the lens forms real images on the opposite side from the (real) object and the mirror forms them on the same side.

QUESTIONS

1. If a mirror reverses right and left, why doesn't it reverse up and down?
2. Is it possible to photograph a virtual image?
3. What approximations were made in deriving the mirror equation (Eq. 42–4):

$$\frac{1}{o} + \frac{1}{i} = \frac{2}{r}?$$

4. Can you think of a simple test or observation to prove that the law of reflection is the same for all wavelengths, under conditions in which geometrical optics prevails?
5. Under what conditions will a spherical mirror, which may be concave or convex, form (a) a real image, (b) an inverted image, and (c) an image smaller than the object?
6. An unsymmetrical thin lens forms an image of a point object on its axis. Is the image location changed if the lens is reversed?
7. Why has a lens two focal points and a mirror only one?

8. Under what conditions will a thin lens, which may be converging or diverging, form (a) a real image, (b) an inverted image, and (c) an image smaller than the object?

9. Does the apparent depth of an object below water depend on the angle of view of the observer in air? Explain and illustrate with ray diagrams.

10. A skin diver wants to use an air-filled plastic bag as a converging lens for underwater use. Sketch a suitable cross section for the bag.

11. What approximations were made in deriving the thin lens equation (Eq. 42–19):

$$\frac{1}{o} + \frac{1}{i} = \frac{1}{f}?$$

12. Under what conditions will a thin lens have a lateral magnification (a) of -1 and (b) of $+1$?

13. How does the focal length of a glass lens for blue light compare with that for red light, assuming the lens is (a) diverging and (b) converging?

14. Does the focal length of a lens depend on the medium in which the lens is immersed? Is it possible for a given lens to act as a converging lens in one medium and a diverging lens in another medium?

15. Are the following statements true for a glass lens in air? (a) A lens that is thicker at the center than at the edges is a converging lens for parallel light. (b) A lens that is thicker at the edges than at the center is a diverging lens for parallel light. Explain and illustrate, using wavefronts.

16. Under what conditions would the lateral magnification, ($m = -i/o$) for lenses and mirrors become infinite? Is there any practical significance to such a condition?

17. Light rays are reversible. Discuss the situation in terms of objects and images if all rays in Figs. 42–10, 42–14, 42–17, 42–19, 42–23, and 42–25 are reversed in direction.

18. What significance can be given to the origin of coordinates in the graphical representation of the thin-lens formula (Fig. 42–27)?

19. In connection with Fig. 42–24a, we pointed out that all rays originating on the same wavefront in the incident wave have the same optical path length to the image point. Discuss this in connection with Fermat's principle (Section 41–6).

PROBLEMS

1. Solve Example 2 if the angle between the mirrors is (a) 45°, (b) 60°, (c) 120°, the object always being placed on the bisector of the mirrors.

2. Two plane mirrors make an angle of 90° with each other. What is the largest number of images of an object placed between them that can be seen by a properly placed eye? The object need *not* lie on the mirror bisector.

3. A small object is 10 cm in front of a plane mirror. If you stand behind the object, 30 cm from the mirror, and look at its image, for what distance must you focus your eyes?

4. A small object O is placed one-third of the way between two parallel plane mirrors as in Fig. 42–28. Trace appropriate bundles of rays for viewing the four images that lie closest to the object.

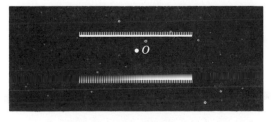

Fig. 42–28

5. Redraw Fig. 42–29 on a large sheet of paper and trace carefully the reflected rays, using the law of reflection. Is a point focus formed? Discuss.

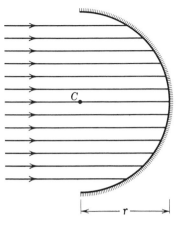

Fig. 42–29

6. Fill in this table, each column of which refers to a spherical mirror. Check your results by graphical analysis. Distances are in centimeters; if a number has no plus or minus sign in front of it, it may have either sign.

	a	b	c	d	e	f	g	h
Type	concave						convex	
f	20		+20			20		
r				−40			40	
i				−10			4	
o	+10	+10	+30	+60				+24
m		+1		−0.5		+0.10		0.50
Real image?		no						
Erect image?								no

7. A short linear object of length l lies on the axis of a spherical mirror, a distance o from the mirror. (a) Show that its image will have a length l' where

$$l' = l\left(\frac{f}{o-f}\right)^2.$$

(b) Show that the *longitudinal magnification* $m'(= l'/l)$ is equal to m^2 where m is the lateral magnification discussed in Section 42–3. (c) Is there any condition such that, neglecting all mirror defects, the image of a small cube would also be a cube?

8. As an example of the effect of relaxing the paraxial ray assumption find, analytically,

the apparent depth of a swimming pool having water ($n = 1.33$) of actual depth 8.0 ft (a) when viewed at normal incidence and (b) when viewed at an angle of 30° from the normal.

9. A layer of water ($n = 1.33$) 2.0 cm thick floats on carbon tetrachloride ($n = 1.46$) 4.0 cm thick. How far below the water surface, viewed at normal incidence, does the bottom of the tank seem to be?

10. Fill out the following table, each column of which refers to a spherical surface separating two media with different indices of refraction. Distances are measured in centimeters.

	a	b	c	d	e	f	g	h
n_1	1.0	1.0	1.0	1.0	1.5	1.5	1.5	1.5
n_2	1.5	1.5	1.5		1.0	1.0	1.0	
o	+10	+10		+20	+10		+70	+100
i		−13	+600	−20	−6	−7.5		+600
r	+30		+30	−20		−30	+30	−30
Real image?								

Draw a figure for each situation and construct the appropriate rays graphically. Assume a point object.

11. Fill in this table, each column of which refers to a thin lens, to the extent possible. Check your results by graphical analysis. Distances are in centimeters; if a number (except in row n) has no plus sign or minus sign in front of it, it may have either sign.

	a	b	c	d	e	f	g	h	i
Type	converging								
f	10	+10	10	10					
r'					+30	−30	−30		
r''					−30	+30	−60		
i									
o	+20	+5	+5	+5	+10	+10	+10	+10	+10
n					1.5	1.5	1.5		
m			>1	<1				0.5	0.5
Real image?									yes
Erect image?								yes	

Draw a figure for each situation and construct the appropriate rays graphically. Assume a finite object.

12. Define and locate the first and second focal points (see p. 966) for a single spherical refracting surface such as that of Fig. 42-17.

13. A luminous object and a screen are a fixed distance D apart. (a) Show that a converging lens of focal length f will form a real image on the screen for two positions that are separated by

$$d = \sqrt{D(D - 4f)}.$$

(b) Show that the ratio of the two image sizes for these two positions is

$$\left(\frac{D - d}{D + d}\right)^2.$$

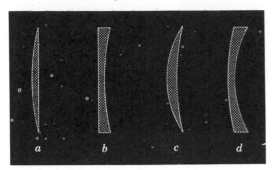

Fig. 42-30

14. Using the lens maker's equation (Eq. 42-18), decide which of the thin lenses in Fig. 42-30 is converging and which diverging for parallel incident light.

15. Two thin lenses of focal length f_1 and f_2 are in contact. Show that they are equivalent to a single thin lens with a focal length given by

$$f = \frac{f_1 f_2}{f_1 + f_2}.$$

16. Show that the distance between an object and its real image formed by a thin converging lens is always greater than four times the focal length of the lens.

17. A double-convex lens is to be made of glass with an index of refraction of 1.50. One surface is to have twice the radius of curvature of the other and the focal length is to be 6.0 cm. What are the radii?

18. The formula

$$\frac{1}{o} + \frac{1}{i} = \frac{1}{f}$$

is called the *Gaussian form* of the thin lens formula. Another form of this formula, the *Newtonian* form, is obtained by considering the distance x from the object to the first focal point and the distance x' from the second focal point to the image. Show that

$$xx' = f.$$

19. A parallel incident beam falls on a solid glass sphere at normal incidence. Locate the image in terms of the index of refraction n and the sphere radius r.

20. An erect object is placed a distance in front of a converging lens equal to twice the focal length f_1 of the lens. On the other side of the lens is a converging mirror of focal length f_2 separated from the lens by a distance $2(f_1 + f_2)$. (a) Find the location, nature and relative size of the final image. (b) Draw the appropriate ray diagram. See Fig. 42-31.

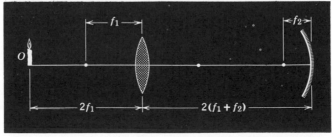

Fig. 42-31

21. An object is placed at a center of curvature of a double-concave lens, both of whose radii of curvature are the same. (a) According to the convention used in this book, what are the signs of the two radii of curvature? (b) Find the location of the image in terms of the radius of curvature r and the index of refraction, n, of the glass. (c) Describe the nature of the image. (d) Verify your result with a ray diagram.

22. *Compound microscope.* Two lenses with their focal points are shown in Fig. 42–32. With the given object, find the image formed by lens 1 and, using this as an object for lens 2, find the final image. Discuss the nature of the two images. Verify your conclusions by copying the figure to scale and drawing a ray diagram.

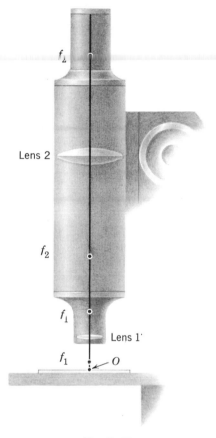

Fig. 42–32

23. An object is 20 cm to the left of a lens with a focal length of +10 cm. A second lens of focal length +12.5 cm is 30 cm to the right of the first lens. (a) Using the image formed by the first lens as the object for the second, find the location and relative size of the final image. (b) Verify your conclusions by drawing the lens system to scale and constructing a ray diagram. (c) Describe the final image.

Interference

CHAPTER 43

43–1 Young's Experiment

In Section 19–7 we saw that if two waves of the same frequency travel in approximately the same direction and have a phase difference that remains constant with time, they may combine so that their energy is not distributed uniformly in space but is a maximum at certain points and a minimum (possibly even zero) at others. The demonstration of such *interference* effects for light by Thomas Young in 1801 first established the wave theory of light on a firm experimental basis. Young was able to deduce the wavelength of light from his experiments, the first measurement of this important quantity.

Young allowed sunlight to fall on a pinhole S_0 punched in a screen A in Fig. 43–1. The emerging light spreads out by diffraction (see Section 42–1) and falls on pinholes S_1 and S_2 punched into screen B. Again diffraction occurs and two overlapping spherical waves expand into the space to the right of screen B.

The condition for geometric optics, namely that $a \gg \lambda$ where a is the diameter of the pinholes, is definitely *not* met in this experiment. The pinholes do not cast geometrical shadows but act as sources of expanding Huygens' wavelets. We are dealing here (and in succeeding chapters) with *wave optics* rather than with geometrical optics.

Figure 43–2, taken from an 1803 paper of Young, shows the region between screens B and C. The blackening represents the minima of the wave disturbance; the white space between represents the maxima. If you hold the page with your eye close to the left edge and look at a grazing angle along the figure, you will see that along lines marked by x's there is cancella-

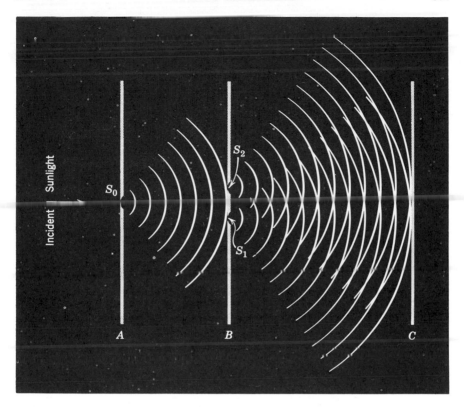

Fig. 43–1 Showing how Thomas Young produced an interference pattern by allowing diffracted waves from pinholes S_1 and S_2 to overlap on screen C.

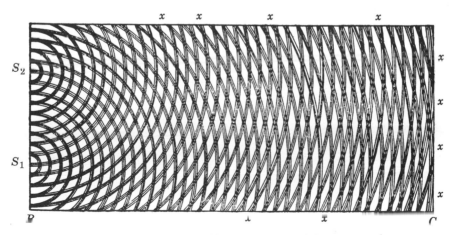

Fig. 43–2 Thomas Young's original drawing showing interference effects in overlapping waves. Place the eye near the left edge and sight at a grazing angle along the figure. (From Thomas Young, *Phil. Transactions*, 1803.)

tion of the wave; between them there is reinforcement. If a screen is placed anywhere across the superimposed waves, we expect to find alternate bright and dark spots on it. Figure 43–3 shows a photograph of such *interference*

 Fig. 43–3 Interference fringes for monochromatic light, made with an arrangement like that of Fig. 43–1.

fringes; in keeping with modern technique, long narrow slits rather than pin-holes were used in preparing this figure.

Interference is not limited to light waves but is a characteristic of all wave phenomena. Figure 43–4, for example, shows the interference pattern of

Fig. 43–4 The interference of water waves in a ripple tank. There is destructive interference along the lines marked "Line of nodes" and constructive interference between these lines. (Courtesy Physical Science Study Committee.)

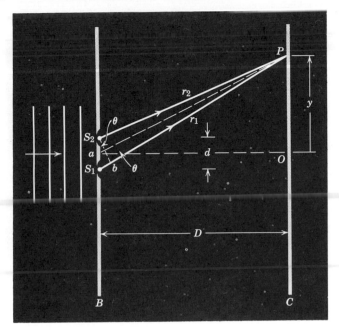

Fig. 43–5 Rays from S_1 and S_2 combine at P. The light falling on screen B has been taken as parallel. Actually, $D \gg d$, the figure being distorted for clarity.

water waves in a shallow *ripple tank*. The waves are generated by two vibrators that tap the water surface in synchronism, producing two expanding spherical waves.

Let us analyze Young's experiment quantitatively, assuming that the incident light consists of a single wavelength only. In Fig. 43–5 P is an arbitrary point on the screen, a distance r_1 and r_2 from the narrow slits S_1 and S_2, respectively. Let us draw a line from S_2 to b in such a way that the lines PS_2 and Pb are equal. If d, the slit spacing, is much smaller than the distance D between the two screens (the ratio d/D in the figure has been exaggerated for clarity), S_2b is then almost perpendicular to both r_1 and r_2. This means that angle S_1S_2b is almost equal to angle PaO, both angles being marked θ in the figure. This is equivalent to saying that the lines r_1 and r_2 may be taken as parallel.

We often put a lens in front of the two slits, as in Fig. 43–6, the screen C being in the focal plane of the lens. Under these conditions light focused at P must have struck the lens parallel to the line Px, drawn from P through the center of the (thin) lens. Under these conditions rays r_1 and r_2 are strictly parallel even though the requirement $D \gg d$ is not met. The lens L may in practice be the lens and cornea of the eye, screen C being the retina.

The two rays arriving at P in Figs. 43–5 or 43–6 from S_1 and S_2 are in phase at the source slits, both being derived from the same wavefront in the incident plane wave. Because the rays have different optical path lengths,

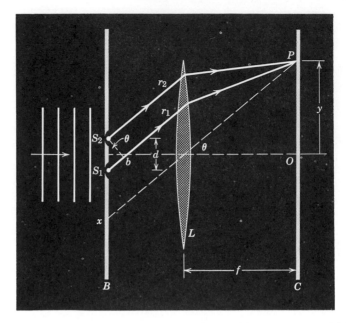

Fig. 43–6   A lens is normally used to produce interference fringes; compare with Fig. 43–5. The figure is again distorted for clarity in that $f \gg d$ in practice.

they arrive at P with a phase difference.   The number of wavelengths contained in S_1b, which is the path difference, determines the nature of the interference at P.

To have a *maximum* at P, S_1b ($= d \sin \theta$) must contain an integral number of wavelengths, or

$$S_1b = m\lambda \qquad m = 0, 1, 2, \ldots,$$

which can be written as

$$d \sin \theta = m\lambda \qquad m = 0, 1, 2, \ldots \text{ (maxima).} \qquad (43\text{–}1)$$

Note that each maximum above O in Figs. 43–5 and 43–6 has a symmetrically located maximum below O.   There is a central maximum described by $m = 0$.

For a *minimum* at P, S_1b ($= d \sin \theta$) must contain a half-integral number of wavelengths, or

$$d \sin \theta = (m - \tfrac{1}{2})\lambda \qquad m = 1, 2, 3, \ldots \text{ (minima).} \qquad (43\text{–}2)$$

If a lens is used as in Fig. 43–6, it may seem that a phase difference should develop between the rays beyond the plane represented by S_2b, the path lengths between this plane and P being clearly different.   In Section 42–5, however, we saw that for such parallel rays focused by a lens the *optical path lengths* are identical.   Two rays with the same optical path lengths contain the same number of wavelengths, so that no phase difference will result because of the light passing through the lens.

▶ **Example 1.** The double-slit arrangement in Fig. 43-5 is illuminated with light from a mercury vapor lamp so filtered that only the strong green line ($\lambda = 5400$ A) is effective. The slits are 0.10 mm apart, and the screen on which the interference pattern appears is 20 cm away. What is the angular position of the first minimum? Of the tenth maximum?

At the first minimum we put $m = 1$ in Eq. 43-2, or

$$\sin \theta = \frac{(m - \frac{1}{2})\lambda}{d} = \frac{(\frac{1}{2})(546 \times 10^{-9} \text{ meter})}{0.10 \times 10^{-3} \text{ meter}} = 0.0027.$$

This value for $\sin \theta$ is so small that we can take it to be the value of θ, expressed in radians; expressed in degrees it is $0.16°$.

At the tenth maximum (not counting the central maximum) we must put $m = 10$ in Eq. 43-1. Doing so and calculating as before leads to an angular position of $3.8°$. For these conditions we see that the angular spread of the first dozen or so fringes is small.

Example 2. In Example 1 what is the linear distance on screen C between adjacent maxima?

If θ is small enough, we can use the approximation

$$\sin \theta \cong \tan \theta \cong \theta.$$

From Fig. 43-5 we see that $\qquad \tan \theta = \dfrac{y}{D}.$

Substituting this into Eq. 43-1 for $\sin \theta$ leads to

$$y = m \frac{\lambda D}{d} \qquad m = 0, 1, 2, \ldots \text{ (maxima)}.$$

The positions of any two adjacent maxima are given by

$$y_m = m \frac{\lambda D}{d}$$

and

$$y_{m+1} = (m + 1) \frac{\lambda D}{d}.$$

Their separation Δy is found by subtracting:

$$\Delta y = y_{m+1} - y_m = \frac{\lambda D}{d}$$

$$= \frac{(546 \times 10^{-9} \text{ meter})(20 \times 10^{-2} \text{ meter})}{0.10 \times 10^{-3} \text{ meter}} = 1.09 \text{ mm}.$$

As long as θ in Figs. 43-5 and 43-6 is small, the separation of the interference fringes is independent of m; that is, the fringes are evenly spaced. Note that if the incident light contains more than one wavelength the separate interference patterns, which will have different fringe spacings, will be superimposed.   ◀

Equation 43-1 can be used to determine the wavelength of light; to quote Thomas Young:

> From a comparison of various experiments, it appears that the breadth of the undulations [that is, the wavelength] constituting the extreme red light must be supposed to be, in air, about one 36 thousandth of an inch, and those of the extreme violet about one 60 thousandth; the mean of the whole spectrum, with respect to the intensity of light, being one 45 thousandth.

Young's value for the average effective wavelength present in sunlight (1/45,000 in.) can be written as 5700 A, which agrees rather well with the wavelength at which the eye sensitivity is a maximum, 5550 A (see Fig. 40–2). It must not be supposed that Young's work was received without criticism. One of his contemporaries, evidently a firm believer in the corpuscular theory of light, wrote:

> We wish to raise our feeble voice against innovations that can have no other effect than to check the progress of science, and renew all those wild phantoms of the imagination which Bacon and Newton put to flight from her temple. This paper contains nothing that deserves the name of either experiment or discovery.

Needless to say, posterity has decided in favor of Young.

43–2 Coherence

Analysis of the derivation of Eqs. 43–1 and 43–2 shows that a fundamental requirement for the existence of well-defined interference fringes on screen C in Fig. 43–1 is that the light waves that travel from S_1 and S_2 to any point P on this screen must have a sharply defined phase difference $\Delta\phi$ that remains constant with time. If this condition is satisfied, a stable, well-defined fringe pattern will appear. At certain points P, $\Delta\phi$ will be given, independent of time, by $n\pi$ where $n = 1, 3, 5, \ldots$ so that the resultant intensity will be strictly zero and will remain so throughout the time of observation. At other points $\Delta\phi$ will be given by $n\pi$ where $n = 0, 2, 4 \ldots$ and the resultant intensity will be a maximum. Under these conditions the two beams emerging from slit S_1 and S_2 are said to be completely *coherent*.

Let the source in Fig. 43–1 be removed and let slits S_1 and S_2 be replaced by two completely independent light sources, such as two fine incandescent wires placed side by side in a glass envelope. No interference fringes will appear on screen C but only a relatively uniform illumination. We can interpret this if we make the reasonable assumption that for completely independent light sources the phase difference between the two beams arriving at P will vary with time in a random way. At a certain instant conditions may be right for cancellation and a short time later (perhaps 10^{-8} sec) they may be right for re-enforcement. This same random phase behavior holds for all points on screen C with the result that this screen is uniformly illuminated. The intensity at any point is equal to the sum of the intensities that each source S_1 and S_2 produces separately at that point. Under these conditions the two beams emerging from S_1 and S_2 are said to be completely *incoherent*.

Note that for completely coherent light beams one (1) combines the amplitudes vectorially, taking the (constant) phase difference properly into account, and then (2) squares this resultant amplitude to obtain a quantity proportional to the resultant intensity. For completely incoherent light beams, on the other hand, one (1) squares the individual amplitudes to obtain quantities proportional to the individual intensities and then (2) adds the individual intensities to obtain the resultant intensity. This procedure is in agreement with the experimental fact that for completely independent light sources the resultant intensity at every point is always greater than the intensity produced at that point by either light source acting alone.

It remains to investigate under what experimental conditions coherent or incoherent beams may be produced and to give an explanation for coherence in terms of the mode of production of the radiation. Consider first a parallel beam of microwave radiation emerging from an antenna connected by a co-axial cable to an oscillator based on an electromagnetic resonant cavity. The cavity oscillations (see Section 38-6) are completely periodic with time and produce, at the antenna, a completely periodic variation of $\mathbf{E}$ and $\mathbf{B}$ with time. The radiated wave at large enough distances from the antenna is well represented by Fig. 39-11. Note that (1) the wave has essentially infinite extent in time, including both future times ($t > 0$, say) and past times ($t < 0$); see Fig. 43-7a. At any point, as the wave passes by, the wave disturbance (i.e., $\mathbf{E}$ or $\mathbf{D}$) varies with time in a perfectly periodic way. (2) The wavefronts at points far removed from the antenna are parallel planes of essentially infinite extent at right angles to the propagation direction. At any instant of time the wave disturbance varies with distance along the propagation direction in a perfectly periodic way.

Two beams generated from a single traveling wave like that of Fig. 39-11 will be completely coherent. One way to generate two such beams is to put an opaque screen containing two slits in the path of the beam. The waves emerging from the slits will always have a constant phase difference at any point in the region in which they overlap and interference fringes will be produced. Coherent radio beams can also be readily established, as can coherent elastic waves in solids, liquids and gases. The two prongs of the vibrating tapper in Fig. 43-4, for example, generate two coherent waves in the water of the ripple tank.

The technique of producing two beams from a single beam (and thus from a single source) tests specifically whether the wavefronts in the single parallel beam are truly planes, that is, whether all points in a plane at right angles to the direction of propagation have the same phase at any given instant. By dividing the beam in another way it is possible to test whether the beam is truly periodic over a large number of cycles of oscillation. This can be done, as we show in detail in Section 43-6, by inserting in the beam at 45° to it a thin sheet of material possessing the property that two beams are produced, one (which will be at right angles to the incident beam) by reflection and a second (which will be in the direction of the incident beam) by transmission. In the visible region such a sheet, called a *half-silvered mirror*, may be formed from a glass plate by depositing on it an appropriately thin film of silver. By appropriate use of mirrors (see Section 43-7) these two sub-beams can be recombined into a single beam traveling in a chosen direction. If the beams travel different distances before they are recombined, we are comparing in the combined beam a sample of the original beam with another sample an arbitrarily large number of cycles away. If the original beam is truly periodic in space and time, the two sub-beams will be completely coherent and interference fringes will be produced when they are recombined.

If we turn from microwave sources to common sources of visible light, such as incandescent wires or an electric discharge passing through a gas, we become aware of a fundamental difference. In both of these sources the fundamental light emission processes occur in individual atoms and these atoms do not act together in a cooperative (i.e., *coherent*) way. The act of light emission by a single atom takes, in a typical case, about 10^{-8} sec and the emitted light is properly described as a *wavetrain* (Fig. 43–7b) rather than as a wave (Fig. 43–7a). For emission times such as these the wave-trains are a few meters long.

Interference effects from ordinary light sources may be produced by putting a very narrow slit (S_0 in Fig. 43–1) directly in front of the source. This insures that the wavetrains that strike slits S_1 and S_2 in screen B in this figure originate from the same small region of the source. The diffracted beams emerging from S_1 and S_2 thus represent the same population of wavetrains and are coherent with respect to each other. If the phase of the light emitted from S_0 changes, this change is transmitted simultaneously to S_1 and S_2. Thus, at any point on screen C, a constant phase difference is maintained between the beams from these two slits and a stationary interference pattern occurs.

If the width of slit S_0 in Fig. 43–1 is gradually increased it will be observed experimentally that the maxima of the interference fringes become reduced in intensity and that the intensity in the fringe minima is no longer strictly zero. In other words, the fringes become less distinct. If S_0 is opened extremely wide, the lowering of the maximum intensity and the raising of the minimum intensity will be such that the fringes disappear, leaving only a uniform illumination. Under these conditions we say that the beams from S_1 and S_2 pass continuously from a condition of complete coherence to one of complete incoherence. When not at either of these two limits the beams are said to be partially coherent.

Partial coherence can also be demonstrated in two beams that are produced, as described on p. 998, by inserting a "half-silvered mirror" in a beam at an angle of 45° to the direction of propagation. The two beams so produced, by reflection and transmission, traverse paths of different lengths before they are recombined. If the path difference is small compared to the average length of a wavetrain, the interference fringes will be sharply defined and will go essentially to zero at their minima. If the path difference is deliberately made longer, the fringes will become less distinct, and finally, when the path difference is larger than the average length of a wavetrain, the fringes will disappear altogether. Thus it is possible once again to progress smoothly in an experimental arrangement from complete coherence, through partial coherence, to complete incoherence.

The lack of coherence of the light from ordinary sources such as glowing wires is due to the fact that the emitting atoms do not act cooperatively

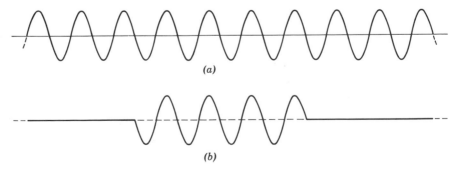

(a)

(b)

Fig. 43–7 (a) A section of an infinite wave and (b) a wavetrain.

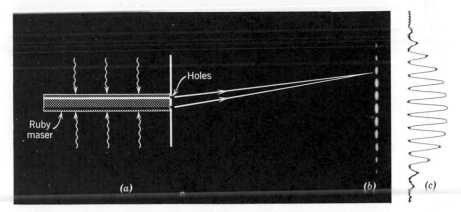

Fig. 43–8 A screen with two small holes is placed against the end of an optical maser. (a) The light passing through the holes forms an interference pattern on a strip of photographic film placed at (b). The fact that the pattern is formed shows that the light emitted from the maser is coherent across the beam cross section. At (b) is shown the image as formed on a photographic strip exposed in this manner. At (c) is an intensity plot of the film made by measuring the degree to which the film has been exposed. (Courtesy of D. F. Nelson and R. J. Collins, Bell Telephone Laboratories.)

(i.e., *coherently*). Since 1960 it has proved possible to construct sources of visible light in which the atoms *do* act cooperatively and in which the emitted light is highly coherent. Such devices are called *optical masers* or *lasers*; * their light output is extremely monochromatic, intense, and highly collimated. The coherence of the emitted light can be demonstrated by placing a screen with two holes in it in the beam emerging from the laser. An interference pattern results, as Fig. 43–8 shows. These methods permit, for the first time, a degree of control of visible light approaching that possible for radio and for microwaves. The practical applications of lasers, which include the amplification of weak light signals, the use of light beams as highly efficient carriers of information from point to point (see problem 13), and the production of high temperatures by intense local heating, remain to be fully exploited.

43–3   Intensity in Young's Experiment

Let us assume that the electric field components of the two waves in Fig. 43–5 vary with time at point P as

$$E_1 = E_0 \sin \omega t \tag{43–3}$$

and

$$E_2 = E_0 \sin (\omega t + \phi) \tag{43–4}$$

where ω ($= 2\pi f$) is the angular frequency of the waves and ϕ is the phase difference between them. Note that ϕ depends on the location of point P,

---

* Laser, like maser, is a coined word, meaning "*light amplification through stimulated emission of radiation*." The interested student is referred to an article called "Optical Masers" by Arthur L. Schawlow, *Scientific American*, June 1961.

which, in turn, for a fixed geometrical arrangement, is described by the angle θ in Figs. 43–5 and 43–6. We assume that the slits are so narrow that the diffracted light from each slit illuminates the central portion of the screen uniformly. This means that near the center of the screen E_0 is independent of the position of P, that is, of the value of θ.

The resultant wave disturbance * at P is found from

$$E = E_1 + E_2 \tag{43–5}$$

and (see Eq. 19–17) proves to be

$$E = E_\theta \sin{(\omega t + \beta)}, \tag{43–6a}$$

where

$$\beta = \tfrac{1}{2}\phi \tag{43–6b}$$

and

$$E_\theta = 2E_0 \cos{\beta} = E_m \cos{\beta}. \tag{43–6c}$$

E_m, the maximum possible amplitude for E_θ, is equal to twice the amplitude of the combining waves ($= 2E_0$), corresponding to complete reinforcement. The student should verify Eq. 43–6 carefully. The amplitude E_θ of the resultant wave disturbance, which determines the intensity of the interference fringes, will turn out to depend strongly on the value of θ, that is, on the location of point P in Figs. 43–5 and 43–6.

In Section 19 6 we showed that the intensity of a wave I, measured perhaps in watts/meter², is proportional to the square of its amplitude. For the resultant wave then, ignoring the proportionality constant,

$$I_\theta \propto E_\theta{}^2. \tag{43–7}$$

This relationship seems reasonable if we recall (Eq. 30–27) that the energy density in an electric field is proportional to the *square* of the electric field strength. This is true for rapidly varying electric fields, such as those in a light wave, as well as for static fields.

The ratio of the intensities of two light waves is the ratio of the squares of the amplitudes of their electric fields. If I_θ is the intensity of the resultant wave at P and I_0 is the intensity that a single wave acting alone would produce, then

$$\frac{I_\theta}{I_0} = \left(\frac{E_\theta}{E_0}\right)^2. \tag{43–8}$$

Combining with Eq. 43–6c leads to

$$I_\theta = 4I_0 \cos^2{\beta} = I_m \cos^2{\beta}. \tag{43–9}$$

---

* The electric field **E** in the light wave rather than the magnetic field **B** is normally identified with the "wave disturbance" because the effects of **B** on the human eye and on various light detectors are exceedingly small. Radiation pressure (Section 40–2) is one such effect. Note too that, although Eq. 43–5 should be a vector equation, in most cases of interest the **E** vectors in the two interfering waves are closely parallel so that an algebraic equation suffices.

Note that the intensity of the resultant wave at any point P varies from zero [for a point at which ϕ ($= 2\beta$) $= \pi$, say] to I_m, which is four times the intensity I_0 of each individual wave [for a point at which ϕ ($= 2\beta$) $= 0$, say]. Let us compute I_θ as a function of the angle θ in Figs. 43-5 or 43-6.

The phase difference ϕ in Eq. 43-4 is associated with the path difference $S_1 b$ in Fig. 43-5 or 43-6. If $S_1 b$ is $\frac{1}{2}\lambda$, ϕ will be π; if $S_1 b$ is λ, ϕ will be 2π, etc. This suggests that

$$\frac{\text{phase difference}}{2\pi} = \frac{\text{path difference}}{\lambda},$$

$$\phi = \frac{2\pi}{\lambda}(d \sin \theta),$$

or, finally, from Eq. 43-6b,

$$\beta = \frac{1}{2}\phi = \frac{\pi d}{\lambda} \sin \theta. \tag{43-10}$$

This expression for β can be substituted into Eq. 43-9 for I_θ, yielding the latter quantity as a function of θ. For convenience we collect here the expressions for the amplitude and the intensity in double-slit interference.

[Eq. 43-6c]	$E_\theta = E_m \cos \beta$ interference	(43-11a)
[Eq. 43-9]	$I_\theta = I_m \cos^2 \beta$ from narrow	(43-11b)
	slits (that is,	
[Eq. 43-10]	$\beta \ (= \frac{1}{2}\phi) = \dfrac{\pi d}{\lambda} \sin \theta$ $a \ll \lambda$	(43-11c)

To find the positions of the intensity maxima, we put

$$\beta = m\pi \qquad m = 0, 1, 2, \ldots$$

in Eq. 43-11b. From Eq. 43-11c this reduces to

$$d \sin \theta = m\lambda \qquad m = 0, 1, 2, \ldots \text{ (maxima)},$$

which is the equation derived in Section 43-1 (Eq. 43-1). To find the intensity minima we write

$$\frac{\pi d \sin \theta}{\lambda} = (m - \tfrac{1}{2})\pi \qquad m = 1, 2, 3, \ldots \text{ (minima)},$$

which reduces to the previously derived Eq. 43-2.

Figure 43-9 shows the intensity pattern for double-slit interference. The horizontal solid line is I_0; this describes the (uniform) intensity pattern on the screen if one of the slits is covered up. If the two sources were incoherent the intensity would be uniform over the screen and would be $2I_0$; see the horizontal dashed line in Fig. 43-9. For coherent sources we expect the

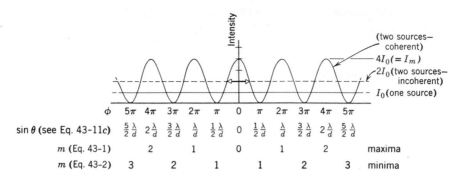

ϕ	5π	4π	3π	2π	π	0	π	2π	3π	4π	5π	
$\sin\theta$ (see Eq. 43-11c)	$\frac{5}{2}\frac{\lambda}{d}$	$2\frac{\lambda}{d}$	$\frac{3}{2}\frac{\lambda}{d}$	$\frac{\lambda}{d}$	$\frac{1}{2}\frac{\lambda}{d}$	0	$\frac{1}{2}\frac{\lambda}{d}$	$\frac{\lambda}{d}$	$\frac{3}{2}\frac{\lambda}{d}$	$2\frac{\lambda}{d}$	$\frac{5}{2}\frac{\lambda}{d}$	
m (Eq. 43-1)		2		1		0		1		2		maxima
m (Eq. 43-2)	3		2		1		1		2		3	minima

Fig. 43–9 The intensity pattern for double-slit interference. The heavy arrow in the central peak represents the half-width of the peak. This figure is constructed on the assumption that the two interfering waves each illuminate the central portion of the screen uniformly, that is, I_0 is independent of position as shown.

energy to be merely redistributed over the screen, since energy is neither created nor destroyed by the interference process. Thus the *average* intensity in the interference pattern should be $2I_0$, as for incoherent sources. This follows at once if, in Eq. 43–11b, we substitute one-half for the cosine-squared term and if we recall that $I_m = 4I_0$. We have seen several times that the average value of the square of a sine or a cosine term over one or more half-cycles is one-half.

43–4 Adding Wave Disturbances

In Section 43–3 we combined two time-varying wave disturbances, namely

$$E_1 = E_0 \sin \omega t \tag{43-3}$$

and $\qquad\qquad E_2 = E_0 \sin(\omega t + \phi), \tag{43-4}$

which have the same angular frequency ω and amplitude E_0 but which have a phase difference ϕ between them. In this case the result (Eqs. 43–11a and c) is easily obtained algebraically.

In later chapters we will want to add larger numbers of wave disturbances, often an infinite number, with infinitesimal individual amplitudes. Since analytic methods become more difficult in such cases we describe a graphical method, illustrating it by rederiving Eq. 43–11a.

A sinusoidal wave disturbance such as that represented by Eq. 43–3 can be represented graphically, using a rotating vector. In Fig. 43–10a a vector of magnitude E_0 is allowed to rotate about the origin in a counterclockwise direction with an angular frequency ω. Following electrical engineering practice we call such a rotating vector a *phasor*. The alternating wave disturbance E_1 (Eq. 43–3) is represented by the projection of this phasor on the vertical axis.

A second wave disturbance E_2, which has the same amplitude E_0 but a phase difference ϕ with respect to E_1,

$$E_2 = E_0 \sin (\omega t + \phi), \tag{43–4}$$

can be represented graphically (Fig. 43–10b) as the projection on the vertical axis of a second phasor of magnitude E_0 which makes an angle ϕ with the first phasor. As this figure shows, the sum E of E_1 and E_2 is the sum of the projections of the two phasors on the vertical axis. This is revealed more clearly if the phasors are redrawn, as in Fig. 43–10c, placing the foot of one arrow at the head of the other, maintaining the proper phase difference, and letting the whole assembly rotate counterclockwise about the origin.

In Fig. 43–10c E can also be regarded as the projection on the vertical axis of a phasor of length E_θ, which is the vector sum of the two phasors of magnitude E_0. Note that the (algebraic) sum of the projections of the two phasors is equal to the projection of the (vector) sum of the two phasors.

In most problems in optics we are concerned only with the *amplitude* E_θ of the resultant wave disturbance and not with its time variation. This is because the eye and other common measuring instruments respond to the resultant intensity of the light (that is, to the square of the amplitude) and cannot detect the rapid time variations that characterize visible light. For sodium light, for example ($\lambda = 5890$ A), the frequency f ($= \omega/2\pi$) is 5.1×10^{14} cycles/sec. Often, then, we need not consider the rotation of the phasors but can confine our attention to finding the magnitude of the resultant phasor.

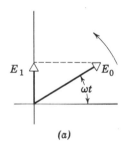

(a)

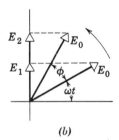

(b)

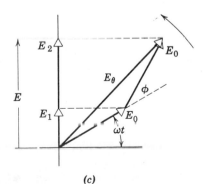

(c)

Fig. 43–10 (a) A wave disturbance E_1 is represented by a rotating vector or *phasor*. (b) Two wave disturbances E_1 and E_2, with a phase difference ϕ between them, are so represented. These two phasors can represent the two wave disturbances in the double-slit problem; see Eqs. 43–3 and 43–4. (c) Another way of drawing (b).

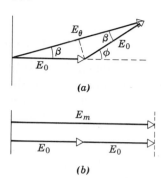

(a)

(b)

Fig. 43–11   (a) A construction to find the amplitude E_θ of two wave disturbances of amplitude E_0 and phase difference ϕ.   (b) The maximum possible amplitude for these wave disturbances occurs for $\phi = 0$ and has the value $E_m = 2E_0$.

Figure 43–11a shows the phasors for double-slit interference at time $t = 0$; compare Fig. 43–10c.   We see that

$$E_\theta = 2E_0 \cos \beta = E_m \cos \beta,$$

in which, from the theorem that the exterior angle of a triangle (ϕ) is equal to the sum of its two opposite interior angles ($\beta + \beta$),

$$\beta = \tfrac{1}{2}\phi.$$

This is exactly the result arrived at earlier algebraically; compare Eqs. 43–11a and c.

In a more general case we might want to find the resultant of a number (>2) of sinusoidally varying wave disturbances.   The general procedure is the following:

1. Construct a series of phasors representing the functions to be added. Draw them end to end, maintaining the proper phase relationships between adjacent phasors.

2. Construct the vector sum of this array.   Its length gives the amplitude of the resultant.   The angle between it and the first phasor is the phase of the resultant with respect to this first phasor.   The projection of this phasor on the vertical axis gives the time variation of the resultant wave disturbance.

▶ **Example 3.**   Find graphically the resultant $E(t)$ of the following wave disturbances:

$$E_1 = 10 \sin \omega t$$
$$E_2 = 10 \sin (\omega t + 15°)$$
$$E_3 = 10 \sin (\omega t + 30°)$$
$$E_4 = 10 \sin (\omega t + 45°).$$

Figure 43–12 in which E_0 equals 10, shows the assembly of four phasors that represents these functions.   Their vector sum, by graphical measurement, has an amplitude E_R of 38 and a phase ϕ_0 with respect to E_1 of 23°.   In other words

$$E(t) = E_1 + E_2 + E_3 + E_4 = 38 \sin (\omega t + 23°).$$

Check this result by trigonometric calculation.   ◀

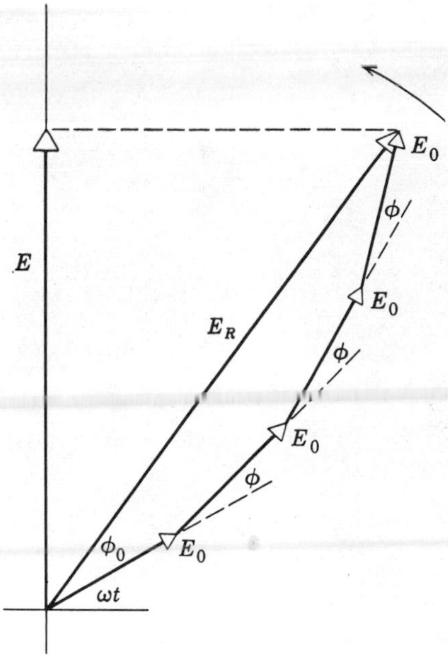

Fig. 43-12 Example 3. Four wave disturbances are added graphically, using the method of phasors.

43-5   Interference from Thin Films

The colors of soap bubbles, oil slicks, and other thin films are the result of interference.   Figure 43-13 shows interference effects in a thin vertical film of soapy water illuminated by monochromatic light.

Figure 43-14 shows a film of uniform thickness d and index of refraction n, the eye being focused on spot a. The film is illuminated by a broad source of monochromatic light S. There exists on this source a point P such that two rays, identified by the single and double arrows, respectively, can leave P and enter the eye as shown, after passing through point a. These two rays follow

Fig. 43-13 A soapy water film on a wire loop, viewed by reflected light. The black segment at the top is not a tear. It arises because the film, by drainage, is so thin here that there is destructive interference between the light reflected from its front surface and that reflected from its back surface. Recall that these two waves differ in phase by 180°

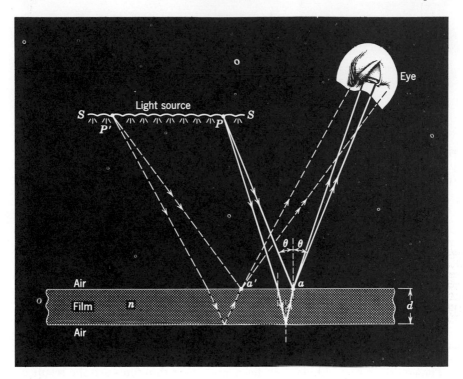

Fig. 43–14   Interference by reflection from a thin film, assuming an extended source S.

different paths in going from P to the eye, one being reflected from the upper surface of the film, the other from the lower surface.   Whether point a appears bright or dark depends on the nature of the interference between the two waves that diverge from a.   These waves are coherent because they both originate from the same point P on the light source.

If the eye looks at another part of the film, say a', the light that enters the eye must originate from a different point P' of the extended source, as suggested by the dashed lines in Fig. 43–14.

For near-normal incidence ($\theta \cong 0$ in Fig. 43–14) the geometrical path difference for the two rays from P will be close to $2d$.   We might expect the resultant wave reflected from the film near a to be an interference maximum if the distance $2d$ is an integral number of wavelengths.   This statement must be modified for two reasons.

First, the wavelength must refer to the wavelength of the light in the film λ_n and not to its wavelength in air λ; that is, we are concerned with optical path lengths rather than geometrical path lengths.   The wavelengths λ and λ_n (see Eq. 41–11) are related by

$$\lambda_n = \lambda/n. \tag{43–12}$$

To bring out the second point, let us assume that the film is so thin that $2d$ is very much less than a wavelength.   The phase difference between the two waves would be close to zero on our assumption, and we would expect such a film to appear bright on reflection. However, it appears dark. This is clear from Fig. 43–13, in which the action of gravity produces a wedge-shaped film, extremely thin at its top edge. As drainage continues, the dark area increases in size. To explain this and many similar phenomena, we assume that one or the other of the two rays of Fig. 43–14 suffers an abrupt phase change of π ($= 180°$) associated either with reflection at the air-film interface or transmission through it. As it turns out, the ray reflected from the upper surface suffers this phase change. The other ray is not changed abruptly in phase, either on transmission through the upper surface or on reflection at the lower surface.

In Section 19–9 we discussed phase changes on reflection for transverse waves in strings. To extend these ideas, consider the composite string of Fig. 43–15, which consists of two parts with different masses per unit length, stretched to a given tension. If a pulse moves to the right in Fig. 43–15a, approaching the junction, there will be a reflected and a transmitted pulse,

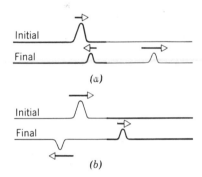

Fig. 43–15 Phase changes on reflection at a junction between two stretched composite strings. (a) Incident pulse in heavy string and (b) incident pulse in light string.

the reflected pulse being *in phase* with the incident pulse. In Fig. 43–15b the situation is reversed, the incident pulse now being in the less massive string. In this case the reflected pulse will differ in phase from the incident pulse by π ($-180°$). In each case the transmitted pulse will be in phase with the incident pulse.

Figure 43–15a suggests a light wave in glass, say, approaching a surface beyond which there is a less optically dense medium (one of lower index of refraction) such as air. Figure 43–15b suggests a light wave in air approaching glass. To sum up the optical situation, when reflection occurs from an interface beyond which the medium has a *lower* index of refraction, the reflected wave undergoes *no phase change;* when the medium beyond the interface has a *higher* index, there is a phase change of π.* The transmitted wave does not experience a change of phase in either case.

---

* These statements, which can be proved rigorously from Maxwell's equations (see also Section 43–6), must be modified for light falling on a less dense medium at an angle such that total internal reflection occurs. They must also be modified for reflection from metallic surfaces.

We are now able to take into account both factors that determine the nature of the interference, namely, differences in optical path length and phase changes on reflection. For the two rays of Fig. 43–14 to combine to give a *maximum* intensity, assuming normal incidence, we must have

$$2d = (m + \tfrac{1}{2})\lambda_n \qquad m = 0, 1, 2, \ldots .$$

The term $\tfrac{1}{2}\lambda_n$ is introduced because of the phase change on reflection, a phase change of 180° being equivalent to half a wavelength. Substituting λ/n for λ_n yields finally

$$2dn = (m + \tfrac{1}{2})\lambda \qquad m = 0, 1, 2, \ldots \text{ (maxima).} \qquad (43\text{--}13)$$

The condition for a *minimum* intensity is

$$2dn = m\lambda \qquad m = 0, 1, 2, \ldots \text{ (minima).} \qquad (43\text{--}14)$$

These equations hold when the index of refraction of the film is either greater or less than the indices of the media on *each* side of the film. Only in these cases will there be a relative phase change of 180° for reflections at the two surfaces. A water film in air and an air film in the space between two glass plates provide examples of cases to which Eqs. 43–13 and 43–14 apply. Example 5 provides a case in which they do not apply.

If the film thickness is not uniform, as in Fig. 43–13, where the film is wedge-shaped, constructive interference will occur in certain parts of the film and destructive interference will occur in others. Lines of maximum and of minimum intensity will appear—these are the interference fringes. They are called *fringes of constant thickness*, each fringe being the locus of points for which the film thickness d is a constant. If the film is illuminated with white light rather than monochromatic light, the light reflected from various parts of the film will be modified by the various constructive or destructive interferences that occur. This accounts for the brilliant colors of soap bubbles and oil slicks.

Only if the film is "thin," which implies that d is no more than a few wavelengths of light, will fringes of the type described, that is, fringes that appear localized on the film and associated with a variable film thickness, be possible. For very thick films (say $d \cong 1$ cm), the path difference between the two rays of Fig. 43–14 will be many wavelengths and the phase difference at a given point on the film will change rapidly as we move even a small distance away from a. For "thin" films, however, the phase difference at a also holds for reasonably nearby points; there is a characteristic "patch brightness" for any point on the film, as Fig. 43–13 shows. Interference fringes can be produced for thick films; they are not localized on the film but are at infinity. See Section 43–7.

▶ **Example 4.** A water film ($n = 1.33$) in air is 3200 A thick. If it is illuminated with white light at normal incidence, what color will it appear to be in reflected light?

By solving Eq. 43–13 for λ,

$$\lambda = \frac{2dn}{m + \tfrac{1}{2}} = \frac{(2)(3200 \text{ A})(1.33)}{m + \tfrac{1}{2}} = \frac{8500 \text{ A}}{m + \tfrac{1}{2}} \qquad \text{(maxima).}$$

From Eq. 43–14 the minima are given by

$$\lambda = \frac{8500 \text{ A}}{m} \qquad \text{(minima)}.$$

Maxima and minima occur for the following wavelengths:

m	0 (max)	1 (min)	1 (max)	2 (min)	2 (max)
λ, A	17000	8500	5700	4250	3400

Only the maximum corresponding to $m = 1$ lies in the visible region (see Fig. 40–2); light of this wavelength appears yellow-green. If white light is used to illuminate the film, the yellow-green component will be enhanced when viewed by reflection.

Example 5. *Nonreflecting glass.* Lenses are often coated with thin films of transparent substances like MgF_2 ($n = 1.38$) in order to reduce the reflection from the glass surface, using interference. How thick a coating is needed to produce a minimum reflection at the center of the visible spectrum (5500 A)?

We assume that the light strikes the lens at near-normal incidence (θ is exaggerated for clarity in Fig. 43–16), and we seek destructive interference between rays r and r_1. Equation 43–14 does not apply because in this case a phase change of 180° is associated with *each* ray, for at *both* the upper and lower surfaces of the MgF_2 film the reflection is from a medium of greater index of refraction.

There is no net change in phase produced by the two reflections, which means that the optical path difference for destructive interference is $(m + \frac{1}{2})\lambda$ (compare Eq. 43–13), leading to

$$2dn = (m + \tfrac{1}{2})\lambda \qquad m = 0, 1, 2, \ldots \text{ (minima)}.$$

Solving for d and putting $m = 0$ yields

$$d = \frac{(m + \frac{1}{2})\lambda}{2n} = \frac{\lambda}{4n} = \frac{5500 \text{ A}}{(4)(1.38)} = 1000 \text{ A}.$$

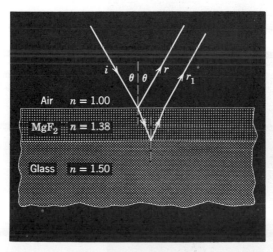

Fig. 43–16 Example 5. Unwanted reflections from glass can be reduced by coating the glass with a thin transparent film.

Example 6. *Newton's rings.* Figure 43–17 shows a lens of radius of curvature R resting on an accurately plane glass plate and illuminated from above by light of wavelength λ. Figure 43–18 shows that circular interference fringes (Newton's rings) appear, associated with the variable thickness air film between the lens and the plate. Find the radii of the circular interference maxima.

Here it is the ray from the *bottom* of the (air) film rather than from the top that undergoes a phase change of 180°, for it is the one reflected from a medium of higher refractive index. The condition for a maximum remains unchanged, however (Eq. 43–13), and is

$$2d = (m + \tfrac{1}{2})\lambda \qquad m = 0, 1, 2, \ldots, \qquad (43\text{-}15)$$

the index of refraction of the air film being assumed to be unity. From Fig. 43–17 we can write

$$d = R - \sqrt{R^2 - r^2} = R - R\left[1 - \left(\frac{r}{R}\right)^2\right]^{\frac{1}{2}}.$$

If $r/R \ll 1$, the square bracket can be expanded by the binomial theorem, keeping only two terms, or

$$d = R - R\left[1 - \frac{1}{2}\left(\frac{r}{R}\right)^2 + \cdots\right] \cong \frac{r^2}{2R}.$$

Combining with Eq. 43–15 yields

$$r = \sqrt{(m + \tfrac{1}{2})\lambda R} \qquad m = 0, 1, 2, \ldots,$$

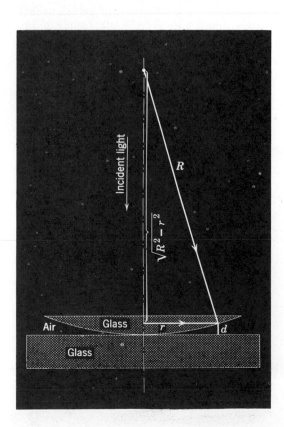

Fig. 43–17 Example 6. Apparatus for observing Newton's rings.

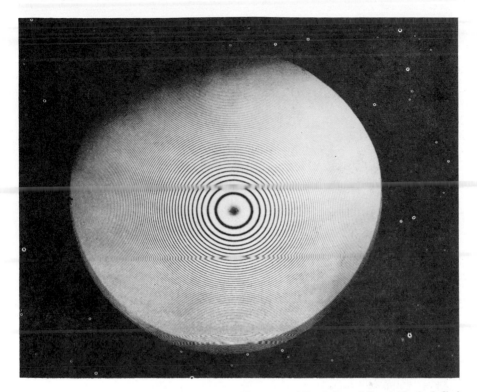

Fig. 43–18   Example 6.   Newton's rings.   (Courtesy of Bausch and Lomb Optical Co.)

which gives the radii of the bright rings. If white light is used, each spectrum component will produce its own set of circular fringes, the sets all overlapping.   ◀

43–6   Phase Changes on Reflection

G. G. Stokes (1819–1903) used the principle of optical reversibility to investigate the reflection of light at an interface between two media. The principle states that if there is no absorption of light a light ray that is reflected or refracted will retrace its original path if its direction is reversed. This reminds us that any mechanical system can run backward as well as forward, provided there is no absorption of energy because of friction, etc.

Figure 43–19a shows a wave of amplitude E reflected and refracted at a surface separating media 1 and 2, where $n_2 > n_1$. The amplitude of the reflected wave is $r_{12}E$, in which r_{12} is an *amplitude reflection coefficient*. The amplitude of the refracted wave is $t_{12}E$, where t_{12} is an *amplitude transmission coefficient*.

We consider only the possibility of phase changes of 0 or 180°. If $r_{12} = +0.5$, for example, we have a reduction in amplitude on reflection by one-half and no change in phase. For $r_{12} = -0.5$ we have a phase change of 180° because

$$E \sin (\omega t + 180°) = -E \sin \omega t.$$

Figure 43–19b suggests that if we reverse these two rays they should combine to produce the original ray reversed in direction. Ray $r_{12}E$, identified by the single arrows in the figure, is reflected and refracted, producing the rays of amplitudes

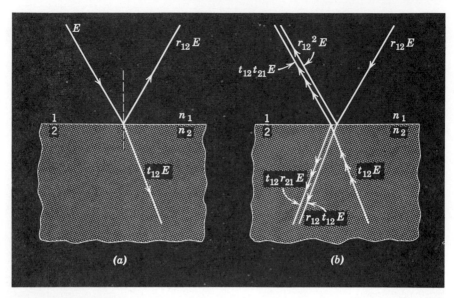

Fig. 43–19 (a) A ray is reflected and refracted at an air-glass interface. (b) The optically reversed situation; the two rays in the lower left must cancel.

$r_{12}^2 E$ and $r_{12}t_{12}E$. Ray $t_{12}E$, identified by the triple arrows, is also reflected and refracted, producing the rays of amplitudes $t_{12}t_{21}E$ and $t_{12}r_{21}E$ as shown. Note that r_{12} describes a ray in medium 1 reflected from medium 2, and r_{21} describes a ray in medium 2 reflected from medium 1. Similarly, t_{12} describes a ray that passes from medium 1 to medium 2; t_{21} describes a ray that passes from medium 2 to medium 1.

The two rays in the upper left of Fig. 43–19b must be equivalent to the incident ray of Fig. 43–19a, reversed; the two rays in the lower left of Fig. 43–19b must cancel. This second requirement leads to

$$r_{12}t_{12}E + t_{12}r_{21}E = 0,$$

or
$$r_{12} = -r_{21}.$$

This result tells us that if we compare a wave reflected from medium one with one reflected from medium 2, they behave differently in that one or the other undergoes a phase change of 180°. We must rely on experiment to show that, as we pointed out earlier, the ray reflected from the more optically dense medium is the one that experiences the phase change of 180°.

43–7 Michelson's Interferometer

An interferometer is a device that can be used to measure lengths or changes in length with great accuracy by means of interference fringes. We describe the form originally built by Michelson in 1881.

Consider light that leaves point P on extended source S (Fig. 43–20) and falls on half-silvered mirror M. This mirror has a silver coating just thick enough to transmit half the incident light and to reflect half; in the figure we have assumed that this mirror, for convenience, possesses negligible thickness. At M the light divides into two waves. One proceeds by transmission toward mirror M_1; the other proceeds by reflection toward M_2. The waves are reflected at each of these mirrors and are sent back along their directions of incidence, each wave eventually entering the eye E. Since the waves are coherent, being derived from the same point on the source, they will interfere.

If the mirrors M_1 and M_2 are exactly perpendicular to each other, the effect is that of light from an extended source S falling on a uniformly thick slab of air, between glass, whose thickness is equal to $d_2 - d_1$. Interference fringes appear, caused by small changes in the angle of incidence of the light from different points on the extended source as it strikes the equivalent air film. For *thick* films a path difference of one wavelength can be brought about by a very small change in the angle of incidence.

If M_2 is moved backward or forward, the effect is to change the thickness of the equivalent air film. Suppose that the center of the (circular) fringe pattern appears bright and that M_2 is moved just enough to cause the first bright circular fringe to move to the center of the pattern. The path of the light beam striking M_2 has been changed by one wavelength. This means (because the light passes twice through the equivalent air film) that the mirror must have moved one-half a wavelength.

The interferometer is used to measure changes in length by counting the number of interference fringes that pass the field of view as mirror M_2 is moved. Length measurements made in this way can be accurate if large numbers of fringes are counted.

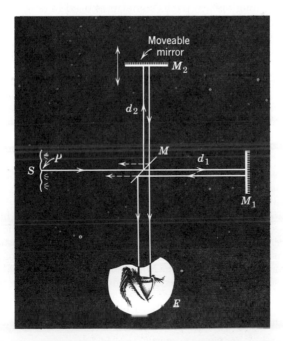

Fig. 43–20 Michelson's interferometer, showing the path of a particular ray originating at point P of an extended source S.

Michelson measured the length of the standard meter, kept in Paris, in terms of the wavelength of certain monochromatic red light emitted from a light source containing cadmium. He showed that the standard meter was equivalent to 1,553,163.5 wavelengths of the red cadmium light.

Physicists have long speculated on the advantages of discarding the standard meter bar as the basic standard of length and of *defining* the meter in terms of the wavelength of some carefully chosen monochromatic radiation. This would make the primary length standard readily available in laboratories all over the world. It would improve the accuracy of length measurements, since one would no longer need to compare an unknown object with a standard object (the meter bar), using interferometer techniques, but could measure the unknown object *directly* and in an absolute sense, using these techniques. There is the additional advantage that if the standard meter bar were destroyed it could never be replaced, whereas light sources and interferometers will (presumably) always be available.

In 1961 such an atomic standard of length was adopted by international agreement. Quoting from an article * describing the event:

> The wavelength of the orange-red light of krypton-86 has replaced the platinum iridium bar as the world standard of length. Formerly the wavelength of this light was defined as a function of the length of the meter bar. Now the meter is defined as a multiple (1,650,763.73) of the wavelength of the light.

The light from krypton-86 was used in preference to that from cadmium or other sources because it produces sharper interference fringes in the interferometer over the long optical paths sometimes used in length measurement.

43–8 Michelson's Interferometer and Light Propagation

In Section 40–4 we presented Einstein's hypothesis, now well verified, that in free space light is propagated with the same speed c no matter what the relative velocity of the source and the observer may be. We pointed out that this hypothesis contradicted the views of nineteenth-century physicists regarding wave propagation. It was difficult for these physicists, trained as they were in the classical physics of the time, to believe that a wave could be propagated without a medium. If such a medium could be established, the speed c of light would naturally be construed as the speed *with respect to that medium*, just as the speed of sound always refers to a medium such as air.

Although no medium for light propagation was obvious, the physicists postulated one, called the *ether* † and hypothesized that its properties were such that it was undetectable by ordinary means such as weighing.

In 1881 (24 years before Einstein's hypothesis) A. A. Michelson set himself the task of forcing the ether, assuming that it existed, to submit to direct physical verification. In particular, Michelson, later joined by E. W. Morley, tried to measure the speed u with which the earth moves through the ether. Michelson's interferometer was their instrument of choice for this now-famous Michelson-Morley experiment.

The earth together with the interferometer moving with velocity **u** through the ether is equivalent to the interferometer at rest with the ether streaming through it with velocity $-\mathbf{u}$, as shown in Fig. 43–21. Consider a wave moving along the path MM_1M and one moving along MM_2M. The first corresponds classically to a man

---

* *Scientific American*, p.75, December 1960.

† More fully, the *luminiferous* (or light-carrying) *ether*.

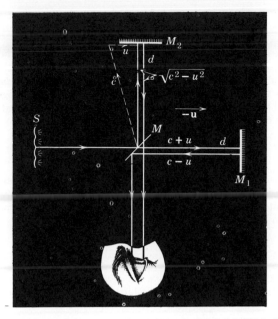

Fig. 43–21   The "ether" is streaming with velocity —**u** through Michelson's interferometer. The wave speeds shown are on the basis of the (incorrect) ether hypothesis.

rowing a boat a distance d downstream and the same distance upstream; the second corresponds to rowing a boat a distance d across a stream and back.

On the ether hypothesis the speed of light on the path MM_1 is $c + u$; on the return path M_1M it is $c - u$. The time required for the complete trip is

$$t_1 = \frac{d}{c + u} + \frac{d}{c - u} = d\,\frac{2c}{c^2 - u^2} = \frac{2d}{c}\,\frac{1}{1 - (u/c)^2}.$$

The speed of light, *on the ether hypothesis*, for path MM_2 is $\sqrt{c^2 - u^2}$, as Fig. 43–21 suggests. This same speed holds for the return path M_2M, so that the time required for this complete path is

$$t_2 = \frac{2d}{\sqrt{c^2 - u^2}} = \frac{2d}{c}\,\frac{1}{\sqrt{1 - (u/c)^2}}.$$

The difference of time for the two paths is

$$\Delta t = t_1 - t_2$$

$$= \frac{2d}{c}\left\{\left[1 - \left(\frac{u}{c}\right)^2\right]^{-1} - \left[1 - \left(\frac{u}{c}\right)^2\right]^{-\frac{1}{2}}\right\}.$$

Assuming $u/c \ll 1$, we can expand the quantities in the square brackets by using the binomial theorem, retaining only the first two terms. This leads to

$$\Delta t = \frac{2d}{c}\left\{\left[1 + \left(\frac{u}{c}\right)^2 + \cdots\right] - \left[1 + \frac{1}{2}\left(\frac{u}{c}\right)^2 + \cdots\right]\right\}$$

$$= \frac{2d}{c}\left\{\frac{1}{2}\left(\frac{u}{c}\right)^2\right\} = \frac{du^2}{c^3}. \tag{43–16}$$

Now let the entire interferometer be rotated through 90°. This will interchange the roles of the two light paths, MM_1M now being the "cross-stream" path and MM_2M the "down- and upstream" path. The time difference between the two waves entering the eye is also reversed; this changes the phase difference between the combining waves and alters the positions of the interference maxima. *The experiment consists of looking for a shift of the interference fringes as the apparatus is rotated.*

The *change* in time difference is $2\Delta t$, which corresponds to a fringe shift of $2\Delta t/T$ where T ($= \lambda/c$) is the period of vibration of the light. The expected maximum shift in the number of fringes on a 90° rotation (see Eq. 43–16) is

$$\Delta N = \frac{2\Delta t}{T} = \frac{2\Delta tc}{\lambda} = \frac{2d}{\lambda}\left(\frac{u}{c}\right)^2. \tag{43–17}$$

In the Michelson-Morley interferometer let $d = 11$ meters (obtained by multiple reflection in the interferometer) and $\lambda = 5.9 \times 10^{-7}$ meter. If u is assumed to be roughly the orbital speed of the earth, then $u/c \cong 10^{-4}$. The expected maximum fringe shift when the interferometer is rotated through 90° is then

$$\Delta N = \frac{2d}{\lambda}\left(\frac{u}{c}\right)^2 = \frac{(2)(11 \text{ meters})}{5.9 \times 10^{-7} \text{ meter}}(10^{-4})^2 = 0.4.$$

Even though a shift of only about 0.4 of a fringe was expected, Michelson and Morley were confident that they could observe a shift of 0.01 fringe. *They found from their experiment, however, that there was no observable fringe shift!*

The analogy between a light wave in the supposed ether and a boat moving in water, which seemed so evident in 1881, is simply incorrect. The derivation based on this analogy is incorrect for light waves. When the analysis is carried through on Einstein's hypothesis, the observed negative result is clearly predicted, the speed of light being c for all paths. The motion of the earth around the sun and the rotation of the interferometer have, in Einstein's view, no effect whatever on the speed of the light waves in the interferometer.

It should be made clear that although Einstein's hypothesis is completely consistent with the negative result of the Michelson-Morley experiment this experiment standing alone cannot serve as a proof for Einstein's hypothesis. Einstein said that no number of experiments, however large, could prove him right but that a single experiment could prove him wrong. Our present-day belief in Einstein's hypothesis rests on consistent agreement in a large number of experiments designed to test it. The "single experiment" that might prove Einstein wrong has never been found.

QUESTIONS

1. Is Young's experiment an interference experiment or a diffraction experiment, or both?

2. Do interference effects occur for sound waves? Recall that sound is a longitudinal wave and that light is a transverse wave.

3. In Young's double-slit interference experiment, using a monochromatic laboratory light source, why is screen A in Fig. 43–1 necessary? What would happen if one gradually enlarged the hole in this screen?

4. Describe the pattern of light intensity on screen C in Fig. 43–5 if one slit is covered with a red filter and the other with a blue filter, the incident light being white.

5. Is coherence important in reflection and refraction?

6. Define carefully, and distinguish between, the angles θ and ϕ that appear in Eq. 43–10.

7. If one slit in Fig. 43–5 is covered, what change occurs in the intensity of light in the center of the screen?

8. What changes occur in the pattern of interference fringes if the apparatus of Fig. 43–5 is placed under water?

9. What are the requirements for a maximum intensity when viewing a thin film by *transmitted* light?

10. In a Newton's rings experiment, is the central spot, as seen by reflection, dark or light? Explain.

11. Why must the film of Fig. 43–14 be "thin" for us to see an interference pattern of the type described?

12. Why do coated lenses (see Example 5) look purple by reflected light?

13. A person wets his eyeglasses to clean them. As the water evaporates he notices that for a short time the glasses become markedly more nonreflecting. Explain.

14. A lens is coated to reduce reflection, as in Example 5. What happens to the energy that had previously been reflected? Is it absorbed by the coating?

15. Very small changes in the angle of incidence do not change the interference conditions much for "thin" films but they do change them for "thick" films. Why?

16. The directional characteristics of a certain radar antenna as a receiver of radiation are known. What can be said about its directional characteristics as a transmitter?

17. A person in a dark room, looking through a small window, can see a second person standing outside in bright sunlight. The second person cannot see the first person. Is this a failure of the principle of optical reversibility? Assume no absorption of light.

18. Why is it necessary to rotate the interferometer in the Michelson-Morley experiment?

19. How is the negative result of the Michelson-Morley experiment interpreted according to Einstein's theory of relativity?

20. If interference between light waves of different frequencies is possible, one should observe light beats, just as one obtains sound beats from two sources of sound with slightly different frequencies. Discuss how one might experimentally look for this possibility.

21. In Young's double-slit experiment suppose that screen A in Fig. 43–1 contained *two* very narrow parallel slits instead of one. (a) Show that if the spacing between these slits is properly chosen the interference fringes can be made to disappear. (b) Under these conditions, would you call the beams emerging from slits S_1 and S_2 in screen B coherent? They do not produce interference fringes. (c) Discuss what would happen to the interference fringes in the case of a single slit in screen A if the slit width were gradually increased.

PROBLEMS

1. Design a double-slit arrangement that will produce interference fringes 1° apart on a distant screen. Assume sodium light ($\lambda = 5890$ A).

2. Two point sources in Fig. 43–22 emit coherent waves. Show that curves, such as that given, over which the phase difference for rays r_1 and r_2 is a constant are hyperbolas. Extend the analysis to three dimensions. (Hint: A constant phase difference implies a constant difference in length between r_1 and r_2.)

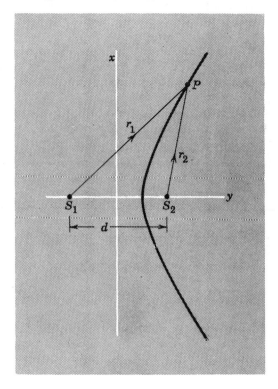

Fig. 43–22

3. A double-slit arrangement produces interference fringes for sodium light ($\lambda = 5890$ A) that are 0.20° apart. What is the angular fringe separation if the entire arrangement is immersed in water?

4. A double-slit arrangement produces interference fringes for sodium light ($\lambda = 5890$ A) that are 0.20° apart. For what wavelength would the angular separation be 10% greater?

5. A thin flake of mica ($n = 1.58$) is used to cover one slit of a double-slit arrangement. The central point on the screen is occupied by what used to be the seventh bright fringe. If $\lambda = 5500$ A, what is the thickness of the mica?

6. Sodium light ($\lambda = 5890$ A) falls on a double slit of separation $d = 2.0$ mm. D in Fig. 43–5 is 4 cm. What per cent error is made in locating the tenth bright fringe if it is *not* assumed that $D \gg d$?

7. Sodium light ($\lambda = 5890$ A) falls on a double slit of separation $d = 0.20$ mm. A thin lens ($f = +1.0$ meter) is placed near the slit as in Fig. 43–6. What is the linear fringe separation on a screen placed in the focal plane of the lens?

8. S_1 and S_2 in Fig. 43–23 are effective point sources of radiation, excited by the same oscillator. They are coherent and in phase with each other. Placed 1.0 meters apart, they emit equal amounts of power in the form of 1.0-meter wavelength electromagnetic waves. (a) Find the positions of the first (that is, the nearest), the second, and the third maxima of the received signal, as the detector is moved out along Ox. (b) Is the intensity at the nearest minimum equal to zero? Justify your answer.

Fig. 43–23

9. One of the slits of a double-slit system is wider than the other, so that the amplitude of the light reaching the central part of the screen from one slit, acting alone, is twice that from the other slit, acting alone. Derive an expression for I_θ in terms of θ, corresponding to Eqs. 43–11b and c.

10. Show that the half-width $\Delta\theta$ of the double-slit interference fringes (see arrow in Fig. 43–9) is given by

$$\Delta\theta = \frac{\lambda}{2d}$$

if θ is small enough so that $\sin\theta \cong \theta$.

11. Find the sum of the following quantities (a) by the vector method and (b) analytically:

$$y_1 = 10\sin\omega t$$

$$y_2 = 8\sin(\omega t + 30°).$$

12. Add the following quantities graphically, using the vector method:

$$y_1 = 10\sin\omega t$$

$$y_2 = 15\sin(\omega t + 30°)$$

$$y_3 = 5\sin(\omega t - 45°).$$

13. The frequency width of a standard television channel is 4×10^6 cycles/sec. If it were possible to transmit television signals in the visible portion of the electromagnetic spectrum, possibly by using optical maser or laser techniques, how many such standard channels would be available for allocation in the visible spectrum? Assume that this spectrum extends from 4000 to 7000 A.

14. In a Newton's rings experiment the radius of curvature R of the lens is 5.0 meters and its diameter is 2.0 cm. (a) How many rings are produced? (b) How many rings would be seen if the arrangement were immersed in water ($n = 1.33$)? Assume that $\lambda = 5890$ A.

15. The diameter of the tenth bright ring in a Newton's rings apparatus changes from 1.40 to 1.27 cm as a liquid is introduced between the lens and the plate. Find the index of refraction of the liquid.

16. A broad source of light (λ = 6800 A) illuminates normally two glass plates 12 cm long that touch at one end and are separated by a wire 0.048 mm in diameter at the other (Fig. 43–24). How many bright fringes appear over the 12-cm distance?

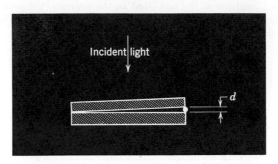

Incident light

d

Fig. 43–24

17. A thin film 4×10^{-5} cm thick is illuminated by white light normal to its surface. Its index of refraction is 1.5. What wavelengths within the visible spectrum will be intensified in the reflected beam?

18. White light reflected at perpendicular incidence from a soap film has, in the visible spectrum, an interference maximum at 6300 A and a minimum at 4500 A, with no minimum in between. If n = 1.33 for the film, what is the film thickness, assumed uniform?

19. A plane wave of monochromatic light falls normally on a uniformly thin film of oil which covers a glass plate. The wavelength of the source can be varied continuously. Complete destructive interference of the reflected light is observed for wavelengths of 5000 and 7000 A and for no other wavelengths in between. If the index of refraction of the oil is 1.30 and that of the glass is 1.50, find the thickness of the oil film.

20. In Example 5 assume that there is zero reflection for light of wavelength 5500 A at normal incidence. Calculate the factor by which the reflection is diminished by the coating at 4500 and at 6500 A.

21. A plane monochromatic light wave in air falls at normal incidence on a thin film of oil which covers a glass plate. The wavelength of the source may be varied continuously. Complete destructive interference in the reflected beam is observed for wavelengths of 5000 and 7000 A and for no other wavelength in between. The index of refraction of glass is 1.50. Show that the index of refraction of the oil must be less than 1.50.

22. White light reflected at perpendicular incidence from a soap bubble has, in the visible spectrum, a single interference maximum (at λ = 6000 A) and a single minimum at the violet end of the spectrum. If n = 1.33 for the film, calculate its thickness.

23. If mirror M_2 in Michelson's interferometer is moved through 0.233 mm, 792 fringes are counted. What is the wavelength of the light?

24. A thin film with n = 1.40 for light of wavelength 5890 A is placed in one arm of a Michelson interferometer. If a shift of 7.0 fringes occurs, what is the film thickness?

25. (a) What is the wavelength of the orange-red line of krypton-86 in angstrom units? Take 1 A = 10^{-10} meter exactly. (b) Does this question really make sense, in view of the fact that the meter is defined in terms of this wavelength? Explain.

26. A Michelson interferometer is used with a sodium discharge tube as a light source. The yellow sodium light consists of two wavelengths, 5890 and 5896 A. It is observed that the interference pattern disappears and reappears periodically as one moves mirror M_2 in Fig. 43–20. (a) Explain this effect. (b) Calculate the change in path difference between two successive reappearances of the interference pattern.

Diffraction

CHAPTER 44

44-1 Introduction

Diffraction, which is illustrated in Fig. 42–3, is the bending of light around an obstacle such as the edge of a slit. We can see the diffraction of light by looking through a crack between two fingers at a distant light source such as a tubular neon sign or by looking at a street light through a cloth umbrella. Usually diffraction effects are small and must be looked for carefully. Also, most sources of light have an extended area so that a diffraction pattern produced by one point of the source will overlap that produced by another. Finally, common sources of light are not monochromatic. The patterns for the various wavelengths overlap and again the effect is less apparent.

Diffraction was discovered by Francesco Maria Grimaldi (1618–1663), and the phenomenon was known both to Huygens (1629–1695) and to Newton (1642–1727). Newton did not see in it any justification for a wave theory for light. Huygens, although he believed in a wave theory, did not believe in diffraction! He imagined his secondary wavelets to be effective only at the point of tangency to their common envelope, thus denying the possibility of diffraction. In his words:

> And thus we see the reasons why light . . . proceeds only in straight lines in such a way that it does not illuminate any object except when the path from the source to the object is open along such a line.

Fresnel (1788–1827) correctly applied Huygens' principle (which is called the Huygens-Fresnel principle in Europe) to explain diffraction. In these early days the light waves were believed to be mechanical waves in an all-

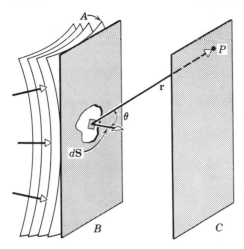

Fig. 44–1 Light is diffracted at the aperture in screen B and illuminates screen C. The intensity at P is found by dividing the wavefront at B into elementary radiators $d\mathbf{S}$ and combining their effects at P.

pervading ether. We have seen (Section 39–5) how Maxwell (1831–1879) showed that light waves were not mechanical in nature but electromagnetic. Einstein (1879–1955) rounded out our modern view of light waves by eliminating the need to postulate an ether (see Section 40–4).

Figure 44–1 shows a general diffraction situation. Surface A is a wavefront that falls on B, which is an opaque screen containing an aperture of arbitrary shape; C is a diffusing screen that receives the light that passes through this aperture. This pattern of light intensity on C can be calculated by subdividing the wavefront into elementary areas $d\mathbf{S}$, each of which becomes a source of an expanding Huygens' wavelet. The light intensity at an arbitrary point P is found by superimposing the wave disturbances (that is, the $\mathbf{E}$ vectors) caused by the wavelets reaching P from all these elementary radiators.

The wave disturbances reaching P differ in amplitude and in phase because (a) the elementary radiators are at varying distances from P, (b) the light leaves the radiators at various angles to the normal to the wavefront (see p. 928), and (c) some radiators are blocked by screen B; others are not. Diffraction calculations—simple in principle—may become difficult in practice. The calculation must be repeated for every point on screen C at which we wish to know the light intensity. We followed exactly this program in calculating the double-slit intensity pattern in Section 43–3. The calculation there was simple because we assumed only two elementary radiators, the two narrow slits.

Figure 44–2a shows the general case of *Fresnel diffraction*, in which the light source and/or the screen on which the diffraction pattern is displayed are a finite distance from the diffracting aperture; the wavefronts that fall on the diffracting aperture in this case and that leave it to illuminate any point P of the diffusing screen are not planes; the corresponding rays are not parallel.

A simplification results if source S and screen C are moved to a large distance from the diffraction aperture, as in Fig. 44–2b. This limiting case is called *Fraunhofer diffraction*. The wavefronts arriving at the diffracting aperture from the distant source S are planes, and the rays associated with these wavefronts are parallel to each other. Similarly, the wavefronts arriving at any point P on the distant screen C are planes, the corresponding rays

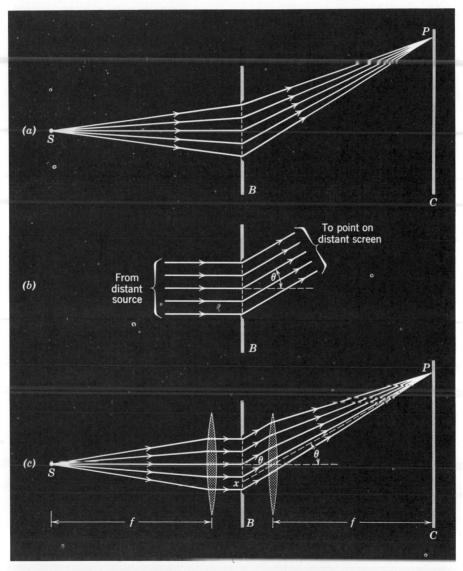

Fig. 44–2 (a) Fresnel diffraction. (b) Source S and screen C are moved to a large distance, resulting in Fraunhofer diffraction. (c) Fraunhofer diffraction conditions produced by lenses, leaving source S and screen C in their original positions.

also being parallel. Fraunhofer conditions can be established in the laboratory by using two converging lenses, as in Fig. 44–2c. The first of these converts the diverging wave from the source into a plane wave. The second lens causes plane waves leaving the diffracting aperture to converge to point P. All rays that illuminate P will leave the diffracting aperture parallel to the dashed line Px drawn from P through the center of this second (thin) lens. We assumed Fraunhofer conditions for Young's double-slit experiment in Section 43–1 (see Fig. 43–5).

Although Fraunhofer diffraction is a limiting case of the more general Fresnel diffraction, it is an important limiting case and is easier to handle mathematically. This book deals only with Fraunhofer diffraction.

44–2 Single Slit

Figure 44–3 shows a plane wave falling at normal incidence on a long narrow slit of width a. Let us focus our attention on the central point P_0 of screen C. The rays extending from the slit to P_0 all have the same optical path lengths, as we saw in Section 42–5. Since they are in phase at the plane of the slit, they will still be in phase at P_0, and the central point of the diffraction pattern that appears on screen C has a maximum intensity.

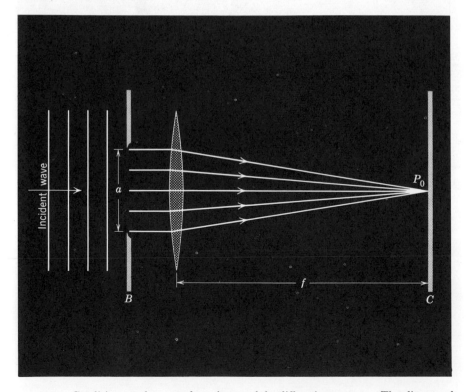

Fig. 44–3 Conditions at the central maximum of the diffraction pattern. The slit extends a distance above and below the figure, this distance being much greater than the slit width a.

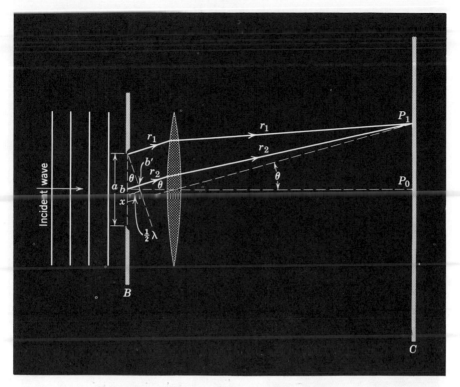

Fig. 44–4 Conditions at the first minimum of the diffraction pattern.

We now consider another point on the screen. Light rays which reach P_1 in Fig. 44–4 leave the slit at an angle θ as shown. Ray r_1 originates at the top of the slit and ray r_2 at its center. If θ is chosen so that the distance bb' in the figure is one-half a wavelength, r_1 and r_2 will be out of phase and will produce no effect at P_1.* In fact, every ray from the upper half of the slit will be canceled by a ray from the lower half, originating at a point $a/2$ below the first ray. The point P_1, the first minimum of the diffraction pattern, will have zero intensity (compare Fig. 42–3).

The condition shown in Fig. 44–4 is

$$\frac{a}{2} \sin \theta = \frac{\lambda}{2},$$

or
$$a \sin \theta = \lambda. \qquad (44\text{–}1)$$

As we stated earlier (see Fig. 42–1), the central maximum becomes wider as the slit is made narrower. If the slit width is as small as one wavelength ($a = \lambda$), the first minimum occurs at $\theta = 90°$, which implies that the central maximum fills the entire forward hemisphere. We assumed a condition ap-

---

* Whatever phase relation exists between r_1 and r_2 at the plane represented by the sloping dashed line in Fig. 44–4 that passes through b' also exists at P_1, not being affected by the lens (see Section 42–5).

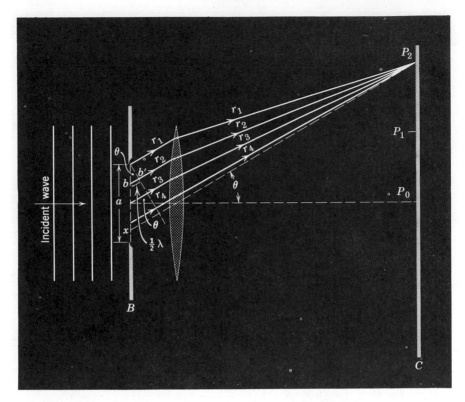

Fig. 44–5 Conditions at the second minimum of the diffraction pattern.

proaching this in our discussion of Young's double-slit interference experiment in Section 43–1.

In Fig. 44–5 the slit is divided into four equal zones, with a ray leaving the top of each zone. Let θ be chosen so that the distance bb' is one-half a wavelength. Rays r_1 and r_2 will then cancel at P_2. Rays r_3 and r_4 will also be half a wavelength out of phase and will also cancel. Consider four other rays, emerging from the slit a given distance below the four rays above. The two rays below r_1 and r_2 will cancel uniquely, as will the two rays below r_3 and r_4. We can proceed across the entire slit and conclude again that no light reaches P_2; we have located a second point of zero intensity.

The condition described (see Fig. 44–5) requires that

$$\frac{a}{4} \sin \theta = \frac{\lambda}{2},$$

or

$$a \sin \theta = 2\lambda.$$

By extension, the general formula for the minima in the diffraction pattern on screen C is

$$a \sin \theta = m\lambda \qquad m = 1, 2, 3, \ldots \text{ (minima)}. \qquad (44\text{--}2)$$

There is a maximum approximately halfway between each adjacent pair of minima. The student should consider the simplification that has resulted in this analysis by examining Fraunhofer (Fig. 44–2c) rather than Fresnel conditions (Fig. 44–2a).

▶ **Example 1.** A slit of width a is illuminated by white light. For what value of a will the first minimum for red light ($\lambda = 6500$ A) fall at $\theta = 30°$?

At the first minimum we put $m = 1$ in Eq. 44–2. Doing so and solving for a yields

$$a = \frac{m\lambda}{\sin\theta} = \frac{(1)(6500 \text{ A})}{\sin 30°} = 13{,}000 \text{ A.}$$

Note that the slit width must be twice the wavelength in this case.

Example 2. In Example 1 what is the wavelength λ' of the light whose first diffraction maximum (not counting the central maximum) falls at $\theta = 30°$, thus coinciding with the first minimum for red light?

This maximum is about halfway between the first and second minima. It can be found without too much error by putting $m = 1.5$ in Eq. 44–2, or

$$a \sin\theta \cong 1.5\lambda'.$$

From Example 1, however, $a \sin\theta = \lambda.$

Dividing gives $\lambda' = \dfrac{\lambda}{1.5} = \dfrac{6500 \text{ A}}{1.5} = 4300 \text{ A.}$

Light of this color is violet. The second maximum for light of wavelength 4300 A will *always* coincide with the first minimum for light of wavelength 6500 A, no matter what the slit width. If the slit is relatively narrow, the angle θ at which this overlap occurs will be relatively large.   ◀

44–3   Single Slit—Qualitative

Figure 44–6 shows a slit of width a divided into N parallel strips of width Δx. Each strip acts as a radiator of Huygens' wavelets and produces a characteristic wave disturbance at point P, whose position on the screen, for a particular arrangement of apparatus, can be described by the angle θ.

If the strips are narrow enough—which we assume—all points on a given strip have essentially the same optical path length to P, and therefore all the light from the strip will have the same phase when it arrives at P. The amplitudes ΔE_0 of the wave disturbances at P from the various strips may be taken as equal if θ in Fig. 44–6 is not too large.

We limit our considerations to points that lie in, or infinitely close to, the plane of Fig. 44–6. It can be shown that this procedure is valid for a slit whose length is much greater than its width a. We made this same assumption tacitly both earlier in this chapter and in Chapter 43; see Figs. 43–5 and 44–3, for example.

The wave disturbances from adjacent strips have a constant phase difference $\Delta\phi$ between them at P given by

$$\frac{\text{phase difference}}{2\pi} = \frac{\text{path difference}}{\lambda},$$

or $$\Delta\phi = \left(\frac{2\pi}{\lambda}\right)(\Delta x \sin\theta), \qquad (44\text{–}3)$$

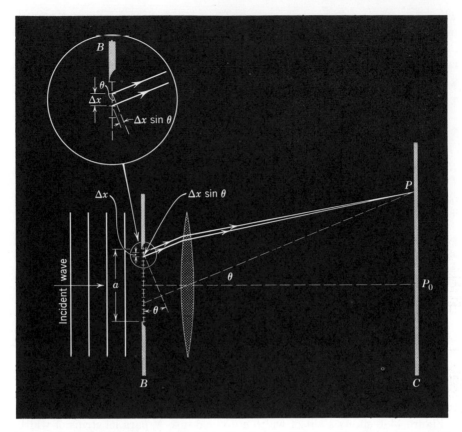

Fig. 44–6 A slit of width a is divided into N strips of width Δx. The insert shows conditions at the second strip more clearly. In the differential limit the slit is divided into an infinite number of strips (that is, $N \to \infty$) of differential width dx. For clarity in this and the following figure, we take $N = 18$.

where $\Delta x \sin \theta$ is, as the figure insert shows, the path difference for rays originating at the top edges of adjacent strips. Thus, at P, N vectors with the same amplitude ΔE_0, the same frequency, and the same phase difference $\Delta\phi$ between adjacent members combine to produce a resultant disturbance. We ask, for various values of $\Delta\phi$ [that is, for various points P on the screen, corresponding to various values of θ (see Eq. 44–3)], what is the amplitude E_θ of the resultant wave disturbance? We find the answer by representing the individual wave disturbances ΔE_0 by phasors and calculating the resultant phasor amplitude, as described in Section 43–4.

At the center of the diffraction pattern θ equals zero, and the phase shift between adjacent strips (see Eq. 44–3) is also zero. As Fig. 44–7a shows, the phasor arrows in this case are laid end to end and the amplitude of the resultant has its maximum value E_m. This corresponds to the center of the central maximum.

As we move to a value of θ other than zero, $\Delta\phi$ assumes a definite nonzero value (again see Eq. 44–3), and the array of arrows is now as shown in Fig. 44–7b. The resultant amplitude E_θ is less than before. Note that the length of the "arc" of small arrows is the same for both figures and indeed for all figures of this series. As θ increases further, a situation is reached (Fig. 44–7c) in which the chain of arrows curls around through 360°, the tip of the last arrow touching the foot of the first arrow. This corresponds to $E_\theta = 0$, that is, to the first minimum. For this condition the ray from the top of the slit (1 in Fig. 44–7c) is 180° out of phase with the ray from the center of the slit ($\frac{1}{2}N$ in Fig. 44–7c). These phase relations are consistent with Fig. 44–4, which also represents the first minimum.

As θ increases further, the phase shift continues to increase, and the chain of arrows coils around through an angular distance greater than 360°, as in Fig. 44–7d, which corresponds to the first maximum beyond the central maximum. This maximum is much smaller than the central maximum. In making this comparison, recall that the arrows marked E_θ in Fig. 44–7 correspond to the *amplitudes* of the wave disturbance and not to the *in-*

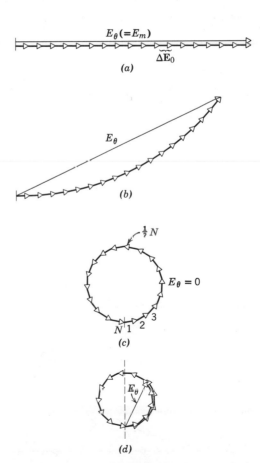

Fig. 44–7 Conditions at (a) the central maximum, (b) a direction slightly removed from the central maximum, (c) the first minimum, and (d) the first maximum beyond the central maximum for single-slit diffraction. This figure corresponds to $N = 18$ in Fig. 44–6.

tensity. The amplitudes must be squared to obtain the corresponding relative intensities (see Eq. 43–7).

44–4 Single Slit—Quantitative

The "arc" of small arrows in Fig. 44–8 shows the phasors representing, in amplitude and phase, the wave disturbances that reach an arbitrary point P on the screen of Fig. 44–6, corresponding to a particular angle θ. The resultant amplitude at P is E_θ. If we divide the slit of Fig. 44–6 into infinitesimal strips of width dx, the arc of arrows in Fig. 44–8 approaches the arc of a circle, its radius R being indicated in that figure. The length of the arc is E_m, the amplitude at the center of the diffraction pattern, for at the center of the pattern the wave disturbances are all in phase and this "arc" becomes a straight line as in Fig. 44–7a.

The angle ϕ in the lower part of Fig. 44–8 is revealed as the difference in phase between the infinitesimal vectors at the left and right ends of the arc E_m. This means that ϕ is the phase difference between rays from the top and the bottom of the slit of Fig. 44–6. From geometry we see that ϕ is also the angle between the two radii marked R in Fig. 44–8. From this figure we can write

$$E_\theta = 2R \sin \frac{\phi}{2}.$$

In radian measure ϕ, from the figure, is

$$\phi = \frac{E_m}{R}.$$

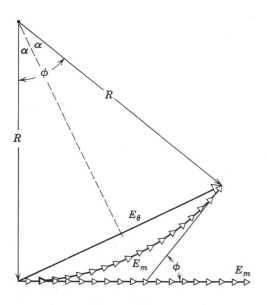

Fig. 44–8 A construction used to calculate the intensity in single-slit diffraction. The situation corresponds to that of Fig. 44–7.

Combining yields
$$E_\theta = \frac{E_m}{\phi/2} \sin \frac{\phi}{2},$$

or
$$E_\theta = E_m \frac{\sin \alpha}{\alpha}, \tag{44-4}$$

in which
$$\alpha = \frac{\phi}{2}. \tag{44-5}$$

From Fig. 44–6, recalling that ϕ is the phase difference between rays from the top and the bottom of the slit and that the path difference for these rays is $a \sin \theta$, we have

$$\frac{\text{phase difference}}{2\pi} = \frac{\text{path difference}}{\lambda},$$

or
$$\phi = \left(\frac{2\pi}{\lambda}\right)(a \sin \theta).$$

Combining with Eq. 44–5 yields

$$\alpha = \frac{\phi}{2} = \frac{\pi a}{\lambda} \sin \theta. \tag{44-6}$$

Equation 44–4, taken together with the definition of Eq. 44–6, gives the amplitude of the wave disturbance for a single-slit diffraction pattern at any angle θ. The intensity I_θ for the pattern is proportional to the square of the amplitude, or

$$I_\theta = I_m \left(\frac{\sin \alpha}{\alpha}\right)^2. \tag{44-7}$$

For convenience we display together, and renumber, the formulas for the amplitude and the intensity in single-slit diffraction.

[Eq. 44–4]
$$E_\theta = E_m \frac{\sin \alpha}{\alpha} \tag{44-8a}$$

single-

[Eq. 44–7]
$$I_\theta = I_m \left(\frac{\sin \alpha}{\alpha}\right)^2 \tag{44-8b}$$

slit

diffraction

[Eq. 44–6]
$$\alpha \left(= \tfrac{1}{2}\phi\right) = \frac{\pi a}{\lambda} \sin \theta \tag{44-8c}$$

Figure 44–9 shows plots of I_θ for several values of the ratio a/λ. Note that the pattern becomes narrower as a/λ is increased; compare this figure with Figs. 42–1 and 42–3.

Minima occur in Eq. 44–8b when

$$\alpha = m\pi \qquad m = 1, 2, 3, \ldots. \tag{44-9}$$

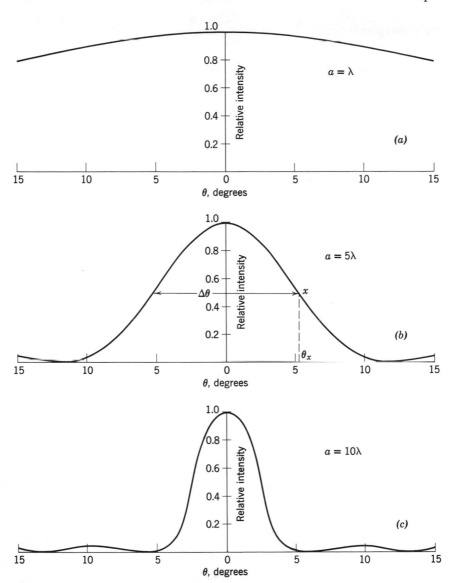

Fig. 44–9 The relative intensity in single-slit diffraction for three values of the ratio a/λ. The arrow in (*b*) shows the half-width $\Delta\theta$ of the central maximum.

Combining with Eq. 44–8*c* leads to

$$a \sin \theta = m\lambda \qquad m = 1, 2, 3, \ldots \text{ (minima)},$$

which is the result derived in the preceding section (Eq. 44–2). In that section, however, we derived *only* this result, obtaining no quantitative information about the intensity of the diffraction pattern at places in which it was not zero. Here (Eqs. 44–8) we have complete intensity information.

▶ **Example 3.** *Intensities of the secondary diffraction maxima.* Calculate, approximately, the relative intensities of the secondary maxima in the single-slit Fraunhofer diffraction pattern.

The secondary maxima lie approximately halfway between the minima and are found (compare Eq. 44–9) from

$$\alpha \cong (m + \tfrac{1}{2})\pi \qquad m = 1, 2, 3, \ldots.$$

Substituting into Eq. 44–8b yields

$$I_\theta = I_m \left[\frac{\sin (m + \tfrac{1}{2})\pi}{(m + \tfrac{1}{2})\pi}\right]^2,$$

which reduces to

$$\frac{I_\theta}{I_m} = \frac{1}{(m+\tfrac{1}{2})^2\pi^2}.$$

This yields, for $m = 1, 2, 3, \ldots, I_\theta/I_m = 0.045, 0.016, 0.0083$, etc. The successive maxima decrease rapidly in intensity.

Example 4. *Width of the central diffraction maximum.* Derive the *half-width* $\Delta\theta$ of the central maximum in a single-slit Fraunhofer diffraction (see Fig. 44–9b). The half-width is the angle between the two points in the pattern where the intensity is one-half that at the center of the pattern.

Point x in Fig. 44–9b is so chosen that $I_\theta = \tfrac{1}{2}I_m$, or, from Eq. 44–8b,

$$\frac{1}{2} = \left(\frac{\sin \alpha_x}{\alpha_x}\right)^2.$$

This equation cannot be solved analytically for α_x. It can be solved graphically, as accurately as one wishes, by plotting the quantity $(\sin \alpha_x/\alpha_x)^2$ as ordinate versus α_x as abscissa and noting the value of α_x at which the curve intersects the line "one-half" on the ordinate scale (see Problem 5). However, if only an approximate answer is desired, it is often quicker to use trial-and-error methods.

We know that α equals π at the first minimum; we guess that α_x is perhaps $\pi/2$ ($= 90° = 1.57$ radians). Trying this in Eq. 44–8b yields

$$\frac{I_\theta}{I_m} = \left[\frac{\sin (\pi/2)}{\pi/2}\right]^2 = 0.4.$$

This intensity ratio is *less* than 0.5, so that α_x must be *less* than 90°. After a few more trials we find easily enough that

$$\alpha_x = 1.40 \text{ radians} = 80°$$

does yield a ratio close to the correct value of 0.5.

We now use Eq. 44–8c to find the corresponding angle θ:

$$\alpha_x = \frac{\pi a}{\lambda} \sin \theta_x = 1.40,$$

or, noting that $a/\lambda = 5$ for Fig. 44–9b,

$$\sin \theta_x = \frac{1.40\lambda}{\pi a} = \frac{1.40}{5\pi} = 0.0892.$$

The half-width $\Delta\theta$ of the central maximum (see Fig. 44–9b) is given by

$$\Delta\theta = 2\theta_x = 2 \sin^{-1} 0.0892 = 2 \times 5.1° = 10.2°,$$

which is in agreement with the figure.   ◀

44–5 Diffraction at a Circular Aperture

Diffraction will occur when a wavefront is partially blocked off by an opaque object such as a metal disk or an opaque screen containing an aperture. Here we consider diffraction at a circular aperture of diameter d, the aperture constituting the boundary of a circular lens.

Our previous treatment of lenses was based on geometrical optics, diffraction being specifically assumed not to occur. A rigorous analysis would be based from the beginning on wave optics, since geometrical optics is always an approximation, although often a good one. Diffraction phenomena would emerge in a natural way from such a wave-optical analysis.

Figure 44–10 shows the image of a distant point source of light (a star) formed on a photographic film placed in the focal plane of a converging lens. It is not a point, as the (approximate) geometrical optics treatment suggests, but a circular disk surrounded by several progressively fainter secondary rings. Comparison with Fig. 42–3c leaves little doubt that we are dealing with a diffraction phenomenon in which, however, the aperture is a circle rather than a long narrow slit. The ratio d/λ, where d is the diameter of the lens (or of a circular aperture placed in front of the lens), determines the scale of the diffraction pattern, just as the ratio a/λ does for a slit.

Analysis shows that the first minimum for the diffraction pattern of a circular aperture of diameter d, assuming Fraunhofer conditions, is given by

$$\sin \theta = 1.22 \frac{\lambda}{d}. \tag{44–10}$$

This is to be compared with Eq. 44–1, or

$$\sin \theta = \frac{\lambda}{a},$$

which locates the first minimum for a long narrow slit of width a. The factor 1.22 emerges from the mathematical analysis when we integrate over the elementary radiators into which the circular aperture may be divided.

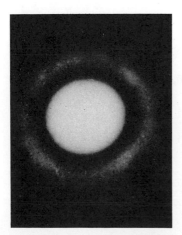

Fig. 44–10 The image of a star formed by a converging lens is a diffraction pattern. Note the central maximum, sometimes called the Airy disk (after Sir George Airy, who first solved the problem of diffraction at a circular aperture in 1835), and the circular secondary maximum. Other secondary maxima occur at larger radii but are too faint to be seen.

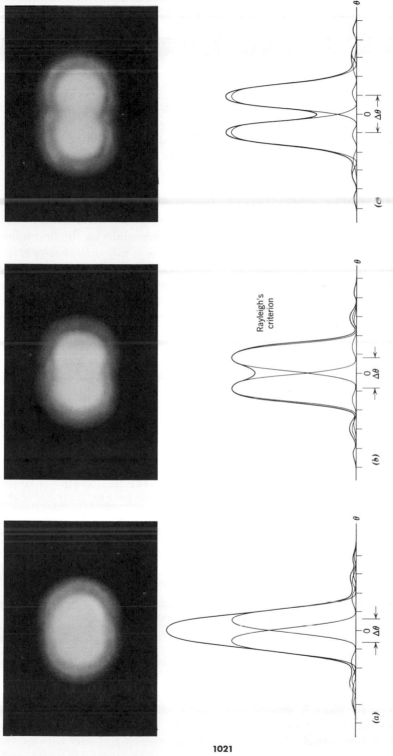

Fig. 44-11 The images of two distant point objects are formed by a converging lens whose diameter (= 10 cm) is 200,000 times the effective wavelength (= 5000 A). Sketches of the images as they appear in the focal plane of the lens are shown with the corresponding intensity plots below them. (*a*) The angular separation of the objects (see vertical ticks) is so small that the images are not resolved. (*b*) The objects are farther apart and the images meet Rayleigh's criterion for resolution. (*c*) The objects are still farther apart and the images are well resolved.

In actual lenses the image of a distant point object will be somewhat larger than that shown in Fig. 44–10 and may not have radial symmetry. This is caused by the various lens "defects" mentioned on p. 969. However, even if all of these defects could be eliminated by suitable shaping of the lens surfaces or by introducing correcting lenses, the diffraction pattern of Fig. 44–10 would remain. It is an inherent property of the lens aperture and of the wavelength of light used.

The fact that lens images are diffraction patterns is important when we wish to distinguish two distant point objects whose angular separation is small. Figure 44–11 shows the visual appearances and the corresponding intensity patterns for two distant point objects with small angular separations. In (a) the objects are not resolved; that is, they cannot be distinguished from a single point object. In (b) they are barely resolved and in (c) they are fully resolved.

In Fig. 44–11b the angular separation of the two point sources is such that the maximum of the diffraction pattern of one source falls on the first minimum of the diffraction pattern of the other. This is called *Rayleigh's criterion*. This criterion, though useful, is arbitrary; other criteria for deciding when two objects are resolved are sometimes used. From Eq. 44–10, two objects that are barely resolvable by Rayleigh's criterion must have an angular separation θ_R of

$$\theta_R = \sin^{-1} \frac{1.22\lambda}{d}.$$

Since the angles involved are rather small, we can replace $\sin \theta_R$ by θ_R, or

$$\theta_R = 1.22 \frac{\lambda}{d}. \tag{44–11}$$

If the angular separation θ between the objects is greater than θ_R, we can resolve the two objects; if it is less, we cannot.

▶ **Example 5.** A converging lens 3.0 cm in diameter has a focal length f of 20 cm. (a) What angular separation must two distant point objects have to satisfy Rayleigh's criterion? Assume that $\lambda = 5500$ A.

From Eq. 44–11,

$$\theta_R = 1.22 \frac{\lambda}{d} = \frac{(1.22)(5.5 \times 10^{-7} \text{ meter})}{3.0 \times 10^{-2} \text{ meter}} = 2.2 \times 10^{-5} \text{ radian.}$$

(b) How far apart are the centers of the diffraction patterns in the focal plane of the lens? The linear separation is

$$x = f\theta = (20 \text{ cm})(2.2 \times 10^{-5} \text{ radian}) = 44{,}000 \text{ A.}$$

This is 8.0 wavelengths of the light employed.   ◀

When one wishes to use a lens to resolve objects of small angular separation, it is desirable to make the central disk of the diffraction pattern as small as possible. This can be done (see Eq. 44–11) by increasing the lens diameter or by using a shorter wavelength. One reason for constructing large telescopes is to produce *sharper* images so that celestial objects can be examined in finer detail. The images are also *brighter*, not only because the energy is concentrated into a smaller diffraction disk but because the larger lens collects more light. Thus fainter objects, for example, more distant stars, can be seen.

To reduce diffraction effects in *microscopes* we often use ultraviolet light, which, because of its shorter wavelength, permits finer detail to be examined than would be possible for the same microscope operated with visible light. We shall see in Chapter 48 that beams of electrons behave like waves under some circumstances. In the *electron microscope* such beams may have an effective wavelength of 0.04 A, of the order of 10^5 times shorter than visible light ($\lambda \cong 5000$ A). This permits the detailed examination of tiny objects like viruses. If a virus were examined with an optical microscope, its structure would be hopelessly concealed by diffraction.

44–6 Double Slit

In Young's double-slit experiment (Section 43–1) we assume that the slits are arbitrarily narrow (that is, $a \ll \lambda$), which means that the central part of the diffusing screen was uniformly illuminated by the diffracted waves from each slit. When such waves interfere, they produce fringes of uniform intensity, as in Fig. 43–9. This idealized situation cannot occur with actual slits because the condition $a \ll \lambda$ cannot usually be met. Waves from the two actual slits combining at different points of the screen will have intensities that are *not* uniform but are governed by the diffraction pattern of a single slit. The effect of relaxing the assumption that $a \ll \lambda$ in Young's experiment is to leave the fringes relatively unchanged in location but to alter their intensities.

The interference pattern for infinitesimally narrow slits is given by Eq. 43–11b and c or, with a small change in nomenclature,

$$I_{\theta,\text{int}} = I_{m,\text{int}} \cos^2 \beta, \tag{44–12}$$

where
$$\beta = \frac{\pi d}{\lambda} \sin \theta. \tag{44–13}$$

The intensity for the diffracted wave from either slit is given by Eqs. 44–8b and c, or, with a small change in nomenclature,

$$I_{\theta,\text{dif}} = I_{m,\text{dif}} \left(\frac{\sin \alpha}{\alpha}\right)^2, \tag{44–14}$$

where
$$\alpha = \frac{\pi a}{\lambda} \sin \theta. \tag{44–15}$$

The combined effect is found by regarding $I_{m,\text{int}}$ in Eq. 44–12 as a variable amplitude, given in fact by $I_{\theta,\text{dif}}$ of Eq. 44–14. This assumption, for the combined pattern, leads to

$$I_\theta = I_m (\cos \beta)^2 \left(\frac{\sin \alpha}{\alpha}\right)^2, \tag{44–16}$$

in which we have dropped all subscripts referring separately to interference and diffraction.

Let us express this result in words. At any point on the screen the available light intensity from each slit, considered separately, is given by the diffraction pattern of that slit (Eq. 44–14). The diffraction patterns for the two slits, again considered separately, coincide because parallel rays in

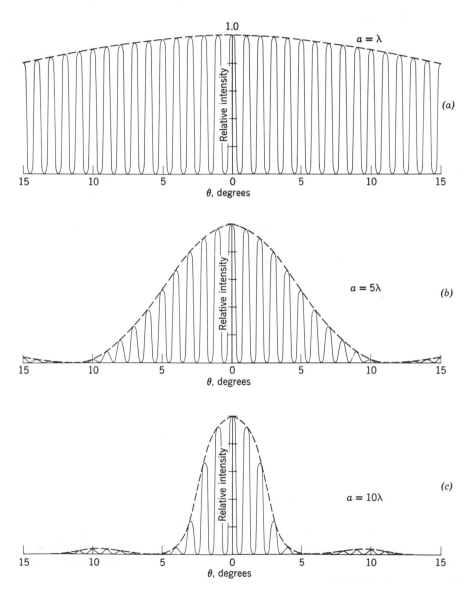

Fig. 44–12 Interference fringes for a double slit with slit separation $d = 50\lambda$. Three different slit widths, described by $a/\lambda = 1$, 5, and 10 are shown.

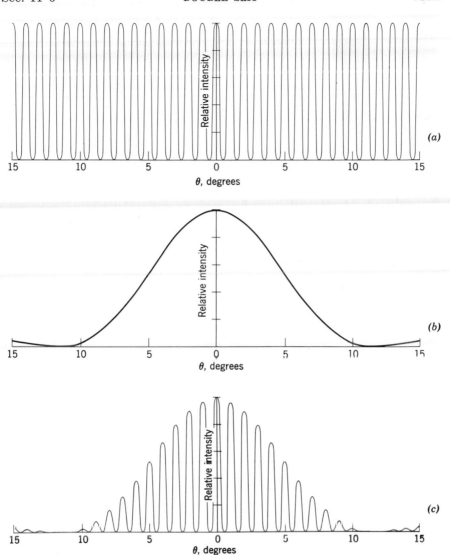

Fig. 44–13 (a) The "interference factor" and (b) the "diffraction factor" in Eq. 44–16 and (c) their product; compare Fig. 44–12b.

Fraunhofer diffraction are focused at the same spot (see Fig. 44–5). Because the two diffracted waves are coherent, they will interfere.

The effect of interference is to redistribute the available energy over the screen, producing a set of fringes. In Section 43–1, where we assumed $a \ll \lambda$, the available energy was virtually the same at all points on the screen so that the interference fringes had virtually the same intensities (see Fig. 43–9). If we relax the assumption $a \ll \lambda$, the available energy is *not* uniform over the screen but is given by the diffraction pattern of a slit of width a. In this

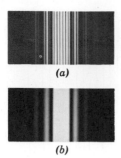

(a)

(b)

Fig. 44–14 (a) Interference fringes for a double-slit system in which the slit width is *not* negligible in comparison to the wavelength. The fringes are modulated in intensity by the diffraction pattern of a single slit. (b) If one of the slits is covered up, the interference fringes disappear and we see the single slit diffraction pattern. (Courtesy G. H. Carragan, Rensselaer Polytechnic Institute.)

case the interference fringes will have intensities that are determined by the intensity of the diffraction pattern at the location of a particular fringe. Equation 44–16 is the mathematical expression of this argument.

Figure 44–12 is a plot of Eq. 44–16 for $d = 50\lambda$ and for three values of a/λ. It shows clearly that for narrow slits ($a = \lambda$) the fringes are nearly uniform in intensity. As the slits are widened, the intensities of the fringes are markedly modulated by the "diffraction factor" in Eq. 44–16, that is, by the factor $(\sin \alpha/\alpha)^2$.

Equation 44–16 shows that the fringe envelopes of Fig. 44–12 are precisely the single-slit diffraction patterns of Fig. 44–9. This is especially clear in Fig. 44–13, which shows, for the curve of Fig. 44–12b, (a) the "interference factor" in Eq. 44–16 (that is, the factor $\cos^2 \beta$), (b) the "diffraction factor" $(\sin \alpha/\alpha)^2$, and (c) their product.

If we put $a = 0$ in Eq. 44–16, then (see Eq. 44–15) $\alpha = 0$ and $\sin \alpha/\alpha \cong \alpha/\alpha = 1$. Thus this equation reduces, as it must, to the intensity equation for a pair of vanishingly narrow slits (Eq. 44–12). If we put $d = 0$ in Eq. 44–16, the two slits coalesce into a single slit of width a, as Fig. 44–15 shows; $d = 0$ implies $\beta = 0$ (see Eq. 44–13) and $\cos^2 \beta = 1$. Thus Eq. 44–16 reduces, as it must, to the diffraction equation for a single slit (Eq. 44–14).

Figure 44–14 shows some actual double-slit interference photographs. The uniformly spaced interference fringes and their intensity modulation by the diffraction pattern of a single slit is clear. If one slit is covered up, as in Fig. 44–14b, the interference fringes disappear and we see the diffraction pattern of a single slit.

▶ **Example 6.** Starting from the curve of Fig. 44–12b, what is the effect of (a) increasing the slit width, (b) increasing the slit separation, and (c) increasing the wavelength?

(a) If we increase the slit width a, the envelope of the fringe pattern changes so that its central peak is sharper (compare Fig. 44–12c). The fringe spacing, which depends on d/λ, does not change.

(b) If we increase d, the fringes become closer together, the envelope of the pattern remaining unchanged.

(c) If we increase λ, the envelope becomes broader and the fringes move further apart. Increasing λ is equivalent to decreasing both of the ratios a/λ and d/λ. The general relationship of the envelope to the fringes, which depends only on d/a, does not change with wavelength.

Example 7. In double-slit Fraunhofer diffraction what is the fringe spacing on a screen 50 cm away from the slits if they are illuminated with blue light ($\lambda = 4800$ A), if $d = 0.10$ mm, and if the slit width $a = 0.02$ mm? What is the linear distance from the central maximum to the first minimum of the fringe envelope?

The intensity pattern is given by Eq. 44–16, the fringe spacing being determined by the interference factor $\cos^2 \beta$. From Example 2, Chapter 43, we have

$$\Delta y = \frac{\lambda D}{d},$$

where D is the distance of the screen from the slits. Substituting yields

$$\Delta y = \frac{(480 \times 10^{-9} \text{ meter})(50 \times 10^{-2} \text{ meter})}{0.10 \times 10^{-3} \text{ meter}} = 2.4 \times 10^{-3} \text{ meter} = 2.4 \text{ mm}.$$

The distance to the first minimum of the envelope is determined by the diffraction factor $(\sin \alpha / \alpha)^2$ in Eq. 44–16. The first minimum in this factor occurs for $\alpha = \pi$. From Eq. 44–15,

$$\sin \theta = \frac{\alpha \lambda}{\pi a} = \frac{\lambda}{a} = \frac{480 \times 10^{-9} \text{ meter}}{0.02 \times 10^{-3} \text{ meter}} = 0.024.$$

This is so small that we can assume that $\theta \cong \sin \theta \cong \tan \theta$, or

$$y = D \tan \theta \cong D \sin \theta = (50 \text{ cm})(0.024) = 1.2 \text{ cm}.$$

There are about ten fringes in the central peak of the fringe envelope.

Example 8. What requirements must be met for the central maximum of the envelope of the double-slit Fraunhofer pattern to contain exactly eleven fringes?

The required condition will be met if the sixth minimum of the interference factor $(\cos^2 \beta)$ in Eq. 44–16 coincides with the first minimum of the diffraction factor $(\sin \alpha / \alpha)^2$.

The sixth minimum of the interference factor occurs when

$$\beta = \tfrac{11}{2}\pi$$

in Eq. 44–12.

The first minimum in the diffraction term occurs for

$$\alpha = \pi.$$

Dividing (see Eqs. 44–13 and 44–15) yields

$$\frac{\beta}{\alpha} = \frac{d}{a} = \frac{11}{2}.$$

This condition depends only on the slit geometry and not on the wavelength. For long waves the pattern will be broader than for short waves, but there will always be eleven fringes in the central peak of the envelope. ◀

The double-slit problem as illustrated in Fig. 44–12 combines interference and diffraction in an intimate way. At root both are superposition effects and depend on adding wave disturbances at a given point, taking phase differences properly into account. If the waves to be combined originate from a *finite* (and usually small) number of elementary coherent radiators, as in Young's double-slit experiment, we call the effect *interference*. If the waves to be combined originate by subdividing a wave into *infinitesimal* coherent radiators, as in our treatment of a single slit (Fig. 44–6), we call the effect *diffraction*. This distinction between interference and diffraction is convenient and useful. However, it should not cause us to lose sight of the fact that both are superposition effects and that often both are present simultaneously, as in Young's experiment.

QUESTIONS

1. Why is the diffraction of sound waves more evident in daily experience than that of light waves?

2. Why do radio waves diffract around buildings, although light waves do not?

3. A loud-speaker horn has a rectangular aperture 4 ft high and 1 ft wide. Will the pattern of sound intensity be broader in the horizontal plane or in the vertical?

4. A radar antenna is designed to give accurate measurements of the height of an aircraft but only reasonably good measurements of its direction in a horizontal plane. Must the height-to-width ratio of the radar reflector be less than, equal to, or greater than unity?

5. A person holds a single narrow vertical slit in front of the pupil of his eye and looks at a distant light source in the form of a long heated filament. Is the diffraction pattern that he sees a Fresnel or a Fraunhofer pattern?

6. In a single-slit Fraunhofer diffraction, what is the effect of increasing (a) the wavelength and (b) the slit width?

7. Sunlight falls on a single slit of width 10^4 A. Describe qualitatively what the resulting diffraction pattern looks like.

8. In Fig. 44–5 rays r_1 and r_3 are in phase; so are r_2 and r_4. Why isn't there a *maximum* intensity at P_2 rather than a minimum?

9. Describe what happens to a Fraunhofer single-slit diffraction pattern if the whole apparatus is immersed in water.

10. Distinguish clearly between θ, α, and ϕ in Eq. 44–8c.

11. Do diffraction effects occur for virtual images as well as for real images? Explain.

12. Do diffraction effects occur for images formed by (a) plane mirrors and (b) spherical mirrors? Explain.

13. If we were to redo our analysis of the properties of lenses in Section 42–5 by the methods of geometrical optics but *without* restricting our considerations to paraxial rays and to "thin" lenses, would diffraction phenomena, such as that of Fig. 44–10, emerge from the analysis? Discuss.

14. Distinguish carefully between interference and diffraction in Young's double-slit experiment.

15. In what way are interference and diffraction similar? In what way are they different?

16. In double-slit interference patterns such as that of Fig. 44–14a we said that the interference fringes were modulated in intensity by the diffraction pattern of a single slit. Could we reverse this statement and say that the diffraction pattern of a single slit is intensity-modulated by the interference fringes? Discuss.

PROBLEMS

1. In a single-slit diffraction pattern the distance between the first minimum on the right and the first minimum on the left is 5.2 mm. The screen on which the pattern is displayed is 80 cm from the slit and the wavelength is 5460 A. Calculate the slit width.

2. A plane wave (λ = 5900 A) falls on a slit with a = 0.40 mm. A converging lens (f = +70 cm) is placed behind the slit and focuses the light on a screen. What is the linear distance on the screen from the center of the pattern to (a) the first minimum and (b) the second minimum?

3. A single slit is illuminated by light whose wavelengths are λ_a and λ_b, so chosen that the first diffraction minimum of λ_a coincides with the second minimum of λ_b. (a) What relationship exists between the two wavelengths? (b) Do any other minima in the two patterns coincide?

4. (a) Show that the values of α at which intensity maxima for single-slit diffraction occur can be found exactly by differentiating Eq. 44–8b with respect to α and equating to zero, obtaining the condition

$$\tan \alpha = \alpha.$$

(b) Find the values of α satisfying this relation by plotting graphically the curve $y = \tan \alpha$ and the straight line $y = \alpha$ and finding their intersections. (c) Find the (nonintegral) values of m corresponding to successive maxima in the single-slit pattern. Note that the secondary maxima do not lie exactly halfway between minima.

5. In Example 3 solve the transcendental equation

$$\frac{1}{2} = \left(\frac{\sin \alpha_x}{\alpha_x}\right)^2$$

graphically for α_x, to an accuracy of three significant figures.

6. (a) In Fig. 44–7d, why is E_θ, which represents the first maximum beyond the central maximum, not vertical? (b) Calculate the angle it makes with the vertical, assuming the slit to be divided into infinitesimal strips of width dx.

7. What is the half-width of a diffracted beam for a slit whose width is (a) 1, (b) 5, and (c) 10 wavelengths?

8. (a) A circular diaphragm 0.60 meter in diameter oscillates at a frequency of 25,000 cycles/sec in an underwater source of sound for submarine detection. Far from the source the sound intensity is distributed as a Fraunhofer diffraction pattern for a circular hole whose diameter equals that of the diaphragm. Take the speed of sound in water to be 1450 meters/sec and find the angle between the normal to the diaphragm and the direction of the first minimum. (b) Repeat for a source having an (audible) frequency of 1000 cycles/sec.

9. The two headlights of an approaching automobile are 4 ft apart. At what maximum distance will the eye resolve them? Assume a pupil diameter of 5.0 mm and λ = 5500 A. Assume also that this distance is determined only by diffraction effects at the circular pupil aperture.

10. The wall of a large room is covered with acoustic tile in which small holes are drilled 5.0 mm from center to center. How far can a person be from such a tile and still distinguish the individual holes, assuming ideal conditions? Assume the diameter of the pupil to be 4.0 mm and λ to be 5500 A.

11. (a) How small is the angular separation of two stars if their images are barely resolved by the Thaw refracting telescope at the Allegheny Observatory in Pittsburgh? The lens diameter is 30 in. and its focal length is 46 ft. Assume λ = 5000 A. (b) Find the distance between these barely resolved stars if each of them is 10 light years distant from the earth. (c) For the image of a single star in this telescope, find the diameter of the first dark ring in the diffraction pattern, as measured on a photographic plate placed at the

focal plane. Assume that the star image structure is associated entirely with diffraction at the lens aperture and not with (small) lens "errors."

12. Find the separation of two points on the moon's surface that can just be resolved by the 200-in. telescope at Mount Palomar, assuming that this distance is determined by diffraction effects. The distance from the earth to the moon is 240,000 miles.

13. Construct qualitative vector diagrams like those of Fig. 44–7 for the double-slit interference pattern. For simplicity, consider $d = 2a$ (see Fig. 44–15). Can you interpret the main features of the intensity pattern this way?

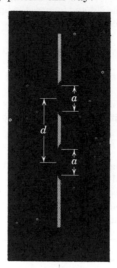

Fig. 44–15

14. Suppose that, as in Example 8, the envelope of the central peak contains eleven fringes. How many fringes lie between the first and second minima of the envelope?

15. For $d = 2a$ in Fig. 44–15, how many interference fringes lie in the central diffraction envelope?

16. If we put $d = a$ in Fig. 44–15, the two slits coalesce into a single slit of width $2a$. Show that Eq. 44–16 reduces to the diffraction pattern for such a slit.

17. (a) Design a double-slit system in which the fourth fringe, not counting the central maximum, is missing. (b) What other fringes, if any, are also missing?

Gratings and Spectra

CHAPTER 45

45–1 Introduction

In connection with Young's experiment (Sections 43–1 and 43–3) we discussed the interference of two coherent waves formed by diffraction at two elementary radiators (pinholes or slits). In our first treatment we assumed that the slit width was much less than the wavelength, so that light diffracted from each slit illuminated the observation screen essentially uniformly. Later, in Section 44–6, we took the slit width into account and showed that the intensity pattern of the interference fringes is modulated by a "diffraction factor" $(\sin \alpha/\alpha)^2$ (see Eq. 44–16).

Here we extend our treatment to cases in which the number N of radiators or diffracting centers is larger—and usually much larger—than two. We consider two situations:

1. An array of N parallel equidistant slits, called a *diffraction grating*.

2. A three-dimensional array of periodically arranged radiators—the atoms in a crystalline solid such as NaCl. In this case the average spacing between the elementary radiators is so small that interference effects must be sought at wavelengths much smaller than those of visible light. We speak of *X-ray diffraction*.

In each case we distinguish carefully between the diffracting properties of a single radiator (slit or atom) and the interference of the waves diffracted, coherently, from the assembly of radiators.

45 2 Multiple Slits

A logical extension of Young's double-slit interference experiment is to increase the number of slits from two to a larger number N. An arrangement like that of Fig. 45–1, usually involving many more slits, is called a *diffrac-*

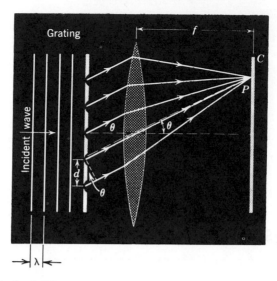

Fig. 45-1   An idealized diffraction grating containing five slits. The slit width a is shown for convenience to be considerably smaller than λ, although this condition is not realized in practice. The figure is distorted in that f is much greater than d in practice.

tion grating. As for a double slit, the intensity pattern that results when monochromatic light of wavelength λ falls on a grating consists of a series of interference fringes. The *angular separations* of these fringes are determined by the ratio λ/d, where d is the spacing between the centers of adjacent slits. The relative *intensities* of these fringes are determined by the diffraction pattern of a single grating slit, which depends on the ratio λ/a, where a is the slit width.

Figure 45–2, which compares the intensity patterns for $N = 2$ and $N = 5$, shows clearly that the "interference" fringes are modulated in intensity by a "diffraction" envelope, as in Fig. 44–14. Figure 45–3 presents a theoretical calculation of the intensity patterns for a few fringes near the centers of the patterns of Fig. 45–2. These two figures show that increasing N (a) does not change the spacing between the (principal) interference fringe maxima,

(a) $N = 2$

(b) $N = 5$

Fig. 45-2   Intensity patterns for "gratings" with (a) $N = 2$ and (b) $N = 5$ for the same value of d and λ. Note how the intensities of the fringes are modulated by a diffraction envelope as in Fig. 44–14; thus the assumption $a \ll \lambda$ is not realized in these actual "gratings." For $N = 5$ three very faint secondary maxima, not visible in this photograph, appear between each pair of adjacent primary maxima.

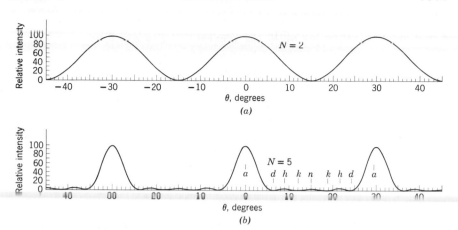

Fig. 45–3 Calculated intensity patterns for (a) a two-slit and (b) a five-slit grating for the same value of d and λ. This figure shows the sharpening of the principal maxima and the appearance of faint secondary maxima for $N > 2$. The letters on the five-slit pattern refer to Fig. 45–5. The figure assumes slits with $a \ll \lambda$ so that the principal maxima are of uniform intensity.

provided d and λ remain unchanged, (b) sharpens the (principal) maxima, and (c) introduces small secondary maxima between the principal maxima. Three such secondaries are present (but not readily visible) between each pair of adjacent principal maxima in Fig. 45–2b.

A principal maximum in Fig. 45–1 will occur when the path difference between rays from adjacent slits ($= d \sin \theta$) is given by

$$d \sin \theta = m\lambda \qquad m = 0, 1, 2, \ldots \qquad \text{(principal maxima)}, \qquad (45\text{–}1)$$

where m is called the *order number*. This equation is identical with Eq. 43–1, which locates the intensity maxima for a double slit. The *locations* of the (principal) maxima are thus determined only by the ratio λ/d and are independent of N. As for the double slit, the ratio a/λ determines the relative *intensities* of the principal maxima but does not alter their locations appreciably.

The sharpening of the principal maxima as N is increased can be understood by a graphical argument, using phasors. Figures 45–4a and b show conditions at any of the principal maxima for a two-slit and a nine-slit grating. The small arrows represent the amplitudes of the wave disturbances arriving at the screen at the position of each principal maximum. For simplicity we consider the central principal maximum only, for which $m = 0$, and thus $\theta = 0$, in Eq. 45–1.

Consider the angle $\Delta\theta_0$ corresponding to the position of zero intensity that lies on either side of the central principal maximum. Figures 45–4c and d show the phasors at this point. The phase difference between waves from adjacent slits, which is zero at the central principal maximum, must increase by an amount $\Delta\phi$ chosen so that the array of phasors just closes on itself, yielding zero resultant intensity. For $N = 2$, $\Delta\phi = 2\pi/2 \, (= 180°)$; for $N = 9$, $\Delta\phi = 2\pi/9 \, (= 40°)$. In the general case it is given by

$$\Delta\phi = \frac{2\pi}{N}.$$

This increase in phase difference for adjacent waves corresponds to an increase in the path difference Δl given by

$$\frac{\text{phase difference}}{2\pi} = \frac{\text{path difference}}{\lambda},$$

or

$$\Delta l = \left(\frac{\lambda}{2\pi}\right)\Delta\phi = \left(\frac{\lambda}{2\pi}\right)\left(\frac{2\pi}{N}\right) = \frac{\lambda}{N}.$$

From Fig. 45–1, however, the path difference Δl at the first minimum is also given by $d \sin \Delta\theta_0$, so that we can write

$$d \sin \Delta\theta_0 = \frac{\lambda}{N},$$

or

$$\sin \Delta\theta_0 = \frac{\lambda}{Nd}.$$

Since $N \gg 1$ for actual gratings, $\sin \Delta\theta_0$ will ordinarily be quite small (that is, the lines will be sharp), and we may replace it by $\Delta\theta_0$ to good approximation, or

$$\Delta\theta_0 = \frac{\lambda}{Nd} \qquad \text{(central principal maximum).} \qquad (45\text{–}2)$$

This equation shows specifically that if we increase N for a given λ and d,

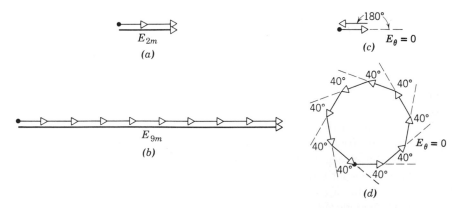

Fig. 45–4 Drawings (*a*) and (*b*) show conditions at the central principal maximum for a two-slit and a nine-slit grating, respectively. Drawings (*c*) and (*d*) show conditions at the minimum of zero intensity that lies on either side of this central principal maximum. In going from (*a*) to (*c*) the phase shift between waves from adjacent slits changes by 180° ($\Delta\phi = 2\pi/2$); in going from (*b*) to (*d*) it changes by 40° ($\Delta\phi = 2\pi/9$).

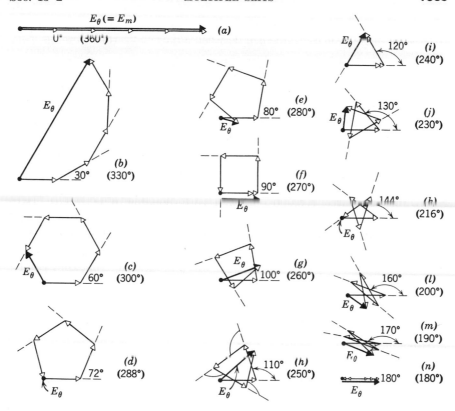

Fig. 45–5 The figures taken in sequence from (a) to (n) and then from (n) to (a) show conditions as the intensity pattern of a five-slit grating is traversed from the central principal maximum to an adjacent principal maximum. Phase differences between waves from adjacent slits are shown directly or, when going from (n) to (a), in parentheses. Principal maxima occur at (a), secondary maxima at, or near, (h) and (n), and points of zero intensity at (d) and (k). Compare Fig. 45–3b.

$\Delta\theta_0$ will decrease, which means that the central principal maximum becomes sharper.

We state without proof,* and for later use, that for principal maxima other than the central one (that is, for $m \neq 0$) the angular distance between the position θ_m of the principal maximum of order m and the minimum that lies on either side is given by

$$\Delta\theta_m = \frac{\lambda}{Nd\cos\theta_m} \qquad \text{(any principal maximum).} \qquad (45\text{--}3)$$

For the central principal maximum we have $m = 0$, $\theta_m = 0$, and $\Delta\theta_m = \Delta\theta_0$, so that Eq. 45–3 reduces, as it must, to Eq. 45–2.

The origin of the secondary maxima that appear for $N > 2$ can also be understood using the phasor method. Figure 45–5a shows conditions at the central principal maximum for a five-slit grating. The vectors are in

---

* See Problem 15.

phase. As we depart from the central maximum, θ in Fig. 45–1 increases from zero and the phase difference between adjacent vectors increases from zero to $\Delta\phi = \dfrac{2\pi}{\lambda} d \sin\theta$. Successive figures show how the resultant wave amplitude E_θ varies with $\Delta\phi$. The student should verify by graphical construction that a given figure represents conditions for both $\Delta\phi$ and $2\pi - \Delta\phi$. Thus we start at $\Delta\phi = 0$, proceed to $\Delta\phi = 180°$, and then trace backward through the sequence, following the phase differences shown in parentheses, until we reach $\Delta\phi = 360°$. This sequence corresponds to traversing the intensity pattern from the central principal maximum to an adjacent one. Figure 45–5, which should be compared with Fig. 45–3b, shows that for $N = 5$ there are three secondary maxima, corresponding to $\Delta\phi = 110°$, $180°$, and $250°$. The student should make a similar analysis for $N = 3$ and should show that only one secondary maximum occurs. In actual gratings, which commonly contain 10,000 to 50,000 "slits," the secondary maxima lie so close to the principal maxima or are so reduced in intensity that they cannot be distinguished from them experimentally.

45–3 Diffraction Gratings

The *grating spacing* d for a typical grating that contains 12,000 "slits" distributed over a 1-in. width is 2.54 cm/12,000, or 21,000 A. Gratings are often used to measure wavelengths and to study the structure and intensity of spectrum lines. Few devices have contributed more to our knowledge of modern physics.

Gratings are made by ruling equally spaced parallel grooves on a glass or a metal * plate, using a diamond cutting point whose motion is automatically controlled by an elaborate ruling engine. Once such a master grating has been prepared, replicas can be formed by pouring a collodion solution on the grating, allowing it to harden, and stripping it off. The stripped collodion, fastened to a flat piece of glass or other backing, forms a good grating.

Figure 45–6 shows a cross section of a common type of grating ruled on glass. In the rudimentary grating of Fig. 45–1 open slits were separated by opaque strips; the *amplitude* of the wave disturbance varied in a periodic way as the grating was crossed, dropping to zero on the opaque strips. The grating of Fig. 45–6 is transparent everywhere, so that there is little periodic change in amplitude as the grating is crossed. The effect of the rulings is to change the *optical thickness* of the grating in a periodic way, rays traversing the grating between the rulings (b in Fig. 45–6) containing more wavelengths than rays traversing the grating in the center of the rulings (a in Fig. 45–6). This results in a periodic change of *phase* as one crosses the grating at right angles to the rulings. Reflection gratings also depend for their operation on a periodic change in phase of the reflected wave as one crosses the grating, the change in amplitude under these conditions being negligible. The principal maxima for *phase gratings*, assuming that the incident light falls on the grating at right angles, can be given by the same formula derived earlier for idealized amplitude or slit gratings,

---

* Gratings ruled on metal are called *reflection gratings* because the interference effects are viewed in reflected rather than in transmitted light. Many research gratings are the reflection type; commonly they are ruled on the surface of a concave mirror, which eliminates the need for lenses.

Fig. 45–6 An enlarged cross section of a diffraction grating ruled on glass. Such gratings, in which the phase of the emerging wave changes as one crosses the grating, are called *phase gratings*.

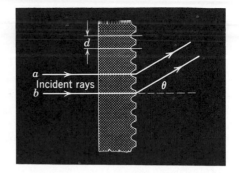

namely

$$d \sin \theta = m\lambda \qquad m = 0, 1, 2\ldots,$$

where d is the distance between the rulings and the integer m is called the *order* of the particular principal maximum. Essentially all gratings used in the visible spectrum, whether of the transmission type, as in Fig. 45–6, or the reflection type, are phase gratings.

Figure 45–7 shows a simple grating spectroscope, used for viewing the spectrum of a light source, assumed to emit a number of discrete wavelengths, or *spectrum lines*. The light from source S is focused by lens L_1 on a slit S_1 placed in the focal plane of lens L_2. The parallel light emerging from collimator C falls on grating G. Parallel rays associated with a particular interference maximum occurring at angle θ fall on lens L_3, being brought to a focus in plane F-F'. The image formed in this plane is examined, using a magnifying lens arrangement E, called an eyepiece. A symmetrical inter-

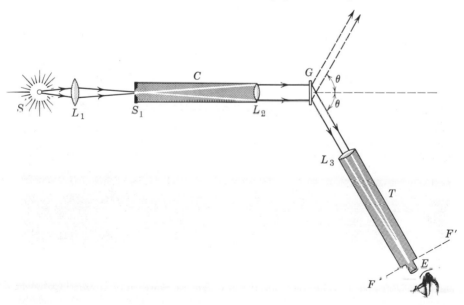

Fig. 45–7 A simple type of grating spectroscope used to analyze the wavelengths of the light emitted by source S.

ference pattern is formed on the other side of the central position, as shown
by the dotted lines. The entire spectrum can be viewed by rotating telescope T through various angles. Instruments used for scientific research or
in industry are more complex than the simple arrangement of Fig. 45–7.
They invariably employ photographic or photoelectric recording and are
called *spectrographs*. Figure 47–12 shows a small portion of the spectrum of
iron, produced by examining the light produced in an arc struck between iron
electrodes, using a research type spectrograph with photographic recording.
Each line in the figure represents a different wavelength that is emitted from
the source.

Grating instruments can be used to make absolute measurements of wavelength, since the grating spacing d in Eq. 45–1 can be measured accurately
with a traveling microscope. Several spectra are normally produced in such
instruments, corresponding to $m = \pm 1, \pm 2$, etc., in Eq. 45–1 (see Fig. 45–8).
This may cause some confusion if the spectra overlap. Further, this multiplicity of spectra reduces the recorded intensity of any given spectrum line
because the available energy is divided among a number of spectra.

This disadvantage of the grating instrument can be overcome by shaping the
profile of the grating grooves so that a large fraction of the light is thrown into a
particular order on a particular side (for a given wavelength). This technique, called
blazing, so alters the diffracting properties of the individual grooves (by controlling
their profiles) that the light of wavelength λ diffracted by a single groove has a sharp
peak of maximum intensity at a selected angle θ ($\neq 0$).

Light can also be analyzed into its component wavelengths if the grating
in Fig. 45–7 is replaced by a prism. In a *prism spectrograph* each wavelength

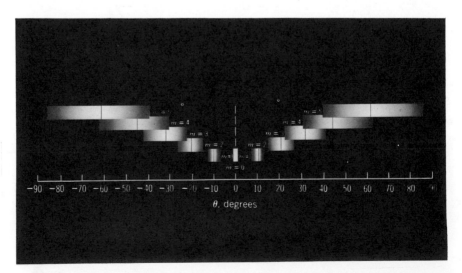

Fig. 45–8 Example 1. The spectrum of white light as viewed in a grating instrument
like that of Fig. 45–7. The different orders, identified by the order number *m*, are shown
separated vertically for clarity. As actually viewed, they would not be so displaced.
The central line in each order corresponds to λ = 5500 A.

in the incident beam is deflected through a definite angle θ, determined by the index of refraction of the prism material for that wavelength. Curves such as Fig. 41–2, which gives the index of refraction of fused quartz as a function of wavelength, show that the shorter the wavelength, the larger the angle of deflection θ. Such curves vary from substance to substance and must be found by measurement. Prism instruments are not adequate for accurate *absolute* measurements of wavelength because the index of refraction of the prism material at the wavelength in question is usually not known precisely enough. Both prism and grating instruments make accurate *comparisons* of wavelength, using a suitable comparison spectrum such as that shown in Fig. 47–12, in which careful absolute determinations have been made of the wavelengths of the spectrum lines. The prism instrument has an advantage over a grating instrument (unblazed) in that its light energy is concentrated into a single spectrum so that brighter lines may be produced.

▶ **Example 1.** A grating with 8000 rulings/in. is illuminated with white light at perpendicular incidence. Describe the diffraction pattern. Assume that the wavelength of the light extends from 4000 to 7000 A.

The grating spacing d is 2.54 cm/8000, or 31,700 A. The central or zero-order maximum corresponds to $m = 0$ in Eq. 45–1. All wavelengths present in the incident light are superimposed at $\theta = 0$, as Fig. 45–8 shows.

The first-order diffraction pattern corresponds to $m = 1$ in Eq. 45–1. The 4000-A line occurs at an angle given by

$$\theta = \sin^{-1}\frac{m\lambda}{d} = \sin^{-1}\frac{(1)(4000\ A)}{31,700\ A} = \sin^{-1}0.126 = 7.3°.$$

In the same way the angle for the 7000-A line is found to be 12.8°, and the entire pattern of Fig. 45–8 can be calculated. Note that the *first-order spectrum* ($m = 1$) is isolated but that the second-, third-, and fourth-order spectra overlap.

Example 2. A diffraction grating has 10^4 rulings uniformly spaced over 1 in. It is illuminated at normal incidence by yellow light from a sodium vapor lamp. This light contains two closely spaced lines (the well-known *sodium doublet*) of wavelengths 5890.0 and 5895.9 A. (*a*) At what angle will the first-order maximum occur for the first of these wavelengths?

The grating spacing d is 10^{-4} in., or 25,400 A. The first-order maximum corresponds to $m = 1$ in Eq. 45–1. We thus have

$$\theta = \sin^{-1}\frac{m\lambda}{d} = \sin^{-1}\frac{(1)(5890\ A)}{25,400\ A} = \sin^{-1}0.232 = 13.3°.$$

(*b*) What is the angular separation between the first-order maxima for these lines?

The straightforward way to find this separation is to repeat this calculation for $\lambda = 5895.9$ A and to subtract the two angles. A difficulty, which can best be appreciated by carrying out the calculation, is that we must carry a large number of significant figures to obtain a meaningful value for the difference between the angles. To calculate the difference in angular positions *directly*, let us write down Eq. 45–1, solved for $\sin \theta$, and differentiate it, treating θ and λ as variables:

$$\sin \theta = \frac{m\lambda}{d}$$

$$\cos \theta\ d\theta = \frac{m}{d}\ d\lambda.$$

If the wavelengths are close enough together, as in this case, $d\lambda$ can be replaced by $\Delta\lambda$, the actual wavelength difference; $d\theta$ then becomes $\Delta\theta$, the quantity we seek. This gives

$$\Delta\theta = \frac{m\,\Delta\lambda}{d\cos\theta} = \frac{(1)(5.9\text{ A})}{(25{,}400\text{ A})(\cos 13.3°)} = 2.4 \times 10^{-4}\text{ radian} = 0.014°.$$

Note that although the wavelengths involve five significant figures our calculation, done this way, involves only two or three, with consequent reduction in numerical manipulation.   ◀

The quantity $d\theta/d\lambda$, called the *dispersion D* of a grating, is a measure of the angular separation produced between two incident monochromatic waves whose wavelengths differ by a small wavelength interval. From this example we see that

$$D = \frac{d\theta}{d\lambda} = \frac{m}{d\cos\theta}. \tag{45-4}$$

45–4   Resolving Power of a Grating

To distinguish light waves whose wavelengths are close together, the principal maxima of these wavelengths formed by the grating should be as narrow as possible. Expressed otherwise, the grating should have a high *resolving power R*, defined from

$$R = \frac{\lambda}{\Delta\lambda}. \tag{45-5}$$

Here λ is the mean wavelength of two spectrum lines that can barely be recognized as separate and $\Delta\lambda$ is the wavelength difference between them. The smaller $\Delta\lambda$ is, the closer the lines can be and still be resolved; hence the greater the resolving power R of the grating. It is to achieve a high resolving power that gratings with many rulings are constructed.

The resolving power of a grating is usually determined by the same consideration (that is, the Rayleigh criterion) that we used in Section 44–5 to determine the resolving power of a lens. If two principal maxima are to be barely resolved, they must, according to this criterion, have an angular separation $\Delta\theta$ such that the maximum of one line coincides with the first minimum of the other; see Fig. 44–11. If we apply this criterion, we can show that

$$R = Nm, \tag{45-6}$$

where N is the total number of rulings in the grating and m is the order. As expected, the resolving power is zero for the central principal maximum ($m = 0$), all wavelengths being undeflected in this order.

Let us derive Eq. 45–6. The angular separation between two principal maxima whose wavelengths differ by $\Delta\lambda$ is found from Eq. 45–4, which we recast as

$$\Delta\theta = \frac{m\,\Delta\lambda}{d\cos\theta}. \tag{45-4}$$

The Rayleigh criterion (Section 44–5) requires that this be equal to the angular separation between a principal maximum and its adjacent minimum. This is given from Eq. 45–3, dropping the subscript m in $\cos \theta_m$, as

$$\Delta\theta_m = \frac{\lambda}{dN \cos \theta}. \tag{45–3}$$

Equating Eqs. 45–4 and 45–3 leads to

$$R \; (= \lambda/\Delta\lambda) = Nm,$$

which is the desired relation.

▶ **Example 3.** In Example 2 how many rulings must a grating have if it is barely to resolve the sodium doublet in the third order?

From Eq. 45–5 the required resolving power is

$$R = \frac{\lambda}{\Delta\lambda} = \frac{5890 \text{ A}}{(5895.9 - 5890.0)\text{A}} = 1000.$$

From Eq. 45–6 the number of rulings needed is

$$N = \frac{R}{m} = \frac{1000}{3} = 330.$$

This is a modest requirement.   ◀

The resolving power of a grating must not be confused with its dispersion. Table 45–1 shows the characteristics of three gratings, each illuminated with light of $\lambda = 5890$ A, the diffracted light being viewed in the first order ($m = 1$ in Eq. 45–1).

Table 45–1

SOME CHARACTERISTICS OF THREE GRATINGS
($\lambda = 5890$ A, $m = 1$)

Grating	N	d, A	θ	R	D 10^{-3} degrees/A
A	10,000	25,400	13.3°	10,000	2.32
B	20,000	25,400	13.3°	20,000	2.32
C	10,000	13,700	25.5°	10,000	4.64

The student should verify that the values of D and R given in the table can be calculated from Eqs. 45–4 and 45–6, respectively.

For the conditions of use noted in Table 45–1, gratings A and B have the same *dispersion* and A and C have the same *resolving power*. Figure 45–9 shows the intensity patterns that would be produced by these gratings for two incident waves of wavelengths λ_1 and λ_2, in the vicinity of $\lambda = 5890$ A. Grating B, which has high resolving power, has narrow intensity maxima and is inherently capable of distinguishing lines that are much closer together in wavelength than those of Fig. 45–9. Grating C, which has high dispersion, produces twice the angular separation between rays λ_1 and λ_2 that grating B does.

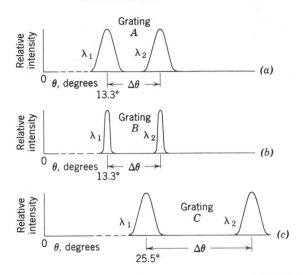

Fig. 45–9   The intensity patterns for light of wavelengths λ_1 and λ_2 near 5890 A, incident on the gratings of Table 45–1.   Grating B has the highest resolving power and grating C the highest dispersion.

▶ **Example 4.**   The grating of Example 1 has 8000 lines illuminated by light from a mercury vapor discharge.   (*a*) What is the expected dispersion, in the third order, in the vicinity of the intense green line ($\lambda = 5460$ A)?   Noting that $d = 31{,}700$ A, we have, from Eq. 45–1,

$$\theta = \sin^{-1}\frac{m\lambda}{d} = \sin^{-1}\frac{(3)(5460 \text{ A})}{31{,}700 \text{ A}} = \sin^{-1}0.517 = 31.1°.$$

From Eq. 45–4 we have

$$D = \frac{m}{d\cos\theta} = \frac{3}{(31{,}700 \text{ A})(\cos 31.1°)} = 1.1 \times 10^{-4} \text{ radian/A} = 6.3 \times 10^{-3} \text{ deg/A}.$$

(*b*) What is the expected resolving power of this grating in the fifth order?   Equation 45–6 gives

$$R = Nm = (8000)(5) = 40{,}000.$$

Thus near $\lambda = 5460$ A a wavelength difference $\Delta\lambda$ given by Eq. 45–5, or

$$\Delta\lambda = \frac{\lambda}{R} = \frac{5460 \text{ A}}{40{,}000} = 0.14 \text{ A},$$

can be distinguished.   ◀

45–5   X-ray Diffraction

Figure 45–10 shows how X-rays are produced when electrons from a heated filament F are accelerated by a potential difference V and strike a metal target T.   X-rays are electromagnetic radiation with wavelengths of the order of 1 A.   This value is to be compared to 5500 A for the center of the visible spectrum.   For such small wavelengths a standard optical diffraction grating, as normally employed, cannot be used.   For $\lambda = 1$ A and $d = 30{,}000$ A,

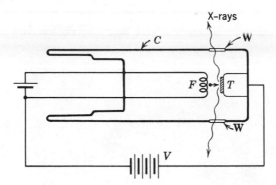

Fig. 45-10 X-rays are generated when electrons from heated filament F, accelerated by potential difference V, are brought to rest on striking metallic target T. W is a "window" —transparent to X-rays—in the evacuated metal container C.

for example, Eq. 45-1 shows that the first-order maximum occurs at

$$\theta = \sin^{-1} \frac{m\lambda}{d} = \sin^{-1} \frac{(1)(1 \text{ A})}{3 \times 10^4 \text{ A}} = \sin^{-1} 0.33 \times 10^{-4} = 0.002°.$$

This is too close to the central maximum to be practical. A grating with $d \cong \lambda$ is desirable, but, since X-ray wavelengths are about equal to atomic diameters, such gratings cannot be constructed mechanically.

In 1912 it occurred to the German physicist Max von Laue that a crystalline solid, consisting as it does of a regular array of atoms, might form a natural three-dimensional "diffraction grating" for X-rays. Figure 45-11 shows that if a collimated beam of X-rays, continuously distributed in wavelength, is allowed to fall on a crystal, such as sodium chloride, intense beams corresponding to constructive interference from the many diffracting centers

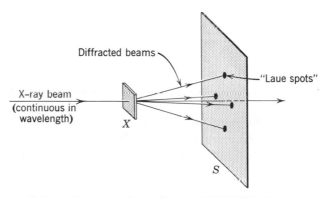

Fig. 45-11 A nonmonochromatic beam of X-rays falls on a crystal X, which may be NaCl. Strong diffracted beams appear in certain directions, forming a so-called Laue pattern on a photographic film S.

Fig. 45–12 Laue X-ray diffraction pattern from sodium chloride. A crystal of ordinary table salt was used in making this plate. (Courtesy of W. Arrington and J. L. Katz, X-ray Laboratory, Rensselaer Polytechnic Institute.)

of which the crystal is made up appear in certain sharply defined directions. If these beams fall on a photographic film, they form an assembly of "Laue spots." Figure 45–12, which is an actual example of these spots, shows that the hypothesis of Laue is indeed correct. The atomic arrangements in the crystal can be deduced from a careful study of the positions and intensities of the Laue spots * in much the same way that we might deduce the structure of an optical grating (that is, the detailed profile of its slits) by a study of the positions and intensities of the lines in the interference pattern.

Figure 45–13 shows how sodium and chlorine atoms (strictly, Na^+ and Cl^- ions) are stacked to form a crystal of sodium chloride. This pattern, which has *cubic* symmetry, is one of the many atomic arrangements exhibited

---

* Other experimental arrangements have supplanted the Laue technique to a considerable extent today; the principle remains unchanged, however.

by solids.   The model represents the *unit cell* for sodium chloride.   This is
the smallest unit from which the crystal may be built up by repetition in
three dimensions.   The student should verify that no smaller assembly of
atoms possesses this property.   For sodium chloride the length of the cube
edge of the unit cell is 5.62737 A.

Each unit cell in sodium chloride has four sodium ions and four chlorine
ions associated with it.   In Fig. 45–13 the sodium ion in the center belongs
entirely to the cell shown.   Each of the other twelve sodium ions shown is
shared with three adjacent unit cells so that each contributes one-fourth of
an ion to the cell under consideration.   The total number of sodium ions is
then $1 + \frac{1}{4}(12) = 4$.   By similar reasoning the student can show that although there are fourteen chlorine ions in Fig. 45–13 only four are associated
with the unit cell shown.

The unit cell is the fundamental repetitive diffracting unit in the crystal,
corresponding to the slit (and its adjacent opaque strip) in the optical dif-

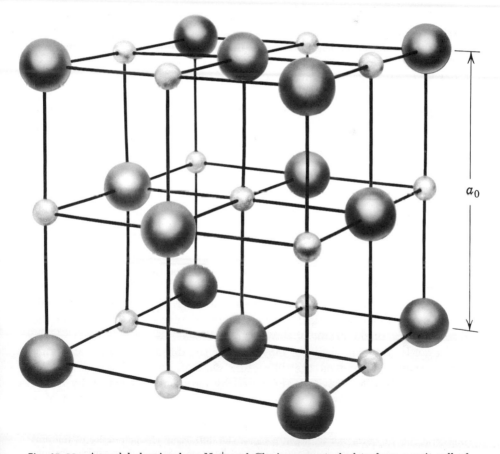

a_0

Fig. 45–13   A model showing how Na^+ and Cl^- ions are stacked to form a unit cell of
NaCl.   The small spheres represent sodium ions, the large ones chlorine.   The edge a_0
of the (cubical) unit cell is 5.62737 A.

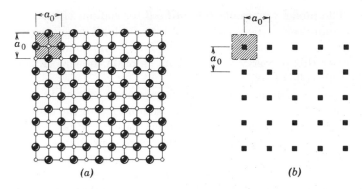

Fig. 45–14 (*a*) A section through a crystal of sodium chloride, showing the sodium and chlorine ions. (*b*) The corresponding unit cells in this section, each cell being represented by a small black square.

fraction grating of Fig. 45–1. Figure 45–14*a* shows a particular plane in a sodium chloride crystal. If each unit cell intersected by this plane is represented by a small cube, Fig. 45–14*b* results. The student may imagine each of these figures extended indefinitely in three dimensions.

Let us treat each small cube in Fig. 45–14*b* as an elementary diffracting center, corresponding to a slit in an optical grating. The *directions* (but not the intensities) of all the diffracted X-ray beams that can emerge from a sodium chloride crystal (for a given X-ray wavelength and a given orientation of the incident beam) are determined by the geometry of this three-dimensional lattice of diffracting centers. In exactly the same way the *directions* (but not the intensities) of all the diffracted beams that can emerge from a particular optical grating (for a given wavelength and orientation of the incident beam) are determined only by the geometry of the grating, that is, by the grating spacing *d*. Representing the unit cell by what is essentially a point, as in Fig. 45–14*b*, corresponds to representing the slits in a diffraction grating by lines, as we did in discussing Young's experiment in Section 43–1.

The *intensities* of the lines from an optical diffraction grating are determined by the diffracting characteristics of a single slit, as Fig. 44–14 shows. In the idealized case of Fig. 45–1 these characteristics depend on the slit width *a*. In practical optical gratings these characteristics depend on the detailed shape of the profile of the grating rulings.

In exactly the same way the *intensities* of the diffracted beams emerging from a crystal depend on the diffracting characteristics of the unit cell.* Fundamentally the X-rays are diffracted by electrons, diffraction by nuclei being negligible in most cases. Thus the diffracting characteristics of a

---

* For some directions in which a beam might be expected to emerge, from interference considerations, no beam will be found because the diffracting characteristics of the unit cell are such that no energy is diffracted in that direction. Similarly, in optical gratings some lines, permitted by interference considerations, may not appear if their predicted positions coincide with a null in the single-slit diffraction pattern (see Fig. 44–12).

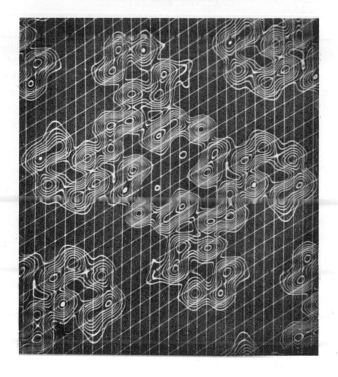

(a)

(b)

Fig. 45–15 (a) A photograph of an oscilloscope screen arranged to display projected electron density contours for phthalocyanine ($C_{32}H_{18}N_8$). Such plots, constructed electronically from X-ray diffraction data by an analog computer, provide a vivid picture of the structure of molecules. (Courtesy of Ray Pepinsky.) (b) A structural representation of the molecule phthalocyanine. The student should make a detailed comparison with (a), locating the various atoms identified in (b). Note that hydrogen atoms, which contain only a single electron, are not prominent in (a).

unit cell depend on how the electrons are distributed throughout the volume of the cell. By studying the *directions* of diffracted X-ray beams, we can learn the basic symmetry of the crystal. By also studying the *intensities* we can learn how electrons are distributed in the unit cell. Figure 45–15 shows the average density of electrons projected onto a particular plane through a unit cell of a crystal of phthalocyanine. This remarkable figure suggests something of the full power of X-ray methods for studying the structure of solids.

45–6   Bragg's Law

Bragg's law predicts the conditions under which diffracted X-ray beams from a crystal are possible. In deriving it, we ignore the structure of the unit cell, which is related only to the intensities of these beams. The dashed sloping lines in Fig. 45–16a represent the intersection with the plane of the figure of an arbitrary set of planes passing through the elementary diffracting centers. The perpendicular distance between adjacent planes is d. Many other such families of planes, with different *interplanar spacings*, can be defined.

Figure 45–16b shows a plane wave that lies in the plane of the figure falling on one member of the family of planes defined in Fig. 45–16a, the incident rays making an angle θ with the plane.* Consider a family of diffracted rays lying in the plane of Fig. 45 16b and making an angle β with the plane containing the elementary diffracting centers. The diffracted rays will combine to produce maximum intensity if the path difference between adjacent rays is an integral number of wavelengths or

$$ae - bd = h(\cos \beta - \cos \theta) = l\lambda \qquad l = 0, 1, 2, \ldots. \qquad (45\text{–}7)$$

For $l = 0$ this leads to $\qquad\qquad \beta = \theta,$

and the plane of atoms acts like a mirror for the incident wave, no matter what the value of θ.

For other values of l, β does not equal θ, but the diffracted beam can always be regarded as being "reflected" from a *different* set of planes than that shown in Fig. 45–16a with a different interplanar spacing d. Since we wish to describe each diffracted beam as a "reflection" from a particular set of planes and since we are dealing in the present argument only with the particular set of planes shown in Fig. 45–16a we ignore all values of l other than $l = 0$ in Eq. 45–7. It can also be shown that a plane of diffracting centers acts like a mirror (that is, $\beta = \theta$) whether or not the incident wave lies in the plane of Fig. 45–16b.

Figure 45–16c shows an incident wave striking the *family* of planes, a single member of which was considered in Fig. 45–16b. For a single plane, mirror-like "reflection" occurs for *any* value of θ, as we have seen. To have a constructive interference in the beam diffracted from the entire family of planes

---

* In X-ray diffraction it is customary to specify the direction of a wave by giving the angle between the ray and the plane (the *glancing angle*) rather than the angle between the ray and the normal.

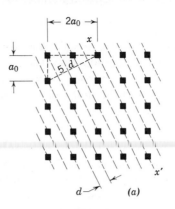

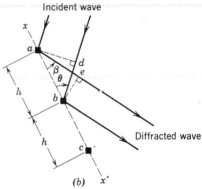

Fig. 45–16 (*a*) A section through the NaCl unit cell lattice of Fig. 45–14*b*. The dashed sloping lines represent an arbitrary family of planes, with interplanar spacing *d*. (*b*) An incident wave falls, at grazing angle *θ*, on one of the planes, *xx'*, shown in (*a*). (*c*) An incident wave falls on the entire family of planes shown in (*a*). A strong diffracted wave is formed.

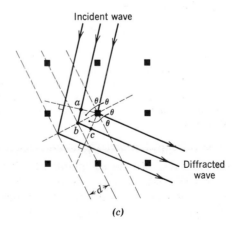

in the direction θ, the rays from the separate planes must reinforce each other. This means that the path difference for rays from adjacent planes (abc in Fig. 45–16c) must be an integral number of wavelengths or

$$2d \sin \theta = m\lambda \qquad m = 1, 2, 3, \ldots . \qquad (45\text{–}8)$$

This relation is called *Bragg's law* after W. L. Bragg who first derived it. The quantity d in this equation (the interplanar spacing) is the perpendicular distance between the planes. For the planes of Fig. 45–16a analysis shows that d is related to the unit cell dimension a_0 by

$$d = \frac{a_0}{\sqrt{5}}. \qquad (45\text{–}9)$$

If an incident *monochromatic* X-ray beam falls at an *arbitrary* angle θ on a particular set of atomic planes, a diffracted beam will *not* result because Eq. 45–8 will not, in general, be satisfied. If the incident X-rays are *continuous* in wavelength, diffracted beams will result when wavelengths given by

$$\lambda = \frac{2d \sin \theta}{m} \qquad m = 1, 2, 3, \ldots$$

are present in the incident beam (see Eq. 45–8).

▶ **Example 5.** At what angles must an X-ray beam with $\lambda = 1.10$ A fall on the family of planes represented in Fig. 45–16c if a diffracted beam is to exist? Assume the material to be sodium chloride.

The interplanar spacing d for these planes is given by Eq. 45–9 or

$$d = \frac{a_0}{\sqrt{5}} = \frac{5.63 \text{ A}}{2.24} = 2.52 \text{ A}.$$

Equation 45–8 gives

$$\sin \theta = \frac{m\lambda}{2d} = \frac{(m)(1.10 \text{ A})}{(2)(2.52 \text{ A})} = 0.218m.$$

Diffracted beams are possible at $\theta = 12.6°$ ($m = 1$), $\theta = 25.9°$ ($m = 2$), $\theta = 40.9°$ ($m = 3$), and $\theta = 60.7°$ ($m = 4$). Higher-order beams cannot exist because they require $\sin \theta$ to exceed unity. Actually, the odd-order beams ($m = 1, 3$) prove to have zero intensity because the unit cell in cubic crystals such as NaCl has diffracting properties such that the intensity of the light scattered in these orders is zero (see Problem 26). ◀

X-ray diffraction is a powerful tool for studying the arrangements of atoms in crystals. To do so quantitatively requires that the wavelength of the X-rays be known. In one of several approaches to this problem the unit cell dimension for NaCl * is determined by a method that does not involve X-rays. X-ray diffraction measurements on NaCl can then be used to determine the wavelength of the X-ray beam which in turn can be used to determine the structures of solids other than NaCl.

---

* In practice, calcite ($CaCO_3$) proves to be more useful as a standard crystal for a number of technical reasons.

If ρ is the measured density of NaCl, we have, for the unit cell of Fig. 45-13,* recalling that each unit cell contains four NaCl "molecules,"

$$\rho = \frac{m}{V} = \frac{4m_{NaCl}}{a_0^{3}}.$$

Here m_{NaCl}, the mass of a NaCl molecule, is given by

$$m_{NaCl} = \frac{M}{N_0},$$

where M is the molecular weight of NaCl and N_0 is Avogadro's number. Combining these two equations and solving for a_0 yields

$$a_0 = \left(\frac{4M}{N_0\rho}\right)^{\frac{1}{3}},$$

which permits us to calculate a_0. Once a_0 is known, the wavelengths of monochromatic X-ray beams can be found, using Bragg's law (Eq. 45–8).

QUESTIONS

1. Discuss this statement: "A diffraction grating can just as well be called an interference grating."

2. For the simple spectroscope of Fig. 45-7, show (a) that θ increases with λ for a grating and (b) that θ decreases with λ for a prism.

3. You are given a photograph of a spectrum on which the angular positions and the wavelengths of the spectrum lines are marked. (a) How can you tell whether the spectrum was taken with a prism or a grating instrument? (b) What information could you gather about either the prism or the grating from studying such a spectrum?

4. Assume that the limits of the visible spectrum are 4300 and 6800 A. Is it possible to design a grating, assuming that the incident light falls normally on it, such that the first-order spectrum *barely overlaps* the second-order spectrum?

5. (a) Why does a diffraction grating have closely spaced rulings? (b) Why does it have a large number of rulings?

6. The relation $R = Nm$ suggests that the resolving power of a given grating can be made as large as desired by choosing an arbitrarily high order of diffraction. Discuss.

7. Show that at a given wavelength and a given angle of diffraction the resolving power of a grating depends only on its width W ($= Nd$).

8. According to Eq. 45–3 the principal maxima become wider (that is, $\Delta\theta_m$ increases) the higher the order m (that is, the larger θ_m becomes). According to Eq. 45–6 the resolving power becomes greater the higher the order m. Explain this apparent paradox.

9. Is the pattern of Fig. 45–12 more properly described as a diffraction pattern or as an interference pattern?

10. For a given family of planes in a crystal, can the wavelength of incident X-rays be (a) too large or (b) too small to form a diffracted beam?

11. If a parallel beam of X-rays of wavelength λ is allowed to fall on a randomly oriented crystal of any material, generally no intense diffracted beams will occur. Such beams

* This relation cannot be written down unless it is known that the structure of NaCl is cubic. This can be determined, however, by inspection of the symmetry of the spots in Fig. 45–12; the wavelength of the X-rays need not be known.

appear if (a) the X-ray beam consists of a continuous distribution of wavelengths rather than a single wavelength or (b) the specimen is not a single crystal but a finely divided powder.   Explain.

12. Why cannot a simple cube of edge $a_0/2$ in Fig. 45–13 be used as a unit cell for sodium chloride?

13. How would you *measure* (a) the dispersion D and (b) the resolving power R for either a prism or a grating spectrograph.

PROBLEMS

1. Given a grating with 4000 lines/cm, how many orders of entire visible spectrum (4000–7000 A) can be produced?

2. Derive this expression for the intensity pattern for a three-slit "grating":

$$I_\theta = \tfrac{1}{9}I_m(1 + 4\cos\phi + 4\cos^2\phi),$$

where

$$\phi = \frac{2\pi d\,\sin\theta}{\lambda}.$$

Assume that $a \ll \lambda$ and be guided by the derivation of the corresponding double-slit formula (Eq. 43–9).

3. (a) Using the result of Problem 2, show that the half-width of the fringes for a three-slit diffraction pattern, assuming θ small enough so that $\sin\theta \cong \theta$, is

$$\Delta\theta \cong \frac{\lambda}{3.2d}.$$

(b) Compare this with the expression derived for the two-slit pattern in Problem 10, Chapter 43.   (c) Do these results support the conclusion that for a fixed slit spacing the interference maxima become sharper as the number of slits is increased?

4. Using the result of Problem 2, show that a three-slit "grating" has only one secondary maximum.   Find its location and its relative intensity.

5. A grating designed for use in the infrared region of the electromagnetic spectrum is "blazed" to concentrate all its intensity in the first order ($m = 1$) for $\lambda = 80,000$ A.   If visible light (4000 A $< \lambda <$ 7000 A) were allowed to fall on this grating, what visual appearance would the diffracted beams present?

6. The central intensity maximum formed by a grating, along with its subsidiary secondary maxima, can be viewed as the diffraction pattern of a single "slit" whose width is that of the entire grating.   Treating the grating as a single wide slit, assuming that $m = 0$, and using the methods of Section 44–4, show that Eq. 45–2 can be derived.

7. A grating has 8000 rulings/in.   For what wavelengths in the visible spectrum can fifth-order diffraction be observed?

8. A diffraction grating has 5000 rulings/in., and a strong diffracted beam is noted at $\theta = 30°$.   (a) What are the possible wavelengths of the incident light?   (b) How could you identify them in an actual case?

9. A diffraction grating 2.0 cm wide has 6000 rulings.   At what angles will maximum-intensity beams occur if the incident radiation has a wavelength of 5890 A?

10. Assume that the limits of the visible spectrum are arbitrarily chosen as 4300 and 6800 A.   Design a grating that will spread the first-order spectrum through an angular range of 20°.

11. A grating has 8000 rulings/in. and is illuminated at normal incidence by white light.   A spectrum is formed on a screen 30 cm from the grating.   If a 1.0-cm square hole is cut in the screen, its inner edge being 5.0 cm from the central maximum, what range of wavelengths passes through the hole?

12. Assume that light is incident on a grating at an angle ψ as shown in Fig. 45–17. Show that the condition for a diffraction maximum is

$$d(\sin \psi + \sin \theta) = m\lambda \qquad m = 0, 1, 2, \ldots.$$

Only the special case $\psi = 0$ has been treated in this chapter (compare Eq. 45–1).

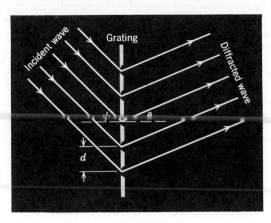

Fig. 45–17

13. Show that in a grating with alternately transparent and opaque strips of *equal* width all the even orders (except $m = 0$) are absent.

14. A transmission grating with $d = 1.50 \times 10^{-4}$ cm is illuminated at various angles of incidence by light of wavelength 6000 A. Plot as a function of angle of incidence (0 to 90°) the angular deviation of the first-order diffracted beam from the incident direction.

15. Derive Eq. 45–3, that is, the expression for $\Delta\theta_m$, the angular distance between a principal maximum of order m and either adjacent minimum.

16. A three-slit grating has separation d between adjacent slits. If the middle slit is covered up, will the half-width of the intensity maxima become broader or narrower? See Problem 3 and also Problem 10, Chapter 43.

17. A grating has 40,000 rulings spread over 3.0 in. (a) What is its expected dispersion D for sodium light ($\lambda = 5890$ A) in the first three orders? (b) What is its resolving power in these orders?

18. In a particular grating the sodium doublet (see Example 2) is viewed in third order at 80° to the normal and is barely resolved. Find (a) the grating spacing and (b) the total width of the rulings.

19. A source containing a mixture of hydrogen and deuterium atoms emits a red doublet at $\lambda = 6563$ A whose separation is 1.8 A. Find the minimum number of lines needed in a diffraction grating which can resolve these lines in the first order.

20. Show that the dispersion of a grating can be written as

$$D = \frac{\tan \theta}{\lambda}.$$

21. A grating has 6000 rulings/cm and is 6.0 cm wide. (a) What is the smallest wavelength interval that can be resolved in the third order at $\lambda = 5000$ A? (b) For this wavelength and this grating, can the resolution be improved? How?

22. Light containing a mixture of two wavelengths, 5000 A and 6000 A, is incident normally on a diffraction grating. It is desired (1) that the first and second principal maxima for each wavelength appear at $\theta \le 30°$, (2) that the dispersion be as high as possible, *and* (3) that the third order for 6000 A be a missing order. (a) What is the separation

between adjacent slits? (b) What is the smallest possible individual slit width? (c) Name *all* orders for 6000 A that actually appear on the screen with the values chosen in (a) and (b).

23. Light of wavelength 6000 A is incident normally on a diffraction grating. Two *adjacent* principal maxima occur at $\sin \theta = 0.2$ and $\sin \theta = 0.3$, respectively. The fourth order is a missing order. (a) What is the separation between adjacent slits? (b) What is the smallest possible individual slit width? (c) Name *all* orders actually appearing on the screen with the values chosen in (a) and (b).

24. An optical grating with a spacing $d = 15,000$ A is used to analyze soft X-rays of wavelength $\lambda = 5.0$ A. The angle of incidence θ is $90° - \gamma$, where γ is a *small* angle. The first order maximum is found at an angle $\theta = 90° - 2\beta$. Find the value of β.

25. Monochromatic X-rays ($\lambda = 1.20$ A) fall on a crystal of sodium chloride, making an angle of 45° with a reference line as shown in Fig. 45–18. Through what angles must the crystal be turned to give a diffracted beam associated with the planes shown? Assume that the crystal is turned about an axis that is perpendicular to the plane of the page. Ignore the possibility (see Problem 26) that some of these beams may be of zero intensity.

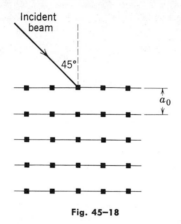

Fig. 45–18

26. *Missing orders in X-ray diffraction.* In Problem 25 the $m = 1$ beam, permitted by interference considerations, has zero intensity because of the diffracting properties of the unit cell for this geometry of beams and crystal. Prove this. (Hint: Show that the "reflection" from an atomic plane through the top of a layer of unit cells is canceled by a "reflection" from a plane through the middle of this layer of cells. All odd-order beams prove to have zero intensity.)

27. Assume that the incident X-ray beam in Fig. 45–18 is not monochromatic but contains wavelengths in a band from 0.95 to 1.30 A. Will diffracted beams, associated with the planes shown, occur? Assume $a_0 = 2.75$ A.

28. In comparing the wavelengths of two monochromatic X-ray lines, it is noted that line A gives a first-order reflection maximum at a glancing angle of 30° to the smooth face of a crystal. Line B, known to have a wavelength of 0.97 angstroms, gives a third-order reflection maximum at an angle of 60° from the same face of the same crystal. Find the wavelength of line A.

Polarization

CHAPTER 46

46–1 Polarization

Light, like all electromagnetic radiation, is predicted by electromagnetic theory to be a *transverse wave*, the directions of the vibrating electric and magnetic vectors being at right angles to the direction of propagation instead of parallel to it as in a longitudinal wave. The transverse waves of Figs. 46–1 and 39–11 have the additional characteristic that they are *plane-polarized*. This means that the vibrations of the **E** vector are parallel to each other for all points in the wave. At any such point the vibrating **E** vector and the direction of propagation form a plane, called the *plane of vibration;* in a plane-polarized wave all such planes are parallel.

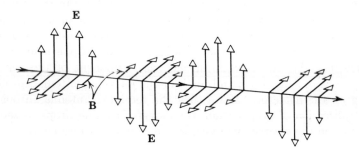

Fig. 46–1 An instantaneous "snapshot" of a plane-polarized wave showing the vectors **E** and **B** along a particular ray. The wave is moving to the right with speed *c*. The plane containing the vibrating **E** vector and the direction of propagation is a *plane of vibration*.

The transverse nature of light waves cannot be deduced from the interference or diffraction experiments so far described because longitudinal waves such as sound waves also show these effects. An experimental basis for believing that light waves are transverse was provided by Thomas Young in 1817. Two of his contemporaries, Dominique-François Arago (1786–1853) and Augustin Jean Fresnel (1788–1827), were able, by allowing a light beam to fall on a crystal of calcite, to produce two separate beams (see Section 46–4). Astonishingly, these beams, although coherent, produced no interference fringes but only a uniform illumination. Young deduced from this that light must be a transverse wave and that the planes of vibration in the two beams must be at right angles to each other. Wave disturbances that act at right angles to each other cannot show interference effects; the student is asked to prove this in Problem 9. Young's words to Arago were these:

> I have been reflecting on the possibility of giving an imperfect explanation of the affection of light which constitutes polarization without departing from the genuine doctrine of undulations. It is a principle in this theory that all undulations are simply propagated through homogeneous mediums in concentric spherical surfaces like the undulations of sound, consisting simply in the direct and retrograde motions of the particles in the direction of the radius with their concomitant condensation and rarefactions [that is, longitudinal waves]. And yet, it is possible to explain in this theory a transverse vibration, propagated also in the direction of the radius, and with equal velocity, the motions of the particles being in a certain constant direction with respect to that radius; and this is a *polarization*.

Note how Young presents the possibility of a transverse vibration as a novel idea, light having been generally—but incorrectly—assumed to be a longitudinal vibration.

In a plane-polarized transverse wave it is necessary to specify two directions, that of the wave disturbance (**E**, say) and that of propagation. In a longitudinal wave these directions are identical. In plane-polarized transverse waves, but not in longitudinal waves, we may thus expect a lack of symmetry about the direction of propagation. Electromagnetic waves in the radio and microwave range exhibit this lack of symmetry readily. Such a wave, generated by the surging of charge up and down in the dipole that forms the transmitting antenna of Fig. 46–2, has (at large distances from the dipole and at right angles to it) an electric field vector parallel to the dipole axis. When this plane-polarized wave falls on a second dipole connected to a microwave detector, the alternating electric component of the wave will cause electrons to surge back and forth in the receiving antenna, producing a reading on the detector. If we turn the receiving antenna through 90° about the direction of propagation, the detector reading drops to zero. In this orientation the electric field vector is not able to cause charge to move along the dipole axis because it points at right angles to this axis. We can reproduce the experiment of Fig. 46–2 by turning the receiving antenna of a television set (assumed an electric dipole type) through 90° about an axis that points toward the transmitting station.

Common sources of visible light differ from radio and microwave sources

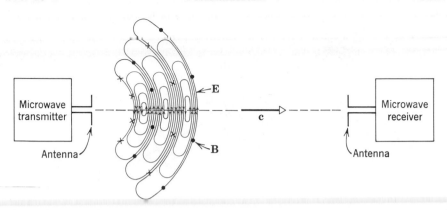

Fig. 46–2 The vectors **E** in the transmitted wave are parallel to the axis of the receiving antenna so that the wave will be detected. If the receiving antenna is rotated through 90° about the direction of propagation, no signal will be detected.

in that the elementary radiators, that is, the atoms and molecules, act independently. The light propagated in a given direction consists of independent wavetrains whose planes of vibration are randomly oriented about the direction of propagation, as in Fig. 46–3b. Such light, though still transverse, is *unpolarized*. The random orientation of the planes of vibration produces symmetry about the propagation direction, which, on casual study, conceals the true transverse nature of the waves. To study this transverse nature, a way must be found to unsort the different planes of vibration.

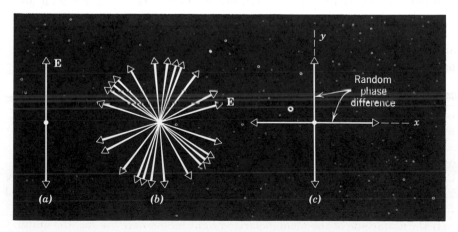

Fig. 46–3 (a) A plane-polarized transverse wave moving toward the reader, showing only the electric vector. (b) An unpolarized transverse wave viewed as a random superposition of many plane-polarized wavetrains. (c) A second, completely equivalent, description of an unpolarized transverse wave; here the unpolarized wave is viewed as two plane-polarized waves *with a random phase difference*. The orientation of the x and y axes about the propagation direction is completely arbitrary.

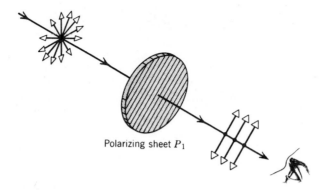

Fig. 46-4   A polarizing sheet produces plane-polarized light from unpolarized light.   The parallel lines, which are not actually visible on the sheet, suggest the characteristic polarizing direction of the sheet.

46-2   Polarizing Sheets

Figure 46-4 shows unpolarized light falling on a sheet of commercial polarizing material called *Polaroid*.*   There exists in the sheet a certain characteristic polarizing direction, shown by the parallel lines.   *The sheet will transmit only those wave-train components whose electric vectors vibrate parallel to this direction and will absorb those that vibrate at right angles to this direction.*   The emerging light will be plane-polarized.   This polarizing direction is established during the manufacturing process by embedding certain long-chain molecules in a flexible plastic sheet and then stretching the sheet so that the molecules are aligned parallel to each other.   Polarizing sheets 2 ft wide and 100 ft long may be produced.

In Fig. 46-5 the polarizing sheet or *polarizer* lies in the plane of the page and the direction of propagation is into the page.   The arrow E shows the plane of vibration of a randomly selected wavetrain falling on the sheet.   Two vector components, E_x (of magnitude $E \sin \theta$) and E_y (of magnitude $E \cos \theta$), can replace E, one parallel to the polarizing direction and one at right angles to it.   Only the former will be transmitted; the other is absorbed within the sheet.

Let us place a second polarizing sheet P_2 (usually called, when so used, an *analyzer*) as in Fig. 46-6.   If P_2 is rotated about the direction of propagation, there are two positions, 180° apart, at which the transmitted light intensity is almost zero; these are the positions in which the polarizing directions of P_1 and P_2 are at right angles.

If the amplitude of the plane-polarized light falling on P_2 is E_m, the amplitude of the light that emerges is $E_m \cos \theta$, where θ is the angle between the polarizing directions of P_1 and P_2.   Recalling that the intensity of the light

---

* There are other ways of producing polarized light without using this well-known commercial product.   We mention some of them below.

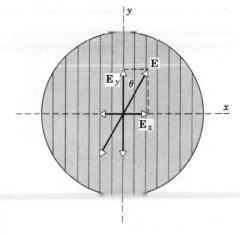

Fig. 46–5　A wavetrain **E** is equivalent to two component wavetrains $\mathbf{E}_y$ and $\mathbf{E}_x$. Only the former is transmitted by the polarizer.

beam is proportional to the square of the amplitude, we see that the transmitted intensity I varies with θ according to

$$I = I_m \cos^2 \theta, \qquad (46\text{–}1)$$

in which I_m is the maximum value of the transmitted intensity. It occurs when the polarizing directions of P_1 and P_2 are parallel, that is, when $\theta = 0$ or 180°. Figure 46–7a, in which two overlapping polarizing sheets are in the parallel position ($\theta = 0$ or 180° in Eq. 46–1) shows that the light transmitted through the region of overlap has its maximum value. In Fig. 46–7b one or the other of the sheets has been rotated through 90° so that θ in Eq. 46–1 has the value 90 or 270°; the light transmitted through the region of overlap is now a minimum.

Equation 46–1, called the law of Malus, was discovered by Étienne Louis Malus (1775–1812) experimentally in 1809, using polarizing techniques other

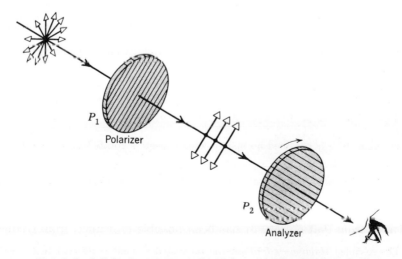

P_1

Polarizer

P_2

Analyzer

Fig. 46–6　Unpolarized light is not transmitted by crossed polarizing sheets.

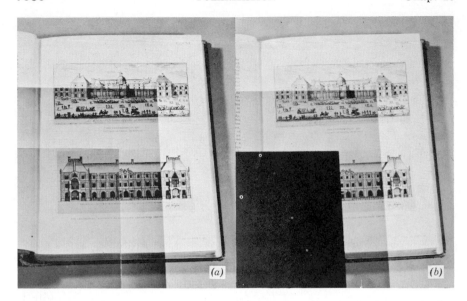

Fig. 46–7 Two square sheets of Polaroid are laid over a book. In (a) the axes of polarization of the two sheets are parallel and light passes through both sheets. In (b) one sheet has been rotated 90° and no light passes through. The book is opened to an illustration of the Luxembourg Palace in Paris. Malus discovered the phenomenon of polarization by reflection while looking at sunlight reflected off the palace windows through a calcite crystal.

than those so far described (see Section 46–3). Equation 46–1 describes precisely the lack of symmetry about the propagation direction that must be exhibited by plane-polarized transverse waves. Longitudinal waves could not possibly show such effects. Interestingly enough the human eye, under certain conditions, can detect polarized light.*

▶ **Example 1.** Two polarizing sheets have their polarizing directions parallel so that the intensity I_m of the transmitted light is a maximum. Through what angle must either sheet be turned if the intensity is to drop by one-half?

From Eq. 46–1, since $I = \frac{1}{2}I_m$, we have

$$\tfrac{1}{2}I_m = I_m \cos^2 \theta$$

or
$$\theta = \cos^{-1} \pm \frac{1}{\sqrt{2}} = \pm 45°, \pm 135°.$$

The same effect is obtained no matter which sheet is rotated or in which direction. ◀

Historically polarization studies were made to investigate the nature of light. Today we reverse the procedure and deduce something about the nature of an object from the polarization state of the light emitted by or scattered from that object. It has been possible to deduce, from studies of

---

* The so-called *Haidinger's brushes*; the interested student is referred to *Concepts of Classical Optics*, John Strong, W. H. Freeman & Co., 1958.

the polarization of light reflected from them, that the grains of cosmic dust present in our galaxy have been oriented in the weak galactic magnetic field ($\sim 2 \times 10^{-4}$ gauss) so that their long dimension is parallel to this field. Polarization studies have shown that Saturn's rings consist of ice crystals. The size and shape of virus particles can be determined by the polarization of ultraviolet light scattered from them. Much useful information about the structure of atoms and nuclei is gained from polarization studies of their emitted radiations in all parts of the electromagnetic spectrum. Thus we have a useful research technique for structures ranging in size from a galaxy ($\sim 10^{+20}$ meters) to a nucleus ($\sim 10^{-14}$ meter). Polarized light also has many practical applications in industry and in engineering science.

46–3 Polarization by Reflection

Malus discovered in 1809 that light can be partially or completely polarized by reflection. Anyone who has watched the sun's reflection in water, while wearing a pair of sunglasses made of polarizing sheet, has probably noticed the effect. It is necessary only to tilt the head from side to side, thus rotating the polarizing sheets, to observe that the intensity of the reflected sunlight passes through a minimum.

Figure 46–8 shows an unpolarized beam falling on a glass surface. The **E** vector for each wavetrain in the beam can be resolved into two components, one perpendicular to the plane of incidence — which is the plane of Fig. 46–8 — and one lying in this plane. The first component, represented by the dots, is called the *σ-component*, from the German *senkrecht*, meaning perpendicular. The second component, represented by the arrows, is called the *π-component* (for *parallel*). On the average, for completely unpolarized incident light, these two components are of equal amplitude.

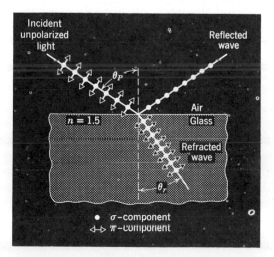

Fig. 46–8 For a particular angle of incidence θ_p, the reflected light is completely polarized, as shown. The transmitted light is partially polarized.

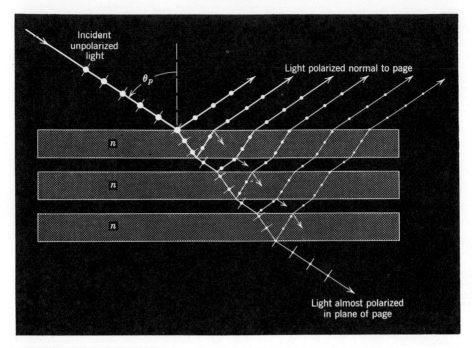

Fig. 46-9 Polarization of light by a stack of glass plates. Unpolarized light is incident on a stack of glass plates at Brewster's angle θ_p. (Polarization in the plane of the page is shown by the short lines and polarization normal to the page by the dots.) All light reflected out of the original ray is polarized normal to the page. After passing through several reflecting interfaces, the light in the original ray no longer contains any appreciable component polarized normal to the page.

Experimentally, for glass or other dielectric materials, there is a particular angle of incidence, called the *polarizing angle* θ_p, at which the reflection coefficient for the π-component is zero. This means that the beam reflected from the glass, although of low intensity, is plane-polarized, with its plane of vibration at right angles to the plane of incidence. This polarization of the reflected beam can easily be verified by analyzing it with a polarizing sheet.

The π-component at the polarizing angle is entirely refracted; the σ-component is only partially refracted. Thus the transmitted beam, which is of high intensity, is only partially polarized. By using a stack of glass plates rather than a single plate, reflections from successive surfaces occur and the intensity of the emerging reflected (σ-component) beam can be increased (see Fig. 46–9). By the same token, the σ-components are progressively removed from the transmitted beam, making it more completely π-polarized.

At the polarizing angle it is found experimentally that the reflected and the refracted beams are at right angles, or (Fig. 46–8)

$$\theta_p + \theta_r = 90°.$$

From Snell's law, $n_1 \sin \theta_p = n_2 \sin \theta_r.$

Combining these equations leads to

$$n_1 \sin \theta_p = n_2 \sin (90° - \theta_p) = n_2 \cos \theta_p$$

or $$\tan \theta_p = \frac{n_2}{n_1}, \qquad (46\text{--}2)$$

where the incident ray is in medium one and the refracted ray in medium two. This can be written as

$$\tan \theta_p = n, \qquad (46\text{--}3)$$

where n $(= n_2/n_1)$ is the index of refraction of medium two with respect to medium one. Equation 46–3 is known as *Brewster's law* after Sir David Brewster (1781–1868), who deduced it empirically in 1812. It is possible to prove this law rigorously from Maxwell's equations.

▶ **Example 2.** We wish to use a plate of glass ($n = 1.50$) as a polarizer. What is the polarizing angle? What is the angle of refraction?
From Eq. 46–3,
$$\theta_p = \tan^{-1} 1.50 = 56.3°.$$

The angle of refraction follows from Snell's law:

$$(1) \sin \theta_n = n \sin \theta_r$$

or $$\sin \theta_r = \frac{\sin 56.3°}{1.50} = 0.555 \qquad \theta_r = 33.7°. \qquad ◀$$

46–4 Double Refraction

In earlier chapters we assumed that the speed of light, and thus the index of refraction, is independent of the direction of propagation in the medium and of the state of polarization of the light. Liquids, amorphous solids such as glass, and crystalline solids having cubic symmetry normally show this behavior and are said to be *optically isotropic*. Many other crystalline solids are optically *anisotropic* (that is, not isotropic).*

Solids may be anisotropic in many properties. Mica cleaves readily in one plane only; a cube of crystalline graphite does not have the same electric resistance between all pairs of opposite faces; a cube of crystalline nickel magnetizes more readily in certain directions than in others, etc. If a solid is a mixture of a large number of tiny crystallites, it may appear to be isotropic because of the random orientations of the crystallites. Powdered

---

* Many transparent amorphous solids such as glasses and plastics become optically anisotropic when they are mechanically stressed. This fact is useful in engineering design studies in that strains in gears, bridge structures, etc., can be studied quantitatively by building plastic models, stressing them appropriately, and examining the optical anisotropy that results, using polarization techniques. The interested student should consult "Photo-elasticity," a chapter by H. T. Jessop in Vol. 6 of the *Encyclopedia of Physics*, edited by H. Flugge (1958), Springer Verlag, Berlin.

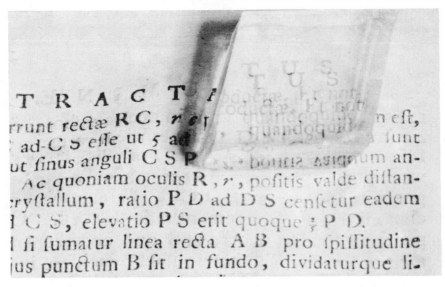

Fig. 46–10 Two images, one polarized 90° relative to the other, are formed by a calcite crystal. The book on which the crystal is lying is Huygens' *Opera Reliqua*, wherein the phenomenon of birefringence is discussed.

mica, for example, compacted to a solid mass with a binder, does not exhibit the cleavage properties that characterize the crystallites making it up.

Figure 46–10, in which a polished crystal of calcite ($CaCO_3$) is laid over some printed letters, shows the optical anisotropy of this material; *the image appears double.* Figure 46–11 shows a beam of unpolarized light falling on a calcite crystal at right angles to one of its faces. The single beam splits into two at the crystal surface. The "double-bending" of a beam transmitted through calcite, exhibited in Figs. 46–10 and 46–11, is called *double refraction.*

If the two emerging beams in Fig. 46–11 are analyzed with a polarizing sheet they are found to be plane-polarized with their planes of vibration at right angles to each other, a fact discovered by Huygens in 1678. Huygens used a second calcite crystal to investigate the polarization states of the beams labeled *o* and *e* in the figure.

If experiments are carried out at various angles of incidence, one of the beams in Fig. 46–11 (represented by the *ordinary ray,* or *o*-ray) will be found to obey Snell's law of refraction at the crystal surface, just like a ray passing from one isotropic medium into another. The second beam (represented by the *extraordinary ray,* or *e*-ray) will not. In Fig. 46–11, for example, the angle of incidence for the incident light is zero but the angle of refraction of the *e*-ray, contrary to the prediction of Snell's law, is not. In general, the *e*-ray does not even lie in the plane of incidence.

This difference between the waves represented by the *o*- and *e*-rays with respect to Snell's law can be explained in these terms:

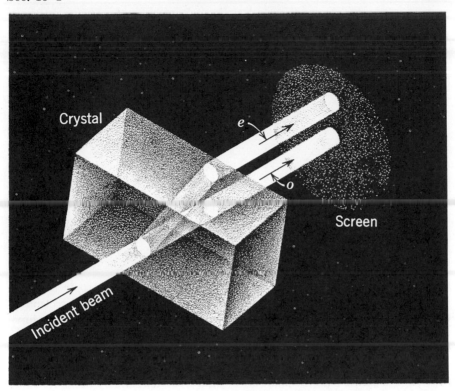

Fig. 46–11   A beam of unpolarized light falling on a calcite crystal is split into two beams which are polarized at right angles to each other.

1. The o-wave travels in the crystal with the same speed v_o in all directions. In other words, the crystal has, for this wave, a single index of refraction n_o, just like an isotropic solid.

2. The e-wave travels in the crystal with a speed that varies with direction from v_o to a larger value (for calcite) v_e. In other words, the index of refraction, defined as c/v, varies with direction from n_o to a smaller value (for calcite) n_e.

The quantities n_o and n_e are called the *principal indices of refraction* for the crystal. Problem 7 suggests how to measure them. Table 46–1 shows these indices for six doubly refracting crystals. For three of them the e-wave is slower; for the other three it is faster. Some doubly refracting crystals (mica, topaz, etc.) are more complex optically than calcite and require *three* principal indices of refraction for a complete description of their optical properties. Crystals whose basic crystal structure is cubic (see Fig. 45–13) are optically isotropic, requiring only *one* index of refraction.

The behavior for the speeds of the two waves traveling in calcite is summarized by Fig. 46–12, which shows two wave surfaces spreading out from an imaginary point light source S imbedded in the crystal. The o-wave sur-

Table 46–1

PRINCIPAL INDICES OF REFRACTION OF
SEVERAL DOUBLY REFRACTING CRYSTALS
(For sodium light, $\lambda = 5890$ A)

Crystal	Formula	n_o	n_e	$n_e - n_o$
Ice	H_2O	1.309	1.313	$+0.004$
Quartz	SiO_2	1.544	1.553	$+0.009$
Wurzite	ZnS	2.356	2.378	$+0.022$
Calcite	$CaCO_3$	1.658	1.486	-0.172
Dolomite	$CaO \cdot MgO \cdot 2CO_2$	1.681	1.500	-0.181
Siderite	$FeO \cdot CO_2$	1.875	1.635	-0.240

face is a sphere, as we would expect if the medium were isotropic. The *e*-wave surface is an ellipsoid of revolution about a characteristic direction in the crystal called the *optic axis*. The two wave surfaces represent light having two different polarization states. If we consider for the present only rays lying in the plane of Fig. 46–12, then (*a*) the plane of polarization for the *o*-rays is perpendicular to the figure, as suggested by the dots, and (*b*) that for the *e*-rays coincides with the plane of the figure, as suggested by the short lines. We describe the polarization states more fully at the end of this section.

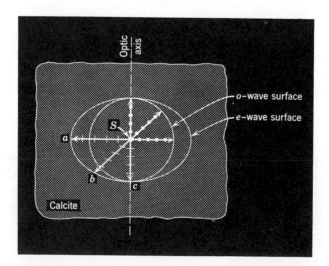

Fig. 46–12 Huygens' wave surfaces generated by a point source S imbedded in calcite. The polarization states for three *o*-rays and three *e*-rays are shown by the dots and lines, respectively. Note that in general (ray Sb) the bars representing the polarization direction are not perpendicular to the *e*-rays.

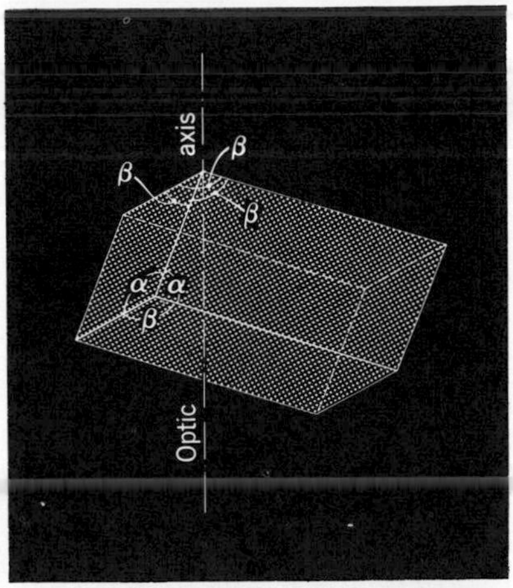

Fig. 46–13 A calcite crystal; α is $78°\ 13'$; β is $102°\ 21'$.

Figure 46–13, which shows a typical calcite crystal that may be obtained by cleavage from a naturally occurring crystal, shows how to locate the optic axis. The edges of calcite crystals may have any lengths but the angles at which the edges intersect always have one or another of two values, $78°\ 13'$ or $102°\ 21'$. The optic axis is found by erecting a line at either of the two corners where three obtuse angles meet (the "blunt" corners), making equal angles with the crystal edges. *Any line in the crystal parallel to this line is also an optic axis.*

We can use Huygens' principle to study the propagation of light waves in doubly refracting crystals. Figure 46–14a shows the special case in which unpolarized light falls at normal incidence on a calcite slab cut from a crystal in such a way that the optic axis is normal to the surface. Consider a wavefront that, at time $t = 0$, coincides with the crystal surface. Following Huygens, we may let any point on this surface serve as a radiating center for a double set of Huygens' wavelets, such as those in Fig. 46–12. The plane of tangency to these wavelets represents the new position of this wavefront at a later time t. The incident beam in Fig. 46–14a is propagated through the crystal without deviation at speed v_o. The beam emerging from the slab will have the same polarization character as the incident beam. The calcite slab, in these special circumstances only, behaves like an isotropic material, and no distinction can be made between the o- and the e-waves.

Figure 46–14b shows two views of another special case, namely, unpolarized incident light falling at right angles on a slab cut so that the optic axis is parallel to its surface. In this case also the incident beam is propagated without deviation. However, we can now identify o- and e-waves that travel through the crystal with different speeds, v_o and v_e, respectively. These waves are polarized at right angles to each other.

Some doubly refracting crystals have the interesting property, called *dichroism*, in which one of the polarization components is strongly absorbed within the crystal, the other being transmitted with little loss. Dichroism, illustrated in Fig. 46–15, is the basic operating principle of the commercial Polaroid sheet. The many small crystallites, imbedded in a plastic sheet with their optic axes parallel, have a polarizing action equivalent to that of a single large crystal slab.

Figure 46–14c shows unpolarized light falling at normal incidence on a calcite slab cut so that its optic axis makes an arbitrary angle with the crystal surface. Two spatially separated beams are produced, as in Fig. 46–11. They travel through the crystal at different speeds, that for the o-wave being v_o and that for the e-wave being intermediate between v_o and v_e.

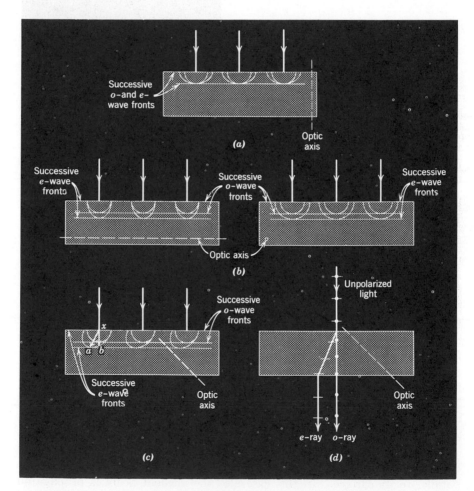

Fig. 46–14 Unpolarized light falls at normal incidence on slabs cut from a calcite crystal. The Huygens' wavelets are appropriate sections of the figure of revolution about the optic axis represented by Fig. 46–15. (a) No double refraction or speed difference occurs. (b) No double refraction occurs but there is a speed difference. (c) Both double refraction and a speed difference occur. (d) Same as (c) but showing the polarization states and the emerging rays.

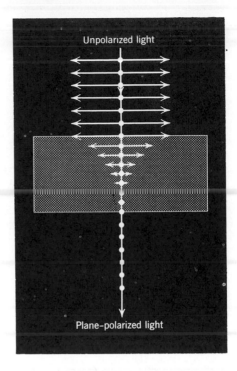

Fig. 46-15 Showing the absorption of one polarization component inside a dichroic crystal of the type used in Polaroid sheets.

Note that ray xa represents the shortest *optical* path for the transfer of light energy from point x to the e-wavefront. Energy transferred along any other ray, in particular along ray xb, would have a longer transit time, a consequence of the fact that the speed of e-waves varies with direction.* Figure 46-14d represents the same case as Fig. 46-14c. It shows the rays emerging from the slab, as in Fig. 46-11, and makes clear that the emerging beams are polarized at right angles to each other, that is, they are *cross-polarized*.

We now seek to understand, in terms of the atomic structure of optically anisotropic crystals, how cross-polarized light waves with different speeds can exist. Light is propagated through a crystal by the action of the vibrating **E** vectors of the wave on the electrons in the crystal. These electrons, which experience electrostatic restoring forces if they are moved from their equilibrium positions, are set into forced periodic oscillation about these positions and pass along the transverse wave disturbance that constitutes the light wave. The strength of the restoring forces may be measured by a force constant k, as for the simple harmonic oscillator discussed in Chapter 15 (see Eq. 15-2).

In optically isotropic materials the force constant k is the same for all directions of displacement of the electrons from their equilibrium positions. In doubly refracting crystals, however, k varies with direction. For electron displacements that lie in a plane at right angles to the optic axis k has the constant value k_o, no matter how the displacement is oriented in this plane. For displacements parallel to the

---

* The student who has not previously read Section 41-6 on Fermat's principle may care to do so now.

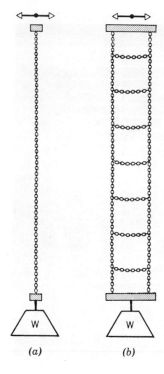

(a)   *(b)*

Fig. 46–16 Two views of a one-dimensional mechanical model for double refraction.

optic axis, k has the larger value (for calcite) k_e.* Note carefully that the speed of a wave in a crystal is determined by the direction in which the **E** vectors vibrate and *not* by the direction of propagation. It is the transverse **E**-vector vibrations that call the restoring forces into play and thus determine the wave speed. Note too that the stronger the restoring force, that is, the larger k, the faster the wave. For waves traveling along a stretched cord, for example, the restoring force for the transverse displacements is determined by the tension F in the cord. Equation 19–12 shows that an increase in F means an increase in the wave speed v.

Figure 46–16, a long weighted "tire chain" supported at its upper end, provides a one-dimensional mechanical analogy for double refraction. It applies specifically to o- and e-waves traveling at right angles to the optic axis, as in Fig. 46–14b. If the supporting block is oscillated, as in Fig. 46–16a, a transverse wave travels along the chain with a certain speed. If the block is oscillated lengthwise, as in Fig. 46–16b, another transverse wave is also propagated. The restoring force for the second wave is greater than for the first, the chain being more rigid in the plane of Fig. 46–16b than in the plane of Fig. 46–16a. Thus the second wave travels along the chain with a greater speed.

In the language of optics we would say that the speed of a transverse wave in the chain depends on the orientation of the plane of vibration of the wave. If we oscillate the top of the chain in a random way, the wave disturbance at a point along the chain can be described as the sum of two waves, polarized at right angles and traveling with different speeds. This corresponds exactly to the optical situation of Fig. 46–14b.

---

* For doubly refracting crystals with $n_e > n_o$ (see Table 46–1) k for displacements parallel to the optic axis is *smaller* than for those at right angles to it. Also, for crystals with three principal indices of refraction, there will be three principal force constants. Such crystals have two optic axes and are called *biaxial*. The crystals listed in Table 46–1 have only a single optic axis and are called *uniaxial*.

For waves traveling parallel to the optic axis, as in Fig. 46–14a, or for waves in optically isotropic materials, the appropriate mechanical analogy is a single weighted hanging chain. Here there is only one speed of propagation, no matter how the upper end is oscillated. The restoring forces are the same for all orientations of the plane of polarization of waves traveling along such a chain.

These considerations allow us to understand more clearly the polarization states of the light represented by the double-wave surface of Fig. 46–12. For the (spherical) o-wave surface, the E-vector vibrations must be everywhere at right angles to the optic axis. If this is so, the same force constant k_o will always be operative, and the o-waves will travel with the same speed in all directions. More specifically, if we draw a ray in Fig. 46–12 from S to the o-wave surface, considered three-dimensionally (that is, as a sphere), the E-vector vibrations will always be at right angles to the plane defined by this ray and the optic axis. Thus these vibrations will always be at right angles to the optic axis.

For the (ellipsoidal) e-wave surface, the E-vector vibrations in general have a component parallel to the optic axis. For rays such as Sa in Fig. 46–12 or for the e-rays of Fig. 46–14b, the vibrations are completely parallel to this axis. Thus a relatively strong force constant (in calcite) k_e is operative, and the wave speed v_e will be relatively high. For e-rays, such as Sb in Fig. 46–12, the parallel component of the E-vector vibrations is less than 100%, so that the corresponding wave speed will be less than v_e. For ray Sc, in Fig. 46–12, the parallel component is zero, and the distinction between o- and e-rays disappears.

46–5   Circular Polarization

Let plane-polarized light of angular frequency ω ($= 2\pi f$) fall at normal incidence on a slab of calcite cut so that the optic axis is parallel to the face of the slab, as in Fig. 46–17. The two waves that emerge will be plane-polarized at right angles to each other, and, if the incident plane of vibration is at 45° to the optic axis, they will have equal amplitudes. Since the waves travel through the crystal at different speeds, there will be a phase difference ϕ between them when they emerge from the crystal. If the crystal thickness is chosen so that (for a given frequency of light) $\phi - 90°$, the slab is called a *quarter-wave plate*. The emerging light is said to be *circularly polarized*.

In Section 15–7 we saw that the two emerging plane-polarized waves just described (vibrating at right angles with a 90° phase difference) can be represented as the projections on two perpendicular axes of a vector rotating with

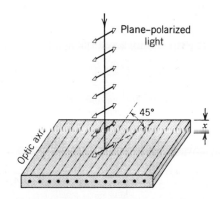

Fig. 46–17   Plane-polarized light falls on a doubly refracting slab of thickness x cut with its optic axis parallel to the surface. The plane of vibration of the incident light is oriented to make an angle of 45° with the optic axis.

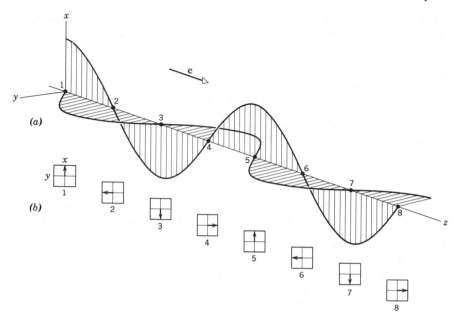

Fig. 46–18 (*a*) Two plane-polarized waves of equal amplitude and at right angles to each other are moving in the *z* direction. They differ in phase by 90°; where one wave has maximum values, the other is zero. (*b*) Views of the resultant amplitude of the approaching wave as seen by observers located at the positions shown on the *z* axis. Note that each observer will see the resultant vector rotate clockwise with time.

angular frequency ω about the propagation direction. These two descriptions of circularly polarized light are completely equivalent. Figure 46–18 clarifies the relationship between these two descriptions.

▶ **Example 3.** A quartz quarter-wave plate is to be used with sodium light ($\lambda = 5890$ A). What must its thickness be?

Two waves travel through the slab at speeds corresponding to the two principal indices of refraction given in Table 46–1 ($n_e = 1.553$ and $n_o = 1.544$). If the crystal thickness is x, the number of wavelengths of the first wave contained in the crystal is

$$N_e = \frac{x}{\lambda_e} = \frac{xn_e}{\lambda},$$

where λ_e is the wavelength of the *e*-wave in the crystal and λ is the wavelength in air. For the second wave the number of wavelengths is

$$N_o = \frac{x}{\lambda_o} = \frac{xn_o}{\lambda},$$

where λ_o is the wavelength of the *o*-wave in the crystal. The difference $N_e - N_o$ must be one-fourth, or

$$\frac{1}{4} = \frac{x}{\lambda}(n_e - n_o).$$

This equation yields

$$x = \frac{\lambda}{4(n_e - n_o)} = \frac{5890 \text{ A}}{(4)(1.553 - 1.544)} = 0.016 \text{ mm.}$$

This plate is rather thin; most quarter-wave plates are made from mica, splitting the sheet to the correct thickness by trial and error.

Example 4. A beam of circularly polarized light falls on a polarizing sheet. Describe the emerging beam.

The circularly polarized light, as it enters the sheet, can be represented by

$$E_x = E_m \sin \omega t$$

and

$$E_y = E_m \cos \omega t,$$

where x and y represent arbitrary perpendicular axes. These equations correctly represent the fact that a circularly polarized wave is equivalent to two plane-polarized waves with equal amplitude and a 90° phase difference.

The resultant amplitude in the incident circularly polarized wave is

$$E_{cp} = \sqrt{E_x^2 + E_y^2} = \sqrt{E_m^2 (\sin^2 \omega t + \cos^2 \omega t)} = E_m,$$

an expected result if the circularly polarized wave is represented as a rotating vector. The resultant intensity in the incident circularly polarized wave is proportional to E_m^2, or

$$I_{cp} \propto E_m^2. \tag{46–4}$$

Let the polarizing direction of the sheet make an arbitrary angle θ with the x axis as shown in Fig. 46–19. The instantaneous value of the plane-polarized wave transmitted by the sheet is

$$\begin{aligned} E &= E_y \sin \theta + E_x \cos \theta \\ &= E_m \cos \omega t \sin \theta + E_m \sin \omega t \cos \theta \\ &= E_m \sin (\omega t + \theta). \end{aligned}$$

The intensity of the wave transmitted by the sheet is proportional to E^2, or

$$I \propto E_m^2 \sin^2 (\omega t + \theta).$$

The eye and other measuring instruments respond only to the average intensity $\bar{I}$, which is found by replacing $\sin^2 (\omega t + \theta)$ by its average value over one or more cycles $(= \frac{1}{2})$, or

$$\bar{I} \propto \tfrac{1}{2} E_m^2.$$

Comparison with Eq. 46–4 shows that inserting the polarizing sheet reduces the intensity by one-half. The orientation of the sheet makes no difference, since θ does not

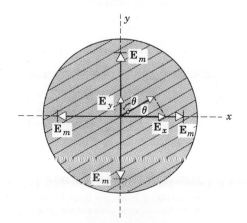

Fig. 46–19 Circularly polarized light falls on a polarizing sheet. $\mathbf{E}_x$ and $\mathbf{E}_y$ are instantaneous values of the two components, their maximum values being $\mathbf{E}_m$.

appear in this equation; this is to be expected if circularly polarized light is represented by a rotating vector, all azimuths about the propagation direction being equivalent. Inserting a polarizing sheet in an *unpolarized* beam has just the same effect, so that a simple polarizing sheet cannot be used to distinguish between unpolarized and circularly polarized light.

Example 5.   A beam of light is thought to be circularly polarized.   How may this be verified?

Insert a quarter-wave plate.   If the beam is circularly polarized, the two components will have a phase difference of 90° between them.   The quarter-wave plate will introduce a further phase difference of ±90° so that the emerging light will have a phase difference of either zero or 180°.   In either case the light will now be *plane-polarized* and can be made to suffer complete extinction by rotating a polarizer in its path.

Does the quarter-wave plate have to be oriented in any particular way to carry out this test?

Example 6.   A plane-polarized light wave of amplitude E_0 falls on a calcite quarter-wave plate with its plane of vibration at 45° to the optic axis of the plate, which is taken as the y axis; see Fig. 46–20.   The emerging light will be circularly polarized. In what direction will the rotating electric vector appear to rotate?   The direction of propagation is out of the page.

The wave component whose vibrations are parallel to the optic axis (the e-wave) can be represented as it emerges from the plate as

$$E_y = (E_0 \cos 45°) \sin \omega t = \frac{1}{\sqrt{2}} E_0 \sin \omega t = E_m \sin \omega t.$$

The wave component whose vibrations are at right angles to the optic axis (the o-wave) can be represented as

$$E_x = (E_0 \sin 45°) \sin (\omega t - 90°) = -\frac{1}{\sqrt{2}} E_0 \cos \omega t = -E_m \cos \omega t,$$

the 90° phase shift representing the action of the quarter-wave plate.   Note that E_x

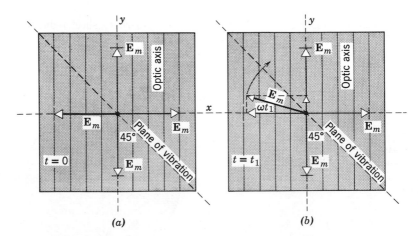

(a)   (b)

Fig. 46–20   Plane-polarized light falls from behind on a quarter-plate oriented so that the light emerging from the page is circularly polarized.   In this case the electric vector E_m rotates clockwise as seen by an observer facing the light source.

reaches its maximum value one-fourth of a cycle *later* than E_y does, for, in calcite, wave E_x (the *o*-wave) travels *more slowly* than wave E_y (the *e*-wave).

To decide the direction of rotation, let us locate the tip of the rotating electric vector at two instants of time, (*a*) $t = 0$ and (*b*) a short time t_1 later chosen so that ωt_1 is a small angle. At $t = 0$ the coordinates of the tip of the rotating vector (see Fig. 46–20*a*) are

$$E_y = 0 \quad \text{and} \quad E_x = -E_m.$$

At $t = t_1$ these coordinates become, approximately,

$$E_y = E_m \sin \omega t_1 \cong E_m(\omega t_1)$$

$$E_x = -E_m \cos \omega t_1 \cong -E_m.$$

Figure 46–20*b* shows that the vector that represents the emerging circular polarized light is rotating clockwise; by convention such light is called *right-circularly polarized*, the observer always being considered to face the light source.

If the plane of vibration of the incident light in Fig. 46–20 is rotated through $\pm 90°$, the emerging light will be *left-circularly polarized*.   ◀

46–6 Angular Momentum of Light

That light waves can deliver *linear momentum* to an absorbing screen or to a mirror is in accord with classical electromagnetism, with quantum physics, and with experiment. The facts of circular polarization suggest that light so polarized might also have *angular* momentum associated with it. This is indeed the case; once again the prediction is in accord with classical electromagnetism and with quantum physics. Experimental proof was provided in 1936 by Beth, who showed that when circularly polarized light is produced in a doubly refracting slab the slab experiences a reaction torque.

The angular momentum carried by light plays a vital role in understanding the emission of light from atoms and of γ-rays from nuclei. If light carries away angular momentum as it leaves the atom, the angular momentum of the residual atom must change by exactly the amount carried away; otherwise the angular momentum of the isolated system *atom plus light* will not be conserved.

Classical and quantum theory both predict that if a beam of circularly polarized light is completely absorbed by an object on which it falls, an angular momentum given by

$$L = \frac{U}{\omega} \tag{46–5}$$

is transferred to the object, where U is the amount of absorbed energy and ω the angular frequency of the light. The student should verify that the dimensions in Eq. 46–5 are consistent.

46–7 Scattering of Light

A light wave, falling on a transparent solid, causes the electrons in the solid to oscillate periodically in response to the time-varying electric vector of the incident wave. The wave that travels through the medium is the resultant of the incident wave and of the radiations from the oscillating electrons. The resultant wave has a maximum intensity in the direction of the incident beam, falling off rapidly on either side. The lack of sideways scattering, which would be essentially complete in a large "perfect" crystal, comes about because the oscillating charges in the medium act cooperatively or coherently.

When light passes through a gas, we find much more sideways scattering. The oscillating electrons in this case, being separated by relatively large distances and not being bound together in a rigid structure, act independently rather than cooperatively. Thus the rigid cancellation of wave disturbances that are not in the forward direction is less likely to occur; there is more sideways scattering.

Light scattered sideways from a gas can be wholly or partially polarized, even though the incident light is unpolarized. Figure 46–21 shows an unpolarized beam moving upward on the page and striking a gas atom at *a*. The electrons at *a* will oscillate in response to the electric components of the incident wave, their motion being equivalent to two oscillating dipoles whose axes are represented by the arrow and the dot at *a*. An oscillating dipole does not radiate along its own line of action. Thus an observer at *b* would receive no radiation from the dipole represented by the arrow at *a*. The radiation reaching him would come entirely from the dipole represented by the dot at *a*; thus this radiation would be plane-polarized, the plane of vibration passing through the line *ab* and being normal to the page.

Observers at *c* and *d* would detect partially polarized light, since the dipole represented by the arrow at *a* would radiate somewhat in these directions. Observers viewing the transmitted or the back-scattered light would not detect any polarization effects because both dipoles at *a* would radiate equally in these two directions.

A familiar example is the scattering of sunlight by the molecules of the earth's atmosphere. If the atmosphere were not present, the sky would appear black except when we looked directly at the sun. This has been verified

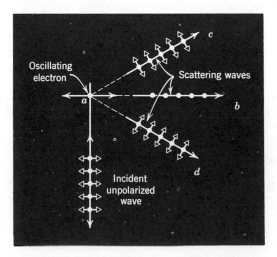

Fig. 46–21 Light is polarized either partially (*c* and *d*) or completely (*b*) by scattering from a gas molecule at *a*.

by measurements made in rockets and satellites above the atmosphere. We can easily check with a polarizer that the light from the cloudless sky is at least partially polarized. This fact is used in polar exploration in the so-called *solar compass*. In this device we establish direction by noting the nature of the polarization of the scattered sunlight. As is well known, magnetic compasses are not useful in these regions. It has been learned * that bees orient themselves in their flights between their hive and the pollen sources by means of polarization of the light from the sky; bees' eyes contain built-in polarization-sensing devices.

It still remains to be explained why the light scattered from the sky is predominantly blue and why the light received directly from the sun—particularly at sunset when the length of the atmosphere that it must traverse is greatest—is red. The cross section of an atom or molecule for light scattering depends on the wavelength, blue light being scattered more effectively than red light. Since the blue light is largely scattered, the transmitted light will have the color of normal sunlight with the blues largely removed; it is therefore more reddish in appearance.

The fact that the scattering cross section for blue light is higher than that for red light can be made reasonable. An electron in an atom or molecule is bound there by strong restoring forces. It has a definite natural frequency, like a small mass suspended in space by an assembly of springs. The natural frequency for electrons in atoms and molecules is usually in a region corresponding to violet or ultraviolet light.

When light is allowed to fall on such bound electrons, it sets up forced oscillations at the frequency of the incident light beam. In mechanical resonant systems it is possible to "drive" the system most effectively if we impress on it an external force whose frequency is as close as possible to that of the natural resonant frequency. In the case of light the blue is closer to the natural resonant frequency of the bound electron than is the red light. Therefore, we would expect the blue light to be more effective in causing the electron to oscillate, and thus it will be more effectively scattered.

46–8 Double Scattering

When X-rays were discovered in 1898, there was much speculation whether they were waves or particles. In 1906 they were established as transverse waves by Charles Glover Barkla (1877–1944) by means of a polarization experiment.

When the unpolarized X-rays strike scattering block S_1 in Fig. 46–22, they set the electrons into oscillatory motion. The considerations of the preceding section require that the X-rays scattered toward the second block be plane-polarized as shown in the figure. Let this wave be scattered from the second scattering block, and let us examine the radiation scattered from it by rotating a detector D in a plane at right angles to the line joining the blocks. The electrons will oscillate parallel to each other, and the positions of maximum and zero intensity will be as shown. A plot of detector reading as a function of the angle ϕ supports the hypothesis that X-rays are transverse waves. If the X-rays were a stream of particles or a longitudinal wave, these effects could by no means be so readily understood. Thus Barkla's important experiment established that X-rays are a part of the electromagnetic spectrum.

---

* See *Scientific American*, p. 60, July 1955, and *Bees: Their Vision, Chemical Sense, and Language*, K. von Frisch, Cornell University Press, 1950.

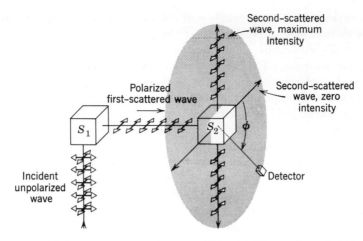

Fig. 46–22   A double-scattering experiment used by Barkla to show that X-rays are transverse waves.

In his later studies the student will learn that beams of particles such as electrons, protons, and pions can be viewed as waves. Scattering (including double scattering) techniques are often used to investigate the polarization characteristics of such beams.

QUESTIONS

1. Why do sunglasses made of polarizing materials have a marked advantage over those that simply depend on absorption effects?

2. Unpolarized light falls on two polarizing sheets so oriented that no light is transmitted. If a third polarizing sheet is placed between them, can light be transmitted?

3. Can polarization by reflection occur if the light is incident on the interface from the side with the higher index of refraction (glass to air, for example)?

4. Is the optic axis of a doubly refracting crystal simply a line or a direction in space? Has it a direction sense, like an arrow? What about the characteristic direction of a polarizing sheet?

5. Devise a way to identify the polarizing direction of a sheet of Polaroid.

6. If ice is doubly refracting (see Table 46–1), why don't we see two images of objects viewed through an ice cube?

7. From Table 46–1, would you expect a quarter-wave plate made from calcite to be thicker than one made from quartz?

8. Does the e-wave in doubly refracting crystals always travel at a speed given by c/n_e?

9. In Fig. 46–14a and b describe qualitatively what happens if the incident beam falls on the crystal with an angle of incidence that is not zero. Assume in each case that the incident beam remains in the plane of the figure.

10. Devise a way to identify the direction of the optic axis in a quarter-wave plate.

11. If plane-polarized light falls on a quarter-wave plate with its plane of vibration making an angle of (a) $0°$ or (b) $90°$ with the axis of the plate, describe the transmitted light. (c) If this angle is arbitrarily chosen, the transmitted light is called *elliptically polarized;* describe such light.

12. What would be the action of a *half-wave plate* (that is, a plate twice as thick as a

quarter-wave plate) on (a) plane-polarized light (assume the plane of vibration to be at 45° to the optic axis of the plate), (b) circularly polarized light, and (c) unpolarized light?

13. You are given an object which may be (a) a disk of grey glass, (b) a polarizing sheet, (c) a quarter-wave plate, or (d) a half-wave plate (see Question 12). How could you identify it?

14. Can a plane-polarized light beam be represented as a sum of two circularly polarized light beams of opposite rotation? What effect has changing the phase of one of the circular components on the resultant beam?

15. How can a right-circularly polarized light beam be transformed into a left-circularly polarized beam?

16. Could (a) a radar beam and (b) a sound wave in air be circularly polarized?

17. A beam of light is said to be unpolarized, plane-polarized, or circularly polarized. How could you choose among them experimentally?

18. A parallel beam of light is absorbed by an object placed in its path. Under what circumstances will (a) linear momentum and (b) angular momentum be transferred to the object?

19. When observing a clear sky through a polarizing sheet, one finds that the intensity varies by a factor of two on rotating the sheet. This does not happen when one views a cloud through the sheet. Can you devise an explanation?

PROBLEMS

1. Unpolarized light falls on two polarizing sheets placed one on top of the other. What must be the angle between the characteristic directions of the sheets if the intensity of the transmitted light is (a) one-third the maximum intensity of the transmitted beam or (b) one-third the intensity of the incident beam? Assume that the polarizing sheet is ideal, that is, that it reduces the intensity of unpolarized light by exactly 50%.

2. An unpolarized beam of light is incident on a group of four polarizing sheets which are lined up so that the characteristic direction of each is rotated by 30° clockwise with respect to the preceding sheet. What fraction of the incident intensity is transmitted?

3. Describe the state of polarization represented by these sets of equations:

(a) $E_x = E \sin (kz - \omega t)$

$E_y = E \cos (kz - \omega t)$,

(b) $E_x = E \cos (kz - \omega t)$

$E_y = E \cos \left(kz - \omega t + \frac{\pi}{4} \right)$,

(c) $E_x = E \sin (kz - \omega t)$

$E_y = -E \sin (kz - \omega t)$.

4. (a) At what angle of incidence will the light reflected from water be completely polarized? (b) Does this angle depend on the wavelength of the light?

5. Calculate the range of polarizing angles for white light incident on fused quartz. Assume that the wavelength limits are 4000 and 7000 A and use the dispersion curve of Fig. 41-2.

6. A narrow beam of unpolarized light falls on a calcite crystal cut with its optic axis as shown in Fig. 46-23. (a) For $t = 1.0$ cm and for $\theta_i = 45°$, calculate the perpendicular distance between the two emerging rays x and y. (b) Which is the o-ray and which the e-ray? (c) What are the states of polarization of the emerging rays? (d) Describe what

happens if a polarizer is placed in the incident beam and rotated. (Hint: Inside the crystal the **E**-vector vibrations for one ray are always perpendicular to the optic axis and for the other ray they are always parallel. The two rays are described by the indices n_o and n_e; *in this plane* each ray obeys Snell's law.)

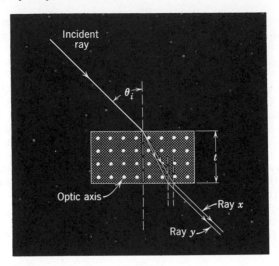

Fig. 46–23

7. A prism is cut from calcite so that the optic axis is parallel to the prism edge as shown in Fig. 46–24. Describe how such a prism might be used to measure the two principal

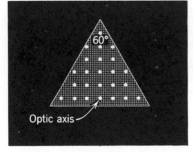

Fig. 46–24

indices of refraction for calcite. (Hint: See hint in Problem 6; see also Example 3, Chapter 41.)

8. How thick must a sheet of mica be if it is to form a quarter-wave plate for yellow light ($\lambda = 5890$ A)? Mica cleaves in such a way that the appropriate indices of refraction, for transmission at right angles to the cleavage plane, are 1.6049 and 1.6117.

9. Prove that two plane-polarized light waves of equal amplitude, their planes of vibration being at right angles to each other, cannot produce interference effects. (Hint: Prove that the intensity of the resultant light wave, averaged over one or more cycles of oscillation, is the same no matter what phase difference exists between the two waves.)

10. Show that in a parallel beam of circularly polarized light the angular momentum per unit volume L_v is given by

$$L_v = \frac{P}{\omega c},$$

where P is the power per unit area (watts/cm^2, say) of the beam. Start from Eq. 46–5.

11. Assume that a parallel beam of circularly polarized light whose intensity is 100 watts is absorbed by an object. At what rate is angular momentum transferred to the object? If the object is a flat disk of diameter 5.0 mm and mass 1.0×10^{-2} gm, after how long a time (assuming it is free to rotate about its axis) would it attain an angular speed of 1.0 rev/sec? Assume a wavelength of 5000 A.

Light and Quantum Physics

CHAPTER 47

47-1 Sources of Light

We have studied the propagation, reflection, refraction, diffraction, polarization, scattering, and interference of light. This chapter deals in part with the *production* of light and with the way that such studies led, in 1900, to the birth of modern quantum physics.

The most common light sources are heated solids and gases through which an electric discharge is passing. The tungsten filament of an incandescent lamp and the familiar neon sign are examples in each category. By analyzing the light from a source with a spectrometer, we can learn how strongly it radiates at various wavelengths. Figure 47–1, which is typical of spectra for heated solids, shows the results of such measurements for a heated tungsten ribbon at 2000°K.

The ordinate $\mathcal{R}_\lambda$ in Fig. 47–1 is called the *spectral radiancy*, defined so that the quantity $\mathcal{R}_\lambda \, d\lambda$ is the rate at which energy is radiated per unit area of surface for wavelengths lying in the interval λ to $\lambda + d\lambda$. Typical units for $\mathcal{R}_\lambda$ are watts/cm^2-μ; the corresponding units of $\mathcal{R}_\lambda \, d\lambda$ are watts/cm^2. In measuring $\mathcal{R}_\lambda$, all radiation emerging into the forward hemisphere is included.

Sometimes we wish to discuss the radiated energy without regard to its wavelength. An appropriate quantity here is the *radiancy* $\mathcal{R}$, defined as the rate per unit surface area at which energy is radiated into the forward hemisphere, appropriate units being watts/cm^2. It can be found by integrating the radiation present in all wavelength intervals:

$$\mathcal{R} = \int_0^\infty \mathcal{R}_\lambda \, d\lambda. \tag{47-1}$$

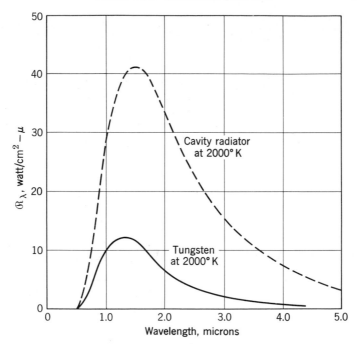

Fig. 47–1 The spectral radiancy of tungsten at 2000°K. The dashed curve refers to a cavity radiator at the same temperature. One micron $(1\ \mu) = 10^{-6}$ meter $= 10^4$ A.

The radiancy $\mathcal{R}$ can be interpreted as the area under the plot of $\mathcal{R}_\lambda$ against λ. In Fig. 47–1 this area—and thus $\mathcal{R}$—is 23.5 watts/cm². The student should note the formal similarity between such curves and the Maxwell speed distribution curve of Section 24–2.

For every material there exists a family of spectral radiancy curves like that of Fig. 47–1, one curve for every temperature. If such families of curves are compared, no obvious regularities stand out. A quantitative understanding in terms of a basic theory presents serious difficulties. Fortunately, it is possible to work with an *idealized heated solid*, called a *cavity radiator*. Its light-emitting properties prove to be independent of any particular material and to vary in a simple way with temperature. In much the same way it proved convenient earlier to deal with an ideal gas rather than to analyze the properties of the infinite variety of real gases. The cavity radiator is the *ideal solid* as far as its light-emitting characteristics are concerned. We shall describe in the next two sections how the theoretical study of cavity radiation in 1900 by the German physicist Max Planck (1858–1947) laid the foundations of modern quantum physics.

47–2 Cavity Radiators

Let us construct a cavity in each of three metal blocks through the walls of which a small hole is drilled. Let the blocks be made of any suitable materials; for example, tungsten, tantalum, and molybdenum. Let each block be raised to the same uniform temperature (say 2000°K) as determined by a suitable thermometer. Finally, let us observe the blocks by their emitted light in a dark room. Measurements of $\mathcal{R}$ and $\mathcal{R}_\lambda$ show the following:

1. The radiation from the cavity interior is always more intense than the radiation from the outside wall. Comparison of the two curves in Fig. 47–1 makes this clear for tungsten. For the three materials given, at 2000°K the ratio of the radiancy for the outside surface to that for the cavity is 0.259 (tungsten), 0.212 (molybdenum), and 0.232 (tantalum).

2. At a given temperature the radiancy of the hole is *identical for all three radiators*, in spite of the fact that the radiancies of the outer surfaces are different. At 2000°K the cavity radiancy (that is, the hole radiancy) is 90.0 watts/cm².

3. In contrast to the radiancy of the outer surfaces, the cavity radiancy $\mathcal{R}_c$ varies with temperature in a simple way, namely as

$$\mathcal{R}_c = \sigma T^4, \tag{47–2}$$

where σ is a universal constant (the Stefan-Boltzmann constant) whose measured value is 5.67×10^{-8} watt/(meter²)(°K⁴). The radiancy of the outer surfaces varies with temperature in a more complicated way and is different for different materials. It is often written as

$$\mathcal{R} = e\mathcal{R}_c = e\sigma T^4, \tag{47–3}$$

where e, the *emissivity*, depends on the material and the temperature.

4. $\mathcal{R}_\lambda$ for the cavity radiation varies with temperature in the way shown in Fig. 47–2. These curves depend only on the temperature and are quite independent of the material and of the shape and size of the cavity.

Figure 47–3 shows an actual cavity, consisting of a hollow thin-walled cylinder of tungsten heated by sending an electric current through it. The cylinder is mounted in an evacuated glass bulb, and a tiny hole is drilled

Fig. 47–2 The spectral radiancy for cavity radiation at three different temperatures.

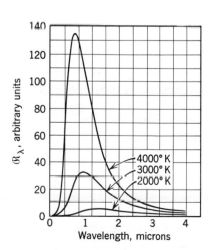

Fig. 47–3 Photograph of an incandescent tungsten tube with a small hole drilled in its wall. The radiation emerging from the hole is cavity radiation.

through the cylinder wall. It is clear from the photograph that the radiancy of the cavity interior is greater than that of the cavity walls.

Many of the facts just given about cavity radiation can be deduced from Fig. 47–4, which shows two cavities made of different materials, of arbitrary shapes, and with the same wall temperature T. Radiation, described by $\mathfrak{R}_A$, goes from cavity A to cavity B and radiation described by $\mathfrak{R}_B$ moves in the opposite direction. If these two rates of energy transfer are not equal, one end of the composite block will start to heat up and the other end will start to cool down, which is a violation of the second law of thermodynamics. (Why?) Thus we must have

$$\mathfrak{R}_A = \mathfrak{R}_B = \mathfrak{R}_c, \tag{47–4}$$

where $\mathfrak{R}_c$ describes the total radiation for *all* cavities.

Not only the total radiation but also the distribution of radiant energy with wavelength must be the same for each cavity in Fig. 47–4. This can be shown by placing a filter between the two cavity openings, so chosen that it permits only a selected narrow band of wavelengths to pass. Applying the same argument, we can show that we must have

$$\mathfrak{R}_{\lambda A} = \mathfrak{R}_{\lambda B} = \mathfrak{R}_{\lambda c}, \tag{47–5}$$

where $\mathfrak{R}_{\lambda c}$ is a spectral radiancy characteristic of all cavities.

Fig. 47–4 Two radiant cavities initially at the same temperature are placed together as shown.

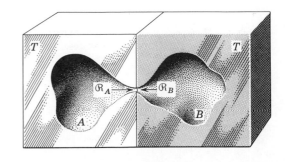

47–3   Planck's Radiation Formula

A theoretical explanation for the cavity radiation was the outstanding unsolved problem in physics during the years before the turn of the present century. A number of capable physicists advanced theories based on classical physics, which, however, had only limited success. Figure 47–5, for example, shows the theory of Wien; the fit to the experimental points is reasonably good, within the experimental error of the data, but definitely not exact. Wien's formula is

$$\Re_\lambda = \frac{c_1}{\lambda^5} \frac{1}{e^{c_2/\lambda T}},$$

where c_1 and c_2 are constants that must be determined empirically by fitting the theoretical formula to the experimental data.

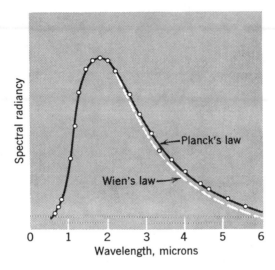

Fig. 47–5 The circles show the experimental spectral radiancy data of Coblentz for cavity radiation. The theoretical formulas of Wien and Planck are also shown, Planck's providing an excellent fit to the data.

In 1900 Max Planck pointed out that if Wien's formula were modified in a simple way it would prove to fit the data precisely. Planck's formula, announced to the Berlin Physical Society on October 19, 1900, was

$$\Re_\lambda = \frac{c_1}{\lambda^5} \frac{1}{e^{c_2/\lambda T} - 1}. \tag{47–6}$$

This formula, though interesting and important, was still empirical at that stage and did not constitute a theory.

Planck sought such a theory in terms of a detailed model of the atomic processes taking place at the cavity walls. He assumed that the atoms that make up these walls behave like tiny electromagnetic oscillators, each with a characteristic frequency of oscillation. The oscillators emit electromagnetic energy into the cavity and absorb electromagnetic energy from it. Thus it should be possible to deduce the characteristics of the cavity radiation from those of the oscillators with which it is in equilibrium.

Planck was led to make two radical assumptions about the atomic oscillators. As eventually formulated, these assumptions are the following:

1. An oscillator cannot have *any* energy but only energies given by *

$$E = nh\nu, \tag{47-7}$$

where ν is the oscillator frequency, h is a constant (now called *Planck's constant*), and n is a number (now called a *quantum number*) that can take on only integral values. Equation 47-7 asserts that the oscillator energy is *quantized*.

2. The oscillators do not radiate energy continuously, but only in "jumps," or *quanta*. These quanta of energy are emitted when an oscillator changes from one to another of its quantized energy states. Thus, if n changes by one unit, Eq. 47-7 shows that an amount of energy given by

$$\Delta E = \Delta nh\nu = h\nu \tag{47-8}$$

is radiated. As long as an oscillator remains in one of its quantized states (or *stationary states* as they are called), it neither emits nor absorbs energy.

These assumptions were radical ones and, indeed, Planck himself resisted accepting them wholeheartedly for many years. In his words, "My futile attempts to fit the elementary quantum of action [that is, the quantity h] somehow into the classical theory continued for a number of years, and they cost me a great deal of effort."

Consider the application of Planck's hypotheses to a large-scale oscillator such as a mass-spring system or an LC circuit. It would be a stoutly defended common belief that oscillations in such systems could take place with *any* value of total energy and not with only certain discrete values. In the decay of such oscillations (by friction in the mass-spring system or by resistance and radiation in the LC circuit), it would seem that the mechanical or electromagnetic energy would decrease in a perfectly continuous way and not by "jumps." There is no basis in everyday experience, however, to dismiss Planck's assumptions as violations of "common sense," for Planck's constant proves to have a very small value, namely

$$h = 6.625 \times 10^{-34} \text{ joule-sec.}$$

The following example makes this clear.

---

* Later developments show that the correct formula for a harmonic oscillator is

$$E = (n + \tfrac{1}{2})h\nu.$$

This change makes no difference to Planck's conclusions, however.

▶ **Example 1.** A mass-spring system has a mass $m = 1.0$ kg and a spring constant $k = 20$ nt/meter and is oscillating with an amplitude of 1.0 cm. (*a*) If its energy is quantized according to Eq. 47–7, what is the quantum number n? (*b*) If n changes by unity, what fractional change in energy occurs?

(*a*) From Eq. 15–8 the frequency is

$$\nu = \frac{1}{2\pi}\sqrt{\frac{k}{m}} = \frac{1}{2\pi}\sqrt{\frac{20 \text{ nt/meter}}{1.0 \text{ kg}}} = 0.71 \text{ cycles/sec.}$$

From Eq. 8–8 the mechanical energy is

$$E = \tfrac{1}{2}kx_{\max}^2 = \tfrac{1}{2}(20 \text{ nt/meter})(10^{-2} \text{ meter})^2 = 1.0 \times 10^{-3} \text{ joule.}$$

From Eq. 47–7 the quantum number is

$$n = \frac{E}{h\nu} = \frac{1.0 \times 10^{-3} \text{ joule}}{(6.6 \times 10^{-34} \text{ joule-sec})(0.71 \text{ cycles/sec})} = 2.1 \times 10^{30}.$$

(*b*) If n changes by unity, the fractional change in energy is given by dividing Eq. 47–8 by Eq. 47–7, or

$$\frac{\Delta E}{E} = \frac{h\nu}{nh\nu} = \frac{1}{n} = \sim 10^{-30}.$$

Thus for large-scale oscillators the quantum numbers are enormous and the quantized nature of the energy of the oscillations will not be apparent. Similarly, we are not aware in large-scale experiments of the discrete nature of mass and the quantized nature of charge, that is, of the existence of atoms and electrons.   ◀

On the basis of his two assumptions, Planck was able to derive his radiation law (Eq. 47–6) entirely from theory, receiving a Nobel prize for this accomplishment in 1918. His theoretical expressions for the hitherto empirical constants c_1 and c_2 were

$$c_1 = 2\pi c^2 h \quad \text{and} \quad c_2 = \frac{hc}{k},$$

where k is Boltzmann's constant (see Section 23–5) and c is the speed of light. By inserting the experimental values for c_1 and c_2, Planck was able to derive the values of both h and k. Planck described his theory to the Berlin Physical Society on December 14, 1900. Quantum physics dates from that day. Planck's ideas soon received re-enforcement from Einstein, who, in 1905, applied the concepts of energy quantization to a new area of physics, the photoelectric effect.

Before discussing this effect, it is important to realize that although Planck had quantized the energies of the oscillators in the cavity walls he *still treated the radiation within the cavity* as an electromagnetic wave. Einstein's analysis of the photoelectric effect first pointed out the inadequacy of the wave picture of light in certain situations.

47–4 Photoelectric Effect

Figure 47–6 shows an apparatus used to study the photoelectric effect. Monochromatic light, falling on metal plate A, will liberate *photoelectrons*, which can be detected as a current if they are attracted to metal cup B by

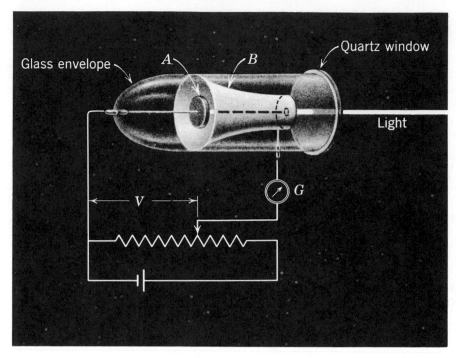

Fig. 47–6   An apparatus used to study the photoelectric effect. V cannot only be varied continuously but can be reversed in sign by a switching arrangement not shown.

means of a potential difference V applied between A and B. Galvanometer G serves to measure this *photoelectric current*.

Figure 47–7 (curve a) is a plot of the photoelectric current in an apparatus like that of Fig. 47–6, as a function of the potential difference V. If V is made large enough, the photoelectric current reaches a certain limiting value at which *all* photoelectrons ejected from plate A are collected by cup B.

If V is reversed in sign, the photoelectric current does not immediately drop to zero, which proves that the electrons are emitted from A with a finite velocity. Some will reach cup B in spite of the fact that the electric field opposes their motion. However, if this reversed potential difference is made large enough, a value V_0 (the *stopping potential*) is reached at which the photoelectric current does drop to zero. This potential difference V_0, multiplied by electron charge, measures the kinetic energy K_{max} of the *fastest* ejected photoelectron. In other words,

$$K_{max} = eV_0. \tag{47–9}$$

Here K_{max} turns out to be independent of the intensity of the light as shown by curve b in Fig. 47–7, in which the light intensity has been reduced to one-half.

Figure 47–8 shows the stopping potential V_0 as a function of the frequency of the incident light for sodium. Note that there is a definite cutoff frequency

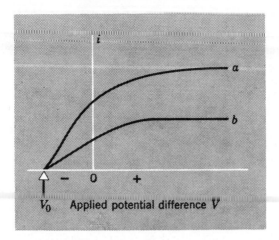

Fig. 47–7 Some data taken with the apparatus of Fig. 47–6. The applied potential difference V is called positive when the cup B in Fig. 47–6 is positive with respect to the photoelectric surface A. In curve b the incident light intensity has been reduced to one-half that of curve a.

ν_0, below which no photoelectric effect occurs. These data were taken by R. A. Millikan (1868–1953), whose painstaking work on the photoelectric effect won him the Nobel prize in 1923. Because the photoelectric effect is largely a surface phenomenon, it is necessary to avoid oxide films, grease, or other surface contaminants. Millikan devised a technique to cut shavings from the metal surface under vacuum conditions, a "machine shop *in vacuo*" as he called it.

Three major features of the photoelectric effect cannot be explained in terms of the wave theory of light:

Fig. 47–8 A plot of Millikan's measurements of the stopping potential at various frequencies for sodium. The cutoff frequency ν_0 is 4.39×10^{14} cycles/sec.

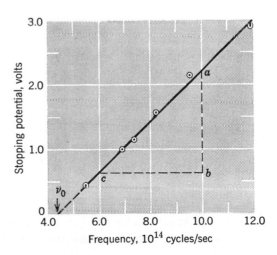

1. Wave theory suggests that the kinetic energy of the photoelectrons should increase as the light beam is made more intense. However, Fig. 47–7 shows that K_{max} $(= eV_0)$ *is independent of the light intensity;* this has been tested over a range of intensities of 10^7.

2. According to the wave theory, the photoelectric effect should occur for *any* frequency of the light, provided only that the light is intense enough. However, Fig. 47–8 shows that there exists, for each surface, *a characteristic cutoff frequency* v_0. For frequencies less than this, the photoelectric effect disappears, no matter how intense the illumination.

3. If the energy of the photoelectrons is "soaked up" from the incident wave by the metal plate, it is not likely that the "effective target area" for an electron in the metal is much more than a few atomic diameters. Thus, if the light is feeble enough, there should be a measurable time lag (see Example 2) between the impinging of the light on the surface and the ejection of the photoelectron. During this interval the electron should be "soaking up" energy from the beam until it had accumulated enough energy to escape. However, *no detectable time lag has ever been measured.* This disagreement is particularly striking when the photoelectric substance is a gas; under these circumstances the energy of the emitted photoelectron must certainly be "soaked out of the beam" by a single atom.

▶ **Example 2.** A metal plate is placed 5 meters from a monochromatic light source whose power output is 10^{-3} watt. Consider that a given ejected photoelectron may collect its energy from a circular area of the plate as large as ten atomic diameters $(10^{-9}$ meter$)$ in radius. The energy required to remove an electron through the metal surface is about 5.0 ev. *Assuming light to be a wave,* how long would it take for such a "target" to soak up this much energy from such a light source?

The target area is $\pi (10^{-9}$ meter$)^2$ or 3×10^{-18} meter^2; the area of a 5-meter sphere centered on the light source is $4\pi (5$ meters$)^2 \cong 300$ meters^2. Thus, if the light source radiates uniformly in all directions, the rate P at which energy falls on the target is given by

$$P = (10^{-3} \text{ watt}) \left(\frac{3 \times 10^{-18} \text{ meter}^2}{300 \text{ meters}^2}\right) = 10^{-23} \text{ joule/sec.}$$

Assuming that all this power is absorbed, we may calculate the time required from

$$t = \left(\frac{5 \text{ ev}}{10^{-23} \text{ joule/sec}}\right) \left(\frac{1.6 \times 10^{-19} \text{ joule}}{1 \text{ ev}}\right) \cong 20 \text{ hr.}$$

However, *no detectable time lag can be measured under any circumstances.* ◀

47–5 Einstein's Photon Theory

Einstein succeeded in explaining the photoelectric effect by making a remarkable assumption, namely, that the energy in a light beam travels through space in concentrated bundles, called *photons.* The energy E of a single photon (see Eq. 47–8) is given by

$$E = h\nu. \tag{47–10}$$

Recall that Planck believed that light, although emitted from its source discontinuously, travels through space as an electromagnetic wave. Einstein's hypothesis suggests that light traveling through space behaves not like a wave at all but like a particle. Millikan, whose experiments verified Einstein's ideas in every detail, spoke of Einstein's "bold, not to say reckless, hypothesis."

Applying the photon concept to the photoelectric effect, Einstein wrote

$$h\nu = E_0 + K_{max} \qquad (47\text{--}11)$$

where $h\nu$ is the energy of the photon. Equation 47-11 says that a photon carries an energy $h\nu$ into the surface. Part of this energy (E_0) is used in causing the electron to pass through the metal surface. The excess energy ($h\nu - E_0$) is given to the electron in the form of kinetic energy; if the electron does not lose energy by internal collisions as it escapes from the metal, it will exhibit it all as kinetic energy after it emerges. Thus K_{max} represents the *maximum* kinetic energy that the photoelectron can have outside the surface; in nearly all cases it will have less energy than this because of internal losses.

Consider how Einstein's photon hypothesis meets the three objections raised against the wave-theory interpretation of the photoelectric effect. As for objection 1 (the lack of dependence of K_{max} on the intensity of illumination), there is complete agreement of the photon theory with experiment. Doubling the light intensity merely doubles the number of photons and thus doubles the photoelectric current; it does not change the energy ($= h\nu$) of the individual photons or the nature of the individual photoelectric processes described by Eq. 47-11.

Objection 2 (the existence of a cutoff frequency) follows from Eq. 47-11. If K_{max} equals zero, we have

$$h\nu_0 = E_0,$$

which asserts that the photon has just enough energy to eject the photoelectrons and none extra to appear as kinetic energy. This quantity E_0 is called the work function of the substance. If ν is reduced below ν_0, the individual photons, no matter how many of them there are (that is, no matter how intense the illumination), will not have enough energy to eject photoelectrons.

Objection 3 (the absence of a time lag) follows from the photon theory because the required energy is supplied in a concentrated bundle. It is *not* spread uniformly over a large area, as in the wave theory.

Although the photon hypothesis certainly fits the facts of photoelectricity, it seems to be in direct conflict with the wave theory of light which, as we have seen in earlier chapters, has been verified in many experiments. Our modern view of the nature of light is that *it has a dual character, behaving like a wave under some circumstances and like a particle, or photon, under others.* We discuss the wave-particle duality at length in Chapter 48. Meanwhile, let us continue our studies of the firm experimental foundation on which the photon concept rests.

Let us rewrite Einstein's photoelectric equation (Eq. 47–11) by substituting eV_0 for K_{max} (see Eq. 47–9). This yields, after rearrangement,

$$V_0 = \frac{h}{e}\nu - \frac{E_0}{e}. \tag{47–12}$$

Thus Einstein's theory predicts a linear relationship between V_0 and ν, in complete agreement with experiment; see Fig. 47–8. The slope of the experimental curve in this figure should be h/e, or

$$\frac{h}{e} = \frac{ab}{bc} = \frac{2.20 \text{ volt} - 0.65 \text{ volt}}{(10 \times 10^{14} - 6 \times 10^{14}) \text{ cycles/sec}} = 3.9 \times 10^{-15} \text{ volt-sec.}$$

We can find h by multiplying this ratio by the electron charge e,

$$h = (3.9 \times 10^{-15} \text{ volt-sec})(1.6 \times 10^{-19} \text{ coul}) = 6.2 \times 10^{-34} \text{ joule-sec.}$$

From a more careful analysis of this and other data, including data taken with lithium surfaces, Millikan found the value $h = 6.57 \times 10^{-34}$ joule-sec, with an accuracy of about 0.5%. This agreement with the value of h derived from Planck's radiation formula is a striking confirmation of Einstein's photon concept.

▶ **Example 3.** Deduce the work function for sodium from Fig. 47–8.

The intersection of the straight line in Fig. 47–8 with the horizontal axis is the cutoff frequency ν_0. Substituting these values yields

$$E_0 = h\nu_0 = (6.63 \times 10^{-34} \text{ joule-sec})(4.39 \times 10^{14} \text{ cycles/sec})$$

$$= 2.92 \times 10^{-19} \text{ joule} = 1.82 \text{ ev.} \qquad ◀$$

47–6 The Compton Effect

Compelling confirmation of the concept of the photon as a concentrated bundle of energy was provided in 1923 by A. H. Compton (1892–1962) who earned a Nobel prize for this work in 1927.* Compton allowed a beam of X-rays of sharply defined wavelength λ to fall on a graphite block, as in Fig. 47–9, and he measured, for various angles of scattering, the intensity of the scattered X-rays as a function of their wavelength. Figure 47–10 shows his experimental results. We see that although the incident beam consists essentially of a single wavelength λ the scattered X-rays have intensity peaks at *two* wavelengths; one of them is the same as the incident wavelength, the other, λ', being larger by an amount $\Delta\lambda$. This so-called *Compton shift* $\Delta\lambda$ varies with the angle at which the scattered X-rays are observed.

The presence of a scattered wave of wavelength λ' cannot be understood if the incident X-rays are regarded as an electromagnetic wave like that of Fig. 39–11. On this picture the incident wave of frequency ν causes electrons in the scattering block to oscillate at that same frequency. These oscillating electrons, like charges surging back and forth in a small radio transmitting

---

* For an historical account of Compton's researches read "The Scattering of X Rays as Particles," A. H. Compton, p. 817, *Am. J. Phys.*, December 1961.

Fig. 47–9   Compton's experimental arrangement. Monochromatic X-rays of wavelength λ fall on a graphite scatterer. The distribution of intensity with wavelength is measured for X-rays scattered at any selected angle φ. The scattered wavelengths are measured by observing Bragg reflections from a crystal; see Eq. 45–8. Their intensities are measured by a detector, such as an ionization chamber.

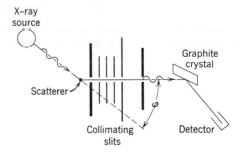

antenna, radiate electromagnetic waves that again have this same frequency ν. Thus, on the wave picture the scattered wave should have the same frequency ν and the same wavelength λ as the incident wave.

Compton * was able to explain his experimental results by postulating that the incoming X-ray beam was not a wave but an assembly of photons of energy E ($= h\nu$) and that these photons experienced billiard-ball-like collisions with the free electrons in the scattering block. The "recoil" photons emerging from the block constitute, on this view, the scattered radiation. Since the incident photon transfers some of its energy to the electron with

* P. W. Debye simultaneously and independently offered the same interpretation.

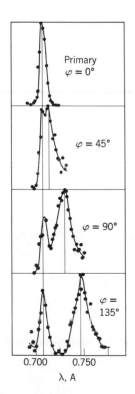

Fig. 47–10 Compton's experimental results. The solid vertical line on the left corresponds to the wavelength λ, that on the right to λ'. Results are shown for four different angles of scattering φ. Note that the Compton shift Δλ for $\varphi = 90°$ is $h/m_0c = 0.242$ A.

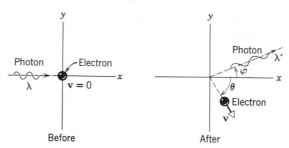

Fig. 47–11 A photon of wavelength λ is incident on an electron at rest. On collision, the photon is scattered at an angle φ with increased wavelength λ', while the electron moves off with speed v in direction θ.

which it collides, the scattered photon must have a lower energy E'; it must therefore have a lower frequency $\nu'(= E'/h)$, which implies a larger wavelength $\lambda'(= c/\nu')$. This point of view accounts, at least qualitatively, for the wavelength shift $\Delta\lambda$. Notice how different this particle model of X-ray scattering is from that based on the wave picture. Now let us analyze a single photon-electron collision quantitatively.

Figure 47–11 shows a collision between a photon and an electron, the electron assumed to be initially at rest and essentially free, that is, not bound to the atoms of the scatterer. Let us apply the law of conservation of energy to this collision. Since the recoil electrons may have a speed v that is comparable with that of light, we must use the relativistic expression for the kinetic energy of the electron. From Eqs. 47–10 and 8–14 we may write

$$h\nu = h\nu' + (m - m_0)c^2,$$

in which the second term on the right is the relativistic expression for the kinetic energy of the recoiling electron, m being the relativistic mass and m_0 the rest mass of that particle. Substituting c/λ for ν (and c/λ' for ν') and using Eq. 8–13 to eliminate the relativistic mass m leads us to

$$\frac{hc}{\lambda} = \frac{hc}{\lambda'} + m_0c^2 \left(\frac{1}{\sqrt{1 - (v/c)^2}} - 1 \right). \qquad (47\text{–}13)$$

Now let us apply the (vector) law of conservation of linear momentum to the collision of Fig. 47–11. We first need an expression for the momentum of a photon. In Section 40–2 we saw that if an object completely absorbs an energy U from a parallel light beam that falls on it the light beam, according to the wave theory of light, will simultaneously transfer to the object a linear momentum given by U/c. On the photon picture we imagine this momentum to be carried along by the individual photons, each photon transporting linear momentum in amount $p = h\nu/c$, where $h\nu$ is the photon energy. Thus, if we substitute λ for c/ν, we can write

$$p = \frac{E}{c} = \frac{h\nu}{c} = \frac{h}{\lambda}. \qquad (47\text{–}14)$$

This conclusion, that the momentum of a photon is given by h/λ, may also be deduced from the theory of relativity.

For the electron, the relativistic expression for the linear momentum is given by Eq. 9–15, or

$$p_e = \frac{m_0 v}{\sqrt{1 - (v/c)^2}}.$$

We can then write for the conservation of the x component of linear momentum

$$\frac{h}{\lambda} = \frac{h}{\lambda'} \cos \varphi + \frac{m_0 v}{\sqrt{1 - (v/c)^2}} \cos \theta \qquad (47\text{--}15)$$

and for the y component

$$0 = \frac{h}{\lambda'} \sin \varphi - \frac{m_0 v}{\sqrt{1 - (v/c)^2}} \sin \theta. \qquad (47\text{--}16)$$

Our immediate aim is to find $\Delta\lambda \ (= \lambda' - \lambda)$, the wavelength shift of the scattered photons, so that we may compare it with the experimental results of Fig. 47–10. Compton's experiment did not involve observations of the recoil electron in the scattering block. Of the five collision variables (λ, λ', v, φ, and θ) that appear in the three equations (47–13, 47–15, and 47–16) we may eliminate two. We chose to eliminate v and θ, which deal only with the electron, thereby reducing the three equations to a single relation among the variables.

Carrying out the necessary algebraic steps (see Problem 15) leads to this simple result:

$$\Delta\lambda \ (= \lambda' - \lambda) = \frac{h}{m_0 c} (1 - \cos \varphi). \qquad (47\text{--}17)$$

Thus the Compton shift $\Delta\lambda$ depends only on the scattering angle φ and *not* on the initial wavelength λ. Equation 47–17 predicts within experimental error the experimentally observed Compton shifts of Fig. 47–10. Note from the equation that $\Delta\lambda$ varies from zero (for $\varphi = 0$, corresponding to a "grazing" collision in Fig. 47–11, the incident photon being scarcely deflected) to $2h/m_0 c$ (for $\varphi = 180°$, corresponding to a "head-on" collision, the incident photon being reversed in direction).

It remains to explain the presence of the peak in Fig. 47–10 for which the wavelength does *not* change on scattering. This peak can be understood as resulting from a collision between a photon and electrons bound in an ionic core in the scattering block. During photon collisions the bound electrons behave like the free electrons that we considered in Fig. 47–11, with the exception that their effective mass is much greater. This is because the ionic core as a whole recoils during the collision. The effective mass M for a carbon scatterer is approximately the mass of a carbon nucleus. Since this nucleus contains 6 protons and 6 neutrons, we have approximately that $M = 12 \times 1840m_0 = 22{,}000m_0$. If we replace m_0 by M in Eq. 47–17, we see that the Compton shift for collisions with tightly bound electrons is immeasurably small.

As in the cavity radiation problem (see Eq. 47–7) and the photoelectric effect (see Eq. 47–11), Planck's constant h is centrally involved in the Compton effect. The quantity h is the central constant of quantum physics. In a universe in which $h = 0$ there would be no quantum physics and classical physics would be valid in the sub-atomic domain. In particular, as Eq. 47–17 shows, there would be no Compton effect (that is, $\Delta\lambda = 0$) in such a universe.

▶ **Example 4.** X-rays with $\lambda = 1.00$ A are scattered from a carbon block. The scattered radiation is viewed at 90° to the incident beam. (a) What is the Compton shift $\Delta\lambda$? (b) What kinetic energy is imparted to the recoiling electron?

(a) Putting $\varphi = 90°$ in Eq. 47–17, we have, for the Compton shift,

$$\Delta\lambda = \frac{h}{m_0 c}(1 - \cos\varphi)$$

$$= \frac{6.63 \times 10^{-34} \text{ joule-sec}}{(9.11 \times 10^{-31} \text{ kg})(3.00 \times 10^8 \text{ meters/sec})}(1 - \cos 90°)$$

$$= 2.43 \times 10^{-12} \text{ meter} = 0.0243 \text{ A.}$$

(b) If we put K for the kinetic energy of the electron, we can write Eq. 47–13 as

$$\frac{hc}{\lambda} = \frac{hc}{\lambda'} + K.$$

Since $\lambda' = \lambda + \Delta\lambda$, we obtain

$$\frac{hc}{\lambda} = \frac{hc}{\lambda + \Delta\lambda} + K,$$

which reduces to

$$K = \frac{hc\,\Delta\lambda}{\lambda(\lambda + \Delta\lambda)}$$

$$= \frac{(6.63 \times 10^{-34} \text{ joule-sec})(3.00 \times 10^8 \text{ meters/sec})(2.43 \times 10^{-12} \text{ meter})}{(1.00 \times 10^{-10} \text{ meter})(1.00 + 0.024) \times 10^{-10} \text{ meter}}$$

$$= 4.73 \times 10^{-17} \text{ joule} = 295 \text{ ev.}$$

The student may show that the initial photon energy E in this case $(= h\nu = hc/\lambda)$ is 12,400 ev so that the photon lost about 2.3% of its energy in this collision. A photon whose energy was ten times as large $(= 124{,}000 \text{ ev})$ can be shown to lose 23% of its energy in a similar collision. This follows from the fact that $\Delta\lambda$ does not depend on the initial wavelength. Hence more energetic X-rays, which have smaller wave-lengths, will experience a larger *per cent* increase in wavelength and thus a larger per cent loss in energy.   ◀

47–7   Line Spectra

We have seen how Planck successfully explained the nature of the radiation from heated solid objects of which the cavity radiator formed the prototype. Such radiations form *continuous spectra* and are contrasted with *line spectra* such as that of Fig. 47–12, which shows the radiation emitted from iron ions

Wavelength, A

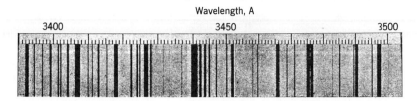

Fig. 47–12 A small portion of the spectrum of iron, in the region 3400 to 3500 A.

and atoms in an electric arc struck between iron electrodes. We shall see that Planck's quantization ideas, suitably extended, lead to an understanding of line spectra also. The prototype for the study of line spectra is that of atomic hydrogen; being the simplest atom it has the simplest spectrum.

Line spectra are common in all parts of the electromagnetic spectrum. Figure 47–13 shows a spectrum of the γ-rays ($\lambda \cong 10^{-12}$ meter) emitted from a particular radioactive nucleus, an isotope of mercury. Figure 47–14 shows a spectrum of X-rays ($\lambda \cong 10^{-10}$ meter) emitted from a molybdenum target when struck by a 35-kev electron beam. The sharp emission lines are superimposed on a continuous background.

Figure 47–15 shows a spectrum associated with the molecule HCl. It occurs in the infrared, with $\lambda \cong 10^{-6}$ meter. This is an *absorption* spectrum rather than an emission spectrum, as in Fig. 47–12. Experiment shows that isolated atoms and molecules absorb radiation, as well as emit it, at discrete wavelengths.

Figure 47–16 shows a portion of the absorption spectrum of ammonia (NH$_3$) in the microwave region ($\lambda \cong 10^{-2}$ meter). Finally, Fig. 47–17 shows how radiation in the radio-frequency region ($\lambda \cong 43$ meters) is absorbed by hydrogen molecules placed in a magnetic field.

Fig. 47–13 A wavelength plot for a gamma ray emitted by the nucleus Hg^{198}. (From data by Du-Mond and co-workers.)

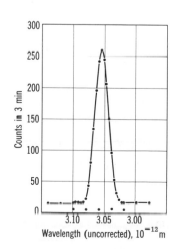

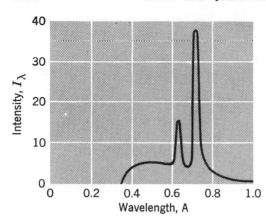

Fig. 47-14 X-rays from a molybdenum target struck by 35-kev electrons. Note the two sharp lines rising above a broad continuous base. The wavelength of the most intense line is 7.1×10^{-11} meter or 0.71 A. (From data by Ulrey.)

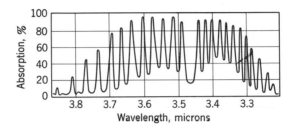

Fig. 47-15 An absorption spectrum of the HCl molecule near $\lambda = 3.5 \times 10^{-6}$ meter = 3.5 μ. (From data by E. S. Imes.)

Fig. 47-16 An oscilloscope trace showing one strong line and four weak lines in the absorption spectrum of ammonia at microwave frequencies.

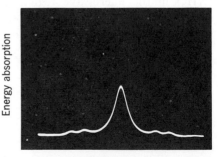

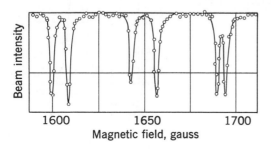

Fig. 47-17 A portion of the absorption spectrum of the protons in molecular hydrogen at $\lambda \cong 43$ meters. In this technique the frequency is left fixed and the sample is placed in a magnetic field, which is varied to scan the spectrum. (From data by Kellogg, Rabi, and Zacharias.)

47–8   The Hydrogen Atom

Figure 47–18 shows the spectrum of hydrogen. A theoretical interpretation of the hydrogen spectrum, based on quantum ideas, was first given by Niels Bohr in 1913.

We might wish to associate the frequency of an emitted spectrum line with the frequency of an electron revolving in an orbit inside the atom. Classical electromagnetism predicts that charges will radiate energy when they are accelerated. In this way electromagnetic waves are emitted from a radio transmitting antenna in which electrons are caused to surge back and forth. This radiation represents a loss of energy for the moving electrons which, in a radio antenna, is compensated for by supplying energy from an oscillator. In an isolated atom, however, no energy is supplied from external sources. We would expect the frequency of the electron and thus that of the emitted radiation to change continuously as the energy drains away. This prediction of classical theory cannot be reconciled with the existence of sharp spectrum lines. Thus classical physics cannot explain the hydrogen, or any other, spectrum.

Bohr circumvented this difficulty by assuming that, like Planck's oscillators, the hydrogen atom exists in certain *stationary states* in which it does not radiate. Radiation occurs *only* when the atom makes a transition from one state, with energy E_k, to a state with lower energy E_j. In equation form

$$h\nu = E_k - E_j, \qquad (47\text{--}18)$$

where $h\nu$ is the quantum of energy carried away by the photon that is emitted from the atom during the transition.

To learn the allowed frequencies predicted by Eq. 47–18, it is necessary to know the energies of the various stationary states in which a hydrogen atom can exist. This calculation was first carried out by Bohr on the basis of a specific model for the hydrogen atom put forward by him. Bohr's model was highly successful for hydrogen and had a tremendous influence on the

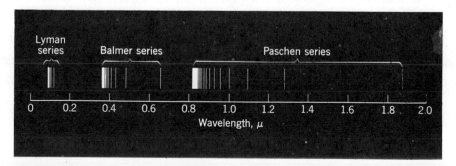

Fig. 47–18 The spectrum of hydrogen. It consists of a number of series of lines, three of which are shown. Within each series the spectrum lines follow a regular pattern, approaching a so-called *series limit* at the short-wave end of the series.

further development of the subject; it is now regarded as an important preliminary stage in the development of a more complete theory of quantum physics.

Let us assume that the electron in the hydrogen atom moves in a circular orbit of radius r centered on its nucleus. We assume that the nucleus, which is a single proton, is so massive that the center of mass of the system is essentially at the position of the proton. Let us calculate the energy E of such an atom.

Writing Newton's second law for the motion of the electron, we have (using Coulomb's law)

$$F = ma,$$

or

$$\frac{e^2}{4\pi\epsilon_0 r^2} = m\frac{v^2}{r}.$$

This allows us to calculate the kinetic energy of the electron, which is

$$K = \tfrac{1}{2}mv^2 = \frac{e^2}{8\pi\epsilon_0 r}. \tag{47–19}$$

The potential energy U of the proton-electron system is given by

$$U = V(-e) = -\frac{e^2}{4\pi\epsilon_0 r}, \tag{47–20}$$

where V ($= e/4\pi\epsilon_0 r$) is the potential of the proton at the radius of the electron.

The total energy E of the system is

$$E = K + U = -\frac{e^2}{8\pi\epsilon_0 r}. \tag{47–21}$$

Since the orbit radius can apparently take on any value, so can the energy E. The problem of quantizing E reduces to that of quantizing r.

Every property of the orbit is fixed if the radius is given. Equations 47–19, 47–20, and 47–21 show this specifically for the energies K, U, and E. From Eq. 47–19 we can show that the *linear speed* v for the electron is also given in terms of r by

$$v = \sqrt{\frac{e^2}{4\pi\epsilon_0 mr}}. \tag{47–22}$$

The *rotational frequency* ν_0 follows at once from

$$\nu_0 = \frac{v}{2\pi r} = \sqrt{\frac{e^2}{16\pi^3\epsilon_0 mr^3}}. \tag{47–23}$$

The *linear momentum p* follows from Eq. 47–22:

$$p = mv = \sqrt{\frac{me^2}{4\pi\epsilon_0 r}}. \tag{47-24}$$

The *angular momentum L* is given by

$$L = pr = \sqrt{\frac{me^2 r}{4\pi\epsilon_0}}. \tag{47-25}$$

Thus if r is known, the orbit parameters K, U, E, v, v_o, p, and L are also known. If any one of these quantities is quantized, all of them must be.

At this stage Bohr had no rules to guide him and so made (after some indirect reasoning which we do not reproduce) a bold hypothesis, namely, that the necessary quantization of the orbit parameters shows up most simply when applied to the angular momentum and that, specifically, L can take on only values given by

$$L = n\frac{h}{2\pi} \qquad n = 1, 2, 3, \ldots. \tag{47-26}$$

Planck's constant appears again in a fundamental way; the integer n is a *quantum number.*

Combining Eqs. 47–25 and 47–26 leads to

$$r = n^2 \frac{h^2\epsilon_0}{\pi m e^2} \qquad n = 1, 2, 3, \ldots, \tag{47-27}$$

which tells how r is quantized. Substituting Eq. 47–27 into Eq. 47–21 produces

$$E = -\frac{me^4}{8\epsilon_0^2 h^2}\frac{1}{n^2} \qquad n = 1, 2, 3, \ldots, \tag{47-28}$$

which gives directly the energy values of the allowed stationary states.

Figure 47–19 shows the energies of the stationary states and their associated quantum numbers. Equation 47–27 shows that the orbit radius increases as n^2. The upper level in Fig. 47–19, marked $n = \infty$, corresponds to a state in which the electron is completely removed from the atom (that is, $E = 0$ and $r = \infty$). Figure 47–19 also shows some of the quantum jumps that take place between the different stationary states.

Combining Eqs. 47–18 and 47–28 allows us to write a completely theoretical formula for the frequencies of the lines in the hydrogen spectrum. It is

$$\nu = \frac{me^4}{8\epsilon_0^2 h^3}\left(\frac{1}{j^2} - \frac{1}{k^2}\right) \tag{47-29}$$

in which j and k are integers describing, respectively, the lower and the upper stationary states. The corresponding wavelengths can easily be

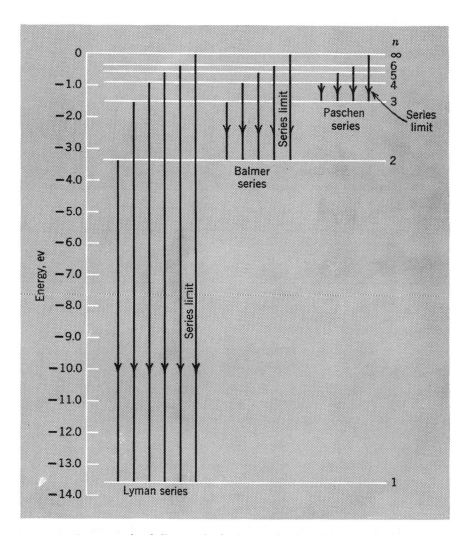

Fig. 47–19 An energy level diagram for hydrogen showing the quantum number n for each level and some of the transitions that appear in the spectrum. An infinite number of levels is crowded in between the levels marked $n = 6$ and $n = \infty$. Compare this figure carefully with Fig. 47–18.

found from $\lambda - c/\nu$. Table 47–1 shows some wavelengths so calculated; it should be compared carefully with Figs. 47–18 and 47–19.

Table 47–1

THE HYDROGEN SPECTRUM

(Some selected lines)

Name of series	Quantum Number		Wavelength, A
	j (lower state)	h (upper state)	
Lyman	1	2	1216
	1	3	1026
	1	4	970
	1	5	949
	1	6	940
	1	∞	912
Balmer	2	3	6563
	2	4	4861
	2	5	4341
	2	6	4102
	2	7	3970
	2	∞	3650
Paschen	3	4	18751
	3	5	12818
	3	6	10938
	3	7	10050
	3	8	9546
	3	∞	8220

▶ **Example 5.** Calculate the binding energy of the hydrogen atom (the energy binding the electron to the nucleus) from Eq. 47–28.

The binding energy is numerically equal to the energy of the lowest state in Fig. 47–19. The largest negative value of E in Eq. 47–28 is found for $n = 1$. This yields

$$E = -\frac{me^4}{8\epsilon_0^2 h^2}$$

$$= -\frac{(9.11 \times 10^{-31} \text{ kg})(1.60 \times 10^{-19} \text{ coul})^4}{(8)(8.85 \times 10^{-12} \text{ coul}^2/\text{nt-m}^2)^2(6.63 \times 10^{-34} \text{ joule-sec})^2}$$

$$= -2.17 \times 10^{-18} \text{ joule} = -13.6 \text{ ev},$$

which agrees with the experimentally observed binding energy for hydrogen. ◀

47–9   The Correspondence Principle

Although all theories in physics have limitations, they usually do not break down abruptly but in a continuous way, yielding results that agree less and less well with experiment. Thus the predictions of Newtonian mechanics become less and less accurate as the speed is made to approach that of light. A similar relationship must exist between quantum physics and classical physics; it remains to find the circumstances under which the latter theory is revealed as a special case of the former.

The radius of the lowest energy state in hydrogen (the so-called *ground state*) is found by putting $n = 1$ in Eq. 47–27; it turns out to be 5.3×10^{-11} meter. If $n = 10,000$, however, the radius is $(10,000)^2$ times as large or 5.3 mm. This "atom" is so large that we suspect that its behavior should be accurately described by classical physics. Let us test this by computing the frequency of the emitted light on the basis of both classical and quantum assumptions. These calculations should differ at small quantum numbers but should agree at large quantum numbers. The fact that *quantum physics reduces to classical physics at large quantum numbers* is called the *correspondence principle*. This principle, credited to Niels Bohr, was very useful during the years in which quantum physics was being developed. Bohr, in fact, based his theory of the hydrogen atom on correspondence principle arguments.

Classically, the frequency of the light emitted from an atom is equal to ν_0, its frequency of revolution * in its orbit. This can be expressed in terms of a quantum number n by combining Eqs. 47–23 and 47–27 to obtain

$$\nu_0 = \frac{me^4}{8\epsilon_0^2 h^3} \frac{2}{n^3}. \tag{47–30}$$

Quantum physics predicts that the frequency ν of the emitted light is given by Eq. 47–29. Considering a transition between an orbit with quantum number $k = n$ and one with $j = n - 1$ leads to

$$\nu = \frac{me^4}{8\epsilon_0^2 h^3} \left[\frac{1}{(n-1)^2} - \frac{1}{n^2} \right]$$

$$= \frac{me^4}{8\epsilon_0^2 h^3} \left[\frac{2n-1}{(n-1)^2 n^2} \right]. \tag{47–31}$$

As $n \to \infty$ the expression in the square brackets above approaches $2/n^3$ so that $\nu \to \nu_0$ as $n \to \infty$. Table 47–2 illustrates this example of the correspondence principle.

---

* Integral multiples of the frequency also exist but may be ignored without affecting the present argument.

Table 47–2

THE CORRESPONDENCE PRINCIPLE AS APPLIED TO THE
HYDROGEN ATOM

Quantum Number, n	Frequency of Revolution in Orbit (Eq. 47–30) cycles/sec	Frequency of Transition to Next Lowest State (Eq. 47–31) cycles/sec	Difference, %
2	8.20×10^{14}	24.6×10^{14}	67
5	5.26×10^{13}	7.38×10^{13}	29
10	6.57×10^{12}	7.72×10^{12}	14
50	5.25×10^{10}	5.42×10^{10}	30
100	6.578×10^{9}	6.677×10^{9}	1.5
1,000	6.5779×10^{6}	6.5878×10^{6}	0.15
10,000	6.5779×10^{3}	6.5789×10^{3}	0.015

QUESTIONS

1. "Pockets" formed by the coals in a coal fire seem brighter than the coals themselves. Is the temperature in such pockets appreciably higher than the surface temperature of an exposed glowing coal?

2. The relation $R = \sigma T^4$ (Eq. 47–2) is exact for true cavities and holds for all temperatures. Why don't we use this relation as the basis of a definition of temperature at, say, 100°C?

3. Do all incandescent solids obey the fourth-power law of temperature, as Eq. 47–3 seems to suggest?

4. A hole in the wall of a cavity radiator is sometimes called a *black body*. Why?

5. It is stated that if we look into a cavity whose walls are maintained at a constant temperature no details of the interior are visible. Does this seem reasonable?

6. How can a *photon* energy be given by $E = h\nu$ (Eq. 47–10) when the very presence of the frequency ν in the formula implies that light is a *wave*?

7. In the photoelectric effect, why does the existence of a cutoff frequency speak in favor of the photon theory and against the wave theory?

8. Why are photoelectric measurements so sensitive to the nature of the photoelectric surface?

9. Does Einstein's theory of photoelectricity, in which light is postulated to be a photon, invalidate Young's interference experiment?

10. List and discuss carefully the assumptions made by Planck in connection with the cavity radiation problem, by Einstein in connection with the photoelectric effect, and by Bohr in connection with the hydrogen atom problem.

11. In Bohr's theory for the hydrogen atom orbits, what is the implication of the fact that the potential energy is negative and is greater in magnitude than the kinetic energy?

12. Can a hydrogen atom absorb a photon whose energy exceeds its binding energy (13.6 ev)?

13. Discuss Example 1 in terms of the correspondence principle.

14. According to classical mechanics, an electron moving in an orbit should be able to do so with any angular momentum whatever. According to Bohr's theory of the hydrogen atom, however, the angular momentum is quantized according to $L = nh/2\pi$. Reconcile these two statements, using the correspondence principle.

PROBLEMS

1. At what wavelength does a cavity radiator at 6000°K radiate most copiously? Solve either analytically or graphically.

2. Using Fig. 47–1, verify that the emissivity of tungsten at 2000°K is 0.259.

3. A cavity radiator at 6000°K has a hole 0.10 mm in diameter drilled in its wall. At what rate do photons in the range 5500 to 5510 A escape from this hole?

4. A cavity whose walls are held at 4000°K has a circular aperture 5.0 mm in diameter. (a) At what rate does energy in the visible range (defined to extend from 0.40 to 0.70 μ) escape from this hole? (b) What fraction of the total radiation escaping from the cavity does this represent? Solve either analytically or graphically.

5. Show that Wien's law (p. 1085) is a special case of Planck's law (Eq. 47–6) for short wavelengths or low temperatures.

6. Solar radiation falls on the earth at a rate of 1.9 cal/cm²-min. How many photons/cm²-min is this, assuming an average wavelength of 5500 A?

7. A spectral emission line, important in radioastronomy, has a wavelength of 21 cm. To what photon energy does this correspond?

8. The energy required to remove an electron from sodium is 2.3 ev. Does sodium show a photoelectric effect for orange light, with $\lambda = 6800$ A?

9. Light of a wavelength 2000 A falls on an aluminum surface. In aluminum 4.2 ev are required to remove an electron. What is the kinetic energy of (a) the fastest and (b) the slowest emitted photoelectrons? (c) What is the stopping potential? (d) What is the cutoff wavelength for aluminum?

10. The work function for a clean lithium surface is 2.3 ev. Make a rough plot of the stopping potential V_0 versus the frequency of the incident light for such a surface.

11. In Example 2 suppose that the "target" is a single gas atom of 1.0 A radius and that the intensity of the light source is reduced to 10^{-5} watt. If the binding energy of the most loosely bound electron in the atom is 20 ev, what time lag for the photoelectric effect is expected on the basis of the wave theory of light?

12. A 100-watt sodium vapor lamp radiates uniformly in all directions. (a) At what distance from the lamp will the average density of photons be 10/cm³? (b) What is the average density of photons 2.0 meters from the lamp? Assume the light to be monochromatic, with $\lambda = 5890$ A.

13. Show, by analyzing a collision between a photon and a free electron (using relativistic mechanics), that it is impossible for a photon to give *all* of its energy to the free electron. In other terms, the photoelectric effect cannot occur for completely free electrons; the electrons must be bound in a solid or in an atom.

14. Calculate the per cent change in photon energy for a Compton collision with φ in Fig. 47–11 equal to 90° for radiation in (a) the microwave range, with $\lambda = 3.0$ cm, (b) the visible range, with $\lambda = 5000$ A, (c) the X-ray range, with $\lambda = 1.00$ A, and (d) the gamma ray range, the energy of the gamma-ray photons being 1.0 Mev. What are your conclusions about the importance of the Compton effect in these various regions of the electromagnetic spectrum, judged solely by the criterion of energy loss in a single Compton encounter?

15. Carry out the necessary algebra to eliminate v and θ from Eqs. 47–13, 47–15, and 47–16 to obtain the Compton shift relation (Eq. 47–17).

16. (a) Using Bohr's formula, calculate the three longest wavelengths in the Balmer series. (b) Between what wavelength limits does the Balmer series lie?

17. In the ground state of the hydrogen atom, according to Bohr's theory, what are (a) the quantum number, (b) the orbit radius, (c) the angular momentum, (d) the linear momentum, (e) the angular velocity, (f) the linear speed, (g) the force on the electron, (h) the acceleration of the electron, (i) the kinetic energy, (j) the potential energy, and (k) the total energy?

18. How do the quantities (b) to (k) in Problem 17 vary with the quantum number?

19. How much energy is required to remove an electron from a hydrogen atom in a state with $n = 8$?

20. A hydrogen atom is excited from a state with $n = 1$ to one with $n = 4$. (a) Calculate the energy that must be absorbed by the atom. (b) Calculate and display on an energy-level diagram the different photon energies that may be emitted if the atom returns to its $n = 1$ state. (c) Calculate the recoil speed of the hydrogen atom, assumed initially at rest, if it makes the transition from $n = 4$ to $n = 1$ in a single quantum jump.

21. A hydrogen atom in a state having a *binding energy* (this is the energy required to remove an electron) of 0.85 ev makes a transition to a state with an *excitation energy* (this is the difference in energy between the state and the ground state) of 10.2 ev. (a) Find the energy of the emitted photon. (b) Show this transition on an energy-level diagram for hydrogen, labeling the appropriate quantum numbers.

22. Show on an energy-level diagram for hydrogen the quantum numbers corresponding to a transition in which the wavelength of the emitted photon is 1216 A.

23. A neutron, with kinetic energy of 6.0 ev, collides with a resting hydrogen atom in its ground state. Apply the laws of conservation of momentum and of energy to this collision and show that it must be elastic (that is, *kinetic* energy must be conserved).

24. Apply Bohr's theory to singly ionized helium, that is, to a helium atom with one electron removed. What relationship exists between this spectrum and the hydrogen spectrum?

25. Using Bohr's theory, calculate the energy required to remove the electron from singly ionized helium.

26. *Positronium.* Apply Bohr's theory to the positronium atom. This consists of a positive and a negative electron revolving around their center of mass, which lies halfway between them. (a) What relationship exists between this spectrum and the hydrogen spectrum? (b) What is the radius of the ground state orbit? (Hint: It will be necessary to analyze this problem from first principles because this "atom" has no nucleus; both particles revolve about a point halfway between them.)

27. *Muonic atoms.* Apply Bohr's theory to a muonic atom, which consists of a nucleus of charge Ze with a negative muon (an elementary particle with a charge of $-e$ and a mass m that is 207 times as large as the electron mass; see Appendix F) circulating about it. Calculate (a) the radius of the first Bohr orbit, (b) the ionization energy, and (c) the wavelength of the most energetic photon that can be emitted. Assume that the muon is circulating about a hydrogen nucleus ($Z = 1$).

28. If an electron is rotating in an orbit at frequency ν_0, classical electromagnetism predicts that it will radiate energy not only at this frequency but also at $2\nu_0$, $3\nu_0$, $4\nu_0$, etc.; see footnote on p. 1104. Show that this is also predicted by Bohr's theory of the hydrogen atom in the limiting case of large quantum numbers.

29. In Table 47–2 show that the quantity in the last column is given by

$$\frac{100(\nu - \nu_0)}{\nu} \cong \frac{150}{n}$$

for large quantum numbers.

30. If the angular momentum of the earth due to its motion around the sun were quantized according to Bohr's relation $L = nh/2\pi$, what would the quantum number be? Could such quantization be detected if it existed?

Waves and Particles

CHAPTER 48

48–1 Matter Waves

In 1924 Louis de Broglie of France reasoned that (a) nature is strikingly symmetrical in many ways; (b) our observable universe is composed entirely of light and matter; (c) if light has a dual, wave-particle nature, perhaps matter has also. Since matter was then regarded as being composed of particles, de Broglie's reasoning suggested that one should search for a wave-like behavior for matter.

De Broglie's suggestion might not have received serious attention had he not predicted what the expected wavelength of the so-called matter waves would be. We recall that about 1680 Huygens put forward a wave theory of light that did not receive general acceptance, in part because Huygens was not able to state what the wavelength of the light was. When Thomas Young rectified this defect in 1800, the wave theory of light started on its way to acceptance.

De Broglie assumed that the wavelength of the predicted matter waves was given by the same relationship that held for light namely, Eq. 47–14, or

$$\lambda = \frac{h}{p}, \tag{48–1}$$

which connects the wavelength of a light wave with the momentum of the associated photons. The dual nature of light shows up strikingly in this equation and also in Eq. 47–10 ($E = h\nu$). Each equation contains within its structure both a wave concept (ν and λ) and a particle concept (E and p). *De Broglie predicted that the wavelength of matter waves would also be given by Eq. 48–1, where p would now be the momentum of the particle of matter.*

▶ **Example 1.** What wavelength is predicted by Eq. 48–1 for a beam of electrons whose kinetic energy is 100 ev?

The velocity of the electrons is found from $K = \frac{1}{2}mv^2$, or

$$v = \sqrt{\frac{2K}{m}} = \sqrt{\frac{(2)(100 \text{ ev})(1.6 \times 10^{-19} \text{ joule/ev})}{9.1 \times 10^{-31} \text{ kg}}}$$

$$= 5.9 \times 10^6 \text{ meters/sec.}$$

The momentum follows from

$$p = mv = (9.1 \times 10^{-31} \text{ kg})(5.9 \times 10^6 \text{ meters/sec}) = 5.4 \times 10^{-24} \text{ kg-m/sec.}$$

The wavelength (called the *de Broglie wavelength*) is found from Eq. 48–1 or

$$\lambda = \frac{h}{p} = \frac{6.6 \times 10^{-34} \text{ joule-sec}}{5.4 \times 10^{-24} \text{ kg-m/sec}} = 1.2 \text{ A.}$$

This is the same order of magnitude as the size of an atom or the spacing between adjacent planes of atoms in a solid. ◀

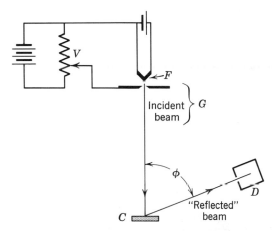

Fig. 48–1 The apparatus of Davisson and Germer. Electrons from filament F are accelerated by a variable potential difference V. After "reflection" from crystal C they are collected by detector D.

In 1926 Elsasser pointed out that the wave nature of matter might be tested in the same way that the wave nature of X-rays was first tested, namely, by allowing a beam of electrons of the appropriate energy to fall on a crystalline solid. The atoms of the crystal serve as a three-dimensional array of diffracting centers for the electron "wave"; we should look for strong diffracted peaks in certain characteristic directions, just as for X-ray diffraction.

This idea was tested by C. J. Davisson and L. H. Germer in this country and by G. P. Thomson in Scotland.* Figure 48–1 shows the apparatus of

---

* For an historical account of Thomson's researches see "Early Work in Electron Diffraction," Sir George Thomson, p. 821, *Am. J Phys.*, December, 1961.

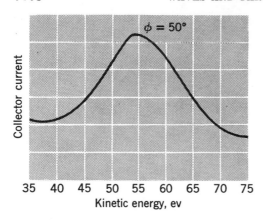

Davisson and Germer. Electrons from a heated filament are accelerated by a variable potential difference V and emerge from the "electron gun" G with kinetic energy eV. This electron beam is allowed to fall at normal incidence on a single crystal of nickel at C. Detector D is set at a particular angle ϕ and readings of the intensity of the "reflected" beam are taken at various values of the accelerating potential V. Figure 48–2 shows that a strong beam occurs at $\phi = 50°$ for $V = 54$ volts.

All such strong "reflected" beams can be accounted for by assuming that the electron beam has a wavelength, given by $\lambda = h/p$, and that "Bragg reflections" occur from certain families of atomic planes precisely as described for X-rays in Section 45–5.

Figure 48–3 shows such a Bragg reflection, obeying the Bragg relationship

$$m\lambda = 2d \sin \theta \qquad m = 1, 2, 3, \ldots. \qquad (48\text{–}2)$$

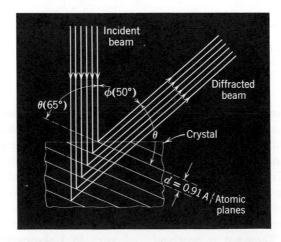

Fig. 48–3 The strong diffracted beam at $\phi = 50°$ and $V = 54$ volts arises from wave-like "reflection" from the family of atomic planes shown, for $d = 0.91$ A. The Bragg angle θ is 65°. For simplicity, refraction of the diffracted wave as it leaves the surface is ignored.

For the conditions of Fig. 48–3 the effective interplanar spacing d can be shown by X-ray analysis to be 0.91 A. Since ϕ equals 50°, it follows that θ equals $90° - \frac{1}{2} \times 50°$ or 65°. The wavelength to be calculated from Eq. 48–2, if we assume $m = 1$, is

$$\lambda = 2d \sin \theta = 2(0.91 \text{ A})(\sin 65°) = 1.65 \text{ A}.$$

The wavelength calculated from the de Broglie relationship $\lambda = h/p$ is, for 54-ev electrons (see Example 1), 1.64 A. This excellent agreement, combined with much similar evidence, is a convincing argument for believing that electrons are wave-like in some circumstances.

Not only electrons but all other particles, charged or uncharged, show wave-like characteristics. Beams of slow neutrons from nuclear reactors are routinely used to investigate the atomic structure of solids. Figure 48–4 shows a "neutron diffraction pattern" for finely powdered lead.

The evidence for the existence of matter waves with wavelengths given by Eq. 48–1 is strong indeed. Nevertheless, the evidence that matter is

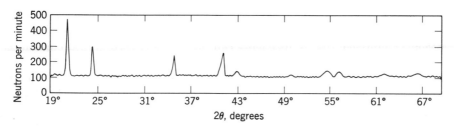

Fig. 48–4 A diffraction pattern for powdered lead, using a monochromatic neutron beam from a nuclear reactor. The peaks represent "Bragg reflections" from the various atomic planes, θ being the corresponding "Bragg angle."

composed of particles remains equally strong; see Fig. 10–10. Thus, for matter as for light, we must face up to the existence of a dual character; *matter behaves in some circumstances like a particle and in others like a wave.*

48–2 Atomic Structure and Standing Waves

The motion of electrons in beams is not bounded or limited in the beam direction. We can make an analogy to a sound wave in a long gas-filled tube, a wave traveling down a long string, or an electromagnetic wave in a long waveguide. All four cases can be described by appropriate traveling waves and, significantly, waves of *any* wavelength (within a certain range) can be propagated.

Let these last three waves be *bounded* by imposing physical restrictions. For the sound wave this corresponds to inserting end walls on a section of the long gas-filled pipe, thus forming an acoustic resonant cavity (Section 38–5). For the waves in the string it corresponds to removing a finite section of string and clamping it at each end, as a violin string (Section 20–5).

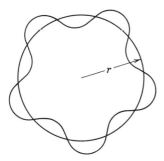

Fig. 48–5 Showing how an electron wave can be adjusted in wavelength to fit an integral number of times around the circumference of a Bohr orbit of radius r. This concept, like the Bohr orbit concept, is now regarded as oversimplified.

For the electromagnetic wave it corresponds to inserting end caps on a finite length of waveguide, thus forming an electromagnetic resonant cavity (Section 38–6).

Two important changes occur: (*a*) the motions are now represented by *standing* rather than traveling waves and (*b*) *only certain wavelengths (or frequencies) can now exist*. This *quantization* of the wavelength is a direct result of bounding or limiting the wave. We expect that if electrons are limited in their motions by being localized in an atom that (*a*) the electron motion can be represented by a standing matter wave, and (*b*) the electron motion will become quantized, that is, its energy can take on only certain discrete values.

De Broglie was able to derive the Bohr quantization condition for angular momentum by applying proper *boundary conditions* to matter waves in the hydrogen atom. Figure 48–5 suggests an instantaneous "snapshot" of a standing matter wave associated with an orbit of radius r. The de Broglie wavelength ($\lambda = h/p$) has been chosen so that the orbit of radius r contains an integral number n of the matter waves, or

$$\frac{2\pi r}{\lambda} = \frac{2\pi r}{(h/p)} = n \qquad n = 1, 2, 3, \ldots.$$

This leads at once to

$$L = pr = n\frac{h}{2\pi} \qquad n = 1, 2, 3, \ldots,$$

which is the Bohr quantization condition for L.

48–3   Wave Mechanics

The idea that the stationary states in atoms correspond to standing matter waves was taken up by Erwin Schrödinger in 1926 and used by him as the foundation of *wave mechanics*, one of several equivalent formulations of quantum physics.

An important quantity in wave mechanics is the *wave function* Ψ, which measures the "wave disturbance" of matter waves. For waves on strings the "wave disturbance" may be measured by a transverse displacement y; for sound waves it may be measured by a pressure variation p; for electromagnetic waves it may be measured by the electric field vector $\mathbf{E}$.

We make the physical meaning of the wave disturbance Ψ clear in Section 48-4 Meanwhile, let us study the wave function $\Psi(x, t)$ for a simple, one dimensional problem, that of the possible motions a particle of mass m confined between rigid walls of separation l as in Fig. 48-6b. The wave function can be obtained by analogy with a known mechanical problem, that of the natural modes of vibration of a string of length l, clamped at each end as in Fig. 48-6a.

In the vibrating string the boundary conditions require that nodes exist at each end. This means that the wavelength λ must be chosen so that

$$l = n\frac{\lambda}{2} \qquad n = 1, 2, 3, \ldots,$$

or that the wavelength λ is "quantized" by the requirement that

$$\lambda = \frac{2l}{n} \qquad n = 1, 2, 3, \ldots. \tag{48-3}$$

The wave disturbance for the string is represented by a standing wave whose equation was shown in Section 19-9 to be

$$y = y_m \sin kx \cos \omega t,$$

where $\omega \ (= 2\pi f)$ is the angular frequency of the wave and $k \ (= 2\pi/\lambda)$ is the wave number. Since λ is quantized, k must be also, or

$$k = \frac{2\pi}{\lambda} = \frac{n\pi}{l} \qquad n = 1, 2, 3, \ldots.$$

which leads to

$$y = \left[y_m \sin \frac{n\pi x}{l} \right] \cos \omega t \qquad n = 1, 2, 3, \ldots. \tag{48-4}$$

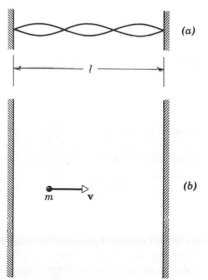

(a)

(b)

Fig. 48-6 (a) A stretched string of length l clamped between rigid supports. (b) A particle of mass m and velocity v confined to move between rigid walls a distance l apart.

$m \longrightarrow v$

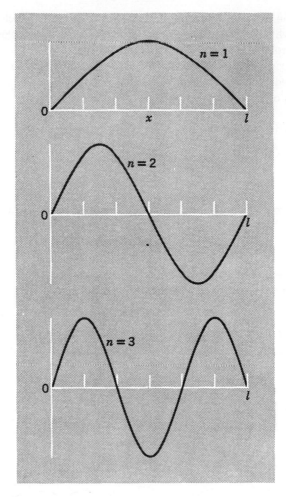

Fig. 48–7   Three quantized modes of vibration for the string of Fig. 48–6a. The figure also represents three of the quantized wave functions for the particle of Fig. 48–6b. The ordinate is a displacement amplitude in the first case and a wave-function amplitude in the second.

Inspection of Eq. 48–4 shows that no matter what value of n is selected nodes exist at $x = 0$ and at $x = l$, as required by the boundary conditions. Figure 48–7 shows plots of the quantity in the square brackets in this equation (the amplitude of the standing wave) for the modes of vibration of the string corresponding to $n = 1$, 2, and 3.

Consider now the particle confined between rigid walls. Since the walls are assumed to be perfectly rigid, the particle cannot penetrate them so that Ψ, which represents the particle motion in some way not yet clearly specified (see Section 48–4), must vanish at $x = 0$ and $x = l$. The allowed wavelengths of the matter waves must be given by Eq. 48–3, or

$$\lambda = \frac{2l}{n}.$$

Replacing λ by h/p (see Eq. 48-1) leads to

$$p = \frac{nh}{2l}, \tag{48-5}$$

which shows that the *linear momentum* of the particle is quantized. The momentum p ($= mv$) is related to the energy E (which is entirely kinetic and is equal to $\frac{1}{2}mv^2$) by

$$p = \sqrt{2mE}. \tag{48-6}$$

Combining Eqs. 48-5 and 48-6 leads to the quantization condition for E, or

$$E = n^2 \frac{h^2}{8ml^2} \qquad n = 1, 2, 3, \ldots. \tag{48-7}$$

The particle cannot have any energy, as we would expect classically, but only energies given by Eq. 48-7.

The matter wave is described, in strict analogy with Eq. 48-4, by

$$\Psi = \left[\Psi_m \sin \frac{n\pi x}{l} \right] \cos \omega t \qquad n = 1, 2, 3, \ldots. \tag{48-8}$$

Figure 48-7 can serve equally well to show how the amplitude of the standing matter waves for the states of motion corresponding to $n = 1$, 2, and 3 varies throughout the box. We see clearly in this problem how the act of localizing or bounding a particle leads to energy quantization.

▶ **Example 2.** Consider an electron ($m = 9.1 \times 10^{-31}$ kg) confined by electrical forces to move between two rigid "walls" separated by 1.0×10^{-9} meter, which is about five atomic diameters. Find the quantized energy values for the three lowest stationary states.

From Eq. 48-7, for $n = 1$, we have

$$E = n^2 \frac{h^2}{8ml^2} = (1)^2 \frac{(6.6 \times 10^{-34} \text{ joule-sec})^2}{(8)(9.1 \times 10^{-31} \text{ kg})(1.0 \times 10^{-9} \text{ meter})^2}$$

$$= 6.0 \times 10^{-20} \text{ joule} = 0.38 \text{ ev}.$$

The energies for the next two states ($n = 2$ and $n = 3$) are $2^2 \times 0.38$ ev $= 1.5$ ev and $3^2 \times 0.38$ ev $= 3.4$ ev.

Example 3. Consider a grain of dust ($m = 1.0$ μgm $= 1.0 \times 10^{-9}$ kg) confined to move between two rigid walls separated by 0.1 mm ($= 10^{-4}$ meter). Its speed is only 10^{-6} meter/sec, so that it requires 100 sec to cross the gap. What quantum number describes this motion?

The energy is

$$E \ (= K) = \frac{1}{2}mv^2 = \frac{1}{2}(10^{-9} \text{ kg})(10^{-6} \text{ meter/sec})^2$$

$$= 5 \times 10^{-22} \text{ joule}.$$

Solving Eq. 48–7 for n yields

$$n = \sqrt{8mE}\,\frac{l}{h} = \sqrt{(8)(10^{-9}\text{ kg})(5 \times 10^{-22}\text{ joule})}\left(\frac{10^{-4}\text{ meter}}{6.6 \times 10^{-34}\text{ joule-sec}}\right)$$

$$= 3 \times 10^{14}.$$

Even in these extreme conditions the quantized nature of the motion would never be apparent; we cannot distinguish experimentally between $n = 3 \times 10^{14}$ and $n = 3 \times 10^{14} + 1$. Classical physics, which fails completely for the problem of Example 2, works extremely well for this problem. ◀

48–4 Meaning of Ψ

Max Born first suggested that the quantity Ψ^2 at any particular point is a measure of *the probability that the particle will be near that point*. More exactly, if a volume element dV is constructed at that point, the probability that the particle will be found in the volume element at a given instant is $\Psi^2\,dV$. This interpretation of Ψ provides a statistical connection between

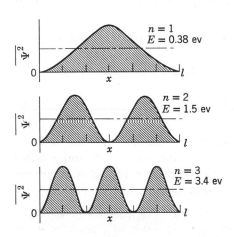

Fig. 48–8 The "probability functions" for three states of motion of the particle of Fig. 48–6b, along with the corresponding quantized energies for the conditions of Example 2. The horizontal lines show the predictions of classical mechanics, in which the probability function is constant for all positions of the particle.

the wave and the associated particle; it tells us where the particle is *likely to be*, not where it *is*.

For the particle confined between rigid walls the probability that the particle will lie between two planes that are distance x and $x + dx$ from one wall (see Fig. 48–8) is given by

$$\Psi^2\,dx = \Psi_m{}^2 \sin^2\frac{n\pi}{l}x\,\cos^2\omega t\,dx.$$

Since we are more interested in the particle's spatial location than in its time behavior, we average Ψ^2 over one cycle of the motion. This is equivalent to replacing $\cos^2\omega t$ by its average value for one cycle, namely one-half, or

$$\overline{\Psi^2} = \tfrac{1}{2}\Psi_m{}^2 \sin^2\frac{n\pi x}{l} \qquad n = 1, 2, 3, \dots. \tag{48–9}$$

Figure 48–8 shows $\overline{\Psi^2}$ for the three stationary states corresponding to $n = 1, 2,$ and 3. Note that for $n = 1$ the particle is more likely to be near the center than the ends. This is in sharp contradiction to the results of classical physics, according to which the particle has the same probability of being located anywhere between the walls, as shown by the horizontal line in Fig. 48–8.

The problem of a particle confined between rigid walls has little real application in physics. We would prefer to illustrate the wave mechanics of Schrödinger by applying it to a more experimentally realizable situation, such as the hydrogen atom. Only mathematical complexity prevents us from doing this. We state without proof that when this problem is solved by wave mechanics the motion of the electron in the ground state of the atom, defined by putting $n = 1$ in Eq. 47–28, is described by the following wave function,

$$\Psi = \frac{1}{\sqrt{\pi a^3}} e^{-r/a} \cos \omega t, \qquad (48\text{--}10)$$

where
$$a = \frac{h^2 \epsilon_0}{\pi m e^2}.$$

Putting $n = 1$ in Eq. 47–27 shows that a is the radius of the ground-state orbit in Bohr's theory. This special interpretation has little meaning in wave mechanics; a is taken here merely as a convenient unit of length when dealing with atomic problems, having the value 0.529 A.

▶ **Example 4.** Consider two hypothetical spherical shells centered on the nucleus of a hydrogen atom with radii r and $r + dr$. What is the probability $P(r)$ that the electron will lie between these shells, as a function of r?

This probability is $\Psi^2 \, dV$, where dV is the volume between the shells, or $4\pi r^2 \, dr$. Thus

$$\Psi^2 \, dV = \left(\frac{1}{\sqrt{\pi a^3}} e^{-r/a} \cos \omega t \right)^2 (4\pi r^2 \, dr) = P(r) \, dr.$$

Averaging over the time (that is, replacing $\cos^2 \omega t$ by $\frac{1}{2}$) yields for the probability $\overline{P(r)}$

$$\overline{P(r)} = \frac{2r^2}{a^3} e^{-2r/a}.$$

Figure 48–9 shows a plot of this function. Note that the most probable location for the electron corresponds to the first Bohr radius. Thus in wave mechanics we do not say that the electron in the $n = 1$ state in hydrogen goes around the nucleus in a circular orbit of 0.529 A radius but only that the electron is more likely to be found at this distance from the nucleus than at any other distance, either larger or smaller. ◀

Fig. 48–9 The probability function for the ground state of the hydrogen atom, as calculated from wave mechanics. The separation between the nucleus and the electron is r; a is the radius of the first Bohr orbit (0.529 × 10⁻¹⁰ meter), used here merely as a convenient unit of distance.

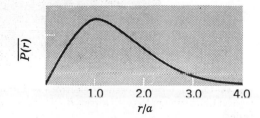

48–5   The Uncertainty Principle

Only those quantities that can be measured have any real meaning in physics. If we could focus a "super" microscope on an electron in an atom and see it moving around in an orbit, we would declare that such orbits have meaning. However, we shall show that *it is fundamentally impossible to make such an observation*—even with the most ideal instruments that could conceivably be constructed. Therefore, we declare that such orbits have no physical meaning.

We observe the moon traveling around the earth by means of the sunlight that it reflects in our direction. Now light transfers linear momentum to an object from which it is reflected. In principle, this reflected light would disturb the course of the moon in its orbit, although a little thought shows that this disturbing effect is negligible.

For electrons the situation is quite different. Here, too, we can hope to "see" the electron only if we reflect light, or another particle, from it. In this case the recoil that the electron experiences when the light (photon) bounces from it completely alters the electron's motion in a way that cannot be avoided or even corrected for.

It is not surprising that the probability curve of Fig. 48–9 is the most detailed information that we can hope to obtain, by measurement, about the distribution of negative charge in the hydrogen atom. If orbits such as those envisaged by Bohr existed, they would be broken up completely in our attempts to verify their existence. Under these circumstances, we prefer to say that it is the probability function, and not the orbits, that represents physical reality.

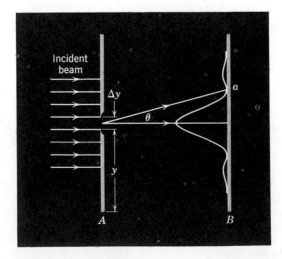

Fig. 48–10 An incident beam of electrons is diffracted at the slit in screen A, forming a typical diffraction pattern on screen B. If the slit is made narrower, the pattern becomes wider.

Our inherent inability to describe the motions of electrons in a classical way finds expression in the *uncertainty principle*, enunciated by Werner Heisenberg in 1927. To formulate this principle, consider a beam of monoenergetic electrons of speed v_0 moving from left to right in Fig. 48–10. Let us set ourselves the task of measuring the position of a particular electron in the vertical (y) direction and also its velocity component v_y in this direction. If we succeed in carrying out these measurements with unlimited accuracy, we can then claim to have established the position and motion of the electron (or one component of it at least) with precision. However, we shall see that *it is impossible to make these two measurements simultaneously with unlimited accuracy.*

To measure y we block the beam with an absorbing screen A in which we put a slit of width Δy. If an electron gets through the slit, its vertical position must be known to this accuracy. By making the slit narrower, we can improve the accuracy of this vertical position measurement as much as we wish.

Since the electron is a wave, it will undergo diffraction at the slit, and a photographic plate placed at B in Fig. 48–10 will reveal a typical *diffraction pattern*. The existence of this diffraction pattern means that there is an uncertainty in the values of v_y possessed by the electrons emerging from the slit. Let v_{ya} be the value of v_y that corresponds to an electron landing at the first minimum on the screen, marked by point a and described by a characteristic angle θ_a. We take v_{ya} as a *rough* measure of the uncertainty Δv_y in v_y for electrons emerging from the slit.

The first minimum in the diffraction pattern is given by Eq. 44–2, or

$$\sin \theta_a = \frac{\lambda}{\Delta y}.$$

If we assume that θ_a is small enough, we can write this equation as

$$\theta_a \cong \frac{\lambda}{\Delta y}. \tag{48–11}$$

To reach point a, $v_{ya}\ (= \Delta v_y)$ must be such that

$$\theta_a \cong \frac{\Delta v_y}{v_0}. \tag{48–12}$$

Combining Eqs. 48–11 and 48–12 leads to

$$\frac{\Delta v_y}{v_0} = \frac{\lambda}{\Delta y},$$

which we rewrite as $\Delta v_y\, \Delta y \cong \lambda v_0.$ \hfill (48–13)

Now λ, the wavelength of the electron beam, is given by h/p or h/mv_0; substituting this into Eq. 48–13 yields

$$\Delta v_y\, \Delta y \cong \frac{h v_0}{m v_0}.$$

We rewrite this as $\Delta p_y\, \Delta y \cong h.$ \hfill (48–14)

In Eq. 48–14 $\Delta p_y\ (= m\, \Delta v_y)$ is the uncertainty in our knowledge of the vertical momentum of the electrons; Δy is the uncertainty in our knowledge of their vertical position. The equation tells us that, since the product of these uncertainties is a constant, *we cannot measure p_y and y simultaneously with unlimited accuracy.*

If we want to improve our measurement of y (that is, if we want to reduce Δy), we use a finer slit. However (see Eq. 48–11), this will produce a wider diffraction pattern. A wider pattern means that our knowledge of the vertical momentum component of the electron has deteriorated, or, in other words, Δp_y has increased; this is exactly what Eq. 48–14 predicts.

The limits on measurement imposed by Eq. 48–14 have nothing to do with the crudity of our measuring instruments. We are permitted to postulate the existence of the finest conceivable measuring equipment. Equation 48–14 represents a *fundamental* limitation, imposed by nature.

Equation 48–14 is a derivation, for a special case, of a general principle known as the *uncertainty principle*. As applied to position and momentum measurements, it asserts that

$$\Delta p_x \, \Delta x \gtrsim h$$

$$\Delta p_y \, \Delta y \gtrsim h$$

$$\Delta p_z \, \Delta z \gtrsim h. \qquad (48\text{–}15)$$

Thus no component of the motion of an electron, free or bound, can be described with unlimited precision.

Planck's constant h probably appears nowhere that has more deep-seated significance than in Eq. 48–15. If this product had been zero instead of h, the classical ideas about particles and orbits would be correct; it would then be possible to measure both momentum and position with unlimited precision. The fact that h appears means that the classical ideas are wrong; the magnitude of h tells us under what circumstances these classical ideas must be replaced by quantum ideas. Gamow * has speculated, in an interesting and readable fantasy, what our world would be like if the constant h were much larger than it is, so that nonclassical ideas would be apparent to our sense perceptions.

▶ **Example 5.** An electron has a speed of 300 meters/sec, accurate to 0.01%. With what fundamental accuracy can we locate the position of this electron?

The electron momentum is

$$p = mv = (9.1 \times 10^{-31} \text{ kg})(300 \text{ meters/sec}) = 2.7 \times 10^{-28} \text{ kg-m/sec.}$$

The uncertainty in momentum is given to be 0.01% of this, or

$$\Delta p = (0.0001)(2.7 \times 10^{-28} \text{ kg-m/sec}) = 2.7 \times 10^{-32} \text{ kg-m/sec.}$$

The minimum uncertainty in position, from Eq. 48–15, is

$$\Delta x = \frac{h}{\Delta p} = \frac{6.6 \times 10^{-34} \text{ joule-sec}}{2.7 \times 10^{-32} \text{ kg-m/sec}}$$

$$= 2.4 \text{ cm.}$$

If the electron momentum has really been determined by measurement to have the accuracy stated, there is no hope whatever that its position can be known to any better accuracy than that stated, namely about 1 in. The concept of the electron as a tiny dot is not very valid under these circumstances.

▶ **Example 6.** A bullet has a speed of 300 meters/sec, accurate to 0.01%. With what fundamental accuracy can we locate its position? Its mass is 50 gm (= 0.05 kg).

This example is the same as Example 5 in every respect save the mass of the particle involved. The momentum is

$$p = mv = (0.05 \text{ kg})(300 \text{ meters/sec}) = 15 \text{ kg-m/sec}$$

and $\qquad \Delta p = (0.0001)(15 \text{ kg-m/sec}) = 1.5 \times 10^{-3} \text{ kg-m/sec.}$

Equation 48–15 yields

$$\Delta x = \frac{6.6 \times 10^{-34} \text{ joule-sec}}{1.5 \times 10^{-3} \text{ kg-m/sec}} = 4.4 \times 10^{-31} \text{ meter.}$$

---

* *Mr. Tompkins in Wonderland*, Macmillan, 1940.

This is so far beyond the possibility of measurement (a nucleus is only about 10^{-15} meter in diameter) that we can assert that for heavy objects like bullets the uncertainty principle sets no limits whatever on our measuring procedures. Once again the correspondence principle shows us how quantum physics reduces to classical physics under the appropriate circumstances.   ◄

The uncertainty relation shows us why it is possible for both light and matter to have a dual, wave-particle, nature. It is because these two views, so obviously opposite to each other, can never be brought face to face in the same experimental situation. If we devise an experiment that forces the electron to reveal its wave character strongly, its particle character will always be inherently fuzzy. If we modify the experiment to bring out the particle character more strongly, the wave character necessarily becomes fuzzy. Matter and light are like coins that can be made to display either face at will but not both simultaneously. Niels Bohr first pointed out in his *principle of complementarity* how the ideas of wave and of particle complement rather than contradict each other.

QUESTIONS

1. How can the *wavelength* of an electron be given by $\lambda = h/p$ when the very presence of the momentum p in this formula implies that the electron is a particle?

2. How could Davisson and Germer be sure that the "54-volt" peak of Fig. 48–2 was a first-order diffraction peak, that is, that $m = 1$ in Eq. 48–2?

3. In a repetition of Thomson's experiment for measuring e/m for the electron (see Section 33–8), a beam of 10^4-ev electrons is collimated by passage through a slit of width 0.50 mm. Why is the beam-like character of the emerging electrons not destroyed by diffraction of the electron wave at this slit?

4. Why is the wave nature of matter not more apparent to our daily observations?

5. Apply the correspondence principle to the problem of a particle confined between rigid walls, showing that those features which seem "strange" (that is, the quantization of energy and the nonuniformity of the probability functions of Fig. 48–8) become undetectable experimentally at large quantum numbers.

6. In the $n = 1$ mode, for a particle confined between rigid walls, what is the probability that the particle will be found in a small volume element at the surface of either wall?

7. A standing wave can be viewed as the superposition of two traveling waves. Can you apply this to the problem of a particle confined between rigid walls, giving an interpretation in terms of the motion of the electron?

8. What is the physical significance of the wave function Ψ?

9. Why does the concept of Bohr orbits violate the uncertainty principle?

10. How can the predictions of wave mechanics be so exact if the only information we have about the positions of the electrons is statistical?

11. Make up some numerical examples to show the difficulty of getting the uncertainty principle to reveal itself during experiments with an object whose mass is about 1 gm.

12. Figure 48–8 shows that for $n = 3$ the probability function for a particle confined between rigid walls is zero at two points between the walls. How can the particle ever move across these positions? (Hint: Consider the implications of the uncertainty principle.)

13. The uncertainty principle can be stated in terms of angular quantities (compare Eq. 48–15) as

$$\Delta L \; \Delta \phi \gtrsim h$$

where ΔL is the uncertainty in the *angular* momentum and $\Delta \phi$ the uncertainty in the *angular* position. For electrons in atoms the angular momentum has definite quantized values, with no uncertainty whatever. What can we conclude about the uncertainty in the angular position and about the validity of the orbit concept?

PROBLEMS

1. A bullet of mass 40 gm travels at 1000 meters/sec. (a) What wavelength can we associate with it? (b) Why does the wave nature of the bullet not reveal itself through diffraction effects?

2. What wavelength do we associate with a beam of neutrons whose energy is 0.025 ev?

3. An electron and a photon each have a wavelength of 2.0 A. What are their (a) momenta and (b) energies?

4. The 50-Bev electron accelerator to be built at Stanford will provide an electron beam of small wavelength, suitable for probing the fine details of nuclear structure by scattering experiments. What will this wavelength be and how does it compare to the size of an average nucleus? (Hint: At these energies it is necessary to use the extreme relativistic relationship between momentum and energy, namely $p = E/c$. This is the same relationship used for light (Section 40–2) and is justified whenever the kinetic energy of a particle is very much greater than its rest energy m_0c^2, as in this case.)

5. In the experiment of Davisson and Germer (a) at what angles would the second- and third-order diffracted beams corresponding to the strong maximum of Fig. 48–2 occur, provided they are present, and (b) at what angle would the first-order diffracted beam occur if the accelerating potential were changed from 54 to 60 volts?

6. Make a plot of de Broglie wavelength against kinetic energy for (a) electrons and (b) protons. Restrict the range of energy values to those in which classical mechanics applies reasonably well. A convenient criterion is that the maximum kinetic energy on each plot be only about, say, 5% of the rest energy m_0c^2 for the particular particle.

7. What is the wavelength of a hydrogen atom moving with a velocity corresponding to the mean kinetic energy for thermal equilibrium at 20°C?

8. If an electron moves from a state represented by $n = 3$ in Fig. 48–8 to one represented by $n = 2$ in that figure, emitting electromagnetic radiation in the process, what are (a) the energy of the emitted single photon and (b) the corresponding wavelength?

9. A particle is confined between rigid walls separated by a distance l. What is the probability that it will be found within a distance $l/3$ of one wall (a) for $n = 1$, (b) for $n = 2$, (c) for $n = 3$, and (d) under the assumptions of classical physics?

10. In the ground state of the hydrogen atom show that the probability P_r that the electron lies *within* a sphere of radius r is given by

$$P_r = 1 - e^{-2r/a}\left(\frac{2r^2}{a^2} + \frac{2r}{a} + 1\right).$$

Does this yield expected values for (a) $r = 0$ and (b) $r = \infty$? (c) State clearly the difference in meaning between this expression and that given on p. 1117.

11. In the ground state of the hydrogen atom, what is the probability that the electron will lie within a sphere whose radius is that of the first Bohr orbit?

12. The uncertainty in the position of an electron is given as about 0.5 A, which is the radius of the first Bohr orbit in hydrogen. What is the uncertainty in the linear momentum of the electron?

13. Show that if the uncertainty in the location of a particle is equal to its de Broglie wavelength the uncertainty in its velocity is equal to its velocity.

14. The highest achievable resolving power of a microscope is limited only by the wavelength used; that is, the smallest detail that can be separated is about equal to the wavelength. Suppose one wishes to "see" inside an atom. Assuming the atom to have a diameter of 1.0 A, this means that we wish to resolve detail of separation about 0.1 A. (a) If an electron microscope is used, what minimum energy of electrons is needed? (b) If a light microscope is used, what minimum energy of photons is needed? (c) Which microscope seems more practical for this purpose? Explain.

15. A microscope using photons is employed to locate an electron in an atom to within a distance of 0.1 A. What is the uncertainty in the momentum of the electron located in this way?

Appendices

Appendices

Fundamental and Derived Physical Constants

APPENDIX A

These data are a summary of hundreds of physical measurements made over the years by physicists in all parts of the world. They have been subjected to exhaustive statistical analysis and, with their accompanying standard errors, represent the best values to date.

For most problem work three significant figures suffice, and the "computational" (rounded) values may be used. The best value has the same units as the computational value.

The data are largely based on the review article by E. R. Cohen in *Nuovo Cimento*, Suppl. to Vol. VI, Ser. X (1957), and are on the physical scale $O^{16} = 16.0000$ amu.

Name	Symbol	Computational Value	Best Experimental Value
Speed of light	c	3.00×10^8 meters/sec	$(2.997930 \pm 0.000003) \times 10^8$
Universal gravitational constant	G	6.67×10^{-11} nt-m^2/kg^2	$(6.673 \pm 0.003) \times 10^{-11}$
Avogadro's number	N_0	6.02×10^{23}/mole	$(6.02486 \pm 0.00016) \times 10^{23}$
Universal gas constant	R	8.32 joules/(mole)(K°) 0.0821 liter-atm/(mole)(K°)	8.31696 ± 0.00034
Standard volume of ideal gas	–	2.24×10^{-2} meter^3 22.4 liter	$(2.24207 \pm 0.00006) \times 10^{-2}$
Planck's constant	h	6.63×10^{-34} joule-sec	$(6.62517 \pm 0.00023) \times 10^{-34}$
Boltzmann's constant	k	1.38×10^{-23} joule/K°	$(1.38044 \pm 0.00007) \times 10^{-23}$
Stefan-Boltzmann constant	σ	5.67×10^{-8} joule/(K°^{4})(meter^2)(sec)	$(5.6687 \pm 0.0010) \times 10^{-8}$
Mechanical equivalent of heat	J	4.19 joules/cal	4.1855 ± 0.0004
Triple point of water	–	273.16°K	273.16°K exactly
Ice point of water	–	273.15°K	273.1500 ± 0.0002
Maximum density of water (at 3.98°C and 1 atm)	–	1 gm/cm^3	0.999973 gm/cm^3 1.000000 gm/ml
Permeability constant	μ_0	1.26×10^{-6} henry/meter	$4\pi \times 10^{-7}$ exactly
Permittivity constant	ϵ_0	8.85×10^{-12} farad/meter	$(8.85415 \pm 0.00002) \times 10^{-12}$
Electronic charge	e	1.60×10^{-19} coul	$(1.60206 \pm 0.00003) \times 10^{-19}$
Electronic rest mass	m_e	9.11×10^{-31} kg	$(9.1083 \pm 0.0003) \times 10^{-31}$ $(5.48763 \pm 0.00006) \times 10^{-4}$ amu
Proton rest mass	m_p	1.67×10^{-27} kg	$(1.67239 \pm 0.00004) \times 10^{-27}$ 1.007593 ± 0.000003 amu
Neutron rest mass	m_n	1.67×10^{-27} kg	$(1.67470 \pm 0.00004) \times 10^{-27}$ 1.008982 ± 0.000003 amu
Mass-energy relation	$c^2 = E/m$	8.99×10^{16} meters^2/sec^2 931 Mev/amu	$(8.98758 \pm 0.00003) \times 10^{16}$ (931.141 ± 0.010)
Magnetic moment of electron	–	9.28×10^{-24} joule-m^2/weber	$(9.2837 \pm 0.0002) \times 10^{-24}$
Compton wavelength of electron	$\lambda = \dfrac{h}{m_e c} = 2.43 \times 10^{-12}$ meter		$(0.40606 \pm 0.00000) \times 10^{-12}$
First Bohr orbit radius in hydrogen atom	$a_0 = \dfrac{h^2 \epsilon_0}{4\pi m_e e^2} = 5.29 \times 10^{-11}$ meter		$(5.29172 \pm 0.00002) \times 10^{-11}$

3

Miscellaneous Terrestrial Data

APPENDIX B

Standard atmosphere	1.013×10^5 nt/meter^2
	14.70 lb/in^2
	2117 lb/ft^2
Density of dry air at STP [a]	1.293 kg/meter^3
	2.458×10^{-3} slug/ft^2
Speed of sound in dry air at STP	331.4 meters/sec
	1089 ft/sec
	742.5 miles/hr
Acceleration of gravity, g (standard value) [b]	9.80665 meters/sec^2
	32.1740 ft/sec^2
Solar constant [c]	1340 watts/m^2
	1.92 cal/cm^2-min
Mean total solar radiation	3.92×10^{26} watts
Equatorial radius of earth	6.378×10^6 meters
	3963 miles
Polar radius of earth	6.357×10^6 meters
	3950 miles
Volume of earth	1.087×10^{21} meter^3
	3.838×10^{22} ft^3
Radius of sphere having same volume	6.371×10^6 meters
	3959 miles
	2.090×10^7 ft
Mean density of earth	5522 kg/meter^3
Mass of earth	5.983×10^{24} kg
Mean orbital speed of earth	29,770 meters/sec
	18.50 miles/sec
Mean angular speed of rotation of earth	7.29×10^{-5} radians/sec
Earth's magnetic field, B (at Washington, D. C.)	5.7×10^{-5} weber/meter^2
Earth's magnetic dipole moment	6.4×10^{21} amp-m^2

[a] STP = standard temperature and pressure = 0°C at 1 atm.

[b] This value, used for barometer corrections, legal weights, etc., was adopted by the International Committee on Weights and Measures in 1901.   It approximates 45° latitude at sea level.

[c] The solar constant is the solar energy falling per unit time at normal incidence on unit area of the earth's surface.

APPENDIX C

Body	Mass (Earth = 1)	Distance from Sun		Sidereal Period, days	Mean Specific Gravity
		Km	Miles		
Sun	329,390	–	–	–	1.42
Mercury	0.0549	58×10^6	36.0×10^6	87.97	5.61
Venus	0.8073	108×10^6	67.1×10^6	244.70	5.16
Earth	1.0000	149×10^6	92.9×10^6	365.26	5.52
Mars	0.1065	228×10^6	141.7×10^6	686.98	3.95
Jupiter	314.5	778×10^6	483.4×10^6	4,332.59	1.34
Saturn	94.07	1426×10^6	886.1×10^6	10,759.20	0.69
Uranus	14.40	2869×10^6	1782.7×10^6	30,685.93	1.36
Neptune	16.72	4495×10^6	2793.1×10^6	60,187.64	1.30
Pluto	–	5900×10^6	3666.1×10^6	90,885	–
Moon	0.01228	[b] 38×10^4	[b] 23.9×10^4	27.32	3.36

Body and Symbol [c]	Diameter		Acceleration Due to Gravity at Surface	
	Km	Miles	Cm/sec^2	Ft/sec^2
Sun ⊙	1,390,600	864,100	27,440	900.3
Mercury ☿	5,140	3,194	302	12.0
Venus ♀	12,620	7,842	882	28.9
Earth ⊕, ⊖, ♁	12,756	7,926	980	32.2
Mars ♂	6,860	4,263	392	12.9
Jupiter ♃	143,600	89,229	2,646	86.8
Saturn ♄	120,600	74,937	1,176	38.6
Uranus ♁, ♅	53,400	33,181	980	32.2
Neptune ♆	49,700	30,882	980	32.2
Moon ☽	3,476	2,159.9	167	5.47

[a] From the *Handbook of Chemistry and Physics*, Chemical Rubber Publishing Company.
[b] Distance to Earth.
[c] These symbols are often used in astronomy.

Periodic Table of the Elements

APPENDIX D

Atomic weights are based on those adopted by the International Union of Chemistry. For artificially produced elements, the approximate atomic weight of the most stable isotope is given in brackets.

Period	Series	I	II	III	IV	V	VI	VII	VIII			O
1	1	1 H 1.0080										2 He 4.003
2	2	3 Li 6.940	4 Be 9.013	5 B 10.82	6 C 12.011	7 N 14.008	8 O 16.0000	9 F 19.00				10 Ne 20.183
3	3	11 Na 22.991	12 Mg 24.32	13 Al 26.98	14 Si 28.09	15 P 30.975	16 S 32.066	17 Cl 35.457				18 A 39.944
4	4	19 K 39.100	20 Ca 40.08	21 Sc 44.96	22 Ti 47.90	23 V 50.95	24 Cr 52.01	25 Mn 54.94	26 Fe 55.85	27 Co 58.94	28 Ni 58.71	
	5	29 Cu 63.54	30 Zn 65.38	31 Ga 69.72	32 Ge 72.60	33 As 74.91	34 Se 78.96	35 Br 79.916				36 Kr 83.80

5												
6	37 Rb 85.48	38 Sr 87.63	39 Y 88.92	40 Zr 91.22	41 Nb 92.91	42 Mo 95.95	43 Tc [99]	44 Ru 101.1	45 Rh 102.91	46 Pd 106·4		
7	47 Ag 107.880	48 Cd 112.41	49 In 114.82	50 Sn 118.70	51 Sb 121.76	52 Te 127.61	53 I 126.91	44 Ru 101.1	45 Rh 102.91	46 Pd 106·4	54 Xe 131.30	
8	55 Cs 132.91	56 Ba 137.36	57–71 Lanthanide series a	72 Hf 178.50	73 Ta 180.95	74 W 183.86	75 Re 186.22	76 Os 190.2	77 Ir 192.2	78 Pt 195·09		
9	79 Au 197.0	80 Hg 200.61	81 Tl 204.39	82 Pb 207.21	83 Bi 209.00	84 Po 210	85 At [210]				86 Rn 222	
10	87 Fr [223]	88 Ra 226.05	89– Actinide series b									

a Lanthanide series:

57 La 138.92	58 Ce 140.13	59 Pr 140.92	60 Nd 144.27	61 Pm [147]	62 Sm 150.35	63 Eu 152.0	64 Gd 157.26	65 Tb 158.93	66 Dy 162.51	67 Ho 164.94	68 Er 167.27	69 Tm 168.94	70 Yb 173.04	71 Lu 174.99

b Actinide series:

89 Ac 227	90 Th 232.05	91 Pa 231	92 U 238.07	93 Np [237]	94 Pu [242]	95 Am [243]	96 Cm [245]	97 Bk [249]	98 Cf [249]	99 E [253]	100 Fm [255]	101 Md [256]	102 No	103

The Greek Alphabet

Alpha	A	α
Beta	B	β
Gamma	Γ	γ
Delta	Δ	δ
Epsilon	E	ϵ
Zeta	Z	ζ
Eta	H	η
Theta	Θ	θ, ϑ
Iota	I	ι
Kappa	K	κ
Lambda	Λ	λ
Mu	M	μ
Nu	N	ν
Xi	Ξ	ξ
Omicron	O	o
Pi	Π	π
Rho	P	ρ
Sigma	Σ	σ, s
Tau	T	τ
Upsilon	Υ	υ
Phi	Φ	ϕ, φ
Chi	X	χ
Psi	Ψ	ψ
Omega	Ω	ω

Properties of the Elementary Particles

APPENDIX F

This table must be regarded as a progress report in this field, since many of the properties are not well understood. Also, new particles appear and old particles become reclassified. The data are primarily from two review articles: A. M. Shapiro, *Review of Modern Physics*, **28**, 164 (1956) and M. Gell-Mann and E. P. Rosenbaum, *Scientific American*, **197-1**, 72 (July 1957). All data in ⟨ ⟩ are theoretically predicted and/or have not yet been completely verified experimentally.

Type	Name	Symbol, Charge and Relation [a] — Matter	Antimatter	Rest Mass [b]	Spin [c]	Mean Life, sec	Decay Products [d]
Massless	Photon	γ^0		0	1	stable	—
	Neutrino	ν^0	$\bar{\nu}^0$	⟨0⟩	$\frac{1}{2}$	stable	—
	Electron (positron)	e^-	e^+	1.0000	$\frac{1}{2}$	stable	—
L-mesons	Muon (mu meson)	μ^-	μ^+	206.7	$\langle\frac{1}{2}\rangle$	2.22×10^{-6}	$e^- + \nu + \bar{\nu}$
	Pion (pi meson)	π^-	π^+	273.1	0	2.53×10^{-8}	$\mu^- + \bar{\nu}$
		π^0		264.3	0	$(1-5) \times 10^{-15}$	$\gamma + \gamma$, $\gamma + e^+ + e^-$ [e], $2e^+ + 2e^-$ [f]
K-mesons [g]		K^+	K^-	966.5	⟨0⟩	1.2×10^{-8}	$\pi^+ + \pi^+ + \pi^-$, $\pi^+ + \pi^0 + \pi^0$ $\mu^+ + \nu, e^+ + ? + \ast$[h] $\pi^+ + \pi^0, \mu^+ + \pi^0 + \nu$

		Symbol (j)	Antiparticle	Mass (b)	Spin (i)	Mean life (s)	Decay products (d)
K-mesons		K_1^0	$\langle \overline{K_1^0} \rangle$	965		1.3×10^{-10}	$\pi^+ + \pi^-,\ \langle \pi^0 + \pi^0 \rangle$
		K_2^0	$\langle \overline{K_2^0} \rangle$	965		$(\sim 100) \times 10^{-6}$	$\pi^+ + e^- + \bar{\nu},\ \pi^- + \ldots + \mu^+ + \nu + \pi^0$ $\pi^+ + \mu^- + \bar{\nu},\ \pi^- + \ldots + \nu,\ \pi^+ + \pi^- + \pi^0 + \pi^0$ $\pi^+ + \mu^- + \bar{\nu},\ \pi^0 + \pi^0 + \pi^0$
Nucleons	Proton	p^+	$\overline{p}^-$	1836.1	$\tfrac{1}{2}$	stable	—
	Neutron	n^0	$\overline{n}^0$	1838.6	$\tfrac{1}{2}$	1100	$p^+ + e^- + \bar{\nu}$
Hyperons	Lambda particle	Λ^0	$\overline{\Lambda}^0$	2182	$\tfrac{1}{2}$	2.7×10^{-10}	$p^+ + \pi^-,\ n + \pi^0$
	Sigma particle	Σ^+	$\langle \overline{\Sigma}^+ \rangle$	2325	$\tfrac{1}{2}$	0.7×10^{-10}	$p^+ + \pi^0,\ n + \pi^+$
		Σ^0	$\overline{\Sigma}^0$	2324	$\tfrac{1}{2}$	?	$\Lambda^0 + \gamma$
		Σ^-	$\langle \overline{\Sigma}^- \rangle$	2341	$\tfrac{1}{2}$	1.5×10^{-10}	$n + \pi^-$
	Xi particle	$\langle \Xi^0 \rangle$ Ξ^-	$\langle \overline{\Xi}^+ \rangle$ $\langle \overline{\Xi}^0 \rangle$	2585	$\langle \tfrac{1}{2} \rangle$	10^{-9} to 10^{-10}	$\Lambda^0 + \pi^-$

(a) The charge is given by the superscript and is in units of electron charge. For example, μ^+ has a positive charge of the same magnitude as that of the electron; ν^0 is uncharged. Symbols in the shaded region represent antimatter; particles and corresponding antiparticles are placed symmetrically about the dotted center line. Particles on the center line are their own antiparticles. For example, the positron (e^+) is the antiparticle of the electron (e^-), whereas the photon (γ^0) is its own antiparticle. A dash over a symbol (say $\overline{\nu}^0$) is to be read 'anti-____' (anti-ν^0); however, it is seen that this notation is not always used (namely, e^+, e^-).

(b) The rest mass of each particle is given as a multiple of the electron mass. For example, the mass of μ^- is $206.7 \times m_e = 206.7 \times 9.11 \times 10^{-31}$ kg.

(c) The spin is the angular momentum each particle has owing to rotation about its own axis and is given in units of $\hbar = h/2\pi$, where h is Planck's constant.

(d) The decay products are for the decay of particles (unshaded region). For the decay of the corresponding antiparticle, antiparticles are written for each component of the decay product. For example, we see $\pi^- \rightarrow \mu^- + \bar{\nu}$ so $\pi^+ \rightarrow \mu^+ + \nu$.

(e) Rarely; about once in 80 decays.

(f) Very rarely; about once in 25,600 decays.

(g) The K-mesons in general are not (yet) well understood. The multiplicity of decay schemes might suggest that several particles are lumped together here under one classification, but, on the contrary, some authorities feel that even the K_1^0 and K_2^0 are one and the same. (The notation employed here is that of Gell-Mann and Rosenbaum.)

(h) The spin of the K_1^0 is an integer $\neq$ ...

(i) Perhaps $e^+ + \pi^0 + \nu$ or $e^+ + \ldots + \gamma + \nu$.

(j) The K_1^0 and K_2^0-particles are thought by some to be the same. See note (g).

Symbols, Dimensions, and Units
for Physical Quantities

APPENDIX G

All units and dimensions are in the mksq (rationalized) system.   The primary units can be found by reading kilograms for M, meters for L, seconds for T, and coulombs for Q. The symbols are those used in the text.

Quantity	Symbol	Dimensions	Derived Units
Acceleration	**a**	LT^{-2}	meters/sec^2
Angular acceleration	α	T^{-2}	radians/sec^2
Angular displacement	θ	–	radian
Angular frequency and speed	ω	T^{-1}	radians/sec
Angular momentum	**L**	ML^2T^{-1}	kg-m^2/sec
Angular velocity	**ω**	T^{-1}	radians/sec
Area	A, S	L^2	meter^2
Displacement	**r, d**	L	meter
Energy, total	E	ML^2T^{-2}	joule
kinetic	K	ML^2T^{-2}	joule
potential	U	ML^2T^{-2}	joule
Force	**F**	MLT^{-2}	newton
Frequency	f, ν	T^{-1}	cycles/sec
Gravitational field strength	**g**	LT^{-2}	nt/kg
Gravitational potential	V	L^2T^{-2}	joules/kg
Length	l	L	meter
Mass	m	M	kilogram
Mass density	ρ	ML^{-3}	kg/m^3
Momentum	**p**	MLT^{-1}	kg-m/sec^2
Period	T	T	second
Power	P	ML^2T^{-3}	watt
Pressure	p	$ML^{-1}T^{-2}$	nt/m^2
Rotational inertia	I	ML^2	kg-m^2
Time	t	T	second
Torque	τ	ML^2T^{-2}	nt-m
Velocity	**v**	LT^{-1}	meters/sec
Volume	V	L^3	meter^3
Wavelength	λ	L	meter
Work	W	ML^2T^{-2}	joule
Entropy	S	ML^2T^{-2}	joules/K$^\circ$
Internal energy	U	ML^2T^{-2}	joule
Heat	Q	ML^2T^{-2}	joule
Temperature	T	–	Kelvin degree

Quantity	Symbol	Dimensions	Derived Units
Capacitance	C	$M^{-1}L^{-2}T^2Q^2$	farad
Charge	q	Q	coulomb
Conductivity	σ	$M^{-1}L^{-3}TQ^2$	(ohm-meter)$^{-1}$
Current	i	$T^{-1}Q$	ampere
Current density	$\mathbf{j}$	$L^{-2}T^{-1}Q$	amp/meter^2
Electric dipole moment	$\mathbf{p}$	LQ	coul-meter
Electric displacement	$\mathbf{D}$	$M^{-2}Q$	coul/meter^2
Electric field strength	$\mathbf{E}$	$MLT^{-2}Q^{-1}$	volts/meter
Electric flux	Φ_E	$ML^3T^{-2}Q^{-1}$	volt-meter
Electric potential	V	$ML^2T^{-2}Q^{-1}$	volt
Electromotive force	$\mathcal{E}$	$ML^2T^{-2}Q^{-1}$	volt
Inductance	L	ML^2Q^{-2}	henry
Magnetic dipole moment	$\boldsymbol{\mu}$	$L^2T^{-1}Q$	amp-meter^2
Magnetic field strength	$\mathbf{H}$	$MT^{-1}Q$	amp-meter
Magnetic flux	Φ_B	$ML^2T^{-1}Q^{-1}$	weber = volt-sec
Magnetic induction	$\mathbf{B}$	$MT^{-1}Q^{-1}$	webers/meter^2
Magnetization	$\mathbf{M}$	$L^{-1}T^{-1}Q$	amp/meter
Permeability	μ	MLQ^{-2}	henrys/meter
Permittivity	ϵ	$M^{-1}L^{-3}T^2Q^2$	farads/meter
Resistance	R	$ML^2T^{-1}Q^{-2}$	ohm
Resistivity	ρ	$ML^3T^{-1}Q^{-2}$	ohm-meter
Voltage	V	$ML^2T^{-2}Q^{-1}$	volt

Conversion Factors[a]

APPENDIX H

Conversion factors for common and not-so-common units may be read off directly from the tables below. For example, 1 degree = 2.778×10^{-3} revolutions, so $16.7° = 16.7 \times 2.778 \times 10^{-3}$ rev. The mksq quantities are capitalized in each table.

PLANE ANGLE

	°	′	″	RADIAN	rev
1 degree =	1	60	3600	1.745×10^{-2}	2.778×10^{-3}
1 minute =	1.667×10^{-2}	1	60	2.909×10^{-4}	4.630×10^{-5}
1 second =	2.778×10^{-4}	1.667×10^{-2}	1	4.848×10^{-6}	7.716×10^{-7}
1 RADIAN =	57.30	3438	2.063×10^{5}	1	0.1592
1 revolution =	360	2.16×10^{4}	1.296×10^{6}	6.283	1

1 rev = 2π radians = 360°   1° = 60′ = 3600″

SOLID ANGLE

1 sphere = 4π steradians = 12.57 steradians

LENGTH

	cm	METER	km	in.	ft	mile
1 centimeter =	1	10^{-2}	10^{-5}	0.3937	3.281×10^{-2}	6.214×10^{-6}
1 METER =	100	1	10^{-3}	39.37	3.281	6.214×10^{-4}
1 kilometer =	10^{5}	1000	1	3.937×10^{4}	3281	0.6214
1 inch =	2.540	2.540×10^{-2}	2.540×10^{-5}	1	8.333×10^{-2}	1.578×10^{-5}
1 foot =	30.48	0.3048	3.048×10^{-4}	12	1	1.894×10^{-4}
1 statute mile =	1.609×10^{5}	1609	1.609	6.336×10^{4}	5280	1

1 foot = 1200/3937 meter   1 micron = 10^{-6} meter   1 fathom = 6 ft
1 meter = 3937/1200 ft   1 millimicron (mμ) = 10^{-9} meter   1 yard = 3 ft
1 angstrom (A) = 10^{-10} meter   1 light-year = 9.4600×10^{12} km   1 rod = 16.5 ft
1 X-unit = 10^{-13} meter   1 parsec = 3.084×10^{13} km   1 mil = 10^{-3} in.
1 nautical mile = 1852 meters = 1.1508 statute miles = 6076.10 ft

[a] Adapted in part from G. Shortley and D. Williams, *Elements of Physics*, Prentice-Hall, Inc., New York, Second Edition, 1955.

AREA

	METER^2	cm^2	ft^2	in.^{2}	circ mil
1 SQUARE METER =	1	10^4	10.76	1550	1.974 × 10^9
1 square centimeter =	10^{-4}	1	1.076 × 10^{-3}	0.1550	1.974 × 10^5
1 square foot =	9.290 × 10^{-2}	929.0	1	144	1.833 × 10^8
1 square inch =	6.452 × 10^{-4}	6.452	6.944 × 10^{-3}	1	1.273 × 10^6
1 circular mil =	5.067 × 10^{-10}	5.067 × 10^{-6}	5.454 × 10^{-9}	7.854 × 10^{-7}	1

1 square mile = 27,878,400 ft^2 = 640 acres   1 acre = 43,560 ft^2
1 barn = 10^{-28} meter^2

VOLUME

	METER^3	cm^3	1	ft^3	in.^{3}
1 CUBIC METER =	1	10^6	1000	35.31	6.102 × 10^4
1 cubic centimeter =	10^{-6}	1	1.000 × 10^{-3}	3.531 × 10^{-5}	6.102 × 10^{-2}
1 liter =	1.000 × 10^{-3}	1000	1	3.531 × 10^{-2}	61.02
1 cubic foot =	2.832 × 10^{-2}	2.832 × 10^4	28.32	1	1728
1 cubic inch =	1.639 × 10^{-5}	16.39	1.639 × 10^{-2}	5.787 × 10^{-4}	1

1 U. S. fluid gallon = 4 U. S. fluid quarts = 8 U. S. pints = 128 U. S. fluid ounces = 231 in.^{3}
1 British imperial gallon = the volume of 10 lb of water at 62°F = 277.42 in.^{3}
1 liter = the volume of 1 kg of water at its maximum density = 1000.028 cm^3

MASS

Note: Those quantities to the right of and below the heavy lines are not mass units at all but are often used as such. When we write, for example,

$$1 \text{ kg ``='' } 2.205 \text{ lb}$$

this means that a kilogram is a *mass* that *weighs* 2.205 pounds. Clearly this "equivalence" is approximate (depending on the value of g) and is meaningful only for terrestrial measurements. Thus, care must be employed when using the factors in the shaded portion of the table.

	gm	KG	slug	amu	oz	lb	ton
1 gram =	1	0.001	6.852 × 10^{-5}	6.024 × 10^{23}	3.527 × 10^{-2}	2.205 × 10^{-3}	1.102 × 10^{-6}
1 KILOGRAM =	1000	1	6.852 × 10^{-2}	6.024 × 10^{26}	35.27	2.205	1.102 × 10^{-3}
1 slug =	1.459 × 10^4	14.59	1	8.789 × 10^{27}	514.8	32.17	1.609 × 10^{-2}
1 amu =	1.660 × 10^{-24}	1.660 × 10^{-27}	1.137 × 10^{-28}	1	5.855 × 10^{-26}	3.660 × 10^{-27}	1.829 × 10^{-30}
1 ounce (avoirdupois) =	28.35	2.835 × 10^{-2}	1.943 × 10^{-3}	1.708 × 10^{25}	1	6.250 × 10^{-2}	3.125 × 10^{-5}
1 pound (avoirdupois) =	453.6	0.4536	3.108 × 10^{-2}	2.732 × 10^{26}	16	1	0.0005
1 ton =	9.072 × 10^5	907.2	62.16	5.465 × 10^{29}	3.2 × 10^4	2000	1

DENSITY

Note: Those quantities to the right or below the heavy line are weight densities and, as such, are dimensionally different from mass densities. Care must be used. (See note for mass table.)

	slug/ft^3	KG/METER^3	gm/cm^3	lb/ft^3	lb/in.^{3}
1 slug per ft^3 =	1	515.4	0.5154	32.17	1.862×10^{-2}
1 KILOGRAM per METER^3 =	1.940×10^{-3}	1	0.001	6.243×10^{-2}	3.613×10^{-5}
1 gram per cm^3 =	1.940	1000	1	62.43	3.613×10^{-2}
1 pound per ft^3 =	3.108×10^{-2}	16.02	1.602×10^{-2}	1	5.787×10^{-4}
1 pound per in.^{3} =	53.71	2.768×10^4	27.68	1728	1

TIME

	yr	day	hr	min	SEC
1 year =	1	365.2	8.766×10^3	5.259×10^5	3.156×10^7
1 day =	2.738×10^{-3}	1	24	1440	8.640×10^4
1 hour =	1.141×10^{-4}	4.167×10^{-2}	1	60	3600
1 minute =	1.901×10^{-6}	6.944×10^{-4}	1.667×10^{-2}	1	60
1 SECOND =	3.169×10^{-8}	1.157×10^{-5}	2.778×10^{-4}	1.667×10^{-2}	1

1 year = 365.24219879 days

SPEED

	ft/sec	km/hr	METER/SEC	miles/hr	cm/sec	knot
1 foot per second =	1	1.097	0.3048	0.6818	30.48	0.5925
1 kilometer per hour =	0.9113	1	0.2778	0.6214	27.78	0.5400
1 METER per SECOND =	3.281	3.6	1	2.237	100	1.944
1 mile per hour =	1.467	1.609	0.4470	1	44.70	0.8689
1 centimeter per second =	3.281×10^{-2}	3.6×10^{-2}	0.01	2.237×10^{-2}	1	1.944×10^{-2}
1 knot =	1.688	1.852	0.5144	1.151	51.44	1

1 knot = 1 nautical mile/hr   1 mile/min = 88 ft/sec = 60 miles/hr

FORCE

Note: Those quantities to the right of and below the heavy lines are not force units at all but are often used as such, especially in chemistry. For instance, if we write

$$1 \text{ gram-force "}=\text{" } 980.7 \text{ dynes,}$$

we mean that a gram-*mass* experiences a *force* of 980.7 dynes in the earth's gravitational field. Thus, care must be employed when using the factors in the shaded portion of the table.

	.dyne	NT	lb	pdl	gf	kgf
1 dyne =	1	10^{-5}	2.248×10^{-6}	7.233×10^{-5}	1.020×10^{-3}	1.020×10^{-6}
1 NEWTON =	10^5	1	0.2248	7.233	102.0	0.1020
1 pound =	4.448×10^5	4.448	1	32.17	453.6	0.4536
1 poundal =	1.383×10^4	0.1383	3.108×10^{-2}	1	14.10	1.410×10^{-2}
1 gram-force =	980.7	9.807×10^{-3}	2.205×10^{-3}	7.093×10^{-2}	1	0.001
1 kilogram-force =	9.807×10^5	9.807	2.205	70.93	1000	1

$$1 \text{ kgf} = 9.80665 \text{ nt} \qquad 1 \text{ lb} = 32.17398 \text{ pdl}$$

PRESSURE

	atm	dyne/cm²	inch of water	cm Hg	NT/METER²	lb/in.²	lb/ft²
1 atmosphere =	1	1.013×10^6	406.8	76	1.013×10^5	14.70	2116
1 dyne per cm² =	9.869×10^{-7}	1	4.015×10^{-4}	7.501×10^{-5}	0.1	1.450×10^{-5}	2.089×10^{-3}
1 inch of water at 4° C [a] =	2.458×10^{-3}	2491	1	0.1868	249.1	3.613×10^{-2}	5.202
1 centimeter of mercury at 0°C [a] =	1.316×10^{-2}	1.333×10^4	5.353	1	1333	0.1934	27.85
1 NEWTON per METER² =	9.869×10^{-6}	10	4.015×10^{-3}	7.501×10^{-4}	1	1.450×10^{-4}	2.089×10^{-2}
1 pound per in.² =	6.805×10^{-2}	6.895×10^4	27.68	5.171	6.895×10^3	1	144
1 pound per ft² =	4.725×10^{-4}	478.8	0.1922	3.591×10^{-2}	47.88	6.944×10^{-3}	1

[a] Where the acceleration of gravity has the standard value 9.80665 meters/sec².

$$1 \text{ bar} = 10^6 \text{ dyne/cm}^2 \qquad 1 \text{ millibar} = 10^3 \text{ dyne/cm}^2$$

ENERGY, WORK, HEAT

The electron volt (ev) is the kinetic energy an electron gains from being accelerated through the potential difference of one volt in an electric field. The Mev is the kinetic energy it gains from being accelerated through a million-volt potential difference.

The last two items in this table are not properly energy units but are included for convenience. They arise from the relativistic mass-energy equivalence formula $E = mc^2$ and represent the energy released if a kilogram or atomic mass unit (amu) is destroyed completely. Again, care should be used when employing this table.

	Btu	erg	ft-lb	hp-hr	JOULES	cal	kw-hr	ev	Mev	kg	amu
1 British thermal unit =	1	1.055×10^{10}	777.9	3.929×10^{-4}	1055	252.0	2.930×10^{-4}	6.585×10^{21}	6.585×10^{15}	1.174×10^{-14}	7.074×10^{12}
1 erg =	9.481×10^{-11}	1	7.376×10^{-8}	3.725×10^{-14}	10^{-7}	2.389×10^{-8}	2.778×10^{-14}	6.242×10^{11}	6.242×10^{5}	1.113×10^{-24}	670.5
1 foot-pound =	1.285×10^{-3}	1.356×10^{7}	1	5.051×10^{-7}	1.356	0.3239	3.766×10^{-7}	8.464×10^{18}	8.464×10^{12}	1.509×10^{-17}	9.092×10^{9}
1 horsepower-hour =	2545	2.685×10^{13}	1.980×10^{6}	1	2.685×10^{6}	6.414×10^{5}	0.7457	1.676×10^{25}	1.676×10^{19}	2.988×10^{-11}	1.800×10^{16}
1 JOULE =	9.481×10^{-4}	10^{7}	0.7376	3.725×10^{-7}	1	0.2389	2.778×10^{-7}	6.242×10^{18}	6.242×10^{12}	1.113×10^{-17}	6.705×10^{9}
1 calorie =	3.968×10^{-3}	4.186×10^{7}	3.087	1.559×10^{-6}	4.186	1	1.163×10^{-6}	2.613×10^{19}	2.613×10^{13}	4.659×10^{-17}	2.807×10^{10}
1 kilowatt-hour =	3413	3.6×10^{13}	2.655×10^{6}	1.341	3.6×10^{6}	8.601×10^{5}	1	2.247×10^{25}	2.270×10^{19}	4.007×10^{-11}	2.414×10^{16}
1 electron volt =	1.519×10^{-22}	1.602×10^{-12}	1.182×10^{-19}	5.967×10^{-26}	1.602×10^{-19}	3.827×10^{-20}	4.450×10^{-26}	1	10^{-6}	1.783×10^{-36}	1.074×10^{-9}
1 million electron volts =	1.519×10^{-16}	1.602×10^{-6}	1.182×10^{-13}	5.967×10^{-20}	1.602×10^{-13}	3.827×10^{-14}	4.450×10^{-20}	10^{6}	1	1.783×10^{-30}	1.074×10^{-3}
1 kilogram =	8.521×10^{13}	8.987×10^{23}	6.629×10^{16}	3.348×10^{10}	8.987×10^{16}	2.147×10^{16}	2.497×10^{10}	5.610×10^{35}	5.610×10^{29}	1	6.025×10^{26}
1 atomic mass unit =	1.415×10^{-13}	1.492×10^{-3}	1.100×10^{-10}	5.558×10^{-17}	1.492×10^{-10}	3.564×10^{-11}	4.145×10^{-17}	9.31×10^{8}	931.0	1.660×10^{-27}	1

1 m-kgf = 9.807 joules   1 watt-sec = 1 joule = 1 nt-m   1 cm-dyne = 1 erg

POWER

	Btu/hr	ft-lb/min	ft-lb/sec	hp	cal/sec	kw	WATTS
1 British thermal unit per hour =	1	12.97	0.2161	3.929×10^{-4}	7.000×10^{-2}	2.930×10^{-4}	0.2930
1 foot-pound per minute =	7.713×10^{-2}	1	1.667×10^{-2}	3.030×10^{-5}	5.399×10^{-3}	2.260×10^{-5}	2.260×10^{-2}
1 foot-pound per second =	4.628	60	1	1.818×10^{-3}	0.3239	1.356×10^{-3}	1.356
1 horsepower =	2545	3.3×10^{4}	550	1	178.2	0.7457	745.7
1 calorie per second =	14.29	1.852×10^{2}	3.087	5.613×10^{-3}	1	4.186×10^{-3}	4.186
1 kilowatt =	3413	4.425×10^{4}	737.6	1.341	238.9	1	1000
1 WATT =	3.413	44.26	0.7376	1.341×10^{-3}	0.2389	0.001	1

ELECTRIC CHARGE

	abcoul	amp-hr	COUL	faraday	statcoul
1 abcoulomb (1 emu) =	1	2.778×10^{-3}	10	1.036×10^{-4}	2.998×10^{10}
1 ampere-hour =	360	1	3600	3.730×10^{-2}	1.079×10^{13}
1 COULOMB =	0.1	2.778×10^{-4}	1	1.036×10^{-5}	2.998×10^{9}
1 faraday =	9652	26.81	9.652×10^{4}	1	2.893×10^{14}
1 statcoulomb (1 esu) =	3.336×10^{-11}	9.266×10^{-14}	3.336×10^{-10}	3.456×10^{-15}	1

1 electronic charge = 1.602×10^{-19}

ELECTRIC CURRENT

	abamp	AMP	statamp
1 abampere (1 emu) =	1	10	2.998×10^{10}
1 AMPERE =	0.1	1	2.998×10^{9}
1 statampere (1 esu) =	3.336×10^{-11}	3.336×10^{-10}	1

ELECTRIC POTENTIAL, ELECTROMOTIVE FORCE

	abv	VOLTS	statv
1 abvolt (1 emu) =	1	10^{-8}	3.336×10^{-11}
1 VOLT =	10^{8}	1	3.336×10^{-3}
1 statvolt (1 esu) =	2.998×10^{10}	299.8	1

ELECTRIC RESISTANCE

	abohm	OHMS	statohm
1 abohm (1 emu) =	1	10^{-9}	1.113×10^{-21}
1 OHM =	10^9	1	1.113×10^{-12}
1 statohm (1 esu) =	8.987×10^{20}	8.987×10^{11}	1

ELECTRIC RESISTIVITY

	abohm-cm	μohm-cm	ohm-cm	statohm-cm	OHM-M	ohm-circ mil /ft
1 abohm-centimeter (1 emu) =	1	0.001	10^{-9}	1.113×10^{-21}	10^{-11}	6.015×10^{-3}
1 micro-ohm-centimeter- =	1000	1	10^{-6}	1.113×10^{-18}	10^{-8}	6.015
1 ohm-centimeter =	10^9	10^6	1	1.113×10^{-12}	0.01	6.015×10^6
1 statohm-centimeter (1 esu) =	8.987×10^{20}	8.987×10^{17}	8.987×10^{11}	1	8.987×10^9	5.406×10^{18}
1 OHM-METER =	10^{11}	10^8	100	1.113×10^{-10}	1	6.015×10^8
1 ohm-circular mil per foot =	166.2	0.1662	1.662×10^{-7}	1.850×10^{-19}	1.662×10^{-9}	1

CAPACITANCE

	abf	FARADS	μf [a]	statf
1 abfarad (1 emu) =	1	10^9	10^{15}	8.987×10^{20}
1 FARAD =	10^{-9}	1	10^6	8.987×10^{11}
1 microfarad =	10^{-15}	10^{-6}	1	8.987×10^5
1 statfarad (1 esu) =	1.113×10^{-21}	1.113×10^{-12}	1.113×10^{-6}	1

[a] This unit is frequently abbreviated as mf.

INDUCTANCE

	abhenry	HENRYS	μh	mh	stathenry
1 abhenry (1 emu) =	1	10^{-9}	0.001	10^{-6}	1.113×10^{-21}
1 HENRY =	10^9	1	10^6	1000	1.113×10^{-12}
1 microhenry =	1000	10^{-6}	1	0.001	1.113×10^{-18}
1 millihenry =	10^6	0.001	1000	1	1.113×10^{-15}
1 stathenry (1 esu) =	8.987×10^{20}	8.987×10^{11}	8.987×10^{17}	8.987×10^{14}	1

MAGNETIC FLUX

	maxwell	kiloline	WEBER
1 maxwell (1 line or 1 emu) =	1	0.001	10^{-8}
1 kiloline =	1000	1	10^{-5}
1 WEBER =	10^8	10^5	1

1 esu = 299.8 webers

MAGNETIC INDUCTION B

	gauss	kiloline/in.^{2}	WEBER/METER^2	milligauss	γ
1 gauss (line per cm^2) =	1	6.452×10^{-3}	10^{-4}	1000	10^5
1 kiloline per in.^{2} =	155.0	1	1.550×10^{-2}	1.550×10^5	1.550×10^7
1 WEBER per METER^2 =	10^4	64.52	1	10^7	10^9
1 milligauss =	0.001	6.452×10^{-6}	10^{-7}	1	100
1 gamma =	10^{-5}	6.452×10^{-8}	10^{-9}	0.01	1

1 esu = 2.998×10^6 webers /meter^2

MAGNETOMOTIVE FORCE

	abamp-turn	AMP-TURN	gilbert
1 abampere-turn =	1	10	12.57
1 AMPERE-TURN =	0.1	1	1.257
1 gilbert =	7.958×10^{-2}	0.7958	1

1 pragilbert = 4π amp-turn   1 esu = 2.655×10^{-11} amp-turn

MAGNETIC FIELD STRENGTH H

	abamp-turn/cm	amp-turn/cm	amp-turn/in.	AMP-TURN/METER	oersted
1 abampere-turn per centimeter =	1	10	25.40	1000	12.57
1 ampere-turn per centimeter =	0.1	1	2.540	100	1.257
1 ampere-turn per inch =	3.937×10^{-2}	0.3937	1	39.37	0.4947
1 AMPERE-TURN per METER =	0.001	0.01	2.540×10^{-2}	1	1.257×10^{-2}
1 oersted =	7.958×10^{-2}	0.7958	2.021	79.58	1

1 oersted = 1 gilbert   1 esu = 2.655×10^{-9} amp-turn/meter
1 praoersted = 4π amp-turn/meter

Mathematical Formulas

Series expansions (these expansions converge for $-1 < x < 1$, except as noted)

$$\frac{1}{1+x} = 1 - x + x^2 - x^3 + \cdots$$

$$\sqrt{1+x} = 1 + \frac{x}{2} - \frac{x^2}{8} + \frac{x^3}{16} - \cdots$$

$$\frac{1}{\sqrt{1+x}} = 1 - \frac{x}{2} + \frac{3x^2}{8} - \frac{5x^3}{16} + \cdots$$

$$e^x = 1 + x + \frac{x^2}{2} + \frac{x^3}{6} + \cdots \qquad (-\infty < x < \infty)$$

x in radians

$$\sin x = x - \frac{x^3}{6} + \frac{x^5}{120} - \cdots \qquad (-\infty < x < \infty)$$

$$\cos x = 1 - \frac{x^2}{2} + \frac{x^4}{24} - \cdots \qquad (-\infty < x < \infty)$$

$$\tan x = x + \frac{x^3}{3} + \frac{2x^5}{15} + \cdots \qquad (-\pi/2 < x < \pi/2)$$

$$(x + y)^n = x^n + \frac{n}{1!}x^{n-1}y + \frac{n(n-1)}{2!}x^{n-2}y^2 + \cdots \qquad (x^2 > y^2)$$

Quadratic formula

If $ax^2 + bx + c = 0$, then $x = \dfrac{-b \pm \sqrt{b^2 - 4ac}}{2a}$.

Trigonometric functions of angle θ

$$\sin \theta = \frac{y}{r} \qquad \cos \theta = \frac{x}{r}$$

$$\tan \theta = \frac{y}{x} \qquad \cot \theta = \frac{x}{y}$$

$$\sec \theta = \frac{r}{x} \qquad \csc \theta = \frac{r}{y}$$

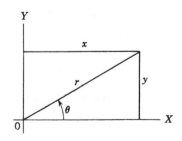

Pythagorean theorem

$$x^2 + y^2 = r^2$$

Trigonometric identities

$$\sin^2 \theta + \cos^2 \theta = 1 \qquad \sec^2 \theta - \tan^2 \theta = 1 \qquad \csc^2 \theta - \cot^2 \theta = 1$$

$$\sin (\alpha \pm \beta) = \sin \alpha \cos \beta \pm \cos \alpha \sin \beta$$

$$\cos (\alpha \pm \beta) = \cos \alpha \cos \beta \mp \sin \alpha \sin \beta$$

$$\tan (\alpha \pm \beta) = \frac{\tan \alpha \pm \tan \beta}{1 \mp \tan \alpha \tan \beta}$$

$$\sin 2\theta = 2 \sin \theta \cos \theta$$

$$\cos 2\theta = \cos^2 \theta - \sin^2 \theta = 2 \cos^2 \theta - 1 = 1 - 2 \sin^2 \theta$$

$$\sin \theta = \frac{e^{i\theta} - e^{-i\theta}}{2i} \qquad \cos \theta = \frac{e^{i\theta} + e^{-i\theta}}{2}$$

$$e^{\pm i\theta} = \cos \theta \pm i \sin \theta$$

Vector products

$$\mathbf{a} \cdot \mathbf{b} = \mathbf{b} \cdot \mathbf{a} \qquad \mathbf{a} \cdot \mathbf{b} = ab \cos \theta \;\Big| \;\text{where } \theta \text{ is the smaller}$$

$$\mathbf{a} \times \mathbf{b} = -\mathbf{b} \times \mathbf{a} \qquad |\mathbf{a} \times \mathbf{b}| = ab \sin \theta \;\Big|\; \text{angle between } \mathbf{a} \text{ and } \mathbf{b}$$

Mathematical signs and symbols

$=$ equals

$\cong$ equals approximately

$\neq$ is not equal to

$\equiv$ is identical to, is defined as

$>$ is greater than ($\gg$ is much greater than)

$<$ is less than ($\ll$ is much less than)

$\geq$ is more than or equal to (or, is no less than)

$\leq$ is less than or equal to (or, is no more than)

$\pm$ plus or minus (e.g., $\sqrt{4} = \pm 2$)

$\propto$ is proportional to (e.g., Hooke's law: $F \propto x$, or $F = -kx$)

Σ the sum of

$\bar{x}$ the average value of x

Values of Trigonometric Functions

APPENDIX J

Angle		Sine	Cosine	Tan-gent	Angle		Sine	Cosine	Tan-gent
Degrees	Radians				Degrees	Radians			
0	0.0000	0.000	1.000	0.000					
1	0.0175	.018	1.000	.018	31	0.5411	0.515	0.857	0.601
2	0.0349	.035	0.999	.035	32	0.5585	.530	.848	.625
3	0.0524	.052	.999	.052	33	0.5760	.545	.839	.649
4	0.0698	.070	.998	.070	34	0.5934	.559	.829	.675
5	0.0873	.087	.996	.088	35	0.6109	.574	.819	.700
6	0.1047	.105	.995	.105	36	0.6283	.588	.809	.727
7	0.1222	.122	.993	.123	37	0.6458	.602	.799	.754
8	0.1396	.139	.990	.141	38	0.6632	.616	.788	.781
9	0.1571	.156	.988	.158	39	0.6807	.629	.777	.810
10	0.1745	.174	.985	.176	40	0.6981	.643	.766	.839
11	0.1920	.191	.982	.194	41	0.7156	.656	.755	.869
12	0.2094	.208	.978	.213	42	0.7330	.669	.743	.900
13	0.2269	.225	.974	.231	43	0.7505	.682	.731	.933
14	0.2443	.242	.970	.249	44	0.7679	.695	.719	.966
15	0.2618	.259	.966	.268	45	0.7854	.707	.707	1.000
16	0.2793	.276	.961	.287	46	0.8029	.719	.695	1.036
17	0.2967	.292	.956	.306	47	0.8203	.731	.682	1.072
18	0.3142	.309	.951	.325	48	0.8378	.743	.669	1.111
19	0.3316	.326	.946	.344	49	0.8552	.755	.656	1.150
20	0.3491	.342	.940	.364	50	0.8727	.766	.643	1.192
21	0.3665	.358	.934	.384	51	0.8901	.777	.629	1.235
22	0.3840	.375	.927	.404	52	0.9076	.788	.616	1.280
23	0.4014	.391	.921	.425	53	0.9250	.799	.602	1.327
24	0.4189	.407	.914	.445	54	0.9425	.809	.588	1.376
25	0.4363	.423	.906	.466	55	0.9599	.819	.574	1.428
26	0.4538	.438	.899	.488	56	0.9774	.829	.559	1.483
27	0.4712	.454	.891	.510	57	0.9948	.839	.545	1.540
28	0.4887	.470	.883	.532	58	1.0123	.848	.530	1.600
29	0.5061	.485	.875	.554	59	1.0297	.857	.515	1.664
30	0.5236	.500	.866	.577	60	1.0472	.866	.500	1.732

Angle		Sine	Cosine	Tan-gent	Angle		Sine	Cosine	Tan-gent
Degrees	Radians				Degrees	Radians			
61	1.0647	0.875	0.485	1.804	76	1.3265	0.970	0.242	4.011
62	1.0821	.883	.470	1.881	77	1.3439	.974	.225	4.331
63	1.0996	.891	.454	1.963	78	1.3614	.978	.208	4.705
64	1.1170	.899	.438	2.050	79	1.3788	.982	.191	5.145
65	1.1345	.906	.423	2.145	80	1.3963	.985	.174	5.671
66	1.1519	.914	.407	2.246	81	1.4137	.988	.156	6.314
67	1.1694	.921	.391	2.356	82	1.4312	.990	.139	7.115
68	1.1868	.927	.375	2.475	83	1.4486	.993	.122	8.144
69	1.2043	.934	.358	2.605	84	1.4661	.995	.105	9.514
70	1.2217	.940	.342	2.747	85	1.4835	.996	.087	11.43
71	1.2392	.946	.326	2.904	86	1.5010	.998	.070	14.30
72	1.2566	.951	.309	3.078	87	1.5184	.999	.052	19.08
73	1.2741	.956	.292	3.271	88	1.5359	.999	.035	28.64
74	1.2915	.951	.276	3.487	89	1.5533	1.000	.018	57.29
75	1.3090	.966	.259	3.732	90	1.5708	1.000	.000	∞

Nobel Prize Winners in Physics[a]

APPENDIX K

1901	Wilhelm Konrad Röntgen	1845–1923	German	Discovery of X-rays.
1902	Hendrik Antoon Lorentz	1853–1928	Dutch	Influence of magnetism on the
	Pieter Zeeman	1865–1943	Dutch	phenomena of radiation.
1903	Henri Becquerel	1852–1908	French	Discovery of the radioactive elements of radium and polonium.
	Pierre Curie	1850–1906	French	
	Marie Curie	1867–1934	French	
1904	Baron Rayleigh	1842–1919	English	Discovery of argon.
1905	Philipp Lenard	1862–1947	German	Research in cathode rays.
1906	Sir Joseph John Thomson	1856–1940	English	Conduction of electricity through gases.
1907	Albert A. Michelson	1852–1931	U. S.	Spectroscopic and metrological investigations.
1908	Gabriel Lippmann	1845–1921	French	Photographic reproduction of colors.
1909	Guglielmo Marconi	1874–1937	Italian	Development of wireless telegraphy.
	Karl Ferdinand Braun	1850–1918	German	
1910	Johannes Diderik van der Waals	1837–1923	Dutch	Equations of state of gases and fluids.
1911	Wilhelm Wien	1864–1928	German	Laws of heat radiation.
1912	Nils Gustaf Dalen	1869–1937	Swedish	Coast lighting.
1913	Heike Kamerlingh-Onnes	1853–1926	Dutch	Properties of matter at low temperatures; production of liquid helium.
1914	Max von Laue	1879–	German	Diffraction of X-rays in crystals.
1915	Sir William Henry Bragg	1862–1942	English	Study of crystal structure by means of X-rays.
	William Lawrence Bragg	1890–	English— his son	
1916	(No award)			
1917	Charles Glover Barkla	1877–1944	English	Discovery of the characteristic Röntgen radiation of elements.
1918	Max Planck	1858–1947	German	Discovery of the elemental quantum.
1919	Johannes Stark	1874–1957	German	Discovery of the Doppler effect in canal rays and the division of spectral lines in the electric field.
1920	Charles Edouard Guillaume	1861–1938	Swiss	Discovery of the anomalies of nickel-steel alloys.
1921	Albert Einstein	1879–1955	German	Founder of theory of relativity and discoverer of law of photoelectric effect.
1922	Niels Bohr	1885–	Danish	Study of structure and radiations of atoms.
1923	Robert Andrews Millikan	1868–1953	U. S.	Work on elementary electric charge and the photoelectric effect.
1924	Karl Manne Siegbahn	1886–	Swedish	Discoveries in the area of X-ray spectra.
1925	James Franck	1882–	German	Laws governing collision between electron and atom.
	Gustav Hertz	1887–	German	
1926	Jean Perrin	1870–1942	French	Discovery of the equilibrium of sedimentation.
1927	Arthur H. Compton	1892–	U. S.	Discovery of the dispersion of X-rays.
	Charles T. R. Wilson	1869–	English	Method of rendering discernible the courses of electrically charged particles by water condensation.
1928	Sir Owen Williams Richardson	1879–1959	English	Discovery of the law known by his name (the dependency of the emission of electrons on temperature).

1929	Louis-Victor de Broglie	1892–	French	Wave nature of electrons.
1930	Sir Chandrasekhara Raman	1888–	Indian	Works on the diffusion of light and discovery of the effect known by his name.
1931	(No award)			
1932	Werner Heisenberg	1901–	German	Creation of quantum mechanics.
1933	Paul Adrien Maurice Dirac	1902–	English	Discovery of new fertile forms of
	Erwin Schrödinger	1887–	Austrian	the atomic theory.
1934	(No award)			
1935	James Chadwick	1891–	English	Discovery of the neutron.
1936	Victor Hess	1883–	Austrian	Discovery of cosmic radiation.
	Carl David Anderson	1905–	U. S.	Discovery of the positron.
1937	Clinton Joseph Davisson	1881–1958	U. S.	Discovery of diffraction of elec-
	George P. Thomson	1892–	English	trons by crystals.
1938	Enrico Fermi	1901–1954	Italian	Artificial radioactive substances.
1939	E. O. Lawrence	1901–1958	U. S.	Invention of the cyclotron.
1940–				
1942	(No award)			
1943	Otto Stern	1888–	U. S.	Detection of magnetic move- ments of protons.
1944	Isidor Isaac Rabi	1898–	U. S.	Studies of atom's nucleus.
1945	Wolfgang Pauli	1900–	Austrian	Exclusion principle.
1946	Percy Williams Bridgman	1882–	U. S.	High-pressure physics.
1947	Sir Edward Appleton	1892–	English	Discovery of Appleton layer.
1948	Patrick Maynard Stuart Blackett	1897–	English	Discoveries in cosmic radiation.
1949	Hideki Yukawa	1907–	Japanese	Theoretical work on meson.
1950	Cecil Frank Powell	1903–	English	Photographic method of study- ing atomic nuclei; discoveries about mesons.
1951	Sir John Douglas Cockcroft	1897–	English	Transmutation of atomic nu-
	Ernest Thomas Sinton Walton	1903–	Irish	clei by artificially accelerated atomic particles.
1952	Felix Bloch	1905–	U. S.	Measure of magnetic fields in
	Edward Mills Purcell	1912–	U. S.	atomic nuclei.
1953	Frits Zernike	1888–	Dutch	Introduction of phase contrast microscopy.
1954	Max Born	1882–	English [b]	Work in mathematics which en- abled physicists to understand atom behavior.
	Walther Bothe	1891–1957	German	Analysis of cosmic radiation; "the coincidence method."
1955	Willis E. Lamb, Jr.	1913–	U. S.	Work with atomic measurements.
	Polykarp Kusch	1911–	U. S.	
1956	John Bardeen	1908–	U. S.	Invention and development of
	Walter H. Brattain	1902–	U. S.	transistor.
	William B. Shockley	1910–	U. S. [c]	
1957	Chen Ning Yang	1922–	China [d]	Overthrow of principle of con-
	Tsung Dao Lee	1926–	China [d]	servation of parity.
1958	Pavel A. Čerenkov	1904?–	Russian	Discovery and interpretation of
	Ilya M. Frank	1908?–	Russian	Čerenkov effect.
	Igor Y. Tamm	1895–	Russian	
1959	Owen Chamberlain	1920–	U. S.	Discovery of the antiproton.
	Emilio Gino Segré	1905–	U. S. [e]	
1960	Donald A. Glaser	1926–	U. S.	Invention of bubble chamber.
1961	Robert L. Hofstadter	1915–	U. S.	Electromagnetic structure of nu- cleons from high-energy elec- tron scattering.
	Rudolf L. Mössbauer	1929–	German	Discovery of recoilless resonance absorption of gamma rays in nuclei.

[a] From the *Encyclopaedia Britannica*.
[b] Born in Germany; naturalized British citizen.
[c] Born in England; naturalized U. S. citizen.
[d] Both have permanent U. S. resident status.
[e] Born in Italy; naturalized U. S. citizen.

Answers to Problems

Chapter 1
1. 0.0254 in.
3. 186 miles
5. 2.30 hr

Chapter 2
1. $|\mathbf{D}| = 11{,}200$ km
3. 81.0 miles, 39.6° N of E
7. (a) $A_x = -2.83$ meters
   $A_y = -2.83$ meters
   $B_x = 5$ meters
   $B_y = 0$
   $C_x = 3$ meters
   $C_y = 5.2$ meters,
   (b) $D_x = 5.17$ meters
   $D_y = 2.37$ meters,
   (c) 5.69 meters, 24.6° N of E
9. 10 meters, 37° above x-axis.
11. $c_x + d_x = 2$ miles,
   $c_y + d_y = 4$ miles,
   $c_z + d_z = 4$ miles
13. (a) 21 ft
19. (a) 30.0 units², (b) 52.0 units²

Chapter 3
1. (a) 5.71 ft/sec, (b) 7.00 ft/sec
5. 2985 ft/sec² upward
9. 8.0×10^{14} meters/sec²
11. 10 cm
13. (a) 300 ft, (b) 60 ft/sec.
19. (a) 40 ft/sec

21. $\frac{1}{16}$ ft
23. (a) 17.0 sec, (b) 293 meters
25. (a) LT^{-2} (ft/sec²), LT^{-3} (ft/sec³);
   (b) 24 ft; (c) -16 ft;
   (d) 0, 3, 0, -9, -24 ft/sec;
   (e) 6, 0, -6, -12, -18 ft/sec²

Chapter 4
1. 10 ft/sec
3. (a) 3 sec, (b) 2400 ft, (c) -96 ft/sec
5. (a) 12.4 sec, (b) 3220 ft
11. 18.4 ft/sec
15. 8.0 meters/sec².
17. (a) $V = V_0 \cos \theta_0$, (b) $a = g$,
   (c) $a \perp V$,
   (d) $R = (V_0^2 \cos^2 \theta_0)/g$
19. 9×10^{22} meters/sec²
21. A factor of 17
23. (a) 60° from upstream, (b) 1.16 hr,
   (c) 1.33 hr, (d) 1.33 hr,
   (e) cross stream

Chapter 5
1. $a_1/a_2 = m_2/m_1$
3. 1 meter/sec², 36.9° from F_2 toward F_1
5. (a) 1.64×10^{-15} nt,
   (b) $F_g = 8.93 \times 10^{-30}$ nt
7. 1.54 cm
9. 1 nt
11. (a) 2.2×10^{-3} nt, (b) 3.7×10^{-3} nt
13. (a) 3.2 ft/sec², (b) 57.6 lb

15. (a) 2 ft, (b) $\frac{1}{2}$ sec, (c) 8 ft/sec
17. 6750 and 5250 lb.
19. (a) $\theta = $ arc tan (a/g), (b) 8.87°
21. 42.7 lb, 10.7 ft/sec^2

Chapter 6

1. 110 lb
3. (a) 0.376 ft/sec^2, 0.794 ft/sec^2;
    (b) 0.041, 0.027
5. (a) 0.031 lb, (b) 0.125
7. 0.75
9. 40 lb
11. (a) 15 lb, (b) 6.4 ft/sec^2
13. $V_0{}^2/(4g \sin \phi)$
15. $\sqrt{Rg}$
17. (a) 9.06×10^{22} meters/sec^2 toward center; (b) 8.25×10^{-8} nt, parallel to acceleration
19. (a) 15.1°, (b) 0.27

Chapter 7

1. (a) 52 lb, (b) −260 ft-lb,
    (c) 300 ft-lb, (d) −40 ft-lb,
    (e) 0, (f) 0
3. (a) 50 lb; (b) No; (c) Yes, 100 ft-lb;
    (d) No
9. (a) 1.83×10^5 ft-lb,
    (b) 305.0 ft-lb/sec
11. Boy: 4.82 meters/sec,
    Man: 2.41 meters/sec
13. (a) 2.9×10^7 meters/sec,
    (b) 1.31×10^6 ev
17. 4.70×10^6 ev

Chapter 8

1. 16 ft/sec
3. (a) $V = 2\sqrt{gl}$, $T = 5mg$; (b) 70.5°.
5. $\frac{1}{4}\rho g A (h_2 - h_1)^2$.
7. (a) $\sqrt{65}mg$, (b) $3R$
9. $-\frac{1}{2}Kx^2$
11. (a) $\dfrac{Ke^2}{2}\left(\dfrac{1}{R_2} - \dfrac{1}{R_1}\right)$,

    (b) $-Ke^2\left(\dfrac{1}{R_2} - \dfrac{1}{R_1}\right)$,

    (c) $\dfrac{Ke^2}{2}\left(\dfrac{1}{R_2} - \dfrac{1}{R_1}\right)$

15. 7.2 meters/sec
17. $mgl/50$
19. (a) 5.79×10^{-13} joule, (b) 0.08
21. (a) 0.01, 0.023; (b) 1, 0.30
23. 26.5 mev

Chapter 9

3. 6.46×10^{-11} meter
5. 6.75×10^{-12} meter below on line of symmetry

7. $4a/3\pi$ from flat base along line of symmetry
9. (a) halfway between a line of centers,
    (b) $\frac{1}{10}$ cm toward heavier from midpoint of line of centers,
    (c) 0.0016 g down
11. $\frac{1}{200}$ ft/sec
13. $\dfrac{wu}{W + w}$
15. $10\sqrt{2}$, 135° from either
17. 1.06×10^5 ft
19. (a) 58.8 kg/sec, (b) 176.4 kg/sec
21. 5120 lb, 5590 hp

Chapter 10

1. 2.5 meters/sec
3. 8.8 meters/sec
5. 3500 ft/sec.
7. 307 meters/sec.
9. (a) 4.1 ft/sec, 2.4×10^3 joules;
    (b) $U_{32} = 3.3$ ft/sec, $U_{24} = 5.3$ ft/sec.
11. 11.25 lb.
13. $v_0 = \left(2E\dfrac{M + m}{Mm}\right)^{1/2}$
15. (a) $\left(\dfrac{m}{m + M}\right)^2 \dfrac{V^2}{2g}$,

    (b) $\dfrac{1}{2}\dfrac{m^2}{m + M}V^2$.
19. 1.9 meters/sec, 30° to initial direction.
21. 116.5° from B.
23. (a) $\left(\dfrac{2m_n}{m_n + m_h}\right) V_n$, (b) 1.14 amu.
25. 90 barns.

Chapter 11

1. (a) 15.7 radians/sec^2, (b) 420 rev.
3. 8 sec.
5. $6bt - 12ct^2$.
7. (a) $6.34\pi \times 10^{-8}$ radians/sec,
    $9.5\pi \times 10^3$ meters/sec.
9. (a) 70.4 radians/sec,
    (b) −13.1 radians/sec^2, (c) 236 ft.
11. 0.12 radians/sec.
13. (a) $a_r = -\omega^2 r$, $a_T = \alpha r$,
    (b) $\sqrt{3}/2$ radians.

Chapter 12

7. 2.5 ft-lb.
9. $(l\omega)^2/6g$.
11. T up = T down = $mg\left(\dfrac{I}{I + mr^2}\right)$
13. 1.39×10^{-2} kg-m^2.
15. $g/2$.
17. 32%.

19. (a) 11.2 ft, (b) 7/5 sec.

21. $\frac{2}{3}$ g, 1 lb.

23. 10.5 lb, -0.053 g.

25. 6.5 ft above floor, 1.25 ft from wall.

27. 5.4 meters/sec.

Chapter 13

5. $8 \times 10^{-4}\%$.

7. 0.77 radian/sec.

9. (a) 3 rev/sec, (b) 237 joules.

11. $d = \sqrt{a^2 - g^2/\omega^4}$ for $\omega \geq \sqrt{g/a}$

13. (a) $\frac{1}{4}MR^2\omega_0^2$, $\frac{1}{2}MR^2\omega_0$; (b) $\frac{1}{2}\dfrac{\omega_0^2R^2}{g}$;

(c) $1/2, \left(\dfrac{M}{2} - m\right)R^2\omega_0$,

$\frac{1}{2}\left(\dfrac{M}{2} - m\right)R^2\omega_0^2$.

17. 2.1 rad/sec, downward.

Chapter 14

1. $W\left[\dfrac{h(2r - h)}{(r - h)^2}\right]^{\frac{1}{2}}$

3. 74.4 gm.

5. 1875 lb.

7. (a) $\dfrac{px}{l \sin \theta}$; (b) $F_H = \dfrac{px}{l} \cot \theta$,

$F_V = p\left(1 - \dfrac{x}{l}\right)$

9. 625 lb.

11. $N_A = 120$ lb, $N_E = 72$ lb, $T = 48$ lb.

13. 23.1 nt; 6.9 m/sec², 45° below horizontal.

15. $F_A = 87$ lb, $F_B = 150$ lb,
$F_C = F_D = 100$ lb.

Chapter 15

1. 0.28 sec.

3. (a) 3 meters, (b) $-9\pi\sqrt{3}$ meters/sec,
(c) $-27\pi^2$ meters/sec²,
(d) $\pi/3$ radians, (e) 3π radians/sec,
(f) $\frac{2}{3}$ sec.

5. 3.1×10^{-2} meter.

9. 710 nt/meter.

11. 0.2 meter, 1.6 cps.

13. 19.4 lb.

15. $\frac{3}{4}, \frac{1}{4}, A\sqrt{2}/2$.

19. 8.15×10^{-1} ft.

21. (a) 0.35/sec⁻¹, (b) 0.39/sec⁻¹.

23. 1.64 sec, 1.54 sec, 1.94 sec.

27. (a) 0.47/sec⁻¹, (b) 4 ft.

29. 10.9 sec.

Chapter 16

1. 8.7×10^6 ft.

3. 4.8 sec.

7. (b) 84.2 min.

9. (a) 2.56×10^4 ft/sec, (b) 87 min.

11. 2.5×10^4 km

13. (a) $\frac{1}{2}$, (b) $\frac{1}{2}$, (c) 8.6×10^7 ft-lb.

15. 1.88 earth years.

17. (b) 1.04×10^4 meters/sec;
(c) 1.90×10^3 meters/sec,
6.17×10^5 meters/sec.

19. (a) 7.1 radians/sec,
(b) 2×10^8 meters/sec.

23. 1.15%.

25. (a) 0, (b) -10^{-9} joule/kg,
(c) -5.0×10^{-10} joule/kg.

Chapter 17

1. 239 lb/in²

3. (b) 5980 lb.

5. (a) $\frac{1}{2}\rho g D^2 W$, $\rho g \dfrac{D^3 W}{6}$;
(b) $D/3$ up from bottom.

13. 500 ft².

15. 1.93 ft.

17. $\dfrac{0.96 - 100 \, \rho^2}{(8 - \rho)\rho}$ %, ρ in gm/cm³.

Chapter 18

1. 29 ft/sec.

3. 1.08×10^5 ft-lb.

7. $v = 4.1$ meters/sec.
$v' = 21$ meters/sec.
$Av = 8.1 \times 10^{-3}$ cubic meters/sec.

9. 109 lb/in.².

11. (a) $2[h(H - h)]^{\frac{1}{2}}$

15. 788 lb, 248 lb up.

17. 410 meters/sec.

Chapter 19

3. (a) 10 cm, 1 vps, 200 cm/sec, 200 cm;
(b) 62.8 cm/sec.

5. (a) 0.117 meter, (b) 180°.

7. 129 meters/sec.

11. (b) 5.67×10^{-17} joule/meter³

13. 5 cm.

17. (a) 2.5 cm, 120 cm/sec;
(b) 3.0 cm; (c) 0.

19. 8.1 lb.

Chapter 20

1. 16.6 meters, 0.017 meter.

3. 10^5 vps.

7. (a) $\dfrac{l(V - v)}{Vv}$, (b) 1630 ft.

11. 3.6×10^{-8} meter.

13. (a) 5×10^3 vps, (b) $\dfrac{A_sBD}{A_sAD} = \dfrac{1}{2}$.

15. $\dfrac{2n + 1}{8}$ meter $n = 0, 1, 2, 3$.

17. (a) 82.5 vps, (b) 81.7 nt.

19. 0.552 meter, 0.414 meter.

21. $\frac{1}{50}$

25. (a) 971 vps, (b) 1031 vps, (c) 0

27. 29.6°

Chapter 21

1. 1.37

3. (a) 10^4°F; (b) 37.0°C; (c) 73.9°C;
(d) 56.7°C, −56.7°C; (e) −297°F

5. 91 C°

7. 3.84 × 10^{-2} in.

9. 46.4 cm

11. 1.002 in.

17. 28.9 cm^3

21. 7.44 × 10^{-4} (C°)$^{-1}$

Chapter 22

1. 1.17 C°

3. 194 watts

5. 0.13 Btu/lb

9. 0.59 cal/gm-C°

11. $B\dfrac{t^2}{12}$

13. 150 C°

17. (a) 1.4 × 10^{-5} k-cal/m²-sec,
(b) 6.2 × 10^{14} k-cal

19. 4.19 joules/cal

Chapter 23

1. 106 cm^3

3. 653 joules

5. 27 lb/in.²

7. (a) 565 × 10^{-23} joule,
772 × 10^{-23} joule;
(b) 3390 joule, 4632 joule

Chapter 26

1. 0.12 amp.

5. 6.0 × 10^{-8} coul.

9. (a) 5.7 × 10^{13} coul,
(b) no,
(c) 660 tons.

13. (b) Along the body diagonal.

17. (a) 510 nt,
(b) 7.7 × 10^{28} meters/sec².

9. (a) 1.01 × 10^4°K, 16.2 × 10^4°K;
(b) 450°K, 7200°K

11. 3.67 × 10^{16}

13. (a) 11, (b) 1

17. 3.11 × 10^3 joule/kg-K°

19. 220 cal, 43%

25. (a) 1390°K, (b) 730°K

27. (a) 8 atm, (b) 600°K

29. (a) 2.5 atm, 336°K; (b) $V_f = 0.41V_i$

Chapter 24

1. 3.2 × 10^{-8} cm

3. (a) 3.5 × 10^{10} molecules/cm³,
(b) 1.6 × 10^4 cm

5. (a) 7.1 × 10^3 meters/sec,
(b) 2 × 10^{-8} cm,
(c) 5 × 10^{10} per sec

7. 1.5 cm/sec

11. $RT \ln \dfrac{V_f - b}{V_i - b} + a\left(\dfrac{1}{V_f} - \dfrac{1}{V_i}\right)$

13. (a) 3.2 × 10^6 nt/meter²,
(b) 4.1 × 10^6 nt/meter²

Chapter 25

1. 5.02 × 10^4 joules

3. 58%

5. (a) 2090 joules, (b) 375 cal,
(c) 1570 joules

7. 6.5

9. $eK = T_2/T_1$

11. 13 joules

15. 1.424 cal/K°

17. 0.1 cal/K°

3. ±2.4 × 10^{-8} coul.

7. (a) $Q = -2\sqrt{2}q$,
(b) no.

11. 3.8 × 10^{-5} coul, 1.2 × 10^{-5} coul.

15. (a) 6.3 × 10^{11},
(b) 7.3 × 10^{-13}.

Chapter 27

5. 5.6 × 10^{-11} coul.

9. (a) The larger charge produces a field of 13 × 10^4 nt/coul at the site of the smaller; the smaller charge produces a field of 5.3 × 10^4 nt/coul at the site of the larger.
(b) 1.1 × 10^{-2} nt, repulsive.

11. E lies in the median plane and points radially away from the charge axis.

13. 1.0 × 10^5 nt, pointing up.

17. $E = q/8\pi\epsilon_0 a^2$, pointing along the axis of symmetry and away from the hemisphere.

21. (a) $E = \dfrac{1}{4\pi\epsilon_0} \dfrac{qx}{(a^2 + x^2)^{3/2}}$,

(b) $E = \dfrac{1}{2\pi^2\epsilon_0} \dfrac{(q_1 - q_2)a}{(a^2 + x^2)^{3/2}}$.

25 (a) 1.5×10^3 nt/coul,

(b) 2.4×10^{-16} ul (up),

(c) 1.6×10^{-26} nt,

(d) 1.5×10^{10}.

27. (a) 7.1 cm,

(b) 2.9×10^{-8} sec,

(c) 11%.

29. $\dfrac{dE}{dz} = -\dfrac{8q}{\pi\epsilon_0 l^3}$, where l is the distance between the charges; yes.

31. 1.64×10^{-19} coul.

Chapter 28

1. $\pi R^2 E$ (an expected result).

3. $EA \cos\theta$.

7. (a) 1.0×10^6 nt/coul,

(b) $E = 0$.

9. (a) $E = \sigma/\epsilon_0$, to the left,

(b) $E = 0$,

(c) $E = \sigma/\epsilon_0$, to the right.

11. 4.9×10^{-10} coul.

13. 0.44 mm.

19. (a) $E = \dfrac{q}{2\pi\epsilon_0 lr}$ (radially inward), where l is the length of the cylinders,

(b) $-q$ on inner surface and $-q$ on outer surface,

(c) $E = \dfrac{q}{2\pi\epsilon_0 lr}$ (radially outward).

21. 2.5×10^{-9} coul/meter^2.

23. 1.9×10^2 nt,

2.9×10^{28} meters/sec^2.

25. (a) 1.1 nt meters^2/coul,

(b) 9.3×10^{-12} coul.

Chapter 29

1. 0.89 mm.

3. 900 volts.

5. (a) Between the charges a distance of 25 cm from $+q$ and outside the charges a distance of 50 cm from $+q$.

(b) Outside the charges a distance of 140 cm from $+q$.

7. $V_A - V_B = \dfrac{q}{2\pi\epsilon_0} \dfrac{d}{a(a + d)}$.

9. 1.9×10^{-29} coul meter; text value (0.61×10^{-29} coul meter) is lower and correct; the assumptions made in this problem are oversimplified.

11. 99 tons.

13. -6.4×10^{-7} joule.

15. (a) -0.12 volt,

(b) 1.8×10^{-8} nt/coul, radially inward.

17. 2900 volts.

21. No.

23. (a) -180 volts,

(b) $+2900$ volts and -9000 volts.

27. $-0.21q^2/\epsilon_0 a$.

29. (a) 1.1×10^{17} volts/meter,

(b) 4.6×10^{21} volts/meter, assuming a nuclear radius of 5×10^{-15} meter.

31. (a) 2.6×10^5 volts,

(b) $\dfrac{\sqrt{5}}{3} c = 0.745$ c.

33. 9.0 kw.

35. (a) 3.2×10^{-13} joule,

(b) 1.6×10^{-13} joule,

(c) proton.

Chapter 30

1. (a) $q_2 = q_8 = 4.8 \times 10^{-4}$ coul,

$V_2 = 240$ volts,

$V_8 = 60$ volts;

3. 43 $\mu\mu$f.

    (b) $q_2 = 2.0 \times 10^{-4}$ coul,
        $q_8 = 7.7 \times 10^{-4}$ coul,
        $V_2 = V_8 = 96$ volts;
    (c) $q_2 = q_8 =$ zero,
        $V_2 = V_8 =$ zero.

11. 3.2 μf.   **13.** 4 μf.

15. 7.3 μf.   **21.** Mica.

23. Assuming $\kappa = 5.4$:
    (a) 10^4 volts/meter,
    (b) $+5.0 \times 10^{-9}$ coul, on the positive plate,
    (c) -4.1×10^{-9} coul, next to the positive plate.

25. 0.63 meter^2.   **27.** 0.11 joule/meter^3.

31. (a) 1.3×10^{-7} joule,   **33.** 7.0×10^{-6} coul.
    (b) no.

35. 7.0¢.   **37.** (a) $q_1 = q_2 = 3.3 \times 10^{-4}$ coul,
                     $q_3 = 4.0 \times 10^{-4}$ coul;
            (b) $V_1 = 33$ volts,
                     $V_2 = 67$ volts,
                     $V_3 = 100$ volts;
            (c) $U_1 = 5.4 \times 10^{-3}$ joule,
                     $U_2 = 10.9 \times 10^{-3}$ joule,
                     $U_3 = 2.0 \times 10^{-2}$ joule.

Chapter 31

1. (a) 1200 coul,   **3.** (a) 2.4, iron being larger;
    (b) 7.5×10^{21} electrons.   (b) no.

5. 6.7×10^{-6} coul/meter^2.   **7.** 54 ohms.

9. (a) 2.2×10^{-7} ohm,   **11.** (a) 260°C,
    (b) nickel ($\rho = 6.8 \times 10^{-8}$ ohm -meter).   (b) yes.

13. 0.39% (ρ),   **17.** 11 ohms.
    0.0017% (l),
    0.0034% (A).

19. (a) 4.9×10^6 amp/meter^2,   **21.** 620 watts.
    (b) 8.4×10^{-2} volt/meter,
    (c) 26 volts,
    (d) 640 watts.

23. (a) 8.7%,
    (b) smaller.

Chapter 32

1. 1.1×10^4 joules.   **3.** -0.62%.

7. (a) 990 ohms,   **9.** $V_d - V_c = 1.3$ volts.
    (b) 9.9×10^{-4} watt.

11. (a) 120 ohms,   **13.** (a) $R = \frac{1}{2}r$,
    (b) $i_1 = 0.051$ amp,   (b) $E^2/2r$.
        $i_2 = i_3 = 0.019$ amp,
        $i_4 = 0.013$ amp.

17. 38 ohms.   **19.** (a) 10 ohms,
                     (b) 14 ohms,
                     (c) 10 ohms.

21. series: $i = \dfrac{2}{R + 2r}$.
    parallel: $i = \dfrac{2}{2R + r}$.

(a) Put R_1 roughly in the middle of its range; adjust current roughly with R_2; make fine adjustment with R_1.

(b) Relatively large percentage changes in R_1 cause only small percentage changes in the resistance of the parallel combination, thus permitting fine adjustment. The ratio is 1:21.

27. 2.7%.   **29.** 4.6 time constants.

33. (a) 9.5×10^{-5} coul/sec,
(b) 1.1×10^{-6} watt,
(c) 2.7×10^{-6} watt,
(d) 3.8×10^{-6} watt.

Chapter 33

1. (a) East,
(b) 6.3×10^{14} meters/sec^2,
(c) 3.0 mm.

3. 7.5 nt, perpendicular to the wire and to **B**.

5. See Appendix.   **7.** 3.8 coul.

9. 520 gauss, normal to plane of tracks.

11. 4.3×10^{-3} nt-meter. The torque vector is parallel to the long side of the coil and points down.

15. (a) 1.4×10^{-4} meter/sec,
(b) 4.5×10^{-23} nt (down),
(c) 2.8×10^{-4} volt/meter (down),
(d) 5.7×10^{-6} volt (top +, bottom −),
(e) same as (b).

17. (a) $K_p = K_d = \frac{1}{2}K_\alpha$,
(b) $R_d = 14$ cm.
(c) $R_\alpha = 14$ cm.

19. (a) 2.6×10^7 motors/sec,
(b) 1.1×10^{-7} sec,
(c) 14 Mev,
(d) 7.0×10^6 volts.

23. 1.6×10^{-8} weber/meter^2, horizontal and at right angles to the equator.

25. $T = 3.6 \times 10^{-10}$ sec,
$p = 0.17$ mm,
$r = 1.5$ mm.

27. 2.11×10^{-25} kg or 127 proton masses.

29. (a) Increase,
(b) decrease.

31. (a) 8.5 Mev,
(b) 0.80 weber/meter^2,
(c) 34 Mev,
(d) 24 mc/sec
(e) 34 Mev, 1.6 webers/meter^2,
34 Mev, 12 mc/sec.

33. 1.4.   **35.** 3800 meters/sec.

Chapter 34

1. 7.9×10^{-3} weber/meter^2.

3. (a) 3.2×10^{-16} nt, parallel to current;
(b) 3.2×10^{-16} nt, radially outward if **v** is parallel to the current;
(c) zero.

7. 1.0×10^{-6} weber/meter.

9. $B = 0$ along a line parallel to the wire and 4.0 mm from it. If the current is horizontal and points toward the observer and the external field points horizontally from left to right, the line is directly above the wire.

11. 8.0×10^{-5} weber/meter^2, up.   **13.** 3.2×10^{-3} nt, toward the long wire.

23. (a) 1.0×10^{-3} weber/meter^2, out of figure;
(b) 8.0×10^{-4} weber/meter^2, out of figure.

27. (a) 9.4×10^{-5} weber/meter^2,
(b) 1.5×10^{-6} nt-meter.

Chapter 35

1. 2.0×10^{-2} coul.
9. $V_m = \pi^2 B R^2 f$,
   $i_m = \pi^2 B R^2 f / R_M$
13. (a) 3.1×10^{-2},
    (b) left to right.

3. Zero.
11. 3.0×10^{-4} volt.
17. (a) 4.4×10^7 meters/sec^2, to the right;
    (b) zero;
    (c) 4.4×10^7 meters/sec^2, to the left.

Chapter 36

1. Let the current charge at 10 amp/sec.
9. 12 sec.
15. (a) 10 amp,
    (b) 100 joules.
21. (a) 2.5×10^{-6} joule/meter,
    (b) 14×10^{-6} joule/meter,
    (c) 0.8×10^{-6} joule/meter.

7. 1.0×10^{-7} weber.
13. 27 amp/sec.
17. 0.63 joule/meter^3.

23. 1.5×10^8 volt/meter.

Chapter 37

1. (a) 5.0×10^7 amp,
   (b) yes,
   (c) no.
5. (a) 7.6 amp meter^2,
   (b) 11 nt-meter.
11. (a) 1.8 webers/meter^2,
    (b) 6.5×10^{-23} joule.

3. (a) 1.4×10^{11} volts/meter,
   (b) 2.8×10^{-3} weber/meter^2.

9. 7.5×10^{-6} weber/meter^2.

Chapter 38

1. 600, 710, 1100, and 1300 cycles/sec.

15. $\omega = \sqrt{\dfrac{1}{L_1 C_1}} = \sqrt{\dfrac{1}{L_2 C_2}}$.

21. (a) 1.4×10^{14} volts/meter-sec,
    (b) 9.9×10^{-6} weber/meter^2.

13. (a) 35 cycles/sec.
    (b) 38 or 33 cycles/sec.

19. $i_d = \epsilon_0 \pi r^2 \dfrac{dE}{dt}$ $(r \lessgtr R)$,

    $i_d = \epsilon_0 \pi R^2 \dfrac{dE}{dt}$ $(r \gtrless R)$.

Chapter 39

3. 4.9 cm, 5.2×10^8 meters/sec
   $(= 1.7\ c)$.
13. (a) $a^2 E B / \mu_0$
    for faces parallel to xy-plane, zero for others;
    (b) zero.
15. 1000 volts/meter,
    3.4×10^{-6} weber/meter^2.

9. 18 cm, 12 cm.

Chapter 40

1. (a) 5100 A and 6100 A,
   (b) 5.5×10^{14} cycles/sec and 1.8×10^{-15} sec.
3. $F_{\text{rad}} = 6.0 \times 10^8$ nt,
   $F_{\text{gr}} = 3.6 \times 10^{22}$ nt.
11. 0.13.
15. 3.8×10^{-2} A.

7. 1.3×10^{-7} nt/meter^2.

13. (b) 7.3 (cycles/sec)/(miles/hour).
17. Yellow-orange.

Chapter 41

3. 2.05×10^8 meters/sec.
15. (b) 0.17.

5. 1.56.

19. Cover the center of each face with a circle of radius 0.33 cm. The fraction covered is 0.35.

Chapter 42

1. (a) 7,
    (b) 5,
    (c) 2.

3. 40 cm.

6. Alternate vertical columns:
    (a) +, +40, −20, +2, no, yes;
    (c) concave, +40, +60, −2, yes, no;
    (e) convex, −20, +20, +0.5, no, yes;
    (g) −20, −, −, +5, +0.80, no, yes.

7. Object at center of curvature.

9. 4.24 cm.

10. Alternate vertical columns:
    (a) −18, no;
    (c) +71, yes;
    (e) +30, no;
    (g) −26, no.

11. Alternate vertical columns:
    (a) +, X, X, +20, X, −1, yes, no;
    (c) converging, +, X, X, −10, X, no, yes;
    (e) converging, +30, −15, +1.5, no, yes;
    (g) diverging, −120, −9.2, +0.92, no, yes;
    (i) converging, +3.3, X, X, +5, X, −, no.

17. 4.5 cm, 9.0 cm.

19. Assuming the light is incident from the left, a distance of $-\dfrac{r(n-2)}{2(n-1)}$ to the right of the right edge of the sphere.

21. (a) R' is negative and R'' is positive,
    (b) $i = \dfrac{-2r}{n+1}$,
    (c) virtual and erect.

23. (a) Coincides in location with original object and is enlarged 5.0 times,
    (c) virtual and inverted.

Chapter 43

1. Slit separation must be 0.034 mm.

3. 0.15°.

5. 6.6×10^{-3} mm.

7. 3.0 mm.

9. $I = \dfrac{I_m}{4}\left[1 + 8\cos^2\left(\dfrac{\pi d \sin\theta}{\lambda}\right)\right].$

11. $y = 17.4 \sin(\omega t + 13.3°).$

13. 80 million.

15. 1.21.

17. 4800 A (blue).

19. 6700 A.

23. 5880 A.

25. 6057.8021 A.

Chapter 44

1. 0.17 mm.

3. (a) $\lambda_a = 2\lambda_b$,
    (b) coincidences occur when $m_b = 2m_a$.

5. 79.7°.

7. (a) 52.9°,
    (b) 10.2°,
    (c) 5.1°.

9. 9100 meters.

11. (a) 0.16 sec of arc,
    (b) 7.4×10^7 km,
    (c) 2.2×10^{-4} mm.

15. 3.

17. (a) Must have $d = 4a$,
    (b) Every fourth fringe is missing.

Chapter 45

 1. Three complete orders.
 5. The intensity would be concentrated near the twentieth order for blue and the eleventh order for red. The orders would overlap to such an extent as to appear almost white.
 7. All wavelengths shorter than 6300 A.
 9. $0°$, $\pm10°$, $\pm21°$, $\pm32°$, $\pm45°$, and $\pm62°$.
11. 5200 A to 6200 A.   17. (a) $0.0032°/A$,
                                                $0.0077°/A$,
                                                $0.024°/A$;
                                            (b) 40,000,
                                                80,000,
                                                120,000.
19. 3600 lines.
21. (a) 4.6×10^{-2} A.
    (b) No. The resolution could normally be improved by going to a higher order diffraction, but in this case $m = 3$ is the highest order that can exist (assuming that the light falls on the grating at right angles).
23. (a) 6×10^4 A,
    (b) 1.5×10^4 A,
    (c) 0, 1, 2, 3, 5, 6, 7, 9. The tenth order is at $\theta = 90°$.
25. $33°$, $20°$, $5.2°$ (all clockwise);   27. Yes, $n = 3$ for $\lambda = 1.29$ A,
    $14°$ (counterclockwise). $n = 4$ for $\lambda = 0.97$ A.

Chapter 46

 1. (a) $\pm55°$,
    (b) $\pm35°$.
 3. Assuming that a right-handed coordinate system is used,
    (a) circular, counterclockwise as seen facing the source;
    (b) elliptical, counterclockwise as seen facing the source, major axis of ellipse along $y = x$;
    (c) plane, along $y = -x$.
 5. $55°30'$ to $55°46'$.   11. 2.7×10^{-14} kg-meter^2/sec^2,
                                                2.1 hr.

Chapter 47

 1. 4.8 A.   3. 6.2×10^{23} photons/sec.
 7. 5.9×10^{-6} ev.   9. (a) 2.0 ev,
                                                (b) zero,
                                                (c) 2.0 volts,
                                                (d) 3000 A.
11. 100 years.   17. (a) 1,
                                                (b) 5.3×10^{-11} meter,
                                                (c) 1.1×10^{-34} joule-sec,
                                                (d) 2.0×10^{-24} kg-meter/sec,
                                                (e) 4.1×10^{15} radians/sec,
                                                (f) 2.2×10^6 meters/sec,
                                                (g) 8.2×10^{-8} nt,
                                                (h) 9.0×10^{22} meters/sec^2
                                                (i) $+13.6$ ev,
                                                (j) -27.2 ev,
                                                (k) -13.6 ev.

19. +0.21 ev.   **21.** 2.6 ev.

25. +54 ev, assuming the electron to be in its ground state initially.

27. (a) 2.6×10^{-13} meter,

(b) 2800 ev,

(c) 4.4 A.

Chapter 48

1. (a) 1.7×10^{-35} meter.

3. (a) 3.3×10^{-24} kg-meter/sec, for each;

(b) 38 ev for the electron and 6200 ev for the photon.

5. (a) Higher orders cannot exist for this accelerating potential and for these planes.

(b) 59°; the crystal must be rotated with respect to the incident beam to satisfy Bragg's law for this new wavelength.

7. 1.5 A.   **9.** (a) 0.20,

(b) 0.40,

(c) 0.33,

(d) 0.33.

11. 0.32.   **15.** 6.6×10^{-23} kg-meter/sec.

Index